Visit classzone.com and get connected

Online resources provide instruction, practice, and learning support correlated to your text.

- **Videos and Animations** are referenced at point-of-use in the Teacher's Edition to aid in student comprehension.

- **Interactive Review Games** reinforce key material for every chapter.

- **The Activity Maker** allows teachers to create and edit Review Games, Flipcards and Crossword Puzzles.

- **Science Links** offer additional science and teaching resources.

Gain immediate access to *ClassZone's* teacher resources.

MCDLANSTUWW6A

Use this code to create your own username and password.

World of Chemistry

Zumdahl/Zumdahl/DeCoste

Teacher's Edition

World of Chemistry

Steven S. Zumdahl
University of Illinois

Susan L. Zumdahl
University of Illinois

Donald J. DeCoste
University of Illinois

McDougal Littell

A Houghton Mifflin Company
Evanston, Illinois • Boston • Dallas

Dedication

For Olivia, Madeline, and Michael
Jessica, Joshua, Moriah, David, Lucia, and Alexander
Who bring love, laughter, and joy
to all of us

Printed in the U.S.A.

Library of Congress Catalog Card Number: 2006927587

ISBN-10: 0-618-80748-9
ISBN-13: 978-0-618-80748-2

1 2 3 4 5 6 7 8 9-WEB-10 09 08 07 06

Reviewers/Panelists

Robert Blaus
York High School
Elmhurst, Illinois

Connie Grosse
El Dorado High School
Placentia, California

Bernadette Gruca-Peal
Archdiocese of Chicago Schools
Queen of Peace High School
Chicago, Illinois

Janet Jones
Chicago Public Schools
Sullivan High School
Chicago, Illinois

Ray Lesniewski
Jones Academic Magnet High School
Chicago, Illinois

Ann Levinson
Niles Township Community High School
Skokie, Illinois

John Little
St. Mary's High School
Stockton, California

Lee Slick
Morgan Park High School
Chicago, Illinois

Carl Wasik
Chicago Public Schools
Curie High School
Chicago, Illinois

About the Authors

Steven S. Zumdahl earned a B.S. in Chemistry from Wheaton College (IL) and a Ph.D. from the University of Illinois, Urbana-Champaign. He has been a faculty member at the University of Colorado-Boulder, Parkland College (IL), and the University of Illinois at Urbana-Champaign (UIUC) where he is Professor Emeritus. He has received numerous awards including the National Catalyst Award for Excellence in Chemical Education, the University of Illinois Teaching Award, the UIUC Liberal Arts and Sciences Award for Excellence in Teaching, the UIUC Liberal Arts and Sciences Advising Award, and the School of Chemical Sciences Teaching Award (five times). He is author of several chemistry textbooks. In his leisure time he enjoys traveling and collecting classic cars.

Susan L. Zumdahl earned a B.S. and M.A. in Chemistry at California State University-Fullerton. She has taught science and mathematics at all levels including middle school, high school, community college, and university. At the University of Illinois, Urbana-Champaign, she developed a program for increasing the retention of minorities and women in science and engineering. This program focused on using active learning and peer teaching to encourage students to excel in the sciences. She has coordinated and led workshops and programs for science teachers from elementary through college levels. These programs encourage and support active learning and creative techniques for teaching science. For several years she was director of an Institute for Chemical Education (ICE) field center in Southern California and she has authored several chemistry textbooks. Susan spearheaded the development of a sophisticated Web-based electronic homework system for teaching chemistry. Susan enjoys traveling, classic cars, and gardening in her spare time when she is not playing with her grandchildren.

Donald J. DeCoste is Associate Director of General Chemistry at the University of Illinois, Urbana-Champaign and has been teaching chemistry at the high school and college levels for 20 years. He earned a B.S. in Chemistry and a Ph.D. from the University of Illinois, Urbana-Champaign. At UIUC he has developed chemistry courses for nonscience majors, preservice secondary teachers, and preservice elementary teachers. He teaches courses in introductory chemistry and the teaching of chemistry, and has received the School of Chemical Sciences Teaching Award four times. Don has led workshops for secondary teachers and graduate student teaching assistants, discussing the methods and benefits of getting students more actively involved in class. When not involved in teaching and advising, Don enjoys spending time with his wife and three children.

A Word From the Authors

As the authors of several chemistry programs, we are often asked to describe what makes our approach to teaching chemistry unique. How is the *World of Chemistry* curriculum different from other programs? Because our experience tells us that learning chemistry is not a spectator sport, this curriculum is designed to put students in the center of the learning process. To learn in a meaningful way, students must participate in the process. A knowledge of chemistry is not something a teacher gives to a student—it is something the student must construct for herself or himself with the help of the teacher, the textbook, laboratory exploration, and the other materials provided. Our philosophy is represented throughout our program in several important ways.

An Emphasis on Active Learning

Our experience tells us that there is no better way to learn than to teach someone else. When we try to teach a concept, it soon becomes obvious whether we truly understand. Teaching someone allows us to recognize and "fix" our own misconceptions. However, successful peer teaching activities require much more than simply assigning students to work in groups. The quality of the problems they work on in groups is critical. Based on our extensive experience with active learning in introductory chemistry at the University of Illinois, we have designed **Team Learning Worksheets**, which contain conceptual questions that produce discussion and meaningful learning in a group setting.

A Book Students Can Rely On

One of the great advantages of effective active learning is that it directs students to the textbook. When students confront a concept in group work that they do not understand, they learn much more effectively if they struggle with it rather than having the teacher simply supply the answer. In going from high school to college, students need to become much more independent learners, especially by using the textbooks effectively. Students who are not college bound also need to know how to learn from books since changing job markets necessitate retraining.

Therefore, one of our main goals in constructing this learning package is to make the textbook readable and useful to students both during and after class. The textbook is a central learning resource for students. To engage students as they begin to read the chapter, we have designed **Prereading Questions** that connect what they know to new material. Included within the text material are **Active Reading Questions** that reinforce new concepts and direct students to the Tables and Figures in the text. **Section Review Questions** help students read in a meaningful way by focusing on the main ideas in the section. **Math Tips** and **Reading Tips** provide extra support.

The text also contains many features to help students connect chemistry to their daily lives. **Chemistry Explorers** boxes tell the stories of significant pioneers in the field of chemistry. **Chemistry in Your World** boxes feature interesting applications of chemistry that connect to technology, history, consumer and societal issues, and other areas of interest. **Celebrity Chemical** features emphasize important chemicals and their uses. The **Top Ten** lists and **Critical Thinking** features highlight interesting connections between classroom studies and "real life."

An Emphasis on Problem-Solving and Exploration

The text contains hundreds of worked-out examples that show the systematic thinking needed to solve chemical problems. These examples emphasize understanding concepts rather than rote memorization. To help students think about solving problems logically, we have used a four-step **Problem Solving Strategy:**

1. Where do we want to go?
2. What do we know?
3. How do we get there?
4. Does it make sense?

We apply this strategy in both text and worked-out examples to guide students in developing their own problem-solving sense.

To encourage in-class exploration, we have included several **Hands-On Chemistry Mini-Lab** activities for each chapter. These activities can be used to introduce concepts in a hands-on format. The **Laboratory program** for *World of Chemistry* provides experiments that include traditional, microscale, and computer based formats. All of these labs have been class tested and were constructed to provide an effective balance between structure and exploration.

Assessment and Program Support

The **Chapter Assessment** questions vary in level from simple drill-and-practice exercises to critical thinking exercises that combine several ideas to develop students' critical thinking skills. The **Standardized Test Practice** at the end of each chapter exemplifies a standardized test format.

Our **Meeting Individual Needs Toolkit** collects program materials for students who are achieving at varying levels. The Toolkit offers five sections of materials. The **Math Concepts** materials provide additional explanations and practice to develop stronger math skills. For those students who struggle with reading, our **Reading Concepts** material assists in learning the skills needed to read a textbook independently. **Chapter Summaries** are easy to read and include additional **Active Reading Questions** for students who may be struggling with chapter content. **Leveled Chapter Review Worksheets** are provided at three levels (basic, standard, and challenge) to allow students to review the material at their own level. For students ready for more advanced study, we have designed **Challenge Projects** to help them extend their knowledge beyond the scope of the text.

Additional **Teacher Resources** include **Classroom Activities and Projects** designed to add interest and project-based learning to your curriculum. We have designed a **Chapter Test** for each chapter. In addition, a bank of approximately 1600 test items is available with the **McDougal Littell Test Generator** program. A book of **Standardized Test Practice** has been provided to further prepare students to take standardized tests. A **Solutions Guide** includes complete solutions to all the textbook problems.

Our goals are to interest and motivate students, making them active participants in the process of truly understanding this fascinating and important subject.

Acknowledgements

This was a massive project and we are indebted to many people for their help. We thank the editorial team of Publisher Charles Hartford, Executive Editor Richard Stratton, Vice President, Director of Advanced and Elective Programs Alison Zetterquist and Senior Development Editor Bess Deck for their support throughout the lifespan of this project. We very much appreciate the professional and efficient work of Project Editor Nan Lewis-Schulz and Managing Editor Terry Wilton, who managed the production of this very complex project in a smooth way. The professionals at Mazer Corporation did an exemplary job in the design and production of the new edition of the text. We thank especially Project Manager Grace Ninneman, Designer Angela Rice, Art Buyer Courtney Adams, Production Artists Lesley Hollen and Tim Howard, Proofreader Terri Weiss, Copy Editor Sally Athmer, Executive Editor for Science and Health Joyce Spangler, and Science Editor Bria Youderian. Suzanne Thomas of S & T Technical Aspects was a continual source of ideas, assistance, and support throughout the project.

The 2007 program brought new levels of collaboration within Houghton Mifflin, and we especially thank Science Marketing Director Mark Mine, Science Product Marketing Associate Maggy Tinucci, Science Product Marketing Manager Mitch Coulter, Science Editorial Director Dan Rogers, and Advanced and Elective Markets Marketing Director Chris Tabbert for their guidance and help throughout the project. The McDougal Littell Media Group produced the suite of technology ancillaries, for which we especially thank Executive Producer Madaliene Schalet, Producer David Koning, and Associate Producer Elizabeth Holst.

We are especially grateful to John Little, St. Mary's High School, Stockton, California, and Connie Grosse, El Dorado High School, Placentia, California, who supplied creative and innovative laboratory experiments and who gave us much valuable advice along the way. John also contributed many new standardized test practice items. We also greatly appreciate the efforts of Steve Nelson, Addison Trails High School, Addison, Illinois, who wrote the excellent chapter assessment materials. We are indebted to Gretchen Adams, Chemistry Merit Director, University of Illinois, for her energy, enthusiasm, and willingness to tackle any project we required. She created the new Math Concepts material for the Meeting Individual Needs Toolkit, revised many other supplemental materials, and expanded the Test Item File. We appreciate the detailed work of the many accuracy checkers who contributed to the program.

Finally, we are grateful to all our friends who teach high school who have done so much to encourage and enlighten us over the years. You are a very dedicated, highly professional group of people whom we admire greatly.

Brief Contents

Program Overview

THE VISION FOR HIGH SCHOOL CHEMISTRY

World of Chemistry

Zumdahl/Zumdahl/DeCoste

World of Chemistry provides comprehensive coverage of the **National Science Education Standards.** Sections of the National Standards for grades 9–12 emphasized in this text include:

Unifying Concepts and Processes

- Systems, order, and organization
- Evidence, models, and explanation
- Change, constancy, and measurement
- Form and function

Science as Inquiry

- Abilities necessary to do scientific inquiry
- Understanding about scientific inquiry

Physical Science

- Structure of atoms
- Structure and properties of matter
- Chemical reactions
- Conservation of energy and increase in disorder
- Interactions of energy and matter

Science and Technology

- Abilities of technological design
- Understanding about science and technology

Science in Personal and Social Perspectives

- Environmental quality
- Natural and human-induced hazards
- Science and technology in local, national, and global challenges

History and Nature of Science

- Science as a human endeavor
- Nature of scientific knowledge
- Historical perspectives

Other standards are covered to a lesser extent. A complete correlation to the National Science Education Standards is provided starting on page T-42.

The Balanced Equation

World of Chemistry is a high-school chemistry program that presents the right balance of concepts and applications, emphasizes active learning, and encourages students to solve problems creatively.

Teacher's Edition Content Overview

Student Edition

The chapter begins with **In Your Life**, connecting the chapter content to students' prior knowledge and everyday experiences. This reinforces the text's emphasis on conceptual understanding and helps draw students comfortably into the material.

Prereading Questions help students focus on what they already know about a topic. Teachers can use these questions to assess students' prior knowledge.

Each **Chapter Opener** provides an engaging full-page photograph tied to the chapter content, plus **Looking Ahead**, a chapter outline that gives students a preview of the topics to be explored.

A comprehensive **Art Program** provides hundreds of photographs and illustrations that clearly represent chemical reactions, phenomena, and processes.

Straightforward **Objectives** lead off each section, giving students a context for their reading.

Key terms are boldfaced and defined when they first appear. They are also listed on the Section Opener, in the Chapter Review, and in the Glossary at the back of the book.

Active Reading Questions help students reinforce important ideas as they read.

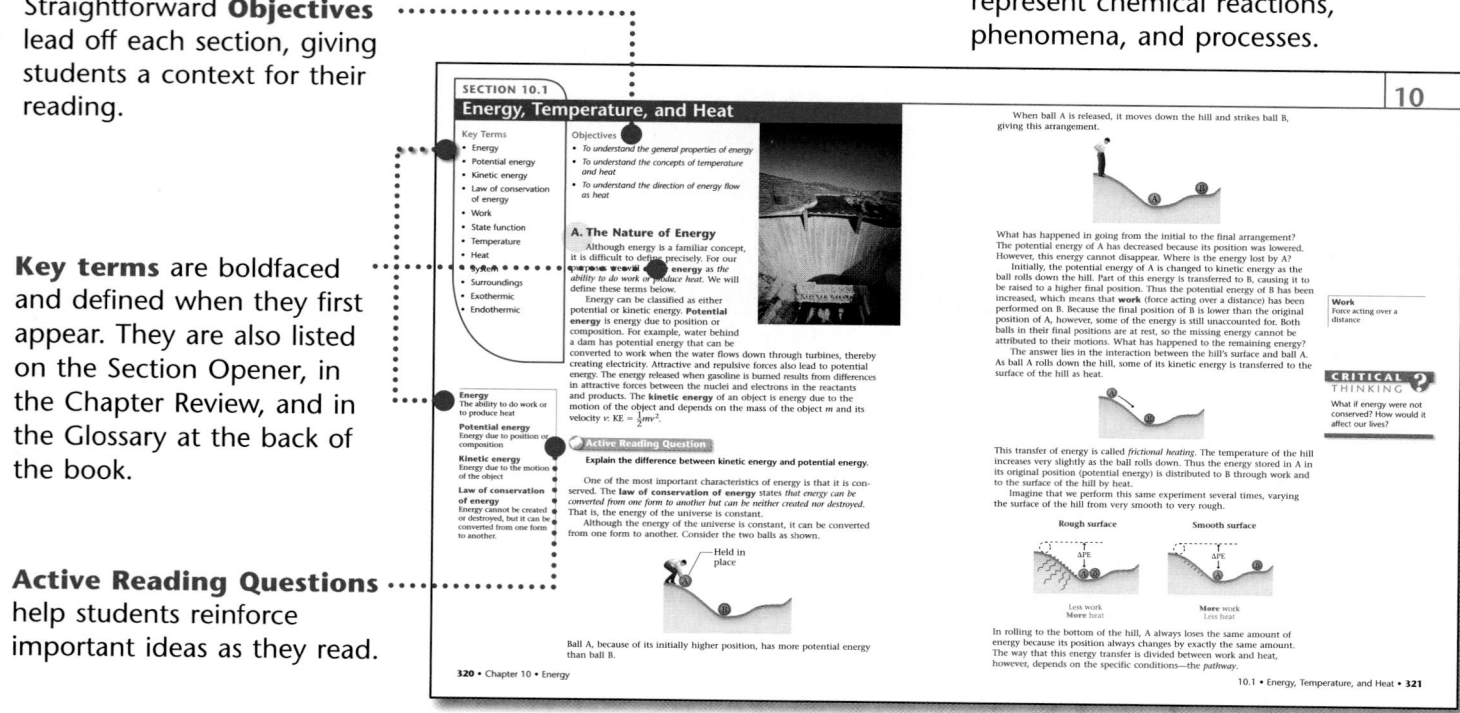

Key Concepts are highlighted to focus students' attention.

Information boxes appear in the margin throughout the text, providing tips that assist students in solving problems, doing calculations, and understanding concepts.

Critical Thinking boxes feature open-ended questions for students to consider. These are particularly useful for generating class discussion.

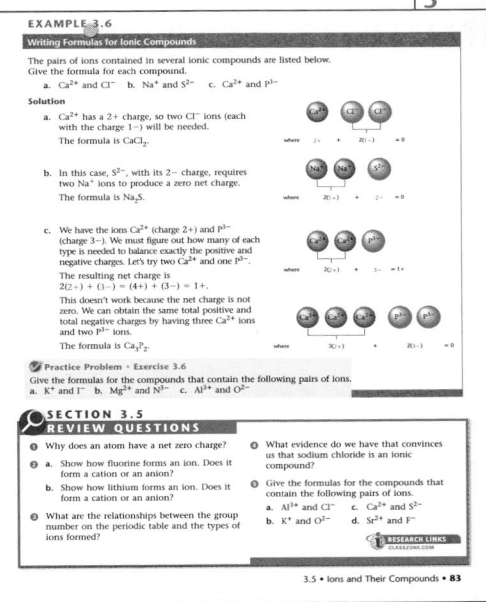

The **Periodic Table** is emphasized throughout. When various elements are introduced in the text, their locations in the periodic table are highlighted visually.

Chemistry in Your World features discuss the latest real-world applications of chemistry to a variety of fields, including science and technology, consumer issues, and history.

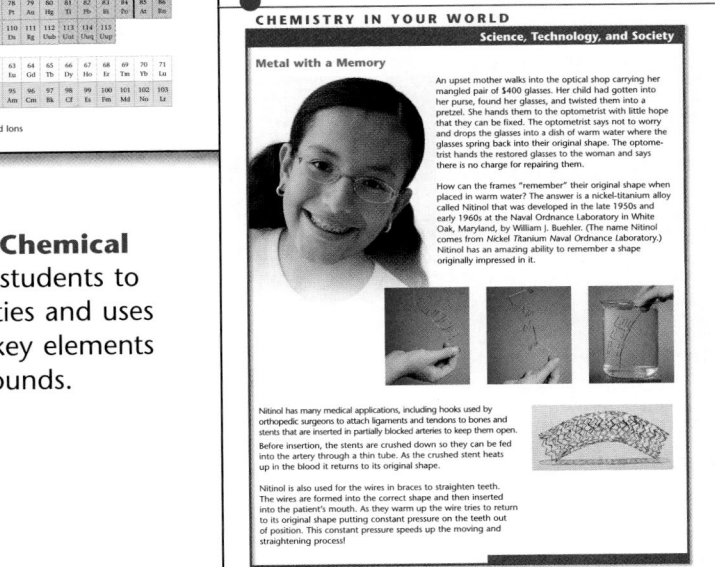

Celebrity Chemical introduces students to the properties and uses of various key elements and compounds.

T-15

Student Edition

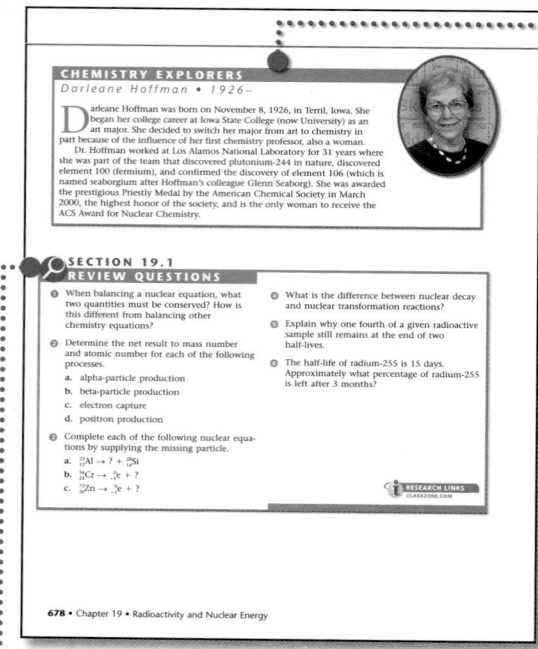

Chemistry Explorers features highlight the contributions of real people to our understanding of chemistry.

CHEMISTRY EXPLORERS
Darleane Hoffman • 1926–

Darleane Hoffman was born on November 8, 1926, in Terril, Iowa. She began her college career at Iowa State College (now University) as an art major. She decided to switch her major from art to chemistry in part because of the influence of her first chemistry professor, also a woman. Dr. Hoffman worked at Los Alamos National Laboratory for 31 years where she was part of the team that discovered plutonium-244 in nature, discovered element 100 (fermium), and confirmed the discovery of element 106 (which is named seaborgium after Hoffman's colleague Glenn Seaborg). She was awarded the prestigious Priestly Medal by the American Chemical Society in March 2000, the highest honor of the society, and is the only woman to receive the ACS Award for Nuclear Chemistry.

SECTION 19.1
REVIEW QUESTIONS

1 When balancing a nuclear equation, what two quantities must be conserved? How is this different from balancing other chemistry equations?

2 Determine the net result to mass number and atomic number for each of the following processes.
 a. alpha-particle production
 b. beta-particle production
 c. electron capture
 d. positron production

3 Complete each of the following nuclear equations by supplying the missing particle.
 a. $^{27}_{13}Al \rightarrow ? + ^{28}_{14}Si$
 b. $^{51}_{24}Cr \rightarrow ^{0}_{-1}e + ?$
 c. $^{72}_{30}Zn \rightarrow ^{0}_{-1}e + ?$

4 What is the difference between nuclear decay and nuclear transformation reactions?

5 Explain why one fourth of a given radioactive sample still remains at the end of two half-lives.

6 The half-life of radium-255 is 15 days. Approximately what percentage of radium-255 is left after 3 months?

678 • Chapter 19 • Radioactivity and Nuclear Energy

Section Review Questions provide ongoing reinforcement and review of the material from each section of the text.

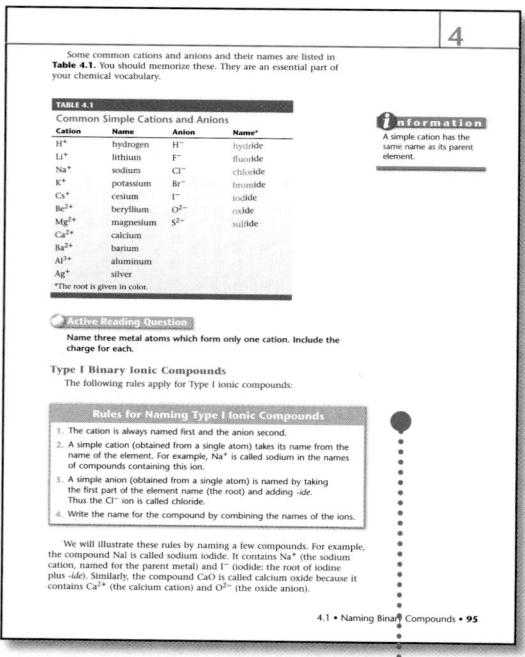

4

Some common cations and anions and their names are listed in **Table 4.1.** You should memorize these. They are an essential part of your chemical vocabulary.

TABLE 4.1
Common Simple Cations and Anions

Cation	Name	Anion	Name*
H⁺	hydrogen	H⁻	hydride
Li⁺	lithium	F⁻	fluoride
Na⁺	sodium	Cl⁻	chloride
K⁺	potassium	Br⁻	bromide
Cs⁺	cesium	I⁻	iodide
Be²⁺	beryllium	O²⁻	oxide
Mg²⁺	magnesium	S²⁻	sulfide
Ca²⁺	calcium		
Ba²⁺	barium		
Al³⁺	aluminum		
Ag⁺	silver		

*The root is given in color.

information
A simple cation has the same name as its parent element.

Active Reading Question
Name three metal atoms which form only one cation. Include the charge for each.

Type I Binary Ionic Compounds
The following rules apply for Type I ionic compounds:

Rules for Naming Type I Ionic Compounds

1. The cation is always named first and the anion second.
2. A simple cation (obtained from a single atom) takes its name from the name of the element. For example, Na⁺ is called sodium in the names of compounds containing this ion.
3. A simple anion (obtained from a single atom) is named by taking the first part of the element name (the root) and adding -ide. Thus the Cl⁻ ion is called chloride.
4. Write the name for the compound by combining the names of the ions.

We will illustrate these rules by naming a few compounds. For example, the compound NaI is called sodium iodide. It contains Na⁺ (the sodium cation, named for the parent metal) and I⁻ (iodide: the root of iodine plus -ide). Similarly, the compound CaO is called calcium oxide because it contains Ca²⁺ (the calcium cation) and O²⁻ (the oxide ion).

4.1 • Naming Binary Compounds • 95

Important **Tools and Rules** are set off from the text in colored boxes and are clearly enumerated for easy reference.

2

Homogeneous and Heterogeneous Mixtures

Mixtures can be classified as either homogeneous or heterogeneous. A **homogeneous mixture** is *the same throughout.* For example, when we dissolve some salt in water and stir well, all regions of the resulting mixture have the same properties. A homogeneous mixture is also called a **solution.** Of course, different amounts of salt and water can be mixed to form various solutions, but a homogeneous mixture (a solution) does not vary in composition from one region of the solution to another (see **Figure 2.13**).

The air around you is a solution—it is a homogeneous mixture of gases. Solid solutions also exist. Brass is a homogeneous mixture of the metals copper and zinc.

A **heterogeneous mixture** contains regions that have different properties from those of other regions. For example, when we pour sand into water, the resulting mixture has one region containing water and another, very different region containing mostly sand (see **Figure 2.14**).

Homogeneous mixture
A mixture that is the same throughout

Solution
A homogeneous mixture

Heterogeneous mixture
A mixture containing regions with differing properties

Figure 2.13 Figure 2.14

Figure 2.13
When table salt is stirred into water (left), a homogeneous mixture called a solution is formed (right).

Figure 2.14
Sand and water do not mix to form a uniform mixture. After the mixture is stirred, the sand settles back to the bottom.

HANDS-ON CHEMISTRY • MINI-LAB •
Mysterious Mixing

Materials
- clear plastic cup
- food coloring
- water

Procedure
1. Fill a clear plastic cup halfway with water.
2. Carefully place a drop of food coloring on the surface of the water.
3. Without disturbing the water, observe the food coloring for a few minutes.
4. How can you make the food coloring mix more quickly with the water? Design an experiment and discuss it with your teacher.
5. Test the experiment.

Results/Analysis
1. Make a list of your observations from step 3.
2. The water does not appear to be moving. What do your observations tell you about the water molecules? Explain your answer.
3. Draw molecular-level pictures that explain your observations.
4. Explain the results of your experiment to make the food coloring mix more quickly with the water.

2.3 • Classifying Matter • 39

Hands-On Chemistry provides mini-labs that can be performed quickly and easily with readily available materials.

Examples are titled for easy reference, and model a thoughtful, step-by-step approach to problem solving.

EXAMPLE 10.3
Calculations Involving Specific Heat Capacity

What quantity of energy (in joules and in calories) is required to heat a piece of iron weighing 1.3 g from 25 °C to 46 °C?

Solution
Where do we want to go?

1.3 g iron
T = 25 °C
? joules
⇨
1.3 g iron
T = 46 °C

What do we know?
- Mass of iron sample = 1.3 g
- Initial temperature = 25 °C
- Final temperature = 46 °C
- Specific heat of iron = 0.45 J/g °C
- 1 cal = 4.184 J

How do we get there?
Our task is to determine how much energy is required (J and cal). It takes 0.45 J to raise the temperature of a 1-g piece of iron by 1 °C.

1.0 g iron
T = 25 °C
0.45 J
⇨
1.0 g iron
T = 26 °C

In this case our sample is 1.3 g, so 1.3 × 0.45 J is required for *each* degree of temperature increase.

1.3 g iron
T = 25 °C
1.3 × 0.45 J
⇨
1.3 g iron
T = 26 °C

MATH
The result you will get on your calculator is 12.285, which rounds to 12.

Because the temperature increase is 21 °C (46 °C − 25 °C = 21 °C), the total amount of energy required is

$$0.45 \frac{J}{g \cdot °C} \times 1.3 \, g \times 21 \, °C = 12 \, J$$

1.3 g iron
T = 25 °C
21 × 1.3 × 0.45 J
⇨
1.3 g iron
T = 46 °C

To calculate this energy in calories, we construct the appropriate conversion factor. We want to change from joules to calories, so cal must be in the numerator and J in the denominator, where it cancels:

$$12 \, J \times = \frac{1 \, cal}{4.184 \, J} = 2.9 \, cal$$

Does it make sense?
The final units of J and cal are energy units as required. The answers have 2 significant figures because all of the measurements are given with 2 significant figures.

Practice Problem • Exercise 10.3
A 5.63-g sample of solid gold is heated from 21 °C to 32 °C. How much energy (in joules and calories) is required?

330 • Chapter 10 • Energy

Most examples are followed by **Practice Problems**, which provide students with opportunities to practice the skills they have just learned.

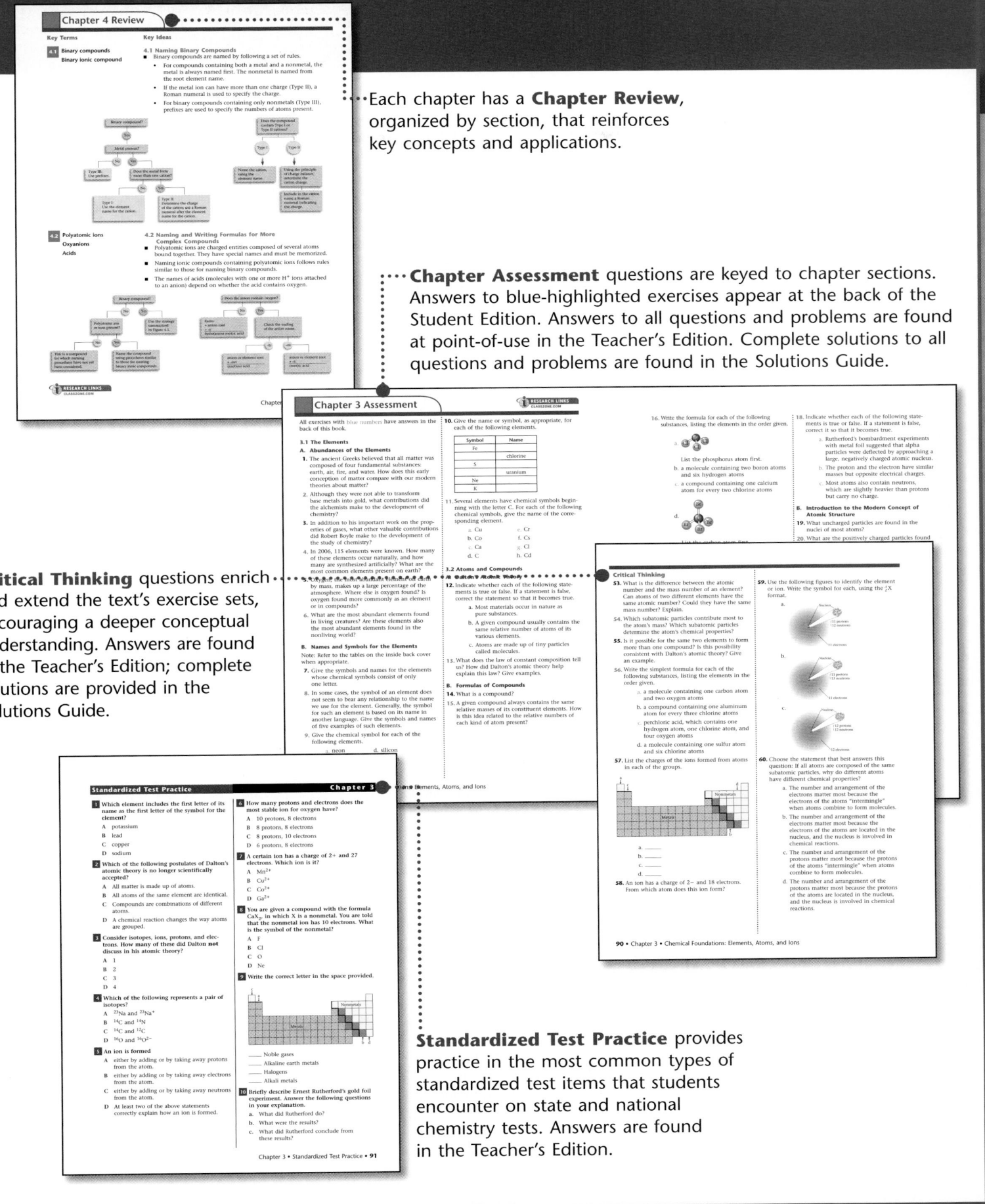

Each chapter has a **Chapter Review**, organized by section, that reinforces key concepts and applications.

Chapter Assessment questions are keyed to chapter sections. Answers to blue-highlighted exercises appear at the back of the Student Edition. Answers to all questions and problems are found at point-of-use in the Teacher's Edition. Complete solutions to all questions and problems are found in the Solutions Guide.

Critical Thinking questions enrich and extend the text's exercise sets, encouraging a deeper conceptual understanding. Answers are found in the Teacher's Edition; complete solutions are provided in the Solutions Guide.

Standardized Test Practice provides practice in the most common types of standardized test items that students encounter on state and national chemistry tests. Answers are found in the Teacher's Edition.

Student Edition

Fostering the development of problem-solving skills is a core principle in the learning approach of the *World of Chemistry*. Early chapters of the text help students understand that to be successful in chemistry, they must learn how to "think like a chemist" by using a systematic approach to exploration.

A four-step problem-solving strategy is formalized in Chapter 5 and used throughout the text to help students develop problem-solving strategies that they can use beyond the classroom.

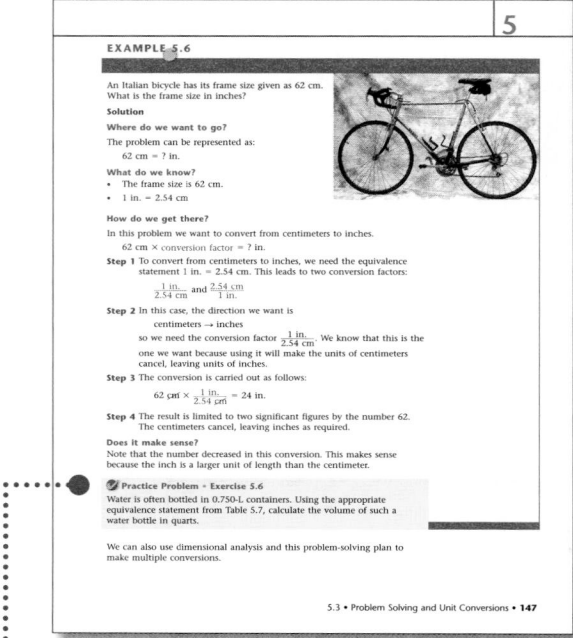

Practice Problems found after Examples give an immediate opportunity for students to apply the skills they have learned.

To emphasize the importance of a logical approach to building chemical knowledge, problem-solving steps are also used in the explanatory text, when appropriate.

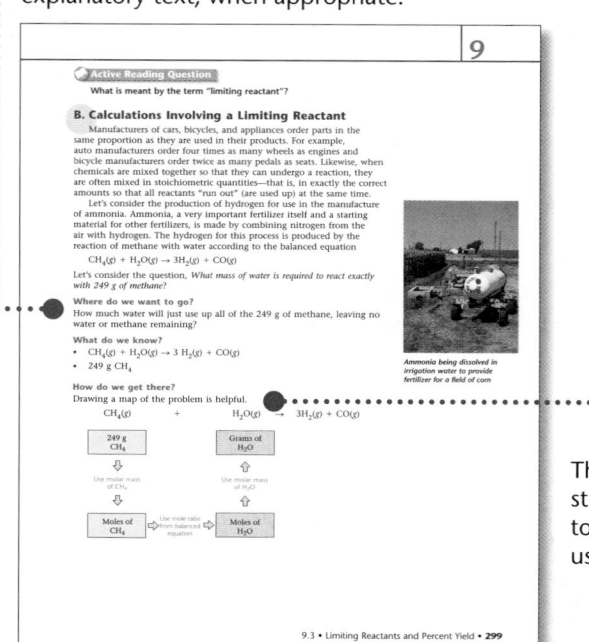

Examples emphasize a broader conceptual understanding rather than rote memorization.

The problem-solving strategy is completed by thinking about whether the answer makes sense.

Throughout the text, students are encouraged to begin solving problems using symbols and diagrams.

Teacher's Edition

Teacher's Edition Features

- Entire content of Student Edition
- Complete section-by-section Chapter Planning Guide
- Wraparound margin notes, including:
  - Chapter Review
  - Teaching Tips
  - More Examples based on in-text Examples
  - Background material
  - Suggestions for setting up and performing in-class demonstrations and activities
  - References to print and technology resources at point-of-use
  - Answers to all questions and problems within the text

Meeting the Standards

World of Chemistry has been correlated to the National Science Education Standards. The standards covered by each Section are indicated in the Chapter Planners. A complete correlation to the standards is provided in the Teacher's Edition starting on page T-42.

A resourceful Teacher's Edition that is straightforward and uncomplicated provides helpful tools and ideas for effective classroom integration.

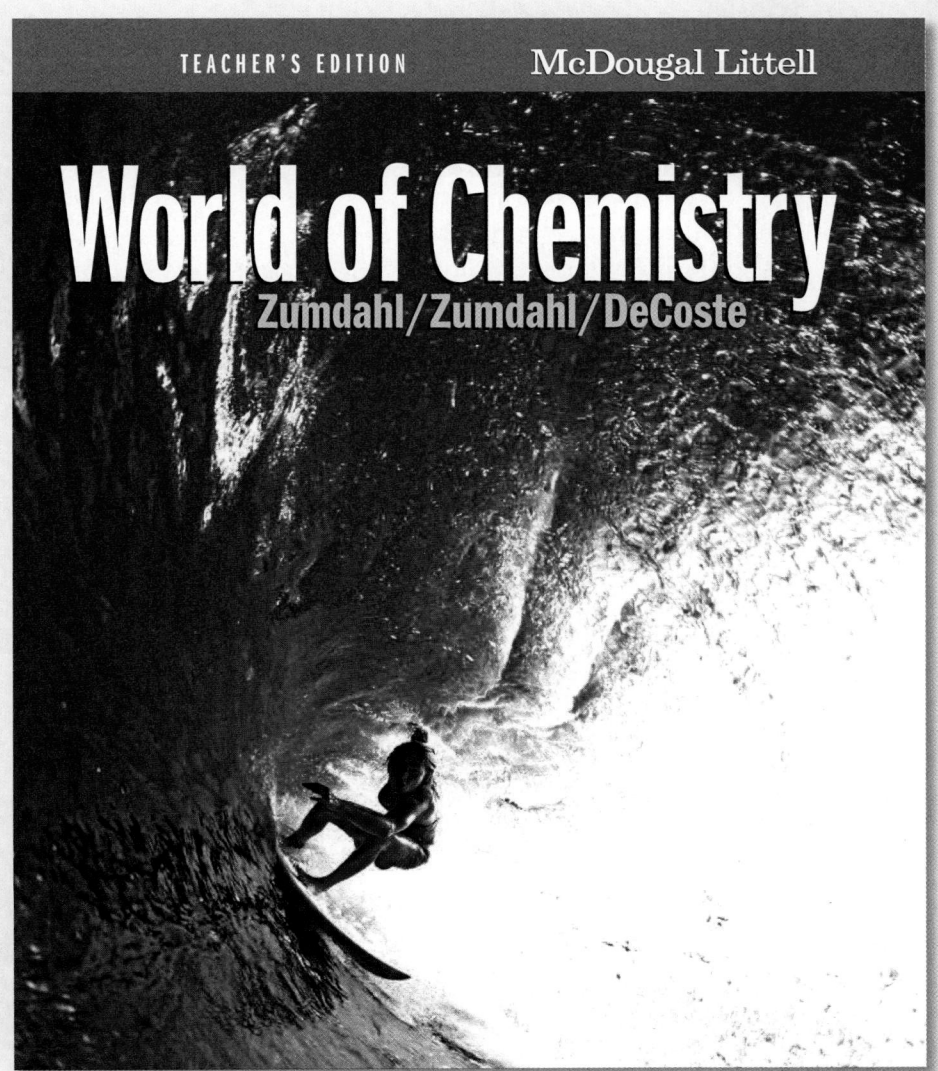

TEACHER'S EDITION McDougal Littell

World of Chemistry
Zumdahl/Zumdahl/DeCoste

Teacher's Edition

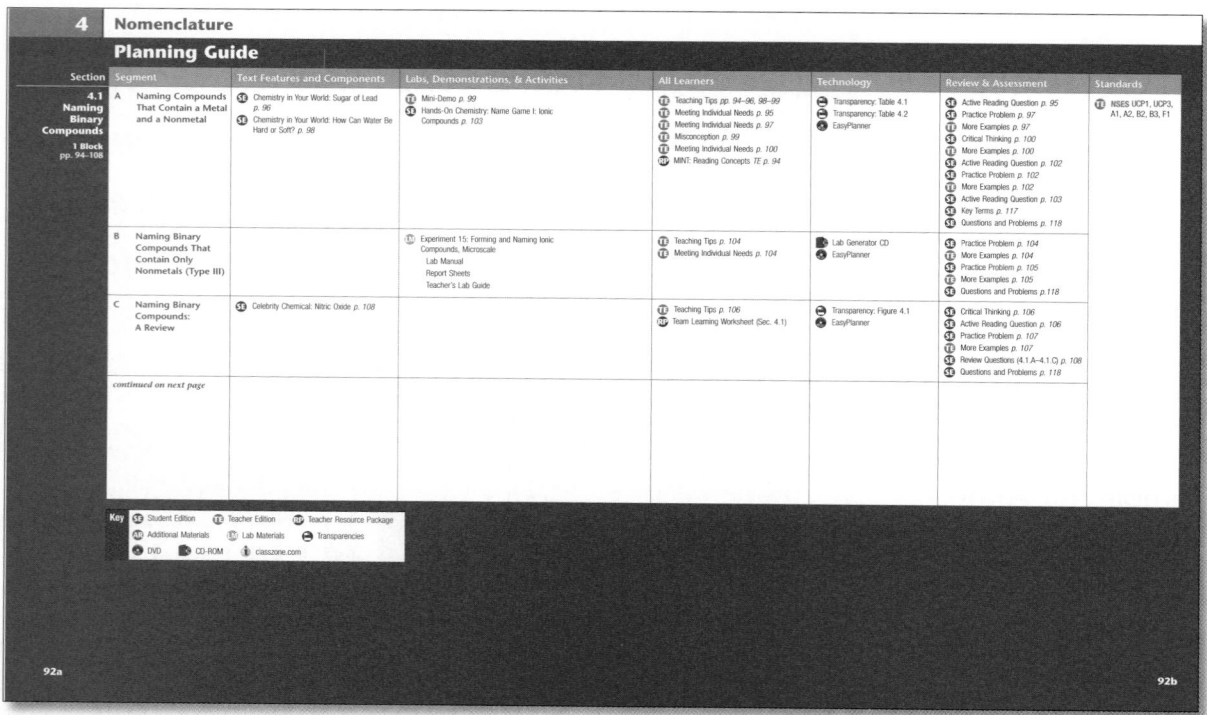

Each Chapter **Planning Guide** provides a section-by-section guide to help with classroom planning and time management. Labs, activities, features, assessments, technology resources, and strategies for all learners are clearly indicated for quick reference. References to National Standards are indicated.

An **Overview** is provided on each chapter opener page. This feature clearly defines the goals for the chapter, allowing for a quick determination of the objectives accomplished within the chapter.

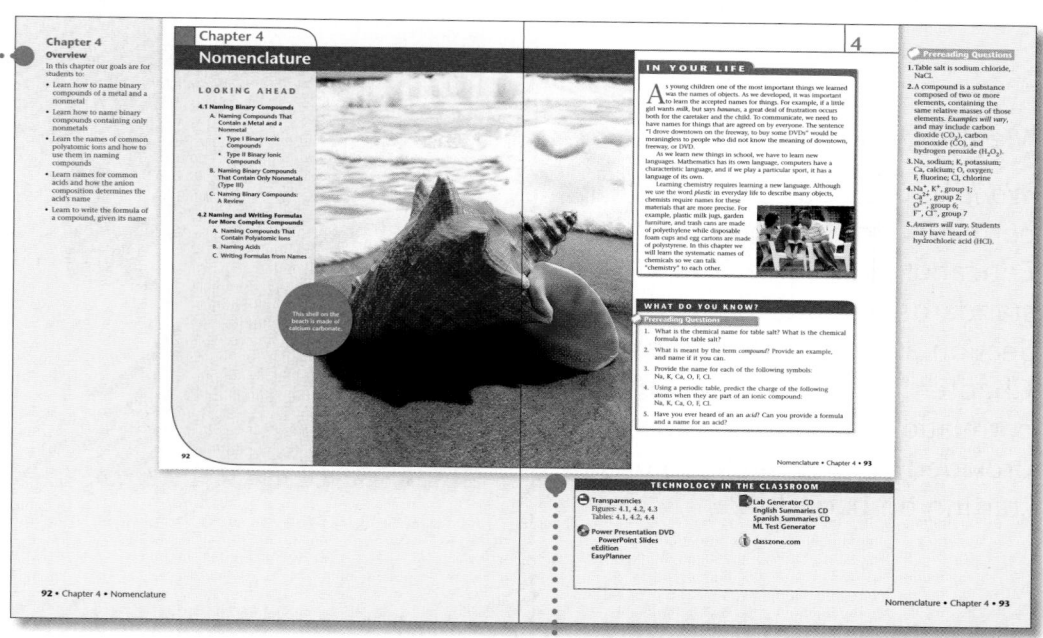

Technology in the Classroom provides a handy overview of available technology resources.

Group Activities and other inclusion strategies appear in appropriate locations throughout the text, providing valuable suggestions to reach all learners.

In-depth **Teaching Tips** provide information and strategies to help present concepts to students who have various learning styles, skill levels, and interests. These ideas can also help trigger prior knowledge, reinforce concepts, and extend the material.

Misconceptions are highlighted throughout the text, and tips are given to clarify misinterpretations, to help you caution students against common mistakes, and to clear up confusion about terms and symbols.

Additional information about the materials and purpose of each **Hands-On Chemistry Mini-Lab** helps you implement these activities quickly and efficiently. Class discussion ideas are presented and questions that are posed in the activity are answered in detail.

Teaching Support boxes provide:
- Demonstrations
- Background Information
- Historical Information
- Tips on Meeting Individual Needs

Mini-Demos suggest ideas for quick, effective classroom demos to introduce or reinforce concepts.

More Examples corresponding to a specific in-text example problem can be used to reinforce new concepts. These examples are similar in style and in substance to the examples in the student text, and all answers are provided.

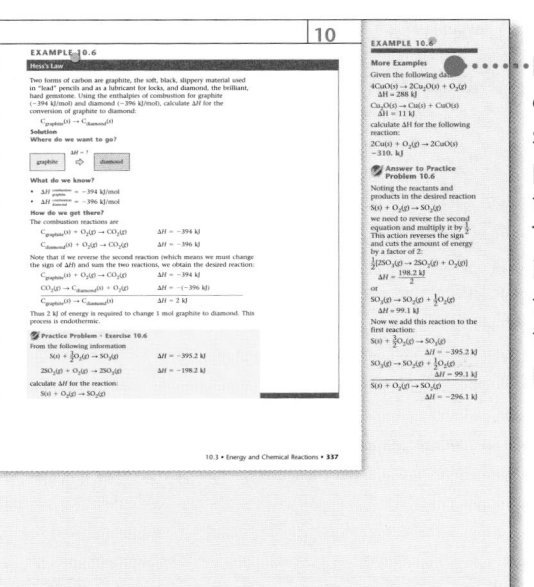

Teacher's Edition

Answers to the Prereading Questions, Active Reading Questions, Questions and Problems, and Critical Thinking questions are provided at point-of-use.

Support on Chapter Review pages directs you to additional assessment resources.

Answers to Standardized Test Practice questions are provided at point-of-use.

Resource Package

Accessible Content

Creative Problem Solving

Real-World Connections

Active Learning

All the Elements for Success

- Laboratory Program
- Assessment Program
- Teacher Resources Program
- Technology Program
- Student Resources Program
- All Learners Program

The World of Chemistry *program includes all of the elements for a successful learning experience. In addition to the Student Edition and the Teacher's Edition, the curriculum includes a wide variety of tools.*

The Laboratory Program *is designed to help students learn chemistry by exploring the chemical nature of matter. In addition to the Mini-labs and Demonstrations explained in the Student and Teacher's Editions, the program includes the following items:*

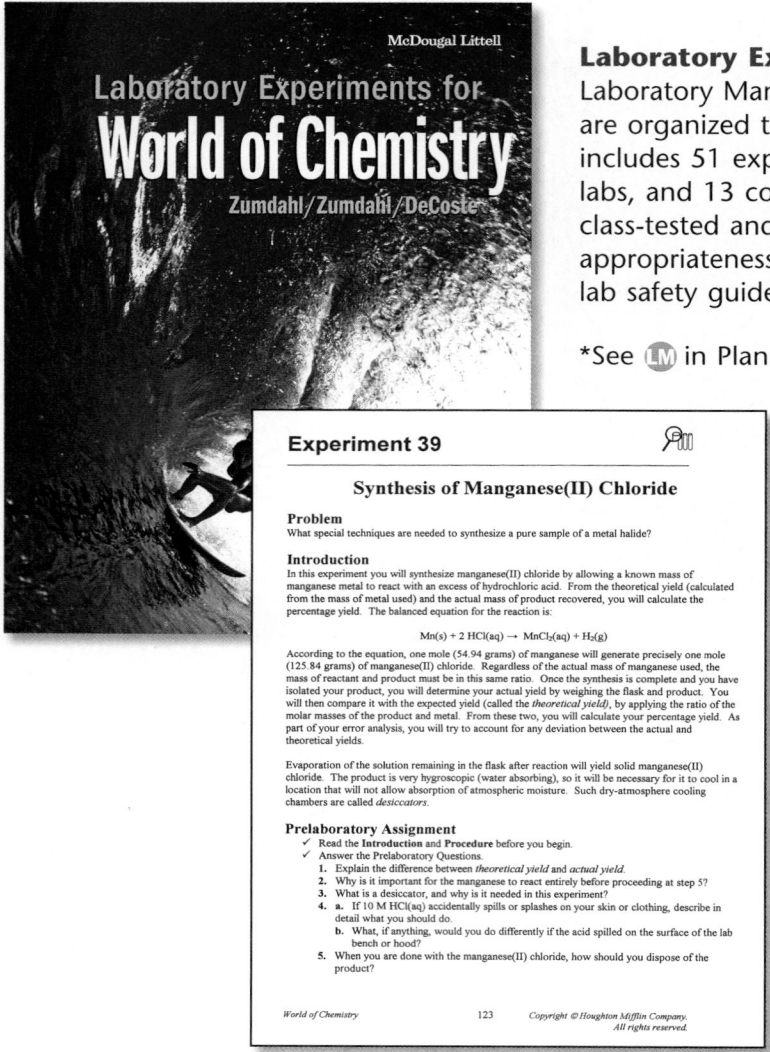

Laboratory Experiments for World of Chemistry* This Laboratory Manual provides 91 engaging experiments, which are organized to match the topics in the text. The manual includes 51 experiments of a traditional nature, 27 microscale labs, and 13 computer-based labs. All experiments have been class-tested and have undergone a safety review to ensure their appropriateness for high school chemistry students. Complete lab safety guidelines are provided throughout the manual.

*See **LM** in Planning Guide

Experiment 39

Synthesis of Manganese(II) Chloride

Problem
What special techniques are needed to synthesize a pure sample of a metal halide?

Introduction
In this experiment you will synthesize manganese(II) chloride by allowing a known mass of manganese metal to react with an excess of hydrochloric acid. From the theoretical yield (calculated from the mass of metal used) and the actual mass of product recovered, you will calculate the percentage yield. The balanced equation for the reaction is:

$$Mn(s) + 2\ HCl(aq) \rightarrow MnCl_2(aq) + H_2(g)$$

According to the equation, one mole (54.94 grams) of manganese will generate precisely one mole (125.84 grams) of manganese(II) chloride. Regardless of the actual mass of manganese used, the mass of reactant and product must be in this same ratio. Once the synthesis is complete and you have isolated your product, you will determine your actual yield by weighing the flask and product. You will then compare it with the expected yield (called the *theoretical yield*), by applying the ratio of the molar masses of the product and metal. From these two, you will calculate your percentage yield. As part of your error analysis, you will try to account for any deviation between the actual and theoretical yields.

Evaporation of the solution remaining in the flask after reaction will yield solid manganese(II) chloride. The product is very hygroscopic (water absorbing), so it will be necessary for it to cool in a location that will not allow absorption of atmospheric moisture. Such dry-atmosphere cooling chambers are called *desiccators*.

Prelaboratory Assignment
✓ Read the **Introduction** and **Procedure** before you begin.
✓ Answer the Prelaboratory Questions.
1. Explain the difference between *theoretical yield* and *actual yield*.
2. Why is it important for the manganese to react entirely before proceeding at step 5?
3. What is a desiccator, and why is it needed in this experiment?
4. a. If 10 M HCl(aq) accidentally spills or splashes on your skin or clothing, describe in detail what you should do.
   b. What, if anything, would you do differently if the acid spilled on the surface of the lab bench or hood?
5. When you are done with the manganese(II) chloride, how should you dispose of the product?

World of Chemistry   123   *Copyright © Houghton Mifflin Company. All rights reserved.*

Teacher's Guide to Accompany Laboratory Experiments* This helpful guide includes general notes about each experiment, detailed hints for teacher laboratory preparation and cleanup, hints for prelaboratory and postlaboratory discussions, lists of materials required, and a key for the student report sheet that contains sample data as well as detailed answers for the questions and calculations.

*See **LM** in Planning Guide

Teacher Resources
Teacher's Guide
to accompany Laboratory Experiments for

McDougal Littell

World of Chemistry

Stev

Experiment 39

Synthesis of Manganese(II) Chloride

Introduction

Intent
Students synthesize a compound, then calculate their percent yield. Because the product is hygroscopic, they must take care to avoid absorption of moisture using a simple, home-made desiccator.

Objectives
1. To synthesize manganese(II) chloride from a known mass of manganese metal and excess hydrochloric acid.
2. To isolate the dry product, and determine the mass and percent yield.
3. To apply extensive error analysis to evaluate the results of the experiment.

Materials (for each lab team of 2 students)

Apparatus	Reagents
Milligram balance (1 for 3-4 groups)	Manganese metal, 0.1 gram
Erlenmeyer flask, 10-mL	10 M hydrochloric acid, 1.5 mL
Sand bath	Boiling stone
Tongs or forceps for handling (hot flask)	
Desiccator	
Safety goggles (2)	
Lab apron (2)	

Preparation Hints
Manganese metal chips of reasonable purity are available from Al...
Crush the chips with a hammer or mortar and pestle. Each studen...
If milligram balances aren't available, consider doubling the mass ...
the time needed for dissolving, so it might be wise to do steps 2-4 ...
experiment the next.

The choice of 10 M hydrochloric acid is arbitrary. It is just dilute ...
45 mL of concentrated acid added to 5 mL of water makes enoug...

Prelaboratory Discussion
Point out the need for caution in handling the acid. Also tell stude...
small amount of manganese sulfide present as an impurity which r...
hydrogen sulfide, H₂S (rotten-egg odor). If students detect this o...
an operating fume hood until the manganese has fully dissolved.

World of Chemistry   219   Copyright ©

Name_____

Section_____ Date_____

Report for Experiment 39

Synthesis of Manganese(II) Chloride

Prelaboratory Questions

1. Explain the difference between *theoretical yield* and *actual yield*.

   The theoretical yield is calculated from the mass of reactants, while the actual yield is the mass of product recovered.

2. Why is it important for the manganese to react entirely before proceeding at step 5?

   Until the manganese has dissolved, it is not manganese chloride. Any undissolved manganese will be recovered as the metal, reducing the yield of product.

3. What is a desiccator, and why is it needed in this experiment?

   A desiccator is a container that maintains a moisture-free atmosphere. It is used here to prevent the MnCl₂ from absorbing moisture during cooling.

4. **a.** If 10 M HCl(aq) accidentally spills or splashes on your skin or clothing, describe in detail what you should do.
   Rinse it off with large volumes of water; tell the teacher.

   b. What, if anything, would you do differently if the acid spilled on the surface of the lab bench or hood?
   Surface spills can first be neutralized with baking soda, then flushed away with large amounts of water.

5. When you are done with the manganese(II) chloride, how should you dispose of the product?

   The flask with the product is to be put in a location designated by the teacher, who will then see to safe disposal. It is not to be washed down the sink.

Data/Observations

Mass of empty Erlenmeyer flask (with boiling stone):	_16.285_	g
Mass of Erlenmeyer flask and manganese metal:	_16.394_	g
Mass of flask and manganese(II) chloride:	_16.549_	g
Final mass of flask and manganese(II) chloride:	_16.542_	g

Appearance of manganese(II) chloride *pale pink, flaky*

Was the reaction between manganese metal and hydrochloric acid endothermic or exothermic? Describe the evidence on which you base your answer.

Exothermic—the flask felt hot and there was steam condensing.

World of Chemistry   221   Copyright © Houghton Mifflin Company.
All rights reserved.

Laboratory

Report Sheets to Accompany Laboratory Experiments*

Student report sheets are provided for all of the experiments in *Laboratory Experiments for World of Chemistry*. The report sheet is an organized form for students to use when answering Prelaboratory Questions, recording their data/observations, and completing their analysis and conclusions.

For teachers who prefer that their students write their own lab reports, the experiments are written to include prelaboratory questions, information on preparing data tables and tables for results, and analysis questions.

*See LM in Planning Guide

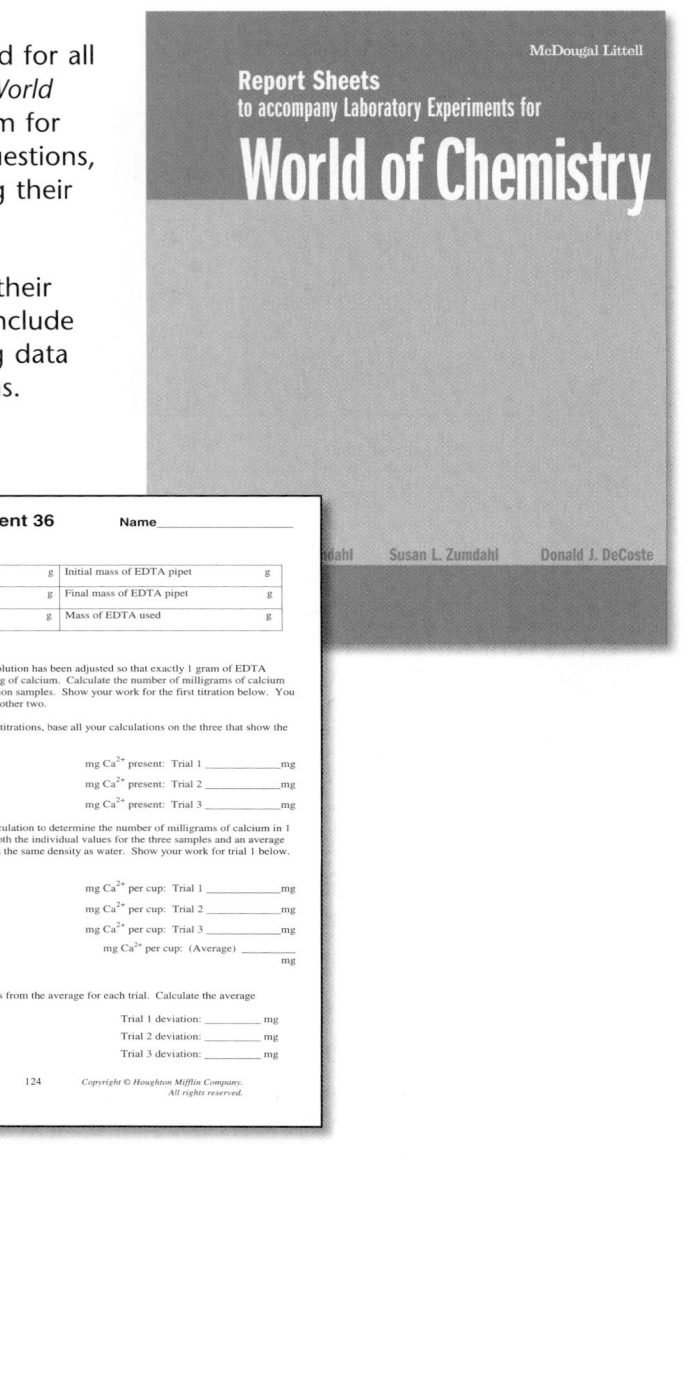

McDougal Littell

Report Sheets
to accompany Laboratory Experiments for

World of Chemistry

...dahl   Susan L. Zumdahl   Donald J. DeCoste

Report for Experiment 36   Name_____

Titration 3:

Initial mass of milk pipet	g	Initial mass of EDTA pipet	g
Final mass of milk pipet	g	Final mass of EDTA pipet	g
Mass of milk used	g	Mass of EDTA used	g

Analysis and Conclusions

1. The concentration of the EDTA solution has been adjusted so that exactly 1 gram of EDTA solution will tie up exactly 1.08 mg of calcium. Calculate the number of milligrams of calcium present in each of your three titration samples. Show your work for the first titration below. You need report only the results of the other two.

    If you carried out more than three titrations, base all your calculations on the three that show the best agreement.

    mg Ca^{2+} present: Trial 1 _____mg

    mg Ca^{2+} present: Trial 2 _____mg

    mg Ca^{2+} present: Trial 3 _____mg

...from the first calculation to determine the number of milligrams of calcium in 1 ...f milk. Report both the individual values for the three samples and an average ...at skim milk has the same density as water. Show your work for trial 1 below.

    mg Ca^{2+} per cup: Trial 1 _____mg

    mg Ca^{2+} per cup: Trial 2 _____mg

    mg Ca^{2+} per cup: Trial 3 _____mg

    mg Ca^{2+} per cup: (Average) _____mg

...vidual deviations from the average for each trial. Calculate the average ...r three trials.

    Trial 1 deviation: _____ mg

    Trial 2 deviation: _____ mg

    Trial 3 deviation: _____ mg

124   *Copyright © Houghton Mifflin Company.*
All rights reserved.

Name_____

Section_____Date_____

Report for Experiment 36

The Calcium Content of Milk

Prelaboratory Questions

1. Why would you expect the calcium in milk to be present as calcium ions, rather than as elemental calcium?

2. According to one source, one cup (~240 mL) of whole milk contains 291 mg of calcium. Use this to calculate the mass percent of calcium in whole milk. Assume the density of milk is 1.0 g/mL.

3. Would you expect the density of milk to be affected by its fat content? Explain. Would increased fat content raise or lower the density? Explain.

Data/Observations

Data Table

Titration 1:

Initial mass of milk pipet	g	Initial mass of EDTA pipet	g
Final mass of milk pipet	g	Final mass of EDTA pipet	g
Mass of milk used	g	Mass of EDTA used	g

Titration 2:

Initial mass of milk pipet	g	Initial mass of EDTA pipet	g
Final mass of milk pipet	g	Final mass of EDTA pipet	g
Mass of milk used	g	Mass of EDTA used	g

World of Chemistry   123   *Copyright © Houghton Mifflin Company.*
All rights reserved.

Assessment

The Assessment Program provides multiple ways to assess student comprehension. The Student Edition offers Prereading and Active Reading Questions, Practice Problems, Section Review Questions, and end-of-chapter problems that also include both Critical Thinking questions and Standardized Test Practice. Answers to all these items, as well as More Examples to assess student comprehension, are found in the Teacher's Edition. In addition, the assessment program includes the following items:

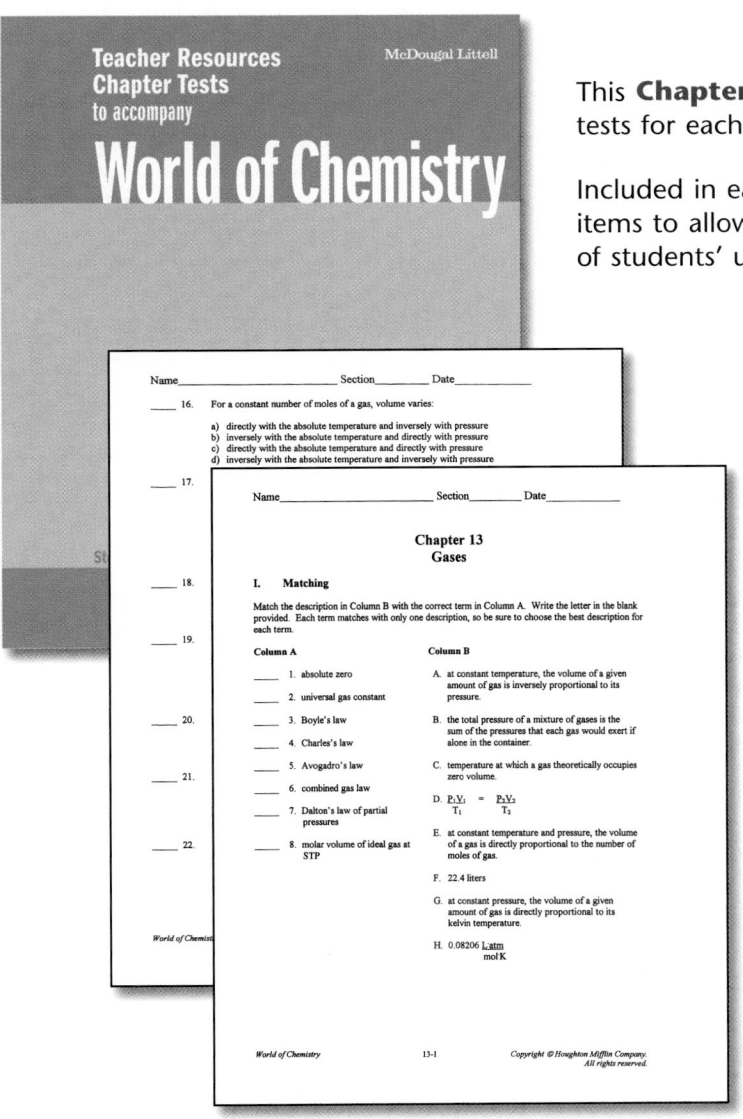

This **Chapter Tests*** resource booklet contains chapter tests for each chapter of *World of Chemistry*.

Included in each chapter test are various styles of test items to allow for a complete, comprehensive assessment of students' understanding of the chapter material:

- Matching items
- Multiple-choice items
- Fill-in-the-blank items
- Free-response items

Answers are provided at the end of the booklet.

*See **RP** in Planning Guide

Assessment

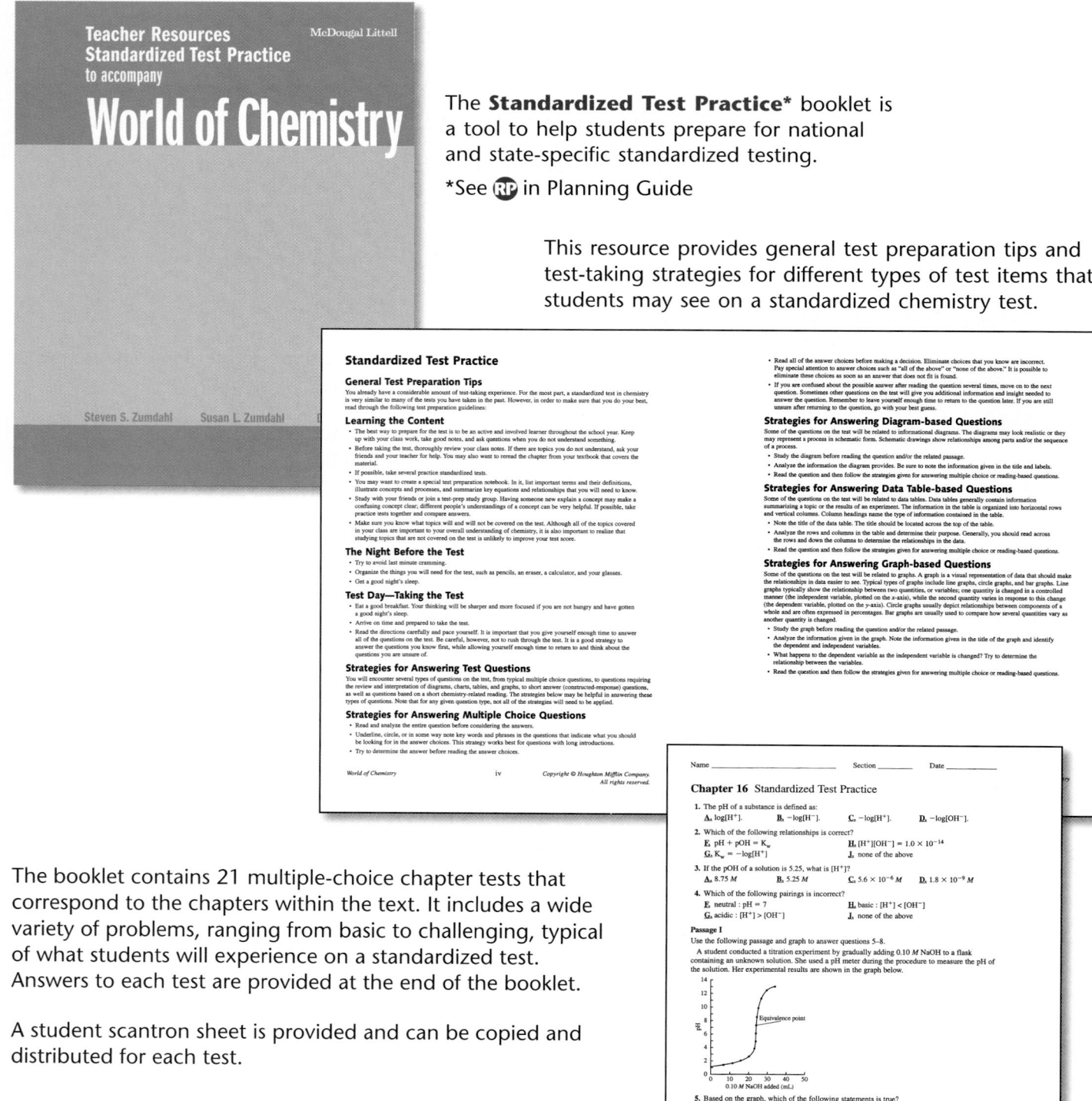

Teacher Resources
Standardized Test Practice
to accompany

McDougal Littell

World of Chemistry

Steven S. Zumdahl   Susan L. Zumdahl

The **Standardized Test Practice*** booklet is a tool to help students prepare for national and state-specific standardized testing.

*See **RP** in Planning Guide

This resource provides general test preparation tips and test-taking strategies for different types of test items that students may see on a standardized chemistry test.

Standardized Test Practice

General Test Preparation Tips
You already have a considerable amount of test-taking experience. For the most part, a standardized test in chemistry is very similar to many of the tests you have taken in the past. However, in order to make sure that you do your best, read through the following test preparation guidelines:

Learning the Content
- The best way to prepare for the test is to be an active and involved learner throughout the school year. Keep up with your class work, take good notes, and ask questions when you do not understand something.
- Before taking the test, thoroughly review your class notes. If there are topics you do not understand, ask your teacher for help. You may also want to reread the chapter from your textbook that covers the material.
- If possible, take several practice standardized tests.
- You may want to create a special test preparation notebook. In it, list important terms and their definitions, illustrate concepts and processes, and summarize key equations and relationships that you will need to know.
- Study with your friends or join a test-prep study group. Having someone new explain a concept may make a confusing concept clear; different people's understandings of a concept can be very helpful. If possible, take practice tests together and compare answers.
- Make sure you know what topics will and will not be covered on the test. Although all of the topics covered in your class are important to your overall understanding of chemistry, it is also important to realize that studying topics that are not covered on the test is unlikely to improve your test score.

The Night Before the Test
- Try to avoid last minute cramming.
- Organize the things you will need for the test, such as pencils, an eraser, a calculator, and your glasses.
- Get a good night's sleep.

Test Day—Taking the Test
- Eat a good breakfast. Your thinking will be sharper and more focused if you are not hungry and have gotten a good night's sleep.
- Arrive on time and prepared to take the test.
- Read the directions carefully and pace yourself. It is important that you give yourself enough time to answer all of the questions on the test. Be careful, however, not to rush through the test. It is a good strategy to answer the questions you know first, while allowing yourself enough time to return to and think about the questions you are unsure of.

Strategies for Answering Test Questions
You will encounter several types of questions on the test, from typical multiple choice questions, to questions requiring the review and interpretation of diagrams, charts, tables, and graphs, to short answer (constructed-response) questions, as well as questions based on a short chemistry-related reading. The strategies below may be helpful in answering these types of questions. Note that for any given question type, not all of the strategies will need to be applied.

Strategies for Answering Multiple Choice Questions
- Read and analyze the entire question before considering the answers.
- Underline, circle, or in some way note key words and phrases in the questions that indicate what you should be looking for in the answer choices. This strategy works best for questions with long introductions.
- Try to determine the answer before reading the answer choices.

- Read all of the answer choices before making a decision. Eliminate choices that you know are incorrect. Pay special attention to answer choices such as "all of the above" or "none of the above." It is possible to eliminate these choices as soon as an answer that does not fit is found.
- If you are confused about the possible answer after reading the question several times, move on to the next question. Sometimes other questions on the test will give you additional information and insight needed to answer the question. Remember to leave yourself enough time to return to the question later. If you are still unsure after returning to the question, go with your best guess.

Strategies for Answering Diagram-based Questions
Some of the questions on the test will be related to informational diagrams. The diagrams may look realistic or they may represent a process in schematic form. Schematic drawings show relationships among parts and/or the sequence of a process.
- Study the diagram before reading the question and/or the related passage.
- Analyze the information the diagram provides. Be sure to note the information given in the title and labels.
- Read the question and then follow the strategies given for answering multiple choice or reading-based questions.

Strategies for Answering Data Table-based Questions
Some of the questions on the test will be related to data tables. Data tables generally contain information summarizing a topic or the results of an experiment. The information in the table is organized into horizontal rows and vertical columns. Column headings name the type of information contained in the table.
- Note the title of the data table. The title should be located across the top of the table.
- Analyze the rows and columns in the table and determine their purpose. Generally, you should read across the rows and down the columns to determine the relationships in the data.
- Read the question and then follow the strategies given for answering multiple choice or reading-based questions.

Strategies for Answering Graph-based Questions
Some of the questions on the test will be related to graphs. A graph is a visual representation of data that should make the relationships in data easier to see. Typical types of graphs include line graphs, circle graphs, and bar graphs. Line graphs typically show the relationship between two quantities, or variables; one quantity is changed in a controlled manner (the independent variable, plotted on the x-axis), while the second quantity varies in response to this change (the dependent variable, plotted on the y-axis). Circle graphs usually depict relationships between components of a whole and are often expressed in percentages. Bar graphs are usually used to compare how several quantities vary as another quantity is changed.
- Study the graph before reading the question and/or the related passage.
- Analyze the information given in the graph. Note the information given in the title of the graph and identify the dependent and independent variables.
- What happens to the dependent variable as the independent variable is changed? Try to determine the relationship between the variables.
- Read the question and then follow the strategies given for answering multiple choice or reading-based questions.

World of Chemistry   iv

Name _____   Section _____   Date _____

Chapter 16 Standardized Test Practice

1. The pH of a substance is defined as:
A. log[H$^+$].   **B.** −log[H$^−$].   **C.** −log[H$^+$].   **D.** −log[OH$^−$].

2. Which of the following relationships is correct?
E. pH + pOH = K$_w$ **H.** [H$^+$][OH$^−$] = 1.0 × 10^{-14}
G. K$_w$ = −log[H$^+$]   **J.** none of the above

3. If the pOH of a solution is 5.25, what is [H$^+$]?
A. 8.75 M **B.** 5.25 M **C.** 5.6 × 10^{-6} M **D.** 1.8 × 10^{-9} M

4. Which of the following pairings is incorrect?
E. neutral : pH = 7   **H.** basic : [H$^+$] < [OH$^−$]
G. acidic : [H$^+$] > [OH$^−$]   **J.** none of the above

Passage I
Use the following passage and graph to answer questions 5–8.

A student conducted a titration experiment by gradually adding 0.10 M NaOH to a flask containing an unknown solution. She used a pH meter during the procedure to measure the pH of the solution. Her experimental results are shown in the graph below.

5. Based on the graph, which of the following statements is true?
A. At the equivalence point, [H$^+$] > [OH$^−$].
B. The titration curve indicates that the unknown liquid is a weak base.
C. The titration curve indicates that the unknown liquid is a weak acid.
D. At the equivalence point, −log[H$^+$] = 7.

World of Chemistry   42

The booklet contains 21 multiple-choice chapter tests that correspond to the chapters within the text. It includes a wide variety of problems, ranging from basic to challenging, typical of what students will experience on a standardized test. Answers to each test are provided at the end of the booklet.

A student scantron sheet is provided and can be copied and distributed for each test.

McDougal Littell Test Generator* The computerized test bank augments the printed Chapter Tests resource by providing a wealth of questions teachers can select or edit to create quizzes and tests. This powerful, easy-to-use program can produce multiple-choice, true/false, short-answer, matching, fill-in-the-blank, and essay questions. Teachers can select questions according to chapter, question format, type, and/or topic.

*See 🛈 in Planning Guide

Test Bank* This teacher resource contains printed versions of approximately 1600 items from the computerized test bank, arranged by chapter. The test items consist of multiple-choice, true-false, short-answer, matching, fill-in-the-blank, and essay questions. The questions do not repeat any items from the Chapter Test resource booklet.

*See 🆁🅿 in Planning Guide

Teacher Resources
Test Bank
to accompany

McDougal Littell

World of Chemistry

Steven S. Zumda

CHAPTER 9

Chemical Quantities

1. The balanced equation $P_4(s) + 6H_2(g) \rightarrow 4PH_3(g)$ tells us that 2 mol H_2
    a. reacts with 1 mol P_4
    b. produces 4 mol PH_3
    c. cannot react with phosphorus
    d. produces 2 mol PH_3
    e. reacts with 2 mol P_4

    ANSWER: d. produces 2 mol PH_3

2. The equation $N_2(g) + 3H_2(g) \rightarrow 2NH_3(g)$ can be interpreted by saying that 1 mol of N_2 reacts with 3 mol of H_2 to form 2 mol of NH_3. T/F _____

    ANSWER: True

3. A balanced chemical equation is one that has the same number of moles of molecules on each side of the equation. T/F _____

    ANSWER: False

4. The balanced equation $2Cu(s) + O_2(g) \rightarrow 2CuO(s)$ tells us that 1 mol of Cu
    a. reacts with 1 mol of O_2
    b. produces 1 mol of CuO
    c. must react with 32 g of O_2
    d. cannot react with oxygen
    e. produces 2 mol of CuO

    ANSWER: b. produces 1 mol of CuO

5. A mole ratio is used to convert the moles of starting substance to the moles of desired substance. T/F _____

    ANSWER: True

117

Teacher Resources

The Teacher Resources Progam *provides teachers with*
additional materials for
classroom assistance and management.

Transparencies* This package features full-color overhead transparency acetates of key illustrations from the text. Each transparency is clearly labeled with the table number or figure number from the text. Each transparency is referenced at point-of-use in the Teacher's Edition.

These visual aids help reinforce important concepts and are particularly helpful to the visual learner.

*See 🚢 in Planning Guide

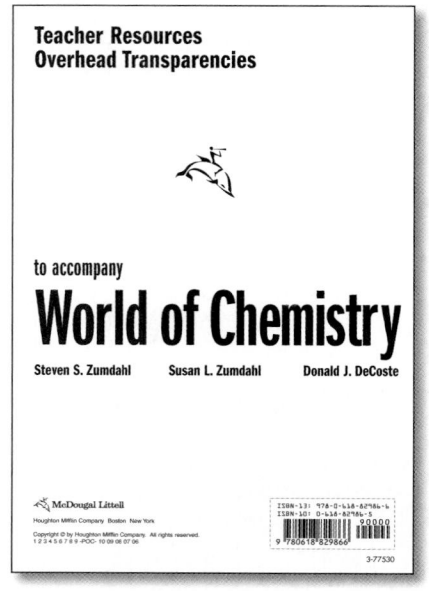

Teacher Resources
Overhead Transparencies

to accompany

World of Chemistry

Steven S. Zumdahl   Susan L. Zumdahl   Donald J. DeCoste

McDougal Littell
Houghton Mifflin Company Boston New York
Copyright © by Houghton Mifflin Company. All rights reserved.
1 2 3 4 5 6 7 8 9 -POO- 10 09 08 07 06

ISBN-13: 978-0-618-82986-6
ISBN-10: 0-618-82986-5   99000
9 780618 829866
3-77530

Figure 10.6

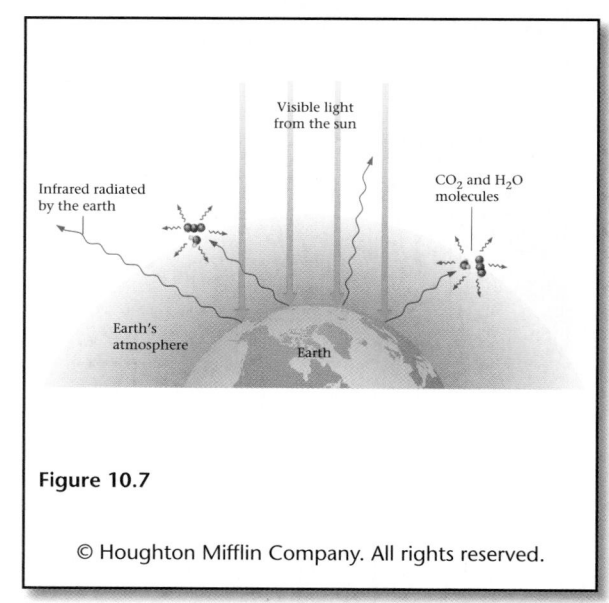

Figure 10.7

Classroom Activities and Projects* This teacher resource contains templates, guidelines, teaching notes, and suggested activities designed to supplement discussions and explanations in the text. Most of the activities and projects are cross-referenced with the appropriate chapters in the text, and are flagged at point-of-use in the Teacher's Edition. This resource also includes quarterly projects and a special Spring Project designed for independent student work.

*See **RP** in Planning Guide

The **Teacher's Solutions Guide*** contains completely worked-out solutions to all of the questions, problems, and critical thinking questions contained in the text at the end of each chapter. Solutions are written in a manner that complements the explanations in the textbook.

*See **RP** in Planning Guide

Technology

The Technology Program *provides a comprehensive collection of technology resources to meet your needs.*

- *Presentation tools help make your presentations more exciting and engaging.*
- *Planning resources streamline preparation and planning time.*
- *Electronic laboratory materials make it easier to take advantage of hands-on learning tools, from quick classroom demos to full-scale laboratory experiments.*

Power Presentations DVD* This DVD collects a wealth of presentation tools in one place for convenience in preparing classroom presentations. The disk contains prepared lecture outlines in PowerPoint that include key figures from the text, video clips and animations, a Media Gallery of art and photos from the text, flipcards for vocabulary review, and a review game to motivate and challenge students to remember important concepts and vocabulary.

*See 🔘 in Planning Guide

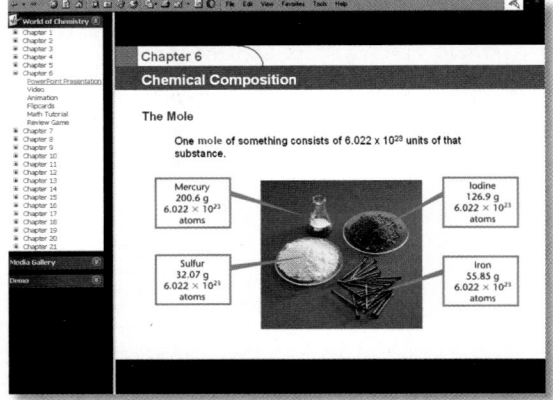

PowerPoint® lecture outlines for each chapter are enhanced with art and tables from the text. Slides can be used as-is, or edited for a custom presentation.

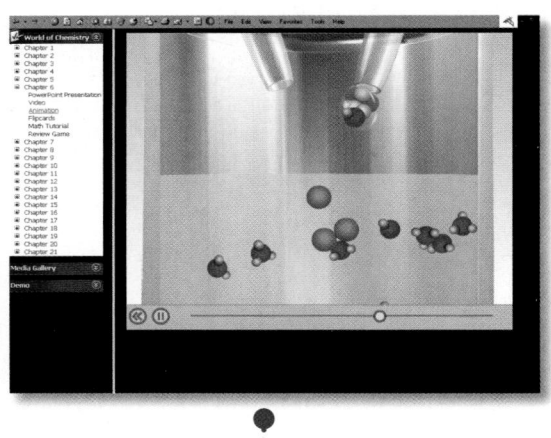

Video clips of chemical phenomena and dozens of **Animations** of molecular-level processes and key chemical concepts are provided for use in classroom presentations. References in the Planning Guide and point-of-use citations in the Teacher's Edition indicate when animations and videos are available to enhance topics in the text.

The **Media Gallery** is a searchable database of selected art and photos from the text that allows you to quickly and easily create a slide show from the images you select.

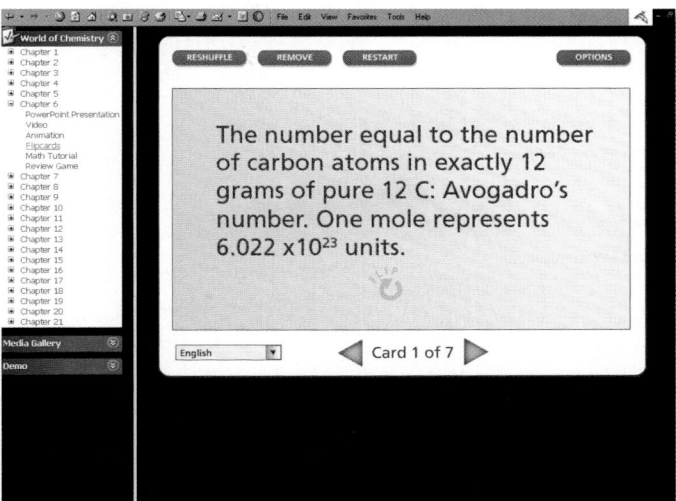

Flipcards of key vocabulary can be used for classroom presentations or as a review game.

The **Review Game** feature offers a quiz-show format in which to review key content from the text. The game can be played by individuals or teams.

Technology

Simplify your lesson planning and save preparation time with the resources available on the EasyPlanner DVD. The Resources2Go flash drive offers convenient and portable one-stop access to multiple program components.

The **EasyPlanner DVD*** contains

- Teacher's Edition
- PDF files of the print ancillary components
- State and national standards
- Customizable lesson plans and a calendar function

The EasyPlanner DVD can be used to view, edit, and customize pre-made lesson plans.

Access to all printed teaching resources is available by chapter and by topic.

*See ⊙ in Planning Guide

Resources2Go is a flash drive containing the EasyPlanner, Test Generator, and the content of the PowerPresentations DVD. Resources2Go is designed to replace the print ancillary package for those teachers who find electronic copy more useful.

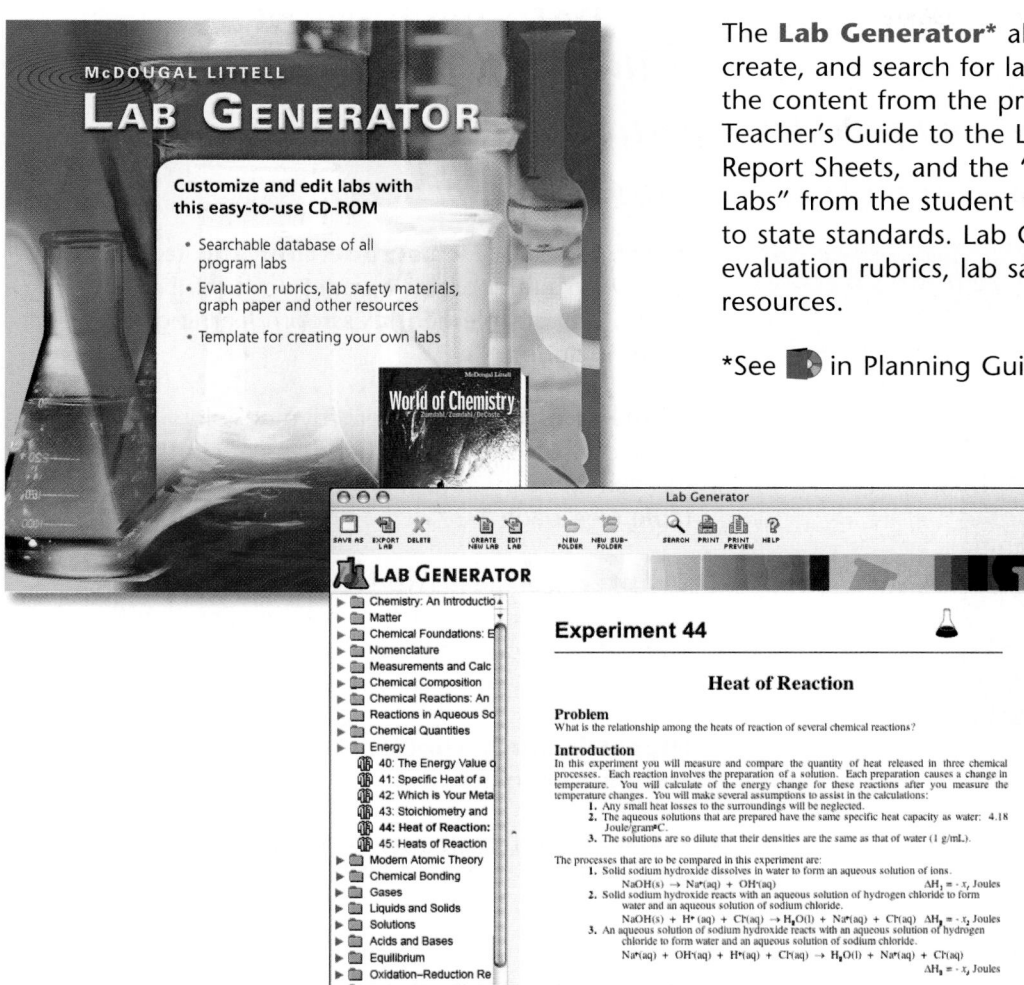

The **Lab Generator*** allows teachers to edit, create, and search for labs. The CD includes all the content from the print Laboratory Manual, the Teacher's Guide to the Laboratory Manual, Student Report Sheets, and the "Hands-On Chemistry Mini-Labs" from the student text. Labs are correlated to state standards. Lab Generator also contains evaluation rubrics, lab safety materials, and other resources.

*See 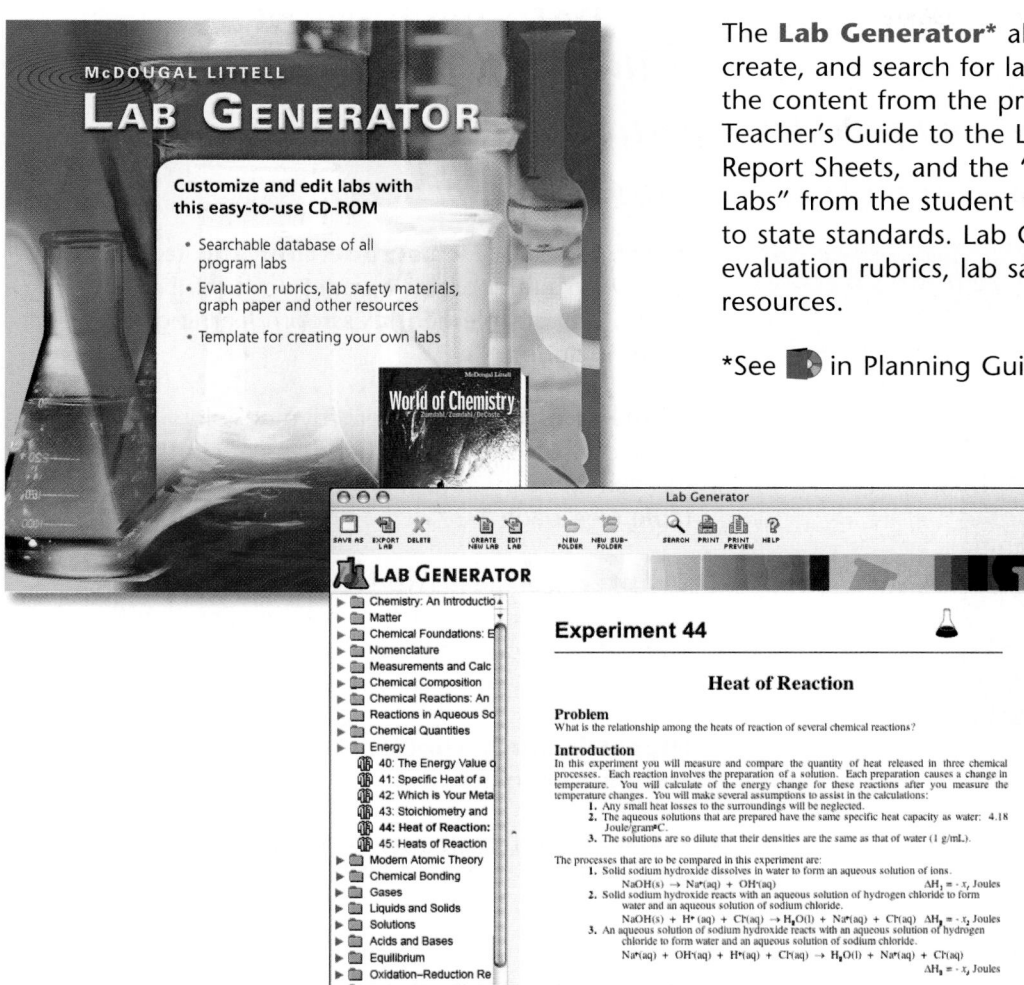 in Planning Guide

Student Resources

The **Student Resources Program** *brings chemical concepts alive, encourages students to be active participants in their own learning, and provides opportunities for review and exploration outside of the classroom experience.*

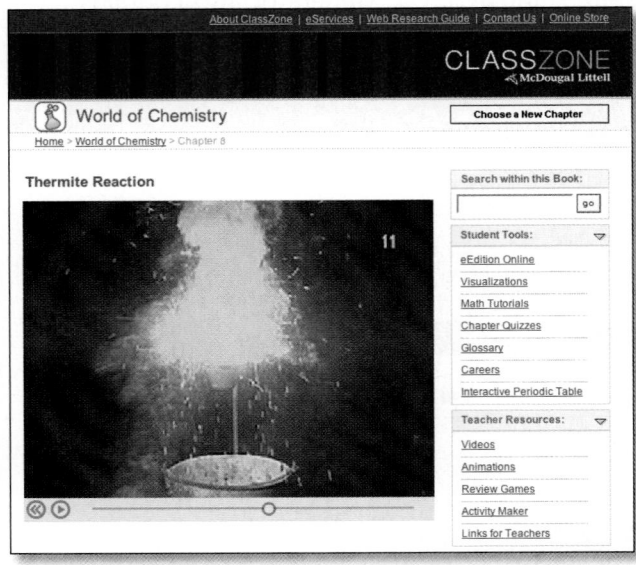

Student Web Site classzone.com This text-specific Web site contains a variety of useful materials that supplement classroom learning. Features include:

- **eEdition online:** An interactive ebook with links to visualizations of chemical concepts, a full-text glossary, and an interactive periodic table (see page T-37)

- **Chapter Quizzes:** Two to three multiple-choice self-grading practice quizzes per chapter. Students can quiz themselves on chapter content and receive an immediate score.

- **Flipcards study tool:** For review of key terms and their definitions

- **Math review content:** Reviews essential math skills

eEdition DVD and **eEdition Online** are two ways of accessing the learning resources available in the eEdition. The eEdition provides the student textbook in an interactive format, with hyperlinks to animations, videos, audio English and Spanish chapter summaries, and to the classzone.com Web site. The eEdition is searchable and offers highlighting and note-taking tools, as well as an interactive glossary.

The World of Chemistry *curriculum supports multiple learning styles and skill levels through the* All Learners Program. *The program includes resources to meet the individual needs of all students. Within the Student Edition, multiple features support math, reading, and critical thinking skills. In the Teacher's Edition, Teaching Tips and the Meeting Individual Needs box features provide point-of-use suggestions for working with students who may be at varying levels. The* All Learners Program *is also supported with the following resources.*

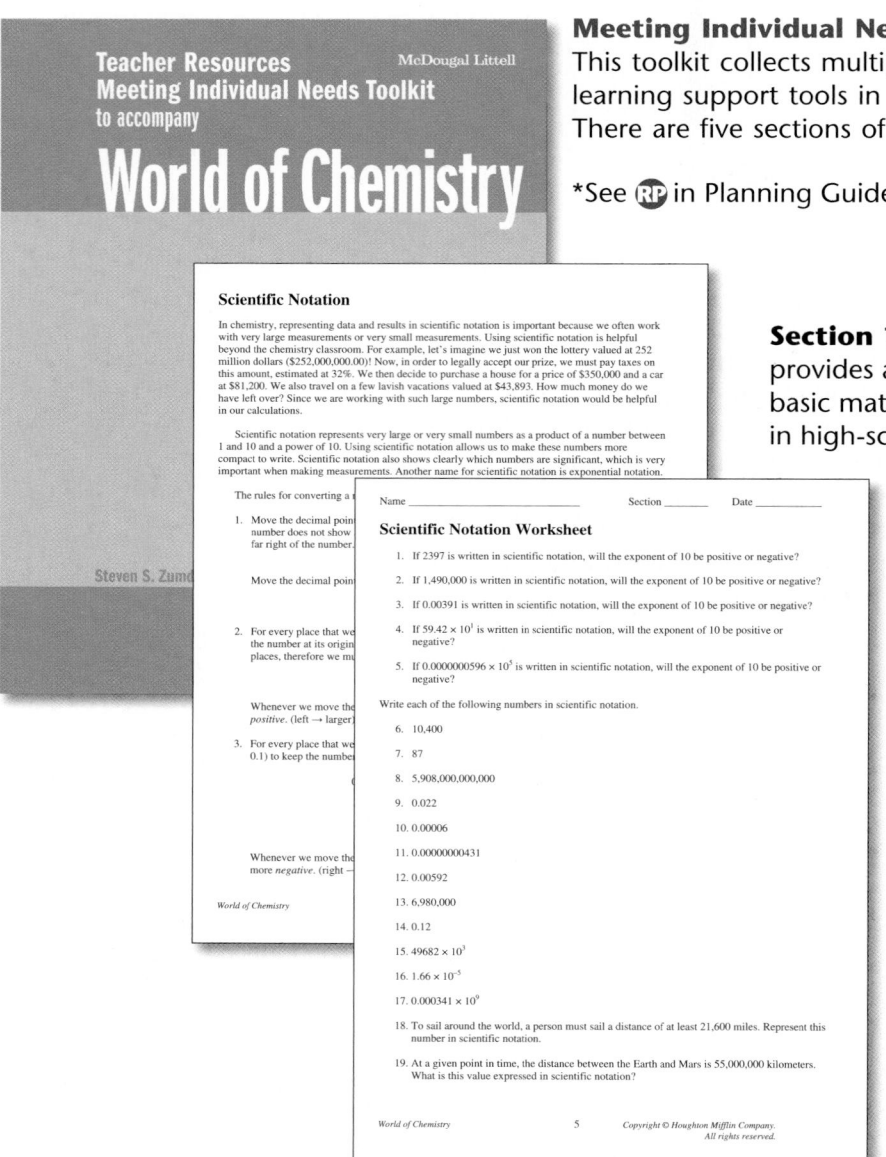

Meeting Individual Needs Toolkit (MINT)*
This toolkit collects multiple teaching and learning support tools in a single ancillary. There are five sections of material.

*See **RP** in Planning Guide

Section 1: Math Concepts
This section provides additional support for eight critical basic math topics that are essential to success in high-school chemistry. For each topic, there is a teaching lesson that includes worked examples and practice problems, followed by a worksheet. Materials can be used by teachers as the basis for a classroom lesson, or as blackline masters for student handouts. Answer keys for all exercises are provided.

Section 2: Reading Concepts

This section supports foundational reading and study skills that students need in order to use their chemistry text effectively. Using examples taken directly from the Student Edition, this section covers topics such as active reading, making and using graphic organizers and outlines, and reading chemical symbols and math notation.

Section 3: Leveled Chapter Review Worksheets

This section offers three levels of review worksheets for chapters in the student text: Basic, Standard, and Challenge. Worksheets are designed for individual students to use for review after studying a chapter.

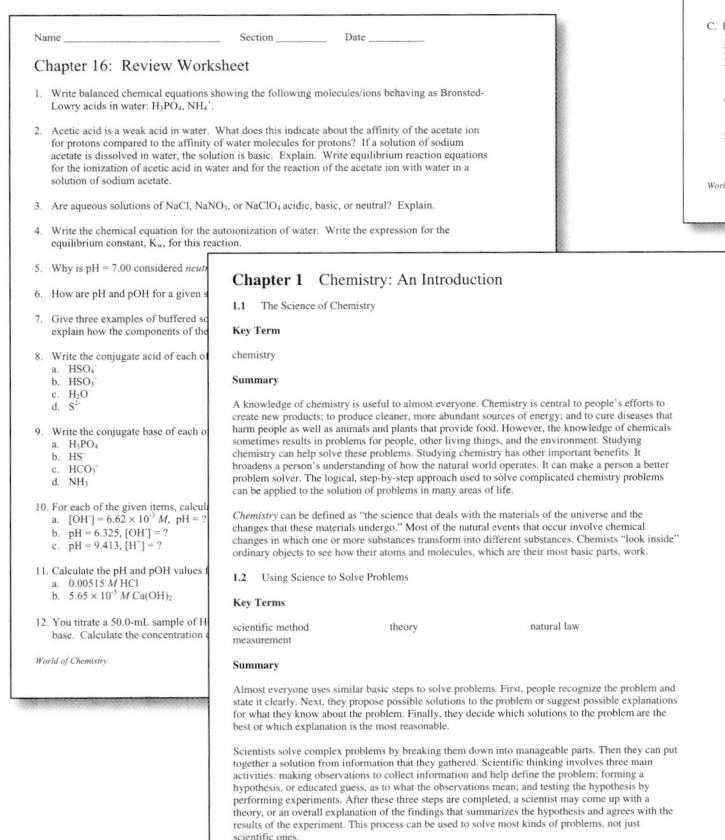

Active Reading

Before You Read

It is a good idea to relate what you already know to what you are going to learn. To help in this, spend some time looking through the chapter before you begin reading each section. Here is a list of what you can do to get the most out of the textbook

- Begin by reading the chapter title page. Read through the section and sub-section titles and see if they sound familiar.
- Read the feature titled "In Your Life". This section explains how what you will learn in the chapter relates to your life. Many times (like Chapter 2, for example) it will contain a few questions that you should consider.
- Read and answer the Prereading Questions that are located on the same page as the "In Your Life" feature. Answer these questions to the best of your abilities, using what you already know. Learning requires that you start with what you already know, and expand it to ...

Making Outlines

An outline is a good way to organize the main ideas of what you have read. The outline is not meant to be a complete representation of everything you have read but should be a summary of the main points. The outline:

- should contain all of the "big ideas".
- may contain examples which are particularly helpful
- should prompt you to remember some of the fine points.

While you do not need to include a discussion of all of the fine points in the chapter, you may include a phrase that triggers you to recall them. This phrase will not mean much to someone who has not read the chapter, but to an active reader of the text, it will be very meaningful.

Because of this, it is important to make your own outlines of the chapters. Using an outline made by a friend when you have not read the text will be of little help because the purpose of the outline is not to teach so much as to organize and remind. To get you started, however, we have provided you with a sample outline for Section 2.1.

Making an outline for Section 2.1 of *World of Chemistry*

An outline for Section 2.1 will include the terms *matter*, *element*, *compound*, *atom*, and *molecule*. It may also include examples of these.

One of many possible outlines for Section 2.1:

A. Matter
 1. Has mass, occupies space
 2. Matter has a variety of forms (solids like a chair, liquids like water, and gases like air are all matter)
 3. Fundamental building blocks of matter are similar in all types of matter (chocolate cake and air).

B. Particulate Nature of Matter
 1. Matter generally appears continuous to the naked eye.
  a. The surface of a table top appears smooth
 2. At high magnification, matter appears to be made of small particles.
  a. Think about sand on the beach or a painting made with dots (Impressionist)

C. Elements and Compounds
 1. All atoms are not alike (copper atoms are different from carbon atoms).
 2. Word analogy: matter is like words, atoms are like letters.
 3. Compounds are made of two or more different types of atoms.
  a. Example: water (hydrogen and oxygen, H_2O)
  b. A compound always has same composition..
 4. Molecules are atoms that are stuck together.
  a. Example: carbon dioxide (O-C-O or CO_2)
  b. All compounds are made of molecules.
 5. Elements contain one type of atom.
  a. Elements can be made of atoms: such as copper or iron
  b. Elements can be made of molecules: such as hydrogen (H-H or H_2).

Name _____   Section _____   Date _____

Chapter 16: Review Worksheet

1. Write balanced chemical equations showing the following molecules/ions behaving as Bronsted-Lowry acids in water: H_3PO_4, NH_4^+.

2. Acetic acid is a weak acid in water. What does this indicate about the affinity of the acetate ion for protons compared to the affinity of water molecules for protons? If a solution of sodium acetate is dissolved in water, the solution is basic. Explain. Write equilibrium reaction equations for the ionization of acetic acid in water and for the reaction of the acetate ion with water in a solution of sodium acetate.

3. Are aqueous solutions of NaCl, $NaNO_3$, or $NaClO_4$ acidic, basic, or neutral? Explain.

4. Write the chemical equation for the autoionization of water. Write the expression for the equilibrium constant, K_w, for this reaction.

5. Why is pH = 7.00 considered *neut...*

6. How are pH and pOH for a given s...

7. Give three examples of buffered so... explain how the components of the...

8. Write the conjugate acid of each of...
 a. HSO_4^-
 b. HSO_3^-
 c. H_2O
 d. S^{2-}

9. Write the conjugate base of each of...
 a. H_3PO_4
 b. HS^-
 c. HCO_3^-
 d. NH_3

10. For each of the given items, calcula...
 a. $[OH^-] = 6.62 \times 10^{-3}$ M, pH = ?
 b. pH = 6.325, $[OH^-]$ = ?
 c. pH = 9.413, $[H^+]$ = ?

11. Calculate the pH and pOH values ...
 a. 0.00515 M HCl
 b. 5.65×10^{-3} M $Ca(OH)_2$

12. You titrate a 50.0-mL sample of H... base. Calculate the concentration ...

World of Chemistry

Chapter 1   Chemistry: An Introduction

1.1   The Science of Chemistry

Key Term

chemistry

Summary

A knowledge of chemistry is useful to almost everyone. Chemistry is central to people's efforts to create new products; to produce cleaner, more abundant sources of energy; and to cure diseases that harm people as well as animals and plants that provide food. However, the knowledge of chemicals sometimes results in problems for people, other living things, and the environment. Studying chemistry can help solve these problems. Studying chemistry has other important benefits. It broadens a person's understanding of how the natural world operates. It can make a person a better problem solver. The logical, step-by-step approach used to solve complicated chemistry problems can be applied to the solution of problems in many areas of life.

Chemistry can be defined as "the science that deals with the materials of the universe and the changes that these materials undergo." Most of the natural events that occur involve chemical changes in which one or more substances transform into different substances. Chemists "look inside" ordinary objects to see how their atoms and molecules, which are their most basic parts, work.

1.2   Using Science to Solve Problems

Key Terms

scientific method   theory   natural law
measurement

Summary

Almost everyone uses similar basic steps to solve problems. First, people recognize the problem and state it clearly. Next, they propose possible solutions to the problem or suggest possible explanations for what they know about the problem. Finally, they decide which solutions to the problem are the best or which explanation is the most reasonable.

Scientists solve complex problems by breaking them down into manageable parts. Then they can put together a solution from information that they gathered. Scientific thinking involves three main activities: making observations to collect information and help define the problem; forming a hypothesis, or educated guess, as to what the observations mean; and testing the hypothesis by performing experiments. After these three steps are completed, a scientist may come up with a theory, or an overall explanation of the findings that summarizes the hypothesis and agrees with the results of the experiment. This process can be used to solve most kinds of problems, not just scientific ones.

Science is a framework for gaining knowledge and putting it together in a way that makes sense. Science is a set of facts, but it is also a plan of action for studying and understanding certain types of information. When scientists use scientific thinking specifically to understand how the world of

Section 4: Chapter Summaries

This section offers easy-to-read chapter summaries and additional Active Reading Questions to help students who are having difficulty comprehending a chapter or section of the text.

Section 5: Challenge Projects

This section offers challenge projects and activities for students who will benefit from the opportunity to stretch their understanding and skills by applying their chemistry knowledge to real-world situations. The projects are appropriate for either group work or individual use.

All Learners

Team Learning Worksheets* These worksheets provide high-quality discussion questions that encourage students to discuss the conceptual aspects of a problem rather than focusing only on the mechanics of an exercise. Worksheets are designed to be used in the classroom with small groups of students. A discussion guide for teachers is provided for each worksheet at the back of the booklet.

*See **RP** in Planning Guide

Teacher Resources
Team Learning Worksheets
to accompany

McDougal Littell

World of Chemistry

Donald J. DeCoste

Name _____ Section _____ Date _____

Group Members _____

Section 14.1: Team Learning Worksheet

1. True or false: Water molecules exhibit London dispersion forces. Explain.

2. Heating a sample of water at 90°C will cause an immediate temperature change of the water. However, heating a sample of water at 100°C will not cause an immediate temperature change. Explain both of these observations.

3. The heat of vaporization of water is almost seven times as great as the heat of fusion of water. Why is this?

4. Wax consists of long chain non-polar hydrocarbons that exhibit London dispersion forces. Water exhibits hydrogen bonding. Individual hydrogen bonding interactions are stronger than individual London dispersion interactions. So how can wax be a solid and water a liquid at normal conditions?

Name _____ Section _____ Date _____

Group Members _____

Section 2.1: Team Learning Worksheet

1. Using microscopic drawings (molecular level), show the difference between a gaseous element and a gaseous compound. Explain your drawings.

2. Heat is applied to an ice cube. Eventually, only steam is present. Draw a molecular level representation of this process. What happens to the size of the molecules? If you collect all of the steam, how would the mass of the steam compare to the mass of the original ice cube?

3. When you are in the room next to your kitchen, you can smell soup cooking. Why is this?

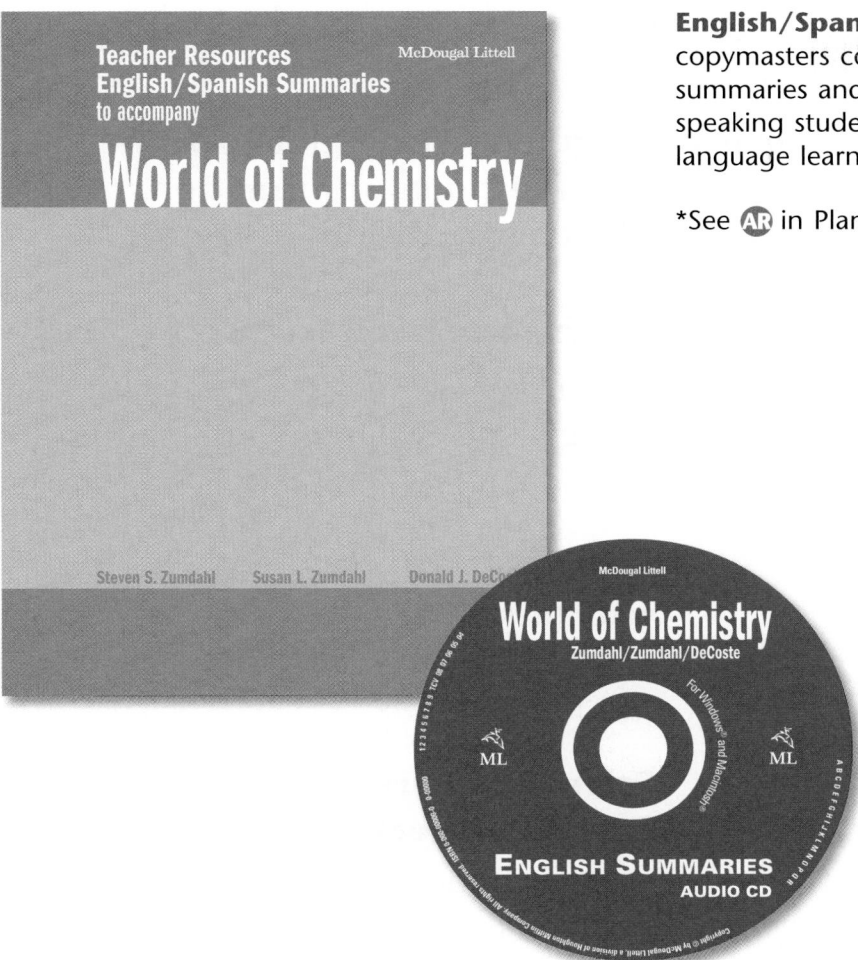

Teacher Resources
English/Spanish Summaries
to accompany

McDougal Littell

World of Chemistry

Steven S. Zumdahl   Susan L. Zumdahl   Donald J. DeCoste

English/Spanish Summaries* These copymasters contain translations of chapter summaries and key terms to help Spanish-speaking students and students who are English-language learners understand key concepts.

*See **AR** in Planning Guide

English and Spanish Summaries on Audio CDs* For further support of Spanish-speaking students, English-language learners, and auditory learners, chapter summaries and key terms are also provided in audio files. These audio summaries can also be accessed in the eEdition at point-of-use.

*See in Planning Guide

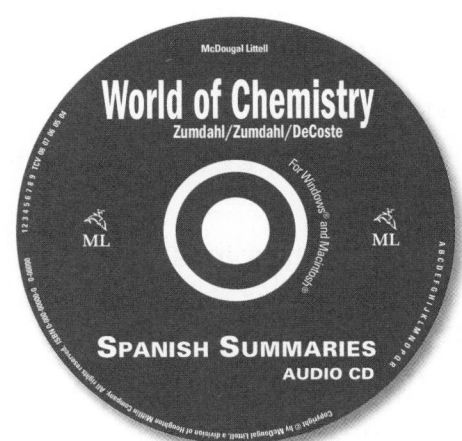

National Science Education Standards (NSES) Correlation to *World of Chemistry*

The table shows the *World of Chemistry* segment correlation to the National Science Education Standards. For additional information, see each chapter Planning Guide in the Teacher's Edition.

Unifying Concepts and Processes

- Systems, order, and organization
- Evidence, models, and explanation
- Change, constancy, and measurement
- Evolution and equilibrium
- Form and function

Science as Inquiry

- Abilities necessary to do scientific inquiry
- Understanding about scientific inquiry

Physical Science

- Structure of atoms
- Structure and properties of matter
- Chemical reactions
- Motions and Forces
- Conservation of energy and increase in disorder
- Interactions of energy and matter

Life Science

- Molecular basis of heredity
- Interdependence of organisms
- Matter, energy, and organization in living systems
- Behavior of organisms

Earth and Space Science

- Geochemical cycles
- Origin and evolution of the earth system
- Origin and evolution of the universe

Science and Technology

- Abilities of technological design
- Understanding about science and technology

Science in Personal and Social Perspectives

- Personal and community health
- Population growth
- Natural resources
- Environmental quality
- Natural and human-induced hazards
- Science and technology in local, national, and global challenges

History and Nature of Science

- Science as a human endeavor
- Nature of scientific knowledge
- Historical perspectives

CODE	STANDARD	SECTION REFERENCE
UNIFYING CONCEPTS AND PROCESSES		
UCP1	Systems, order, and organization	1.1 (pp. 4–8), 1.2 (pp. 9–14), 1.3 (pp. 15–17), 2.1 (pp. 24–30), 2.2 (pp. 31–34), 2.3 (pp. 35–43), 3.1 (pp. 50–55), 3.2 (pp. 56–59), 3.3 (pp. 60–67), 3.4 (pp. 68–75), 3.5 (pp. 76–83), 4.1 (94–108), 4.2 (pp. 109–116), 5.1 (pp. 126–132), 5.2 (pp. 133–142), 5.3 (pp. 143–162), 6.1 (pp. 172–184), 6.2 (pp. 185–195), 6.3 (pp. 196–209), 7 (pp. 218–232), 11.1 (pp. 360–365), 11.3 (pp. 371–376), 11.4 (pp. 377–390), 12.2 (pp. 407–412), 13.1 (pp. 442–457), 13.2 (pp. 458–473), 14.1 (pp. 488–497), 15.1 (pp. 520–527), 15.2 (pp. 528–540), 15.3 (pp. 541–553), 16.1 (pp. 562–572), 16.2 (pp. 573–581), 16.3 (pp. 582–586), 17.1 (pp. 596–604), 17.2 (pp. 605–611), 17.3 (pp. 612–625), 18.1 (pp. 636–641), 18.2 (pp. 642–651), 18.3 (pp. 652–660), 19.1 (pp. 668–678), 19.2 (pp. 679–682), 19.3 (pp. 683–691), 20.1 (pp. 700–717), 20.2 (pp. 718–726), 20.4 (pp. 732–741), 21.1 (pp. 752–761), 21.2 (pp. 762–775)
UCP2	Evidence, models, and explanation	1.1 (pp. 4–8), 1.2 (pp. 9–14), 1.3 (pp. 15–17), 2.1 (pp. 24–30), 2.2 (pp. 31–34), 2.3 (pp. 35–43), 3.1 (pp. 50–55), 3.2 (pp. 56–59), 3.3 (pp. 60–67), 3.4 (pp. 68–75), 3.5 (pp. 76–83), 6.1 (pp. 172–184), 11.1 (pp. 360–365), 11.2 (pp. 366–370), 11.3 (pp. 371–376), 12.1 (pp. 400–406), 12.2 (pp. 407–412), 12.3 (pp. 413–422), 12.4 (pp. 423–433), 13.2 (pp. 458–473), 13.3 (pp. 474–478), 14.3 (pp. 504–511), 16.1 (pp. 562–572), 16.2 (pp. 573–581), 16.3 (pp. 582–586), 17.1 (pp. 596–604), 17.2 (pp. 605–611), 20.1 (pp. 700–717), 20.2 (pp. 718–726), 20.3 (pp. 727–731)
UCP3	Change, constancy, and measurement	2.2 (pp. 31–34), 2.3 (pp. 35–43), 3.2 (pp. 56–59), 3.3 (pp. 60–67), 3.4 (pp. 68–75), 3.5 (pp. 76–83), 4.1 (94–108), 4.2 (pp. 109–116), 5.2 (pp. 133–142), 5.3 (pp. 143–162), 6.1 (pp. 172–184), 6.2 (pp. 185–195), 6.3 (pp. 196–209), 7 (pp. 218–232), 8.1 (pp. 240–253), 8.2 (pp. 254–262), 8.3 (pp. 263–269), 9.1 (pp.280–287), 9.2 (pp. 288–295), 9.3 (pp. 296–308), 11.4 (pp. 377–390), 13.1 (pp. 442–457), 13.2 (pp. 458–473), 13.3 (pp. 474–478), 14.1 (pp. 488–497), 14.2 (pp. 498–503), 15.2 (pp. 528–540), 15.3 (pp. 541–553), 16.2 (pp. 573–581), 16.3 (pp. 582–586), 17.1 (pp. 596–604), 17.2 (pp. 605–611), 17.3 (pp. 612–625), 18.2 (pp. 642–651), 18.3 (pp. 652–660), 19.1 (pp. 668–678), 19.2 (pp. 679–682), 19.3 (pp. 683–691), 20.3 (pp. 727–731), 20.4 (pp. 732–741), 21.1 (pp. 752–761)
UCP4	Evolution and equilibriium	14.2 (pp. 498–503), 17.1 (pp. 596–604), 17.2 (pp. 605–611), 17.3 (pp. 612–625)
UCP5	Form and function	2.1 (pp. 24–30), 3.1 (pp. 50–55), 3.2 (pp. 56–59), 3.3 (pp. 60–67), 3.4 (pp. 68–75), 3.5 (pp. 76–83), 6.2 (pp. 185–195), 6.3 (pp. 196–209), 8.1 (pp. 240–253), 8.2 (pp. 254–262), 8.3 (pp. 263–269), 12.1 (pp. 400–406), 12.3 (pp. 413–422), 12.4 (pp. 423–433), 14.1 (pp. 488–497), 14.2 (pp. 498–503), 14.3 (pp. 504–511), 16.1 (pp. 562–572), 16.3 (pp. 582–586), 18.2 (pp. 642–651), 18.3 (pp. 652–660), 19.2 (pp. 679–682), 19.3 (pp. 683–691), 20.1 (pp. 700–717), 20.2 (pp. 718–726), 20.3 (pp. 727–731), 20.4 (pp. 732–741), 21.1 (pp. 752–761), 21.2 (pp. 762–775)

Standards: NSES

CODE	STANDARD	SECTION REFERENCE
PHYSICAL SCIENCE		
B1	Structure of atoms	2.1 (pp. 24–30), 3.3 (pp. 60–67), 6.1 (pp. 172–184), 6.2 (pp. 185–195), 11.1 (pp. 360–365), 12.1 (pp. 400–406), 12.2 (pp. 407–412), 12.3 (pp. 413–422), 12.4 (pp. 423–433), 19.1 (pp. 668–678), 19.2 (pp. 679–682), 19.3 (pp. 683–691), 20.1 (pp. 700–717)
B2	Structure and properties of matter	2.1 (pp. 24–30), 2.2 (pp. 31–34), 2.3 (pp. 35–43), 3.1 (pp. 50–55), 3.2 (pp. 56–59), 3.3 (pp. 60–67), 4.1 (94–108), 4.2 (pp. 109–116), 6.1 (pp. 172–184), 6.2 (pp. 185–195), 6.3 (pp. 196–209), 9.1 (pp.280–287), 9.2 (pp. 288–295), 9.3 (pp. 296–308), 11.1 (pp. 360–365), 11.4 (pp. 377–390), 12.1 (pp. 400–406), 12.2 (pp. 407–412), 12.3 (pp. 413–422), 12.4 (pp. 423–433), 13.1 (pp. 442–457), 13.2 (pp. 458–473), 13.3 (pp. 474–478), 14.1 (pp. 488–497), 14.2 (pp. 498–503), 14.3 (pp. 504–511), 15.1 (pp. 520–527), 15.2 (pp. 528–540), 15.3 (pp. 541–553), 16.1 (pp. 562–572), 16.2 (pp. 573–581), 16.3 (pp. 582–586), 18.1 (pp. 636–641), 18.2 (pp. 642–651), 18.3 (pp. 652–660), 19.1 (pp. 668–678), 19.2 (pp. 679–682), 19.3 (pp. 683–691), 20.1 (pp. 700–717), 20.2 (pp. 718–726), 20.3 (pp. 727–731), 20.4 (pp. 732–741), 21.1 (pp. 752–761), 21.2 (pp. 762–775)
B3	Chemical reactions	1.1 (pp. 4–8), 2.2 (pp. 31–34), 2.3 (pp. 35–43), 3.2 (pp. 56–59), 3.4 (pp. 68–75), 3.5 (pp. 76–83), 4.1 (94–108), 4.2 (pp. 109–116), 6.1 (pp. 172–184), 6.2 (pp. 185–195), 6.3 (pp. 196–209), 7 (pp. 218–232), 8.1 (pp. 240–253), 8.2 (pp. 254–262), 8.3 (pp. 263–269), 9.1 (pp.280–287), 9.2 (pp. 288–295), 9.3 (pp. 296–308), 15.3 (pp. 541–553), 16.1 (pp. 562–572), 16.3 (pp. 582–586), 17.1 (pp. 596–604), 17.3 (pp. 612–625), 18.1 (pp. 636–641), 18.2 (pp. 642–651), 18.3 (pp. 652–660), 20.1 (pp. 700–717), 20.2 (pp. 718–726), 20.3 (pp. 727–731), 20.4 (pp. 732–741), 21.2 (pp. 762–775)
B4	Motions and forces	13.1 (pp. 442–457), 13.2 (pp. 458–473), 13.3 (pp. 474–478), 14.1 (pp. 488–497), 14.2 (pp. 498–503)
B5	Conservation of energy and increase in disorder	10.1 (pp. 320–325), 10.2 (pp. 326–333), 10.3 (pp. 334–338), 10.4 (pp. 339–350), 14.1 (pp. 488–497), 14.2 (pp. 498–503), 14.3 (pp. 504–511)
B6	Interactions of energy and matter	10.1 (pp. 320–325), 10.2 (pp. 326–333), 10.3 (pp. 334–338), 10.4 (pp. 339–350), 11.1 (pp. 360–365), 11.2 (pp. 366–370), 11.3 (pp. 371–376), 11.4 (pp. 377–390), 17.1 (pp. 596–604)
LIFE SCIENCE		
C2	Molecular basis of heredity	21.2 (pp. 762–775)
C4	Interdependence of organisms	16.1 (pp. 562–572), 17.3 (pp. 612–625), 21.2 (pp. 762–775)
C5	Matter, energy, and organization in living systems	8.3 (pp. 263–269), 9.2 (pp. 288–295), 10.1 (pp. 320–325), 10.2 (pp. 326–333), 14.1 (pp. 488–497), 20.1 (pp. 700–717), 21.1 (pp. 752–761), 21.2 (pp. 762–775)
C6	Behavior of organisms	3.1 (pp. 50–55), 4.2 (pp. 109–116), 7 (pp. 218–232), 9.2 (pp. 288–295), 10.3 (pp. 334–338), 14.1 (pp. 488–497), 16.1 (pp. 562–572), 17.3 (pp. 612–625), 20.2 (pp. 718–726)

Standards: NSES

CODE	STANDARD	SECTION REFERENCE
EARTH AND SPACE SCIENCE		
D2	Geochemical cycles	8.1 (pp. 240–253), 8.2 (pp. 254–262), 10.3 (pp. 334–338)
D3	Origin and evolution of the earth system	6.3 (pp. 196–209), 19.1 (pp. 668–678), 19.2 (pp. 679–682), 19.3 (pp. 683–691)
D4	Origin and evolution of the universe	19.3 (pp. 683–691)
SCIENCE AND TECHNOLOGY		
E1	Abilities of technological design	3.1 (pp. 50–55), 3.2 (pp. 56–59), 3.3 (pp. 60–67), 3.4 (pp. 68–75), 3.5 (pp. 76–83), 5.2 (pp. 133–142), 5.3 (pp. 143–162), 6.1 (pp. 172–184), 7 (pp. 218–232), 8.3 (pp. 263–269), 9.2 (pp. 288–295), 10.4 (pp. 339–350), 11.1 (pp. 360–365), 11.3 (pp. 371–376), 11.4 (pp. 377–390), 12.2 (pp. 407–412), 12.3 (pp. 413–422), 12.4 (pp. 423–433), 13.2 (pp. 458–473), 13.3 (pp. 474–478), 14.3 (pp. 504–511), 16.1 (pp. 562–572), 16.2 (pp. 573–581), 17.1 (pp. 596–604), 17.3 (pp. 612–625), 18.1 (pp. 636–641), 18.2 (pp. 642–651), 18.3 (pp. 652–660), 19.1 (pp. 668–678), 19.2 (pp. 679–682), 19.3 (pp. 683–691), 20.1 (pp. 700–717), 20.4 (pp. 732–741), 21.1 (pp. 752–761), 21.2 (pp. 762–775)
E2	Understanding about science and technology	1.1 (pp. 4–8), 1.2 (pp. 9–14), 3.1 (pp. 50–55), 3.2 (pp. 56–59), 3.3 (pp. 60–67), 3.4 (pp. 68–75), 3.5 (pp. 76–83), 5.1 (pp. 126–132), 5.2 (pp. 133–142), 5.3 (pp. 143–162), 6.1 (pp. 172–184), 7 (pp. 218–232), 8.3 (pp. 263–269), 9.2 (pp. 288–295), 10.4 (pp. 339–350), 11.1 (pp. 360–365), 11.3 (pp. 371–376), 11.4 (pp. 377–390), 12.2 (pp. 407–412), 12.3 (pp. 413–422), 12.4 (pp. 423–433), 13.2 (pp. 458–473), 13.3 (pp. 474–478), 14.3 (pp. 504–511), 16.2 (pp. 573–581), 17.1 (pp. 596–604), 17.3 (pp. 612–625), 18.1 (pp. 636–641), 18.2 (pp. 642–651), 18.3 (pp. 652–660), 19.1 (pp. 668–678), 19.2 (pp. 679–682), 19.3 (pp. 683–691), 20.4 (pp. 732–741), 21.1 (pp. 752–761), 21.2 (pp. 762–775)
SCIENCE IN PERSONAL AND SOCIAL PERSPECTIVES		
F1	Personal and community health	4.1 (pp. 94–108), 6.3 (pp. 196–209), 7 (pp. 218–232), 8.3 (pp. 263–269), 9.2 (pp. 288–295), 13.3 (pp. 474–478), 14.3 (pp. 504–511), 15.1 (pp. 520–527), 16.3 (pp. 582–586), 17.3 (pp. 612–625), 19.1 (pp. 668–678), 19.2 (pp. 679–682), 20.1 (pp. 700–717)
F2	Population growth	21.2 (pp. 762–775)
F3	Natural resources	3.1 (pp. 50–55), 9.2 (pp. 288–295), 10.3 (pp. 334–338), 10.4 (pp. 339–350), 11.3 (pp. 371–376), 15.1 (pp. 520–527), 18.2 (pp. 642–651), 18.3 (pp. 652–660), 19.2 (pp. 679–682), 19.3 (pp. 683–691), 20.1 (pp. 700–717)
F4	Environmental quality	10.3 (pp. 334–338), 10.4 (pp. 339–350), 11.3 (pp. 371–376), 13.3 (pp. 474–478), 15.1 (pp. 520–527), 16.3 (pp. 582–586), 17.1 (pp. 596–604), 17.3 (pp. 612–625), 18.3 (pp. 652–660), 19.3 (pp. 683–691), 20.1 (pp. 700–717)
F5	Natural and human-induced hazards	7 (pp. 218–232), 9.2 (pp. 288–295), 13.3 (pp. 474–478), 15.1 (pp. 520–527), 15.3 (pp. 541–553), 16.3 (pp. 582–586), 17.3 (pp. 612–625), 20.1 (pp. 700–717)
F6	Science and technology in local, national, and global challenges	5.2 (pp. 133–142), 8.3 (pp. 263–269), 9.2 (pp. 288–295), 9.3 (pp. 296–308), 10.3 (pp. 334–338), 10.4 (pp. 339–350), 11.1 (pp. 360–365), 11.3 (pp. 371–376), 12.2 (pp. 407–412), 12.3 (pp. 413–422), 12.4 (pp. 423–433), 13.2 (pp. 458–473), 13.3 (pp. 474–478), 14.3 (pp. 504–511), 15.1 (pp. 520–527), 16.2 (pp. 573–581), 16.3 (pp. 582–586), 17.1 (pp. 596–604), 18.3 (pp. 652–660), 19.1 (pp. 668–678), 19.2 (pp. 679–682), 19.3 (pp. 683–691), 20.1 (pp. 700–717), 20.4 (pp. 732–741), 21.2 (pp. 762–775)

CODE	STANDARD	SECTION REFERENCE
HISTORY AND NATURE OF SCIENCE		
G1	Science as human endeavor	1.1 (pp. 4–8), 1.2 (pp. 9–14), 1.3 (pp. 15–17), 2.3 (pp. 35–43), 3.1 (pp. 50–55), 3.2 (pp. 56–59), 3.3 (pp. 60–67), 3.4 (pp. 68–75), 6.1 (pp. 172–184), 6.2 (pp. 185–195), 6.3 (pp. 196–209), 8.1 (pp. 240–253), 11.1 (pp. 360–365), 11.2 (pp. 366–370), 11.4 (pp. 377–390), 12.3 (pp. 413–433), 13.1 (pp. 442–457), 16.2 (pp. 573–581), 18.1 (pp. 636–641), 18.2 (pp. 642–651), 18.3 (pp. 652–660), 19.1 (pp. 668–678), 19.2 (pp. 679–682), 19.3 (pp. 683–691), 20.1 (pp. 700–717), 20.4 (pp. 732–741)
G2	Nature of scientific knowledge	1.1 (pp. 4–8), 1.2 (pp. 9–14), 1.3 (pp. 15–17), 2.2 (pp. 31–34), 2.3 (pp. 35–43), 3.1 (pp. 50–55), 3.2 (pp. 56–59), 3.3 (pp. 60–67), 3.4 (pp. 68–75), 6.1 (pp. 172–184), 6.2 (pp. 185–195), 6.3 (pp. 196–209), 8.1 (pp. 240–253), 8.2 (pp. 254–262), 11.1 (pp. 360–365), 11.2 (pp. 366–370), 11.4 (pp. 377–390), 12.3 (pp. 413–433), 13.1 (pp. 442–457), 14.3 (pp. 504–511), 16.2 (pp. 573–581), 18.1 (pp. 636–641), 18.2 (pp. 642–651), 18.3 (pp. 652–660), 19.1 (pp. 668–678), 19.2 (pp. 679–682), 19.3 (pp. 683–691), 20.1 (pp. 700–717), 20.4 (pp. 732–741)
G3	Historical perspectives	2.3 (pp. 35–43), 3.1 (pp. 50–55), 3.2 (pp. 56–59), 3.3 (pp. 60–67), 3.4 (pp. 68–75), 5.2 (pp. 133–142), 6.1 (pp. 172–184), 6.3 (pp. 196–209), 7 (pp. 218–232), 9.2 (pp. 288–295), 11.2 (pp. 366–370), 11.4 (pp. 377–390), 12.3 (pp. 413–422), 13.1 (pp. 442–457), 15.3 (pp. 541–553), 16.2 (pp. 573–581), 17.1 (pp. 596–604), 18.2 (pp. 642–651), 18.3 (pp. 652–660), 19.1 (pp. 668–678), 19.2 (pp. 679–682), 19.3 (pp. 683–691), 20.1 (pp. 700–717), 20.4 (pp. 732–741)

CONTENTS

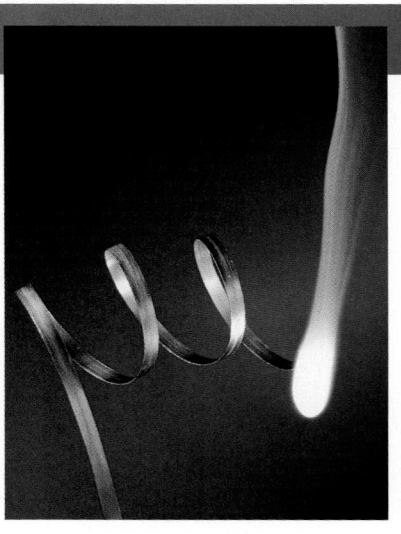

Chapter 4

Chapter 5

Chapter 6

Chapter 7

Chapter 8

Chapter 9

Chapter 10

Chapter 11

Chapter 12

Chemical Bonding   398

Chapter 13

Gases   440

Chapter 14

Chapter 15

Chapter 16

Chapter 17

Chapter 18

Chapter 19

Radioactivity and Nuclear Energy   666

Chapter 20

Organic Chemistry   698

Chapter 21

Biochemistry   750

CELEBRITY CHEMICAL

Top Ten Lists

Consumer Connection

Connection to History

Connection to Biology

Connection to Astronomy

HANDS-ON CHEMISTRY

Overview

In this section our goals are for
students to:

- Understand the importance
  of reading a chemistry
  textbook
- Become efficient and effective
  readers of chemistry
- Develop technical writing skills
- Learn and implement test
  preparation tips for before,
  during, and after a test
- Become familiar with various
  styles of test items

INTRODUCE

Student Preparation

Have students read these
reading support pages before
coming to class.

 Active Learning
Group Activity

After discussing the
information in this feature,
place students in small groups
and have them work together
to preview the textbook.

READING CHEMISTRY

 TEACHING TIPS

- Ask students to write a
  reading agreement in their
  journals to show their
  commitment to the demands
  of the course. Have students
  sign their agreements.
- Use this feature to begin
  focusing on how chemistry
  and reading are integrated.
  Create a bulletin board
  highlighting a reading
  strategy of your choice for
  each chapter. Highlight its
  function and importance.

xxii

Reading Chemistry

Chemistry textbooks are written differently from nontechnical textbooks.
With this in mind, be aware that reading five pages in a chemistry textbook
will probably take much more time than reading five pages in an English or
a history textbook.

If you want to understand this chemistry text, prepare to spend a great deal
of time reading each section within a chapter. If you flip through this book,
you will notice many examples, explanations, diagrams, charts, symbols,
and photos to read, analyze, and interpret. You should read the text in each
section and incorporate these visuals in your reading. You will quickly find
that these visuals are very useful in helping you understand the subject
matter.

**Use these suggestions to become an efficient and
effective reader of chemistry.**

1. **Preview your textbook.**
   To become familiar with the design and structure of your textbook,
   take a look at these key features:
   - Information about the authors, page vi
   - Table of Contents and list of features, pages vii–xxi
   - Appendices, pages A1–A11
   - Glossary, pages A49–A57
   - Index, pages A61–A83
   - Periodic Table, inside back cover

2. **Plan when and where you read.**
   Although you might find that relaxing on the couch at night is a
   comfortable and convenient place to do some of your homework,
   it will not be a good place to read about a chemistry concept.
   - Try to read your chemistry section during daylight hours, or in a
     well-lit area.
   - Sit in a straight-backed chair, such as the chairs in the classroom,
     a kitchen chair, or a desk chair.
   - Read in a quiet atmosphere; turn off your television, radio, or
     earphones.
   - Remember that reading chemistry requires active participation. Make
     sure that you have a pencil, notebook, and any other necessary items
     to help you study.
   - Allow plenty of time to read through each section. Even if a section
     is short, it still requires deep concentration and focus.

3. **Preview each chapter.**
   When you start a new chapter, be sure to preview it before you begin reading a section within the chapter. Taking time to get an overview of the concepts within the chapter will help you become a more efficient learner.

   - Read the title of the chapter and the "Looking Ahead" box. Ask yourself what you have learned previously that may apply to these new concepts.
   - Read the first paragraph of the chapter. This paragraph will give you a quick preview of what will be covered and why this chapter material is important.
   - Read each section title and the corresponding objectives.
   - Glance at the highlighted features, photos, graphs, charts, and symbols in the chapter, to get a sense of the content.
   - Read the Chapter Review found at the end of each chapter. This indicates what is most important and what material you will most likely have to master.

4. **Read each section prior to class.**
   Make sure that you read a section before it is presented in class. By previewing the section, you will be better prepared for class.

   - Note the section title and objectives in your notebook.
   - Make a list of questions you have about the section and of any concepts you need to clarify.
   - Write down any vocabulary, symbols, or structures that you have difficulty interpreting.
   - Try to work through the example problems, and note any steps that confuse you.
   - Attempt to answer the Review Questions at the end of a section.

5. **Reread each section after class.**
   To reinforce the concepts explained during class, read the section again.

   - Highlight in your notes the concepts your teacher emphasized during class.
   - Make flashcards to help you memorize structures, symbols, and vocabulary. Review your flashcards daily.
   - Work through each example problem, and complete the Practice Problem Exercises if they appear at the end of an example.
   - Write a summary of the section. Putting the material in your own words will help you learn this new information.

 TEACHING TIPS

- Now is a good time to tell students that they will need a notebook designated for this course.
- To supplement this feature, use strategies from *Making and Using Flashcards* located in the *Teacher Resources* or on *classzone.com*.
- Ask students to write a paragraph in their journals about the similarities and differences between reading a textbook for a technical course versus reading a novel.
- Consider the questions that students have after they preview a section to determine the technology aids to use.
- Before each chapter, review the strategies explained in *Reading Concepts* and *Math Concepts* located in the *Teacher Resources* to determine the strategies best suited to your class.

Distribute magazines and scientific journals. Have students compare and contrast creative styles of writing with technical writing. Ask students to rewrite one creatively written paragraph as a technical statement.

CRITICAL THINKING ?

Ask students: What if scientists did not conform to a certain style of writing? How could this varying style affect the interpretation of a scientist's research?

Discuss how words can be used to persuade. Point out that research results explained in various styles of writing can lead to a range of interpretations.

Explain how the scientific community relies on clear, quantitative technical descriptions to record, analyze, and explain results.

More Examples

To practice technical writing, have students rewrite these statements.

1. Every minute, the temperature got hotter and hotter by twelve °C.

   The temperature increased at a rate of 12°C per minute.

2. People can use distillation or filtration to separate the things in a mixture. Either method will work just fine.

   The substances that make up mixtures can be separated by two methods: distillation and filtration.

xxiv

Writing Chemistry

Up to this point in your studies, you have learned and practiced many different types and styles of writing. In this class, you will be expected to use technical writing. Technical writing differs from essay, report, letter, and creative writing in many ways. Technical writing is factual, precise, clear, and free of bias and personal opinion. Sentences should be specific and to the point.

For instance, if you were asked to write about the current weather conditions in your area for a technical course, your description should use the technical writing style shown in Example 1, rather than the creative style shown in Example 2.

EXAMPLE 1

Technical Writing Sample

 The temperature is 75 °F. It is sunny with minimal cloud coverage. The wind is blowing north to northwest at 15 miles per hour.

Note that the writer in Example 1 states factual information regarding the temperature and wind speed, includes units of measure, and writes without bias and personal opinion.

EXAMPLE 2

Creative Writing Sample

 It is a beautiful spring day! The sun is shining without a cloud in the sky, the air is light and breezy, and the temperature is simply perfect for a picnic in the park.

Although the writer in Example 2 paints a visual picture of the weather conditions, it would not be an appropriate description in a technical course. There are too many adjectives, there are not enough detailed facts, and the writing contains personal opinion about the weather.

When writing a response to a laboratory question, get right to the point. There is no need for extra words. For instance, you may be asked: "What evidence did you observe that indicates a reaction occurred?"

A good technical response would be:

 A yellow precipitate formed in the container.

The wordy response below would be inappropriate:

 After we observed the reaction for a few minutes, we saw something yellow starting to form at the bottom of the glass. We think that is how we know that a reaction occurred.

To strengthen your skills in technical writing for this chemistry course, as well as for other technical courses, follow these helpful hints.

- Write in third person. Do not use I, we, our, your, my, or us.
- Be specific. Do not ramble to make a point.
- Use the correct verb tense. Use present tense when writing research papers and lab reports and when analyzing data. Use past tense to describe objectives and experimental results.
- Make sure that responses to questions are organized, logical, and precise. A reader should be able to clearly follow your train of thought.
- Avoid stating your opinion. Most of your descriptions and observations should be based on things that can be measured. Keep in mind that your writing should be based on facts, not on the opinion of the observer.
- Write numbers as numerals when they are greater than 10 or when they are linked with a measurement. For example: 230, six, 6 cm.
- Avoid beginning sentences with a number, unless the number is part of a chemical name.
- Include units of measure as part of your data. For example: 50 °F, not 50°; 0.025 M, not 0.025.
- Use scientific notation when appropriate.
- Use the correct number of significant figures when reporting your data.
- Use lowercase for chemical names, unless they are at the beginning of a sentence.
- Make sure that tables, graphs, and diagrams used to help explain a response are completely and accurately labeled.
- Describe a laboratory procedure in detail so that another person can repeat the experiment.
- Make sure that a summary of an experiment includes the meaning of your results and how they are the basis for your conclusions. Incorporate possible sources of error in your description.
- Cite all references.

 Active Learning
Group Activity

Have students research a winner of the Nobel Prize in Chemistry and submit a short technical report.

 TEACHING TIPS

- Assess students on their technical writing skills in their laboratory reports and in their responses to Critical Thinking and Hands-On Chemistry features within the text and Critical Thinking assessment questions at the end of each chapter.
- Tell students to revisit these helpful hints before they turn in a written assignment.
- Review how to cite a reference properly.
- Demonstrate to students how reading aloud what they write can help them identify problems with logic and organization.

 Active Learning
Group Activity

For one of the features in the text, such as a Hands-On Chemistry feature or a Critical Thinking feature, have students exchange written responses with a partner. Students should make suggestions for improving the technical style of the responses.

TEACHING TIPS

- Highlight testing dates in your course outline.
- Review the strategies explained in *Making and Using Flashcards* located in the *Teacher Resources*.
- Additional materials, such as the English/Spanish Summaries and the Meeting Individual Needs features within the text, can be used as tools to help struggling students better comprehend the main points of a chapter.
- Encourage students to write in their journals about fears or apprehension they experience before a test. Help students develop a plan to calm their fears.
- During the week of a test, tell students the style of the test and the approximate number of questions. You may wish to distribute a sample test to give students a visual idea of what to expect.
- Review concepts discussed in the Test-Taking Strategy feature on the Standardized Test Practice page of each chapter in the Teacher's Edition.
- Distribute a reference sheet several days before the test so that students will not spend time memorizing unnecessary information.

xxvi

Testing in Chemistry

The key to earning a successful grade on a chemistry test is to be actively involved in learning the content and to be well-prepared for every class. Chemistry is a cumulative subject, meaning that each section builds on the one before it. Preparation cannot begin the night before the test, but must be ongoing from the first day of class to the last day of class.

Designate a notebook for your chemistry notes and homework. Review your class notes with the corresponding section in the textbook, every day. If you are having trouble remembering new vocabulary words, chemical structures, or formulas, create a set of flashcards. Study your flashcards as often as possible.

Keep in mind that if you find yourself "cramming" for a chemistry test, it is likely that your test grade will reflect a lack of effort. Many of the concepts that you will be learning in this chemistry course will be unfamiliar and challenging. Embrace this challenge by organizing your approach to studying for this course.

Follow these test preparation tips to help you achieve a successful test score.

Before a Chemistry Test

- Read the course outline to know when your tests are scheduled.
- Review your class notes daily, and review the entire section after you have completed it in class. Do not put off reviewing material until right before test time; review needs to be ongoing.
- As you review, ask yourself questions about the material that is difficult for you.
- Create and answer your own test questions about what the teacher emphasized in class.
- Create and study your flashcards.
- Rework any homework problems that you solved incorrectly.
- Find out from your teacher what topics will be covered on the test, the style of the test, and whether a formula reference sheet will be provided.
- Get a good night's sleep before the test. Eat a good breakfast the day of the test so that you can think, process, and recall quickly and accurately.
- Remember to take pencils, erasers, a calculator, and a watch.

During a Chemistry Test

- Relax!
- Read the test directions before you start answering the test questions.
- Look through the test so that you know how many test questions there are, the style of the test items, and what references you have available. This will help determine how much time you should spend on each question.
- If a test question is too hard or too time consuming, skip it and return to it later. Sometimes you may be reminded about a concept or have a thought triggered by another test item. Circle any test items that you skip so that when you go back over the test, you will quickly know which items are not completed.

- Try to save time at the end of the testing period to review and check your answers. Verify that you have completed all parts of each question and that your answers are written clearly.

After a Chemistry Test

- Correct any wrong or incomplete answers.
- If necessary, make changes to your study habits or to your organization to prepare better for the next test.
- Do not give up! Chemistry concepts and applications can be tough to grasp, but with steadfast effort, you will be successful.

Strategies for Various Styles of Test Items

When taking a standardized test, you may encounter various styles of test items, such as multiple choice, gridded response, short answer, and extended response. Each style of question assesses your knowledge and understanding of chemistry, but each is graded differently.

Multiple Choice

A multiple choice test item consists of a test question and four answer choices, such as the following:

> *A compound contains 16% carbon and 84% sulfur by mass. What is the empirical formula of this compound?*
>
> **A** CS_2 **B** C_2S_2 **C** CS **D** C_2S

To answer a multiple choice question:

- Read the entire question slowly before considering any of the answer choices. Take note of key words that indicate what you are being asked to do.
- Try to determine an answer to the question before looking at the answer choices. Be sure to read all of the answer choices before selecting an answer.
- If you are not sure of the answer, try methods such as eliminating answer choices or working backward from the answer choices provided to make an educated guess.
- Completely fill in the correct answer choice on the answer sheet. Verify that the test item number matches the item number on the answer sheet.

xxvii

TEACHING TIPS

- Students should get into the habit of checking their work. A good place to start is with their homework.
- Before a standardized test, tell students whether an omitted answer will count against them.
- After a test, review the correct solution for each test item.
- Make a list of common errors made on the test, and have students work in small groups to develop ways to eliminate or minimize these types of errors on the next exam.
- Use the assessment resources provided in this program to give students practice with various styles of assessment. Resources include Chapter Tests, Standardized Test Practice, Chapter Summaries, Test Bank questions, Active Reading Questions within the text, and Assessment questions at the end of each chapter.
- Select multiple-choice questions from the Chapter Tests or from the Standardized Test Practice booklet that are appropriate to the section you are teaching. Show how to eliminate answer choices by using logic and reasoning. Also review how to use the answer choices to work backward to the question. These strategies are helpful when students are not sure how to solve a problem and when they check an answer.

TEACHING TIP

Use the Critical Thinking assessment questions provided at the end of each chapter to help students practice answering response-type questions.

 Active Learning
Group Activity

Have students work in pairs. Assign each pair a Critical Thinking assessment question from the chapter you are teaching. Each pair should create a scoring rubric for the question. Then have each pair exchange questions with another pair and create a response to the other pair's question. When finished, each pair should return both the question and the response to the original pair for "grading." Students should score the responses based on their scoring rubric and provide a written explanation for the score.

Understanding how a response item is scored will help students remember to answer all parts of a question with a complete and logical explanation.

xxviii

Short Response

Short response test items are structured questions designed to test comprehension and understanding. In a multiple choice or gridded response test item, you simply solve a problem and select or write your answer. In a short response question, however, you must show your work and describe your reasoning process in order to receive full credit.

- Before responding to a short response test item, take time to thoroughly read the question. You may find it helpful to underline key words that signal what should be included in your answer.
- Use the margin of your test page to write a brief outline of your response.
- Use your technical writing skills to write an organized and logical description or explanation.
- Verify that any needed units of measure are included in your answer and that your response contains complete sentences that are free of spelling and grammatical errors.

Extended Response

Extended response test items are usually questions with multiple parts that require a high level of thinking. Because the extended response questions are longer and more involved, your answer may be scored using several points and may involve partial credit.

The following is a sample scoring rubric (method) used to score an answer to an extended response test item.

A Sample Scoring Rubric Method	
4 points:	Student shows a thorough understanding of the concept, correctly answers the question, and provides a complete, detailed explanation.
3 points:	Student shows most of the work and provides an explanation but has a minor error OR student shows all work and arrives at a correct response, but does not provide an explanation.
2 points:	Student shows work but makes major errors resulting in an incorrect response or explanation. Explanation is missing, incorrect, or incomplete.
1 point:	Student shows some work and has an incorrect response without an explanation OR student does not follow directions.

To answer this type of test item, follow the same suggestions given for short response test items. You must also pay attention to the number of parts in the question. Underline key words or phrases in the question, such as *list, explain, solve, compare, contrast, design, identify,* and so on to help you include all aspects of the question in your response.

Gridded Response

When a test item requires you to place your answer in a grid, you must answer the test item correctly *and* fill out accurately the grid on your answer sheet, or the item will be marked as incorrect. The answer to a gridded response test item can be only a positive numerical value, such as a positive integer, a fraction, an improper fraction, or a decimal.

After you work the test item and determine the answer, you must write your answer in the answer boxes at the top of the grid. You must then fill in the corresponding bubble under each box.

- Write your answer with the first digit in the far left answer box, or with the last digit in the far right answer box.
- Write only one digit or symbol in each answer box.
- Do not leave a blank in the middle of an answer.
- Include the decimal point or the fraction bar if it is part of the answer.
- Fill in only one bubble for each answer box that has a number or symbol. Bubbles should be filled in by making a solid black mark.
- Do not grid a mixed number. You must first convert the mixed number to an improper fraction.

Response Grid

- Answer boxes
- Fraction bar bubbles
- Decimal point bubbles
- Number bubbles

EXAMPLES

Whole Number = 50

Decimal = 5.06

Fractions = $^{16}/_5$ = 3.2

Mixed Number = $12\,^1/_5 = ^{61}/_5$

1. [grid] .25 or 1/4

2. [grid] .1725

3. [grid] 2.75 or 2.75

4. [grid] 11/4 or 11/4

5. [grid] .005 or 1/200

6. [grid] .003 or .003

🍎 TEACHING TIP

Review these math skills to help students grid their answers correctly:

- Converting a mixed number to an improper fraction
- Writing a percentage as a decimal or as a fraction
- Converting between a fraction and a decimal

More Examples

Have students grid each of the following.

1. 25%
2. 17.25%
3. $2\frac{3}{4}$
4. $\frac{1}{2}$%
5. 3×10^{-3}

Review the various correct ways to grid each number.

1. [grid] .25 or

Planning Guide

Section	Segment		Text Features and Components	Labs, Demonstrations, & Activities
1.1 **The Science of Chemistry** **0.5 Block** pp. 4–8	A	The Importance of Learning Chemistry	(SE) Celebrity Chemical: Helium *p. 5*	(TE) Teaching Support: Demonstration *pp. 6–7* (RP) Classroom Activities and Projects *TE p. 4*

	B	What Is Chemistry?		(TE) Teaching Support: Additional Activity *pp. 8–9*
				(LM) Experiment 1: Chemistry of Fire
				  Lab Manual
				  Report Sheets
				  Teacher's Lab Guide

1.2
Using Science to Solve Problems
1 Block
pp. 9–14
	A	Solving Everyday Problems		(LM) Experiment 2: Scientific Observations
				  Lab Manual
				  Report Sheets
				  Teacher's Lab Guide

	B	Using Scientific Thinking to Solve a Problem	(SE) Chemistry in Your World: Land Mine Buzzers *p. 10*	

	C	The Scientific Method		(TE) Teaching Support: Additional Activity *p. 12*
				(TE) Teaching Support: Additional Activity *pp. 14–15*
				(RP) Classroom Activities and Projects *TE p. 13*
				(LM) Experiment 3: Observations and Explanations
				  Lab Manual
				  Report Sheets
				  Teacher's Lab Guide

1.3 **Learning Chemistry** **0.5 Block** pp. 15–17	A	Strategies for Learning Chemistry	(SE) Top Ten Reasons for Taking Chemistry *p. 15* (SE) Chemistry in Your World: Learn Chemistry—Prepare for Life *p. 17*	

Key	(SE) Student Edition	(TE) Teacher Edition	(RP) Teacher Resource Package
	(AR) Additional Materials	(LM) Lab Materials	(▤) Transparencies
	(◉) DVD	(▯) CD-ROM	(ⓘ) classzone.com

All Learners	Technology	Review & Assessment	Standards
TE Teaching Tips *pp. 5–6*	**•** Video: Dry Ice and Magnesium **•** Video: Zinc and Iodine **•** Video: Barking Dogs: Reaction of Phosphorus **•** Video: Reactions of Silver(I) **•** EasyPlanner	**SE** Questions and Problems *p. 19*	**TE** **NSES** UCP1, UCP2, A1, A2, B3, E2, G1, G2
TE Teaching Tips *p. 7*	**▮** Lab Generator CD **•** EasyPlanner	**SE** Active Reading Questions *pp. 7–8* **SE** Review Questions (1.1.A–1.1.B) *p. 8* **SE** Key Terms *p. 18* **SE** Questions and Problems *p. 19*	
	▮ Lab Generator CD **•** EasyPlanner	**SE** Questions and Problems *p. 19*	**TE** **NSES** UCP1, UCP2, A1, A2, E2, G1, G2
TE Teaching Tips *pp. 10–11*	**•** EasyPlanner	**SE** Questions and Problems *p. 19*	
TE Teaching Tip *p. 12* **TE** Meeting Individual Needs *p. 13* **TE** Misconception *p. 13*	**▤** Transparency: Figure 1.2 **•** Video: Oxygen, Hydrogen, Soap Bubbles, & Balloons **▮** Lab Generator CD **•** EasyPlanner	**SE** Critical Thinking *p. 14* **SE** Active Reading Question *p. 14* **SE** Review Questions (1.2.A–1.2.C) *p. 14* **SE** Key Terms *p. 18* **SE** Questions and Problems *pp. 19–20*	
TE Teaching Tips *pp. 15–16* **RP** Team Learning Worksheet (Chapter 1)	**▤** Transparency: Figure 1.3 **•** EasyPlanner	**SE** Review Questions (1.3.A) *p. 17* **SE** Questions and Problems *p. 20*	**TE** **NSES** UCP1, UCP2, A1, A2, G1, G2

Resource Materials for Chapter 1

SE Chapter Review *p. 18*

SE Standardized Test Practice *p. 21*

AR English/Spanish Summaries

▮ English Summaries Audio

▮ Spanish Summaries Audio

RP Meeting Individual Needs Toolkit (MINT)
      Chapter Review Worksheets
      Chapter Summaries

RP Solutions Guide

RP Standardized Test Practice

RP Chapter Tests

RP Test Bank

• Test Generator

Chapter 1

Overview

In this chapter our goals are for students to:

- Understand the importance of learning chemistry
- Define chemistry
- Recognize the general steps scientists use in solving problems
- Illustrate the scientific method
- Develop successful strategies for learning chemistry

Chapter 1

Chemistry: An Introduction

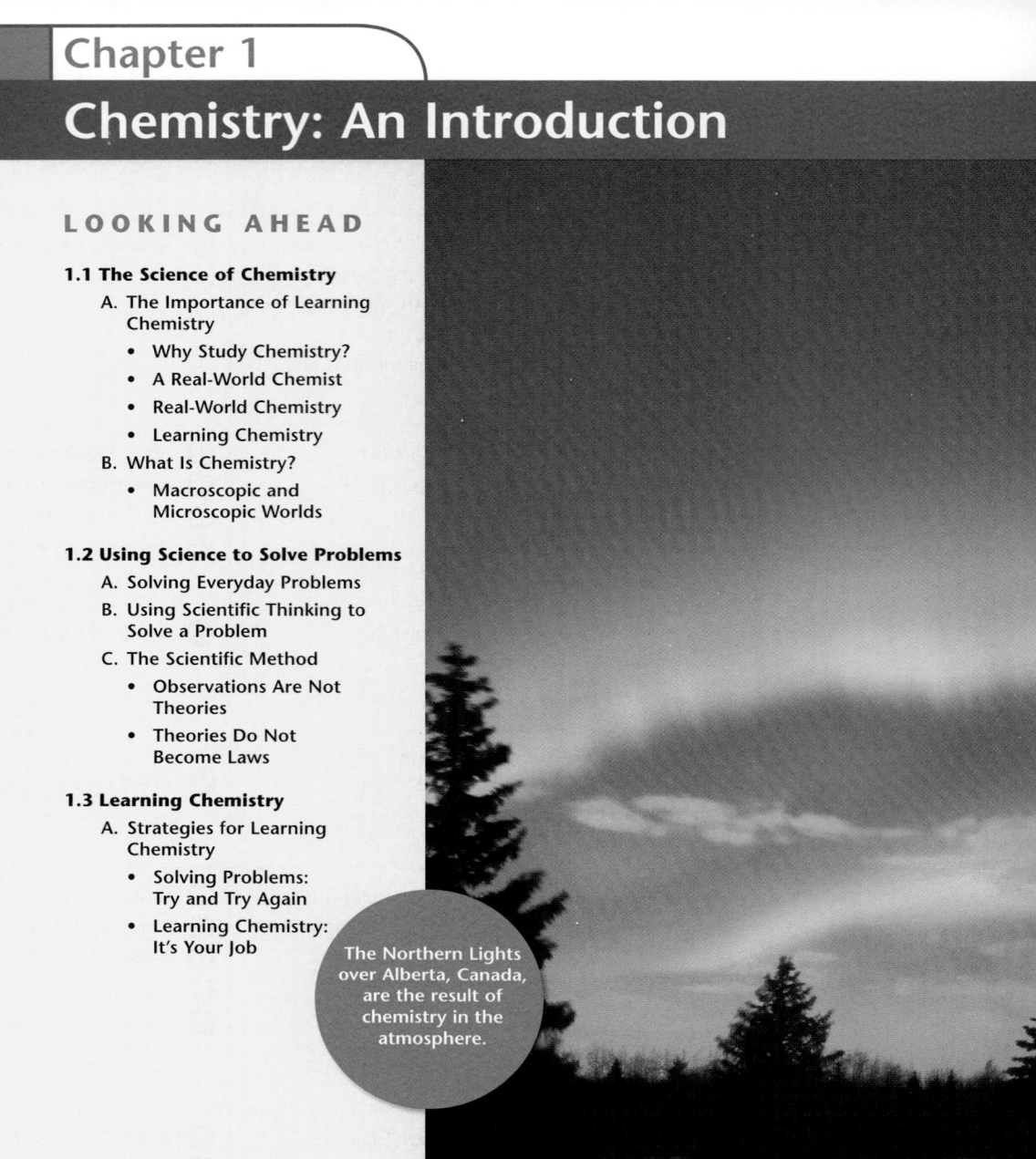

The Northern Lights over Alberta, Canada, are the result of chemistry in the atmosphere.

2

IN YOUR LIFE

Did you ever see a fireworks display on the Fourth of July and wonder how it's possible to produce those beautiful, intricate designs in the air? Have you read about dinosaurs—how they ruled the earth for millions of years and then suddenly disappeared? Although the extinction happened 65 million years ago and may seem unimportant, could the same thing happen to us? Have you ever wondered why an ice cube (pure water) floats in a glass of water (also pure water)? Did you know that the "lead" in your pencil is made of the same substance (carbon) as the diamond in an engagement ring? Did you ever wonder how a corn plant or a palm tree grows seemingly by magic, or why leaves turn beautiful colors in autumn? Do you know how the battery works to start your car or run your calculator? Surely some of these things and many others in the world around you have intrigued you. The fact is that we can explain all of these things in convincing ways by using the models of chemistry and the related physical and life sciences.

WHAT DO YOU KNOW?

Prereading Questions

1. List the first three things you think of when you hear the word *chemistry*.

2. List the first three things you think of when you hear the word *chemist*.

3. Consider a time when you solved a problem in your life. What was the problem? Explain how you went about solving the problem.

Prereading Questions

1. *Answers will vary.* Be prepared to address negative connotations, such as "all chemicals are harmful."

2. *Answers will vary.* Discuss stereotypes of chemists and tell students that they will learn in Chapter 1 that chemists do many different types of work.

3. *Answers will vary.* Have students write the answer to this question in their notebooks and go back to these answers after discussing the scientific method.

TECHNOLOGY IN THE CLASSROOM

 Transparencies
Figures: 1.1, 1.2

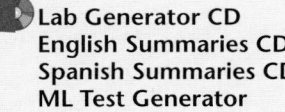 **Power Presentation DVD**
  PowerPoint Slides
  Videos
  Zinc and Iodine
  Dry Ice and Magnesium
  Barking Dogs: Reaction of Phosphorus
  Reactions of Silver(I)
  Oxygen, Hydrogen, Soap Bubbles, and Balloons

eEdition
EasyPlanner

 Lab Generator CD
English Summaries CD
Spanish Summaries CD
ML Test Generator

classzone.com

SECTION 1.1
INTRODUCE

Student Preparation

Assign students to read Section 1.1 and to answer the Review Questions at the end of the section before coming to class.

 Active Learning
Team Learning Worksheet

After introducing the material in Chapter 1 in class, place students in groups and have them work together on **Chapter 1: Team Learning Worksheet.**

 Active Learning
Classroom Activities and Projects

For an early project to introduce students to the elements, see *Element Mobile* located in the *Teacher Resources.*

SECTION 1.1
GUIDE THE LEARNING

Homework

You may wish to assign these selected end-of-chapter problems as homework for this section: 1, 2, 3, 4, 5, 6

Additional end-of-chapter problems can be used for extra practice.

1.1.A The Importance of Learning Chemistry

Objective To understand the importance of learning chemistry

Key Term
• Chemistry

Objectives
• *To understand the importance of learning chemistry*
• *To define chemistry*

A. The Importance of Learning Chemistry

A knowledge of chemistry is useful to almost everyone—chemistry occurs all around us all of the time, and an understanding of chemistry is useful to doctors, lawyers, mechanics, businesspeople, firefighters, and poets, among others. Chemistry is important—there is no doubt about that. It lies at the heart of our efforts to produce new materials that make our lives safer and easier, to produce new sources of energy that are abundant and nonpolluting, and to understand and control the many diseases that threaten us and our food supplies. Even if your future career does not require the daily use of chemical principles, your life will be greatly influenced by chemistry.

Why Study Chemistry?

It is clear that the applications of chemistry have enriched our lives in many ways. However, these applications have brought with them some problems. As a society we tend to be shortsighted; we concentrate too much on present benefits without considering the long-range implications of our actions. As a result, we have damaged the environment. We need to pursue a "greener" approach to the production and use of chemicals. To accomplish this goal, we need to learn more about the chemical nature of the earth.

A Real-World Chemist

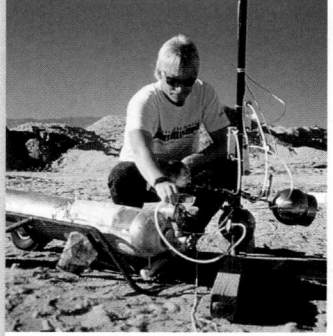

One of the "hottest" fields in the chemical sciences is environmental chemistry—an area that involves studying our environmental ills and finding creative ways to address them. For example, meet Bart Eklund, who works in the atmospheric chemistry field for Radian Corporation in Austin, Texas. Eklund's interest in a career in environmental science started with chemistry and ecology courses he took in college. The diverse nature of environmental problems has allowed Eklund to pursue his interest in several fields at the same time.

Bart Eklund's career demonstrates how chemists help solve our environmental problems. It is how we use our chemical knowledge that makes all the difference.

Eklund's Career Highlights

- Spending a winter month doing air sampling in the Grand Tetons, where he also met his wife and learned to ski;
- Driving sampling pipes by hand into the rocky ground of Death Valley Monument in California;
- Getting to work in and see Alaska, Yosemite Park, Niagara Falls, Hong Kong, the People's Republic of China, Mesa Verde, New York City, and dozens of other interesting places.

Real-World Chemistry

An example that shows how technical knowledge can be a "double-edged sword" is the case of chlorofluorocarbons (CFCs). When the compound called Freon-12 was first synthesized, it was hailed as a near-miracle substance. Because of its noncorrosive nature and its unusual ability to resist decomposition, Freon-12 seemed ideal for refrigeration and air-conditioning systems and many other applications. For years everything seemed fine—the CFCs actually replaced more dangerous materials, such as the ammonia used earlier in refrigeration systems. The CFCs were definitely viewed as "good guys." But then a problem was discovered—the ozone in the upper atmosphere that protects us from the high-energy radiation of the sun began to decline. What was happening to cause the destruction of the vital ozone?

A chemist in the laboratory

CELEBRITY CHEMICAL — Helium (He)

Have you ever heard recordings of deep-sea divers' voices? They sound a lot like Donald Duck. It's the helium gas mixed with the oxygen gas in the "air" that the divers are breathing that produces the effect. Normal air is about 8/10 nitrogen and 2/10 oxygen. This mixture doesn't work for diving because too much nitrogen dissolves in the blood at the high pressures under the ocean. When the diver returns to the surface, this nitrogen can form bubbles leading to the "bends"—a terribly painful condition that can be fatal. Helium does not dissolve in the blood easily, so it does not lead to the bends readily.

Helium is a very interesting substance. You are no doubt familiar with it because you have had balloons filled with helium. If you let go of a helium-filled balloon, it floats up and away from you. That's because helium is lighter than air.

The helium we use for deep-sea diving and filling balloons is separated from natural gas as it is brought to the surface. This helium was formed in the depths of the earth by radioactive decay and remains trapped with the natural gas deposits.

Helium has many uses. For example, it is used to fill blimps and weather balloons. In addition, because of its very low boiling point (−452 °F), it is used as an extreme coolant in scientific experiments.

For a "light-weight," helium is pretty important.

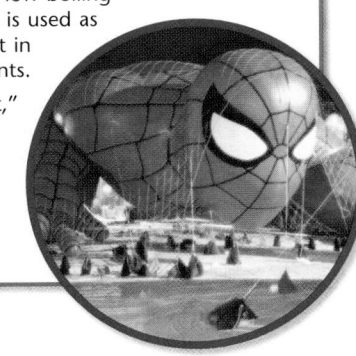

Spider-Man balloon filled with helium

1.1 • The Science of Chemistry • 5

CELEBRITY CHEMICAL

Helium (He)

Encourage students to recognize that they are already familiar with uses of elements and compounds in their daily lives. The Celebrity Chemical feature highlights the uses of chemicals.

Additional Activity: Use this feature to begin focusing on an Element of the Week. Feature a bulletin board with a celebrity element each week. Highlight its properties, uses, and characteristics.

Student Project: Assign an element to each student. Have students create mobiles for their elements, including their elements' names, symbols, properties, uses, and characteristics. Use the mobiles to decorate the classroom for parent night.

TEACHING TIP

Use Bart Eklund as an example of a real-life chemist. Have students compare their original ideas about chemists (from the second Prereading Question for this chapter) to what they have read about Bart Eklund.

Videos

There are several videos available to show your students chemical reactions. These include:
Dry Ice and Magnesium
Zinc and Iodine
Barking Dogs: Reaction of Phosphorus
Reactions of Silver(I)

 TEACHING TIP

Many students will view the term *chemical* negatively (notice whether this is the case when students answer the first Prereading Question for this chapter). While it is true that sometimes chemicals are harmful to the environment, it is also true that all substances (such as water and oxygen) are chemicals. In addition, use the story of CFCs to discuss how chemists work to fix problems caused by some chemicals.

Much to everyone's amazement, the culprits turned out to be the CFCs. Large quantities of CFCs had leaked and drifted into the upper atmosphere, where they reacted to destroy ozone molecules. This process allowed more harmful radiation to reach the earth's surface (see **Figure 1.1**). Thus a substance that possessed many advantages in earthbound applications turned against us in the atmosphere. Who could have guessed it would end this way?

The good news is that the U.S. chemical industry is leading the way to find environmentally safe alternatives to CFCs, and the levels of CFCs in the atmosphere are already dropping.

The story of the CFCs shows that we can respond relatively quickly to a serious environmental problem if we decide to do so. Also, it is important to understand that chemical manufacturers have a new attitude about the environment—they are now among the leaders in finding ways to address our environmental problems.

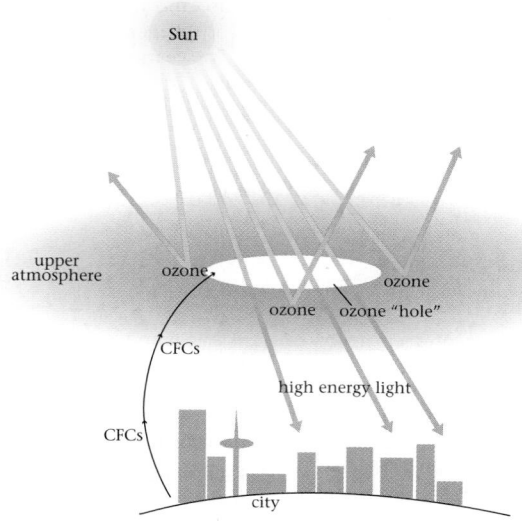

Figure 1.1
Destruction of ozone molecules in the upper atmosphere occurs when CFCs drift up from populated areas.

Learning Chemistry

Learning chemistry is both interesting and important. A chemistry course can do more than simply help you learn the principles of chemistry, however. A major byproduct of your study of chemistry is that you will become a better problem solver. One reason that chemistry has the reputation of being "tough" is that it often deals with rather complicated systems that require some effort to figure out. Although this complexity may seem to be a disadvantage at first, you can turn it to your advantage if you have the right attitude.

6 • Chapter 1 • Chemistry: An Introduction

Teaching Support
DEMONSTRATION

Carbon Tower

Materials
• 250-mL beaker
• Paper towels
• Concentrated sulfuric acid
• Sucrose
• Stirring rod

Procedure Place 50 g of sucrose in the beaker. Place the beaker on a mat of paper towels in a fume hood. Add 50 mL concentrated sulfuric acid to the sugar and observe.

Teaching Notes Have students note the color changes as the reaction proceeds—white, yellow, brown, black. Ask students which element found in sugar could account for this color change.

Although learning chemistry is often not easy, it's never impossible. In fact, anyone who is interested, patient, and willing to work can learn chemistry. In this book, we will try very hard to help you understand what chemistry is and how it works, and to point out how chemistry applies to the things going on in your life.

Our sincere hope is that this text will motivate you to learn chemistry, make its concepts understandable to you, and demonstrate how interesting and vital the study of chemistry is.

B. What Is Chemistry?

Chemistry can be defined as the science that deals with the materials of the universe and the changes that these materials undergo.

> **Chemistry**
> The science of materials and the changes that these materials undergo

Chemists are involved in activities as diverse as examining the fundamental particles of matter, looking for molecules in space, making new materials of all types, using bacteria to produce such chemicals as insulin, and finding new methods for early detection of disease.

Chemistry is often called the central science—and with good reason. Most of the phenomena that occur in the world around us involve chemical changes—changes in which one or more substances become different substances. Here are some examples of chemical changes:

- Wood burns in air, forming water, carbon dioxide, and other substances.
- A plant grows by assembling simple substances into more complex substances.
- The steel in a car rusts.
- Eggs, flour, sugar, and baking powder are mixed and baked to yield a cake.
- The definition of the term *chemistry* is learned and stored in the brain.
- Emissions from a power plant lead to the formation of acid rain.

Active Reading Question

What types of things does a real-world chemist do?

Macroscopic and Microscopic Worlds

As we proceed, you will see how the concepts of chemistry allow us to understand the nature of these and other changes. To understand these processes and the many others that occur around us, chemists take a special view of things. Chemists "look inside" ordinary objects to observe how the fundamental components are behaving.

To understand how this approach works, consider a tree. When we view a tree from a distance, we see the tree as a whole. The trunk, the branches, and the leaves all blend together to give the tree. We call this overall view of the tree the *macroscopic* picture.

As we get closer to the tree, we begin to see the detail—pieces of bark, individual leaves, large and tiny branches, and so on. Now imagine that we examine a single leaf. We see veins, variation in color, surface irregularities, and more. Our curiosity is whetted. What lies inside the leaf? What causes it to change from a bud in the spring to a green leaf in the summer and

1.1 • The Science of Chemistry • **7**

(continued)

Note the steam emitted from the black carbon residue that rises out of the beaker. Ask students to propose an explanation for the source of the steam.

Safety and Disposal The reaction releases SO_2 gas, which is irritating to some students. The smell of the reaction is of burned sugar. Make sure you do not handle the tower

unless you wash it with sodium bicarbonate solution. Place the washed tower in a trash can. Clean the beaker with soap and water.

1.1.B What Is Chemistry?
Objective To define chemistry

LABORATORY
EXPERIMENT 1:
Chemistry of Fire, Traditional

 TEACHING TIPS

- Connecting the real world to the atomic/molecular world is difficult for many students. Encourage students to visualize the atomic/molecular world by drawing pictures.

- Discuss students' ideas of what everyday objects look like on an atomic/molecular level. Include in your discussion examples such as air, water, salt, and sugar. Don't worry about the details here. The idea is to get students thinking and ready to continue with Chapter 2. Further detail will be developed there. Student responses will give you an idea of the perceptions they hold as the course begins.

Active Reading Question

Answers will vary, but include: chemists produce new materials, produce new sources of energy, and understand and control diseases.

Answers will vary, but can include: wood burning, plants growing, leaves changing colors, metal rusting, and food cooking.

SECTION 1.1
ASSESS

 SECTION 1.1
Review Questions

1. CFCs have both good and bad characteristics. They are not corrosive, resist decomposing, and replace more dangerous chemicals. Unfortunately, CFCs also break down the ozone in the upper atmosphere, letting more radiation reach the surface of the earth.

2. Most phenomena involve chemical changes, making chemistry central to everything.

3. A *microscopic* picture allows us to think about the atoms and molecules that make up matter; technically it is what we can see through a microscope, but chemists sometimes use the term to go even further (to the atom and molecule level). A *macroscopic* picture is the view we see with our naked eyes.

4. Chemistry is the science that deals with the materials of the universe and the changes that these materials undergo.

5. A chemist may produce new materials, produce new sources of energy, and control diseases.

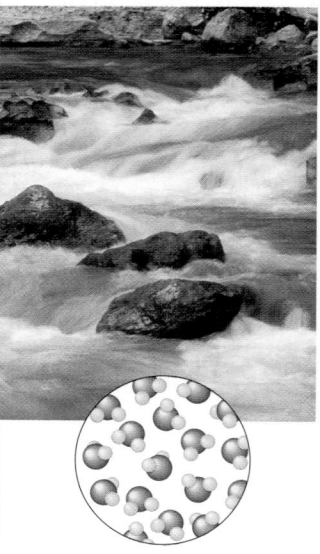

The macroscopic view of water (the mountain stream) and the microscopic view (the individual water molecules)

then to a red or golden color in the fall? To answer these questions, we need a microscope. As we examine the leaf under a microscope, we see cells and motion. Because we don't "live" in this *microscopic* world, the common-place leaf becomes fascinating and mysterious.

When we speak of "motion" in the macroscopic world, we refer to the swaying of the tree and the rustling of the leaves. In the microscopic world, "motion" refers to the cells acting as tiny machines that absorb energy from the sun and nutrients from the air and the soil. We are now in the microscopic world, but as chemists, we want to go even further. What are the building blocks of the cells and what are the components of the water that contains the dissolved nutrients?

Think about water, a very familiar substance. In the macroscopic world, it flows and splashes over rocks in mountain streams and freezes on ponds in the winter. What is the microscopic nature of water? As you may know already, water is composed of tiny molecules that we can represent as

 or

Here H represents a hydrogen atom and O represents an oxygen atom. We often write this molecule as H_2O because it contains two hydrogens (H) and one oxygen (O).

This is the microscopic world of the chemist—a world of molecules and atoms. This is the world we will explore in this book. One of our main goals is to connect the macroscopic world in which you live to the microscopic world that makes it all work. We think you will enjoy the trip!

Active Reading Question

What are some examples of chemistry that you see in everyday life?

 SECTION 1.1
REVIEW QUESTIONS

❶ How do CFC's illustrate that technical advances can be a "double-edged" sword?

❷ Why is chemistry often called a central science?

❸ What is the difference between a *microscopic* picture and a *macroscopic* picture?

❹ What is chemistry?

❺ Name three activities that a chemist may do.

RESEARCH LINKS
CLASSZONE.COM

8 • Chapter 1 • Chemistry: An Introduction

Teaching Support
ADDITIONAL ACTIVITY

Name Game This whole-class activity is intended to help students learn about the scientific method.

Start by thinking of a category for a name such as "female name with five letters." Don't tell students the category, but tell them you are thinking of a name, and ask someone to guess it. If students guess a

name outside of the category, tell them the guess is incorrect. If they guess a name in your chosen category, say "That could be right." You might write the answers in columns on the board labeled *correct* and *incorrect*. After several correct answers, ask students to determine the category.

What can students learn from this game? First, scientists make observations and try to look for patterns. They develop hypotheses to explain these patterns. Some of these

Using Science to Solve Problems

Objectives

- *To understand scientific thinking*
- *To illustrate scientific thinking*
- *To describe the method scientists use to study nature*

Key Terms

- Scientific method
- Theory
- Natural law
- Measurement

A. Solving Everyday Problems

One of the most important things we do in everyday life is solve problems. In fact, most of the decisions you make each day can be described as solving problems.

It's 8:30 A.M. on Friday. Which is the best way to drive to school to avoid traffic congestion?

You have two tests on Monday. Should you divide your study time equally or allot more time to one than to the other?

Your car stalls at a busy intersection and your little brother is with you. What should you do next?

These are everyday problems of the type we all face. What process do we use to solve them? You may not have thought about it before, but there are several steps that almost everyone uses to solve problems:

1. Recognize the problem and state it clearly. Some information becomes known, or something happens that requires action. In science we call this step **making an observation.**

2. Propose possible solutions to the problem or possible explanations for the observation. In scientific language, suggesting such a possibility is called **formulating a hypothesis.**

3. Decide which of the solutions is the best, or decide whether the explanation proposed is reasonable. To do this, we search our memory for any pertinent information or we seek new information. In science we call searching for new information **performing an experiment.**

As we will see, citizens as well as scientists use these same procedures to study what happens in the world around us. The important point here is that scientific thinking can help you in all parts of your life. It's worthwhile to learn how to think scientifically—whether you want to be a scientist, an auto mechanic, a doctor, a politician, or a poet!

B. Using Scientific Thinking to Solve a Problem

To illustrate how science helps us solve problems, consider a true story about two people, David and Susan (not their real names). Several years ago David and Susan were healthy 40-year-olds living in California, where David was serving in the Air Force. Gradually Susan became quite ill, showing flulike symptoms including nausea and severe muscle pains. Even her personality changed: she became uncharacteristically grumpy. She seemed like a totally different person from the healthy, happy woman of a few

---

Student Preparation

Assign students to read Section 1.2 and to answer the Review Questions at the end of the section before coming to class.

🔺 LABORATORY
EXPERIMENT 2:
Scientific Observations, Traditional

SECTION 1.2
GUIDE THE LEARNING

Homework

You may wish to assign these selected end-of-chapter problems as homework for this section: 7, 8, 10, 11, 12, 14

Additional end-of-chapter problems can be used for extra practice.

1.2.A Solving Everyday Problems

Objective To recognize the general steps scientists use in solving problems

1.2.B Using Scientific Thinking to Solve a Problem

Objective To illustrate the scientific method

(continued)

hypotheses sound sensible initially but later turn out to be incorrect. These mistakes can usually be discovered by making more observations. Although we can never be sure that the hypothesis is correct, we can become more confident as we make more observations that fit. After many different names have been presented, the "female five-letter name" category will become apparent. Discuss how this exercise relates to the scientific method (students made observations, looked for patterns, and developed a hypothesis; they then used new observations to refine the theory).

months earlier. Following her doctor's orders, she rested and drank plenty of fluids, including large quantities of orange juice from her favorite mug, part of a 200-piece set of pottery dishes recently purchased in Italy. However, she just became sicker, developing extreme abdominal cramps and severe anemia.

During this time David also became ill and exhibited symptoms much like Susan's: weight loss, excruciating pain in his back and arms, and uncharacteristic fits of temper. The disease became so serious that he retired early from the Air Force and the couple moved to Seattle. For a short time their health improved, but after they unpacked all their belongings (including those pottery dishes), their health began to deteriorate again. Susan's body became so sensitive that she could not tolerate the weight of a blanket. She was near death. What was wrong? The doctors didn't know, but one of them suggested that she might have porphyria, a rare blood disease.

Desperate, David began to search the medical literature himself. One day while he was reading about porphyria, a statement jumped off the page: "Lead poisoning can sometimes be confused with porphyria." Could the problem be lead poisoning?

We have described a very serious problem with life-or-death implications. What should David do next? Overlooking for a moment the obvious response of calling the couple's doctor immediately to discuss the possibility of lead poisoning, could David solve the problem by scientific thinking? Let's use the three steps of the scientific approach to attack the problem one part at a time. This is important: usually we solve complex problems by breaking them down into manageable parts. We can then assemble the solution to the overall problem from the answers we have found "from the parts."

CHEMISTRY IN YOUR WORLD

Science, Technology, and Society

Land Mine Buzzers

An estimated 100 million plastic land mines are scattered throughout the earth on former battlefields. Every day, these hidden mines kill or maim 60 people. Finding these mines is very difficult—they were designed to resist detection. Scientists are now enthusiastic about a new way to identify the mines—with honeybees. Previous work has shown that bees foraging in chemically contaminated areas carry these substances back to their hives. The hope is that bees searching for food in mined areas will bring back traces of the explosives from "leaky" mines, alerting people to nearby danger. Scientists also plan to train bees to seek out explosives by associating the scents of the explosive compounds with food. The researchers will keep track of the bees' movements by fitting electronic identification tags (about the size of a grain of rice) on the bees' backs.

If this idea works, it would be an inexpensive, safe method for characterizing a minefield. These "mine buzzers" would be much safer than the current practice of prodding the soil with pokers.

Chemistry in Your World

Land Mine Buzzers

"Land Mine Buzzers" features honeybees, which provide some fascinating examples of chemistry in action. For example, honeybees from a given hive carry one or more chemicals on their bodies that enable them to recognize one another as "friends." A honeybee entering a hive that has the "wrong" chemical signature will be attacked immediately and killed.

TEACHING TIP

Now would be an excellent time to have students discuss their answers to the third Prereading Question for this chapter. Have students discuss the problems they solved and compare these to the story of David and Susan. Especially emphasize how David and Susan took a large problem and broke it into smaller more manageable questions. This is a good approach to problem solving.

What Is the Disease?			
Observation	Hypothesis	Experiment	Results
David and Susan are ill with specific systems.	The disease is lead poisoning.	Look up symptoms of lead poisoning.	Symptoms match almost exactly.

Is It Lead Poisoning?			
Observation	Hypothesis	Experiment	Results
Lead poisoning results from high levels of lead in the blood.	David and Susan have high levels of lead in their blood.	Perform blood analysis.	High levels of lead in both people's blood.

Where Is the Lead Coming From?			
Observation	Hypothesis	Experiment	Results
There is lead in the couple's blood.	The lead is in their food and drink when they purchase it.	Determine whether anyone else shopping at the store has symptoms (no one does).	Moving to a new area (and new store) did not solve the problem.
The food they bought is free of lead.	The dishes they use at home are the source of the lead.	Determine whether the dishes contain lead.	Analysis of the pottery showed that lead was present in the glaze.
Lead is present in the dishes, so they could be a source of lead poisoning.	The lead is being leached into their food.	Place a beverage (such as orange juice) in one of the cups. Analyze the beverage for lead.	High levels of lead in the drink, so the dishes are the source of the lead poisoning.

After many applications of the scientific method, the problem is solved. We can summarize the answer to the problem (David and Susan's illness) as follows: the Italian pottery they used for everyday dishes contained a lead glaze that contaminated their food and drink with lead. This lead accumulated in their bodies to the point at which it interfered seriously with normal functions and produced severe symptoms. This overall explanation, which summarizes the hypotheses that agree with the experimental results, is called a *theory* in science. This explanation accounts for the results of all of the experiments performed.*

We could continue to use the scientific method to study other aspects of this problem, such as the following:

What types of food or drink leach the most lead from the dishes?

Do all pottery dishes with lead glazes produce lead poisoning?

As we answer questions by using the scientific method, other questions naturally arise. By repeating the three steps again and again, we can come to understand a given phenomenon thoroughly.

---

*"David" and "Susan" recovered from their lead poisoning and are now publicizing the dangers of using lead-glazed pottery. This happy outcome is the answer to the third part of their overall problem, "Can the disease be cured?" They simply stopped using that pottery for food and beverages.

TEACHING TIP

Emphasize that scientists find both answers and more questions as they use the scientific method to solve a problem. This idea will come up repeatedly as students learn about models of the atom in Chapters 3 and 11. The scientific method is more like a loop than a line that has a definite end. This is the nature of science.

1.2.C The Scientific Method

Objective To describe the method scientists use to study nature

 LABORATORY

EXPERIMENT 3:
Observations and Explanations

 TEACHING TIP

While the scientific method is presented in steps, it cannot be emphasized enough that the process does not end at the experiment step. Point out the last sentence of step three: Experiments always produce new observations, and these observations bring us back to the beginning of the process. Figure 1.2 is a graphic representation of this process.

TECHNOLOGY

⊙ **Video**

Oxygen, Hydrogen, Soap Bubbles, and Balloons

This video shows balloons containing hydrogen and oxygen being ignited. Have students use their knowledge of the scientific method to determine what might cause the balloons to make such a loud noise.

Scientific method
Systematic process for studying nature that involves observations, hypotheses, and experiments

Measurement
A quantitative observation

ℹ️ **nformation**

Quantitative observations involve a number. Qualitative observations do not.

C. The Scientific Method

Science is a framework for gaining and organizing knowledge. Science is not simply a set of facts but also a plan of action—a *procedure* for processing and understanding certain types of information. Although scientific thinking is useful in all aspects of life, in this text we will use it to understand how the natural world operates. The process that lies at the center of scientific inquiry is called the **scientific method**, which consists of the following steps:

Steps in the Scientific Method

1. **State the problem and collect data (make observations).** Observations may be *qualitative* (the sky is blue; water is a liquid) or *quantitative* (water boils at 100 °C; a certain chemistry book weighs 4.5 pounds). A qualitative observation does not involve a number. A quantitative observation is called a **measurement** and does involve a number (and a unit, such as pounds or inches). We will discuss measurements in detail in Chapter 5.

2. **Formulate hypotheses.** A hypothesis is a *possible* explanation for the observation.

3. **Perform experiments.** An experiment is something we do to test the hypothesis. We gather new information that allows us to decide whether the hypothesis is supported by the new information we have learned from the experiment. Experiments always produce new observations, and these observations bring us back to the beginning of the process.

To explain the behavior of a given part of nature, we repeat these steps many times. Gradually, we gather the knowledge necessary to understand what is going on.

When we have a set of hypotheses that agrees with our various observations, we assemble them into a theory that is often called a *model*. A **theory** (model) is a set of tested hypotheses that gives an overall explanation of some part of nature (see **Figure 1.2**).

Observations Are Not Theories

It is important to distinguish between observations and theories.

> An observation is something that is witnessed and can be recorded. A theory is an interpretation—a possible explanation of why nature behaves in a particular way.

Theories inevitably change as more information becomes available. For example, the motions of the sun and stars have remained virtually the same over the thousands of years during which humans have been observing them, but our explanations—our theories—have changed greatly since ancient times.

Teaching Support
ADDITIONAL ACTIVITY

A Model Activity Bring some models (toys) to class and place them on the front desk. Examples include a car, truck, horse, boat, and molecule (ball-and-stick methane is a simple one). Tell the class you are going to point to an item, and they are to shout out its name. Expect to be greeted with shouts of "car," "truck,"

and so on. Write these names on the board, thank students for being so responsive, but inform them that they are wrong. Ask them to reconsider. You will probably be greeted with more specifics, such as "blue car." Again, thank them, but tell them they are wrong. Ask students to talk with one another. Eventually someone may say "model car," "toy horse," or something similar. Congratulate

them on their thinking skills. (If they do not come to this conclusion, help them by saying things such as "What makes a car a car?" or "Can I drive this car?") Discuss the nature and purpose of models in science. In particular, make sure that students understand the difference between a scientific model and "reality."

Figure 1.2
The various parts of the scientific method

 MISCONCEPTION
Chemistry

Some students believe that a theory becomes a law once the theory has been accepted. Theories never become laws. Laws tell us what happens, whereas theories are our attempts to explain why things happen.

Active Learning
Classroom Activities and Projects

For a project in which students use scientific thinking to solve real-world problems, see *Applying the Scientific Method* located in the *Teacher Resources*.

The point is that we don't stop asking questions just because we have devised a theory that seems to account satisfactorily for some aspect of natural behavior. We continue doing experiments to refine our theories. We do this by using the theory to make a prediction and then performing an experiment (making a new observation) to see whether the results match this prediction.

Always remember that theories (models) are human inventions. They represent our attempts to explain observed natural behavior in terms of our human experiences. We must continue to do experiments and refine our theories to be consistent with new knowledge if we hope to approach a more nearly complete understanding of nature.

Theories Do Not Become Laws

As we observe nature, we often see that the same observation applies to many different systems. For example, studies of innumerable chemical changes have shown that the total mass of the materials involved is the same before and after the change. We often summarize such generally observed behavior into a statement called a **natural law**. The observation that the total mass of materials is not affected by a chemical change in those materials is called the law of conservation of mass.

You must recognize the difference between a law and a theory. A law is a summary of observed (measurable) behavior, whereas a theory is an explanation of behavior.

> A law tells what happens; a theory (model) is our attempt to explain why it happens.

Natural law
Statement that summarizes generally observed behavior

Meeting Individual Needs
ENGLISH LANGUAGE LEARNERS

Use a real-life situation that is familiar to students to help them understand the meanings of observation and theory. For example, point out that roadway systems are designed based on these concepts. Explain that a person assigned to study traffic patterns at a given location, over a period of time, makes a list of observations about the time intervals in a day when traffic is light, medium, and heavy. A person studying these observations would then theorize as to what causes the traffic patterns. For instance, patterns may be caused by commuting times for work/school, sporting event traffic, weather, and so on. These observations and theories can be used by city engineers to determine whether a traffic light needs to be installed or whether new roads should be constructed to help the flow of traffic.

If this were true, the people solving the problems would be objective and interested in only the facts rather than being influenced by special interests. It does not mean, however, that problems would be solved easily or that all problems would be solved. For example, scientists continue to debate the causes of the ozone hole and the greenhouse effect.

Active Reading Question

In solving a problem, we first need to make observations to understand the problem. We propose a solution to the problem and then test this solution. We may need to modify or completely change the solution depending on how well it works. In science, however, we do not stop asking questions just because an explanation seems to explain our theory. Scientists are always interested in refining theories to make them better.

SECTION 1.2
ASSESS

SECTION 1.2
Review Questions

1. *Answers will vary.* Look for proper labeling of the steps used in the example and for logic in the student answers.

2. An observation can be witnessed and recorded. A theory is an interpretation of why something occurred or why nature behaves in a particular way. Students will have various observations and theories. Have them explain their examples.

3. State the problem, collect data, formulate hypotheses, perform experiments, refine hypotheses (collect more data, etc.).

4. A theory is an interpretation.

CRITICAL ?
THINKING

What if everyone in the government used the scientific method to analyze and solve society's problems, and politics were never involved in the solutions?

Write a paragraph explaining how this approach would be different from the present situation, and whether it would be better or worse.

In this section, we have described the scientific method (which is summarized in **Figure 1.2**) as it might ideally be applied. However, it is important to remember that science does not always progress smoothly and efficiently. Scientists are human. They have prejudices, they misinterpret data, they can become emotionally attached to their theories and thus lose objectivity, and they may play politics. Science is affected by profit motives, budgets, fads, wars, and religious beliefs.

Galileo, for example, was forced to deny his astronomical observations in the face of strong religious resistance. Lavoisier, the father of modern chemistry, was beheaded because of his politics. And great progress in the chemistry of nitrogen fertilizers resulted from the desire to produce explosives to fight wars. The progress of science is often slowed more by the frailties of humans and their institutions than by the limitations of scientific measuring devices. The scientific method is only as effective as the humans using it. It does not automatically lead to progress.

Active Reading Question

In what ways is using a scientific approach to solving a problem similar to approaches you have used in solving problems in everyday life? In what ways is it different?

SECTION 1.2
REVIEW QUESTIONS

❶ Describe how you would set up an experiment to test the relationship between doing chemistry homework and the final grade in the course.

Apply a scientific approach to solving this problem. Label each of your steps appropriately.

❷ What is the difference between an observation and a theory? Give an example of each (different from the ones in your book!)

❸ What are the steps in the scientific method?

❹ Which is an interpretation—a law or a theory?

RESEARCH LINKS
CLASSZONE.COM

Teaching Support
ADDITIONAL ACTIVITY

Can a Tape Recorder Learn? Bring a tape recorder with a blank tape to class. Tell students you are going to teach it the names of some of your students. Walk over to a student and say "The name of this student is [push Record] (name)." Repeat this step with a few more students. Then rewind the tape, go back to the first student, and ask "What is this student's name?" Press Play. Repeat this

step for the next few students. Ask the class, "Did I teach the tape recorder? Did the tape recorder learn?" Discuss learning and teaching with your students.

Most students will state that the tape recorder is not learning. Push students a little further and say, "But didn't the tape recorder get all of the answers right? Wouldn't it deserve an 'A'?" Most students will tell you "no"; use this reply to your advantage.

Learning Chemistry

Objective

• *To develop successful strategies for learning chemistry*

A. Strategies for Learning Chemistry

Chemistry courses have a universal reputation for being difficult. There are some good reasons for this. For example, as we have already discussed, we live in the macroscopic world; but to understand this world, we need to think in terms of the unfamiliar microscopic world. In addition, the language of chemistry is unfamiliar in the beginning; many terms and definitions need to be memorized. As with any language, *you must know the vocabulary* before you can communicate effectively. We will try to help you by pointing out those things that need to be memorized.

But memorization is only the beginning. Don't stop there or your experience with chemistry will be frustrating. Memorization is not the same as understanding. We can teach a parrot to say anything we can say, but the parrot does not understand the meaning of its words. You need to memorize facts, but you also need to strive to understand the fundamental ideas—the models of chemistry. Be willing to do some thinking, and learn to trust yourself to figure things out. To solve a typical chemistry problem, you must sort through the given information and decide what is really crucial.

Solving Problems: Try and Try Again

It is important to realize that chemical systems tend to be complicated—there are typically many components—and we must make approximations in describing them. Therefore, trial and error play a major role in solving chemical problems. In tackling a complicated system, a practicing chemist really does not expect to be right the first time he or she analyzes the problem. The usual practice is to make several simplifying assumptions and then give it a try. If the answer obtained doesn't make sense, the chemist adjusts the assumptions, using feedback from the first attempt, and tries again.

The point is this: in dealing with chemical systems, do not expect to understand everything immediately. In fact, it is typical (even for an experienced chemist) *not* to understand at first. Make an attempt to solve the problem and then analyze the feedback. *It is not a disaster to make a mistake as long as you learn from it.*

The only way to develop your confidence as a problem solver is to practice solving problems. To help you, this book contains many examples worked out in detail. Follow these examples carefully, making sure you understand each step. These examples are followed by a Practice Problem that you should try on your own. Use the practice problems to test whether you are understanding the material as you go along.

Top Ten Reasons for Taking Chemistry

1. Do experiments using fire and chemicals.
2. Learn to answer chemistry questions on game shows.
3. Learn to solve problems.
4. See cool demonstrations in class.
5. Learn to use and dispose of household chemicals safely.
6. Wear fashionable lab aprons and goggles.
7. Learn to think like a scientist.
8. Impress your friends by using words like *molarity* and *stoichiometry*.
9. Find a practical use for the math you've been learning.
10. Meet the most interesting people—the people who teach it!

Learning Chemistry: It's Your Job

In the process of learning chemistry, you are at the center. No one can learn it for you, but there are many ways we can help you.

To learn something new, you first need to gather information. One way to do so is by making your own observations. **Hands-On Chemistry Mini-Labs** and **Chemistry in the Laboratory** experiments have exactly that goal. Another way to collect information is to read a book. Because textbooks contain so much information, it is important, especially at first, to focus on the main ideas. We have designed **Active Reading Questions** to help you concentrate on the most important ideas as you read the text. These Active Reading questions should be answered *before* you go to class. Don't worry if you can't answer all of them completely—they are meant to help you start thinking about the material.

When you have done the initial reading and attempted to answer the Active Reading questions, you are ready for class. In class your teacher will help you to better understand these ideas. Then you will work with your classmates on the **Team Learning Worksheets,** teaching and learning from each other. The Team Learning Worksheets enable you to check your understanding with the help of other members of your class.

Next, you can practice individually by doing homework problems from the Section Review and the Chapter Assessment that give you a chance to see how much you understand and which ideas you need to work on.

After you have completed your homework, you are ready for a quiz, which gives you the chance to show what you know. Now you are ready to apply your knowledge to your further study of chemistry. This student-centered method for learning chemistry is summarized in **Figure 1.3.**

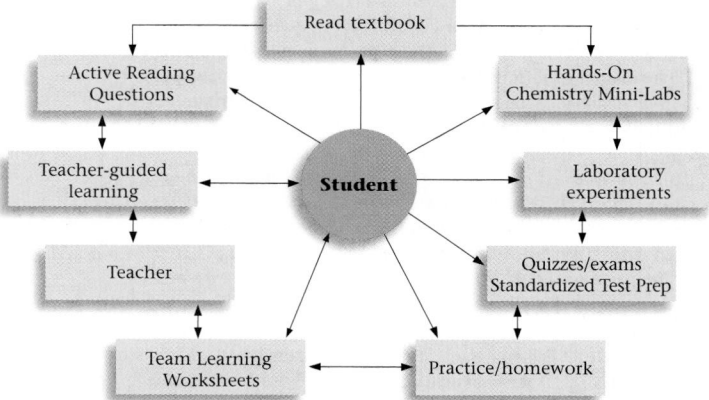

Figure 1.3
Student-centered learning

Chemistry in Your World

Learn Chemistry—Prepare for Life

Analogies for Teaching and Learning

Materials
- 0.10 *M* HCl
- 0.10 *M* NaOH
- Water
- Vegetable oil
- Universal indicator
- 1-L Erlenmeyer flask
- 250-mL Erlenmeyer flask (4)

Empty Pitcher: Show students a large flask filled with water and an empty 250-mL flask. Explain that in this analogy the teacher is the large flask, the small flask is the student, and the water is knowledge. The student starts out empty (knowing nothing). The teacher pours knowledge into the student. Discuss the problems with this analogy. First, students do come into class with ideas about the subject material, even if some are mistaken.

Second, the knowledge that students attain is not the same as the knowledge the teacher has; knowledge is not simply transferred. Finally, learning is not a passive activity.

Oil and Water: Once again, a flask of water represents the teacher. Another flask with some vegetable oil represents the student. This exercise shows that students come with knowledge and that this knowledge is different from the teacher's knowledge. The knowledge

CHEMISTRY IN YOUR WORLD

Consumer Connection

Learn Chemistry—Prepare for Life

What is the purpose of education?

Some people seem to equate education with the storage of facts in the brain. These people apparently believe that education simply means memorizing the answers to all of life's present and future problems. Although this idea is clearly unreasonable, many students behave as though it were their guiding principle. These students want to memorize lists of facts and to reproduce them on tests. They regard as unfair any exam questions that require some original thought or some processing of information. Indeed, it might be tempting to reduce education to a simple filling up with facts because that approach can produce short-term satisfaction for both student and teacher. Of course, storing facts in the brain *is* important. You cannot function without knowing that red means stop, electricity is dangerous, ice is slippery, and so on.

However, mere recall of abstract information, without the ability to process it, makes you little better than a talking encyclopedia. Successful people have several common characteristics. They have a thorough knowledge of their fields, the ability to recognize and solve problems, and the ability to communicate effectively. Typically, they also have a high level of motivation.

How does studying chemistry help you achieve these characteristics? The fact that chemical systems are complicated is really a blessing, though one that

is well disguised. Studying chemistry will not by itself make you a good problem solver; but it can help you develop a positive, aggressive attitude toward problem solving, and it can help boost your confidence. Learning to "think like a chemist" can be valuable to anyone in any field. People who are trained as chemists often excel not only in chemical research and production but also in personnel, marketing, sales, development, finance, and management. The point is that much of what you learn in this course can be applied to any career. So be careful not to take too narrow a view of this course. Look beyond short-term frustration to long-term benefits.

It may not be easy to learn to be a good problem solver, but it's well worth the effort.

Learning chemistry is both fun and important.

SECTION 1.3 REVIEW QUESTIONS

❶ What resources are available to help you learn chemistry?

❷ What characteristics do former chemistry students find most important to their success? Which of these are easiest for you? Which are most difficult?

❸ Why does trial and error play a major role in problem solving?

RESEARCH LINKS
CLASSZONE.COM

1.3 • Learning Chemistry • **17**

SECTION 1.3
ASSESS

SECTION 1.3
Review Questions

1. Text
   Experiments
   Activities
   Guided interactive learning
   Team worksheets
   Homework
   Quizzes/exams
   Teacher
   Classmates

2. Knowledge of fundamentals in the field
   Ability to recognize and solve problems
   Ability to communicate effectively
   High level of motivation
   Students' answers regarding their personal strengths and weaknesses will vary.

3. Since a theory is an interpretation, it must always be refined by further experimentation. Theories are not reality, and will always include simplifying errors.

(continued)

(water) flows from the teacher to the student, and it takes a lot of work to get it to mix with the student's initial knowledge. This analogy is demonstrated by capping the flask, which represents the student, and mixing it vigorously. Show students the product of this work and let them watch as the water and oil slowly separate. "This is a lot of work for nothing. If learning is truly like this—that is, 'cram

as much as you can in your head for a test, and then let it out afterward'— then we are all wasting our time." In this analogy the teacher is doing all of the work.

Active Learning: In this case, the teacher's knowledge is represented by an aqueous acidic solution. The student is represented by a basic solution containing several drops of universal indicator. When the acidic solution (knowledge) flows, the student's

knowledge changes (shown by a change in color). As in the oil and water analogy, the student begins with some knowledge (different from the teacher). Students do not just take the knowledge, but the new knowledge interacts with what students already know. New knowledge changes their understanding, and they don't end up just like the teacher. The interaction is achieved by students taking an active role in understanding the material.

Chapter 1 Review

Key Terms

Key Ideas

1.1 The Science of Chemistry

- Chemistry is important to everyone because chemistry occurs all around us in our daily lives.

- Chemistry is the science that deals with the materials of the universe and the changes that these materials undergo.

- Chemistry "looks inside" ordinary objects to study how their components behave.

1.2 Using Science to Solve Problems

- Scientific thinking helps us solve all types of problems that we confront in our lives.

- Scientific thinking involves observations that enable us to clearly define both a problem and the construction and evaluation of possible explanations or solutions to the problem.

- The scientific method is a procedure for processing the information that flows from the world around us in which we

  - Make observations.
  - Formulate hypotheses.
  - Perform experiments.

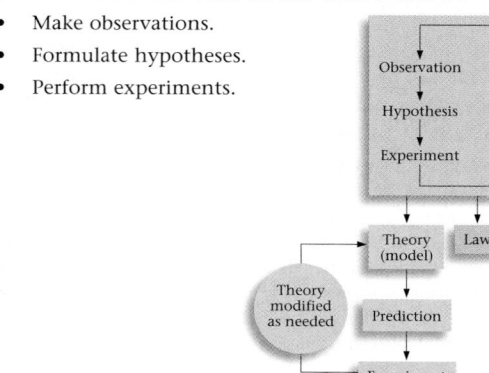

- Models represent our attempt to understand the world around us.
  - Models are not the same as "reality."
  - Elementary models are based on the properties of atoms and molecules.

1.3 Learning Chemistry

- Understanding chemistry takes hard work and patience.

- As you learn chemistry, you should be able to understand, explain, and predict phenomena in the macroscopic world by using models based in the microscopic world.

- Understanding is different from memorizing.

- It is okay to make mistakes as long as you learn from them.

RESEARCH LINKS
CLASSZONE.COM

Meeting Individual Needs
CHAPTER SUMMARY

A **Chapter Summary** that includes additional Active Reading Questions for Chapter 1 is available.

Assessment Resources
CHAPTER 1

Chapter 1 Test

TECHNOLOGY

 Computerized Test Bank for Chapter 1

All exercises with blue numbers have answers in the back of this book.

1.1 The Science of Chemistry

A. The Importance of Learning Chemistry

1. The first few paragraphs of this book asked you if you had ever wondered how and why various things in everyday life behave the way they do. Surely there are many other such phenomena that have intrigued you. List five of these and present them in class for discussion with your instructor and fellow students.

2. Chemistry is used in many professions, and a basic understanding of chemistry is of great importance. Suggest two ways that each of the following professionals might make use of chemistry in their jobs.

    a. physician   e. photographer

    b. lawyer   f. farmer

    c. pharmacist   g. nurse

    d. artist

3. This section presents several ways in which our day-to-day lives have been enriched by chemistry. List three materials or processes involving chemistry that you believe have contributed to such an enrichment, and explain your choices.

4. The text admits that there has been a "dark side" to our use of chemicals and chemical processes, and uses the example of chlorofluorocarbons (CFCs) to explain this. List three additional improper or unfortunate uses of chemicals or chemical processes, and explain your reasoning.

B. What Is Chemistry?

5. This textbook provides a specific definition of chemistry: the study of the materials of which the universe is made and the transformations that these materials undergo. Obviously, such a general definition has to be very broad and nonspecific. From your point of view at this time, how would *you* define chemistry? In your mind, what are chemicals? What do chemists do?

6. We use chemical reactions in our everyday lives, not just in the science laboratory. Give at least five examples of chemical transformations that you make use of in your daily activities. Identify the "chemical" in each of your examples, and how you recognize that a chemical change has taken place.

1.2 Using Science to Solve Problems

A. Solving Everyday Problems

7. Discuss two situations in which you have analyzed a problem such as those presented in this section. What hypotheses did you suggest? How did you test those hypotheses?

B. Using Scientific Thinking to Solve a Problem

8. Consider the lead poisoning case given in this section. Discuss how David and Susan analyzed the situation and arrived at the theory that the lead glaze on the pottery was responsible for their symptoms.

C. The Scientific Method

9. What are the three operations involved in applying the scientific method? How does the scientific method help us understand our observations of nature?

10. As part of a science project, you study traffic patterns in your city at an intersection in the middle of downtown. You set up a device that counts the cars passing through this intersection for a 24-hour period during a weekday. The graph of hourly traffic looks like this:

    a. At what time(s) does the highest number of cars pass through the intersection?

    b. At what time(s) does the lowest number of cars pass through the intersection?

    c. Briefly describe the trend in numbers of cars over the course of the day.

    d. Provide a hypothesis explaining the trend in numbers of cars over the course of the day.

    e. Provide a possible experiment that could test your hypothesis.

have been developed for determining whether a person has a genetic likelihood of developing a particular disease may also be used to make it difficult or impossible for that person to obtain health or life insurance.

5. *Answers will vary.*

6. *Answers will depend on students' choices.*

7. *Answers will depend on students' experience.*

8. David and Susan first recognized the problem (unexplained medical problems). A possible explanation was then proposed (the glaze on their china might be causing the lead poisoning). The explanation was tested by experiment (it was determined that the china did contain lead). A full scenario is given in the text.

9. Recognizing the problem and stating it clearly; proposing possible solutions to or explanations of the problem; performing experiments to test the solutions or explanations and then refining or changing the solution or explanation

10. (a) Between 8 A.M. and 9 A.M. (b) Between 12 A.M. and 1 A.M., and between 10 P.M. and 11 P.M. (c) The number of cars starts out low, increases until early morning and then decreases and levels off. The number of cars then increases toward 5 P.M. and then drops off quickly. (d) Between 8 A.M. and 9 A.M. many people are going to work and between 5 P.M. and 6 P.M. they are returning home. (e) Check the traffic patterns on weekends and holidays. If the hypothesis is correct, you would expect not to see dramatic changes at 8 A.M. and 5 P.M. on these days.

Chapter 1 Assessment

1. *Answers will vary.*

2. (a) physician (cellular processes; drug mechanisms) (b) lawyer (understanding forensic reports; examination of the crime scene) (c) pharmacist (drug interactions; dosages) (d) artist (properties of paints and thinners; properties of sculpture media)

(e) photographer (film-developing process; properties of papers and coatings) (f) farmer (fertilizers; plant hormones) (g) nurse (drug interactions; dosages)

3. *Answers will vary.* New drugs and treatments and new materials (such as special plastics and comfortable contact lenses) are probable answers.

4. Unfortunately, many examples exist. Chemical and biological weapons are produced in some countries. Although the development of plastics has been a boon in many endeavors, their use also depletes fossil fuel reserves and increases our solid waste problems. Although biotechnology has produced many exciting new drugs and treatments, the testing procedures that

11. (a) quantitative
    (b) qualitative
    (c) quantitative
    (d) qualitative
    (e) quantitative
    (f) qualitative
    (g) quantitative

12. A hypothesis is a possible explanation of a single observed phenomenon. A theory or model consists of a set of tested hypotheses that give an overall explanation of some part of nature.

13. A natural law is a summary of observed, measurable behavior that occurs repeatedly and consistently. A theory is an attempt to explain such behavior.

14. "Every time we let go of something heavy, it falls to the ground" is a law. "For example, when an apple breaks from a branch of a tree, it falls to the ground" is an observation. "This happens because apples are attracted to earth" is a theory.

15. When a scientist formulates a hypothesis, he or she wants it to be proved correct. Financial success and prestige are dependent on publishing and producing such ideas.

16. Most applications of chemistry are oriented toward the interpretation of observations that solve problems. Although memorization of facts may aid in these endeavors, it is the ability to combine, relate, and synthesize information that is most important in the study of chemistry.

17. When we study chemistry, at least at first, we try to be as general as possible. In this way the basic principles learned can be applied to many situations. By learning to interpret and solve less complex problems, students can extend this strategy to more complex real-life situations.

11. Which of the following are quantitative observations and which are qualitative observations?
    a. My waist size is 31 inches.
    b. My eyes are blue.
    c. My right index finger is 1/4 inch longer than my left.
    d. The leaves of most trees are green in summer.
    e. An apple is more than 95% water.
    f. Chemistry is an easy subject.
    g. My score on the last chemistry exam was 90%.

12. What is the difference between a hypothesis and a theory? How are the two similar? How do they differ?

13. What is a natural law? Give examples of such laws. How does a law differ from a theory?

14. For the following passage, label each statement as "observation," "theory," or "law."

Every time we let go of something heavy, it falls to the ground. For example, when an apple breaks from a branch of a tree, it falls to the ground. This happens because apples are attracted to earth.

15. Discuss several political, social, or personal considerations that might affect a scientist's evaluation of a theory. Give examples of how such external forces have influenced scientists in the past. Discuss methods by which such bias might be excluded from future scientific investigations.

1.3 Learning Chemistry
A. Strategies for Learning Chemistry

16. In some academic subjects, it may be possible to receive a good grade primarily by memorizing facts. Why is chemistry not one of these subjects?

17. Why is the ability to solve problems important in the study of chemistry? Why is it that the method used to attack a problem is as important as the answer itself?

18. Students approaching the study of chemistry must learn certain basic facts (such as the names and symbols of the most common elements), but it is much more important that they learn to think critically and to go beyond the specific examples discussed in class or in the textbook. Explain how learning to do this might be helpful in any career, even one far removed from chemistry.

18. In real-life situations, the problems and applications likely to be encountered are not simple textbook examples. You must be able to observe an event, hypothesize a cause, and then test this hypothesis. You must be able to carry what has been learned in class forward to new, different situations.

1 Chemists are involved in activities such as

  A   producing new materials.

  B   producing new sources of energy.

  C   understanding and controlling various diseases.

  D   All of the above

2 Which of the following is another term for quantitative observation?

  A   theory

  B   measurement

  C   hypothesis

  D   natural law

Use the information in the following paragraph for questions 3–5.

Ronika and Thomas are eating raisins and drinking ginger ale. Thomas accidentally drops a raisin into his ginger ale. Both he and Ronika notice that the raisin falls to the bottom of the glass. Soon, the raisin rises to the surface of the ginger ale, and then sinks. Within a couple of minutes, it rises and sinks again. Ronika asks "I wonder why that happened?" Thomas says, "I don't know, but let's see if it works in water." Ronika fills a glass with water and drops a raisin into the glass. After a few minutes, Thomas says, "No, it doesn't go up and down in the water." Ronika closely observes the raisins in the two cups and states, "Look, there are bubbles on the raisin in the ginger ale but not on the raisin in the water." Thomas says "It must be the bubbles that make the raisin rise." Ronika asks, "OK, but then why does it sink again?"

3 Which of the following items from the passage is an *observation*?

  A   Accidentally dropping the raisin into the ginger ale

  B   Claiming that the bubbles make the raisin rise

  C   Asking "I wonder why that happened?"

  D   Noticing the raisin sinks in the ginger ale

4 Which of the following from the passage is a *theory*?

  A   Asking "I wonder why that happened?"

  B   Noticing that the raisin does not rise and sink in the water

  C   Claiming that the bubbles make the raisin rise

  D   Wondering why the raisin sinks after it rises to the surface of the ginger ale

5 Which of the following from the passage is an *experiment*?

  A   Claiming that the bubbles make the raisin rise

  B   Dropping a raisin into water

  C   Asking "I wonder why that happened?"

  D   Wondering why the raisin sinks after it rises to the surface of the ginger ale

6 What does a chemist mean by a "microscopic view" of the world, and why is taking such a view important to a chemist?

For questions 7–10, label each of the following statements as true or false. For the statements that you label false, provide an explanation.

7 We can prove a theory to be correct by performing the right experiment.

8 If a theory is accepted for a long time, it eventually becomes a law.

9 A law is a summary of observed behavior.

10 A theory is an attempt to explain what happens in an experiment.

Chapter 1
Standardized Test Practice

1. D

2. B

3. D

4. C

5. B

6. When chemists refer to a "microscopic view," they consider the individual atoms and molecules of a substance. Chemistry is concerned with matter and its changes, and to understand these changes, we need to deal with the atoms and molecules that make up a substance.

7. False. We cannot prove a theory to be correct; we can only support a theory. We can prove a theory to be incorrect.

8. False. A law is a summary of observations. Theories may be generally accepted, but they are explanations of "why," not a summary of "what."

9. True.

10. False. A theory is an attempt to explain why nature behaves in a certain way. A law is a summary of what happens.

Test-Taking Strategy

Advise students to read direction lines preceding a grouping of questions, as in questions 3–5. Encourage students to refer back to the given passage when answering these three questions in order to understand the context of each of the answer choices.

Assessment Resources
CHAPTER 1

For additional practice with standardized testing, see *Standardized Test Practice* located in the *Teacher Resources*.

2 | Matter

Planning Guide

Section	Segment	Text Features and Components	Labs, Demonstrations, & Activities
2.1 The Nature of Matter **0.5 Block** pp. 24–30	**A** The Particulate Nature of Matter		(RP) Classroom Activities and Projects *TE p. 24*
	B Elements and Compounds	(SE) Top Ten Elements in the Universe *p. 25* (SE) Chemistry in Your World: Carbon—Element of Many Forms *p. 28*	(TE) Mini-Demo *p. 25* (TE) Teaching Support: Demonstration *pp. 26–27*
	C The States of Matter		(TE) Mini-Demos *p. 29* (TE) Teaching Support: Demonstration *p. 29* (SE) Hands-On Chemistry: Full or Empty? *p. 30*
2.2 Properties of Matter **1.5 Blocks** pp. 31–34	**A** Physical and Chemical Properties and Changes		(LM) Experiment 4: Physical and Chemical Changes Lab Manual Report Sheets Teacher's Lab Guide (LM) Experiment 5: Household Chemistry Lab Manual Report Sheets Teacher's Lab Guide
	continued on next page		

Key (SE) Student Edition (TE) Teacher Edition (RP) Teacher Resource Package (AR) Additional Materials (LM) Lab Materials (📄) Transparencies (💿) DVD (CD) CD-ROM (ℹ️) classzone.com

22a

All Learners	Technology	Review & Assessment	Standards
TE Teaching Tip *p. 24* **RP** MINT: Reading Concepts *TE p. 24*	● EasyPlanner	**SE** Active Reading Question *p. 25* **SE** Key Terms *p. 44* **SE** Questions and Problems *p. 45*	**TE** **NSES** UCP1, UCP2, UCP5, A1, A2, B1, B2
TE Teaching Tips *pp. 25, 27* **RP** MINT: Reading Concepts *TE p. 25* **RP** MINT: Challenge Projects *TE p. 27*	● EasyPlanner	**SE** Critical Thinking *p. 26* **SE** Active Reading Question *p. 29* **SE** Key Terms *p. 44* **SE** Questions and Problems *p. 45*	
RP Team Learning Worksheet (Sec. 2.1)	● EasyPlanner	**SE** Active Reading Question *p. 29* **SE** Review Questions (2.1.A–2.1.C) *p. 30* **SE** Key Terms *p. 44* **SE** Questions and Problems *p. 45*	
TE Meeting Individual Needs *p. 32* **TE** Teaching Tips *pp. 32, 33*	▦ Transparency: Figure 2.8 ● Video: Electrolysis of Water ▮ Lab Generator CD ● EasyPlanner	**SE** Active Reading Question *p. 31* **SE** Practice Problem *p. 31* **TE** More Examples *p. 31* **SE** Active Reading Question *p. 33* **SE** Practice Problem *p. 34* **TE** More Examples *p. 34* **SE** Review Questions (2.2.A) *p. 34* **SE** Key Terms *p. 44* **SE** Questions and Problems *p. 45*	**TE** **NSES** UCP1, UCP2, UCP3, A1, A2, B2, B3, G2

Planning Guide

Section	Segment		Text Features and Components	Labs, Demonstrations, & Activities
2.3 Classifying Matter **2.5 Blocks** pp. 35–43	A	**Mixtures and Pure Substances**	**TE** Teaching Support: Historical Note *p. 37* **SE** Chemistry in Your World: Alchemical Cymbals *p. 38*	**TE** Mini-Demo *p. 38* **SE** Hands-On Chemistry: Mysterious Mixing *p. 39*

	B	**Separation of Mixtures**	**SE** Celebrity Chemical: Hydrogen Peroxide *p. 43*	**TE** Teaching Support: Demonstration *p. 41*
				TE Group Activity *p. 42*
				LM Experiment 6: Properties of Matter
				LM Experiment 7: Separation Challenge
				LM Experiment 8: Sludge Text
				LM Experiment 9: Separation of Mixtures
				LM Experiment 10: Distillation
				    Lab Manual
				    Report Sheets
				    Teacher's Lab Guide

Key
SE Student Edition   **TE** Teacher Edition   **RP** Teacher Resource Package
AR Additional Materials   **LM** Lab Materials   **⬛** Transparencies
⊙ DVD   **▮** CD-ROM   **ⓘ** classzone.com

All Learners	Technology	Review & Assessment	Standards
(TE) Teaching Tips *pp. 35, 37, 39* (TE) Misconception *p. 36* (TE) Meeting Individual Needs *p. 36*	(•) EasyPlanner	(SE) Active Reading Question *p. 38* (SE) Practice Problem *p. 40* (TE) More Examples *p. 40* (SE) Key Terms *p. 44* (SE) Questions and Problems *p. 46*	(TE) **NSES** UCP1, UCP2, UCP3, A1, A2, B2, B3, G1, G2, G3
(TE) Meeting Individual Needs *p. 40* (RP) Team Learning Worksheet (Sec. 2.2–2.3)	(≡) Transparency: Figure 2.19 (▮) Lab Generator CD (•) EasyPlanner	(SE) Review Questions (2.3.A–2.3.B) *p. 43* (SE) Key Terms *p. 44* (SE) Questions and Problems *p. 46*	

Resource Materials for Chapter 2

(SE) Chapter Review *p. 44*

(SE) Critical Thinking *p. 46*

(SE) Standardized Test Practice *p. 47*

(AR) English/Spanish Summaries

(▮) English Summaries Audio

(▮) Spanish Summaries Audio

(RP) Meeting Individual Needs Toolkit (MINT)
    Reading Concepts
    Challenge Projects
    Chapter Review Worksheets
    Chapter Summaries

(RP) Solutions Guide

(RP) Standardized Test Practice

(RP) Chapter Tests

(RP) Test Bank

(ⓘ) Test Generator

Chapter 2
Overview

In this chapter our goals are for students to:

- Learn about the composition of matter
- Learn the difference between elements and compounds
- Learn to distinguish between physical and chemical properties and changes
- Learn to distinguish between mixtures and pure substances
- Learn two methods of separating mixtures

Chapter 2

Matter

Chemical reactions cause the leaves to change color in the fall.

22

Prereading Questions

1. Atoms make up molecules; a molecule is two or more atoms bonded together.

2. *Answers will vary.* Water is a good example because we often see it as a solid (ice), a liquid (water), and a gas (steam).

3. *Answers will vary.*

IN YOUR LIFE

As you look around you, you must wonder about the properties of matter. How do plants grow and why are they green? Why is the sun hot? Why does soup get hot in a microwave oven? Why does wood burn whereas rocks do not? What is a flame? How does soap work? Why does soda fizz when you open the bottle? When iron rusts, what's happening? And why doesn't aluminum rust? How does a cold pack for an athletic injury, which is stored for weeks or months at room temperature, suddenly get cold when you need it? How does a hair permanent work?

The answers to these and endless other questions lie in the domain of chemistry. In this chapter we begin to explore the nature of matter: how it is organized and how and why it changes. We will also consider the energy that accompanies these changes.

Why does soda fizz when you open the bottle?

WHAT DO YOU KNOW?

Prereading Questions

1. How do atoms differ from molecules?

2. Give an example of each of these: a solid, a liquid, a gas.

3. Describe a chemical change (chemical reaction) you have witnessed outside of school. How do you know that it is a chemical change?

Matter • Chapter 2 • **23**

TECHNOLOGY IN THE CLASSROOM

 Transparencies
Figures: 2.8, 2.19

 Power Presentation DVD
PowerPoint Slides
Video
Electrolysis of Water
eEdition
EasyPlanner

 Lab Generator CD
English Summaries CD
Spanish Summaries CD
ML Test Generator

 classzone.com

Student Preparation

Assign students to read Section 2.1 and to answer the Review Questions at the end of the section before coming to class.

 Active Learning
Team Learning Worksheet

After introducing the material in Section 2.1 in class, place students in groups and have them work together on **Section 2.1: Team Learning Worksheet.**

 Active Learning
Classroom Activities and Projects

For an early project that can be interdisciplinary with Language Arts, see *Element Report* located in the *Teacher Resources.*

Homework

You may wish to assign these selected end-of-chapter problems as homework for this section: 1, 2, 3, 4, 5, 6, 7

Additional end-of-chapter problems can be used for extra practice.

2.1.A The Particulate Nature of Matter

Objective To learn about the composition of matter

 TEACHING TIP

It is important to emphasize an atomic/molecular view of chemistry from the beginning. One reason why students find chemistry difficult is because they do not relate the microscopic view to the macroscopic view. By thinking only in macroscopic terms, ideas such as compound, mixture, and chemical change are often memorized rather than understood.

Key Terms
- Matter
- Atoms
- Compounds
- Molecule
- Elements
- Solid
- Liquid
- Gas

Objectives
- *To learn about the composition of matter*
- *To learn the difference between elements and compounds*
- *To define the three states of matter*

A. The Particulate Nature of Matter

Matter, the "stuff" of which the universe is composed, has two characteristics: it has mass and it occupies space. Matter comes in a great variety of forms: the stars, the air that you are breathing, the gasoline that you put in your car, the chair on which you are sitting, the turkey in the sandwich you may have eaten for lunch, the tissues in your brain that allow you to read and understand this sentence, and so on.

As we look around our world, we are impressed by the great diversity of matter. Given the many forms and types of matter, it seems difficult to believe that all matter is composed of a small number of fundamental particles. It is surprising that the fundamental building blocks in chocolate cake are very similar to the components of air.

The Atomic Nature of Matter

How do we know that matter is composed of the tiny particles we call atoms? After all, they are far too small to be seen with the naked eye. It turns out that after literally thousands of years of speculation, we can finally "see" the atoms that are present in matter. In recent years scientists have developed a device called a scanning tunneling microscope (STM) that, although it works quite differently from an optical microscope, can produce images of atoms.

For example, look at the penny shown in **Figure 2.1.** The small objects represent tiny copper atoms. When chemists look at other metals with powerful microscopes, they see atoms in these substances as well. You can see an example of another metal in **Figure 2.2.**

With ultra-high magnification, objects appear more similar. All objects are made up of small particles called atoms.

All matter consists of tiny particles called atoms. But when you look at objects such as nails or pennies, you don't see these particles. Why not? The atoms are very tiny and can be seen only with a powerful magnifying instrument. You may have encountered the same concept in your life when you looked at a beach from a distance. The sand looks uniform—you can't see the separate particles. As you get close, however, the individual grains of sand become apparent. Observe the Impressionist painting by Seurat shown in the photo on the following page. From a distance the scene looks normal. Only when you stand very close to the painting do you see that it is composed of tiny dots of paint.

So, the conclusion is that although objects in the macroscopic world typically look quite continuous and uniform, they are really particulate in nature—they are made of atoms. We can "see" them with powerful electronic microscopes.

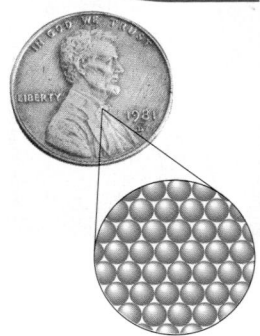

Figure 2.1
The surface of the copper penny is made of copper atoms represented as they would be seen through the lens of a very powerful electronic microscope.

Figure 2.2
A scanning tunneling microscope image of nickel metal. Each peak represents a nickel atom.

Meeting Individual Needs
READING CONCEPTS

To help students better understand how to read this textbook, see *Actively Reading Section 2.1* located in the *Teacher Resources.*

Scientists have developed a scanning tunneling microscope (STM) that can produce images of atoms.

2.1.B Elements and Compounds

Objective To learn the difference between elements and compounds

Active Reading Question

How do we know that all matter is made of atoms?

B. Elements and Compounds

We have just considered the most important idea in chemistry: matter is composed of tiny particles we call **atoms**. If all matter is made up of tiny particles called atoms, are all atoms alike? That is, is copper metal made of the same kind of atoms as gold? The answer is no. Copper atoms and gold atoms are different. Scientists have learned that all matter is composed from about 100 different types of atoms. For example, air is mostly gaseous oxygen and nitrogen. The nitrogen atoms are different from the oxygen atoms, which in turn are different from copper atoms, which differ from gold atoms.

You can think of the matter in the universe like the words in a book. If you break all the words in this book apart into their component letters, you will end up with "large piles" of only 26 letters. The English alphabet allows you to construct thousands of words from just 26 letters. Similarly, all the matter in the universe is constructed by putting approximately 100 types of atoms together in various ways. The different types of matter are like the different words in a book. When we separate all of the universe into its atoms, we find approximately 100 different atoms. We call these 100 types of atoms the *elements* of the universe.

To illustrate this idea, consider the letters A, D, and M. Using these letters you can make many words, such as MAD, DAM, DAD, and MADAM (can you think of others?). Each word represents something very different. Thus, with only three letters, you can represent several unique things or ideas.

Atom
Fundamental unit of which elements are made

Sand on a beach looks uniform from a distance, but up close the irregular sand grains are visible.

The painting "Sunday Afternoon on the Island of La Grande Jatte" by Georges Seurat illustrates the Impressionist style.

Top Ten Elements in the Universe	
Element	Percent (by atoms)
Hydrogen	73.9
Helium	24.0
Oxygen	1.1
Carbon	0.46
Neon	0.13
Iron	0.11
Nitrogen	0.097
Silicon	0.065
Magnesium	0.058
Sulfur	0.044

🍎 TEACHING TIP

Because students have trouble relating microscopic and macroscopic views, we start our discussion with the atom and bypass the traditional historical approach taken by many texts. (This is not to say that we do not value the study of the history of chemistry; in fact, we believe that history helps the material come alive.) Pictures from scanning tunneling microscopes can now "show" us atoms. Therefore, we begin with "we believe in atoms because we can see them." We use this to discuss elements, compounds, mixtures, states of matter, and physical and chemical properties and changes, and students begin their formal study of chemistry by visualizing the microscopic view.

TOP TEN

Have students guess which of these Top Ten elements are found in the top five elements in air. Have them use references to determine the correctness of their predictions. Discuss the differences found.

Have students guess the top element found in the human body. Discuss the importance of this element.

MINI-DEMO

Bring in samples of each element on the Top Ten list. Have students classify the elements by similarities. This activity could be used to lead into a discussion of the states of matter (Section 2.1.C).

2.1 • The Nature of Matter • **25**

Meeting Individual Needs
READING CONCEPTS

Section 2.1 contains several closely related vocabulary terms. Graphic organizers and outlines are good ways for students to organize and remember this information. Have students read *Making and Using Graphic Organizers* and *Making Outlines* located in the *Teacher Resources*. An example outline and an example concept map for Section 2.1 are provided.

CRITICAL THINKING

The scanning tunneling microscope allows us to "see" atoms.

What if you were sent back in time before the invention of the scanning tunneling microscope? Write a paragraph giving evidence to support the theory that all matter is made of atoms and molecules.

Compounds

In much the same way that we can use a few letters to make thousands of words, we can use a few types of atoms to construct all matter. For example, consider the atoms hydrogen, oxygen, and carbon:

Hydrogen   Oxygen   Carbon

Notice that we represent atoms by using spheres. We get this idea from the highly magnified pictures of metals that show the atoms. Notice in Figure 2.1 that atoms look like spheres.

We can combine the hydrogen, oxygen, and carbon atoms in a variety of ways. Just as letters combine to form different words, atoms combine to form different compounds. **Compounds** are substances made by bonding atoms together in specific ways. These substances contain two or more different types of atoms bound together in a particular way. A specific compound consists of the same particles throughout. Table 2.1 shows some examples of atoms combined into compounds.

Table 2.1
Some Common Compounds

Atom Combinations	Name	Characteristics
	carbon monoxide	Carbon monoxide is a poisonous gas.
	carbon dioxide	You breathe out carbon dioxide as a waste material, and plants use carbon dioxide to make oxygen.
	water	Water is the most important liquid on Earth.
	hydrogen peroxide	Hydrogen peroxide is used to disinfect cuts and bleach hair.

Consider a glass of water. If you could magically travel inside the water and examine its individual parts, you would see particles consisting of two hydrogen atoms bonded to an oxygen atom:

Molecule
A collection of atoms bonded together that behave as a unit

We call this particle a molecule. A **molecule** is made up of atoms that are "stuck" together. A glass of water, for example, contains a huge number of molecules packed closely together (see **Figure 2.3**).

Carbon dioxide is another example of a compound. For example, "dry ice"—solid carbon dioxide—contains molecules of the type 🔵 packed together as shown in **Figure 2.4.**

Notice that the particles (molecules) in water are all the same. Likewise, all the molecules in dry ice are the same. However, the molecules in water differ from the molecules in dry ice. Water and carbon dioxide are different compounds.

Discussing Figures 2.3–2.5 provides a good opportunity to distinguish between a microscopic perspective and a macroscopic perspective. The microscopic perspective is important when discussing chemical and physical changes in Section 2.2.

Figure 2.3
A glass of water contains millions of tiny water molecules packed closely together.

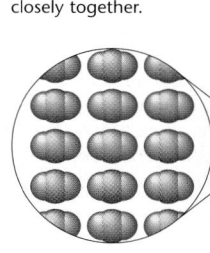

Figure 2.4
Dry ice contains molecules packed closely together.

Elements

Just as hydrogen, oxygen, and carbon can form the compounds carbon dioxide and water, atoms of the same type can also combine with one another to form molecules. For example, hydrogen atoms can pair up , as can oxygen atoms ⬤⬤. For reasons we will consider later, carbon atoms form much larger groups, leading to substances such as diamond, graphite, and buckminsterfullerene.

Because pure hydrogen and oxygen each contains only one type of atom, the substances are called elemental substances or, more commonly, **elements**. Elements are substances that contain only one type of atom. For example, pure gold contains only gold atoms, elemental copper contains only copper atoms, and so on. Thus an element contains only one kind of atom; a sample of iron contains many atoms, but they are all iron atoms. Samples of certain pure elements do contain molecules; for example, hydrogen gas contains H—H (usually written H_2) molecules, and oxygen gas contains O—O (O_2) molecules. However, any pure sample of an element contains only atoms of that element, *never* any atoms of any other element. **Figure 2.5** shows examples of elements.

Elements
Substances containing only one type of atom

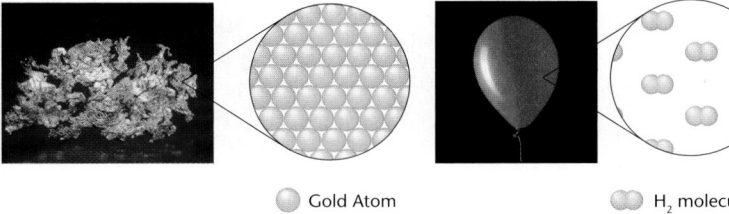

◯ Gold Atom   ⬤⬤ H_2 molecule

Figure 2.5
Gold and hydrogen are both elements. Gold consists of gold atoms packed together as a solid. Hydrogen is an element that is composed of molecules of hydrogen, not single atoms.

(continued)

Safety and Cleanup Note that 30% hydrogen peroxide is corrosive and should be stored under refrigeration. This demonstration can also be done with 10% hydrogen peroxide, with less dramatic results. The flask remains hot for some time. Dispose of the chemicals using correct procedures for your area.

Meeting Individual Needs
CHALLENGE PROJECTS

For a project on the elements, see *Elements in the News* located in the *Teacher Resources*. This project requires students to research relatively current newspapers and magazines to discover information about the elements.

CHEMISTRY IN YOUR WORLD

Science, Technology, and Society

Carbon—Element of Many Forms

Did you know that the "lead" in your pencil and the diamond in an engagement ring are made of exactly the same thing—elemental carbon? It may come as a surprise to learn that the black, slippery material that makes up pencil "lead," which is called **graphite**, has the same composition as the brilliant, hard gemstone called **diamond**. Although both substances are made of carbon atoms, their properties vary dramatically because the carbon atoms are arranged differently in the two substances.

A third form of elemental carbon also exists—**buckminsterfullerene** (see **Figure 2.6**). This strange name comes from a famous industrial designer, Buckminster Fuller, who popularized geodesic domes. The fundamental component of buckminsterfullerene is a C_{60} molecule that has a framework like a geodesic dome. The C_{60} molecule also resembles a soccer ball with its interconnecting hexagons (six-sided polygons) and pentagons (five-sided polygons). Chemists have nicknamed this form of carbon "bucky balls." So there are three forms of elemental carbon: graphite, diamond, and buckminsterfullerene.

Because diamonds are so much more valuable than the other forms of carbon, it has long been the dream of entrepreneurs to make gem-quality diamonds from other carbon-based substances. In fact, we have been able to make artificial diamonds for about 50 years. One of the first crude diamonds was actually made by compressing peanut butter at high pressures and temperatures!

Diamond　　　　　Graphite　　　　　Buckminsterfullerene

Carbon atoms

Figure 2.6
The three forms of the element carbon are diamond, graphite, and buckminsterfullerene.

Chemistry in Your World

Carbon—Element of Many Forms

Although the term is not used in this section, now might be a good time to introduce the term *allotrope*—used when an element exists in several forms. Carbon has three allotropes: diamond, graphite, and buckminsterfullerene. A piece of chicken wire serves as a useful model for graphite; a soccer ball makes a very nice model for buckminsterfullerene; and commercial models are available for diamond, or you can use gumdrops and toothpicks.

Other elements also exist as allotropes. Examples include:

Oxygen	oxygen and ozone
Phosphorus	white, red, and black phosphorus
Tin	white, gray, and brittle tin

A compound always contains atoms of different elements.

For example, water contains hydrogen atoms and oxygen atoms, and there are always exactly twice as many hydrogen atoms as oxygen atoms because water consists of H—O—H 🔵 molecules. A different compound, carbon dioxide, consists of CO_2 🔵 molecules and so contains carbon atoms and oxygen atoms (always in the ratio 1:2).

A compound, although it contains more than one type of atom, always has the same composition—that is, the same combination of atoms.

The properties of a compound are typically very different from those of the elements it contains. For example, the properties of water are quite different from the properties of pure hydrogen and pure oxygen.

🔵 Active Reading Question

Why are hydrogen molecules called "elements," but water molecules are called "compounds"?

C. The States of Matter

Water is one of the most familiar substances in our world. We recognize water in three different states: solid, liquid, and gas. If we lower the temperature of liquid water, it freezes—that is, it changes to ice (solid water). On the other hand, if we heat water to its boiling point, it "disappears" into the air as a gas.

The three states of water have distinctly different properties. If a pond freezes in the winter, you can walk across it. Solid water can support your weight. Conversely, you would never try to walk across the same pond in the summertime!

We can also highlight the differing properties of liquid and solid water with food coloring. A drop of food coloring placed on an ice cube just sits there on top of the ice. In contrast, a drop of food coloring placed in liquid water spreads throughout the liquid. The fact that the food coloring spreads in all directions in the liquid water indicates that the water molecules must be moving, bouncing the "food coloring molecules" around and keeping them suspended. This property is very different from that of ice, where the food coloring does not penetrate the surface. Also, we know that gaseous water is quite different from solid and liquid water because it is invisible to the naked eye, unlike the other states of water.

Like water, all substances exist in the *three states of matter:* solid, liquid, and gas. A **solid** is rigid. It has a fixed shape and volume. A **liquid** has a definite volume but takes the shape of its container (see **Figure 2.7**). A **gas** has no fixed volume or shape. It uniformly fills any container.

🔵 Active Reading Question

What happens to food coloring when we add it to water? How do our observations support the idea that water is made up of moving molecules?

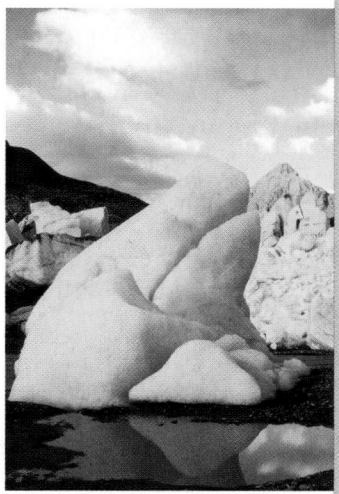

The three states of water: solid (ice), liquid (water), and gas (water vapor in the air)

Solid
Substance with a fixed shape and volume

Liquid
Substance with a definite volume that takes the shape of its container

Gas
Substance with no definite shape or volume

Figure 2.7
Liquid water takes the shape of its container.

🔵 Active Reading Question

Elements are made of only one type of atom and compounds are made of more than one type of atom. A hydrogen molecule consists of two hydrogen atoms (diatomic). A water molecule is made of two hydrogen atoms and an oxygen atom, so water is a compound.

2.1.C The States of Matter
Objective To define the three states of matter

MINI-DEMOS

- Demonstrate the movement of the molecules in water by placing a drop of food coloring in a beaker of water and allowing it to mix without stirring.

- Use small (marble-size) Styrofoam balls to demonstrate the differences among solids, liquids, and gases at the atomic/molecular level. Glue balls together to represent a solid. Place a handful of loose balls in a beaker to represent a liquid. The "liquid" will take the shape of its container. Place a few balls in a quart jar with a lid and shake the jar to represent a gas. If you leave the top off the jar and shake it, the gas will escape from the container.

🔵 Active Reading Question

The food coloring will spread throughout the liquid water in all directions. The food coloring moves in all directions (not just downward from the force of gravity) because water molecules move and allow the "food coloring molecules" to spread in the water.

Teaching Support
DEMONSTRATION

States of Matter

Materials
- Small wooden block
- Colored water
- Balloon
- Several containers with interesting shapes

Procedure Show students the wooden block. Ask what state of matter it is and discuss its definite volume. Ask how its volume might be calculated. Put the block in each of the different-shaped containers to illustrate that solids do not take the shape of their container.

Next, show students the colored water. Ask what state of matter it is and discuss how it can change shape. Pour it from one container to another. Is the volume constant? How could it be measured?

Next, have a student blow up the balloon, but do not tie it closed. Ask what state of matter the air in the balloon is. Ask the student to pour the air into one of the containers. Pour the air from container to container. Discuss its change in shape and whether the volume of the air is constant.

Summarize properties of states of matter.

Extension Place several ice cubes in a beaker. Place the beaker on a hot plate, melt the ice, and bring the water to boiling to show students that one state can change into another. If you have access to dry ice, use a sample to illustrate sublimation.

SECTION 2.1
Review Questions

1. Atoms are the fundamental building blocks of matter. There are the same number of different types of atoms as there are elements. An atom is a single unit of an element. Atoms may be grouped together in elements as pairs or in larger groups. Compounds differ from both atoms and elements because they are composed of two or more different atoms bonded together. The properties of compounds are different from those of the atoms or elements from which they are composed. Millions of compounds exist, but only about 100 elements are known.

2. mist   time   chit   try

   hem   thyme   mister

   cry   chest   sir

   trim   shirt   sit

   met   shim   miter

   mite   stir   chemist

   In this example, an "element" is one type of letter. A "compound" contains more than one type of letter.

3. See Figure 2.8 for molecular pictures of a solid, liquid, and gas. A solid has a fixed shape and volume. A liquid takes the shape of its container and has a fixed volume. A gas has neither a fixed shape nor a fixed volume.

HANDS-ON CHEMISTRY   • MINI-LAB •

Full or Empty?

Materials
- clay
- funnel
- empty soft drink bottle with cap
- water
- large safety pin

Part I: Procedure

1. Use clay to secure a funnel to an empty soft drink bottle. Make sure that the mouth of the bottle is completely covered.
2. Pour water into the funnel, and observe what happens.
3. Develop a method that allows the water to go smoothly into the bottle.
4. Develop a method that allows the water to stay in the funnel.
5. Develop a method that allows the water to periodically squirt into the bottle.

Results/Analysis (Part I)

1. List your observations from step 2.
2. Discuss each of your methods for steps 3–5, and explain why each method works.

Part II: Procedure

1. Fill a plastic soft drink bottle with water, and replace the cap tightly.
2. Using a large safety pin, poke a hole in the side of the container and observe what happens.
3. Hold the bottle over a sink, and unscrew the cap. Observe what happens.

Results/Analysis (Part II)

1. List your observations from step 2, and explain them.
2. List your observations from step 3, and explain them.
3. Relate your findings to those from Part I of this activity.

SECTION 2.1
REVIEW QUESTIONS

❶ How do atoms, compounds, and elements differ?

❷ Consider the letters in the word *chemistry*. Use them to make as many word "compounds" as is possible with 9 elements. How is an element different from a compound?

❸ Draw an "atom" picture of a solid, a liquid, and a gas. Describe the essential differences among them.

RESEARCH LINKS
CLASSZONE.COM

Hands-On Chemistry
MINI-LAB

Full or Empty?

Materials soft drink bottle, funnel, clay, long pin

Purpose Students will understand that air is matter and therefore takes up space.

Discussion

Part I: Air is matter; it has mass and takes up space. For water to enter the soft drink bottle, air must leave. When students first pour water into the funnel with clay completely covering the mouth of the bottle, water cannot easily enter the bottle.

Water does not enter the bottle: If the water is poured quickly such that no water initially enters, the water will stay in the funnel.

Water "squirts" into the bottle: If the water is added relatively slowly at first and some enters the bottle, it pushes air through the water that is being added to

Properties of Matter

Objectives

- *To learn to distinguish between physical and chemical properties*
- *To learn to distinguish between physical and chemical changes*

Key Terms

- Physical properties
- Chemical properties
- Physical changes
- Chemical change

A. Physical and Chemical Properties and Changes

When you see a friend, you immediately respond and call him or her by name. We can recognize a friend because each person has unique characteristics or properties. The person may be thin and tall, may have brown hair and blue eyes, and so on. These characteristics are examples of **physical properties**. Substances also have physical properties. The typical physical properties of a substance include odor, color, volume, state (gas, liquid, or solid), density, melting point, and boiling point.

We can also describe a pure substance in terms of its **chemical properties**, which refer to its ability to form new substances. An example of a chemical change is wood burning in a fireplace, giving off heat and gases and leaving a residue of ashes. In this process, the wood is changed to several new substances. Other examples of chemical changes include the rusting of steel, the digestion of food, and the growth of plants. In a chemical change a given substance changes to a fundamentally different substance or substances.

> **Physical property**
> Characteristic of a substance that can change without the substance's becoming a different substance
>
> **Chemical property**
> Characteristic that describes the ability of a substance to change to a different substance

Active Reading Question

Describe three physical properties of your shampoo.

EXAMPLE 2.1

Identifying Physical and Chemical Properties

Classify each of the following as a physical or a chemical property.

- a. The boiling point of a certain alcohol is 78 °C.
- b. Diamonds are very hard.
- c. Sugar ferments to form alcohol.
- d. A metal wire conducts an electric current.

Solution

Items (a), (b), and (d) are physical properties; they describe characteristics of each substance, and no change in composition occurs. A metal wire has the same composition before and after an electric current has passed through it. Item (c) is a chemical property of sugar. Fermentation of sugars involves the formation of a new substance, alcohol.

Practice Problem • Exercise 2.1

Which of the following are physical properties and which are chemical properties?

- a. Gallium metal melts in your hand.
- b. This page is white.
- c. The copper sheets that form the "skin" of the Statue of Liberty have acquired a greenish coating over the years.

Gallium metal has such a low melting point (30 °C) that it melts from the heat of a hand.

(continued)

the funnel. A bubble of air goes through the water and starts a cycle of air leaving the bottle and water entering the bottle. This cycle can be difficult to achieve.

Water flows smoothly into the bottle: Students should poke a hole through the clay next to the funnel. This hole allows air to leave the bottle continuously, and the water will flow smoothly.

Part II: Water will not come out of the hole until the cap is loosened. For water to leave the bottle, air must enter.

SECTION 2.2
INTRODUCE

Student Preparation

Assign students to read Section 2.2 and to answer the Review Questions at the end of the section before coming to class.

SECTION 2.2
GUIDE THE LEARNING

Homework

You may wish to assign these selected end-of-chapter problems as homework for this section: 8, 9, 10, 11, 12, 13, 14

Additional end-of-chapter problems can be used for extra practice.

2.2.A Physical and Chemical Properties and Changes

Objective To learn to distinguish between physical and chemical properties and changes

Active Reading Question

Answers will vary. Descriptions may include color, scent, viscosity, density, and ability to dissolve in water.

EXAMPLE 2.1

More Examples

Classify each of the following as a physical or chemical property.

1. Ice melts at 0 °C.
   Physical property

2. Propane burns in the air.
   Chemical property

3. Lead is a very dense metal.
   Physical property

4. Leaves turn colors in the fall.
   Chemical property

Answer to Practice Problem 2.1

Items (a) and (b) are physical properties. When solid gallium melts, it forms liquid gallium. Item (c) is a chemical property. Copper reacts with air to form a new substance that is green.

LABORATORY
EXPERIMENT 4:
Physical and Chemical Changes

 LABORATORY
EXPERIMENT 5:
Household Chemistry,
Microscale

 TEACHING TIP

Use Figure 2.8 to emphasize a
molecular perspective as it
relates to the states of matter
and to physical changes. Ice,
liquid water, and steam look
and feel different to us although
they are each composed of water
molecules. It is the spacing and
order of the water molecules
that give the states of matter
different physical properties.

TECHNOLOGY

Figure 2.8

Matter can undergo changes in both its physical and its chemical
properties. To illustrate the fundamental differences between physical and
chemical changes, we will consider water. As we have seen, a sample of
water contains a very large number of individual units (called molecules),
each made up of two atoms of hydrogen and one atom of oxygen—the
familiar H_2O, which can be represented as:

Here the letters stand for atoms and the lines show attachments, called
bonds, between atoms. The molecular model on the right represents water
in a more three-dimensional fashion.

What is really occurring when water undergoes the following changes?

When ice melts, the rigid solid becomes a mobile liquid that takes the
shape of its container. Continued heating brings the liquid to a boil, and
the water becomes a gas or vapor that seems to disappear into the air. The
changes that occur as the substance goes from solid to liquid to gas are
represented in **Figure 2.8.** In ice the water molecules are locked into fixed
positions. In the liquid the molecules are still very close together, but some
motion is occurring; the positions of the molecules are no longer fixed as
they are in ice. In the gaseous state the molecules are much farther apart
and move randomly, hitting each other and the walls of the container.

Figure 2.8
The three states of water, red spheres
represent oxygen atoms and blue spheres
represent hydrogen atoms. (a) Solid: The
water molecules are locked into rigid
positions and are close together. (b) Liquid:
The water molecules are still close together
but can move around to some extent.
(c) Gas: The water molecules are far apart
and move randomly.

Solid (Ice)   Liquid (Water)   Gas (Steam)
   (a)   (b)   (c)

32 • Chapter 2 • Matter

Meeting Individual Needs
ADVANCED LEARNERS

Have advanced learners investigate
additional states of matter such as plasma
and Bose–Einstein Condensates. Have
students present their findings to the class.
Plasma occurs in high energy processes as
near as a fire or as far away as the core of
a star. In 2001, the Nobel Prize for Physics
went to Eric Cornell, Wolfgang Ketterle, and
Carl Wieman, who used lasers, magnets, and
evaporative cooling to discover a new phase
of matter, known as Bose–Einstein
Condensates (BECs).

The most important thing about all these changes is that the water molecules are still intact. The motions of individual molecules and the distances between them change, *but H₂O molecules are still present*. These changes of state are **physical changes** because they do not affect the composition of the substance. In each state we still have water (H_2O), not some other substance.

Now suppose that we run an electric current through water as illustrated in **Figure 2.9.** Something very different happens. The water disappears and is replaced by two new gaseous substances, hydrogen and oxygen. An electric current actually causes the water molecules to come apart—the water *decomposes* to hydrogen and oxygen. We can represent this process as follows:

Electric current

This is a **chemical change** because water (consisting of H_2O molecules) has changed into different substances: hydrogen (containing H_2 molecules) and oxygen (containing O_2 molecules). In this process, the H_2O molecules have been replaced by O_2 and H_2 molecules. Let us summarize as follows.

Water

Oxygen gas forms

Hydrogen gas forms

Electrode

Source of direct current

Figure 2.9
Electrolysis, the decomposition of water by an electric current, is a chemical process.

Physical and Chemical Changes

1. A *physical change* involves a change in one or more physical properties, but no change in the fundamental components that make up the substance. The most common physical changes are changes of state: solid ⟺ liquid ⟺ gas.

2. A *chemical change* involves a change in the fundamental components of the substance; a given substance changes into a different substance or substances. Chemical changes are called reactions: silver tarnishes by reacting with substances in the air; a plant forms a leaf by combining various substances from the air and soil; and so on.

Physical change
Change that does not affect the composition of a substance

Chemical change
Change in which a substance becomes a different substance

 Active Reading Question

Why are changes of state, for example, liquid water changing to steam, not considered to be chemical changes?

2.2 • Properties of Matter • **33**

TECHNOLOGY

 Video
Electrolysis of Water

After the reaction proceeds long enough to see the gases, ask whether anyone knows which is oxygen and which is hydrogen. Have students explain their choices. Point out that in this chemical change, water (H_2O) is taken apart to form hydrogen and oxygen gases. Discuss how this reaction is different from boiling water (although many students indicate that bubbles form in both cases). Explain that boiling water is a physical change in which water liquid is converted to water vapor.

TEACHING TIP

To illustrate the difference between a physical and a chemical change, compare representations (b) and (c) from Figure 2.7, a physical change from liquid water to gaseous water, to the chemical change that occurs when liquid water is electrolyzed to produce the gases H_2 and O_2. Use the equation in the text to represent the electrolysis of water as a chemical change.

 Active Reading Question

In a chemical change, a given substance changes into a new substance or substances. Even though water is not the same phase as ice, for example, water and ice are the same substance. That is, they both contain molecules that consist of two hydrogen atoms and one oxygen atom.

EXAMPLE 2.2

More Examples

Classify each of the following as a chemical or physical change.

1. You make scrambled eggs.
   Chemical change

2. You step on a piece of chalk and it becomes powdered.
   Physical change

3. You light a candle when the electricity goes out.
   Chemical change

4. Steam from your hot shower condenses on a cold mirror.
   Physical change

 Answer to Practice Problem 2.2

a. Milk turns sour because new substances are formed. This is a chemical change.

b. Melting wax is a physical change, a change of state. When wax burns, new substances are formed. This is a chemical change.

SECTION 2.2
ASSESS

 SECTION 2.2 Review Questions

1. Chemical properties relate to the ability to form new substances. Wood burning and iron rusting are two examples of chemical changes.

2. Physical properties are characteristics of a substance such as color, odor, or phase. Water freezing to ice and a glass breaking are two examples of physical changes.

3. Liquid water and gaseous water are both composed of water molecules.

4. a. physical
   b. physical
   c. chemical
   d. chemical
   e. chemical

EXAMPLE 2.2

Identifying Physical and Chemical Changes

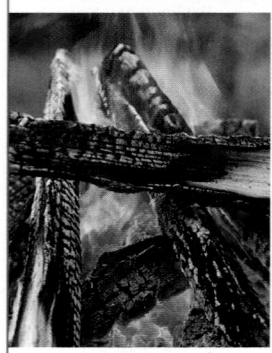

Oxygen combines with the chemicals in wood to produce flames. Is a physical or chemical change taking place?

Classify each of the following as a physical or a chemical change.

a. Iron metal is melted.
b. Iron combines with oxygen to form rust.
c. Wood burns in air.
d. A rock is broken into small pieces.

Solution

a. Melted iron is just liquid iron and could cool again to the solid state. This is a physical change.

b. When iron combines with oxygen, it forms a different substance, rust, that contains iron and oxygen. This is a chemical change because a different substance forms.

c. Wood burns to form different substances (as we will see later, they include carbon dioxide and water). After the fire, the wood is no longer in its original form. This is a chemical change.

d. When the rock is broken up, all the smaller pieces have the same composition as the whole rock. Each new piece differs from the original only in size and shape. This is a physical change.

 Practice Problem • Exercise 2.2

Classify each of the following as a chemical change, a physical change, or a combination of the two.

a. Milk turns sour.
b. Wax is melted over a flame and then catches fire and burns.

 SECTION 2.2
REVIEW QUESTIONS

❶ What is meant by the term *chemical property*? Provide two examples of a chemical change.

❷ What is meant by the term *physical property*? Provide two examples of a physical change.

❸ Why is the boiling of water a physical change if water changes from a liquid to a gas?

❹ Classify the following as physical or chemical changes.
   a. Mothballs gradually vaporize in a closet.
   b. Calcium chloride lowers the temperature at which water freezes and can be used to melt ice on city sidewalks and roadways.
   c. An antacid tablet fizzes and releases carbon dioxide gas when it comes in contact with hydrochloric acid in the stomach.
   d. A flashlight battery corrodes and leaks when stored for a long time.
   e. Whole milk curdles if vinegar is added to it.

❺ Are all physical changes accompanied by chemical changes? Are all chemical changes accompanied by physical changes? Explain.

 RESEARCH LINKS
CLASSZONE.COM

5. Physical changes are not accompanied by chemical changes. In fact, the very nature of a physical change implies no change in the composition of the substance. Chemical changes, on the other hand, are accompanied by physical changes, because the composition of the substance is changed and thus will have new physical properties.

Classifying Matter

Objectives
- *To learn to distinguish between mixtures and pure substances*
- *To learn two methods of separating mixtures*

A. Mixtures and Pure Substances

Virtually all of the matter around us consists of mixtures of substances. For example, if you closely observe a sample of soil, you will see that it has many types of components, including tiny grains of sand and remnants of plants. The air we breathe is a mixture, too. Even the water from a drinking fountain contains many substances besides water.

Mixtures

A **mixture** can be defined as something that has variable composition. For example,

- Wood is a mixture; its composition varies greatly depending on the tree from which it originates.
- Soda is a mixture; it contains many dissolved substances, including carbon dioxide gas.
- Coffee is a mixture; it can be strong, weak, or bitter.
- Although it looks very pure, water pumped from deep in the earth is a mixture; it contains dissolved minerals and gases.
- The most common example of a mixture is the air that surrounds us. If we collect a sample of air from a mountaintop where there is no pollution, we find a mixture containing the substances shown in **Figure 2.10**.

Key Terms
- Mixture
- Alloys
- Pure substance
- Homogeneous mixture
- Solution
- Heterogeneous mixture
- Distillation
- Filtration

Mixture
A substance with variable composition

Figure 2.10
Air is composed of a variety of substances.

2.3 • Classifying Matter • **35**

SECTION 2.3
INTRODUCE

Student Preparation

Assign students to read Section 2.3 and to answer the Review Questions at the end of the section before coming to class.

 Active Learning
Team Learning Worksheet

After introducing the material in Sections 2.2 and 2.3 in class, place students in groups and have them work together on **Sections 2.2–2.3: Team Learning Worksheet.**

SECTION 2.3
GUIDE THE LEARNING

Homework

You may wish to assign these selected end-of-chapter problems as homework for this section: 15, 16, 17, 18, 19, 20, 21, 22

Additional end-of-chapter problems can be used for extra practice.

2.3.A Mixtures and Pure Substances

Objective To learn to distinguish between mixtures and pure substances

🍎 **TEACHING TIP**

Packaged food items, such as dry cake mixes, provide familiar examples of mixtures. Bring in a few examples. You can use the labels on these items when studying nomenclature in Chapter 5.

When we examine each of the substances in air, we find the following:

Nitrogen contains molecules consisting of two atoms of nitrogen.

Oxygen contains molecules consisting of two atoms of oxygen.

Water contains molecules consisting of two hydrogen atoms and one oxygen atom.

Argon contains individual argon atoms.

Carbon dioxide contains molecules consisting of two oxygen atoms and one carbon atom.

Neon contains individual neon atoms.

Helium contains individual helium atoms.

As you can see from the figure, air is a mixture of elements and compounds. Although air has a similar composition everywhere on earth, differences arise depending on where the air is collected. For example, the amount of water vapor changes greatly.

- Air collected over a desert would include very little water vapor.
- In contrast, on a humid day in Florida, air holds a relatively large amount of water.
- Also, the carbon dioxide content of air would be higher in industrial areas due to the burning of fuels.
- Likewise, other substances (pollutants) would be present due to human activities such as driving cars.

Thus air is not exactly the same everywhere. It has a somewhat different composition depending on where you get it. This variation is a characteristic of mixtures.

The composition of mixtures varies, but the composition of compounds is always the same.

Air is only one of the many mixtures we encounter in our daily lives. For example, if you wear a gold ring, you are wearing a mixture. Pure gold, like that found in the bullion stored in Fort Knox, Kentucky, is really quite soft. Because it bends easily, the pure form is not useful for jewelry. Only when we mix gold with other metals such as silver and copper does it become sturdy enough to make rings and chains.

36 • Chapter 2 • Matter

Students can compare their organizer to the one displayed on page 42.

Your ring might be 14-karat gold—that is, it contains 36 atoms of gold for every 25 atoms of silver and for every 39 atoms of copper. Or your ring might be 18-karat gold—that is, it contains 56 atoms of gold for every 20 atoms of silver and for every 24 atoms of copper. Mixtures of metals are called **alloys**. Many gold alloys exist, containing varying amounts of gold, silver, and copper atoms. Alloys are mixtures—their composition varies. They are not compounds like water. Compounds always have the same atomic composition. This is illustrated in **Figure 2.11.**

> **Alloy**
> A mixture of elements that has metallic properties

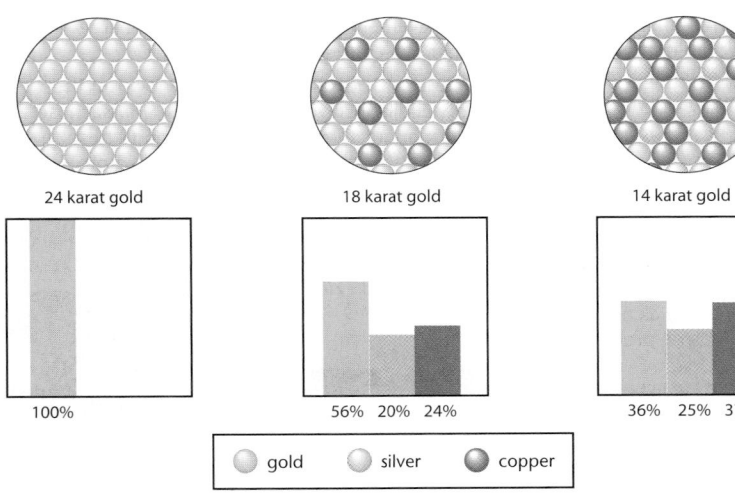

24 karat gold   18 karat gold   14 karat gold

100%   56% 20% 24%   36% 25% 37%

gold   silver   copper

Figure 2.11
Twenty-four-karat gold is an element. It contains only gold atoms. Fourteen-karat and 18-karat gold are alloys. They contain a mixture of different atoms.

It is important to understand the difference between a compound and a mixture. A compound contains only particles of identical atomic composition. Therefore it always has the same composition. See **Figure 2.12** showing water. In contrast, a mixture is a collection of compounds and/or elements that are present in varying amounts. Thus the composition of a mixture depends on how much of each component is used when the mixture is formed.

Pure Substances

Whereas a mixture has variable composition, a **pure substance** always has the same composition. Pure substances are either elements or compounds. For example, pure water is a compound containing individual H_2O molecules. However, as we find it in nature, liquid water always contains other substances in addition to pure water—it is a mixture. This is obvious from the different tastes, smells, and colors of water samples obtained from various locations. However, if we take great pains to purify samples of water from various sources (such as oceans, lakes, rivers, and the earth's interior), we always end up with the same pure substance—water, which is made up of only H_2O molecules.

Pure water always has the same physical and chemical properties and always consists of molecules containing hydrogen and oxygen in exactly the same proportions, regardless of the original source of the water. The properties of a pure substance make it possible to identify that substance conclusively.

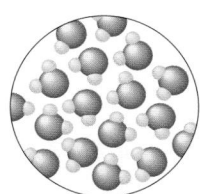

Figure 2.12
Water is a compound. All the components are the same— H_2O molecules.

> **Pure substance**
> Either a pure element or a compound

2.3 • Classifying Matter • **37**

Before class, prepare a mixture of iron filings and sulfur. Show students that a mixture can be separated by physical means—in this case, by using a magnet to separate the iron filings from the sulfur. Place a small amount of the mixture in a test tube. Heat the tube in the flame of a Bunsen burner until it changes to a reddish-brown color. Now use a magnet to show students that the compound, iron sulfide, cannot be separated into iron filings and sulfur.

Active Reading Question

Answers will vary. An example of a mixture is air, and an example of a compound is water. Air contains many substances (mainly nitrogen gas and oxygen gas), but the amounts of each can vary. Water contains hydrogen and oxygen, but the amount is always 2 atoms of hydrogen for every one atom of oxygen.

CHEMISTRY IN YOUR WORLD

Connection to History

Alchemical Cymbals

Chemistry is an ancient science dating back to at least 1000 B.C., when early "chemists" discovered how to isolate metals from ores and how to preserve bodies by using embalming fluids. The Greeks were the first to try to figure out why chemical changes occur. By 400 B.C., they had proposed a system of four elements: fire, earth, water, and air. The next 2000 years of chemical history were dominated by a pseudoscience called *alchemy*. Although many alchemists were fakes and mystics, some were serious scientists who made important discoveries.

In fact, did you know that the cymbals used by more than 60% of the rock bands in the world were invented by an alchemist? The story begins 377 years ago in Constantinople, when an alchemist named Avedis discovered an alloy that produced

better-sounding cymbals. This development was important because at that time cymbals were mainly used by armies to frighten their enemies. To honor his achievement, Avedis was given the name Zildjian, which meant "cymbal maker."

The descendants of that alchemist now run the Avedis Zildjian Company in Norwell, Massachusetts, which manufactures 2000 of the world's best cymbals every day. The musical world—from classical to rock—truly loves alchemical cymbals.

Worker at Avedis Zildjian Company making cymbals

Mixtures can be separated into pure substances: elements and/or compounds.

```
Mixtures  →  Two or
             more pure
             substances
```

For example, we have seen that air can be separated into oxygen (element), nitrogen (element), water (compound), carbon dioxide (compound), argon (element), and other pure substances.

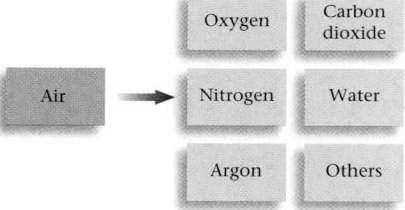
```
        Oxygen    Carbon
                  dioxide
Air  →  Nitrogen  Water
        Argon     Others
```

Active Reading Question

Give an example of a mixture and an example of a compound and explain how they are different.

Alchemical Cymbals

This feature presents an excellent opportunity to talk about alchemy. Alchemy, the pseudo-science that preceded chemistry, was founded on the premise that base metals could be transmuted into gold. This futile dream motivated alchemists and their financial supporters for 17 centuries. The power and influence of the alchemists was very great. In nearly every court in Europe,

men were appointed to the task of discovering how to change lead and iron into gold. Many alchemists were so revered that they were raised almost to the level of nobility, working shoulder to shoulder with their sovereigns. Although many of the alchemists were simply "confidence men," some were genuine seekers of the truth—men like Bernard Trevisan and Philippus Aurelius Theophrastus Bombast von Hohenheim, better known as Paracelsus.

Mysterious Mixing

Materials clear cup, water, food coloring

Purpose Students will understand that water is made of constantly moving particles.

Discussion Liquid water is macroscopica static but microscopically dynamic. This idea surfaces frequently in chemistry

Homogeneous and Heterogeneous Mixtures

Mixtures can be classified as either homogeneous or heterogeneous. A **homogeneous mixture** is *the same throughout*. For example, when we dissolve some salt in water and stir well, all regions of the resulting mixture have the same properties. A homogeneous mixture is also called a **solution**. Of course, different amounts of salt and water can be mixed to form various solutions, but a homogeneous mixture (a solution) does not vary in composition from one region of the solution to another (see **Figure 2.13**).

The air around you is a solution—it is a homogeneous mixture of gases. Solid solutions also exist. Brass is a homogeneous mixture of the metals copper and zinc.

A **heterogeneous mixture** contains regions that have different properties from those of other regions. For example, when we pour sand into water, the resulting mixture has one region containing water and another, very different region containing mostly sand (see **Figure 2.14**).

Homogeneous mixture
A mixture that is the same throughout

Solution
A homogeneous mixture

Heterogeneous mixture
A mixture containing regions with differing properties

Discuss the difference between mixtures and compounds by using a cooking analogy. Just as a mixture of hydrogen (H_2) and oxygen (O_2) is not the same as water (H_2O), a mixture of eggs, flour, sugar, and milk is not a cake. Only when the ingredients react do we get a cake.

Figure 2.13
Figure 2.13
When table salt is stirred into water (left), a homogeneous mixture called a solution is formed (right).

Figure 2.14
Figure 2.14
Sand and water do not mix to form a uniform mixture. After the mixture is stirred, the sand settles back to the bottom.

HANDS-ON CHEMISTRY • MINI-LAB •

Mysterious Mixing

Materials
- clear plastic cup
- food coloring
- water

Procedure

1. Fill a clear plastic cup halfway with water.
2. Carefully place a drop of food coloring on the surface of the water.
3. Without disturbing the water, observe the food coloring for a few minutes.
4. How can you make the food coloring mix more quickly with the water? Design an experiment and discuss it with your teacher.
5. Test the experiment.

Results/Analysis

1. Make a list of your observations from step 3.
2. The water does not appear to be moving. What do your observations tell you about the water molecules? Explain your answer.
3. Draw molecular-level pictures that explain your observations.
4. Explain the results of your experiment to make the food coloring mix more quickly with the water.

2.3 • Classifying Matter • 39

(continued)

(for example, with gases, equilibrium, and kinetics). Although it will take a few minutes for the food coloring to become homogeneously mixed throughout the water, observations should begin immediately. Students should study the directions that the food coloring takes in mixing. While gravity dictates that the drop falls in the water, the food coloring also moves laterally, and will sometimes even rise in the water. This movement indicates that water molecules are "pushing" the food coloring molecules around. By stirring the water, mixing occurs more quickly, a result that molecular theory is able to predict and explain. You can show students what happens when food coloring is added to warm water—introducing that temperature is a measure of kinetic energy, which affects the velocity of the molecules.

Have students draw molecular-level pictures to give you some insight into their ideas. Some students may draw clear water molecules before food coloring is added and colored molecules after mixing has taken place. A correct drawing would show water molecules and food coloring molecules mixed uniformly in solution. This exercise should lead to a good discussion of physical versus chemical changes.

2.3 • Classifying Matter • 39

EXAMPLE 2.3

More Examples

Identify each of the following as a pure substance, a homogeneous mixture, or a heterogeneous mixture.

1. "pure" apple juice
   homogeneous mixture

2. table salt
   pure substance

3. chocolate chip cookies
   heterogeneous mixture

 Answer to Practice Problem 2.3

a. homogeneous mixture of sugar and other substances dispersed uniformly in water

b. homogeneous mixture

c. heterogeneous mixture

d. pure substance, so it always has the same composition (Commercial iodized salt has iodine added to it, so it would be a homogeneous mixture.)

2.3.B Separation of Mixtures

Objective To learn two methods of separating mixtures

🔺 **LABORATORY**
EXPERIMENT 6:
Properties of Matter, Microscale

🔺 **LABORATORY**
EXPERIMENT 7:
Separation Challenge, Microscale

🔺 **LABORATORY**
EXPERIMENT 8:
Sludge Text, Traditional

🔺 **LABORATORY**
EXPERIMENT 9:
Separation of Mixtures, Microscale

🔺 **LABORATORY**
EXPERIMENT 10:
Distillation, Microscale

EXAMPLE 2.3

Distinguishing Between Mixtures and Pure Substances

Identify each of the following as a pure substance, a homogeneous mixture, or a heterogeneous mixture.

    a. gasoline   **c.** air

    b. a stream with gravel at the bottom   **d.** copper metal

Solution

    a. Gasoline is a homogeneous mixture containing many compounds.

    b. A stream with gravel on the bottom is a heterogeneous mixture.

    c. Air is a homogeneous mixture of elements and compounds.

    d. Copper metal is a pure substance (an element).

✅ **Practice Problem • Exercise 2.3**

Classify each of the following as a pure substance, a homogeneous mixture, or a heterogeneous mixture.

    a. maple syrup

    b. the oxygen and helium in a scuba tank

    c. oil and vinegar salad dressing

    d. common salt (sodium chloride)

B. Separation of Mixtures

We have seen that the matter found in nature is typically a mixture of pure substances. For example, seawater is water containing dissolved minerals. We can separate the water from the minerals by boiling, which changes the water to steam (gaseous water) and leaves the minerals behind as solids. If we collect and cool the steam, it condenses to pure water. This separation process, called **distillation**, is shown in **Figure 2.15**.

Distillation
A separation process that depends on the different boiling points of the substances

Figure 2.15
Distillation of a solution consisting of salt dissolved in water. (a) When the solution is boiled, steam is driven off. If this steam is collected and cooled, it condenses to form pure water, which drips into the collection flask. (b) After all of the water has been boiled off, the salt remains in the original flask and the water is in the collection flask.

40 • Chapter 2 • Matter

Before filtration is explained, it may help ELL students to take part in a discussion about real-life filter applications that are helpful to people and the environment. Examples could include: doctors and dentists wearing masks over their faces to prevent the transfer of germs; water being filtered to remove contaminants before being issued as drinking water; filters being used on heating and air conditioning systems to help remove impurities such as dust, smoke, microorganisms, and odors in the air.

When we carry out the distillation of saltwater, water is changed from the liquid state to the gaseous state and then back to the liquid state. These changes of state are examples of physical changes. We are separating a mixture of substances, but we are not changing the composition of the individual substances. We can represent this as shown in **Figure 2.16.**

Saltwater solution
(homogeneous mixture)

Salt + Pure water

Distillation
(physical method)

Figure 2.16
No chemical change occurs when salt water is distilled.

Suppose that we scooped up some sand with our sample of seawater. This sample is a heterogeneous mixture, because it contains an undissolved solid as well as the saltwater solution. We can separate out the sand by simple **filtration**. We pour the mixture onto a mesh, such as a filter paper, which allows the liquid to pass through and leaves the solid behind (see **Figure 2.17**). The salt can then be separated from the water by distillation. The total separation process is represented in **Figure 2.18.** All the changes involved are physical changes.

Filtration
Separation of a solid from a liquid by using filter paper

Mixture of solid and liquid

Stirring rod

Funnel

Filter paper traps solid

Filtrate (liquid component of the mixture)

Figure 2.17
Filtration separates a liquid from a solid. The liquid passes through the filter paper, but the solid particles are trapped.

Use Figure 2.19 to review the material in this section. Have students work in groups to come up with an example for each box in Figure 2.19. A representative of each group can present the results to the class.

TECHNOLOGY

Figure 2.19

Figure 2.18
Separation of a sand-saltwater mixture

We can summarize the description of matter given in this chapter with the diagram shown in **Figure 2.19.** Note that a given sample of matter can be a pure substance (either an element or a compound) or, more commonly, a mixture (homogeneous or heterogeneous).

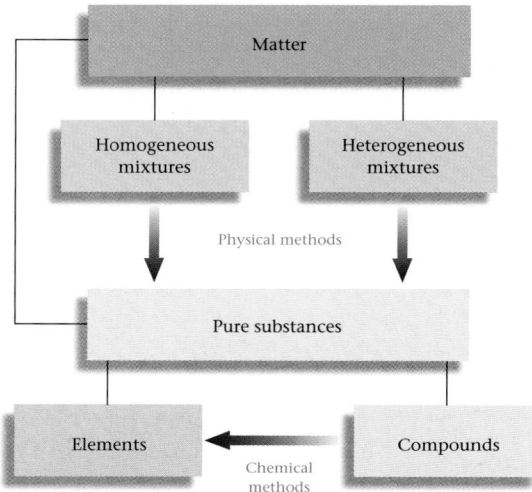

Figure 2.19
The organization of matter

We have seen that all matter exists as elements or can be broken down into elements, the most fundamental substances we have encountered up to this point. We will have more to say about the nature of elements in the next chapter.

CELEBRITY CHEMICAL   Hydrogen Peroxide (H_2O_2)

Hydrogen and oxygen atoms combine to form two different molecules: the very familiar water molecule (H_2O) and the hydrogen peroxide molecule (H_2O_2). Because these molecules have very similar compositions, you might think they should behave in very similar ways. In fact, the properties of water and hydrogen peroxide are very different.

You are already very familiar with water. We drink it, we swim in it, we cook vegetables in it, we wash with it, and so on. Water is essential for life. A few days without it and we die.

Hydrogen peroxide is very different from water. This corrosive liquid would poison us if we were foolish enough to drink it. It is most commonly used as a bleaching agent. For example, hydrogen peroxide bleaches hair by reacting with melanin, the substance responsible for the color of brown and black hair. Hydrogen peroxide changes the

composition of melanin in a way that causes it to lose its color—it turns brown hair blonde. In addition, hydrogen peroxide is used to bleach fibers, such as silk, and to bleach flour, producing the ultra-white powder that consumers demand. Small amounts of hydrogen peroxide are also added to some toothpastes as whitening agents.

One of the most common uses of hydrogen peroxide is to prevent infections in cuts. Sometime in your life when you have cut or scraped yourself, a parent or a nurse probably has applied a liquid to the wound that foamed and burned. That substance was hydrogen peroxide—a powerful *antiseptic* (killer of microorganisms).

Although it looks deceptively similar to water, hydrogen peroxide behaves very differently from water. A small change in the make-up of a molecule can produce big changes in behavior.

SECTION 2.3
REVIEW QUESTIONS

❶ What is meant by the term *mixture*? Provide two examples of a mixture.

❷ Why can't mixtures be classified as pure substances?

❸ Explain the difference between a *heterogeneous mixture* and a *homogeneous mixture*. Provide two examples of each.

❹ Identify the following as *mixtures* or as *pure substances*.
  a. milk
  b. the paper this book is printed on
  c. a teaspoon of sugar
  d. a teaspoon of sugar dissolved in a glass of water
  e. steel

❺ What is another name for a homogeneous mixture?

❻ Classify the following mixtures as *homogeneous* or *heterogeneous*.
  a. vanilla yogurt
  b. vanilla and strawberry swirl yogurt
  c. Italian salad dressing
  d. kitty litter

❼ Explain how you would separate a sugar water solution into sugar (solid) and water. Is this process a distillation or filtration?

RESEARCH LINKS
CLASSZONE.COM

SECTION 2.3
ASSESS

SECTION 2.3
Review Questions

1. A mixture is something that has variable composition. Examples include milk and air.

2. A pure substance always has the same composition; substances can be either elements or compounds.

3. A heterogeneous mixture contains regions that have different properties from other regions. Examples include soil and chunky peanut butter. A homogeneous mixture is the same throughout. Examples include air and brass.

4. a. mixture
   b. mixture
   c. pure substance
   d. mixture
   e. mixture

5. A homogeneous mixture is also called a solution.

6. a. homogeneous
   b. heterogeneous
   c. heterogeneous
   d. heterogeneous

7. Boil the sugar water solution. The sugar is left behind as the water evaporates. If the steam is collected and cooled, it condenses to pure water. This process is called distillation.

CELEBRITY CHEMICAL

Hydrogen Peroxide (H_2O_2)

A small change in the composition of a substance greatly changes its properties. For example, the properties of hydrogen peroxide and water are very different. Other examples are ethanol (CH_3CH_2OH) and methanol (CH_3OH), and carbon monoxide (CO) and carbon dioxide (CO_2).

Chapter 2 Review

Key Terms

2.1 Matter

Atoms

Compounds

Molecule

Elements

Solid

Liquid

Gas

2.2 Physical properties

Chemical properties

Physical change

Chemical change

2.3 Mixture

Alloys

Pure substance

Homogeneous mixture

Solution

Heterogeneous mixture

Distillation

Filtration

RESEARCH LINKS
CLASSZONE.COM

Key Ideas

2.1 The Nature of Matter

■ Matter has mass and occupies space. It is composed of tiny particles called atoms.

■ Matter exists in three states:

- Solid—is a rigid substance with a definite shape
- Liquid—has a definite volume but takes the shape of its container
- Gas—takes the shape and volume of its container

■ Elements contain only one kind of atom—elemental copper contains only copper atoms, and elemental gold contains only gold atoms.

■ Compounds are substances that contain two or more kinds of atoms.

■ Compounds often contain discrete molecules.

■ A molecule contains atoms bound together in a particular way—an example is , the water molecule, which is written H_2O.

2.2 Properties of Matter

■ Matter has both physical and chemical properties.

- Chemical properties describe a substance's ability to change to a different substance.
- Physical properties are the characteristics of a substance that do not involve changing to another substance.
  - ◆ Examples are shape, size, and color.

■ Matter undergoes physical and chemical changes.

- A physical change involves a change in one or more physical properties but no change in composition.
- A chemical change transforms a substance into one or more new substances.

2.3 Classifying Matter

■ Matter can be classified as a mixture or a pure substance.

- A mixture has variable composition.
  - ◆ A homogeneous mixture has the same properties throughout.
  - ◆ A heterogeneous mixture has different properties in different parts of the mixture.
- A pure substance always has the same composition.

■ Mixtures can be separated into pure substances by various means including distillation and filtration.

■ Pure substances are of two types:

- Elements, which cannot be broken down chemically into simpler substances
- Compounds, which can be broken down chemically into elements

---

Meeting Individual Needs

CHAPTER REVIEW

Chapter 2 Review Worksheet at the appropriate level:
   Basic
   Standard
   Challenge

CHAPTER SUMMARY

A **Chapter Summary** that includes additional Active Reading Questions for Chapter 2 is available.

Assessment Resources

CHAPTER 2

Chapter 2 Test

TECHNOLOGY

💻 **Computerized Test Bank for Chapter 2**

All exercises with blue numbers have answers in the back of this book.

2.1 The Nature of Matter

A. The Particulate Nature of Matter

1. How do we "know" that matter is composed of atoms?

2. Why can't we see atoms with the naked eye?

3. Label each of the following as an atomic element, a molecular element, or a compound.

a.
b.
c.
d.

e.
f.
g.

B. Elements and Compounds

4. What does it mean to say that a given compound always has the same composition?

5. How do the properties of a compound, in general, compare with the properties of the elements of which it is composed? Give an example of a common compound and the elements of which it is composed to illustrate your answer.

C. The States of Matter

6. Consider three 10-g samples of water: one as ice, one as a liquid, and one as vapor. How do the volumes of these three samples compare with one another? How is this difference in volume related to the physical state involved?

7. In a sample of a gaseous substance, more than 99% of the overall volume of the sample is empty space. How is this fact reflected in the properties of a gaseous substance, compared with the properties of a liquid or solid substance?

2.2 Properties of Matter

A. Physical and Chemical Properties and Changes

Use the correct term (physical or chemical) to complete each of the following:

8. Copper is a reddish-brown metal that is easily stretched to make wires. These characteristics are examples of _____ properties of copper.

9. When copper metal is heated in concentrated nitric acid, the copper dissolves to form a deep blue solution, and a brown gas is evolved from the acid. These characteristics are examples of _____ changes.

Read the following passage to answer exercises 10 and 11.

Solutions of the substance potassium dichromate are bright orange in color. If a potassium dichromate solution is added to an acidic solution of iron(II) sulfate, the orange color of the potassium dichromate disappears, and the mixture takes on a bright green color as chromium(III) ion forms.

10. From the information above, indicate one *physical* property of potassium dichromate in solution.

11. From the information above, indicate one *chemical* property of potassium dichromate in solution.

12. What is meant by *electrolysis*? Are the changes produced by electrolysis chemical or physical in nature? Give an example to show your reasoning.

13. Classify the following as physical changes, chemical changes, physical properties, and chemical properties.

a. An iron scorches a shirt when you leave it on one spot too long.

b. The tires on your car seem to be getting low in very cold weather.

c. Your grandmother's silver tea set gets black with tarnish over time.

d. Spray-on oven cleaner converts grease in the oven into a soapy material.

e. An ordinary flashlight battery begins to leak with age and can't be recharged.

f. Acids produced by bacteria in plaque cause teeth to decay.

g. Sugar chars if overheated while making homemade candy.

h. Hydrogen peroxide fizzes when applied to a wound.

i. Dry ice "evaporates" without melting as time passes.

14. State the clues that a chemical reaction has taken place.

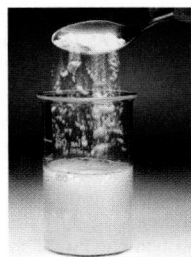

Chapter 2 Assessment

1. We can "see" atoms with a scanning tunneling microscope.

2. Atoms are very tiny.

3. (a) compound
(b) compound
(c) molecular element
(d) atomic element
(e) molecular element
(f) compound
(g) atomic element

4. The molecules of that compound always contain the same types and number of atoms.

5. In general, the properties of a compound are very different from the properties of its constituent elements. For example, the properties of water are very different from the properties of the elements (hydrogen gas and oxygen gas) that form it.

6. Gaseous water has a much larger volume than either the solid or the liquid form. There is a great deal of empty space in the gaseous sample.

7. Because gases are mostly open space, they can be compressed easily to smaller volumes. In solids and liquids, most of the sample's bulk volume is filled with the molecules, leaving little empty space.

8. physical

9. chemical

10. the orange color

11. The substance reacts with iron(II) sulfate.

12. Electrolysis is the passage of an electrical current through a substance or solution to force a chemical reaction to occur. For example, when an electrical current is passed through water, the water molecules undergo a chemical change to form hydrogen gas and oxygen gas.

13. (a) chemical; (b) physical (c) chemical; (d) chemical (e) chemical; (f) chemical (g) chemical; (h) chemical (i) physical; (j) chemical

14. The bubbles suggest that a new product has been formed.

15. *Answers will vary.* Possibilities for heterogeneous mixtures include salad dressing, candy, and pencils; possibilities for solutions include soft drinks, window cleaner, and shampoo.

16. (a) mixture
    (b) mixture
    (c) mixture
    (d) pure substance

17. (a) homogeneous
    (b) heterogeneous
    (c) heterogeneous
    (d) homogeneous
    (e) homogeneous (basically)

18. (a) element
    (b) compound

19. Consider a table salt solution (sodium chloride in water). Because water boils at a much lower temperature than sodium chloride does, the water can be boiled off from the solution, collected, and condensed back into the liquid state.

20. Consider a mixture of table salt (sodium chloride) and sand. Salt is soluble in water, but sand is not. The mixture is added to water, stirred to dissolve the salt, and then filtered. The salt solution passes through the filter, while the sand remains on the filter. The water can then be evaporated from the salt.

21. Add water to the sample and then heat the sample to boiling. This should dissolve the benzoic acid but not the charcoal. The hot sample can be filtered, which will remove the charcoal. As the filtered solution cools, some of the benzoic acid will crystallize. The solution could also be heated carefully to boil off the water, leaving benzoic acid.

22. The solution is heated to vaporize (boil) the water. The water vapor is then cooled so that it condenses back to the liquid state, and the liquid is collected. After all the water is vaporized from the original sample, pure sodium chloride remains. The process consists of physical changes.

23. compound (two different solids form from a pure substance)

24. compound (loses mass when heated)

25. physical

2.3 Classifying Matter

A. Mixtures and Pure Substances

15. Give three examples of heterogeneous *mixtures* and three examples of *solutions* that you might use in everyday life.

16. Classify the following as *mixtures* or as *pure substances*.

    a. a multivitamin tablet

    b. the blue liquid in your car's windshield reservoir

    c. a ham and cheese omelet

    d. a diamond

17. Classify the following mixtures as *homogeneous* or *heterogeneous*.

    a. gasoline

    b. a jar of jelly beans

    c. chunky peanut butter

    d. margarine

    e. the paper on which this question is printed

18. Label each of the following as a heterogeneous mixture, a homogeneous mixture, or a compound.

a.   b.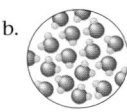

B. Separation of Mixtures

19. Describe how the process of *distillation* could be used to separate a solution into its component substances. Give an example.

20. Describe how the process of *filtration* could be used to separate a mixture into its components. Give an example.

21. In a laboratory experiment, students are asked to determine the relative amounts of benzoic acid and charcoal in a solid mixture. Benzoic acid is relatively soluble in hot water, but charcoal is not. Devise a method for separating the two components of this mixture.

22. Describe the process of distillation depicted in Figure 2.15. Does the separation of the components of a mixture by distillation represent a chemical or a physical change?

Critical Thinking

23. Pure substance X is melted, and the liquid is placed in an electrolysis apparatus like that shown in Figure 2.9. When an electric current is passed through the liquid, a brown solid forms in one chamber and a white solid forms in the other chamber. Is substance X a compound or an element?

24. If a piece of hard white blackboard chalk is heated strongly in a flame, the mass of the piece of chalk will decrease, and eventually the chalk will crumble into a fine white dust. Does this change suggest that the chalk is composed of an element or a compound?

25. During a very cold winter, the temperature may remain below the freezing point for extended periods. However, fallen snow can still disappear, even though it cannot melt. This is possible because a solid can vaporize directly, without passing through the liquid state. Is this process, called sublimation, a physical or a chemical change?

26. Discuss the similarities and differences between a liquid and a gas.

27. Write the correct term: In gaseous substances, the individual molecules are relatively (close/far apart) and are moving freely, rapidly, and randomly.

28. The fact that the substance copper(II) sulfate pentahydrate is bright blue is an example of a _____ property.

29. The fact that the substance copper(II) sulfate pentahydrate combines with ammonia in solution to form a new compound is an example of a _____ property.

26. Liquids and gases flow freely and take the shape of their containers. The molecules in liquids are relatively close together and interact with one another. The molecules in a gas are far apart and do not interact with one another.

27. far apart

28. physical

29. chemical

1 Which of the following is an element?

A air

B water

C salt

D helium

2 Which of the following describes a physical change?

A Cookies burn in the oven.

B A banana ripens.

C Sugar dissolves in coffee.

D Leaves turn colors in the fall.

3 Which of the following is a chemical change?

A Water condenses on a mirror.

B A nail rusts.

C A damp towel dries.

D Peanuts are crushed.

4 Consider the following substances: sodium, sugar, air, iron. How many are *pure* compounds?

A 1

B 2

C 3

D 4

5 A homogeneous mixture is also called _____.

A a heterogeneous mixture

B a pure substance

C a compound

D a solution

6 Which of the following processes requires chemical methods?

A Separating a homogeneous mixture into pure substances

B Breaking a compound into its constituent elements

C Separating a heterogeneous mixture into pure substances

D Distilling a saltwater mixture

Use the following choices to answer questions 7–10.

A

B

C

D

E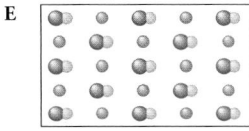

7 Which best represents a solid element?

8 Which best represents a homogeneous mixture of an element and a compound?

9 Which best represents a gaseous compound?

10 Which best represents a heterogeneous mixture of two elements?

11 List one physical property and one chemical property of wood, labeling each.

12 Explain the differences among solids, liquids, and gases both macroscopically and microscopically.

Assessment Resources
CHAPTER 2

For additional practice with standardized testing, see *Standardized Test Practice* located in the *Teacher Resources*.

Chapter 2
Standardized Test Practice

1. D
2. C
3. B
4. A
5. D
6. B
7. B
8. E
9. C
10. D

11. Physical properties of wood include: it is a solid, it floats in water (is less dense than water), and it has color (which varies depending on the type of wood). A chemical property of wood is that it burns in oxygen.

12. Macroscopically, solids have a fixed shape and volume, liquids have definite volume but take the shape of their containers, and gases have no fixed volume or shape. Microscopically, the particles that make up a solid are packed closely together and in a definite order. The particles making up a liquid are also packed rather closely together, but they are not as rigidly held together. They can "slide" over one another. The particles making up a gas are spaced farther apart and move randomly, hitting each other and the walls of the container.

Test-Taking Strategy

Decrease visual distraction by having students use blank index cards to cover the question above and below the one they are answering. Tell students to concentrate on one question at a time, but encourage students to skip a question and circle its number if they are not ready to answer it. Often, answers are triggered by subsequent questions.

Planning Guide

Section	Segment		Text Features and Components	Labs, Demonstrations, & Activities
3.1 The Elements **1 Block** pp. 50–55	A	Abundances of Elements	**SE** Chemistry Explorers: Robert Boyle *p. 50* **SE** Top Ten Elements in the Human Body *p. 51*	**TE** Mini-Demo *p. 51*
	B	Names and Symbols for the Elements	**SE** Chemistry in Your World: Trace Elements: Small but Crucial *p. 53*	**TE** Teaching Support: Demonstration *p. 54*
3.2 Atoms and Compounds **1 Block** pp. 56–59	A	Dalton's Atomic Theory	**SE** Chemistry Explorers: John Dalton *p. 57*	**LM** Experiment 11: Aluminum Atoms Lab Manual Report Sheets Teacher's Lab Guide
	B	Formulas of Compounds	**SE** Celebrity Chemical: Iron *p. 59*	**LM** Experiment 12: Electrolysis Lab Manual Report Sheets Teacher's Lab Guide
3.3 Atomic Structure **0.5 Block** pp. 60–67	A	The Structures of the Atom	**TE** Teaching Support: Historical Note *pp. 60–61* **SE** Chemistry Explorers: Ernest Rutherford *p. 61* **TE** Teaching Support: Background Information *pp. 62–63*	
	B	Introduction to the Modern Concept of Atomic Structure		**SE** Hands-On Chemistry: How Big Is an Atom? *p. 64*
	C	Isotopes		
	continued on next page			

Key   **SE** Student Edition   **TE** Teacher Edition   **RP** Teacher Resource Package

   AR Additional Materials   **LM** Lab Materials   **≣** Transparencies

   ⊙ DVD   **▮** CD-ROM   **⬚** classzone.com

All Learners	Technology	Review & Assessment	Standards
TE Teaching Tips *pp. 50–51* TE Misconception *p. 52*	Transparency: Table 3.1 EasyPlanner	SE Active Reading Questions *p. 51* SE Questions and Problems *p. 86*	TE **NSES** UCP1, UCP2, UCP5, A1, A2, B2, C6, E1, E2, F3, G1, G2, G3
TE Teaching Tips *p. 54* TE Meeting Individual Needs *p. 55* RP MINT: Reading Concepts *TE p. 52*	Transparency: Table 3.3 EasyPlanner	SE Active Reading Questions *p. 54* SE Review Questions (3.1.A–3.1.B) *p. 55* SE Key Terms *p. 84* SE Questions and Problems *p. 86*	
TE Teaching Tip *p. 56*	Lab Generator CD EasyPlanner	SE Active Reading Question *p. 57* SE Key Terms *p. 84* SE Questions and Problems *p. 86*	TE **NSES** UCP1, UCP2, UCP3, UCP5, A1, A2, B2, B3, E1, E2, G1, G2, G3
TE Teaching Tip *p. 57* TE Meeting Individual Needs *p. 58*	Lab Generator CD EasyPlanner	SE Practice Problem *p. 58* TE More Examples *p. 58* SE Review Questions (3.2.A–3.2.B) *p. 59* SE Key Terms *p. 84* SE Questions and Problems *pp. 86–87*	
TE Teaching Tips *pp. 60–62*	Transparency: Figure 3.3 Video: Cathode Ray Tube Animation: Gold Foil Experiment EasyPlanner	SE Active Reading Question *p. 60* SE Critical Thinking *p. 62* SE Active Reading Question *p. 62* SE Key Terms *p. 84* SE Questions and Problems *p. 87*	TE **NSES** UCP1, UCP2, UCP3, UCP5, A1, A2, B1, B2, E1, E2, G1, G2, G3
TE Teaching Tips *p. 63*	EasyPlanner	SE Critical Thinking *p. 63* SE Active Reading Question *p. 64* SE Questions and Problems *p. 87*	
TE Teaching Tips *p. 64* TE Misconception *p. 65* RP Team Learning Worksheet (Sec. 3.1–3.3) RP MINT: Reading Concepts *TE p. 65*	EasyPlanner	SE Active Reading Questions *p. 65* SE Practice Problem *p. 66* TE More Examples *p. 66* SE Practice Problem *p. 67* TE More Examples *p. 67* SE Review Questions (3.3.A–3.3.C) *p. 67* SE Key Terms *p. 84* SE Questions and Problems *pp. 87–88*	

Planning Guide

Section	Segment		Text Features and Components	Labs, Demonstrations, & Activities

3.4 Using the Periodic Table
 1 Block
 pp. 68–75
	A	**Introduction to the Periodic Table**		**TE** Mini-Demo *p. 70*
				 RP Classroom Activities and Projects *TE p. 68*
				 LM Experiment 13: Classifying Elements
				     Lab Manual
				     Report Sheets
				     Teacher's Lab Guide

	B	**Natural States of the Elements**		**TE** Mini-Demo *p. 74* **SE** Hands-On Chemistry: Elementary, My Dear Watson! *p. 75*

3.5 Ions and Their Compounds
 1 Block
 pp. 76–83
	A	**Ions**	**SE** Chemistry in Your World: Miracle Coatings *p. 80*	**LM** Experiment 14: Electric Solutions
				     Lab Manual
				     Report Sheets
				     Teacher's Lab Guide

	B	**Compounds That Contain Ions**		**TE** Teaching Support: Demonstration *pp. 82–83* **RP** Classroom Activities and Projects *TE p. 80*

Key	**SE** Student Edition	**TE** Teacher Edition	**RP** Teacher Resource Package
	AR Additional Materials	**LM** Lab Materials	**▤** Transparencies
	◉ DVD	**�** CD-ROM	**ⓘ** classzone.com

All Learners	Technology	Review & Assessment	Standards
(TE) Teaching Tips *p. 69* (TE) Meeting Individual Needs *p. 70*	(icon) Transparency: Figure 3.7 (icon) Transparency: Figure 3.9 (icon) Lab Generator CD (icon) EasyPlanner	(SE) Active Reading Question *p. 69* (SE) Active Reading Question *p. 70* (SE) Practice Problem *p. 71* (TE) More Examples *p. 71* (SE) Key Terms *p. 85* (SE) Questions and Problems *p. 88*	(TE) **NSES** UCP1, UCP2, UCP3, UCP5, A1, A2, B2, B3, E1, E2, G1, G2, G3
(TE) Misconception *p. 72* (TE) Teaching Tip *p. 73*	(icon) Transparency: Table 3.5 (icon) EasyPlanner	(SE) Active Reading Question *p. 75* (SE) Review Questions (3.4.A–3.4.B) *p. 75* (SE) Key Terms *p. 85* (SE) Questions and Problems *pp. 88–89*	
(TE) Teaching Tips *pp. 76, 78* (TE) Meeting Individual Needs *p. 78* (TE) Misconception *p. 77* (RP) MINT: Reading Concepts *TE p. 76*	(icon) Transparency: Figure 3.15 (icon) Lab Generator CD (icon) EasyPlanner	(SE) Active Reading Question *p. 79* (SE) Key Terms *p. 85* (SE) Questions and Problems *p. 89*	(TE) **NSES** UCP1, UCP2, UCP3, UCP5, A1, A2, B2, B3, E1, E2
(TE) Teaching Tips *p. 81* (RP) Team Learning Worksheet (Sec. 3.4–3.5)	(icon) Animation: Comparison of a Molecular Compound and an Ionic Compound (icon) Animation: Formation of Ionic Compounds (icon) EasyPlanner	(SE) Critical Thinking *p. 82* (SE) Active Reading Question *p. 82* (SE) Practice Problem *p. 83* (TE) More Examples *p. 83* (SE) Review Questions (3.5.A–3.5.B) *p. 83* (SE) Key Terms *p. 85* (SE) Questions and Problems *p. 89*	

Resource Materials for Chapter 3

(SE) Chapter Review *pp. 84–85*

(SE) Critical Thinking *p. 90*

(SE) Standardized Test Practice *p. 91*

(AR) English/Spanish Summaries

(icon) English Summaries Audio

(icon) Spanish Summaries Audio

(RP) Meeting Individual Needs Toolkit (MINT)
    Reading Concepts
    Chapter Review Worksheets
    Chapter Summaries

(RP) Solutions Guide

(RP) Standardized Test Practice

(RP) Chapter Tests

(RP) Test Bank

(icon) Test Generator

Chapter 3
Overview

In this chapter our goals are for students to:

- Learn the names and symbols for some elements
- Learn about the relative abundance of some elements
- Learn Dalton's theory of atoms
- Understand the law of constant composition
- Learn how a formula describes a compound's composition
- Understand Rutherford's experiment and its impact on atomic structure
- Describe important features of subatomic particles
- Learn about isotope, atomic number, and mass number
- Understand the use of the symbol $^{A}_{Z}X$
- Learn the various features of the periodic table
- Learn the properties of metals, nonmetals, and metalloids
- Describe the formation of ions from their parent atoms
- Predict which ion a given element forms by using the periodic table
- Describe how ions combine to form neutral compounds

Chemical Foundations: Elements, Atoms, and Ions

Molten iron is the main component of earth's core.

48

IN YOUR LIFE

The chemical elements are essential to each of us in our daily lives. The most important element is carbon, which is found in virtually all of the molecules that make up the living cell. Although certain elements are present in our bodies in tiny amounts, these elements can have profound effects on our health and behavior. As we will see in this chapter, lithium can be a miracle treatment for someone with manic-depressive disease, and our cobalt levels can have a remarkable impact on behavior. Many elements in our bodies serve no useful purpose, but they are found in the food we eat, the water we drink, and the air we breathe. As a result, the human body typically contains significant amounts of elements such as aluminum, barium, strontium, uranium, and gold, which are usually deposited in the bones or liver.

Many elements have great economic significance. For example, about one billion tons of iron and 60 million tons of aluminum are produced in the world each year and are used mainly in structural materials. Iron is also important in another way that we seldom think about. Earth's core, 4,000 miles in diameter, consists mostly of molten iron. The center of earth's core, with a diameter of about 1,500 miles, may consist of solid iron.

As we will see as we progress in our study of chemistry, most of the chemical elements have an important impact on our lives.

WHAT DO YOU KNOW?

Prereading Questions

1. What elements do you think are most abundant in the human body?

2. Do you know any chemical formulas for compounds? For example, what is the chemical formula for water? What is the chemical formula for table salt? Do you know any other formulas?

3. Have you heard the terms *electrons, protons, neutrons,* or *nucleus*? What do you know about these?

4. What does the term *periodic* mean? How do you think this applies to the term *periodic table*?

5. Name at least one element that normally exists as a solid and at least one element that normally exists as a gas.

Prereading Questions

1. *Answers will vary.*

2. Water is H_2O and table salt is NaCl. *Other answers will vary.*

3. *Answers will vary.* Electrons have a negative charge and are located outside the nucleus. Protons are positively charged and neutrons are neutral; they are located in the nucleus.

4. *Periodic* implies a repeating pattern. Elements in the same column of the periodic table have similar chemical properties.

5. *Answers will vary.* Metals, such as copper, gold, and silver, are generally solid (mercury is an exception as it is a liquid). Oxygen, hydrogen, and nitrogen are common gases.

TECHNOLOGY IN THE CLASSROOM

Transparencies
Figures: 3.3, 3.7, 3.9, 3.15
Tables: 3.1, 3.3, 3.5

Power Presentation DVD
PowerPoint Slides
Animations
Gold Foil Experiment
Comparison of a Molecular Compound and an Ionic Compound
Formation of Ionic Compounds
Video
Cathode Ray Tube
eEdition
EasyPlanner

Lab Generator CD
English Summaries CD
Spanish Summaries CD
ML Test Generator

 classzone.com

Student Preparation

Assign students to read Section 3.1 and to answer the Review Questions at the end of the section before coming to class.

 Active Learning
Team Learning Worksheet

After introducing the material in Sections 3.1 through 3.3 in class, place students in groups and have them work together on **Sections 3.1–3.3: Team Learning Worksheet.**

Homework

You may wish to assign these selected end-of-chapter problems as homework for this section: 1, 4, 5, 7, 10, 11

Additional end-of-chapter problems can be used for extra practice.

 TEACHING TIP

Relate the letters in the alphabet and the elements of various compounds. In the same way that we can make many words from 26 letters, millions of compounds can be made using only the 100 or so elements. Putting the same elements together in different ways results in different compounds with very different properties, as is the case when putting the same letters together in different ways.

The Elements

Key Term
• Element symbols

Objectives
• *To learn about the relative abundances of the elements*
• *To learn the names of some elements*
• *To learn the symbols of some elements*

The Greeks were the first to try to explain why chemical changes occur. By about 400 B.C. they had proposed that all matter was composed of four fundamental substances: fire, earth, water, and air.

The next 2000 years of chemical history were dominated by alchemy. Some alchemists were mystics and fakes who were obsessed with the idea of turning cheap metals into gold. However, many alchemists were sincere scientists and this period saw important events: the elements mercury, sulfur, and antimony were discovered, and alchemists learned how to prepare acids.

As we saw in Chapter 2, all of earth's materials (and those of other parts of the universe) can be broken down chemically into about 100 different elements. At first it might seem amazing that the millions of known substances are composed of so few fundamental elements. Fortunately for those trying to understand and systematize it, nature often uses a relatively small number of fundamental units to assemble even extremely complex materials. For example, proteins, a group of substances that serve the human body in almost uncountable ways, are all made by linking together a few fundamental units to form huge molecules. A nonchemical example is the English language, in which hundreds of thousands of words are constructed from only 26 letters. Compounds are made by combining atoms of the various elements, just as words are constructed from the 26 letters of the alphabet.

Words

bed — a, b, c, d, e, f, g, h, i — chief

fad — bag

Compounds

CO_2 — H, O, N, C — NH_3

H_2O — N_2O

CHEMISTRY EXPLORERS
Robert Boyle • 1627–1691

The first scientist to recognize the importance of careful measurements was Ireland's Robert Boyle. He is best known for his pioneering work on the properties of gases, but Boyle's most important contribution to science was probably his insistence that science should be firmly grounded in experiments. For example, Boyle held no preconceived notions about how many elements there might be. His definition of the term *element* was based on experiments: a substance was an element unless it could be broken down into two or more simpler substances. For example, air could not be an element, as the Greeks believed, because it could be broken down into many substances. As Boyle's experimental definition of an element became generally accepted, the list of known elements grew and the Greek system of four elements died.

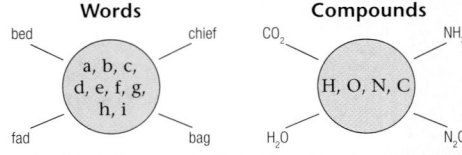

CHEMISTRY EXPLORERS
Robert Boyle

Robert Boyle, the fourteenth child of the Earl of Cork, was born at Lismore Castle, Ireland, on January 25, 1627. Boyle was a true child prodigy who began studies at Eton at age eight (he was already speaking Greek and Latin) and traveled through Europe with a tutor at age eleven. During his travels, he observed demonstrations by the German Otto von Guericke, who had developed an air pump. Guericke's favorite trick was to seal two hemispheres together and then remove the air from inside. The difference in pressure between the atmosphere and the inside of the sphere was so great that teams of horses pulling in opposite directions could not separate them. Guericke would then discreetly let the air back in and separate the hemispheres himself. Boyle was intrigued by this act and proceeded to develop an even better air pump. Using this pump, he evacuated a chamber and demonstrated that

Just as you had to learn the letters of the alphabet before you could learn to read and write, you need to learn the names and symbols of the chemical elements before you can read and write chemistry.

A. Abundances of Elements

At present, about 115 different elements are known, 88 of which occur naturally. (The rest have been made in laboratories.) The elements vary greatly in abundance. In fact, only nine elements account for most of the compounds found in earth's crust. In **Table 3.1,** the elements are listed in order of abundance (mass percent) in earth's crust, oceans, and atmosphere.

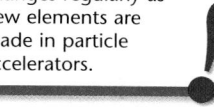
DID YOU KNOW

The number of elements changes regularly as new elements are made in particle accelerators.

Table 3.1

Distribution (Mass Percent) of the 18 Most Abundant Elements in Earth's Crust, Oceans, and Atmosphere

Element	Mass Percent	Element	Mass Percent
oxygen	49.2	titanium	0.58
silicon	25.7	chlorine	0.19
aluminum	7.50	phosphorus	0.11
iron	4.71	manganese	0.09
calcium	3.39	carbon	0.08
sodium	2.63	sulfur	0.06
potassium	2.40	barium	0.04
magnesium	1.93	nitrogen	0.03
hydrogen	0.87	fluorine	0.03
		all others	0.49

Top Ten Elements in the Human Body

Element	Mass Percent
Oxygen	65.0
Carbon	18.0
Hydrogen	10.0
Nitrogen	3.0
Calcium	1.4
Phosphorus	1.0
Magnesium	0.50
Potassium	0.34
Sulfur	0.26
Sodium	0.14

Active Reading Questions

1. **What element is nearly half of earth's crust, oceans, and atmosphere?**

2. **What percent of the mass of the crust, ocean, and atmosphere do the top nine elements make?**

Oxygen, in addition to accounting for about 20 percent of earth's atmosphere (where it occurs as O_2 molecules), is also found in virtually all rocks, sand, and soil on earth's crust. In these materials, oxygen is not present as O_2 molecules but exists in compounds that usually contain silicon and aluminum atoms.

The list of elements found in living matter is very different from that for earth's crust, as shown in the Top Ten. Oxygen, carbon, hydrogen, and nitrogen form the basis for all biologically important molecules. Some elements found in the body (called trace elements) are crucial for life, even though they are present in relatively small amounts **(Table 3.2).** For example, chromium helps the body use sugars to provide energy.

Table 3.2

Trace Elements in the Human Body

Trace Elements

arsenic
chromium
cobalt
copper
fluorine
iodine
manganese
molybdenum
nickel
selenium
silicon
vanadium

3.1 • The Elements • **51**

3.1.A Abundances of Elements

Objective To learn about the relative abundances of the elements and learn the names of some elements

TEACHING TIP

Table 3.1 and the Top Ten features from Chapters 2 and 3 provide good sources for comparisons of the different elements found in the universe, the earth, and the human body. Have students find those in common and tell which one on each list most surprised them and why. If you have samples of the various elements, now is an excellent time to show them to students.

MINI-DEMO

Bring samples of a variety of elements to class. Have students identify them and tell a use for each (if they know one). You can also bring in rocks and minerals and discuss how they are similar and different to elements. While elements and some minerals are pure substances, most minerals and rocks are mixtures. In addition, very few elements are mined as pure substances.

Active Reading Questions

1. oxygen
2. 98.33%

TECHNOLOGY

Table 3.1

(continued)

a feather and a lump of coal both fall at the same rate. He also showed that sound could not travel in a vacuum. Eventually, Boyle carried out his famous experiments in which he discovered the inverse relationship between gas volume and pressure.

In 1661, Boyle published *The Sceptical Chymist,* in which he abandoned the ancient view of the four elements and took the position that an element must be defined by

experiment. Students will learn more about Boyle's work with gases in Chapter 13.

Boyle died in London on December 30, 1691.

Students often have difficulty understanding what is meant by chemical terms such as *element*. It is important to emphasize the various ways we use the term *element* in chemistry. When we say "element," we might mean a single atom, a molecule such as N_2 or O_2, or a large sample such as a bar of aluminum or the graphite ("lead") in a pencil. Help students realize that chemists use terms in many ways and that students need to look at the context of the word to make sure that they understand what is intended. Chemists are accustomed to thinking about things at the macroscopic and microscopic levels simultaneously. Encourage students to think about what they read and to consider how the terms are being used.

3.1.B Names and Symbols for the Elements

Objective To learn the symbols of some elements

One more general comment is important at this point. As we have seen, elements are fundamental to understanding chemistry. However, students may be confused by the many different ways that chemists use the term *element* illustrated below.

Word	Meaning	
Element	**Microscopic form** Single atom of that element	
Element	**Macroscopic form** Sample of that element large enough to weigh on a balance	
Element	**Generic form** When we say the human body contains the element sodium or lithium, we do not mean that free elemental sodium or lithium is present. Rather we mean that atoms of these elements are present in some form.	

B. Names and Symbols for the Elements

The names of the chemical elements have come from many sources. Sometimes the names come from descriptions of the element's properties, sometimes the name reflects the place where the element was discovered, and sometimes the name honors a famous scientist.

Sources of Names of Chemical Elements					
Greek, Latin, or German words describing a property of the element	Latin		Greek		
	gold aurum (shining down)	*lead* plumbum (heavy)	*chlorine* color	*iodine* color	*bromine* stench
Place where the element was discovered	*americium* → America *californium* → California	*germanium* → Germany *polonium* → Poland *francium* → France			
Famous scientists	Albert Einstein *einsteinium*	Alfred Nobel *nobelium*	Marie Curie *curium*		

Using flashcards is a good way for students to learn the names and symbols for the elements. Have students read *Making and Using Flashcards* located in the *Teacher Resources*.

CHEMISTRY IN YOUR WORLD

Trace Elements: Small but Crucial

We all know that certain chemical elements, such as calcium, carbon, nitrogen, and iron, are essential for humans to live. Many other elements, present in tiny amounts, are also essential for life.

In the Body

In Our Personal Environment

Exposure to trace elements in water, food, and air also affects our health. Exposure to aluminum in baked goods and cheese as well as from cookware and utensils is of concern to scientists.

Chromium assists in the metabolism of sugars, cobalt is present in vitamin B_{12}, iodine is necessary for the proper functioning of the thyroid gland, manganese plays a role in maintaining proper calcium levels in the bones, and copper is involved in the production of red blood cells.

In Behavior

Lithium has helped some people with bipolar disorder, a disease in which a person's behavior varies between inappropriate highs and the blackest of depressions.

Studies on inmates at a prison in Illinois have shown that trace elements in the hair of prisoners is related to behaviors. There is an inverse relationship between the levels of cobalt in the hair and the degree of violence in the prisoners.

We often use abbreviations to simplify the written word. For example, it is much easier to put MA on an envelope than to write out Massachusetts, and we often write USA instead of United States of America. Likewise, chemists have invented a set of abbreviations or **element symbols** for the chemical elements. These symbols usually consist of the first letter or the first two letters of the element names. The first letter is always capitalized, and the second is not. For example,

fluorine	F	neon	Ne
oxygen	O	silicon	Si
carbon	C		

Chemistry in Your World

Trace Elements: Small but Crucial

The "Trace Elements: Small but Crucial" feature points out that human behavior has an important chemical component. Elements that are present even in tiny amounts can have a crucial impact on the ways that a body functions. You can use this feature to integrate the study of chemistry with medicine, health, and biology.

1. *Answers will vary.* Three examples are aluminum (Al), cobalt (Co), and barium (Ba).

2. *Answers will vary.* Three examples are antimony (Sb), gold (Au), and tungsten (W).

 TEACHING TIPS

• Water pipes were once made of lead. This is the origin of the word "plumber."

• The only way to learn the symbols for the elements is to memorize them. Some symbol pairs, such as Au/Ag, Na/S, K/P, and Mg/Mn, are easily confused. Have students make flashcards with the element name on one side and the symbol on the other.

• In class, make several groupings of the symbols for the elements, such as the following:

  Symbols unrelated to the name
  Elements beginning with C
  Elements with single-letter symbols
  Elements named after a place
  Elements named after a planet

  Such a system breaks the large group of elements into smaller groups that are easier to learn.

TECHNOLOGY

 Table 3.3

---

 information

In the symbol for an element, only the first letter is capitalized.

Sometimes, however, the two letters used are not the first two letters in the name. For example,

zinc	Zn	cadmium	Cd
chlorine	Cl	platinum	Pt

The symbols for some other elements are based on the original Latin or Greek name.

Current Name	Original Name	Symbol
gold	aurum	Au
lead	plumbum	Pb
sodium	natrium	Na
iron	ferrum	Fe

A list of the most common elements and their symbols is given in **Table 3.3.** You can also see the elements represented on a table in the inside back cover of this text. We will explain the form of this table (which is called the periodic table) in later chapters.

Active Reading Questions

1. Give three examples of elements whose symbols are the first two letters of the name of the element.

2. Give three examples of elements with symbols in which the first letter is not the first letter of the name of the element.

Table 3.3

The Names and Symbols of the Most Common Elements*

Element	Symbol	Element	Symbol
aluminum	Al	lithium	Li
arsenic	As	mercury (hydrargyrum)	Hg
barium	Ba	neon	Ne
boron	B	nitrogen	N
bromine	Br	oxygen	O
calcium	Ca	platinum	Pt
carbon	C	potassium (kalium)	K
chromium	Cr	silicon	Si
cobalt	Co	silver (argentium)	Ag
copper (cuprum)	Cu	sodium (natrium)	Na
gold (aurum)	Au	sulfur	S
lead (plumbum)	Pb	zinc	Zn

*Where appropriate, the original name is shown in parentheses so that you can see the sources of some of the symbols.

54 • Chapter 3 • Chemical Foundations: Elements, Atoms, and Ions

---

Teaching Support
DEMONSTRATION

Check Out This Cereal!

Materials
• Box of cereal (use one with "100% iron" or "reduced iron" on the label) (Total or Special K works well)
• Bar magnet or magnetic stirrer magnet
• Large resealable bag
• Large beaker
• Magnetic stir plate (optional)

Procedure Place about a cup of the cereal in the resealable bag. Have a student crush the cereal into small pieces. Pour the crushed cereal into the beaker and cover it with water. Stir until the cereal becomes soggy. Place the magnetic stirrer into the beaker and place the setup on the stir plate. Start stirring and continue for 15 to 20 minutes. If not using a stir plate, attach the stirrer to a pencil or paint stick and stir the mixture for about 10 minutes.

Remove the magnet from the mixture and show students the dark-colored iron filings on the magnet. You can then remove the filings to a sheet of white paper and show students that the filings are attracted to a magnet held under the paper.

SECTION 3.1
REVIEW QUESTIONS

❶ Give four different chemical meanings for the word element and an example of each.

❷ How many of the Top Ten elements in the human body are also Top Ten elements in the earth's crust, ocean, and atmosphere? What are these elements?

❸ Make a list of elements that you think were named after a place.

❹ Give the symbol for each of the given elements.
   a. Aluminum
   b. Sodium
   c. Mercury
   d. Helium
   e. Oxygen
   f. Potassium

❺ Give the name for each of the given symbols.
   a. Ca
   b. P
   c. S
   d. Si
   e. Mg
   f. C

❻ The graph below shows the mass percentages of the five most abundant elements in the human body. Use this graph to answer the following questions.

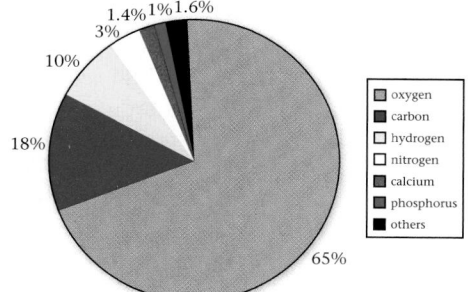

Legend:
- oxygen
- carbon
- hydrogen
- nitrogen
- calcium
- phosphorus
- others

1.4% 1% 1.6%
3%
10%
18%
65%

a. What is the fourth most abundant element by mass in the human body?

b. Which element is almost twice as abundant by mass as hydrogen in the human body?

c. What percentage of the human body is *not* made up of oxygen, carbon, or hydrogen?

RESEARCH LINKS
CLASSZONE.COM

The sand in these dunes at Death Valley National Monument is composed of silicon and oxygen atoms.

SECTION 3.1
Review Questions

1. 1. a single atom; an atom of aluminum
   2. a sample of measurable size; 5.0 g of potassium
   3. a molecule of an element; a molecule of oxygen
   4. one of the building blocks of the universe; helium

2. Six: oxygen, hydrogen, calcium, magnesium, potassium, sodium

3. The list could include berkelium, californium, dubnium, europium, francium, germanium, americium, neptunium, plutonium, polonium, and uranium.

4. a. Al
   b. Na
   c. Hg
   d. He
   e. O
   f. K

5. a. calcium
   b. phosphorus
   c. sulfur
   d. silicon
   e. magnesium
   f. carbon

6. a. nitrogen
   b. carbon
   c. 7%

Meeting Individual Needs
ENGLISH LANGUAGE LEARNERS

Explain that everyone in the world uses the same chemical symbols and that these symbols are simply a shorthand way of representing the elements. To emphasize the importance of the symbols, ask students to share some slang or abbreviations native to their first language. Then compare these to slang or abbreviations used in the English language. Point out how confusing abbreviations can be if you do not understand the language. Discuss the benefits of having a "universal chemistry language" and then have students discuss situations that could occur if scientists around the world did not communicate using the same chemical language.

SECTION 3.2
INTRODUCE

Student Preparation

Assign students to read Section 3.2 and to answer the Review Questions at the end of the section before coming to class.

SECTION 3.2
GUIDE THE LEARNING

Homework

You may wish to assign these selected end-of-chapter problems as homework for this section: 12, 13, 14, 15, 16

Additional end-of-chapter problems can be used for extra practice.

3.2.A Dalton's Atomic Theory

Objective To learn about Dalton's theory of atoms and understand the law of constant composition

 LABORATORY
EXPERIMENT 11:
Aluminum Atoms, Traditional

TEACHING TIP

This section provides a good opportunity to discuss scientific theories. Stress that theories are useful attempts at explanations of observations, and that a theory can change over time. For example, we still accept much of Dalton's atomic theory, although the discovery of isotopes leads us to believe that all atoms of a given element are not identical.

Atoms and Compounds

Key Terms

- Law of constant composition
- Dalton's atomic theory
- Atoms
- Compound
- Chemical formula

Objectives

- *To learn about Dalton's theory of atoms*
- *To understand and illustrate the Law of constant composition*
- *To learn how a formula describes a compound's composition*

A. Dalton's Atomic Theory

As scientists of the eighteenth century studied the nature of materials, several things became clear:

1. Most natural materials are mixtures of pure substances.
2. Pure substances are either elements or combinations of elements called compounds.
3. A given compound always contains the same proportions (by mass) of the elements. For example, water *always* contains 8 g of oxygen for every 1 g of hydrogen, and carbon dioxide *always* contains 2.7 g of oxygen for every 1 g of carbon. This principle became known as the **law of constant composition**. It means that a given compound always has the same composition, regardless of where it comes from.

Law of constant composition
A given compound always contains elements in exactly the same proportion by mass.

John Dalton, an English scientist and teacher, was aware of these observations. In the early 1800s, he offered an explanation for them that became known as **Dalton's atomic theory**. The main ideas of this theory (model) can be stated as follows:

Dalton's Atomic Theory

1. Elements are made of tiny particles called **atoms**.
2. All atoms of a given element are identical.
3. The atoms of a given element are different from those of any other element.
4. Atoms of one element can combine with atoms of other elements to form compounds. A given compound always has the same relative numbers and types of atoms.
5. Atoms are indivisible in chemical processes. That is, atoms are not created or destroyed in chemical reactions. A chemical reaction simply changes the way the atoms are grouped together.

Dalton's model successfully explained important observations such as the law of constant composition. This law makes sense because if a compound always contains the same relative numbers of atoms, it will always contain the same proportions by mass of the various elements.

CHEMISTRY EXPLORERS
John Dalton • 1766–1844

Dalton was an English scientist who made his living as a teacher in Manchester. Although Dalton is best known for his atomic theory, he made contributions in many other areas, including meteorology (he recorded daily weather conditions for 46 years, producing a total of 200,000 data entries). A rather shy man, Dalton was colorblind to red (a special handicap for a chemist) and suffered from lead poisoning contracted from drinking substances that had been drawn through lead pipes.

Like most new ideas, Dalton's model was not accepted immediately. However, Dalton was convinced that he was right and *used his model to predict* how a given pair of elements might combine to form more than one compound. Dalton pictured compounds as collections of atoms. For example, nitrogen and oxygen might form a compound containing one atom of nitrogen and one atom of oxygen (written NO), a compound containing two atoms of nitrogen and one atom of oxygen (written N_2O), or a compound containing one atom of nitrogen and two atoms of oxygen (written NO_2).

NO

NO_2

N_2O

When the existence of these substances was verified, it was a triumph for Dalton's model. Because Dalton was able to predict correctly the formation of multiple compounds between two elements, his atomic theory became widely accepted.

🔖 Active Reading Question

How does Dalton's model explain the law of constant composition?

B. Formulas of Compounds

A **compound** is a distinct substance that is composed of the atoms of two or more elements and always contains exactly the same relative masses of those elements. In light of Dalton's atomic theory, this statement simply means that a compound always contains the same relative numbers of atoms of each element. For example, water always contains two hydrogen atoms for each oxygen atom.

The types of atoms and the number of each type in each unit (molecule) of a given compound are conveniently expressed by a **chemical formula**.

> In a chemical formula, the atoms are indicated by the element symbols and the number of each type of atom is indicated by a subscript, a number that appears to the right of and below the symbol for the element.

The formula for water is written H_2O, indicating that each molecule of water contains two atoms of hydrogen and one atom of oxygen

READING TIP 🔖

Here, *relative* refers to ratios.

Compound
A substance made of two or more different elements joined together in a specific way

---

🔖 Active Reading Question

If a compound always contains the same relative numbers of atoms, it will always contain the same proportions by mass of the various elements.

3.2.B Formulas of Compounds

Objective To learn how a formula describes a compound's composition

🔬 LABORATORY
EXPERIMENT 12:
Electrolysis, Traditional

🍎 TEACHING TIP

Relate the formulas of simple compounds to drawings of the molecules. Write a formula on the board and have students draw a representation of it. Focus on the number and kind of atoms in the molecule; don't worry about shape at this time. Ideas for some interactive examples are H_2O, NH_3, CO_2, and CH_4.

CHEMISTRY EXPLORERS
John Dalton

John Dalton The son of a poor English weaver, Dalton showed an unusual talent for mathematical science at an early age. In fact, he started a school in his village when he was 12 years old. Dalton's consuming interest as a boy was the study of the atmosphere, and he kept meticulous records of the weather for most of his life. Dalton never married, and his only form of relaxation was bowling, which

he did every Thursday afternoon. Dalton was a tall, gaunt fellow who was not an effective public speaker. He was unsuccessful as a lecturer and made his living mainly as a private tutor.

EXAMPLE 3.1

More Examples

Write the formula for each of the following compounds, listing the elements in the order given:

1. A molecule containing six carbon atoms and six hydrogen atoms

    C_6H_6

2. A compound containing half as many calcium atoms as chlorine atoms

    $CaCl_2$

3. A compound containing equal numbers of sodium and nitrogen atoms, but three times as many oxygen atoms as there are sodium atoms

    $NaNO_3$

 Answer to Practice Problem 3.1

a. P_4O_{10}

b. UF_6

c. $AlCl_3$

(the subscript 1 is always understood and not written). Following are some general rules for writing formulas:

Tools for Writing Formulas

1. Each atom present is represented by its element symbol.

2. The number of each type of atom is indicated by a subscript written to the right of the element symbol.

3. When only one atom of a given type is present, the subscript 1 is not written.

EXAMPLE 3.1

Writing Formulas of Compounds

Write the formula for each of the following compounds, listing the elements in the order given.

   a. Each molecule of a compound that has been implicated in the formation of acid rain contains one atom of sulfur and three atoms of oxygen.

   b. Each molecule of a certain compound contains two atoms of nitrogen and five atoms of oxygen.

   c. Each molecule of glucose, a type of sugar, contains six atoms of carbon, twelve atoms of hydrogen, and six atoms of oxygen.

Solution

a. Symbol for sulfur ⎯⎯ ⎯⎯ Symbol for oxygen

$$SO_3$$

One atom of sulfur ↑ ↑ Three atoms of oxygen

b. Symbol for nitrogen ⎯⎯ ⎯⎯ Symbol for oxygen

$$N_2O_5$$

Two atoms of nitrogen ↑ ↑ Five atoms of oxygen

c.

Symbol for carbon ⎯⎯ Symbol for hydrogen ↓ ↓ ↓ ⎯⎯ Symbol for oxygen

$$C_6H_{12}O_6$$

Six atoms of carbon ↑ ↑ ↑ Six atoms of oxygen
Twelve atoms of hydrogen

Practice Problem • Exercise 3.1

Write the formula for each of the following compounds, listing the elements in the order given.

   a. A molecule contains four phosphorus atoms and ten oxygen atoms.

   b. A molecule contains one uranium atom and six fluorine atoms.

   c. A compound contains one aluminum atom for every three chlorine atoms.

58 • Chapter 3 • Chemical Foundations: Elements, Atoms, and Ions

---

Meeting Individual Needs
READING STRATEGIES

Explain that a chemical formula is a simplified way to write a chemical compound. As compounds become more difficult to pronounce, students will appreciate this shorthand notation. Sometimes the readability of a passage becomes difficult when chemical notation is used. Help students make this transition by having them read aloud formulas as they

occur in the text. For instance, in Example 3.1, point out that the accepted way to read the compound SO_3 is "S–O–three," and N_2O_5 is "N–two–O–five."

CELEBRITY CHEMICAL   Iron (Fe)

Iron is a very important element that lies at the very heart of the earth. In fact, molten iron is thought to be the main component of the earth's core. Iron is also the fourth most abundant element in the earth's crust, found mainly in compounds with oxygen.

The earliest evidence of human use of iron dates back to about 4000 B.C. and takes the form of iron beads that are thought to have come from meteors striking the earth. The first humans to obtain iron from the ores found in the earth's crust were the Hittite peoples of Asia Minor in the third millennium B.C. The way in which the Hittites made iron weapons was one of the great military secrets of the ancient world. The process became widely known only after the fall of the Hittites around 1200 B.C., leading to the "Iron Age."

Of course, the major importance of iron in the modern world relates to its presence in steel. Steel is an alloy composed mainly of iron mixed with

carbon and other metals. The principal structural material of our civilization, the annual production of steel amounts to nearly a billion tons.

Although iron is extremely important as a construction material, it is even more important to chemistry in the human body. Without the iron compounds in our systems, we would die immediately. Iron compounds in the blood absorb oxygen from the air and transport it to the tissues, where it is stored by other iron compounds. Still more iron compounds assist oxygen in reacting with the fuel from our food to provide us with the energy to live, work, and play. Iron is truly essential to our lives.

Two iron age axes found in Spain

SECTION 3.2
REVIEW QUESTIONS

❶ What observations led Dalton to propose his model for the atom?

❷ What are the main ideas of Dalton's atomic theory?

❸ How was Dalton able to predict the formation of multiple compounds between the elements?

❹ Did Dalton's model of the atom include protons, neutrons, and electrons inside the atoms? Explain.

❺ What information is given in a chemical formula?

❻ Write the formula for each of the following substances, listing the elements in the order given.

  a. A molecule containing two hydrogen atoms, one sulfur atom, and four oxygen atoms

  b.   List the hydrogen first.

  c. A molecule containing one carbon atom and four hydrogen atoms

  d.   List the carbon first.

  e. A molecule containing one sulfur atom and five fluorine atoms

  f.

RESEARCH LINKS
CLASSZONE.COM

3.2 • Atoms and Compounds • **59**

SECTION 3.2
Review Questions

1. The observations that led Dalton to propose his atomic theory are:

   • Most natural materials are mixtures of pure substances.

   • Pure compounds are either elements or compounds.

   • A given compound always contains the same proportions (by mass) of the elements.

2. The main ideas of Dalton's atomic theory are listed on p. 56.

3. Since Dalton thought of compounds as combinations of atoms of one element with atoms of another element, he predicted that compounds could be made of different amounts of the same elements. Examples include CO and CO_2.

4. Dalton's model of the atom did not include protons, neutrons, or electrons because they were not known at the time he developed his theory.

5. A chemical formula tells us the types of atoms and the number of each atom in each unit (molecule) of a given compound.

6. a. H_2SO_4

   b. H_2O_2

   c. CH_4

   d. CO

   e. SF_5

   f. O_3

CELEBRITY CHEMICAL

Iron (Fe)

Iron is an essential element in the body. Every molecule of hemoglobin contains four ions of iron. Hemoglobin is the component of blood that carries oxygen from the lungs to the tissues of the body. Iron deficiency in the diet causes a person to be fatigued, have a lower resistance to disease, and experience increased heart rate and respiration.

Healthy adults need about 18 mg of iron daily. Iron is found in greatest concentrations in foods such as liver and kidneys. As most students are not fans of these items, they may relate better to high-iron foods such as egg yolks, some vegetables, and shellfish. Humans cannot absorb metallic iron directly. However, metallic iron reacts with the hydrochloric acid in the stomach to produce Fe^{2+} and Fe^{3+}, which can be absorbed by the small intestine and used by the body.

Cereals sometimes have iron added as a food supplement. The demonstration in Section 3.1 graphically shows the iron in cereal, which students find amazing. This iron is metallic iron. In the past, iron deficiency in children was often treated by cooking their meals in an iron skillet. Enough iron reacts with the food being prepared to increase the child's supply of usable iron.

SECTION 3.3
INTRODUCE

Student Preparation

Assign students to read Section 3.3 and to answer the Review Questions at the end of the section before coming to class.

SECTION 3.3
GUIDE THE LEARNING

Homework

You may wish to assign these selected end-of-chapter problems as homework for this section: 17, 20, 21, 24, 25, 28, 29, 30

Additional end-of-chapter problems can be used for extra practice.

3.3.A The Structure of the Atom

Objective To learn about the internal parts of an atom and understand how Rutherford's experiment helps to characterize atomic structure

 TEACHING TIP

This section provides an excellent opportunity to discuss how models change over time when new observations are made. Review the scientific method and how it applies to changing theories.

 Active Reading Question

What causes atoms to "stick together" to form compounds? What is an atom like?

TECHNOLOGY

 Video
Cathode Ray Tube
The cathode ray tube can be used to show how the beam of particles (electrons) can be deflected by a magnet.

SECTION 3.3
Atomic Structure

Key Terms

- Electrons
- Nuclear atom
- Nucleus
- Proton
- Neutron
- Isotopes
- Atomic number
- Mass number

Objectives

- *To learn about the internal parts of an atom*
- *To understand Rutherford's experiment*
- *To describe some important features of subatomic particles*
- *To learn about the terms isotope, atomic number, and mass number*
- *To understand the use of the symbol $_Z^A X$ to describe a given atom*

A. The Structure of the Atom

Dalton's atomic theory, proposed in the early 1800s, provided such a convincing explanation for the composition of compounds that it became generally accepted. Scientists came to believe that *elements consist of atoms and that compounds are a specific collection of atoms* bound together in some way. As does any new theory, Dalton's model of the atom spawned many new questions, including "What causes atoms to 'stick together' to form compounds?" and "What is an atom like?" An atom might be a tiny ball of matter that is the same throughout with no internal structure—like a ball bearing. Or the atom might be composed of parts—it might be made up of a number of subatomic particles. However, if the atom contains parts, there should be some way to break up the atom into its components.

Many scientists pondered the nature of the atom during the 1800s, but it was not until almost 1900 that convincing evidence became available to show that the atom has a number of different parts.

Active Reading Question

What are some questions that Dalton's model of the atom does not answer?

Thomson's Experiment

In the late 1890s, a British physicist named J. J. Thomson used a cathode ray tube (see **Figure 3.1**) to show that the atoms of any element can be made to emit tiny negative particles. (He knew they had a negative charge because he could show that they were repelled by the negative part of an electric field.) Thus he concluded that all types of atoms must contain these negative particles, which are now called **electrons**.

On the basis of his results, Thomson wondered what an atom must be like. Although atoms contain these tiny negative particles, he also knew that whole atoms are not negatively *or* positively charged. He concluded that the atom must also contain positive particles that balance exactly the negative charge carried by the electrons, giving the atom a zero overall charge.

Electron
A negatively charged subatomic particle

Figure 3.1
Schematic of a cathode ray tube. A stream of electrons passes between the electrodes. The fast-moving particles excite the gas in the tube, causing a glow between the plates.

Source of electrical potential

Stream of negative particles (electrons)

Metal plate

Gas-filled glass tube

Metal plate

(−) (+)

Teaching Support
HISTORICAL NOTE

John Joseph (J. J.) Thomson headed the Cavendish Laboratory in Cambridge, England, in 1884 at only 28 years old. He had a gift for designing experiments, but was not mechanically inclined and needed help to build the apparatus used in his experiments. In the 1890s, a common way to study electricity was to build a glass tube with metal electrodes in each end, one of

which was coated with zinc sulfide. When the air was pumped out of the tube, called a **cathode ray tube,** and a battery was hooked to wires connected to the electrodes, a bright, glowing spot was observed in the zinc sulfide. After 10 years, Thomson finally concluded that it must be due to a stream of negative particles that he called corpuscles of electricity—we now call them electrons.

By the time of this discovery in 1897, the Cavendish had become the most distinguished laboratory in England (and

CHEMISTRY EXPLORERS
Ernest Rutherford • 1871–1937

Rutherford was born on a farm in New Zealand. In 1895 he placed second in a scholarship competition to attend Cambridge University, but he was awarded the scholarship when the winner decided to stay home and get married. Rutherford was an intense, hard-driving person who became a master at designing just the right experiment to test a given idea. He was awarded the Nobel Prize in chemistry in 1908.

- Most of your students will not relate to a plum pudding model for the atom. Make a similar analogy using a chocolate chip cookie, with the dough being the uniform positive charge and the scattered chips representing the electrons needed to counterbalance the positive charge.

- Ernest Marsden, Rutherford's undergraduate student, is often credited with discovering the evidence that led Rutherford to decide that particles were being reflected from the nucleus of the gold atoms. Use this opportunity to talk with students about how they might also be involved in research as an undergraduate, and that some discoveries are made by people who have not yet completed their formal education.

The Plum Pudding Model

Given J. J. Thomson's results, it was natural to wonder what the atom might look like. J. J. Thomson and William Thomson (better known as Lord Kelvin, and no relation to J. J.) are credited with proposing that the atom might be something like plum pudding (a pudding with raisins randomly distributed throughout). They reasoned that the atom might be thought of as a uniform "pudding" of positive charge with enough negative electrons scattered within to counterbalance that positive charge (see **Figure 3.2**). Thus the plum pudding model of the atom came into being.

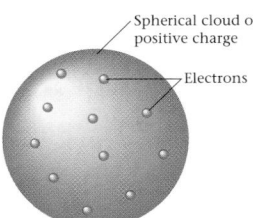

Spherical cloud of positive charge

Electrons

Figure 3.2
One of the early models of the atom was the plum pudding model, in which the electrons were pictured as embedded in a positively charged spherical cloud, much as raisins are distributed in an old-fashioned plum pudding.

Rutherford's Experiment

If you had taken this course in 1910, the plum pudding model would have been the only picture of the atom described. However, our ideas about the atom were changed dramatically in 1911 by a physicist named Ernest Rutherford, who learned physics in J. J. Thomson's laboratory in the late 1890s. By 1911 Rutherford had become a distinguished scientist with many important discoveries to his credit. One of his main areas of interest involved alpha particles (α particles), positively charged particles with a mass approximately 7500 times that of an electron. In studying the flight of these particles through air, Rutherford found that some of the α particles were deflected by something in the air. Puzzled by this observation, he designed an experiment that involved directing α particles toward a thin metal foil. Surrounding the foil was a detector coated with a substance that produced tiny flashes wherever it was hit by an α particle (see **Figure 3.3**). The results of the experiment were very different from those Rutherford anticipated. Although most of the α particles passed straight through the foil, some of them were deflected at large angles, as shown in Figure 3.3, and some were reflected backward.

This outcome was a great surprise to Rutherford. (He described this result as comparable to shooting a gun at a piece of paper and having the bullet bounce back.) Rutherford knew that if the plum pudding model of the atom were correct, the massive α particles would crash through the thin foil like cannonballs through paper (as shown in **Figure 3.4a**). So he expected the α particles to travel through the foil experiencing, at most, very minor deflections of their paths.

TECHNOLOGY

Animation
Gold Foil Experiment

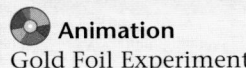

DID YOU KNOW

If the atom were expanded to the size of a huge domed stadium, the nucleus would be only about as big as a fly at the center of the stadium.

(continued)
had acknowledged the growing women's rights movement by allowing women to enter the laboratory). Despite the prominence of Thomson and his laboratory, the suggestion that these negative particles came from inside atoms was not received with enthusiasm by the scientific community. Many physicists did not even believe in the existence of atoms.

CHEMISTRY EXPLORERS
Ernest Rutherford

Rutherford's Nobel Prize in Chemistry was for "his investigations into the disintegration of the elements, and the chemistry of radioactive substances." One could argue that Rutherford was the first successful alchemist because he converted nitrogen to oxygen in 1919 (the nitrogen "disintegrated" upon impact with high-energy alpha particles). He was the first to notice the constant rate of decay of radioactive nuclei, leading to the application of carbon dating, which will be discussed in Chapter 19.

CRITICAL
THINKING

Dalton claimed that atoms are indestructible. Although Dalton never gave a microscopic description of the atom, it is safe to say that "Daltonian atoms" can be described as solid bits of matter. If Dalton's model were correct, Rutherford would have expected most or all of the alpha particles (which would be light relative to the massive gold atoms) to bounce off the gold foil.

In Thomson's model, most of the volume of the atom consists of a positive cloud. Electrons, which have much lower mass than the alpha particles, are embedded in this cloud. Because of this, Rutherford thought that all of the alpha particles would pass through the gold foil. He was quite surprised when some of the alpha particles were actually reflected.

 Active Reading Question

When relatively heavy (compared to electrons), positively charged particles were directed to a thin piece of gold foil, some particles were deflected and some were reflected backward, though most passed straight through. Because most passed through, the atom must be mostly empty space. The deflected particles prove the existence of a small, heavy, positively charged mass in the atom.

 TEACHING TIP

Organize Rutherford's observations and conclusions into a table to help students appreciate the importance of the experiment.

CRITICAL
THINKING ?

You have learned about three different models of the atom: Dalton's model, Thomson's model, and Rutherford's model.

What if Dalton had been correct? What would Rutherford have expected from his experiments with gold foil?

What if Thomson had been correct? What would Rutherford have expected from his experiments with gold foil?

Nuclear atom
A modern concept of the atom as having a dense center of positive charge (the nucleus) surrounded by moving electrons

Nucleus
The relatively small, dense center of positive charge in an atom

Proton
A positively charged subatomic particle located in the atomic nucleus

---

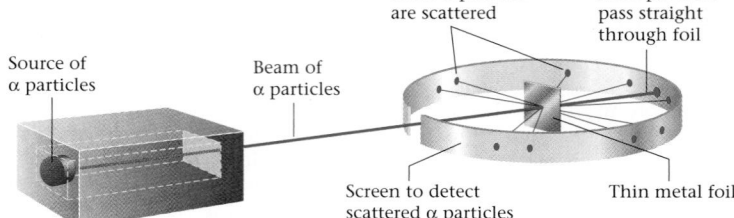

Figure 3.3
Rutherford's experiment on α particle bombardment of metal foil

From these results, Rutherford concluded that the plum pudding model for the atom could not be correct. The large deflections of the α particles could be caused only by a center of concentrated positive charge that would repel the positively charged α particles, as illustrated in **Figure 3.4b.** Most of the α particles passed directly through the foil because the atom is mostly open space. The deflected α particles were those that had a "close encounter" with the positive center of the atom, and the few reflected α particles were those that scored a "direct hit" on the positive center.

The Nuclear Atom In Rutherford's mind, these results could be explained only in terms of a **nuclear atom**—an atom with a dense center of positive charge (the **nucleus**) around which tiny electrons moved in a space that was otherwise empty.

 Active Reading Question

How does Rutherford's experiment support the existence of a positively charged, dense nucleus?

Rutherford concluded that the nucleus must have a positive charge to balance the negative charge of the electrons and that the nucleus must be small and dense. What was it made of? By 1919 Rutherford had concluded that the nucleus of an atom contained what he called protons. A **proton** has the same magnitude (size) of charge as the electron, but its charge is *positive*. We say that the proton has a charge of $1+$ and that the electron has a charge of $1-$.

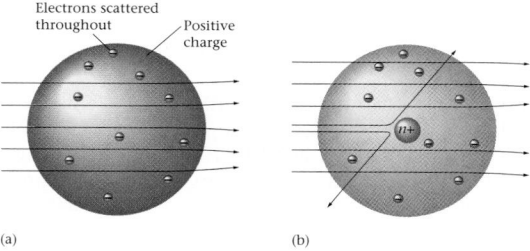

Figure 3.4
(a) The results that the metal foil experiment would have yielded if the plum pudding model had been correct (b) Actual results

62 • Chapter 3 • Chemical Foundations: Elements, Atoms, and Ions

---

Teaching Support
BACKGROUND INFORMATION

Radioactivity was discovered accidentally by Antoine Henri Becquerel in 1896, when he stored a piece of potassium uranyl sulfate in a drawer with some photographic plates and found that the rock emitted radiation that exposed the plates. Although Becquerel was awarded a Nobel Prize for his discovery (in 1903), he didn't understand the composition of the radiation in 1896. The first clue to the nature of radioactivity came in 1897, when J. J. Thomson discovered the corpuscles of electricity, now called electrons. The first person to study radioactivity in a systematic way, however, was Ernest Rutherford. In his studies at the Cavendish Laboratory, Rutherford learned that radioactive materials spewed out huge numbers of particles that traveled at thousands of miles per second. Rutherford found two distinct types of particles, which he named alpha and beta rays (now called particles). He found that

Rutherford reasoned that the hydrogen atom has a single proton at its center and one electron moving through space at a relatively large distance from the proton (the hydrogen nucleus). He also reasoned that other atoms must have nuclei (the plural of *nucleus*) composed of many protons bound together in some way. In addition, in 1932 Rutherford and a coworker, James Chadwick, were able to show that most nuclei also contain a neutral particle that they named the **neutron**. A neutron is slightly more massive than a proton but has no charge.

B. Introduction to the Modern Concept of Atomic Structure

Since the time of Thomson and Rutherford, a great deal has been learned about atomic structure. The simplest view of the atom is that it consists of a tiny nucleus (about 10^{-13} cm in diameter) and electrons that move about the nucleus at an average distance of about 10^{-8} cm from it (see **Figure 3.5**). To visualize how small the nucleus is compared with the size of the atom, consider that if the nucleus were the size of a grape, the electrons would be about one *mile* away on average.

Nucleus

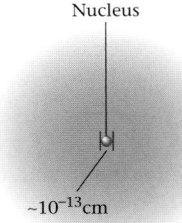

~10^{-13}cm

|—————— ~10^{-8}cm ——————|

Figure 3.5
A nuclear atom viewed in cross section. (The symbol ~ means approximately.) This drawing does not show the actual scale. The nucleus is actually much smaller than the atom itself.

The nucleus contains protons, which have a positive charge equal in magnitude to the electrons' negative charge, and neutrons, which have almost the same mass as protons but no charge. The neutrons' function in the nucleus is not obvious. They may help hold the protons (which repel each other) together to form the nucleus, but we will not be concerned with that here. The relative masses and charges of the electron, proton, and neutron are shown in **Table 3.4.**

An important question arises at this point: *If all atoms are composed of these same components, why do different atoms have different chemical properties?* The answer lies in the number and arrangement of the electrons. The space in which the electrons move accounts for most of the atomic volume. The electrons are the parts of atoms that "intermingle" when atoms combine to form molecules.

Neutron
A subatomic particle with no charge located in the atomic nucleus

CRITICAL THINKING

The average diameter of an atom is 1.3×10^{-10} m.

What if the average diameter of an atom were 1 cm? How tall would you be?

Table 3.4

The Mass and Charge of the Electron, Proton, and Neutron

Particle	Relative Mass*	Relative Charge
electron	1	1−
proton	1836	1+
neutron	1839	none

*The electron is arbitrarily assigned a mass of 1 for comparison.

information

The *chemistry* of an atom arises from its electrons.

3.3 • Atomic Structure • **63**

3.3.B Introduction to the Modern Concept of Atomic Structure
Objective To describe some important features of subatomic particles

 TEACHING TIPS

- Emphasize the tiny size of the nucleus compared to the atom. One example is given in the text: If the nucleus were the size of a grape, the radius of the atom would be about one mile.

- Remind students that questioning theories is what science is all about. Theories are always questioned to refine and improve them or to cause them to be refuted.

CRITICAL THINKING

Assume you are 6 feet tall (1.83 m). If atoms are simply stacked on top of each other, there would be approximately 1.4×10^{10} atoms [$1.83/(1.3 \times 10^{-10})$] from your head to your toes. If each atom were 1 cm, you would be 1.4×10^{10} cm tall, which is approximately 460 million feet tall.

(continued)

while alpha particles were stopped by a sheet of paper, beta particles were highly penetrating. (In 1900, Becquerel showed that beta particles were actually high-speed electrons.)

In 1898, Rutherford moved to McGill University in Canada where he continued his life's work—the study of alpha particles. After four years of work, Rutherford concluded that alpha particles are helium nuclei. One curious fact that Rutherford learned about alpha particles is that they don't travel in a straight line through air, because they are deflected by the oxygen and nitrogen molecules. After moving to the University of Manchester in 1907 and winning the Nobel Prize in 1908, Rutherford was determined to find out how alpha particles were deflected by matter. With the help of his assistant, Hans Geiger, and an undergraduate, Ernest Marsden, he set up an experiment in which alpha particles were directed at a thin metal foil, backed by a metal screen that gave flashes of light when struck by an alpha particle. To see the tiny flashes the scientists had to sit in the absolute dark for more than an hour before the experiment. In 1909, Marsden was able to demonstrate that one in 8000 alpha particles rebounded from the foil—and the age of the nuclear atom was born.

3.3 • Atomic Structure • **63**

The electrons are most responsible for the chemical properties of an element.

3.3.C Isotopes

Objective To learn about the terms *isotope, atomic number,* and *mass number* and to represent an atom using the symbol ${}^{A}_{Z}X$

 TEACHING TIPS

- Students learned in Section 3.3.A that the overall charge on an atom is zero. At this point, you need to emphasize that the charge is zero because the number of negatively charged electrons equals the number of positively charged protons.

- The discussion of protons leads to an excellent example of how and why models change. Dalton's model of the atom did not account for isotopes because he assumed that all atoms of an element are exactly alike. As knowledge expands, models change to accommodate the new information.

HANDS-ON CHEMISTRY • MINI-LAB •

How Big Is an Atom?

Materials
- strip of paper 11″ by 1″
- scissors

Procedure
1. Get a strip of paper 11″ by 1″.
2. Cut the paper in half. Discard one piece.
3. Repeat step 2 keeping track of the number of cuts until you can no longer cut the paper.

Results/Analysis
1. How many times could you cut the paper?
2. How many times would you need to cut the paper to have a piece of paper remaining that is the same width as an atom? (average atom diameter = 1.3×10^{-10} m)

Therefore, the number of electrons a given atom possesses greatly affects the way it can interact with other atoms. As a result, atoms of different elements, which have different numbers of electrons, show different chemical behavior.

Although the atoms of different elements also differ in their numbers of protons, it is the number of electrons that really determines chemical behavior. We will discuss how this happens in later chapters.

 Active Reading Question

Which of the subatomic particles are most responsible for the chemical properties of an element?

information

All atoms of the same element have the same number of protons (the element's atomic number) and the same number of electrons.

In a free atom, the positive and negative charges always balance to yield a net zero charge.

C. Isotopes

We have seen that an atom has a nucleus with a positive charge due to its protons and has electrons in the space surrounding the nucleus at relatively large distances from it.

As an example, consider a sodium atom, which has 11 protons in its nucleus. Because an atom has no overall charge, the number of electrons must equal the number of protons. Therefore, a sodium atom has 11 electrons in the space around its nucleus. It is *always* true that a sodium atom has 11 protons and 11 electrons. However, each sodium atom also has neutrons in its nucleus, and different types of sodium atoms exist that have different numbers of neutrons.

When Dalton stated his atomic theory in the early 1800s, he assumed that all of the atoms of a given element were identical. This idea persisted for over 100 years, until James Chadwick discovered that the nuclei of most atoms contain neutrons as well as protons. (This development is a good example of how a theory changes as new observations are made.) After the discovery of the neutron, Dalton's statement that all atoms of a given element are identical had to be changed to:

"All atoms of the same element contain the same number of protons and electrons, but atoms of a given element may have different numbers of neutrons."

Hands-On Chemistry
MINI-LAB

How Big Is an Atom?

Materials Each student/group will need an 11″ by 1″ piece of paper, a pair of scissors, and a calculator.

Purpose Students will better appreciate the small size of an atom. In addition, they will get practice at problem solving.

Discussion A strip of paper 11″ long is 27.94 cm or 0.2794 m. If this number is divided in half 31 times, you get 1.3×10^{-10}.

A more systematic solution is (disregarding significant figures)

$0.2974 \text{ m}/2^{x} = 1.3 \times 10^{-10}$ m
(x = the number of times the paper needs to be cut in half)

$$0.2794 \text{ m}/1.3 \times 10^{-10} \text{ m} = 2^{x}$$
$$2.149 \times 10^{9} = 2^{x}$$
$$\log(2.149 \times 10^{9}) = x\log 2$$
$$x = \log(2.149 \times 10^{9})/\log 2 = 31$$

Instead of measuring the paper, students can fold the paper in half to see where to cut it. After cutting the paper about six times, it is hard to fold in half. After seven times, it is hard to cut. Most students will find that eight or nine is the maximum number of cuts they can make. While 31 may seem like a small number of cuts to reach atomic size, this means that students would have to cut that paper more than 20 more times to reach the size of an average atom.

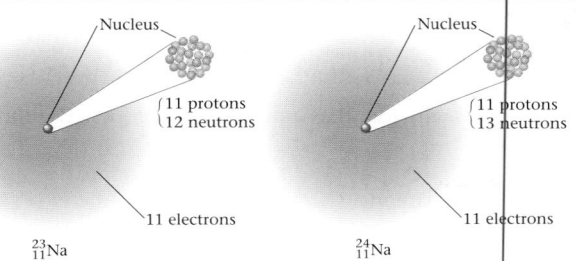

Figure 3.6
Two isotopes of sodium: Both have 11 protons and 11 electrons, but they differ in the number of neutrons in their nuclei.

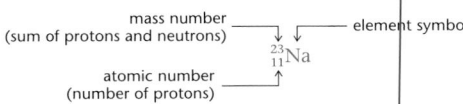

To illustrate this idea, consider the sodium atoms depicted in **Figure 3.6.** These atoms are **isotopes**, or *atoms with the same number of protons but different numbers of neutrons.* The number of protons in a nucleus is called the atom's **atomic number**. The *sum* of the number of neutrons and the number of protons in a given nucleus is called the atom's **mass number**. To specify which of the isotopes of an element we are talking about, we use the following notation:

$$\text{mass number (sum of protons and neutrons)} \searrow \quad \swarrow \text{element symbol}$$
$$^{A}_{Z}X$$
$$\text{atomic number (number of protons)} \nearrow$$

For example, the notation for one particular type of sodium atom is written

$$\text{mass number (sum of protons and neutrons)} \searrow \quad \swarrow \text{element symbol}$$
$$^{23}_{11}Na$$
$$\text{atomic number (number of protons)} \nearrow$$

The particular atom represented above is called sodium-23 because it has a mass number of 23. Let's specify the number of each type of subatomic particle in sodium-23.

- Protons = atomic number = 11
- Electrons = protons = 11
- Neutrons: We need to determine the number of neutrons as follows:

  Mass number = number of protons + number of neutrons

  $$A \quad = \quad Z \quad + \text{ number of neutrons}$$

  $$A - Z \quad = \text{ number of neutrons}$$

This is a general result. You can always determine the number of neutrons present in a given atom by subtracting the atomic number from the mass number. In this case ($^{23}_{11}Na$), we know that $A = 23$ and $Z = 11$. Therefore,

$$A - Z = 23 - 11 = 12 = \text{ number of neutrons}$$

In summary, sodium-23 has 11 electrons, 11 protons, and 12 neutrons.

Isotopes
Atoms with the same number of protons but different numbers of neutrons

Atomic number
The number of protons in the nucleus of a given atom

Mass number
The total number of protons and neutrons in the nucleus of a given atom

MATH

We can solve for the number of neutrons by using algebra, subtracting Z from both sides of the equation.
$$A - Z = Z - Z + \text{number of neutrons}$$

Active Reading Questions

1. How did the discovery of the neutron lead to the concept of isotopes?

2. How does the fact that isotopes exist change Dalton's model?

EXAMPLE 3.2

More Examples

Determine the number of each of the three types of subatomic particles for each of the following:
(**Answers assume each of the below is uncharged.**)

1. $^{60}_{27}Co$

   #protons = #electrons = 27,
   #neutrons = 33 (60 − 27)

2. $^{37}_{17}Cl$

   #protons = #electrons = 17,
   #neutrons = 20 (37 − 17)

3. $^{238}_{92}U$

   #protons = #electrons = 92,
   #neutrons = 146 (238 − 92)

 Answers to Practice Problems 3.2

1. In the symbol $^{90}_{38}Sr$, the number 38 is the atomic number, which represents the number of protons in the nucleus of a strontium atom. Because the atom is neutral overall, it must also have 38 electrons. The number 90 (the mass number) represents the number of protons plus the number of neutrons. Thus, the number of neutrons is $A − Z = 90 − 38 = 52$.

2. The atom $^{201}_{80}Hg$ has 80 protons, 80 electrons, and 201 − 80 = 121 neutrons.

EXAMPLE 3.3

More Examples

Write the symbol for each of the following atoms, and list the number of protons, neutrons, and electrons for each.
(**Answers assume each is uncharged.**)

1. The cesium atom with a mass number of 132.

   $^{132}_{55}Cs$,
   #protons = #electrons = 55,
   #neutrons = 77 (132 − 55)

2. The iron atom with a mass number of 56.

   $^{56}_{26}Fe$,
   #protons = #electrons = 26,
   #neutrons = 30 (56 − 26)

EXAMPLE 3.2

Interpreting Symbols for Isotopes

 information

Isotopes are "top heavy"; that is, the mass number is on the top and the atomic number is on the bottom. For most isotopes, the value of A is greater than the value of Z.

In nature, elements are usually found as a mixture of isotopes. The three isotopes of carbon are:

$^{12}_{6}C$ $^{13}_{6}C$ $^{14}_{6}C$
carbon-12   carbon-13   carbon-14

Determine the number of each of the three types of subatomic particles in each of these carbon atoms.

Solution

The number of protons and electrons is the same in each of the isotopes and is given by the atomic number of carbon, 6. The number of neutrons can be determined by subtracting the atomic number (Z) from the mass number:

$$A − Z = \text{number of neutrons}$$

The numbers of neutrons in the three isotopes of carbon are

$^{12}_{6}C$: number of neutrons = $A − Z = 12 − 6 = 6$
$^{13}_{6}C$: number of neutrons = $13 − 6 = 7$
$^{14}_{6}C$: number of neutrons = $14 − 6 = 8$

In summary,

Symbol	Number of Protons	Number of Electrons	Number of Neutrons
$^{12}_{6}C$	6	6	6
$^{13}_{6}C$	6	6	7
$^{14}_{6}C$	6	6	8

 Practice Problems • Exercise 3.2

1. Strontium-90 occurs in fallout from nuclear testing. It can accumulate in bone marrow and may cause leukemia and bone cancer. Give the number of protons, neutrons, and electrons in the atom symbolized by $^{90}_{38}Sr$.
2. Give the number of protons, neutrons, and electrons in the atom symbolized by $^{201}_{80}Hg$.

EXAMPLE 3.3

Writing Symbols for Isotopes

Magnesium burns in air to give a bright white flame.

Write the symbol for the magnesium atom (atomic number 12) with a mass number of 24. How many electrons and how many neutrons does this atom have?

Solution

The atomic number 12 means that the atom has 12 protons. The element magnesium is symbolized by Mg. The atom is represented as $^{24}_{12}Mg$ and is called magnesium-24. Because the atom has 12 protons, it must also have 12 electrons. The mass number gives the total number of protons and neutrons, which means that this atom has 12 neutrons (24 − 12 = 12).

EXAMPLE 3.4

Calculating Mass Number

Write the symbol for the silver atom ($Z = 47$) that has 61 neutrons.

Solution

The element symbol is $_Z^A\text{Ag}$, where we know that $Z = 47$. We can find A from its definition, $A = Z +$ number of neutrons. In this case,

$$A = 47 + 61 = 108$$

The complete symbol for this atom is $_{47}^{108}\text{Ag}$.

✓ Practice Problem • Exercise 3.4

Give the symbol for the phosphorus atom ($Z = 15$) that contains 17 neutrons.

SECTION 3.3
REVIEW QUESTIONS

① How is Thomson's model of the atom different from Dalton's model of the atom? Draw a picture of each model.

② What caused Rutherford to propose a revised model of the atom? How is the Rutherford model different from the previous models?

③ Copy and complete the following table.

Symbol	Number of protons	Number of neutrons	Number of electrons
$_{15}^{32}\text{P}$			
	29	36	
		21	18

④ Write the symbol for each of the following. Determine the number of protons, neutrons, and electrons in each atom.

  a. A sodium atom with a mass of 24

  b. A carbon atom with a mass of 13

  c. A chlorine atom with a mass of 37

⑤ Write the symbol for each of the following.

  a. The magnesium atom that has 12 neutrons

  b. The bromine atom that has 45 neutrons

  c. The hydrogen atom that has 2 neutrons

⑥ Label the parts of the atom represented below and the charge of each part.

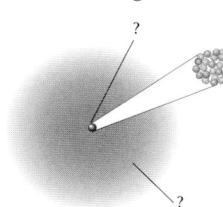

In addition, copy and complete the following table.

Atomic number of the atom	
Name of the element	
Symbol of the element	
Mass number of the atom	
Number of electrons in the atom	

⑦ In two isotopes of the same element, which of the following would be the same and which would be different?

  • atomic number

  • number of protons

  • number of neutrons

  • number of electrons

  • element symbol

RESEARCH LINKS
CLASSZONE.COM

3.3 • Atomic Structure • **67**

EXAMPLE 3.4

More Examples

Write the symbol for each of the following:

1. The krypton atom that has 48 neutrons

   $_{36}^{84}\text{Kr}$

2. The nitrogen atom that has 6 neutrons

   $_{7}^{13}\text{N}$

✓ Answer to Practice Problem 3.4

The atomic number for phosphorus is 15, and the mass number is $15 + 17 = 32$. Thus the symbol for the atom is $_{15}^{32}\text{P}$.

SECTION 3.3
ASSESS

🔍 SECTION 3.3
Review Questions

1. Thomson's model of the atom shows positive charges and negative charges uniformly distributed throughout the atoms. Neutral atoms have equal amounts of positive and negative charges. In Dalton's model, atoms are not charged and are indivisible, containing no positive or negative areas within them.

2. Rutherford proposed a revised model of the atom when he could not explain how an alpha particle could be deflected when passing through a sheet of gold foil. In Rutherford's model of the atom, the mass of the atom is concentrated in a very small area in the center of the atom known as the nucleus. The remainder of the atom is mostly empty space. In the previous models of the atom, the atom was believed to be of approximately uniform density.

3.

Symbol	# of protons	# of neutrons	# of elections
$_{15}^{32}\text{P}$	15	17	15
$_{29}^{65}\text{Cu}$	29	36	29
$_{18}^{39}\text{Ar}$	18	21	18

4. a. $_{11}^{24}\text{Na}$; 11 protons, 13 neutrons, 11 electrons

   b. $_{6}^{13}\text{C}$; 6 protons, 7 neutrons, 6 electrons

   c. $_{17}^{37}\text{Cl}$; 17 protons, 20 neutrons, 17 electrons

5. a. $_{12}^{24}\text{Mg}$

   b. $_{35}^{80}\text{Br}$

   c. $_{1}^{3}\text{H}$

6. Atomic number = 11; name = sodium; symbol = Na; mass number = 23; number of electrons = 11

7. Things that are the same in two isotopes are atomic number, number of protons, number of electrons, and element symbol. Things that are different in two isotopes are number of neutrons and mass.

Assign students to read Section 3.4 and to answer the Review Questions at the end of the section before coming to class.

 Active Learning
Team Learning Worksheet

After introducing the material in Sections 3.4 and 3.5 in class, place students in groups and have them work together on **Sections 3.4–3.5: Team Learning Worksheet.**

SECTION 3.4
GUIDE THE LEARNING

Homework

You may wish to assign these selected end-of-chapter problems as homework for this section: 32, 34, 36, 37, 39, 40, 41, 43

Additional end-of-chapter problems can be used for extra practice.

3.4.A Introduction to the Periodic Table

Objective To learn about various features of the periodic table and learn some of the properties of metals, nonmetals, and metalloids

 LABORATORY
EXPERIMENT 13:
Classifying Elements, Microscale

TECHNOLOGY

 Figure 3.7

Active Learning
Classroom Activities and Projects

For a project to help students understand the periodicity inherent in the periodic table, see *Graphing Periodic Table Properties* located in the *Teacher Resources.* Students can graph these properties now, and you can refer to the graph throughout the year.

SECTION 3.4
Using the Periodic Table

Key Terms
- Periodic table
- Groups
- Alkali metals
- Alkaline earth metals
- Halogens
- Noble gases
- Transition metals
- Metals
- Nonmetals
- Metalloids (semimetals)
- Diatomic molecules

Objectives
- *To learn the various features of the periodic table*
- *To learn some of the properties of metals, nonmetals, and metalloids*
- *To learn the natures of the common elements*

A. Introduction to the Periodic Table

In any room in which chemistry is taught or practiced, you are almost certain to find a chart called the **periodic table** hanging on the wall. This chart shows all of the known elements and gives a good deal of information about each one. As our study of chemistry progresses, the usefulness of the periodic table will become more obvious. This section will simply introduce it.

A simple version of the periodic table is shown in **Figure 3.7.** Note that each box of this table contains a number written over one or two letters.

- The letters are the symbols for the elements.
- The number shown above each symbol is the atomic number (the number of protons and also the number of electrons) for that element.

For example, carbon (C) has atomic number 6, $\boxed{\begin{smallmatrix}6\\C\end{smallmatrix}}$ and lead (Pb) has atomic number 82 $\boxed{\begin{smallmatrix}82\\Pb\end{smallmatrix}}$.

Figure 3.7
The periodic table

Meeting Individual Needs
VISUAL LEARNERS

Hand out an enlarged copy of the periodic table for students to use as part of the note-taking process. As students are introduced to trends, relationships, etc., it will be helpful for students to organize this information directly on the table. Encourage students to use colored pencils to clarify and organize information. They should refer to and update their periodic table as they progress through the course.

Notice that elements 112 through 115 have unusual three-letter designations beginning with U. These are abbreviations for the systematic names of the atomic numbers of these elements. "Regular" names for these elements will be chosen eventually by the scientific community.

> Note that the elements are listed on the periodic table in order of increasing atomic number. They are also arranged in specific horizontal rows and vertical columns.

The elements were first arranged in this way in 1869 by Dmitri Mendeleev, a Russian scientist. Mendeleev arranged the elements in this way because of similarities in the chemical properties of various "families" of elements. For example, fluorine and chlorine are reactive gases that form similar compounds.

Also, Mendeleev knew that sodium and potassium behave very similarly. Thus the name *periodic table* refers to the fact that as we increase the atomic numbers, every so often an element occurs with properties similar to those of an earlier (lower-atomic-number) element. For example, the elements shown vertically below all show similar chemical behavior and so are listed vertically, as a "family" of elements.

Families of elements with similar chemical properties that lie in the same vertical column on the periodic table are called **groups**. Groups are often referred to by the number over the column (see **Figure 3.7**). Note that the group numbers are accompanied by the letter A on the periodic table in Figure 3.7 and on the table inside the back cover of the text. For simplicity we will delete the A when we refer to groups in the text.

Many of the groups have special names (see **Figure 3.8**). For example, the first column of elements (Group 1) has the name **alkali metals**. The Group 2 elements are called the **alkaline earth metals**, the Group 7 elements are the **halogens**, and the elements in Group 8 are called the **noble gases**. A large collection of elements that spans many vertical columns consists of the **transition metals**.

9 F
17 Cl
35 Br
53 I
85 At

i n f o r m a t i o n

Another convention recommended by the International Union of Pure and Applied Chemistry for group designations uses numbers 1 through 18 and includes the transition metals. Do not confuse that system with the one used in this text, in which only the representative elements have group numbers (1 through 8).

Group
A vertical column of elements on the periodic table

Active Reading Question

How are elements in the same family on the periodic table similar?

Figure 3.8
Some groups of elements have special names.

3.4 • Using The Periodic Table • **69**

Figure 3.9

Bring samples of metals, metalloids, and nonmetals to class. Probably the simplest metalloid to bring to class is a piece of silicon. It looks very much like a metal but it is brittle.

Use the samples to illustrate the properties of each group. You might have students classify each item and justify their classifications through the properties.

 Active Reading Question

The periodic table shows which elements are metals, which are nonmetals, and which are metalloids. Also, elements in the same column have similar properties.

Most of the elements are metals. Metals have the following characteristic physical properties:

Physical Properties of Metals

1. Efficient conduction of heat and electricity
2. Malleability (can be hammered into thin sheets)
3. Ductility (can be pulled into wires)
4. A lustrous (shiny) appearance

Copper is a typical metal. It is lustrous (although it tarnishes readily); it is an excellent conductor of electricity (it is widely used in electrical wires); and it is readily formed into various shapes, such as pipes for water systems. Copper is one of the transition metals—the metals shown in the center of the periodic table. Iron, aluminum, and gold are other familiar elements that have metallic properties. All of the elements shown below and to the left of the heavy "stair-step" black line in Figure 3.7 are classified as metals, except for hydrogen (see **Figure 3.9**).

Figure 3.9
The elements classified as metals and as nonmetals

Indonesian men carry chunks of elemental sulfur in baskets.

The relatively small number of elements that appear in the upper righthand corner of the periodic table (to the right of the heavy line in Figures 3.7 and 3.9) are called **nonmetals**. Nonmetals generally lack those properties that characterize metals and show much more variation in their properties than metals do. Whereas almost all metals are solids at normal temperatures, many nonmetals (such as nitrogen, oxygen, chlorine, and neon) are gaseous, and one (bromine) is a liquid. Several nonmetals (such as carbon, phosphorus, and sulfur) are also solids.

The elements that lie close to the "stair-step" line in Figure 3.7 often show a mixture of metallic and nonmetallic properties. These elements, which are called **metalloids** or **semimetals**, include silicon, germanium, arsenic, antimony, and tellurium.

As we continue our study of chemistry, we will see that the periodic table is a valuable tool for organizing knowledge and that it helps us predict the properties we expect a given element to exhibit. We will also develop a model for atomic structure that will explain why various groups of elements have similar chemical properties.

 Active Reading Question

How does the location of an element on the periodic table help you determine its properties?

70 • Chapter 3 • Chemical Foundations: Elements, Atoms, and Ions

Meeting Individual Needs
VISUAL LEARNERS

Help students organize the information in this section by having them create a two-column table with the column headings METALS and NONMETALS. As students read this section, they should complete the table with traits specific to metals and nonmetals.

EXAMPLE 3.5

Interpreting the Periodic Table

For each of the following elements, use the periodic table in the back of the book to

- give the symbol and atomic number.
- specify whether the element is a metal or a nonmetal.
- give the named family to which the element belongs (if any).
  - a. iodine   b. magnesium   c. gold   d. lithium

Solution

a. Iodine (symbol I) is element 53 (its atomic number is 53). Iodine lies to the right of the stair-step line in Figure 3.9 and so is a nonmetal. Iodine is a member of Group 7, the family of halogens.

b. Magnesium (symbol Mg) is element 12 (atomic number 12). Magnesium is a metal and is a member of the alkaline earth metal family (Group 2).

c. Gold (symbol Au) is element 79 (atomic number 79). Gold is a metal and is not a member of a named vertical family. It is classed as a transition metal.

d. Lithium (symbol Li) is element 3 (atomic number 3). Lithium is a metal in the alkali metal family (Group 1).

 Practice Problem • Exercise 3.5

Give the symbol and atomic number for each of the following elements. Also indicate whether each element is a metal or a nonmetal and whether it is a member of a named family.

a. argon   b. chlorine   c. barium   d. cesium

B. Natural States of the Elements

As we have noted, the matter around us consists mainly of mixtures. Most often these mixtures contain compounds, in which atoms from different elements are bound together. Most elements are quite reactive: their atoms tend to combine with those of other elements to form compounds quite readily. As a result, we do not often find elements in nature in pure form—uncombined with other elements. However, there are notable exceptions. The gold nuggets found at Sutter's Mill in California that launched the Gold Rush in 1849 are virtually pure elemental gold. Platinum and silver are also often found in nearly pure form.

DID YOU KNOW

A gold nugget weighing 13 lb, 7 oz, which came to be called Tom's Baby, was found by Tom Grove near Breckenridge, Colorado, on July 23, 1887.

3.4 • Using The Periodic Table • **71**

EXAMPLE 3.5

More Examples

For each of the following elements, use the periodic table to give the symbol and atomic number and to specify whether the element is a metal or nonmetal. Also give the named family to which the element belongs (if any).

1. strontium
   Sr, atomic number = 38. Strontium is a metal and a member of the alkaline earth metal family (Group 2).

2. silicon
   Si, atomic number = 14. Silicon is a metalloid and a member of Group 4.

3. xenon
   Xe, atomic number = 54. Xenon is a nonmetal and a member of the noble gas family (Group 8).

Answer to Practice Problem 3.5

Element	Symbol	Atomic Number	Metal or Non-metal	Family
Argon	Ar	18	Non-metal	Noble gases
Chlorine	Cl	17	Non-metal	Halogens
Barium	Ba	56	Metal	Alkaline earth metals
Cesium	Cs	55	Metal	Alkali metals

3.4.B Natural States of the Elements

Objective To learn the natures of the common elements

Gold, silver, and platinum are members of a class of metals called *noble metals* because they are relatively unreactive. (The term *noble* implies a class set apart.) Other elements that appear in nature in the uncombined state are the elements in Group 8: helium, neon, argon, krypton, xenon, and radon.

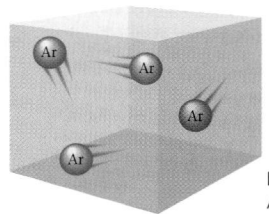

Group 8

| He |
| Ne |
| Ar |
| Kr |
| Xe |
| Rn |

> Because the atoms of these Group 8 elements do not combine readily with those of other elements, we call them the noble gases.

For example, helium gas is found in uncombined form in underground deposits with natural gas.

When we take a sample of air (the mixture of gases that constitute earth's atmosphere) and separate it into its components, we find several pure elements present. One of these is argon. Argon gas consists of a collection of separate argon atoms, as shown in **Figure 3.10.**

Figure 3.10
Argon gas consists of a collection of separate argon atoms.

Diatomic Molecules Air also contains nitrogen gas and oxygen gas. When we examine these two gases, however, we find that they do not contain single atoms, as argon does, but instead contain **diatomic molecules**: molecules made up of *two atoms,* as represented in **Figure 3.11.** In fact, any sample of elemental oxygen gas at normal temperatures contains O$_2$ molecules. Likewise, nitrogen gas contains N$_2$ molecules.

Diatomic molecule
A molecule composed of two atoms

i **nformation**

A molecule is a collection of atoms that behaves as a unit. Molecules are always electrically neutral (zero charge).

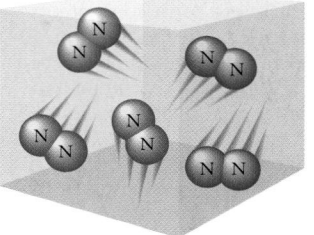

Nitrogen gas contains N$_2$ molecules.

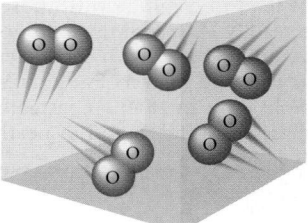

Oxygen gas contains O$_2$ molecules.

Figure 3.11
Gaseous nitrogen and oxygen contain diatomic (two-atom) molecules.

Hydrogen is another element that forms diatomic molecules. Although virtually all of the hydrogen found on earth is present in compounds with other elements (such as with oxygen in water), when hydrogen is prepared as a free element, it contains diatomic H_2 molecules. For example, an electric current can be used to decompose water into elemental hydrogen and oxygen containing H_2 and O_2 molecules, respectively.

Note that only the grouping of the atoms changes in this process; no atoms are created or destroyed. The same number of H atoms and O atoms must be present both before and after the process. For example, the decomposition of two H_2O molecules (containing four H atoms and two O atoms) yields one O_2 molecule (containing two O atoms) and two H_2 molecules (containing a total of four H atoms).

Several other elements, in addition to hydrogen, nitrogen, and oxygen, exist as diatomic molecules. For example, when sodium chloride is melted and subjected to an electric current, chlorine gas is produced (along with sodium metal). This chemical change is represented in **Figure 3.12.** Chlorine gas is a pale green gas that contains Cl_2 molecules.

Chlorine is a member of Group 7, the halogen family. All of the elemental forms of the Group 7 elements contain diatomic molecules. Fluorine is a pale yellow gas containing F_2 molecules. Bromine is a brown liquid made up of Br_2 molecules. Iodine is a lustrous, purple solid that contains I_2 molecules.

Table 3.5 lists the elements that contain diatomic molecules in their pure, elemental forms.

So far we have seen that several elements are gaseous in their elemental forms at normal temperatures (~25 °C). The noble gases (the Group 8 elements) contain individual atoms, whereas several other gaseous elements contain diatomic molecules (H_2, N_2, O_2, F_2, and Cl_2).

Only two elements are liquids in their elemental forms at 25 °C: the nonmetal bromine (containing Br_2 molecules) and the metal mercury. The metals gallium and cesium almost qualify in this category; they are solids at 25 °C, but both melt at ~30 °C.

Group 7

F
Cl
Br
I

Gallium metal has such a low melting point (30 °C) that it melts from the heat of a hand.

MATH

~ means "approximately."

Figure 3.12
(a) Sodium chloride (common table salt) can be decomposed to the elements sodium metal and chlorine gas, shown in (b).

(a)   (b)

3.4 • Using The Periodic Table • **73**

The allotropes of carbon can be illustrated using simple models. Diamond can be represented using a toothpick and gumdrop (or clay) model. Graphite can be shown using pieces of chicken wire. Buckminsterfullerene can be illustrated using a soccer ball.

Table 3.5

Elements That Exist as Diatomic Molecules in Their Elemental Forms

Element Present	Elemental State at 25 °C	Molecule
hydrogen	colorless gas	H_2
nitrogen	colorless gas	N_2
oxygen	pale blue gas	O_2
fluorine	pale yellow gas	F_2
chlorine	pale green gas	Cl_2
bromine	reddish-brown liquid	Br_2
iodine	lustrous, dark-purple solid	I_2

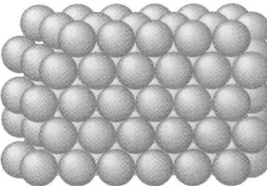

Figure 3.13
In solid metals, the spherical atoms are packed closely together.

Elemental Solids The other elements are solids in their elemental forms at 25 °C. The solid metals contain large numbers of atoms packed together much like marbles in a jar (see **Figure 3.13**).

The structures of solid nonmetallic elements are more varied than those of metals. In fact, different forms of the same element often occur. For example, solid carbon occurs in three forms. Different forms of a given element are called *allotropes*. The three allotropes of carbon are the familiar diamond and graphite forms and a form that has only recently been discovered—buckminsterfullerene. These elemental forms have very different properties because of their different structures (see **Figure 3.14**).

Diamond is the hardest natural substance known and is often used for industrial cutting tools. Diamonds are also valued as gemstones. Graphite, on the other hand, is a rather soft material useful for writing (pencil "lead" is really graphite) and (in the form of a powder) for lubricating locks.

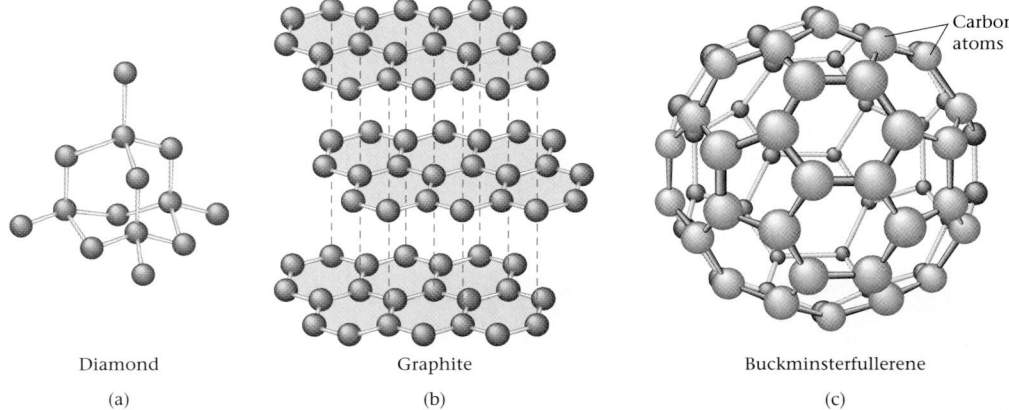

Carbon atoms

Diamond (a)   Graphite (b)   Buckminsterfullerene (c)

Figure 3.14
The three solid elemental (allotropes) forms of carbon: (a) diamond, (b) graphite, and (c) buckminsterfullerene. The representations of diamond and graphite are just fragments of much larger structures that extend in all directions from the parts shown here. Buckminsterfullerene contains C_{60} molecules, one of which is shown.

74 • Chapter 3 • Chemical Foundations: Elements, Atoms, and Ions

The rather odd name given to buckminsterfullerene comes from the structure of the C_{60} molecules of which it is composed. The soccer-ball-like structure contains five- and six-member rings reminiscent of the structure of geodesic domes suggested by the late industrial designer Buckminster Fuller. Other "fullerenes" containing molecules with more than 60 carbon atoms have also recently been discovered, leading to a new area of chemistry.

 Active Reading Question

What does the term *allotrope* mean? Provide an example.

HANDS-ON CHEMISTRY • MINI-LAB •

Elementary, My Dear Watson!

Materials
• index cards

Procedure
1. Make flashcards with the names of the elements in Groups 1–8 on one side and their symbols on the other side.
2. Group the elements according to
   a. their families on the periodic table.
   b. the similarity between their names and their symbols.
   c. the first letter of each symbol.
   d. the state of the element at 25 °C.
   e. whether the element is a metal, a nonmetal, or a metalloid.

Results/Analysis
1. Use your flashcards to learn the names and symbols for these elements.
2. Work in pairs and quiz each other with the flashcards.

SECTION 3.4
REVIEW QUESTIONS

❶ To what does the term *periodic* in *periodic table* refer?

❷ Why are the elements in vertical groups on the periodic table called "families"?

❸ What does the "stair-step" line on the periodic table tell you?

❹ What does the term *noble* mean when referring to *noble metals* and *noble gases*?

❺ Which elements exist naturally as diatomic molecules? Write their formulas.

❻ Which elements are gases at 25 °C? Write their formulas.

❼ Copy the table shown. Then use the periodic table to complete the table.

Name	Symbol	Atomic number	Metal or nonmetal?	Family to which the element belongs
Sodium				
	F			
		4		
Calcium				
		47		

❽ Which two elements are liquids at 25 °C? Write their formulas.

 RESEARCH LINKS CLASSZONE.COM

3.4 • Using The Periodic Table • **75**

Hands-On Chemistry
MINI-LAB

Elementary, My Dear Watson!

Materials Each student/group will need 44 (or more) index cards.

Purpose Students will become more familiar with the periodic table and will learn the names and symbols of some of the elements.

Discussion Although students will generally have access to a periodic table during most exams and quizzes, it is a good idea that they become familiar with the location of elements on the periodic table, some physical properties, and the names and symbols of at least the common elements. You may wish to include some of the more common transition metals in this activity (such as copper, zinc, and silver).

 Active Reading Question

Allotropes are different forms of a given element. For example, carbon can exist as graphite, diamond, or buckminsterfullerene.

SECTION 3.4
ASSESS

SECTION 3.4 Review Questions

1. The term *periodic* refers to the repeating patterns of chemical activity on the periodic table.

2. The properties of elements in vertical groups on the periodic table are similar, just like the characteristics of a particular human family are often similar.

3. The stair-step line on the periodic table marks the division between metals and nonmetals. Elements to the left of the line are metals, and those to the right are nonmetals. Directly adjacent, on either side of the line, are the metalloids.

4. The term *noble* refers to the fact that these metals and gases are relatively unreactive (inert).

5. Elements that form diatomic molecules are hydrogen, H_2; oxygen, O_2; nitrogen, N_2; fluorine, F_2; bromine, Br_2; chlorine, Cl_2; and iodine, I_2.

6. The gaseous elements are hydrogen, H_2; oxygen, O_2; nitrogen, N_2; fluorine, F_2; chlorine, Cl_2; helium, He; neon, Ne; argon, Ar; krypton, Kr; xenon, Xe; and radon, Rn.

7. Sodium, Na, 11, metal, alkali metal (group 1); Fluorine, F, 9, nonmetal, halogen (group 7); Beryllium, Be, 4, metal, alkaline earth metal (group 2); Calcium, Ca, 20, metal, alkaline earth metal (group 2); Silver, Ag, 47, metal, transition metal

8. The liquid elements are mercury (Hg) and bromine (Br_2).

SECTION 3.5
INTRODUCE

Student Preparation

Assign students to read Section 3.5 and to answer the Review Questions at the end of the section before coming to class.

SECTION 3.5
GUIDE THE LEARNING

Homework

You may wish to assign these selected end-of-chapter problems as homework for this section: 46, 47, 48, 49, 50, 52

Additional end-of-chapter problems can be used for extra practice.

3.5.A Ions

Objective To describe the formation of ions from their parent atoms, learn to name them, and predict which ion a given element forms using the periodic table

 LABORATORY
EXPERIMENT 14:
Electric Solutions

 TEACHING TIPS

• Make sure that students realize the atoms of an element are neutral. Charge is shown only for ions.

• Now is an excellent time to teach the notation for writing basic equations. $Na \rightarrow Na^+ + e^-$ shows how a neutral atom can lose an electron to have a positive charge. Students often have difficulty putting the electrons on the correct side when writing these equations.

SECTION 3.5
Ions and Their Compounds

Key Terms

• Ion
• Cation
• Anion
• Ionic compounds

Objectives

• *To describe the formation of ions from their parent atoms*
• *To learn to name ions*
• *To predict which ion a given element forms by using the periodic table*
• *To describe how ions combine to form neutral compounds*

A. Ions

We have seen that an atom has a certain number of protons in its nucleus and an equal number of electrons in the space around the nucleus. This results in an exact balance of positive and negative charges. We say that an atom is a neutral entity—it has *zero net charge*.

We can produce a charged entity, called an **ion**, by taking a neutral atom and adding or removing one or more electrons. For example, a sodium atom ($Z = 11$) has eleven protons in its nucleus and eleven electrons outside its nucleus.

If one of the electrons is lost, there will be eleven positive charges but only ten negative charges. This gives an ion with a net positive one (1+) charge: $(11+) + (10-) = 1+$. We can represent this process as follows: In shorthand form,

$$Na \rightarrow Na^+ + e^-$$

where Na represents the neutral sodium atom, Na^+ represents the 1+ ion formed, and e^- represents an electron.

Ion
An atom or group of atoms that has a positive or negative charge

Neutral sodium
atom (Na)

Sodium ion
(Na^+)

Meeting Individual Needs
READING CONCEPTS

By this point, students have been exposed to a great number of symbols used in chemistry. For additional help with chemical symbols, have students review *Reading Chemical Symbols* located in the *Teacher Resources*.

Cations and Anions

Losing electrons A positive ion, called a **cation** (pronounced *cat' eye on*), is produced when one or more electrons are *lost* from a neutral atom. We have seen that sodium loses one electron to become a 1+ cation. Some atoms lose more than one electron. For example, a magnesium atom typically loses two electrons to form a 2+ cation:

We usually represent this process as follows:

$$Mg \rightarrow Mg^{2+} + 2e^-$$

Cation
A positively charged ion

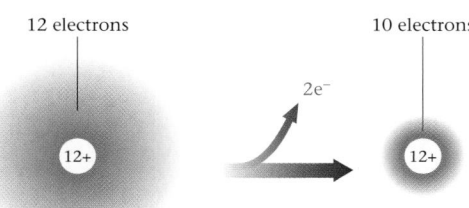

12 electrons   10 electrons

2e⁻

Neutral magnesium   Magnesium ion
atom (Mg)   (Mg²⁺)

Aluminum forms a 3+ cation by losing three electrons: That is,

$$Al \rightarrow Al^{3+} + 3e^-$$

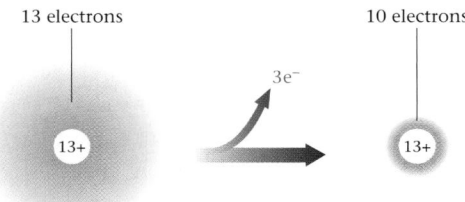

13 electrons   10 electrons

3e⁻

Neutral aluminum   Aluminum ion
atom (Al)   (Al³⁺)

A cation is named using the name of the parent atom. Thus Na^+ is called the sodium ion (or sodium cation), Mg^{2+} is called the magnesium ion (or magnesium cation), and Al^{3+} is called the aluminum ion (or aluminum cation).

ℹ️ nformation

Notice that when electrons are removed from an atom it becomes much smaller.

❓ MISCONCEPTION Chemistry

Emphasize that ions are formed by the gain and loss of electrons. This concept is difficult for students because they tend to think about gain and loss using positive numbers. It is very important that they understand from the beginning that a positive ion is formed by *losing* electrons and a negative ion is formed by *gaining* electrons. In chemistry, the positive number (protons) remains the same.

Anion
A negatively charged ion

Gaining electrons When a neutral atom *gains* electrons, an ion with a negative charge is formed. A negatively charged ion is called an **anion** (pronounced *an' ion*). An atom that gains one extra electron forms an anion with a 1− charge. An example of an atom that forms a 1− anion is the chlorine atom, which has seventeen protons and seventeen electrons. That is,

$$Cl + e^- \rightarrow Cl^-$$

When electrons are added to an atom it becomes much larger.

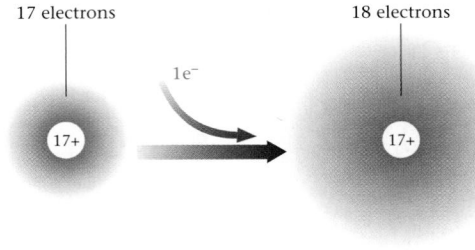

Neutral chlorine atom (Cl)

Chloride ion (Cl⁻)

Note that the anion formed by chlorine has eighteen electrons but only seventeen protons, so the net charge is (18−) + (17+) = 1−. Unlike a cation, which is named for the parent atom, an anion is named by taking the root name of the atom and changing the ending. For example, the Cl⁻ anion produced from the Cl (chlorine) atom is called the chloride ion (or chloride anion). Notice that the word *chloride* is obtained from the root of the atom name (*chlor-*) plus the suffix *-ide*. Other atoms that add one electron to form 1− ions include the following:

fluorine	$F + e^- \rightarrow F^-$	(*fluor*ide ion)
bromine	$Br + e^- \rightarrow Br^-$	(*brom*ide ion)
iodine	$I + e^- \rightarrow I^-$	(*iod*ide ion)

The name of an anion is obtained by adding *-ide* to the root of the atom name.

Note that the name of each of these anions is obtained by adding *-ide* to the root of the atom name.

Some atoms can add two electrons to form 2− anions. Examples include oxygen and sulfur:

oxygen	$O + 2e^- \rightarrow O^{2-}$	(*ox*ide ion)
sulfur	$S + 2e^- \rightarrow S^{2-}$	(*sulf*ide ion)

Note that the names for these anions are derived in the same way as are those for the 1− anions.

Forming ions It is important to recognize that ions are always formed by removing electrons from an atom (to form cations) or adding electrons to an atom (to form anions).

> Ions are never formed by changing the number of protons in an atom's nucleus.

78 • Chapter 3 • Chemical Foundations: Elements, Atoms, and Ions

---

Meeting Individual Needs
READING STRATEGIES

Relate the name of an atom and its corresponding anion to the way we change the ending of a word to indicate verb tense. For example, *walked* and *walking* are forms of the word *walk.* The root of the word stays the same, but the ending is modified when the verb tense changes. This is similar to how the name of an atom changes when it gains an electron.

It is essential to understand that isolated atoms do not form ions on their own. Most commonly, ions are formed when metallic elements combine with nonmetallic elements. As we will discuss in detail in Chapter 8, when metals and nonmetals react, the metal atoms tend to lose one or more electrons, which are, in turn, gained by the atoms of the nonmetal. Thus reactions between metals and nonmetals tend to form compounds that contain metal cations and nonmetal anions. We will have more to say about these compounds later.

Ion Charges and the Periodic Table

We find the periodic table very useful when we want to know what type of ion is formed by a given atom. **Figure 3.15** shows the types of ions formed by atoms in several of the groups on the periodic table. Note that the Group 1 metals all form 1+ ions (M^+), the Group 2 metals all form 2+ ions (M^{2+}), and the Group 3 metals form 3+ ions (M^{3+}). Therefore, for Groups 1 through 3, the charges of the cations formed are identical to the group numbers.

In contrast to the Group 1, 2, and 3 metals, most of the *transition metals* form cations with various positive charges. For these elements, there is no easy way to predict the charge of the cation that will be formed.

Note that metals always form positive ions. This tendency to lose electrons is a fundamental characteristic of metals. Nonmetals, on the other hand, form negative ions by gaining electrons. Note that all Group 7 atoms gain one electron to form 1− ions and that all nonmetals in Group 6 gain two electrons to form 2− ions.

At this point, you should memorize the relationships between the group number and the type of ion formed, as shown in Figure 3.15. You will understand why these relationships exist after we discuss the theory of the atom in more detail in Chapter 11.

nformation

For Groups 1, 2, and 3, the charges of the cations equal the group numbers.

Active Reading Question

How can we use the periodic table to determine the types of ions formed by some atoms?

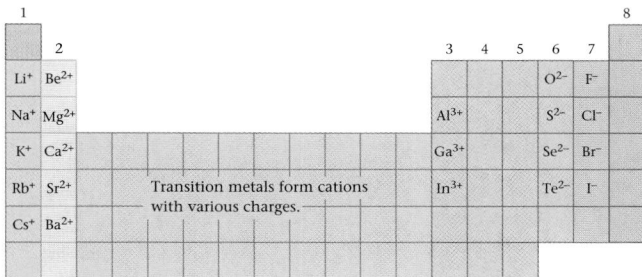

Figure 3.15
The ions formed by selected members of Groups 1, 2, 3, 6, and 7

TEACHING TIPS

- Students need to learn the charges for the ions formed from the elements in Groups 1, 2, 3, 6, and 7 of the periodic table. This effort will help them name compounds correctly later on.

- While students are naming ions and writing their charges, ask them to look for any patterns. They should discover that the nonmetals form ions with negative charges and the metals form ions with positive charges that match their group numbers. They may also notice that transition metals have a variety of charges.

Active Reading Question

Group 1 metals all form 1+ ions, Group 2 metals all form 2+ ions, and Group 3 metals form 3+ ions. Group 6 nonmetals form 2− ions, and Group 7 nonmetals form 1− ions.

TECHNOLOGY

Figure 3.15

CHEMISTRY IN YOUR WORLD

Consumer Connection

Miracle Coatings

Imagine a pair of plastic-lens sunglasses that are unscratchable, even if you drop them on concrete or rub them with sandpaper. Research may make such glasses possible, along with cutting tools that never need sharpening, special glass for windshields and buildings that cannot be scratched by wind-blown sand, and speakers that reproduce sound with a crispness unimagined until now. The secret of such marvels is a thin diamond coating. Diamond is so hard that virtually nothing can scratch it. A thin diamond coating on a speaker cone limits resonance and gives a remarkably pure tone.

But how do you coat something with a diamond? It is nearly impossible to melt diamond (melting point, 3500 °C). And even if diamond were melted, the object being coated would itself melt immediately at this temperature. Surprisingly, a diamond coating can be applied quite easily to something even as fragile as plastic. First, the surface is bathed with a mixture of gaseous methane (CH_4) and hydrogen (H_2). Next, the methane is broken apart into its component elements by an energy source similar to that used in microwave ovens. The carbon atoms freed from the methane then form a thin diamond coating on the surface being treated.

The coating of soft, scratchable materials with a super-tough diamond layer should improve many types of consumer products in the near future.

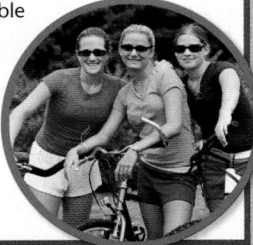

B. Compounds That Contain Ions

 information

Melting means that the solid, in which ions are locked into place, is changed to a liquid, in which the ions can move.

Chemists have good reasons to believe that many chemical compounds contain ions. For instance, consider some of the properties of common table salt, sodium chloride (NaCl). It must be heated to about 800 °C to melt and to almost 1500 °C to boil (compare to water, which boils at 100 °C). As a solid, salt will not conduct an electric current, but when melted it is a very good conductor. Pure water will not conduct electricity (will not allow an electric current to flow), but when salt is dissolved in water, the resulting solution readily conducts electricity (see **Figure 3.16**).

Figure 3.16
(a) Pure water does not conduct a current, so the circuit is not complete and the bulb does not light. (b) Water containing a dissolved salt conducts electricity, and the bulb lights.

(a)   (b)

80 • Chapter 3 • Chemical Foundations: Elements, Atoms, and Ions

Chemists have come to realize that we can best explain these properties of sodium chloride (NaCl) by picturing it as containing Na^+ ions and Cl^- ions packed together as shown in **Figure 3.17.** Because the positive and negative charges attract each other very strongly, salt must be heated to a very high temperature (800 °C) before it melts.

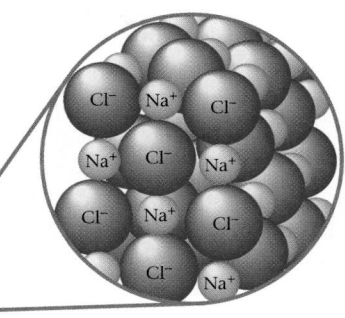

Figure 3.17
The atomic-level view shows the arrangement of sodium ions (Na^+) and chloride ions (Cl^-) in the ionic compound sodium chloride. The photo shows solid sodium chloride highly magnified.

To explore further the significance of the electrical conductivity results, we need to discuss briefly the nature of electric currents. An electric current can travel along a metal wire because *electrons are free to move* through the wire; the moving electrons carry the current. In ionic substances, the ions carry the current. Therefore, substances that contain ions can conduct an electric current *only if the ions can move*—the current travels by the movement of the charged ions. In solid NaCl, the ions are tightly held and cannot move. When the solid melts and becomes a liquid, however, the structure is disrupted and the ions can move. As a result, an electric current can travel through the melted salt.

The same reasoning applies to NaCl dissolved in water. When the solid dissolves, the ions can move around and are dispersed throughout the water, allowing it to conduct a current.

Thus we recognize substances that contain ions by their characteristic properties. They often have very high melting points, and they conduct an electric current when melted or dissolved in water.

Many substances contain ions. In fact, whenever a compound forms between a metal and a nonmetal, it can be expected to contain ions. We call these substances **ionic compounds**.

Ionic compound
A compound that results when a metal reacts with a nonmetal to form cations and anions

Formulas for Ionic Compounds One fact very important to remember is that *a chemical compound must have a net charge of zero*. This fact means that if a compound contains ions, then

1. Both positive ions (cations) and negative ions (anions) must be present.

2. The numbers of cations and anions must be such that the net charge is zero.

TEACHING TIPS

- Students need to think about ionic compounds on the molecular (ionic) level. Have them draw pictures when they begin writing formulas for these compounds. Emphasizing the idea that the compound is composed of both cations and anions lays a strong foundation for understanding the more advanced concepts later in the course. Once students can see the ions in a compound, making the total charge be a net of zero is more understandable. Students can then see how many of each ion are needed to attain a zero charge.

- Point out to students that atoms do not spontaneously gain or lose electrons. The gain and loss of electrons are always paired. One atom loses electrons as another atom simultaneously gains electrons.

Metals and nonmetals form compounds (called ionic compounds) due to the transfer of one or more electrons (from the metal to the nonmetal). The ions formed in this way have a strong attraction for one another. Also, we can predict the formulas of ionic compounds because these compounds are electrically neutral. If subatomic particles had no charge, no ions would form and no ionic attraction would occur. Ionic compounds would be impossible.

 Active Reading Question

The numbers of cations and anions must be such that the net charge is zero.

information

An ionic compound cannot contain only anions or only cations because the net charge of a compound must be zero.

CRITICAL **THINKING**

Thomson and Rutherford helped show that atoms consist of subatomic particles, two of which are charged.

What if subatomic particles had no charge? How would that affect compounds formed between metals and nonmetals?

For example, note that the formula for sodium chloride is written NaCl, indicating one of each type of these elements. This makes sense because sodium chloride contains Na^+ ions and Cl^- ions. Each sodium ion has a 1+ charge and each chloride ion has a 1− charge, so they must occur in equal numbers to give a net charge of zero.

  → NaCl

Charge: 1+ + Charge: 1− Net charge: 0

For *any* ionic compound,
Total charge of cations + Total charge of anions = Zero net charge

Consider an ionic compound that contains the ions Mg^{2+} and Cl^-. What combination of these ions will give a net charge of zero? To balance the 2+ charge on Mg^{2+}, we will need two Cl^- ions to give a net charge of zero.

  → $MgCl_2$

Cation charge: + Anion charge: = Compound net
2+ 2 × (1−) charge: 0

This means that the formula of the compound must be $MgCl_2$. Remember that subscripts are used to give the relative numbers of atoms (or ions).
Now consider an ionic compound that contains the ions Ba^{2+} and O^{2-}. What is the correct formula? These ions have charges of the same size, but opposite sign, so they must occur in equal numbers to give a net charge of zero. The formula of the compound is BaO because (2+) + (2−) = 0.
Similarly, the formula of a compound that contains the ions Li^+ and N^{3-} is Li_3N because three Li^+ cations are needed to balance the charge of the N^{3-} anion.

  → Li_3N

Positive charge: + Negative charge: = Net charge:
3 × (1+) (3−) 0

 Active Reading Question

How does knowing the ions in an ionic compound allow us to determine the chemical formula of the compound?

82 • Chapter 3 • Chemical Foundations: Elements, Atoms, and Ions

Teaching Support
DEMONSTRATION

Conductivity

Materials
- NaCl
- 1 *M* HCl
- 6 beakers
- Wash bottle (for distilled water)
- Conductivity apparatus
- Sugar
- 1 *M* acetic acid
- Distilled water

Procedure Place distilled water in a beaker and tap water in a separate beaker. Ask students to describe the difference between tap water and distilled water. Have them predict the conductivity of each. Test conductivity with apparatus. **Note:** Rinse conductivity apparatus after each test.

Place distilled water in two beakers. Add a spoonful of sugar to one beaker and a spoonful of salt to the other. Test the conductivity of each solution. In a similar manner, test solutions of HCl and acetic

EXAMPLE 3.6

Writing Formulas for Ionic Compounds

The pairs of ions contained in several ionic compounds are listed below. Give the formula for each compound.

a. Ca^{2+} and Cl^- b. Na^+ and S^{2-} c. Ca^{2+} and P^{3-}

Solution

a. Ca^{2+} has a 2+ charge, so two Cl^- ions (each with the charge 1−) will be needed.

The formula is $CaCl_2$.

where   2+   +   2(1−)   = 0

b. In this case, S^{2-}, with its 2− charge, requires two Na^+ ions to produce a zero net charge.

The formula is Na_2S.

where   2(1+)   +   2−   = 0

c. We have the ions Ca^{2+} (charge 2+) and P^{3-} (charge 3−). We must figure out how many of each type is needed to balance exactly the positive and negative charges. Let's try two Ca^{2+} and one P^{3-}.

The resulting net charge is
$2(2+) + (3-) = (4+) + (3-) = 1+.$

This doesn't work because the net charge is not zero. We can obtain the same total positive and total negative charges by having three Ca^{2+} ions and two P^{3-} ions.

The formula is Ca_3P_2.

where   2(2+)   +   3−   = 1+

where   3(2+)   +   2(3−)   = 0

 Practice Problem • Exercise 3.6

Give the formulas for the compounds that contain the following pairs of ions.
a. K^+ and I^- b. Mg^{2+} and N^{3-} c. Al^{3+} and O^{2-}

SECTION 3.5
REVIEW QUESTIONS

❶ Why does an atom have a net zero charge?

❷ a. Show how fluorine forms an ion. Does it form a cation or an anion?

   b. Show how lithium forms an ion. Does it form a cation or an anion?

❸ What are the relationships between the group number on the periodic table and the types of ions formed?

❹ What evidence do we have that convinces us that sodium chloride is an ionic compound?

❺ Give the formulas for the compounds that contain the following pairs of ions.

   a. Al^{3+} and Cl^- c. Ca^{2+} and S^{2-}
   b. K^+ and O^{2-} d. Sr^{2+} and F^-

 RESEARCH LINKS
CLASSZONE.COM

3.5 • Ions and Their Compounds • **83**

EXAMPLE 3.6

More Examples

Use the pairs of ions below to give the formula for the compound containing these ions.

1. Ba^{2+} and O^{2-}
   BaO

2. Al^{3+} and S^{2-}
   Al_2S_3

3. K^+ and P^{3-}
   K_3P

Answer to Practice Problem 3.6

a. KI
   $(1+) + (1-) = 0$

b. Mg_3N_2
   $3(2+) + 2(3-) = 0$

c. Al_2O_3
   $2(3+) + 3(2-) = 0$

SECTION 3.5
ASSESS

SECTION 3.5 Review Questions

1. An atom has a net zero charge because it has an equal number of protons and electrons.

2. a. $F + e^- \rightarrow F^-$; anion

   b. $Li \rightarrow Li^+ + e^-$; cation

3. In general, Group 1 elements form 1+ ions, Group 2 elements form 2+ ions, Group 3 elements form 3+ ions, Group 6 elements form 2− ions, and Group 7 elements form 1− ions.

4. NaCl must be heated to about 800 °C to melt. As a solid, it will not conduct an electric current, but it is a very good conductor when melted. When dissolved in water, the solution readily conducts electricity.

5. a. $AlCl_3$
   b. K_2O
   c. CaS
   d. SrF_2

(continued)

acid. Summarize the results of the test in a table.

Teaching Notes Ask students why distilled water does not conduct electricity but tap water does. What must be present for conductivity to occur? Have students draw molecular-level pictures of the sugar and salt solutions. Based on these results, have them predict what the HCl solution might look

like at the molecular level. Finally, ask students to propose a hypothesis for how the acetic acid solution might differ from the HCl solution.

Chapter 3 Review

Key Terms	Key Ideas

3.1 Element symbols

3.1 The Elements
- All of the materials in the universe can be chemically broken down into about 100 different elements.
- Nine elements account for about 98% of earth's crust, oceans, and atmosphere.
- In the human body, oxygen, carbon, hydrogen, and nitrogen are the most abundant elements.
- Each element has a name and a symbol.
  - The symbol usually consists of the first one or two letters of the element's name.
  - Sometimes the symbol is taken from the element's original Latin or Greek name.

3.2 Law of constant composition
Dalton's atomic theory
Atoms
Compound
Chemical formula

3.2 Atoms and Compounds
- The Law of constant composition states that a given compound always contains the same proportion by mass of the elements of which it is composed.
- Dalton's atomic theory states:
  - All elements are composed of atoms.
  - All atoms of a given element are identical.
  - Atoms of different elements are different.
  - Compounds consist of the atoms of different elements.
  - Atoms are not created or destroyed in a chemical reaction.
- A compound is represented by a chemical formula in which the number and type of atoms present are shown by using the element symbols and subscripts.

3.3 Electrons
Nuclear atom
Nucleus
Proton
Neutron
Isotopes
Atomic number
Mass number

3.3 Atomic Structure
- Experiments by J. J. Thomson and Ernest Rutherford showed that atoms have internal structure.
  - The nucleus, which is at the center of the atom, contains protons (positively charged) and neutrons (uncharged).
  - Electrons move around the nucleus.
    - ◆ Electrons have a small mass (1/1836 of the proton mass).
    - ◆ Electrons have a negative charge equal and opposite to that of the proton.
- Isotopes are atoms with the same number of protons but a different number of neutrons.
- A particular isotope is represented by the symbol $_Z^A X$, in which Z represents the number of protons (atomic number) and A represents the total number of protons and neutrons (mass number) in the nucleus.

RESEARCH LINKS
CLASSZONE.COM

Meeting Individual Needs	**Assessment Resources**
CHAPTER REVIEW	CHAPTER 3

Chapter 3 Review Worksheet at the appropriate level:
   Basic
   Standard
   Challenge
	Chapter 3 Test

CHAPTER SUMMARY	TECHNOLOGY
A **Chapter Summary** that includes additional Active Reading Questions for Chapter 3 is available.	**Computerized Test Bank for Chapter 3**

3.4 Using the Periodic Table

- The periodic table shows all of the known elements in order of increasing atomic number; the table is organized to group elements with similar properties in vertical columns.

- Most elements have metallic properties (the metals) and appear on the left side of the periodic table.

- Nonmetals appear on the right side of the periodic table.

- Metalloids are elements that have some metallic and some nonmetallic properties.

	Alkaline earth metals																	Noble gases
1 1A	2 2A											13 3A	14 4A	15 5A	16 6A	Halogens 17 7A	18 8A	
1 H																	2 He	
3 Li	4 Be											5 B	6 C	7 N	8 O	9 F	10 Ne	
11 Na	12 Mg	3	4	5	6 Transition metals	7	8	9	10	11	12	13 Al	14 Si	15 P	16 S	17 Cl	18 Ar	
19 K	20 Ca	21 Sc	22 Ti	23 V	24 Cr	25 Mn	26 Fe	27 Co	28 Ni	29 Cu	30 Zn	31 Ga	32 Ge	33 As	34 Se	35 Br	36 Kr	
37 Rb	38 Sr	39 Y	40 Zr	41 Nb	42 Mo	43 Tc	44 Ru	45 Rh	46 Pd	47 Ag	48 Cd	49 In	50 Sn	51 Sb	52 Te	53 I	54 Xe	
55 Cs	56 Ba	57 La*	72 Hf	73 Ta	74 W	75 Re	76 Os	77 Ir	78 Pt	79 Au	80 Hg	81 Tl	82 Pb	83 Bi	84 Po	85 At	86 Rn	
87 Fr	88 Ra	89 Ac†	104 Rf	105 Db	106 Sg	107 Bh	108 Hs	109 Mt	110 Uun	111 Ds	112 Rg	113 Uut	114 Uuq	115 Uup				

Alkali metals labels the leftmost column (1A).

*Lanthanides	58 Ce	59 Pr	60 Nd	61 Pm	62 Sm	63 Eu	64 Gd	65 Tb	66 Dy	67 Ho	68 Er	69 Tm	70 Yb	71 Lu
†Actinides	90 Th	91 Pa	92 U	93 Np	94 Pu	95 Am	96 Cm	97 Bk	98 Cf	99 Es	100 Fm	101 Md	102 No	103 Lr

3.5 Ions and Their Compounds

- Atoms can form ions (species with a charge) by gaining or losing electrons.

  - Metals tend to lose one or more electrons to form positive ions called cations; these are generally named by using the name of the parent atom.

  - Nonmetals tend to gain one or more electrons to form negative ions called anions; these are named by using the root of the atom name followed by the suffix -ide.

- The ion that a particular atom will form can be predicted from the atom's position on the periodic table.

  - Elements in Group 1 and 2 form 1+ and 2+ ions, respectively.

  - Group 7 atoms form anions with 1− charges.

  - Group 6 atoms form anions with 2− charges.

- Ions combine to form compounds. Compounds are electrically neutral, so the sum of the charges on the anions and cations in the compound must equal zero.

RESEARCH LINKS
CLASSZONE.COM

Chapter 3 Assessment

1. We still believe that matter is composed of a few simple substances and that the simple substances combine with each other in regular fixed manners. However, our notion of "element" is much different.

2. Alchemists discovered several previously unknown elements (mercury, sulfur, antimony) and were the first to prepare several common acids.

3. Boyle insisted that science be firmly grounded in experiment. His definition of the term *element* was based on observations and experimentation.

4. Approximately 115 elements are known (the number changes frequently); 88 occur naturally; the rest are synthetic. Table 3.1 lists the most common elements on earth.

5. Oxygen is found in rivers, lakes, and oceans (combined with hydrogen in water molecules) and in the earth (most rocks and minerals are oxygen compounds). Oxygen is found most commonly in compounds.

6. The four most abundant elements in living creatures are oxygen, carbon, hydrogen, and nitrogen. In the nonliving world, the most abundant elements are oxygen, silicon, aluminum, and iron.

7. B (boron); C (carbon); F (fluorine); H (hydrogen); I (iodine); K (potassium); N (nitrogen); O (oxygen); P (phosphorus); S (sulfur); U (uranium); V (vanadium); W (tungsten); Y (yttrium)

8. Sb (antimony); Cu (copper); Au (gold); Pb (lead); Hg (mercury); K (potassium); Ag (silver); Na (sodium); Sn (tin); W (tungsten); Fe (iron)

9. (a) Ne
   (b) Ni
   (c) K
   (d) Si
   (e) Ba
   (f) Ag

10. iron; Cl; sulfur; U; neon; potassium

11. (a) copper
    (b) cobalt
    (c) calcium
    (d) carbon
    (e) chromium

All exercises with blue numbers have answers in the back of this book.

3.1 The Elements
A. Abundances of the Elements

1. The ancient Greeks believed that all matter was composed of four fundamental substances: earth, air, fire, and water. How does this early conception of matter compare with our modern theories about matter?

2. Although they were not able to transform base metals into gold, what contributions did the alchemists make to the development of chemistry?

3. In addition to his important work on the properties of gases, what other valuable contributions did Robert Boyle make to the development of the study of chemistry?

4. In 2006, 115 elements were known. How many of these elements occur naturally, and how many are synthesized artificially? What are the most common elements present on earth?

5. Oxygen, the most abundant element on earth by mass, makes up a large percentage of the atmosphere. Where else is oxygen found? Is oxygen found more commonly as an element or in compounds?

6. What are the most abundant elements found in living creatures? Are these elements also the most abundant elements found in the nonliving world?

B. Names and Symbols for the Elements

Note: Refer to the tables on the inside back cover when appropriate.

7. Give the symbols and names for the elements whose chemical symbols consist of only one letter.

8. In some cases, the symbol of an element does not seem to bear any relationship to the name we use for the element. Generally, the symbol for such an element is based on its name in another language. Give the symbols and names of five examples of such elements.

9. Give the chemical symbol for each of the following elements.
   - a. neon
   - b. nickel
   - c. potassium
   - d. silicon
   - e. barium
   - f. silver

10. Give the name or symbol, as appropriate, for each of the following elements.

Symbol	Name
Fe	
	chlorine
S	
	uranium
Ne	
K	

11. Several elements have chemical symbols beginning with the letter C. For each of the following chemical symbols, give the name of the corresponding element.
   - a. Cu
   - b. Co
   - c. Ca
   - d. C
   - e. Cr
   - f. Cs
   - g. Cl
   - h. Cd

3.2 Atoms and Compounds
A. Dalton's Atomic Theory

12. Indicate whether each of the following statements is true or false. If a statement is false, correct the statement so that it becomes true.
   - a. Most materials occur in nature as pure substances.
   - b. A given compound usually contains the same relative number of atoms of its various elements.
   - c. Atoms are made up of tiny particles called molecules.

13. What does the law of constant composition tell us? How did Dalton's atomic theory help explain this law? Give examples.

B. Formulas of Compounds

14. What is a compound?

15. A given compound always contains the same relative masses of its constituent elements. How is this idea related to the relative numbers of each kind of atom present?

(f) cesium
(g) chlorine
(h) cadmium

12. (a) False; most materials occur as mixtures of compounds.
    (b) False; a compound always contains the same relative number of atoms of its various elements.
    (c) False; molecules are made up of tiny particles called atoms.

13. According to Dalton, a given compound always consists of the same number and type of atoms; thus the composition of the compound on a mass percentage basis is always the same.

14. A compound is a distinct substance that is composed of two or more elements and always contains exactly the same relative masses of those elements.

15. According to Dalton, all atoms of the same element are identical; in particular, every atom of a given element has the same mass as every other atom of that element. If a given compound always contains the same relative numbers of atoms of each kind, and those atoms always have the same masses, then

16. Write the formula for each of the following substances, listing the elements in the order given.

a.

List the phosphorus atom first.

b. a molecule containing two boron atoms and six hydrogen atoms

c. a compound containing one calcium atom for every two chlorine atoms

d.

List the carbon atom first.

e. a compound containing two iron atoms for every three oxygen atoms

f. a molecule containing three hydrogen atoms, one phosphorus atom, and four oxygen atoms

3.3 Atomic Structure

A. The Structure of the Atom

17. Indicate whether each of the following statements is true or false. If a statement is false, correct the statement so that it becomes true.

a. In his cathode ray tube experiments, J. J. Thomson obtained beams of different types of particles whose nature depended on which gas was contained in the tube.

b. Thomson assumed that the atom must contain positively charged particles because isolated atoms have no overall charge.

c. In the plum pudding model of the atom, the atom was envisioned as a sphere of negative charge in which positively charged electrons were randomly distributed.

18. Indicate whether each of the following statements is true or false. If a statement is false, correct it so that it becomes true.

a. Rutherford's bombardment experiments with metal foil suggested that alpha particles were deflected by approaching a large, negatively charged atomic nucleus.

b. The proton and the electron have similar masses but opposite electrical charges.

c. Most atoms also contain neutrons, which are slightly heavier than protons but carry no charge.

B. Introduction to the Modern Concept of Atomic Structure

19. What uncharged particles are found in the nuclei of most atoms?

20. What are the positively charged particles found in the nuclei of atoms called?

21. Do the proton and the neutron have exactly the same mass? How do the masses of the proton and the neutron compare with the mass of the electron? Which particles make the greatest contribution to the mass of an atom? Which particles make the greatest contribution to the chemical properties of an atom?

22. Although the nucleus of an atom is very important, it is the _____ of the atom that determine its chemical properties.

C. Isotopes

23. True or false? Atoms that have the same number of neutrons but different numbers of protons are called isotopes.

24. True or false? The mass number of a nucleus represents the number of protons in the nucleus.

25. How was Dalton's atomic theory modified after the discovery that several isotopes of an element may exist?

26. Are all atoms of the same element identical? If not, how do they differ?

19. neutrons

20. protons

21. The proton and neutron have similar, but not identical, masses. Either of these particles has a mass approximately 2000 times greater than the mass of an electron. The combination of the protons and the neutrons makes up the bulk of the mass of the atom. The electrons make the greatest contribution to the chemical properties of the atom.

22. electrons

23. False; atoms that have the same number of protons but different numbers of neutrons are called isotopes.

24. False; the mass number represents the total number of protons and neutrons in the nucleus.

25. Dalton's original theory proposed that all atoms of a given element were identical. We now know that this is not true—isotopes are possible.

26. Atoms of the same element (atoms with the same number of protons in the nucleus) may have different numbers of neutrons, and so will have different masses.

---

the compound made from those elements always contains the same relative masses of its elements.

16. (a) PCl_3
(b) B_2H_6
(c) $CaCl_2$
(d) CBr_4
(e) Fe_2O_3
(f) H_3PO_4

17. (a) False; Thomson obtained beams of identical particles whose nature did not depend on what metal was used to generate them.
(b) True.
(c) False; the atom was envisioned as a sphere of positive charge in which negatively charged electrons were randomly distributed.

18. (a) False; Rutherford's bombardment experiments suggested that alpha particles were being deflected by a dense, positively charged nucleus.
(b) False; the proton and electron do have opposite electrical charges, but the mass of the electron is much smaller than the mass of the proton.
(c) True.

27. (a) 32
  (b) 30
  (c) 24
  (d) 74
  (e) 38
  (f) 27
  (g) 4
  (h) 3

28. (a) $^{17}_{8}O$
  (b) $^{37}_{17}Cl$
  (c) $^{60}_{27}Co$
  (d) $^{57}_{26}Fe$
  (e) $^{131}_{53}I$
  (f) $^{7}_{3}Li$

29. (a) 94p, 150n, 94e
  (b) 95p, 146n, 95e
  (c) 89p, 138n, 89e
  (d) 55p, 78n, 55e
  (e) 77p, 116n, 77e
  (f) 25p, 31n, 25e

30.

Name	Symbol	Atomic Number	Mass Number	Neutrons
sodium	$^{23}_{11}Na$	11	23	12
nitrogen	$^{15}_{7}N$	7	15	8
barium	$^{136}_{56}Ba$	56	136	80
lithium	$^{9}_{3}Li$	3	9	6
boron	$^{11}_{5}B$	5	11	6

31. The elements in the periodic table are listed in order of increasing atomic number (number of protons in the nucleus). The periodic table was previously arranged on the basis of mass.

32. vertical; groups

33. Metals are excellent conductors of heat and electricity. They are also malleable, ductile, and generally shiny (lustrous) when a fresh surface is exposed.

34. Metallic elements are found toward the left and bottom of the periodic table; there are far more metallic elements than nonmetals.

35. Mercury is a liquid under normal conditions.

36. hydrogen, nitrogen, oxygen, fluorine, chlorine, plus all the Group 8 elements (noble gases)

37. The only metal that ordinarily exists as a liquid is mercury. The only nonmetallic element that exists as a liquid under normal conditions is bromine (Br_2). Oxygen and nitrogen are obtainable as liquids but only by compressing the gases at very low temperatures.

27. For each of the following elements, use the periodic table on the inside back cover of this book to write the element's atomic number.

  a. Ge
  b. zinc
  c. Cr
  d. tungsten
  e. Sr
  f. cobalt
  g. Be
  h. lithium

28. Write the atomic symbol $^{A}_{Z}X$ for each of the isotopes described below.

  a. $Z = 8$, number of neutrons = 9
  b. the isotope of chlorine in which $A = 37$
  c. $Z = 27$, $A = 60$
  d. number of protons = 26, number of neutrons = 31
  e. the isotope of I with a mass number of 131
  f. $Z = 3$, number of neutrons = 4

29. How many protons and neutrons are contained in the nucleus of each of the following atoms? Given that each atom is uncharged, how many electrons are present?

  a. $^{244}_{94}Pu$
  b. $^{241}_{95}Am$
  c. $^{227}_{89}Ac$
  d. $^{133}_{55}Cs$
  e. $^{193}_{77}Ir$
  f. $^{56}_{25}Mn$

30. Copy and complete the following table.

Name	Symbol	Atomic Number	Mass Number	Neutrons
sodium		11	23	
	$^{15}_{7}N$			
	$^{136}_{56}Ba$			
lithium				6
boron		5	11	

3.4 Using the Periodic Table

A. Introduction to the Periodic Table

31. What property of the elements is considered when arranging the elements in the periodic table?

32. In which direction on the periodic table, horizontal or vertical, are elements with similar chemical properties aligned? What are families of elements with similar chemical properties called?

33. List the characteristic physical properties that distinguish the metallic elements from the nonmetallic elements.

34. Where are the metallic elements found on the periodic table? Are there more metallic elements or nonmetallic elements?

35. Most, but not all, metallic elements are solids under ordinary laboratory conditions. Which metallic elements are *not* solids?

36. Give several examples of nonmetallic elements that occur in the gaseous state under ordinary conditions.

37. Under ordinary conditions, only a few pure elements occur as liquids. Give an example of a metallic element and a nonmetallic element that ordinarily occur as liquids.

38. What is a *metalloid*? Where are the metalloids found on the periodic table?

39. Write the number and name (if any) of the group (family) to which each of the following elements belongs.

  a. iodine
  b. Ca
  c. Na
  d. lithium
  e. Kr
  f. sodium
  g. Ne

40. Use the tables on the inside back cover of the book to give the chemical symbol, atomic number, and group number of each of the following elements and to specify whether each element is a metal, a metalloid, or a nonmetal.

  a. rubidium
  b. germanium
  c. magnesium
  d. titanium
  e. iodine

B. Natural States of the Elements

41. Are most of the chemical elements found in nature in the elemental form or combined in compounds? Explain.

42. Why are the elements of Group 8 called the noble or inert gas elements?

38. A metalloid is an element that has some properties common to both metallic and nonmetallic elements. The metalloids are found in the "stair-step" region marked on most periodic tables.

39. (a) 7, halogens
  (b) 2, alkaline earth metals
  (c) 1, alkali metals
  (d) 1, alkali metals
  (e) 8, noble gases
  (f) 1, alkali metals
  (g) 8, noble gases

40. (a) rubidium, Rb, atomic number 37, group number 1, metal
  (b) germanium, Ge, atomic number 32, group number 4, metalloid
  (c) magnesium, Mg, atomic number 12, group number 2, metal
  (d) titanium, Ti, atomic number 22, transition metal
  (e) iodine, I, atomic number 53, group number 7, nonmetal

41. Most of the elements are too reactive to be found in uncombined form in nature and are found only in compounds.

42. These elements are found uncombined in nature and do not react readily with other elements. Although these elements were once thought to form no compounds, this now has been shown to be untrue.

43. Give three examples of gaseous elements that exist as diatomic molecules. Give three examples of gaseous elements that exist as single atoms.

44. Most of the elements are solids at 30 °C. Give three examples of elements that are *liquids* and three examples of elements that are *gases* at 30 °C.

3.5 Ions and Their Compounds

A. Ions

45. For each of the positive ions listed in column 1, use the periodic table to find in column 2 the total number of electrons that ion contains. The same answer may be used more than once.

Column 1		Column 2	
[1]	Al^{3+}	[a]	2
[2]	Fe^{3+}	[b]	10
[3]	Mg^{2+}	[c]	21
[4]	Sn^{2+}	[d]	23
[5]	Co^{2+}	[e]	24
[6]	Co^{3+}	[f]	25
[7]	Li^+	[g]	36
[8]	Cr^{3+}	[h]	48
[9]	Rb^+	[i]	76
[10]	Pt^{2+}	[j]	81

46. Complete the following tables.

a.

Cation	# Protons in ion	# Electrons in ion	Formula with O^{2-}
K^+			
Co^{2+}			
Al^{3+}			

b.

Anion	# Protons in ion	# Electrons in ion	Formula with Ca^{2+}
Cl^-			
S^{2-}			
P^{3-}			

47. For the following processes that show the formation of ions, use the periodic table to indicate the number of electrons and protons present in both the *ion* and the *neutral atom* from which the ion is made.

a. $Ca \rightarrow Ca^{2+} + 2e^-$

b. $P + 3e^- \rightarrow P^{3-}$

c. $Br + e^- \rightarrow Br^-$

d. $Fe \rightarrow Fe^{3+} + 3e^-$

e. $Al \rightarrow Al^{3+} + 3e^-$

f. $N + 3e^- \rightarrow N^{3-}$

48. For each of the following atomic numbers, use the periodic table to write the formula (including the charge) for the simple *ion* that the element is most likely to form.

a. 53

b. 38

c. 55

d. 88

e. 9

f. 13

B. Compounds That Contain Ions

49. List some properties of a substance that would lead you to believe that the substance consists of ions. How do these properties differ from those of nonionic compounds?

50. Why does an ionic compound conduct an electric current when the compound is melted but not when it is in the solid state?

51. Why must the total number of positive charges in an ionic compound equal the total number of negative charges?

52. Use the concept that a chemical compound must have a net charge of zero to predict the formula of the simplest compound that the following pairs of ions are most likely to form.

a. Fe^{3+} and P^{3-}

b. Fe^{3+} and S^{2-}

c. Fe^{3+} and Cl^-

d. Mg^{2+} and Cl^-

e. Mg^{2+} and O^{2-}

f. Mg^{2+} and N^{3-}

g. Na^+ and P^{3-}

h. Na^+ and S^{2-}

Chapter 3 • Assessment • **89**

Br^-: 35 protons, 36 electrons
(d) Fe: 26 protons, 26 electrons;
Fe^{3+}: 26 protons, 23 electrons
(e) Al: 13 protons, 13 electrons;
Al^{3+}: 13 protons, 10 electrons
(f) N: 7 protons, 7 electrons;
N^{3-}: 7 protons, 10 electrons

48. (a) I^-
(b) Sr^{2+}
(c) Cs^+
(d) Ra^{2+}
(e) F^-
(f) Al^{3+}

49. A compound that has a high melting point (hundreds of degrees) and that conducts an electrical current when melted or dissolved in water almost certainly consists of ions.

50. In a solid state the ions are rigidly held in fixed positions in the crystal of the substance. For ionic substances to pass an electrical current, the ions must be able to move. This is possible in the liquid state.

51. The total number of positive charges must equal the total number of negative charges so that the crystals of an ionic compound have no net charge. A macroscopic sample of a compound ordinarily has no charge.

52. (a) FeP
(b) Fe_2S_3
(c) $FeCl_3$
(d) $MgCl_2$
(e) MgO
(f) Mg_3N_2
(g) Na_3P
(h) Na_2S

43. Diatomic gases: H_2, N_2, O_2, Cl_2, F_2; monatomic gases: He, Ne, Kr, Xe, Rn, Ar

44. liquids: bromine, gallium, mercury, cesium; gases: hydrogen, nitrogen, oxygen, fluorine, chlorine, the noble gases (helium, neon, argon, krypton, xenon, radon)

45. [1] b; [2] d; [3] b; [4] h; [5] f; [6] e; [7] a; [8] c; [9] g; [10] i

46. (a) K^+: 19 protons, 18 electrons, K_2O;
Co^{2+}: 27 protons, 25 electrons, CoO;
Al^{3+}: 13 protons, 10 electrons, Al_2O_3
(b) Cl^-: 17 protons, 18 electrons, $CaCl_2$;
S^{2-}: 16 protons, 18 electrons, CaS;

P^{3-}: 15 protons, 18 electrons, Ca_3P_2

47. (a) Ca: 20 protons, 20 electrons;
Ca^{2+}: 20 protons, 18 electrons
(b) P: 15 protons, 15 electrons;
P^{3-}: 15 protons, 18 electrons
(c) Br: 35 protons, 35 electrons;

Chapter 3 • Assessment • **89**

53. The atomic number represents the number of protons in the nucleus of an atom. The mass number represents the total number of protons and neutrons. No two elements have the same atomic number. If the total number of protons and neutrons happens to be the same for two atoms, the atoms will have the same mass number.

54. Most of the atom's mass is concentrated in the nucleus; thus the protons and neutrons contribute most to the mass of the atom. The chemical properties of an atom depend on the number and location of the electrons.

55. Yes. For example, carbon and oxygen form carbon monoxide (CO) and carbon dioxide (CO_2). This does not contradict Dalton's theory.

56. (a) CO_2
(b) $AlCl_3$
(c) $HClO_4$
(d) SCl_6

57. (a) 1+
(b) 2−
(c) 2+
(d) 1−

58. sulfur

59. (a) $^{23}_{11}Na$
(b) $^{24}_{11}Na$
(c) $^{24}_{12}Mg$

60. (a) The number and arrangement of the electrons matter most because the electrons of the atoms "intermingle" when atoms combine to form molecules.

Critical Thinking

53. What is the difference between the atomic number and the mass number of an element? Can atoms of two different elements have the same atomic number? Could they have the same mass number? Explain.

54. Which subatomic particles contribute most to the atom's mass? Which subatomic particles determine the atom's chemical properties?

55. Is it possible for the same two elements to form more than one compound? Is this possibility consistent with Dalton's atomic theory? Give an example.

56. Write the simplest formula for each of the following substances, listing the elements in the order given.

    a. a molecule containing one carbon atom and two oxygen atoms

    b. a compound containing one aluminum atom for every three chlorine atoms

    c. perchloric acid, which contains one hydrogen atom, one chlorine atom, and four oxygen atoms

    d. a molecule containing one sulfur atom and six chlorine atoms

57. List the charges of the ions formed from atoms in each of the groups.

    a. _____
    b. _____
    c. _____
    d. _____

58. An ion has a charge of 2− and 18 electrons. From which atom does this ion form?

59. Use the following figures to identify the element or ion. Write the symbol for each, using the ^A_ZX format.

a.

b.

c.

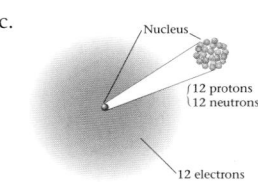

60. Choose the statement that best answers this question: If all atoms are composed of the same subatomic particles, why do different atoms have different chemical properties?

    a. The number and arrangement of the electrons matter most because the electrons of the atoms "intermingle" when atoms combine to form molecules.

    b. The number and arrangement of the electrons matter most because the electrons of the atoms are located in the nucleus, and the nucleus is involved in chemical reactions.

    c. The number and arrangement of the protons matter most because the protons of the atoms "intermingle" when atoms combine to form molecules.

    d. The number and arrangement of the protons matter most because the protons of the atoms are located in the nucleus, and the nucleus is involved in chemical reactions.

1   Which element includes the first letter of its name as the first letter of the symbol for the element?

   A   potassium

   B   lead

   C   copper

   D   sodium

2   Which of the following postulates of Dalton's atomic theory is no longer scientifically accepted?

   A   All matter is made up of atoms.

   B   All atoms of the same element are identical.

   C   Compounds are combinations of different atoms.

   D   A chemical reaction changes the way atoms are grouped.

3   Consider isotopes, ions, protons, and electrons. How many of these did Dalton **not** discuss in his atomic theory?

   A   1

   B   2

   C   3

   D   4

4   Which of the following represents a pair of isotopes?

   A ^{23}Na and $^{23}Na^+$

   B ^{14}C and ^{14}N

   C ^{14}C and ^{12}C

   D ^{16}O and $^{16}O^{2-}$

5   An ion is formed

   A   either by adding or by taking away protons from the atom.

   B   either by adding or by taking away electrons from the atom.

   C   either by adding or by taking away neutrons from the atom.

   D   At least two of the above statements correctly explain how an ion is formed.

6   How many protons and electrons does the most stable ion for oxygen have?

   A   10 protons, 8 electrons

   B   8 protons, 8 electrons

   C   8 protons, 10 electrons

   D   6 protons, 8 electrons

7   A certain ion has a charge of 2+ and 27 electrons. Which ion is it?

   A Mn^{2+}

   B Cu^{2+}

   C Co^{2+}

   D Ga^{2+}

8   You are given a compound with the formula CaX_2, in which X is a nonmetal. You are told that the nonmetal ion has 10 electrons. What is the symbol of the nonmetal?

   A   F

   B   Cl

   C   O

   D   Ne

9   Write the correct letter in the space provided.

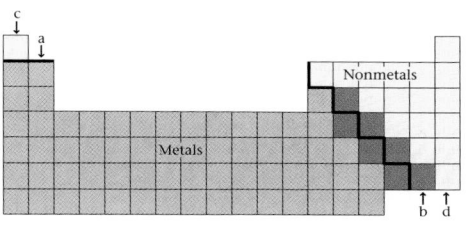

   _____ Noble gases

   _____ Alkaline earth metals

   _____ Halogens

   _____ Alkali metals

10   Briefly describe Ernest Rutherford's gold foil experiment. Answer the following questions in your explanation.

   a.   What did Rutherford do?

   b.   What were the results?

   c.   What did Rutherford conclude from these results?

Chapter 3 • Standardized Test Practice • **91**

1. C

2. B

3. D

4. C

5. B

6. C

7. B

8. A

9. d   Noble gases

   a   Alkaline earth metals

   b   Halogens

   c   Alkali metals

10. a. Rutherford "shot" alpha particles (helium nuclei) at thin gold foil.

   b. Rutherford found that most of the alpha particles went through the gold foil, but that some particles were deflected.

   c. Rutherford concluded that because the alpha particles are relatively heavy and positively charged and a small number were deflected, there must be a small, massive, positively charged part of an atom. He termed this the nucleus.

Test-Taking Strategy

Advise students to read each question carefully. Point out that questions 2 and 3 are both looking for the choice that is NOT true. Explain that there are three choices that support the intent of the problem statement, but that the correct response is the choice that does NOT support the statement.

Assessment Resources
CHAPTER 3

For additional practice with standardized testing, see *Standardized Test Practice* located in the *Teacher Resources*.

Planning Guide

Section	Segment	Text Features and Components	Labs, Demonstrations, & Activities
4.1 Naming Binary Compounds **1 Block** pp. 94–108	**A** **Naming Compounds That Contain a Metal and a Nonmetal**	**SE** Chemistry in Your World: Sugar of Lead *p. 96* **SE** Chemistry in Your World: How Can Water Be Hard or Soft? *p. 98*	**TE** Mini-Demo *p. 99* **SE** Hands-On Chemistry: Name Game I: Ionic Compounds *p. 103*

	B **Naming Binary Compounds That Contain Only Nonmetals (Type III)**		**LM** Experiment 15: Forming and Naming Ionic Compounds, Microscale
			  Lab Manual
			  Report Sheets
			  Teacher's Lab Guide

	C **Naming Binary Compounds: A Review**	**SE** Celebrity Chemical: Nitric Oxide *p. 108*	
	continued on next page		

Key	**SE** Student Edition	**TE** Teacher Edition	**RP** Teacher Resource Package
	AR Additional Materials	**LM** Lab Materials	**🖰** Transparencies
	◉ DVD **▶** CD-ROM	**🛈** classzone.com	

All Learners	Technology	Review & Assessment	Standards
TE Teaching Tips *pp. 94–96, 98–99* **TE** Meeting Individual Needs *p. 95* **TE** Meeting Individual Needs *p. 97* **TE** Misconception *p. 99* **TE** Meeting Individual Needs *p. 100* **RP** MINT: Reading Concepts *TE p. 94*	**Transparency: Table 4.1** **Transparency: Table 4.2** **EasyPlanner**	**SE** Active Reading Question *p. 95* **SE** Practice Problem *p. 97* **TE** More Examples *p. 97* **SE** Critical Thinking *p. 100* **TE** More Examples *p. 100* **SE** Active Reading Question *p. 102* **SE** Practice Problem *p. 102* **TE** More Examples *p. 102* **SE** Active Reading Question *p. 103* **SE** Key Terms *p. 117* **SE** Questions and Problems *p. 118*	**TE** **NSES** UCP1, UCP3, A1, A2, B2, B3, F1
TE Teaching Tips *p. 104* **TE** Meeting Individual Needs *p. 104*	**Lab Generator CD** **EasyPlanner**	**SE** Practice Problem *p. 104* **TE** More Examples *p. 104* **SE** Practice Problem *p. 105* **TE** More Examples *p. 105* **SE** Questions and Problems *p.118*	
TE Teaching Tips *p. 106* **RP** Team Learning Worksheet (Sec. 4.1)	**Transparency: Figure 4.1** **EasyPlanner**	**SE** Critical Thinking *p. 106* **SE** Active Reading Question *p. 106* **SE** Practice Problem *p. 107* **TE** More Examples *p. 107* **SE** Review Questions (4.1.A–4.1.C) *p. 108* **SE** Questions and Problems *p. 118*	

Planning Guide

Section	Segment		Text Features and Components	Labs, Demonstrations, & Activities
4.2 Naming and Writing Formulas for More Complex Compounds 1 Block pp. 109–116	A	**Naming Compounds That Contain Polyatomic Ions**		SE Hands-On Chemistry: Name Game II: Polyatomic Ions *p. 110* LM Experiment 16: Grocery Store Nomenclature Lab Manual Report Sheets Teacher's Lab Guide
	B	**Naming Acids**		LM Experiment 17: Energy Changes in Physical and Chemical Systems, Traditional Lab Manual Report Sheets Teacher's Lab Guide
	C	**Writing Formulas from Names**	SE Chemistry in Your World: Talking Tadpoles *p. 116*	

Key			
	SE Student Edition	TE Teacher Edition	RP Teacher Resource Package
	AR Additional Materials	LM Lab Materials	Transparencies
	DVD	CD-ROM	classzone.com

All Learners	Technology	Review & Assessment	Standards
TE Teaching Tips *pp. 109–110, 112* **TE** Misconception *p. 110* **RP** MINT: Challenge Projects *TE p. 111*	Transparency: Table 4.4 Transparency: Figure 4.2 Lab Generator CD EasyPlanner	**SE** Practice Problem *p. 111* **SE** More Examples *p. 111* **SE** Active Reading Question *p. 111* **SE** Practice Problem *p. 112* **TE** More Examples *p. 112* **SE** Key Terms *p. 117* **SE** Questions and Problems *pp. 118–119*	**TE** **NSES** UCP1, UCP3, A1, A2, B2, B3, C6
TE Teaching Tips *p. 113* **TE** Meeting Individual Needs *p. 113*	Transparency: Figure 4.3 Lab Generator CD EasyPlanner	**TE** More Examples *p. 113* **SE** Key Terms *p. 117* **SE** Questions and Problems *p. 119*	
TE Teaching Tips *p. 114* **RP** Team Learning Worksheet (Sec. 4.2)	EasyPlanner	**SE** Practice Problem *p. 115* **TE** More Examples *p. 115* **SE** Review Questions (4.2.A–4.2.C) *p. 116* **SE** Questions and Problems *p. 119*	

Resource Materials for Chapter 4

SE Chapter Review *p. 117*

SE Critical Thinking *pp. 120–122*

SE Standardized Test Practice *p. 123*

AR English/Spanish Summaries

English Summaries Audio

Spanish Summaries Audio

RP Meeting Individual Needs Toolkit (MINT)
    Reading Concepts
    Challenge Projects
    Chapter Review Worksheets
    Chapter Summaries

RP Solutions Guide

RP Standardized Test Practice

RP Chapter Tests

RP Test Bank

Test Generator

Chapter 4

Overview

In this chapter our goals are for students to:

- Learn how to name binary compounds of a metal and a nonmetal
- Learn how to name binary compounds containing only nonmetals
- Learn the names of common polyatomic ions and how to use them in naming compounds
- Learn names for common acids and how the anion composition determines the acid's name
- Learn to write the formula of a compound, given its name

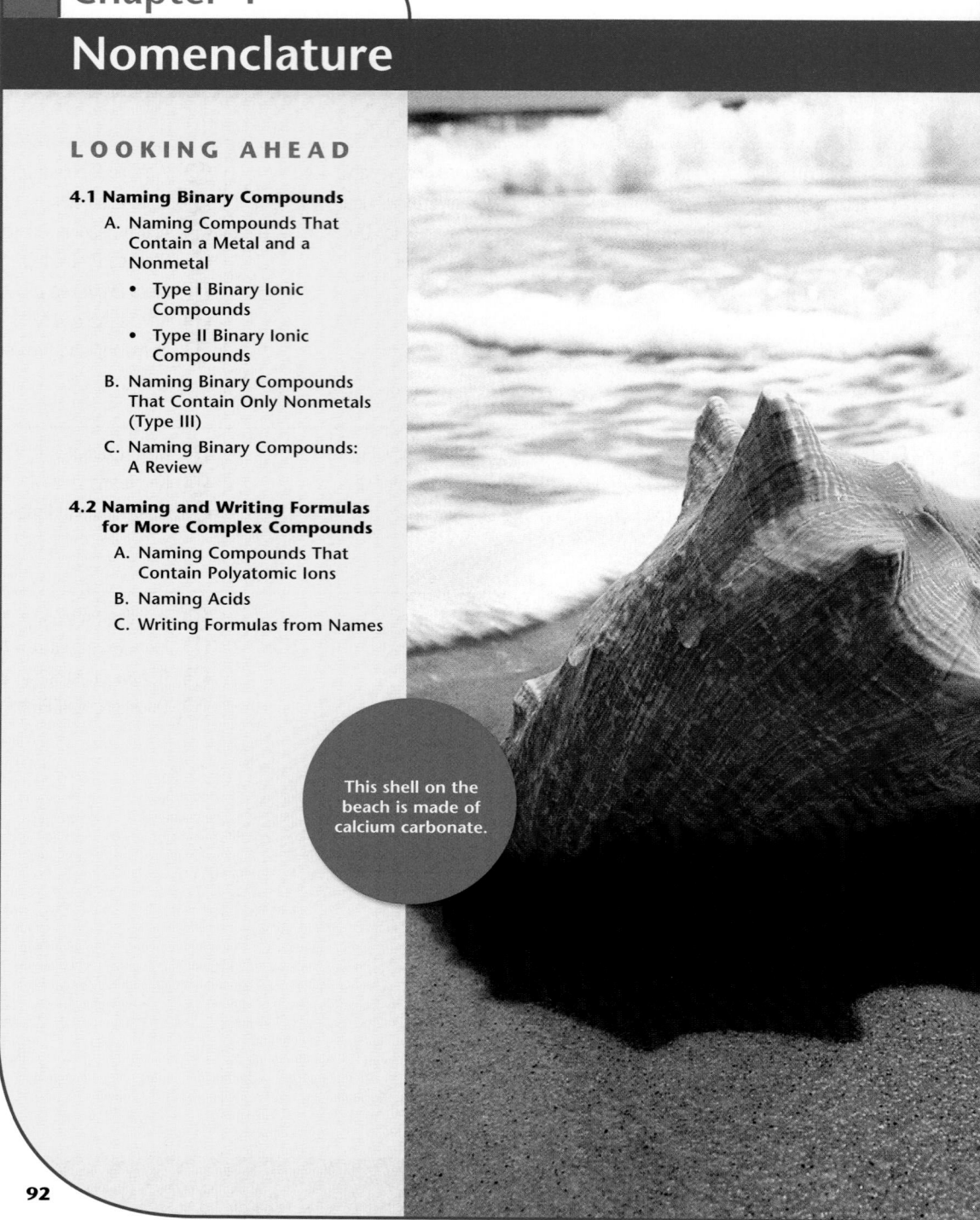

Chapter 4

Nomenclature

LOOKING AHEAD

This shell on the beach is made of calcium carbonate.

92

4

IN YOUR LIFE

As young children one of the most important things we learned was the names of objects. As we developed, it was important to learn the accepted names for things. For example, if a little girl wants *milk*, but says *bananas*, a great deal of frustration occurs both for the caretaker and the child. To communicate, we need to have names for things that are agreed on by everyone. The sentence "I drove downtown on the freeway, to buy some DVDs" would be meaningless to people who did not know the meaning of downtown, freeway, or DVD.

As we learn new things in school, we have to learn new languages. Mathematics has its own language, computers have a characteristic language, and if we play a particular sport, it has a language of its own.

Learning chemistry requires learning a new language. Although we use the word *plastic* in everyday life to describe many objects, chemists require names for these materials that are more precise. For example, plastic milk jugs, garden furniture, and trash cans are made of polyethylene while disposable foam cups and egg cartons are made of polystyrene. In this chapter we will learn the systematic names of chemicals so we can talk "chemistry" to each other.

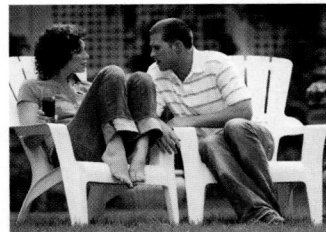

WHAT DO YOU KNOW?

Prereading Questions

1. What is the chemical name for table salt? What is the chemical formula for table salt?

2. What is meant by the term *compound*? Provide an example, and name if it you can.

3. Provide the name for each of the following symbols: Na, K, Ca, O, F, Cl.

4. Using a periodic table, predict the charge of the following atoms when they are part of an ionic compound: Na, K, Ca, O, F, Cl.

5. Have you ever heard of an an *acid*? Can you provide a formula and a name for an acid?

Nomenclature • Chapter 4 • **93**

TECHNOLOGY IN THE CLASSROOM

 Transparencies
Figures: 4.1, 4.2, 4.3
Tables: 4.1, 4.2, 4.4

 Power Presentation DVD
  PowerPoint Slides
  eEdition
  EasyPlanner

 Lab Generator CD
English Summaries CD
Spanish Summaries CD
ML Test Generator

 classzone.com

Assign students to read Section 4.1 and to answer the Review Questions at the end of the section before coming to class.

 Active Learning
Team Learning Worksheet

After introducing the material in Section 4.1 in class, place students in groups and have them work together on **Section 4.1: Team Learning Worksheet.**

Homework

You may wish to assign these selected end-of-chapter problems as homework for this section: 1, 3, 4, 5, 6, 8, 10, 12

Additional end-of-chapter problems can be used for extra practice.

 TEACHING TIP

Stress that learning the language of chemistry by naming compounds and writing their formulas is fundamental to being successful in chemistry. Tell students that they will use this skill for the remainder of the course in everything they do.

4.1.A Naming Compounds That Contain a Metal and a Nonmetal
Objective To learn to name binary compounds of a metal and a nonmetal

 TEACHING TIP

Bring in food labels and have students write formulas for as many of the ingredients as they can. It is encouraging for students to be able to identify more ingredients as they learn more about naming compounds throughout the course.

SECTION 4.1
Naming Binary Compounds

Key Terms
- Binary compound
- Binary ionic compound

Objectives
- *To learn to name binary compounds of a metal and nonmetal*
- *To learn to name binary compounds containing only nonmetals*
- *To summarize the naming of all types of binary compounds*

When chemistry was an infant science, there was no system for naming compounds. Names such as sugar of lead, blue vitriol, quicklime, Epsom salts, milk of magnesia, gypsum, and laughing gas were coined by early chemists. Such names are called *common names*. As our knowledge of chemistry grew, it became clear that using common names for compounds was not practical. More than four million chemical compounds are currently known. Memorizing common names for all these compounds would be impossible.

The solution, of course, is a *system* for naming compounds in which the name tells something about the composition of the compound. After learning the system, you should be able to name a compound when you are given its formula. Conversely, you should be able to construct a compound's formula, given its name. In this chapter we will specify the most important rules for naming compounds other than organic compounds (those based on chains of carbon atoms).

An artist using plaster of Paris, a gypsum plaster

Binary ionic compound
A two-element compound consisting of a cation and an anion

A. Naming Compounds That Contain a Metal and a Nonmetal

As we saw earlier, when a metal such as sodium combines with a nonmetal such as chlorine, the resulting compound contains ions. The metal loses one or more electrons to become a cation, and the nonmetal gains one or more electrons to form an anion. The resulting substance is called a **binary ionic compound**. Binary ionic compounds contain a positive ion (cation), which is always written first in the formula, and a negative ion (anion). *To name these compounds we simply name the ions.*

In this section we will consider binary ionic compounds of two types based on the cations they contain. Certain metal atoms form only one cation. For example,

- The Na atom always forms Na^+, *never* Na^{2+} or Na^{3+},
- Cs always forms Cs^+, Ca always forms Ca^{2+}, and
- Al always forms Al^{3+}.

We will call compounds that contain this type of metal atom Type I binary compounds and the cations they contain Type I cations. Examples of Type I cations are Na^+, Ca^{2+}, Cs^+, and Al^{3+}.

Other metal atoms can form two or more cations. For example,

- Cr can form Cr^{2+} and Cr^{3+} and
- Cu can form Cu^+ and Cu^{2+}.

We will call such ions Type II cations and their compounds Type II binary compounds.

Type I	Type II
Na → Na^+	Cr → Cr^{2+}
Cs → Cs^+	↘ Cr^{3+}
Ca → Ca^{2+}	Cu → Cu^+
Al → Al^{3+}	↘ Cu^{2+}

Type I compounds: The metal present forms only one type of cation.
Type II compounds: The metal present can form two (or more) cations that have different charges.

94 • Chapter 4 • Nomenclature

Meeting Individual Needs
READING CONCEPTS

To assist students in learning how to name chemical compounds, have them make flashcards. If students are unfamiliar with flashcards, have them read *Making and Using Flashcards* located in the *Teacher Resources.*

Some common cations and anions and their names are listed in **Table 4.1.** You should memorize these. They are an essential part of your chemical vocabulary.

 Table 4.1

TABLE 4.1

Common Simple Cations and Anions

Cation	Name	Anion	Name*
H^+	hydrogen	H^-	hydride
Li^+	lithium	F^-	fluoride
Na^+	sodium	Cl^-	chloride
K^+	potassium	Br^-	bromide
Cs^+	cesium	I^-	iodide
Be^{2+}	beryllium	O^{2-}	oxide
Mg^{2+}	magnesium	S^{2-}	sulfide
Ca^{2+}	calcium		
Ba^{2+}	barium		
Al^{3+}	aluminum		
Ag^+	silver		

*The root is given in color.

 information

A simple cation has the same name as its parent element.

 Active Reading Question

Name three metal atoms which form only one cation. Include the charge for each.

Type I Binary Ionic Compounds

The following rules apply for Type I ionic compounds:

Rules for Naming Type I Ionic Compounds

1. The cation is always named first and the anion second.

2. A simple cation (obtained from a single atom) takes its name from the name of the element. For example, Na^+ is called sodium in the names of compounds containing this ion.

3. A simple anion (obtained from a single atom) is named by taking the first part of the element name (the root) and adding *-ide*. Thus the Cl^- ion is called chloride.

4. Write the name for the compound by combining the names of the ions.

We will illustrate these rules by naming a few compounds. For example, the compound NaI is called sodium iodide. It contains Na^+ (the sodium cation, named for the parent metal) and I^- (iodide: the root of iodine plus *-ide*). Similarly, the compound CaO is called calcium oxide because it contains Ca^{2+} (the calcium cation) and O^{2-} (the oxide anion).

TEACHING TIPS

- Students can determine the charges of the ions in Table 4.1 from their positions on the periodic table, with the exception of Ag^+. Students should appreciate that the periodic table contains a great deal of information. It is a valuable resource.

- Type I ionic compounds are named simply by "naming the ions." Type I compounds are relatively easy for students to name. Review the rules for each type of compound as you progress through the chapter. This reinforcement will help students to build upon their knowledge.

 Active Reading Question

Answers will vary. Examples include sodium (Na^+), potassium (K^+), and calcium (Ca^{2+}).

Meeting Individual Needs
VISUAL LEARNERS

Using interactive games will help students memorize common elements, compounds, formulas, etc. Have students create a memory game to play to help remember the common simple cations and anions. On separate index cards, students write the name of each cation or anion. Then they write the corresponding symbols on another set of index cards. They shuffle the sets of cards together and place the cards face down in rows. A student turns over two cards. If the cards are a symbol and name that correspond, then they are a match and the two cards are removed. If not, then the cards are flipped back over and the student tries again for a match.

$$NaI \qquad\qquad CaO$$

Na⁺ ... I⁻ .... Ca²⁺ ... O²⁻
sodium   iodide   calcium   oxide

The rules for naming binary compounds are also illustrated by the following table.

Examples of Binary Ionic Compounds		
Compound	Ions Present	Name
NaCl	Na^+, Cl^-	sodium chloride
KI	K^+, I^-	potassium iodide
CaS	Ca^{2+}, S^{2-}	calcium sulfide
CsBr	Cs^+, Br^-	cesium bromide
MgO	Mg^{2+}, O^{2-}	magnesium oxide

It is important to note that in the *formulas* of ionic compounds, simple ions are represented by the element symbol: Cl means Cl^-, Na means Na^+, and so on. However, when *individual ions* are shown, the charge is always included. Thus the formula of potassium bromide is written KBr, but when the potassium and bromide ions are shown individually, they are written K^+ and Br^-.

CHEMISTRY IN YOUR WORLD

Connection to History

Sugar of Lead

In ancient Roman society it was common to boil fermented grape juice in a lead-lined vessel, driving off much of the water to produce a very sweet, thick syrup called *sapa*. This syrup was often used as a sweetener for many types of food and drink.

We now realize that a major component of this syrup was lead acetate, $Pb(C_2H_3O_2)_2$. This compound has a very sweet taste—hence its original name, sugar of lead.

Many historians believe that the fall of the Roman Empire was due at least in part to lead poisoning, which causes lethargy and mental malfunctions. One major source of this lead was the sapa syrup. In addition, the Romans' highly advanced plumbing system employed lead water pipes, which allowed lead to be leached into their drinking water.

Sadly, this story is more relevant to today's society than you might think. Lead-based solder was widely used for many years to connect the copper pipes in water systems in homes and commercial buildings. There is evidence that dangerous amounts of lead can be leached from these soldered joints into drinking water. In fact, large quantities of lead have been found in the water that some drinking fountains and water coolers dispense. In response to these problems, the U.S. Congress has passed a law banning lead from the solder used in plumbing systems for drinking water.

A carving showing how lead-lined vessels were used

96 • Chapter 4 • Nomenclature

TEACHING TIP

Point out that the net charge of all of the examples of binary ionic compounds given is zero. This rule is very important when trying to determine the formula of a binary ionic compound from its name. The examples given here each have one cation and one anion. Example 4.1 provides examples in which one of the subscripts is greater than one.

Chemistry in Your World

Sugar of Lead

"Sugar of Lead" provides an interesting way to connect history to the chemistry classroom. Many reputable scholars believe that lead poisoning of the ruling classes of Rome was a contributing factor to the fall of the Roman Empire. The syrup called *sapa* was, in effect, the first artificial sweetener—and a very dangerous one at that.

Now might be a good time to discuss other incidences of heavy metal poisoning, such as the "Mad Hatters"—people working in the hat-making industry in England in the eighteenth century who suffered personality changes from being exposed to the mercury compounds used to change wool into felt. It has also been rumored that Charles II of England, an amateur chemist who had a lab in his castle, may have died from mercury poisoning.

Some evidence indicates that Isaac Newton, who dabbled in chemistry as well as physics, may have suffered mercury poisoning severe enough to cause him to interrupt his studies to travel to the country for several months to recover.

EXAMPLE 4.1

Naming Type I Binary Compounds

Name each binary compound.

    a. CsF   **b.** AlCl$_3$ **c.** MgI$_2$

Solution

We will name these compounds by systematically following the rules given on page 95.

    a. CsF

    Step 1 Identify the cation and anion. Cs is in Group 1, so we know it will form the 1+ ion Cs$^+$. Because F is in Group 7, it forms the 1− ion F$^-$.

    Step 2 Name the cation. Cs$^+$ is simply called cesium, the same as the element name.

    Step 3 Name the anion. F$^-$ is called fluoride: we use the root name of the element plus *-ide*.

    Step 4 Name the compound by combining the names of the individual ions. The name for CsF is cesium fluoride. (Remember that the name of the cation is always given first.)

b.

Compound	Ions Present	Ion Names	Comments
AlCl$_3$ Cation →	Al^{3+}	aluminum	Al (Group 3) always forms Al^{3+}.
Anion →	Cl$^-$	chloride	Cl (Group 7) always forms Cl$^-$.

The name of AlCl$_3$ is aluminum chloride.

c.

Compound	Ions Present	Ion Names	Comments
MgI$_2$ Cation →	Mg^{2+}	magnesium	Mg (Group 2) always forms Mg^{2+}.
Anion →	I$^-$	iodide	I (Group 7) gains one electron to form I$^-$.

The name of MgI$_2$ is magnesium iodide.

Practice Problem • Exercise 4.1

Name the following compounds.

    a. Rb$_2$O   **b.** SrI$_2$ **c.** K$_2$S

Let's Review

- Compounds formed from metals and nonmetals are ionic.
- In an ionic compound the cation is always named first.
- The *net* charge on an ionic compound is always zero. In CsF, one of each type of ion (Cs$^+$ and F$^-$) is required: (1+) + (1−) = 0 charge. In AlCl$_3$, however, three Cl$^-$ ions are needed to balance the charge of Al^{3+}: (3+) + 3(1−) = 0 charge. In MgI$_2$, two I$^-$ ions are needed for each Mg^{2+} ion: (2+) + 2(1−) = 0 charge.

4.1 • Naming Binary Compounds • **97**

EXAMPLE 4.1

More Examples

Name each binary compound.

1. KCl
   potassium chloride

2. ZnS
   zinc sulfide

3. CaBr$_2$
   calcium bromide

4. BaH$_2$
   barium hydride

5. Al$_2$S$_3$
   aluminum sulfide

Answer to Practice Problem 4.1

a. rubidium oxide

b. strontium iodide

c. potassium sulfide

Meeting Individual Needs

INCLUSION STRATEGIES

Encourage students to create a table to help organize information when naming binary compounds. Students should also write the Rules for Naming Type I Ionic Compounds on separate index cards. Students can then align the correct rule with the column they need to complete.

Students should use the periodic table when they cannot remember whether a cation has more than one possible charge. Cations from Groups 1, 2, or 3 have only one possible charge, which is the same as the group number. Cations formed from transition metals may have more than one possible charge.

CHEMISTRY IN YOUR WORLD

Science, Technology, and Society

How Can Water Be Hard or Soft?

Water, like most liquids we use every day, is not 100% pure. Floating about in our tap water are all kinds of ions and molecules collected from the places where our water has been. Are these ions and molecules harmful to us? It depends on what they are. The most common impurities in tap water are calcium and magnesium ions. They dissolve into the water as it passes through soil rich in limestone. Calcium and magnesium ions are important in our diets, but when dissolved in water they can have some irritating properties as well. It is "hard" to get soaps to lather—and so we call water with lots of these ions "hard water."

The calcium and magnesium compounds in hard water also leave a white scale or residue inside tea kettles, coffee pots, irons, and other appliances that use water. This scale can build up and keep the appliance from working properly. When soap is used

with hard water, a new compound is formed—calcium or magnesium stearate—that clouds the water and makes a ring in the bathtub and makes clothes appear dingy after washing.

How can we make water soft? Some homeowners install a water softener, which is really an ion exchanger. It is filled with sodium chloride (salt), which exchanges sodium ions for the calcium and magnesium ions in the hard water, making the water soft. How does this exchange alter the behavior of the water? The sodium ions do not react with carbonates to form the white scaly deposits or react with soaps to form soap scum. They produce no negative effects in drinking water, except in people who must limit their sodium intake because of high blood pressure or heart disease. A bonus—your shampoo and soap make much more lather, so less is needed to do the job!

*i*nformation

Type II binary ionic compounds contain a metal that can form more than one type of cation.

Type II Binary Ionic Compounds

So far we have considered binary ionic compounds (Type I) containing metals that always give the same cation. For example, sodium always forms the Na^+ ion, calcium always forms the Ca^{2+} ion, and aluminum always forms the Al^{3+} ion. As we said previously, we can predict with certainty that each Group 1 metal will give a 1+ cation and each Group 2 metal will give a 2+ cation. And aluminum always forms Al^{3+}.

However, many metals can form more than one type of cation. For example, lead (Pb) can form Pb^{2+} or Pb^{4+} in ionic compounds. Also, iron (Fe) can form Fe^{2+} or Fe^{3+}, chromium (Cr) can form Cr^{2+} or Cr^{3+}, gold (Au) can form Au^+ or Au^{3+}, and so on. This means that if we saw the name gold chloride, we wouldn't know whether it referred to the compound AuCl (containing Au^+ and Cl^-) or the compound $AuCl_3$ (containing Au^{3+} and three Cl^- ions). Therefore, we need a way of specifying which cation is present in compounds containing metals that can form more than one type of cation.

Chemists have decided to deal with this situation by using a Roman numeral to specify the charge on the cation. To see how this works, consider the compound $FeCl_2$. Iron can form Fe^{2+} or Fe^{3+}, so we must first decide which of these cations is present. We can determine the

Chemistry in Your World
How Can Water Be Hard or Soft?

"How Can Water Be Hard or Soft?" emphasizes again that the concept of a pure substance is really hypothetical—all substances are contaminated to some extent. This might be a good time to introduce the idea that ions in solution can react to form solids—in this case, soap scum. (The topic of precipitation reactions will be covered in detail in Chapter 8.) Water softening involves exchanging the ions such as Ca^{2+}

and Mg^{2+} that form precipitates with soap, for ions such as Na^+ that do not form solids with the soap anions.

charge on the iron cation, because we know it must balance the charge on the two 1− anions (the chloride ions).

$$FeCl_2$$
$$Fe^{?+} \quad 2Cl^-$$
$$\text{(?+)} + 2\,\text{(1−)} = 0$$
$$2+ \quad + \quad 2- \quad = 0$$

So the charge on Fe = 2+.

The compound $FeCl_2$, then, contains one Fe^{2+} ion and two Cl^- ions. We call this compound iron(II) chloride, where the II tells the charge of the iron cation. That is, Fe^{2+} is called iron(II). Likewise, Fe^{3+} is called iron(III). And $FeCl_3$, which contains one Fe^{3+} ion and three Cl^- ions, is called iron(III) chloride.

> The Roman numeral tells the charge on the ion, not the number of ions present in the compound.

Note that in the above examples the Roman numeral for the cation turned out to be the same as the subscript needed for the anion (to balance the charge). This is often not the case. For example, consider the compound PbO_2.

$$PbO_2$$
$$Pb^{?+} \quad 2O^{2-}$$
$$\text{(?+)} + 2\,\text{(2−)} = 0$$
$$4+ \quad + \quad 4- \quad = 0$$

So the charge on Pb = 4+.

The charge on the lead ion must be 4+ to balance the 4− charge of the two oxide ions. The name of PbO_2 is therefore lead(IV) oxide, where the IV indicates the presence of the Pb^{4+} cation.

There is an older system for naming ionic compounds containing metals that form two cations. The ion with the higher charge has a name ending in *-ic*, and the one with the lower charge has a name ending in *-ous*. In this system, for example, Fe^{3+} is called the ferric ion, and Fe^{2+} is called the ferrous ion. The names for $FeCl_3$ and $FeCl_2$, in this system, are ferric chloride and ferrous chloride, respectively. **Table 4.2** gives both names for many Type II cations. We will use the system of Roman numerals exclusively in this text; the other system is falling into disuse.

information

$FeCl_3$ must contain Fe^{3+} to balance the charge of three Cl^- ions.

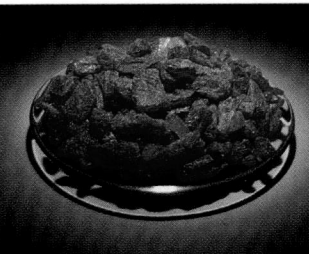

Copper(II) sulfate crystals

TABLE 4.2

Common Type II Cations

Ion	Systematic Name	Older Name	Ion	Systematic Name	Older Name
Fe^{3+}	iron(III)	ferric	Sn^{4+}	tin(IV)	stannic
Fe^{2+}	iron(II)	ferrous	Sn^{2+}	tin(II)	stannous
Cu^{2+}	copper(II)	cupric	Pb^{4+}	lead(IV)	plumbic
Cu^{+}	copper(I)	cuprous	Pb^{2+}	lead(II)	plumbous
Co^{3+}	cobalt(III)	cobaltic	Hg^{2+}	mercury(II)	mercuric
Co^{2+}	cobalt(II)	cobaltous	Hg_2^{2+}*	mercury(I)	mercurous

*Mercury(I) ions always occur bound together in pairs to form Hg_2^{2+}.

TEACHING TIPS

- We use Roman numerals only when they are required for clarity. It is not necessary, for example, to name NaCl sodium(I) chloride, because the sodium ion always has a charge of 1+.

- Stress that the Roman numeral indicates the charge on the cation. It does not indicate the number of anions present in the compound.

- If a cation is not found in Table 4.2, its charge can be obtained from the number and type of anions present in a given compound. This information does not indicate whether a Roman numeral is required in the name of the compound, however.

MISCONCEPTION Chemistry

You cannot emphasize enough that the Roman numeral in a name indicates the charge of the ion, not the subscript in the formula. Because there are many examples in which the Roman numeral and the subscript are the same (such as iron(II) chloride, $FeCl_2$, and iron(III) chloride, $FeCl_3$), students are likely to have this misconception. Use iron(II) oxide (FeO) as a counter-example, and explicitly discuss lead(IV) oxide (PbO_2) as shown in the text.

MINI-DEMO

Bring samples of copper(I) chloride and copper(II) chloride to class. Show students the difference in the compounds' colors, indicating a difference in the copper ions present. Other compounds that show similar differences in color with different ion charges are cobalt(II) chloride and cobalt(III) chloride.

TECHNOLOGY

 Table 4.2

EXAMPLE 4.2

More Examples

Name each binary compound.

1. $CoCl_3$
   cobalt(III) chloride

2. CuI
   copper(I) iodide

3. $SnBr_4$
   tin(IV) bromide

4. $HgCl_2$
   mercury(II) chloride

5. PbS
   lead(II) sulfide

CRITICAL THINKING ?

We modify the system for naming ionic compounds when a transition metal is present because most transition metals can have multiple charges. If transition metals had only one possible charge, a name such as iron oxide would be acceptable (just as potassium oxide is acceptable). We would not need to use the Roman numerals. It is important for students to realize that our rules are always as simple as possible. That is, we never use Roman numerals (or prefixes or suffixes) unless it is necessary to make the name clear. The idea that science keeps rules and models as simple as possible is an important one for students to understand.

To help distinguish between Type I and Type II cations:
- Group 1 and 2 metals are always Type I.
- Transition metals are almost always Type II.

EXAMPLE 4.2

Naming Type II Binary Compounds

Give the systematic name of each of the following compounds.

   a. CuCl **c.** Fe_2O_3 **e.** $PbCl_4$

   b. HgO **d.** MnO_2

Solution

All these compounds include a metal that can form more than one type of cation; thus we must first determine the charge on each cation. We do this by recognizing that a compound must be electrically neutral; that is, the positive and negative charges must balance exactly. We will use the known charge on the anion to determine the charge of the cation.

   a. In CuCl we recognize the anion as Cl^-. To determine the charge on the copper cation, we use the principle of charge balance.

$$\underset{\substack{\text{Charge} \\ \text{on copper} \\ \text{ion}}}{(?+)} + \underset{\substack{\text{Charge} \\ \text{on } Cl^-}}{(1-)} = \underset{\substack{\text{Net charge} \\ \text{(must be zero)}}}{0}$$

In this case, ?+ must be 1+ because $(1+) + (1-) = 0$. Thus the copper cation must be Cu^+. Now we can name the compound by using the regular steps.

Compound	Ions Present	Ion Names	Comments
CuCl — Cation	Cu^+	copper(I)	Copper forms other cations (it is a transition metal), so we must include the I to specify its charge.
CuCl — Anion	Cl^-	chloride	

The name of CuCl is copper(I) chloride.

   b. In HgO we recognize the O^{2-} anion. To yield zero net charge, the cation must be Hg^{2+}.

Compound	Ions Present	Ion Names	Comments
HgO — Cation	Hg^{2+}	mercury(II)	The II is necessary to specify the charge.
HgO — Anion	O^{2-}	oxide	

The name of HgO is mercury(II) oxide.

CRITICAL THINKING ?

We can use the periodic table to predict the stable ions formed by many atoms. For example, the atoms in column 1 always form 1+ ions. The transition metals, however, can form more than one type of stable ion.

What if each transition metal ion had only one possible charge? How would the naming of compounds be different?

Meeting Individual Needs
ENGLISH LANGUAGE LEARNERS

Students may have heard the term *neutral* in other contexts, such as describing color, referring to a person's not taking a position on an issue, or referring to an object's not having distinguishing characteristics. Point out that in this context, *neutral* means no electrical charge, or zero charge.

c. Because Fe_2O_3 contains three O^{2-} anions, the charge on the iron cation must be 3+.

$$2(3+) + 3(2-) = 0$$

Fe^{3+} O^{2-} Net charge

Compound	Ions Present	Ion Names	Comments
Fe_2O_3 Cation → Fe^{3+}		iron(III)	Iron is a transition metal and requires a III to specify the charge on the cation.
Anion → O^{2-}		oxide	

The name of Fe_2O_3 is iron(III) oxide.

d. MnO_2 contains two O^{2-} anions, so the charge on the manganese cation is 4+.

$$(4+) + 2(2-) = 0$$

Mn^{4+} O^{2-} Net charge

Compound	Ions Present	Ion Names	Comments
MnO_2 Cation → Mn^{4+}		manganese (IV)	Manganese is a transition metal and requires a IV to specify the charge on the cation.
Anion → O^{2-}		oxide	

The name of MnO_2 is manganese(IV) oxide.

e. Because $PbCl_4$ contains four Cl^- anions, the charge on the lead cation is 4+.

$$(4+) + 4(1-) = 0$$

Pb^{4+} Cl^- Net charge

Compound	Ions Present	Ion Names	Comments
$PbCl_4$ Cation → Pb^{4+}		lead(IV)	Lead forms both Pb^{2+} and Pb^{4+}, so a Roman numeral is required.
Anion → Cl^-		chloride	

The name for $PbCl_4$ is lead(IV) chloride.

The use of a Roman numeral in a systematic name for a compound is required only when more than one ionic compound forms between a given pair of elements. This occurs most often for compounds that contain transition metals, which frequently form more than one cation.

Metals that form only one cation do not need to be identified by a Roman numeral.

Answers will vary. Examples include iron (Fe^{2+} and Fe^{3+}), copper (Cu^+ and Cu^{2+}), and lead (Pb^{2+} and Pb^{4+}).

EXAMPLE 4.3

More Examples

Name each binary compound.

1. SnI_4
   tin(IV) iodide

2. K_3N
   potassium nitride

3. HgO
   mercury(II) oxide

4. RbF
   rubidium fluoride

5. NaH
   sodium hydride

6. CrF_2
   chromium(II) fluoride

7. $MgBr_2$
   magnesium bromide

8. MnI_2
   manganese(II) iodide

9. Li_2O
   lithium oxide

Answer to Practice Problem 4.3

a. $PbBr_2$ must contain Pb^{2+}—named lead(II)—to balance the charges of the two Br^- ions. Thus the name is lead(II) bromide. The compound $PbBr_4$ must contain Pb^{4+}—named lead(IV)—to balance the charges of the four Br^- ions. The name is therefore lead(IV) bromide.

b. FeS contains the S^{2-} ion, so the iron cation present must be Fe^{2+}, iron(II). The name is iron(II) sulfide. Fe_2S_3 contains three S^{2-} ions and two iron cations of unknown charge. We can determine the iron charge from the following:

$$2(?+) + 3(2-) = 0$$

   ↑   ↑

Iron S^{2-}
charge charge

In this case, ? must be 3 because $2(3+) + 3(2-) = 0$. Thus Fe_2S_3 contains Fe^{3+} and S^{2-}, and its name is iron(III) sulfide.

Common metals that do not require Roman numerals are the Group 1 elements, which form only 1+ ions; the Group 2 elements, which form only 2+ ions; and such Group 3 metals as aluminum and gallium, which form only 3+ ions.

Name three metal atoms which form more than one cation. Include all charges for each.

As shown in Example 4.2, when a metal ion that forms more than one type of cation is present, the charge on the metal ion must be determined by balancing the positive and negative charges of the compound. To do this, you must be able to recognize the common anions and you must know their charges (see Table 4.1).

EXAMPLE 4.3

Naming Binary Ionic Compounds: Summary

Give the systematic name of each of the following compounds.

    a. $CoBr_2$ **c.** Al_2O_3
    b. $CaCl_2$ **d.** $CrCl_3$

Solution

	Compound	Ions and Names	Compound Name	Comments
a.	$CoBr_2$ → Co^{2+} cobalt(II) → Br^- bromide		cobalt(II) bromide	Cobalt is a transition metal; the name of the compound must have a Roman numeral. The two Br^- ions must be balanced by a Co^{2+} cation.
b.	$CaCl_2$ → Ca^{2+} calcium → Cl^- chloride		calcium chloride	Calcium, an alkaline earth metal, forms only the Ca^{2+} ion. A Roman numeral is not necessary.
c.	Al_2O_3 → Al^{3+} aluminum → O^{2-} oxide		aluminum oxide	Aluminum forms only Al^{3+}. A Roman numeral is not necessary.
d.	$CrCl_3$ → Cr^{3+} chromium(III) → Cl^- chloride		chromium(III) chloride	Chromium is a transition metal. The name of the compound must have a Roman numeral. $CrCl_3$ contains Cr^{3+}.

Practice Problem • Exercise 4.3

Give the names of the following compounds.

    a. $PbBr_2$ and $PbBr_4$ **c.** $AlBr_3$ **e.** $CoCl_3$
    b. FeS and Fe_2S_3 **d.** Na_2S

c. Aluminum bromide. Because aluminum forms only Al^{3+}, no Roman numeral is required.

d. Sodium sulfide. Because sodium forms only Na^+, no Roman numeral is needed.

e. The cobalt cation must be Co^{3+}, which is named cobalt(III). Thus the name of $CoCl_3$ is cobalt(III) chloride.

HANDS-ON CHEMISTRY   • MINI-LAB •

Name Game I: Ionic Compounds

Materials
- index cards

Procedure
1. Make two sets of flashcards. Write the name of an ion on one side of a card and its symbol and charge on the other side.
   - Set A: all of the alkali and alkaline earth metals, and iron(II) and iron(III).
   - Set B: all of the nonmetals from Groups 5A, 6A, and 7A.

2. Randomly pick one card from Set A and one card from Set B. Write the proper formula for the ionic compound made from these two ions, and name the compound.

3. Repeat step 2 until you answer ten in a row correctly.

Results/Analysis
1. Make sure that you can write formulas and names when given either the names or the symbols and charges of the ions.

The following flow chart is useful when you are naming binary ionic compounds:

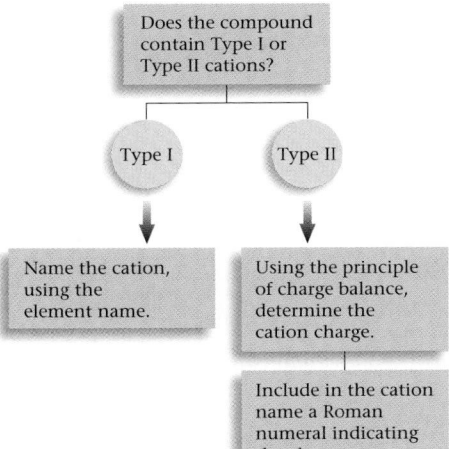

ℹ️ **information**

Sometimes transition metals form only one ion, such as silver, which forms Ag^+; zinc, which forms Zn^{2+}; and cadmium, which forms Cd^{2+}. In these cases, chemists do not use a Roman numeral, although it is not "wrong" to do so.

Active Reading Question

What suffix usually tells you the named compound is a binary compound?

B. Naming Binary Compounds That Contain Only Nonmetals (Type III)

Binary compounds that contain only nonmetals are named in accordance with a system similar in some ways to the rules for naming binary ionic compounds, but there are important differences.

Type III binary compounds contain only nonmetals.

4.1 • Naming Binary Compounds • **103**

Active Reading Question

The suffix *-ide* tells us the named compound is a binary compound.

4.1.B Naming Binary Compounds That Contain Only Nonmetals (Type III)

Objective To learn how to name binary compounds containing only nonmetals

🔬 **LABORATORY**
EXPERIMENT 15:
Forming and Naming Ionic Compounds, Microscale

Hands-On Chemistry
MINI-LAB

Name Game I: Ionic Compounds

Materials Each student/group will need 27 index cards. These can be reused each class period.

Purpose Students will learn to determine the formulas of simple ionic compounds from the elements involved, to name simple ionic compounds, and to determine the formula from the name.

Discussion Understanding chemistry requires that students both understand fundamental principles and know the language of chemistry. They should be familiar with the periodic table, know names and symbols of some elements, and know how to name compounds. You can vary this activity to accommodate time limits.

- Students need to learn the prefixes given in Table 4.3. This effort will make naming compounds and writing formulas much easier.

- Like Roman numerals, prefixes are used only for clarity. For example, two carbon oxides are possible, and we must use prefixes to differentiate between them (carbon monoxide and carbon dioxide). We make the rules more complicated only when it is required.

- At times when naming Type III compounds, two vowels appear together (one from the prefix and one from the root name). We eliminate the vowel on the end of the prefix to make the pronunciation of the name easier. For example, tetraoxide becomes tetroxide and monooxide becomes monoxide.

EXAMPLE 4.4

More Examples

Name the following Type III compounds.

1. I_2O_7
   diiodine heptoxide

2. CO_2
   carbon dioxide

3. CF_4
   carbon tetrafluoride

4. NH_3
   ammonia

5. PCl_3
   phosphorus trichloride

 Answer to Practice Problem 4.4

Compound	Individual Names	Prefixes	Name
a. CCl_4	carbon chloride	none tetra-	carbon tetrachloride
b. NO_2	nitrogen oxide	none di-	nitrogen dioxide
c. IF_5	iodine fluoride	none penta-	iodine pentafluoride

The following rules cover the naming of these compounds.

Rules for Naming Type III Binary Compounds

1. The first element in the formula is named first, and the full element name is used.

2. The second element is named as though it were an anion.

3. Prefixes are used to denote the numbers of atoms present. These prefixes are given in **Table 4.3.**

4. The prefix *mono-* is never used for naming the first element. For example, CO is called carbon monoxide, *not* monocarbon monoxide.

 EXAMPLE 4.4

Naming Type III Binary Compounds

Name the following binary compounds, which contain two nonmetals (Type III).

a. BF_3 b. NO   c. N_2O_5

Solution

a. BF_3

TABLE 4.3

Prefixes Used to Indicate Numbers in Chemical Names

Prefix	Number Indicated
mono-	1
di-	2
tri-	3
tetra-	4
penta-	5
hexa-	6
hepta-	7
octa-	8

Rule 1 Name the first element, using the full element name: boron.

Rule 2 Name the second element as though it were an anion: fluoride.

Rule 3 and 4 Use prefixes to denote numbers of atoms. One boron atom: do not use *mono-* in first position. Three fluorine atoms: use the prefix *tri-*.

The name of BF_3 is boron trifluoride.

b.

Compound	Individual Names	Prefixes	Comments
NO	nitrogen	none	*Mono-* is not used for
	oxide	mono-	the first element.

The name for NO is nitrogen monoxide. Note that the second *o* in *mono-* has been dropped for easier pronunciation. The *common* name for NO, which is often used by chemists, is nitric oxide.

c.

Compound	Individual Names	Prefixes	Comments
N_2O_5	nitrogen	di-	two N atoms
	oxide	penta-	five O atoms

The name for N_2O_5 is dinitrogen pentoxide. The *a* in *penta-* has been dropped for easier pronunciation.

✔ Practice Problem • Exercise 4.4

Name the following compounds.

a. CCl_4 b. NO_2 c. IF_5

Meeting Individual Needs
ENGLISH LANGUAGE LEARNERS

Relate the prefixes given in Table 4.3 to words that are familiar to most students. For instance: *mono-* monopoly, monologue, monorail; *di-* divide; *tri-* triangle, tricycle, trilogy; *penta-* pentagon; *octa-* octopus, octagon.

A piece of copper metal about to be placed in nitric acid

Copper reacts with nitric acid to produce colorless NO, which immediately reacts with the oxygen in the air to form reddish-brown NO_2 gas.

The previous examples illustrate that, to avoid awkward pronunciation, we often drop the final *o* or *a* of the prefix when the second element is oxygen. For example, N_2O_4 is called dinitrogen tetroxide, *not* dinitrogen tetra*o*xide, and CO is called carbon monoxide, *not* carbon mon*o*oxide.

Some compounds are always referred to by their common names. The two best examples are water and ammonia. The systematic names for H_2O and NH_3 are never used.

EXAMPLE 4.5

Naming Type III Binary Compounds: Summary

Name each of the following compounds.

   a. PCl_5 **b.** P_4O_6 **c.** SF_6 **d.** SO_3 **e.** SO_2 **f.** N_2O_3

Solution

Compound	Name
a. PCl_5	phosphorus pentachloride
b. P_4O_6	tetraphosphorus hexoxide
c. SF_6	sulfur hexafluoride
d. SO_3	sulfur trioxide
e. SO_2	sulfur dioxide
f. N_2O_3	dinitrogen trioxide

 Practice Problem • Exercise 4.5

Name the following compounds.

   a. SiO_2 **b.** O_2F_2 **c.** XeF_6

4.1 • Naming Binary Compounds • **105**

EXAMPLE 4.5

More Examples

Name the following Type III compounds.

1. CO
   carbon monoxide
2. NO_2
   nitrogen dioxide
3. SeF_6
   selenium hexafluoride
4. SiO_2
   silicon dioxide
5. H_2O
   water

Answer to Practice Problem 4.5

a. silicon dioxide
b. dioxygen difluoride
c. xenon hexafluoride

Objective To review the naming of Type I, Type II, and Type III binary compounds

 TEACHING TIPS

• Most students can name compounds if they are identified by type. This section provides an opportunity to review the types and have students practice on a variety of compounds rather than just those of a particular type.

• Students may not be aware that the rules for naming compounds are so systematic. Have students use Figure 4.1 (available as a transparency) when naming compounds to see the logical nature behind the rules for naming compounds.

CRITICAL ❓
THINKING

Naming compounds requires certain rules. While some students think this chapter includes many rules, there really are only a few relative to the number of compounds that can be named. At least two major problems arise with common names. First, common names would require a great deal of memorization (the name of each compound would have to be memorized). With a systematic approach, only the rules must be learned. Second, common names are not really common. For example, asking people in different areas if they use a grocery "bag" or "sack," or if they drink "pop" or "soda," shows that "common names" differ from one place to another.

 Active Reading Question

For a compound made of a metal and nonmetal, the numbers of cations and anions must be such that the net charge is zero. Because of this, only one formula is possible. For example, calcium oxide must be CaO (Ca^{2+} and O^{2-}), but carbon oxide is vague.

CRITICAL ❓
THINKING

What if all compounds had only common names? What problems might arise?

C. Naming Binary Compounds: A Review

Because different rules apply for naming various types of binary compounds, we will now consider an overall strategy to use for these compounds. We have considered three types of binary compounds, and naming each type requires a different procedure.

Let's Review

Type I: Ionic compounds with metals that always form a cation with the same charge

Type II: Ionic compounds with metals (usually transition metals) that form cations with various charges

Type III: Compounds that contain only nonmetals

Active Reading Question

Why are prefixes such as "mono-" and "di-" unnecessary for a compound made of a metal and a nonmetal?

In trying to determine which type of compound you are naming, use the periodic table to help you identify metals and nonmetals and to determine which elements are transition metals.

The flow chart given in **Figure 4.1** should help you as you name binary compounds of the various types.

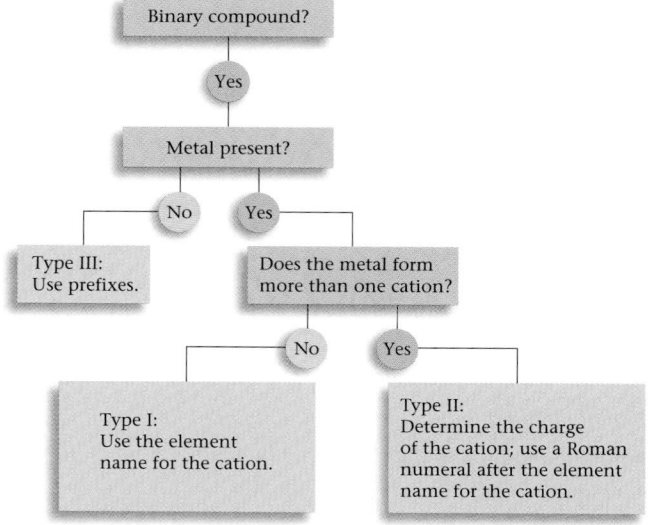

Figure 4.1
A flow chart for naming binary compounds

TECHNOLOGY

 Figure 4.1

EXAMPLE 4.6

Naming Binary Compounds: Summary

Name the following binary compounds.

a. CuO **b.** SrO **c.** B_2O_3 **d.** $TiCl_4$ **e.** K_2S **f.** OF_2 **g.** NH_3

Solution

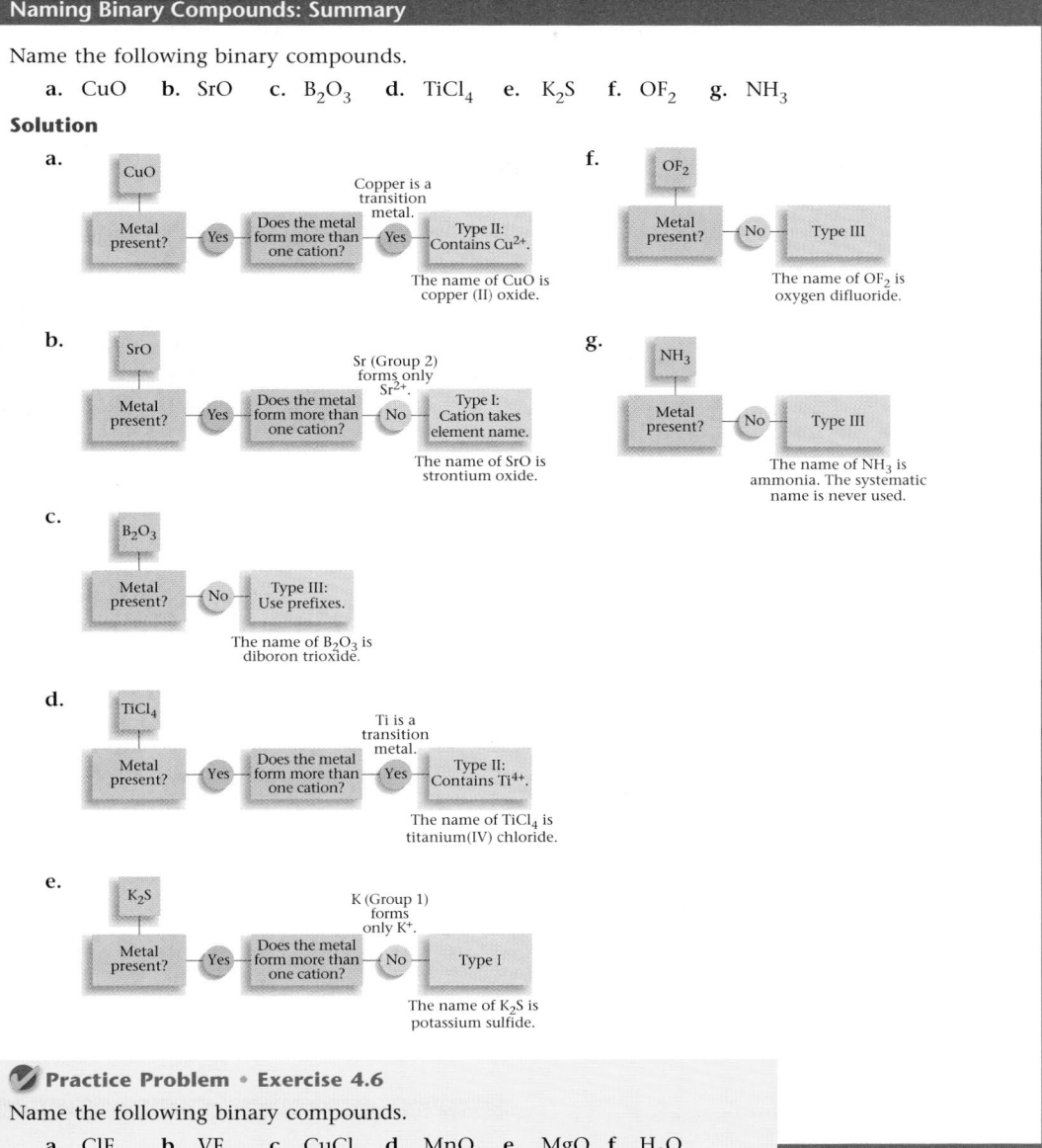

a.
CuO
Metal present? — Yes — Does the metal form more than one cation? — Yes — Copper is a transition metal. — Type II: Contains Cu^{2+}.
The name of CuO is copper (II) oxide.

b.
SrO
Metal present? — Yes — Does the metal form more than one cation? — No — Sr (Group 2) forms only Sr^{2+}. — Type I: Cation takes element name.
The name of SrO is strontium oxide.

c.
B_2O_3
Metal present? — No — Type III: Use prefixes.
The name of B_2O_3 is diboron trioxide.

d.
$TiCl_4$
Metal present? — Yes — Does the metal form more than one cation? — Yes — Ti is a transition metal. — Type II: Contains Ti^{4+}.
The name of $TiCl_4$ is titanium(IV) chloride.

e.
K_2S
Metal present? — Yes — Does the metal form more than one cation? — No — K (Group 1) forms only K^+. — Type I
The name of K_2S is potassium sulfide.

f.
OF_2
Metal present? — No — Type III
The name of OF_2 is oxygen difluoride.

g.
NH_3
Metal present? — No — Type III
The name of NH_3 is ammonia. The systematic name is never used.

✓ Practice Problem • Exercise 4.6

Name the following binary compounds.

a. ClF_3 **b.** VF_5 **c.** CuCl **d.** MnO_2 **e.** MgO **f.** H_2O

EXAMPLE 4.6

More Examples

Name each of the following compounds:

1. AsF_3
arsenic trifluoride

2. Al_2S_3
aluminum sulfide

3. $SnBr_4$
tin(IV) bromide

4. CS_2
carbon disulfide

5. CdS
cadmium sulfide

6. AgCl
silver chloride

7. KI
potassium iodide

8. NO
nitrogen monoxide

9. P_2O_5
diphosphorus pentoxide

10. $FeCl_3$
iron(III) chloride

✓ Answer to Practice Problem 4.6

a. chlorine trifluoride

b. vanadium(V) fluoride

c. copper(I) chloride

d. manganese(IV) oxide

e. magnesium oxide

f. water

**SECTION 4.1
Review Questions**

1. A system for naming compounds is necessary because there are so many different compounds that it would be impossible to memorize all their names. A system makes it possible for each compound to have a unique name that can indicate its chemical composition.

2. A substance is a binary compound if it contains only two different elements.

3. The anions in all types of binary compounds have the ending -*ide*.

4. The cations in Type I compounds are named for the parent atom. In Type II compounds, the cation has the parent atom name followed by a Roman numeral indicating its charge. In Type III compounds, the first element is named as if it were a cation (the name of the parent atom) but it may have a prefix (indicating the number of atoms) if the formula contains more than one atom.

5. a. potassium bromide

   b. tin(II) fluoride

   c. carbon monoxide

   d. copper(I) bromide

   e. magnesium iodide

   f. phosphorus trichloride

6. a. 2+

   b. 1−

   c. 1+

   d. 2−

CELEBRITY CHEMICAL   Nitric Oxide (NO)

Until recently nitric oxide (NO, more correctly called nitrogen monoxide) was primarily viewed as an air pollutant. In the last few years, however, NO has been found to be a potent biological regulator. It turns out that this compound is produced in the body and regulates blood pressure by dilating blood vessels. Studies in the 1990s indicated that NO administered to patients with sickle cell anemia may relieve serious symptoms of that disease. For example, it seems to benefit patients with acute chest syndrome—characterized by chest pain, fever, and high blood pressure in the lungs due to clogged blood vessels—which is the most life-threatening complication of sickle cell disease, especially for children.

Sickle cell anemia is a genetic disease that most often strikes people of West African descent. It causes the red blood cells to be misshapen ("sickle-shaped"), which in turn causes them to stick together and block blood flow. NO is thought to bind to a special site on the hemoglobin molecule (the molecule that carries O_2 from the lungs to the tissues). It is released when blood flow is impaired, causing dilation (expansion) of the blood vessels, thus helping to improve blood flow.

Further tests are now under way to try to discover exactly how NO works to relieve sickle cell symptoms.

A mixture of normal and sickle-shaped red blood cells

**SECTION 4.1
REVIEW QUESTIONS**

❶ Why is a system for naming compounds necessary?

❷ How can you tell whether a substance is a binary compound?

❸ How are the anions in all types of binary compounds similar?

❹ How are the cations different in each type of binary compound?

❺ Use **Figure 4.1** to name these compounds:

   a. KBr   **d.** CuBr

   b. SnF_2 **e.** MgI_2

   c. CO   **f.** PCl_3

❻ List the charges of the ions formed from atoms in each of the groups.

Nonmetals

Metals

a. _____

b. _____

c. _____

d. _____

RESEARCH LINKS
CLASSZONE.COM

CELEBRITY CHEMICAL

Nitric Oxide (NO)

In the last few years, NO has been found to be an important regulator molecule in the human body. Recently, it has been discovered that the "kissing bug," which is found in the tropics and sucks blood from humans much like a mosquito, actually releases NO with its bite. The NO delivered in the bug's saliva expands the victim's

blood vessels and prevents clotting to ensure adequate blood flow. The same molecule in the bug's saliva that transports the NO also prevents the release of histamines, itch-inducing compounds produced by the body's immune system. If the histamines were released, victims would be made aware of the bite and the bug's meal would be interrupted, perhaps fatally.

Naming and Writing Formulas for More Complex Compounds

Objectives

- *To learn the names of common polyatomic ions*
- *To learn to name compounds containing polyatomic ions*
- *To learn how the anion composition determines an acid's name*
- *To learn names for common acids*
- *To learn to write the formula for a compound, given its name*

Key Terms
- Polyatomic ions
- Oxyanions
- Acids

A. Naming Compounds That Contain Polyatomic Ions

A type of ionic compound that we have not yet considered is exemplified by ammonium nitrate, NH_4NO_3, which contains the **polyatomic ions** NH_4^+ and NO_3^-. As their name suggests, polyatomic ions are charged entities composed of several atoms bound together. Polyatomic ions are assigned special names that you *must memorize* to name the compounds containing them. The most important polyatomic ions and their names are listed in **Table 4.4.**

Note in Table 4.4 that several series of polyatomic anions exist that contain an atom of a given element and different numbers of oxygen atoms. These anions are called **oxyanions**. When there are two members in such a series, the name of the one with the smaller number of oxygen atoms ends in *-ite*, and the name of the one with the larger number ends in *-ate*.

Polyatomic ions
An ion consisting of two or more atoms bound together

Oxyanion
A polyatomic ion containing at least one oxygen atom and one or more atoms of at least one other element

TABLE 4.4

Names of Common Polyatomic Ions

Ion	Name	Ion	Name
NH_4^+	ammonium	CO_3^{2-}	carbonate
NO_2^-	nitrite	HCO_3^-	hydrogen carbonate (bicarbonate is a widely used common name)
NO_3^-	nitrate		
SO_3^{2-}	sulfite		
SO_4^{2-}	sulfate	ClO^-	hypochlorite
HSO_4^-	hydrogen sulfate (bisulfate is a widely used common name)	ClO_2^-	chlorite
		ClO_3^-	chlorate
		ClO_4^-	perchlorate
OH^-	hydroxide	$C_2H_3O_2^-$	acetate
CN^-	cyanide	MnO_4^-	permanganate
PO_4^{3-}	phosphate	$Cr_2O_7^{2-}$	dichromate
HPO_4^{2-}	hydrogen phosphate	CrO_4^{2-}	chromate
$H_2PO_4^-$	dihydrogen phosphate	O_2^{2-}	peroxide

DID YOU KNOW

Ionic compounds containing polyatomic ions are not binary compounds, because they contain more than two elements.

SECTION 4.2
INTRODUCE

Student Preparation

Assign students to read Section 4.2 and to answer the Review Questions at the end of the section before coming to class.

 Active Learning
Team Learning Worksheet

After introducing the material in Section 4.2 in class, place students in groups and have them work together on **Section 4.2: Team Learning Worksheet.**

 LABORATORY
EXPERIMENT 16:
Grocery Store Nomenclature

SECTION 4.2
GUIDE THE LEARNING

Homework

You may wish to assign these selected end-of-chapter problems as homework for this section: 15, 18, 19, 21, 22, 24, 25a–d, 26a–c, 27a–c, 28a–d, 29a–f

Additional end-of-chapter problems can be used for extra practice.

4.2.A Naming Compounds That Contain Polyatomic Ions

Objective To learn the names of common polyatomic ions and how to use them in naming compounds

 TEACHING TIP

Use Table 4.4 to help in learning the names of the polyatomic ions. Some groups of ions are related as part of a series, which makes remembering them easier. For example, nitrate and nitrite differ by only one oxygen atom, as do sulfate and sulfite. Show students that the charge is the same but the number of oxygen atoms changes. Also, point out that when hydrogen is added to a polyatomic ion (as in hydrogen carbonate), the charge on the polyatomic ion changes by 1.

TECHNOLOGY

 Table 4.4

TEACHING TIPS

- Chlorine is used to illustrate the series of ions formed between the halogens and oxygen. You can also show how other halogens (bromine, for example) form a series of anions with oxygen.

- If students learn the names and formulas for the -*ate* polyatomic ions and understand the concepts underlying the oxygen and hydrogen anion series, they will be able to write formulas for almost all of the common polyatomic ions.

MISCONCEPTION
Chemistry

Students should think of polyatomic ions as a "unit." Many know that if NaCl is dissolved in water, Na^+ ions and Cl^- ions are present. However, students are often confused about the ions present when $NaNO_3$ is dissolved. Instead of the NO_3^- ion, students may think individual nitrogen and oxygen ions are present.

Note that the SO_3^{2-} anion has very different properties from SO_3 (sulfur trioxide), a pungent, toxic gas.

Except for hydroxide, peroxide, and cyanide, the names of polyatomic ions do not have an -*ide* ending.

For example, SO_3^{2-} is sulfite and SO_4^{2-} is sulfate. When more than two oxyanions make up a series, *hypo*- (less than) and *per*- (more than) are used as prefixes to name the members of the series with the fewest and the most oxygen atoms, respectively. The best example involves the oxyanions containing chlorine:

ClO^-	*hypo*chlor*ite*
ClO_2^-	chlor*ite*
ClO_3^-	chlor*ate*
ClO_4^-	*per*chlor*ate*

Naming ionic compounds that contain polyatomic ions is very similar to naming binary ionic compounds. For example, the compound NaOH is called sodium hydroxide, because it contains the Na^+ (sodium) cation and the OH^- (hydroxide) anion. To name these compounds, you must

- learn to recognize the common polyatomic ions.
- learn the *composition* and *charge* of each of the ions in Table 4.4.

Then when you see the formula $NH_4C_2H_3O_2$, you should immediately recognize its two "parts":

The correct name is ammonium acetate.

When a metal is present that forms more than one cation, a Roman numeral is required to specify the cation charge, just as in naming Type II binary ionic compounds. For example, the compound $FeSO_4$ is called iron(II) sulfate, because it contains Fe^{2+} (to balance the 2− charge on SO_4^{2-}). Note that to determine the charge on the iron cation, you must know that sulfate has a 2− charge.

HANDS-ON CHEMISTRY   • MINI-LAB •

Name Game II: Polyatomic Ions

Materials
- Index cards

Procedure

1. Make flashcards for the common polyatomic ions listed in **Table 4.4.** Write the name on one side and the formula (with charge) on the other side.

2. Group all of the oxyanions together, and arrange these according to suffix (-*ate* or -*ite*). Notice the patterns.

Results/Analysis

1. Learn the names, formulas, and charges for all of the polyatomic ions in **Table 4.4.**

Hands-On Chemistry
MINI-LAB

Name Game II: Polyatomic Ions

Materials Each student/group will need 22 index cards.

Purpose Students will learn the names, formulas, and charges of common polyatomic ions.

Discussion Understanding chemistry requires that students both understand fundamental principles and know the language of chemistry. They should be familiar with the periodic table, know names and symbols of some elements, and know how to name compounds. You can vary this activity to accommodate time limits.

EXAMPLE 4.7

Naming Compounds That Contain Polyatomic Ions

Give the systematic name of each of the following compounds.

- a. Na_2SO_4
- b. KH_2PO_4
- c. $Fe(NO_3)_3$
- d. $Mn(OH)_2$
- e. Na_2SO_3

Solution

Compound	Ions Present	Ion Names	Compound Name
a. Na_2SO_4	two Na^+ SO_4^{2-}	sodium sulfate	sodium sulfate
b. KH_2PO_4	K^+ $H_2PO_4^-$	potassium dihydrogen phosphate	potassium dihydrogen phosphate
c. $Fe(NO_3)_3$	Fe^{3+} three NO_3^-	iron(III) nitrate	iron(III) nitrate
d. $Mn(OH)_2$	Mn^{2+} two OH^-	manganese(II) hydroxide	manganese(II) hydroxide
e. Na_2SO_3	two Na^+ SO_3^{2-}	sodium sulfite	sodium sulfite

 information

Certain transition metals form only one ion. Common examples are zinc (forms only Zn^{2+}) and silver (forms only Ag^+). For these cases the Roman numeral is omitted from the name.

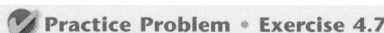 **Practice Problem • Exercise 4.7**

Name each of the following compounds.

- a. $Ca(OH)_2$
- b. Na_3PO_4
- c. $KMnO_4$
- d. $(NH_4)_2Cr_2O_7$
- e. $Co(ClO_4)_2$
- f. $KClO_3$
- g. $Cu(NO_2)_2$

Example 4.7 illustrates that when more than one polyatomic ion appears in a chemical formula, parentheses are used to enclose the ion and a subscript is written after the closing parenthesis. Other examples are $(NH_4)_2SO_4$ and $Fe_3(PO_4)_2$.

In naming chemical compounds, use the strategy summarized in **Figure 4.2.**

 Active Reading Question

How is naming compounds that contain polyatomic ions similar to naming binary ionic compounds? How is it different?

EXAMPLE 4.7

More Examples

Name each of these compounds.

1. $Cu(NO_3)_2$
   copper(II) nitrate
2. $PbCO_3$
   lead(II) carbonate
3. $KHSO_4$
   potassium hydrogen sulfate
4. NH_4I
   ammonium iodide
5. $NaCN$
   sodium cyanide

Answer to Practice Problem 4.7

- a. calcium hydroxide
- b. sodium phosphate
- c. potassium permanganate
- d. ammonium dichromate
- e. cobalt(II) perchlorate (Perchlorate has a 1− charge, so the cation must be Co^{2+} to balance the two ClO_4^- ions.)
- f. potassium chlorate
- g. copper(II) nitrite (This compound contains two NO_2^- (nitrite) ions and thus must contain a Cu^{2+} cation.)

Active Reading Question

It is similar in that the metal ion is named from the metal atom and the anion is the name of the polyatomic ion. It is different because the name of the polyatomic ion is not just the name of the nonmetal with -ide as a suffix.

Meeting Individual Needs
CHALLENGE PROJECTS

For a project involving the use of reference materials such as the CRC Handbook, see *Researching Oxyanions* located in *Teacher Resources*.

TECHNOLOGY

Figure 4.2

🍎 **TEACHING TIP**

Have students use Figure 4.2 along with Figure 4.1 when naming compounds so that they can see that the rules for naming compounds are logical and systematic.

EXAMPLE 4.8

More Examples

Name the following compounds.

1. $Ca(HCO_3)_2$
   calcium hydrogen carbonate

2. MgI_2
   magnesium iodide

3. $KMnO_4$
   potassium permanganate

4. Sb_2O_3
   antimony(III) oxide

5. $Fe(OH)_2$
   iron(II) hydroxide

Answer to Practice Problem 4.8

Compound	Name
a. $NaHCO_3$ Contains Na^+ and HCO_3^-	Sodium hydrogen carbonate, often called sodium bicarbonate (common name)
b. $BaSO_4$ Contains Ba^{2+} and SO_4^{2-}	Barium sulfate
c. $CsClO_4$ Contains Cs^+ and ClO_4^-	Cesium perchlorate
d. BrF_5 Both nonmetals (Type III binary)	Bromine pentafluoride
e. NaBr Contains Na^+ and Br^- (Type I binary)	Sodium bromide
f. KOCl Contains K^+ and OCl^-	Potassium hypochlorite
g. $Zn_3(PO_4)_2$ Contains Zn^{2+} and PO_4^{3-}.	Zinc(II) phosphate

Zn is a transition metal and officially requires a Roman numeral. However, because Zn forms only the Zn^{2+} cation, the II is usually omitted. Thus the name of the compound is usually given as zinc phosphate.

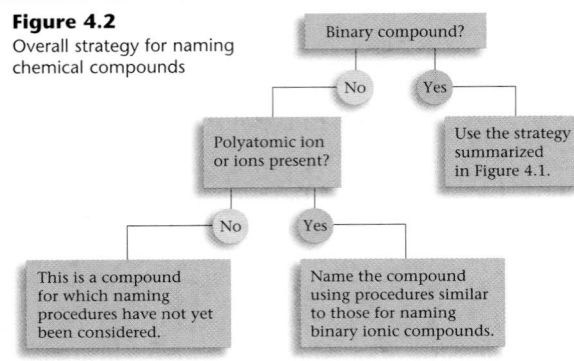
Figure 4.2
Overall strategy for naming chemical compounds

Let's Review

- If the compound being considered is binary, use the procedure summarized in Figure 4.1.
- If the compound has more than two elements, determine whether it has any polyatomic ions.
- Use Table 4.4 to help you recognize these ions until you have committed them to memory.
- If a polyatomic ion is present, name the compound using procedures very similar to those for naming binary ionic compounds.

EXAMPLE 4.8

Summary of Naming Binary Compounds and Compounds That Contain Polyatomic Ions

Name the following compounds.

a. Na_2CO_3 c. PCl_3 e. $CuSO_4$
b. $FeBr_3$ d. $CsClO_4$

Solution

Compound	Name	Comments
a. Na_2CO_3	sodium carbonate	Contains $2Na^+$ and CO_3^{2-}.
b. $FeBr_3$	iron(III) bromide	Contains Fe^{3+} and $3Br^-$.
c. $CsClO_4$	cesium perchlorate	Contains Cs^+ and ClO_4^-.
d. PCl_3	phosphorus trichloride	Type III binary compound (both P and Cl are nonmetals).
e. $CuSO_4$	copper(II) sulfate	Contains Cu^{2+} and SO_4^{2-}.

✓ **Practice Problem • Exercise 4.8**

Name the following compounds.

a. $NaHCO_3$ c. $CsClO_4$ e. NaBr   g. $Zn_3(PO_4)_2$
b. $BaSO_4$ d. BrF_5 f. KOCl

B. Naming Acids

When dissolved in water, certain molecules produce H^+ ions (protons). These substances, which are called **acids**, were first recognized by the sour taste of their solutions. For example, citric acid is responsible for the tartness of lemons and limes. Acids will be discussed in detail later. Here we simply present the rules for naming acids.

An acid can be viewed as a molecule with one or more H^+ ions attached to an anion. The rules for naming acids depend on whether the anion contains oxygen.

Acid
A substance that produces hydrogen ions (H^+) in solution; a proton donor

Rules for Naming Acids

1. If the *anion does not contain oxygen,* the acid is named with the prefix *hydro-* and the suffix *-ic* attached to the root name for the element.

   For example, when gaseous HCl, HCN, and H_2S are dissolved in water, they form the following acids:

Acid	Anion	Name
HCl	Cl^-	hydrochloric acid
HCN	CN^-	hydrocyanic acid
H_2S	S^{2-}	hydrosulfuric acid

2. When the *anion contains oxygen,* the acid name is formed from the root name of the central element of the anion or the anion name, with a suffix of *-ic* or *-ous.* When the anion name ends in *-ate,* the suffix *-ic* is used. For example,

Acid	Anion	Name
H_2SO_4	SO_4^{2-} (sulfate)	sulfuric acid
H_3PO_4	PO_4^{3-} (phosphate)	phosphoric acid
$HC_2H_3O_2$	$C_2H_3O_2^-$ (acetate)	acetic acid

   When the anion name ends in *-ite,* the suffix *-ous* is used in the acid name. For example,

Acid	Anion	Name
H_2SO_3	SO_3^{2-} (sulfite)	sulfurous acid
HNO_2	NO_2^- (nitrite)	nitrous acid

The application of rule 2 can be seen in the names of the acids of the oxyanions of chlorine, as shown below.

Acid	Anion	Name
$HClO_4$	perchlor*ate*	perchlor*ic* acid
$HClO_3$	chlor*ate*	chlor*ic* acid
$HClO_2$	chlor*ite*	chlor*ous* acid
$HClO$	hypochlor*ite*	hypochlor*ous* acid

4.2.B Naming Acids
Objective To learn how the anion composition determines the acid's name and to learn names for common acids

 LABORATORY
EXPERIMENT 17:
Energy Changes in Physical and Chemical Systems, Traditional

 TEACHING TIP

- Students are briefly introduced to acids in this chapter. Acids are reactants in many reactions in upcoming chapters and are used in early experiments, so this brief introduction is important.

- Students should be asked to name the oxyacids containing bromine as well as those containing chlorine. This activity provides an opportunity to review the naming system for the polyatomic ions and extend it to acids.

More Examples

Name the following acids.

1. HF
   hydrofluoric acid

2. H_3PO_3
   phosphorous acid

3. HNO_3
   nitric acid

4. $HBrO_4$
   bromic acid

5. H_2S
   hydrosulfuric acid

Meeting Individual Needs
READING STRATEGIES

As students read this section, have them make a list of any patterns that they notice about naming acids. Once the list is complete, have students go back and mark the patterns that are *always true* or *sometimes true.* As a class, discuss the scenarios for when a pattern is only sometimes true.

Figure 4.3

4.2.C Writing Formulas from Names

Objectives To learn to write the formula of a compound, given its name

 TEACHING TIPS

- Writing formulas from names is usually easier for students than naming formulas because Type I and Type II cations are identified by name. Students must know the polyatomic ions and their charges to write formulas correctly.

- Students often forget to use parentheses in formulas, especially when a polyatomic ion requires a subscript. For example, $Ca(OH)_2$ is frequently written by beginning students as $CaOH_2$. You may want to relate this situation to math and the grouping of algebraic symbols with parentheses.

The rules for naming acids are given in schematic form in **Figure 4.3**. The names of the most important acids are given in **Table 4.5** and **Table 4.6**. These names should be memorized.

Table 4.5	
Names of Acids That Do Not Contain Oxygen	
Acid	**Name**
HF	hydrofluoric acid
HCl	hydrochloric acid
HBr	hydrobromic acid
HI	hydroiodic acid
HCN	hydrocyanic acid
H_2S	hydrosulfuric acid

Table 4.6	
Names of Some Oxygen-Containing Acids	
Acid	**Name**
HNO_3	nitric acid
HNO_2	nitrous acid
H_2SO_4	sulfuric acid
H_2SO_3	sulfurous acid
H_3PO_4	phosphoric acid
$HC_2H_3O_2$	acetic acid

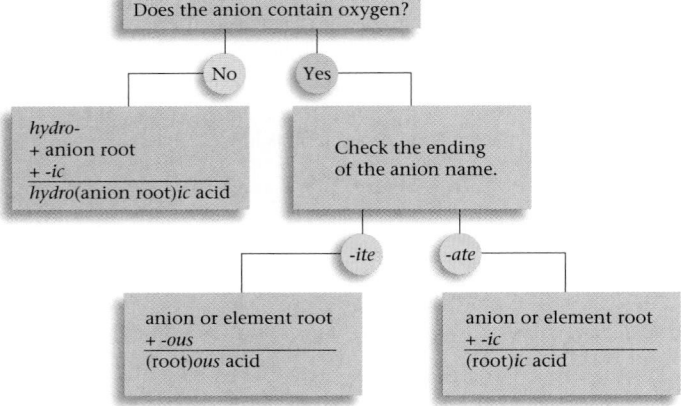

Figure 4.3
A flow chart for naming acids. The acid is pictured as one or more H^+ ions attached to an anion.

C. Writing Formulas from Names

So far we have started with the chemical formula of a compound and decided on its systematic name. Being able to reverse the process is also important. Often a laboratory procedure describes a compound by name, but the label on the bottle in the lab shows only the formula of the chemical it contains. It is essential that you are able to determine the formula of a compound from its name. In fact, you already know enough about compounds to do this.

For example, given the name calcium hydroxide, you can write the formula as $Ca(OH)_2$ because you know that calcium forms only Ca^{2+} ions and that, since hydroxide is OH^-, two of these anions are required to give a neutral compound. Similarly, the name iron(II) oxide implies the formula FeO, because the Roman numeral II indicates the presence of the cation Fe^{2+} and the oxide ion is O^{2-}.

We emphasize at this point that it is essential to learn the name, composition, and charge of each of the common polyatomic anions (and the NH_4^+ cation). If you do not recognize these ions by formula and by name, you will not be able to write the compound's name when given its formula or the compound's formula when given its name. You must also learn the names of the common acids.

EXAMPLE 4.9

Writing Formulas from Names

Give the formula for each of the following compounds.

a. potassium hydroxide   e. calcium chloride
b. sodium carbonate   f. lead(IV) oxide
c. nitric acid   g. dinitrogen pentoxide
d. cobalt(III) nitrate   h. ammonium perchlorate

Solution

Name	Formula	Comments
a. potassium hydroxide	KOH	Contains K^+ and OH^-.
b. sodium carbonate	Na_2CO_3	We need two Na^+ to balance CO_3^{2-}.
c. nitric acid	HNO_3	Common strong acid; memorize.
d. cobalt(III) nitrate	$Co(NO_3)_3$	Cobalt(III) means Co^{3+}; we need three NO_3^- to balance Co^{3+}.
e. calcium chloride	$CaCl_2$	We need two Cl^- to balance Ca^{2+}; Ca (Group 2) always forms Ca^{2+}.
f. lead(IV) oxide	PbO_2	Lead(IV) means Pb^{4+}; we need two O^{2-} to balance Pb^{4+}.
g. dinitrogen pentoxide	N_2O_5	*di-* means two; *pent(a)-* means five.
h. ammonium perchlorate	NH_4ClO_4	Contains NH_4^+ and ClO_4^-.

✔ Practice Problem • Exercise 4.9

Write the formula for each of the following compounds.

a. ammonium sulfate   d. rubidium peroxide
b. vanadium(V) fluoride   e. aluminum oxide
c. disulfur dichloride

4.2 • Naming and Writing Formulas for More Complex Compounds • 115

EXAMPLE 4.9

More Examples

Write the correct formula for each compound.

1. sodium nitrate
   $NaNO_3$

2. ammonium dichromate
   $NH_4Cr_2O_7$

3. mercury(II) iodide
   HgI_2

4. barium carbonate
   $BaCO_3$

5. magnesium bromide
   $MgBr_2$

6. hydrochloric acid
   $HCl(aq)$

7. carbon disulfide
   CS_2

8. nickel(II) perchlorate
   $Ni(ClO_4)_2$

9. cesium fluoride
   CsF

10. hypobromous acid
    $HBrO$

✔ Answer to Practice Problem 4.9

Name	Chemical Formula
a. ammonium sulfate	$(NH_4)_2SO_4$

Two ammonium ions (NH_4^+) are required for each sulfate ion (SO_4^{2-}) to achieve charge balance.

b. vanadium(V) fluoride	VF_5

The compound contains V^{5+} ions and requires five F^- ions for charge balance.

c. disulfur dichloride	S_2Cl_2

The prefix *di-* indicates two of each atom.

d. rubidium peroxide	Rb_2O_2

Because rubidium is in Group 1, it forms only 1+ ions. Thus two $Rb+$ ions are needed to balance the 2− charge on the peroxide ion (O_2^{2-}).

e. aluminum oxide	Al_2O_3

Aluminum forms only 3+ ions. Two Al^{3+} ions are required to balance the charge on the three O^{2-} ions.

SECTION 4.2
Review Questions

1. Ions can be grouped by the first element in the anion (such as sulfur, phosphorus, or nitrogen). The number of oxygen atoms varies, and the presence of hydrogen can also be incorporated into the series.

2. The compound containing a polyatomic ion is named by giving the name for the cation followed by the name for the polyatomic ion (except in the case of the ammonium ion, which is given first because it is a cation). The number of polyatomic ions present is not given in the name.

3. The number of each kind of element or polyatomic ion in a formula is determined by how many are needed to produce a compound that is neutral in charge.

4. The formulas of compounds named as acids begin with H.

5. **a.** perchloric acid
   b. nitrous acid
   c. hydrobromic acid
   d. sulfuric acid

6.

Name	Formula
sodium nitrate	$NaNO_3$
potassium sulfite	K_2SO_3
sodium hydrogen carbonate	$NaHCO_3$
aluminum sulfate	$Al_2(SO_4)_3$
potassium perchlorate	$KClO_4$
copper(II) carbonate	$CuCO_3$
sodium acetate	$NaC_2H_3O_3$
acetic acid	$HC_2H_3O_2$
copper(II) sulfate	$CuSO_4$
calcium hydroxide	$Ca(OH)_2$
nickel(II) carbonate	$NiCO_3$
ammonium nitrate	NH_4NO_3

CHEMISTRY IN YOUR WORLD

Connect to Biology

Talking Tadpoles

It is well known that animals communicate by releasing chemicals that others of the same species receive and "understand." For example, ants use chemicals to signal news about food supplies and danger from predators, and honeybees "recognize" other bees from the same hive by their chemical signals. Now scientists at Yale University have shown that tadpoles send chemical signals to one another.

The experiment involved two groups of tadpoles of red-legged frogs. They were placed in an aquarium partitioned by a screen that allowed water to flow but blocked communications by sight and sound. When a wooden heron (a bird that preys on tadpoles) threatened the tadpoles in the one compartment, those on the other side moved away from the partition and ducked under a shelter. The

researchers concluded that the frightened tadpoles signaled their fear to the tadpoles in the other compartment by releasing a chemical signal that flowed to the other side in the water.

Other water-dwelling animals such as crayfish, hermit crabs, and a fish called the Iowa darter also have been observed to send chemical danger signals when they are threatened. Scientists think that the chemical used to send the signal is the ammonium ion, NH_4^+. Researchers are now trying to find out whether all aquatic species have a common chemical "language" to signal one another, just as ants and bees do.

A California red-legged frog tadpole

SECTION 4.2
REVIEW QUESTIONS

❶ What patterns can you see in Table 4.4 that reduce the number of polyatomic ions you need to memorize? (Hint: Try grouping the ions by common elements or suffixes.)

❷ Once you have identified that a compound contains a polyatomic ion, how is naming it different from naming a binary compound?

❸ When writing a formula from a chemical name, how can you tell how many of each element or polyatomic ion to put in the formula?

❹ How can you tell whether a compound should be named an acid?

❺ Use the flow chart in Figure 4.4 to name the following:
   a. $HClO_4$
   b. HNO_2
   c. HBr
   d. H_2SO_4

❻ Copy and complete the following table.

Name	Formula
	$NaNO_3$
potassium sulfite	
	$NaHCO_3$
aluminum sulfate	
	$KClO_4$
copper(II) carbonate	
	$NaC_2H_3O_2$
acetic acid	
	$CuSO_4$
calcium hydroxide	
	$NiCO_3$
ammonium nitrate	

 RESEARCH LINKS
CLASSZONE.COM

Chemistry in Your World

Talking Tadpoles

Pheromones are the chemicals that a member of a particular species releases to communicate with other members of the species. It is interesting to speculate whether humans emit pheromones.

Plants use chemical signals as well. For example, when attacked by aphids, the wild potato plant manufactures and emits the aphid alarm pheromone to scare off the

invading aphids. Another interesting example is the *Orchidantha* plant in Borneo, which sports a purple flower that emits a foul odor attractive to dung beetles. The plant emits this special fragrance from 7:30 A.M. until midnight, attracting dung beetles to assist in the pollination process.

Chapter 4 Review

Key Terms

Key Ideas

4.1 Naming Binary Compounds

- Binary compounds are named by following a set of rules.
  - For compounds containing both a metal and a nonmetal, the metal is always named first. The nonmetal is named from the root element name.
  - If the metal ion can have more than one charge (Type II), a Roman numeral is used to specify the charge.
  - For binary compounds containing only nonmetals (Type III), prefixes are used to specify the numbers of atoms present.

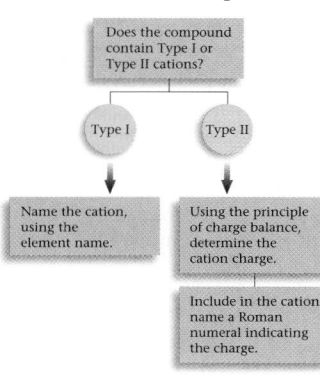

4.2 Polyatomic ions

Oxyanions

Acids

4.2 Naming and Writing Formulas for More Complex Compounds

- Polyatomic ions are charged entities composed of several atoms bound together. They have special names and must be memorized.
- Naming ionic compounds containing polyatomic ions follows rules similar to those for naming binary compounds.
- The names of acids (molecules with one or more H^+ ions attached to an anion) depend on whether the acid contains oxygen.

RESEARCH LINKS
CLASSZONE.COM

Meeting Individual Needs

CHAPTER REVIEW

Chapter 4 Review Worksheet at the appropriate level:
- Basic
- Standard
- Challenge

CHAPTER SUMMARY

A **Chapter Summary** that includes additional Active Reading Questions for Chapter 4 is available.

Assessment Resources

CHAPTER 4

Chapter 4 Test

TECHNOLOGY

💻 **Computerized Test Bank for Chapter 4**

Chapter 4 Assessment

1. A binary compound contains only two elements. Examples are sodium chloride, water, and carbon dioxide.

2. compounds containing a metal and a nonmetal; compounds containing two nonmetals

3. cation, anion

4. cation (positive ion)

5. Sodium chloride consists of Na^+ ions and Cl^- ions in an extended crystal lattice array. No discrete NaCl pairs are present.

6. (a) sodium iodide
   (b) calcium fluoride
   (c) aluminum sulfide
   (d) calcium bromide
   (e) strontium oxide
   (f) silver(I) chloride (silver chloride)
   (g) cesium iodide
   (h) lithium oxide

7. (a) incorrect; BaH_2 is barium hydride
   (b) incorrect; Na_2O is sodium oxide
   (c) correct
   (d) incorrect; SiO_2 is silicon dioxide
   (e) correct

8. (a) iron(III) iodide
   (b) manganese(II) chloride
   (c) mercury(II) oxide
   (d) copper(I) oxide
   (e) copper(II) oxide
   (f) tin(IV) bromide

9. (a) cobaltous chloride
   (b) chromic bromide
   (c) plumbous oxide
   (d) stannic oxide
   (e) ferric oxide
   (f) ferric chloride

10. (a) iodine pentafluoride
    (b) arsenic trichloride
    (c) selenium monoxide
    (d) xenon tetrafluoride
    (e) nitrogen triiodide
    (f) diboron trioxide

11. (a) germanium tetrahydride
    (b) dinitrogen tetrabromide
    (c) diphosphorus pentasulfide
    (d) selenium dioxide
    (e) ammonia
    (f) silicon dioxide

12. (a) diboron hexahydride, nonionic
    (b) calcium nitride, ionic
    (c) carbon tetrabromide, nonionic
    (d) silver sulfide, ionic

All exercises with blue numbers have answers in the back of this book.

4.1 Naming Binary Compounds

A. Naming Compounds That Contain a Metal and a Nonmetal

1. What is a *binary* compound? Give three examples of binary compounds.

2. What are the two major types of binary compounds?

3. In an ionic compound, the positive ion is called the _____ and the negative ion is called the _____ .

4. In naming ionic compounds, we always name the _____ first.

5. Although we write the formula of sodium chloride as NaCl, we realize that NaCl is an ionic compound and contains no molecules. Explain.

6. Give the name of each of the following simple binary ionic compounds.
   - a. NaI
   - b. CaF_2
   - c. Al_2S_3
   - d. $CaBr_2$
   - e. SrO
   - f. AgCl
   - g. CsI
   - h. Li_2O

7. Identify each case in which the name is incorrect. Give the correct name.
   - a. BaH_2, barium hydroxide
   - b. Na_2O, disodium oxide
   - c. $SnCl_4$, tin(IV) chloride
   - d. SiO_2, silver dioxide
   - e. $FeBr_3$, iron(III) bromide

8. Write the name of each of the following ionic substances, using the system that includes a Roman numeral to specify the charge of the cation.
   - a. FeI_3
   - b. $MnCl_2$
   - c. HgO
   - d. Cu_2O
   - e. CuO
   - f. $SnBr_4$

9. Write the name of each of the following ionic substances, using *-ous* or *-ic* endings to indicate the charge of the cation.
   - a. $CoCl_2$
   - b. $CrBr_3$
   - c. PbO
   - d. SnO_2
   - e. Fe_2O_3
   - f. $FeCl_3$

B. Naming Binary Compounds That Contain Only Nonmetals (Type III)

10. Name each of the following binary compounds of nonmetallic elements.
    - a. IF_5
    - b. $AsCl_3$
    - c. SeO
    - d. XeF_4
    - e. NI_3
    - f. B_2O_3

11. Write the name for each of the following binary compounds of nonmetallic elements.
    - a. GeH_4
    - b. N_2Br_4
    - c. P_2S_5
    - d. SeO_2
    - e. NH_3
    - f. SiO_2

C. Naming Binary Compounds: A Review

12. Name each of the following binary compounds, using the periodic table to determine whether the compound is likely to be ionic (containing a metal and a nonmetal) or nonionic (containing only nonmetals).
    - a. B_2H_6
    - b. Ca_3N_2
    - c. CBr_4
    - d. Ag_2S
    - e. $CuCl_2$
    - f. ClF

13. Name each of the following binary compounds, using the periodic table to determine whether the compound is likely to be ionic (containing a metal and a nonmetal) or nonionic (containing only nonmetals).
    - a. $RaCl_2$
    - b. $SeCl_2$
    - c. PCl_3
    - d. Na_3P
    - e. MnF_2
    - f. ZnO

4.2 Naming and Writing Formulas for More Complex Compounds

A. Naming Compounds That Contain Polyatomic Ions

14. What is an *oxyanion*? How is a series of oxyanions named? (Give an example.)

15. Which oxyanion of chlorine contains the most oxygen atoms: hypochlorite, chlorite, or perchlorate?

16. Copy and complete the table by filling in the missing names or formulas of the indicated oxyanions.

BrO^-	
	iodate
IO_4^-	
	hypoiodite

---

13. (a) radium chloride, ionic
    (b) selenium dichloride, nonionic
    (c) phosphorus trichloride, nonionic
    (d) sodium phosphide, ionic
    (e) manganese(II) fluoride, ionic
    (f) zinc oxide, ionic

   (e) copper(II) chloride, ionic
   (f) chlorine monofluoride, nonionic

14. An oxyanion contains a particular element plus oxygen. If there are two oxyanions of that element, the higher oxidation state is given the *-ate* ending and the lower oxidation state is given the *-ite* ending. If there are four oxidation states, the highest is given the prefix *per-* and the lowest is indicated by the prefix *hypo-*. For example: ClO^- (hypochlorite), ClO_2^- (chlorite), ClO_3^- (chlorate), ClO_4^- (perchlorate).

15. perchlorate, ClO_4^-

16. hypobromite; IO_3^-; periodate; IO^-

17. Write the formula for each of the following nitrogen-containing polyatomic ions, including the overall charge of the ion.

    a. nitrate   c. ammonium

    b. nitrite   d. cyanide

18. Write the formula for each of the following chlorine-containing ions, including the overall charge of the ion.

    a. chloride   c. chlorate

    b. hypochlorite   d. perchlorate

19. Write the formulas of the compounds below (refer to your answers to problem 18).

    a. magnesium chloride

    b. calcium hypochlorite

    c. potassium chlorate

    d. barium perchlorate

20. Give the name of each of the following polyatomic anions.

    a. MnO_4^- c. CrO_4^{2-} e. NO_3^-

    b. O_2^{2-} d. $Cr_2O_7^{2-}$ f. SO_3^{2-}

21. Name each of the following compounds, which contain polyatomic ions.

    a. $Fe(NO_3)_3$ d. $Al_2(SO_4)_3$

    b. $Co_3(PO_4)_2$ e. $Cr(C_2H_3O_2)_2$

    c. $Cr(CN)_3$ f. $(NH_4)_2SO_3$

B. Naming Acids

22. Give a simple definition of an *acid*.

23. Many acids contain the element _____ in addition to hydrogen.

24. Name each of the following acids.

    a. HCl   d. HI   g. HBr

    b. H_2SO_4 e. HNO_2 h. HF

    c. HNO_3 f. $HClO_3$ i. $HC_2H_3O_2$

C. Writing Formulas from Names

25. Write formulas for each of the following simple binary ionic compounds.

    a. lithium oxide   e. calcium phosphide

    b. aluminum iodide   f. magnesium fluoride

    c. silver oxide   g. sodium sulfide

    d. potassium nitride h. barium hydride

26. Write the formula for each of the following binary compounds of nonmetallic elements.

    a. carbon dioxide

    b. sulfur dioxide

    c. dinitrogen tetrachloride

    d. carbon tetraiodide

    e. phosphorus pentafluoride

    f. diphosphorus pentoxide

27. Write the formula for each of the following compounds that contain polyatomic ions. Be sure to enclose the polyatomic ion in parentheses if more than one such ion is needed.

    a. calcium phosphate

    b. ammonium nitrate

    c. aluminum hydrogen sulfate

    d. barium sulfate

    e. iron(III) nitrate

    f. copper(I) hydroxide

28. Write the formula for each of the following acids.

    a. hydrocyanic acid   e. hypochlorous acid

    b. nitric acid   f. hydrobromic acid

    c. sulfuric acid   g. bromous acid

    d. phosphoric acid   h. hydrofluoric acid

29. Write the formula for each of the following substances.

    a. lithium chloride

    b. cuprous carbonate

    c. hydrobromic acid

    d. calcium nitrate

    e. sodium perchlorate

    f. aluminum hydroxide

    g. barium hydrogen carbonate

    h. iron(II) sulfate

    i. diboron hexachloride

    j. phosphorus pentabromide

    k. potassium sulfite

    l. barium acetate

---

22. An acid is a substance that produces hydrogen ions, H^+, when dissolved in water.

23. oxygen

24. (a) hydrochloric acid
(b) sulfuric acid
(c) nitric acid
(d) hydroiodic acid
(e) nitrous acid
(f) chloric acid
(g) hydrobromic acid
(h) hydrofluoric acid
(i) acetic acid

25. (a) Li_2O
(b) AlI_3
(c) Ag_2O
(d) K_3N
(e) Ca_3P_2
(f) MgF_2
(g) Na_2S
(h) BaH_2

26. (a) CO_2
(b) SO_2
(c) N_2Cl_4
(d) CI_4
(e) PF_5
(f) P_2O_5

27. (a) $Ca_3(PO_4)_2$
(b) NH_4NO_3
(c) $Al(HSO_4)_3$
(d) $BaSO_4$
(e) $Fe(NO_3)_2$
(f) $CuOH$

28. (a) HCN
(b) HNO_3
(c) H_2SO_4
(d) H_3PO_4
(e) HClO or HOCl
(f) HBr
(g) $HBrO_2$
(h) HF

29. (a) LiCl
(b) Cu_2CO_3
(c) HBr
(d) $Ca(NO_3)_2$
(e) $NaClO_4$
(f) $Al(OH)_3$
(g) $Ba(HCO_3)_2$
(h) $FeSO_4$
(i) B_2Cl_6
(j) PBr_5
(k) K_2SO_3
(l) $Ba(C_2H_3O_2)_2$

---

17. (a) NO_3^-
(b) NO_2^-
(c) NH_4^+
(d) CN^-

18. (a) Cl^-
(b) ClO^-
(c) ClO_3^-
(d) ClO_4^-

19. (a) $MgCl_2$
(b) $Ca(ClO)_2$
(c) $KClO_3$
(d) $Ba(ClO_4)_2$

20. (a) permanganate
(b) peroxide
(c) chromate
(d) dichromate
(e) nitrate
(f) sulfite

21. (a) iron(III) nitrate, ferric nitrate
(b) cobalt(II) phosphate, cobaltous phosphate
(c) chromium(III) cyanide, chromic phosphate
(d) aluminum sulfate
(e) chromium(II) acetate, chromous acetate
(f) ammonium sulfite

30. A moist paste of NaCl would contain Na^+ and Cl^+ ions in solution and would serve as a conductor of electrical impulses.

31. A binary compound is a compound containing two—and only two—elements. A polyatomic anion is several atoms bonded together that, as a whole, carries a negative electrical charge. An oxyanion is a negative ion containing a particular element and one or more oxygen atoms.

32. (a) gold(III) bromide
(b) cobalt(III) cyanide
(c) magnesium hydrogen phosphate
(d) diboron hexahydride (diborane is the common name)
(e) ammonia
(f) silver(I) sulfate (silver sulfate)
(g) beryllium hydroxide

33. (a) ammonium carbonate
(b) ammonium hydrogen carbonate, ammonium bicarbonate
(c) calcium phosphate
(d) sulfurous acid
(e) manganese(IV) oxide
(f) iodic acid
(g) potassium hydride

34. (a) K_2O
(b) MgO
(c) FeO
(d) Fe_2O_3
(e) ZnO
(f) PbO
(g) Al_2O_3

35. M^+ compounds: MD, M_2E, M_3F;
M^{2+} compounds: MD_2, ME, M_3F_2;
M^{3+} compounds: MD_3, M_2E_3, MF

36. See Table 4.A in the *Solutions Guide*.

Critical Thinking

30. Before an electrocardiogram (ECG) is recorded for a cardiac patient, the ECG leads are usually coated with a moist paste containing sodium chloride. What property of an ionic substance such as NaCl is being made use of?

31. What is a *binary* compound? What is a *polyatomic* anion? What is an *oxyanion*?

32. Name the following compounds.
   a. $AuBr_3$
   b. $Co(CN)_3$
   c. $MgHPO_4$
   d. B_2H_6
   e. NH_3
   f. Ag_2SO_4
   g. $Be(OH)_2$

33. Name the following compounds.
   a. $(NH_4)_2CO_3$
   b. NH_4HCO_3
   c. $Ca_3(PO_4)_2$
   d. H_2SO_3
   e. MnO_2
   f. HIO_3
   g. KH

34. Most metallic elements form *oxides*, and often the oxide is the most common compound of the element that is found in the earth's crust. Write the formulas for the oxides of the following metallic elements.
   a. potassium
   b. magnesium
   c. iron(II)
   d. iron(III)
   e. zinc
   f. lead(II)
   g. aluminum

35. Consider the hypothetical metallic element M, which is capable of forming stable simple cations that have charges of 1+, 2+, and 3+, respectively. Consider also the nonmetallic elements D, E, and F, which form anions that have charges of 1−, 2−, and 3−, respectively. Write the formulas of all possible compounds between metal M and nonmetals D, E, and F.

36. Copy and complete Table 4.A (below) by writing the names and formulas for the ionic compounds formed when the cations listed across the top combine with the anions shown in the left column.

TABLE 4.A

Ions	Fe^{2+}	Al^{3+}	Na^+	Ca^{2+}	NH_4^+	Fe^{3+}	Ni^{2+}	Hg_2^{2+}	Hg^{2+}
CO_3^{2-}									
BrO_3^-									
$C_2H_3O_2^-$									
OH^-									
HCO_3^-									
PO_4^{3-}									
SO_3^{2-}									
ClO_4^-									
SO_4^{2-}									
O^{2-}									
Cl^-									

37. Copy and complete Table 4.B (below) by writing the formulas for the ionic compounds formed when the anions listed across the top combine with the cations shown in the left column.

TABLE 4.B

Ions	nitrate	sulfate	hydrogen sulfate	dihydrogen phosphate	oxide	chloride
calcium						
strontium						
ammonium						
aluminum						
iron(III)						
nickel(II)						
silver(I)						
gold(III)						
potassium						
mercury(II)						
barium						

38. Copy and complete the following table. For each of the negative ions listed below, use the periodic table to find the total number of electrons that the ion contains.

Negative Ion	Total number of electrons
Se^{2-}	
S^{2-}	
P^{3-}	
O^{2-}	
N^{3-}	
I^-	
F^-	
Cl^-	
Br^-	
At^-	

39. For each of the following processes that show the formation of ions, complete the process by indicating the number of electrons that must be gained or lost to form the ion. Indicate the total number of electrons in the ion, and in the atom from which it was made.

   a. $Al \rightarrow Al^{3+}$ d. $F \rightarrow F^-$

   b. $S \rightarrow S^{2-}$ e. $Zn \rightarrow Zn^{2+}$

   c. $Cu \rightarrow Cu^+$ f. $P \rightarrow P^{3-}$

40. For each of the following atomic numbers, use the periodic table to write the formula (including the charge) for the simple *ion* that the element is most likely to form.

   a. 36   d. 81

   b. 31   e. 35

   c. 52   f. 87

41. For the following pairs of ions, use the principle of electrical neutrality to predict the formula of the binary compound that the ions are most likely to form.

   a. Na^+ and S^{2-} e. Cu^{2+} and Br^-

   b. K^+ and Cl^- f. Al^{3+} and I^-

   c. Ba^{2+} and O^{2-} g. Al^{3+} and O^{2-}

   d. Mg^{2+} and Se^{2-} h. Ca^{2+} and N^{3-}

42. Give the name of each of the following simple binary ionic compounds.

   a. BeO   e. HCl

   b. MgI_2 f. LiF

   c. Na_2S g. Ag_2S

   d. Al_2O_3 h. CaH_2

37. See Table 4.B in the *Solutions Guide.*

38. total number of electrons: 36; 18; 18; 10; 10; 54; 10; 18; 36; 86

39. (a) Al (13e) $\rightarrow Al^{3+}$ (10e) + 3e$^-$;
(b) S (16e) + 2e$^-$ $\rightarrow S^{2-}$ (18e);
(c) Cu (29e) $\rightarrow Cu^+$ (28e) + 1e$^-$;
(d) F (9e) + e$^-$ $\rightarrow F^-$ (10e);
(e) Zn (30e) $\rightarrow Zn^{2+}$ (28e) + 2e$^-$;
(f) P (15e) + 3e$^-$ $\rightarrow P^{3-}$ (18e)

40. (a) none likely
(b) Ga^{3+}
(c) Te^{2-}
(d) Tl^{3+}
(e) Br^-
(f) Fr^+

41. (a) Na_2S
(b) KCl
(c) BaO
(d) MgSe
(e) $CuBr_2$
(f) AlI_3
(g) Al_2O_3
(h) Ca_3N_2

42. (a) beryllium oxide
(b) magnesium iodide
(c) sodium sulfide
(d) aluminum iodide
(e) hydrogen chloride (gaseous), hydrochloric acid (aqueous)
(f) lithium fluoride
(g) silver(I) sulfide, usually called silver sulfide
(h) calcium hydride

43. (a) incorrect (Si is silicon)
(b) incorrect (Co is cobalt)
(c) incorrect (calcium hydride)
(d) correct
(e) incorrect (phosphorus trihydride)

44. (a) iron(II) bromide
(b) cobalt(II) sulfide
(c) cobalt(III) sulfide
(d) tin(IV) oxide
(e) mercury(I) chloride
(f) mercury(II) chloride

45. (a) xenon hexafluoride
(b) oxygen difluoride
(c) arsenic triiodide
(d) dinitrogen tetraoxide (tetroxide)
(e) dichlorine monoxide
(f) sulfur hexafluoride

46. (a) iron(III) acetate
(b) bromine monofluoride
(c) potassium peroxide
(d) silicon tetrabromide
(e) copper(II) permanganate
(f) calcium chromate

47. (a) lithium dihydrogen phosphate
(b) copper(II) cyanide
(c) lead(II) nitrate
(d) sodium hydrogen phosphate
(e) sodium chlorite
(f) cobalt(III) sulfate

48. (a) $CaCl_2$
(b) Ag_2O
(c) Al_2S_3
(d) $BeBr_2$
(e) H_2S
(f) KH
(g) MgI_2
(h) CsF

49. (a) SO_2
(b) N_2O
(c) XeF_4
(d) P_4O_{10}
(e) PCl_5
(f) SF_6
(g) NO_2

50. (a) NaH_2PO_4
(b) $LiClO_4$
(c) $Cu(HCO_3)_2$
(d) $KC_2H_3O_2$
(e) BaO_2
(f) Cs_2SO_3

51. (a) $AgClO_4$
(b) $Co(OH)_3$
(c) NaClO or NaOCl
(d) $K_2Cr_2O_7$
(e) NH_4NO_2
(f) $Fe(OH)_3$
(g) NH_4HCO_3
(h) $KBrO_4$

43. In which of the following pairs is the name incorrect?
a. SiI_4, silver iodide
b. $CoCl_2$, copper(II) chloride
c. CaH_2, hydrocalcinic acid
d. $Zn(C_2H_3O_2)_2$, zinc acetate
e. PH_3, phosphoric trihydride

44. Write the name of each of the following ionic substances, using the system that includes a Roman numeral to specify the charge of the cation.
a. $FeBr_2$ d. SnO_2
b. CoS   e. Hg_2Cl_2
c. Co_2S_3 f. $HgCl_2$

45. Name each of the following binary compounds.
a. XeF_6 d. N_2O_4
b. OF_2 e. Cl_2O
c. AsI_3 f. SF_6

46. Name each of the following compounds.
a. $Fe(C_2H_3O_2)_3$ d. $SiBr_4$
b. BrF   e. $Cu(MnO_4)_2$
c. K_2O_2 f. $CaCrO_4$

47. Name each of the following compounds, which contain polyatomic ions.
a. LiH_2PO_4 d. Na_2HPO_4
b. $Cu(CN)_2$ e. $NaClO_2$
c. $Pb(NO_3)_2$ f. $Co_2(SO_4)_3$

48. Write the formula for each of the following simple binary ionic compounds.
a. calcium chloride
b. silver(I) oxide (usually called silver oxide)
c. aluminum sulfide
d. beryllium bromide
e. hydrosulfuric acid
f. potassium hydride
g. magnesium iodide
h. cesium fluoride

49. Write the formula for each of the following binary compounds of nonmetallic elements.
a. sulfur dioxide
b. dinitrogen monoxide
c. xenon tetrafluoride
d. tetraphosphorus decoxide
e. phosphorus pentachloride
f. sulfur hexafluoride
g. nitrogen dioxide

50. Write the formula for each of the following ionic substances.
a. sodium dihydrogen phosphate
b. lithium perchlorate
c. copper(II) hydrogen carbonate
d. potassium acetate
e. barium peroxide
f. cesium sulfite

51. Write the formula for each of the following compounds, which contain polyatomic ions. Be sure to enclose the polyatomic ion in parentheses if more than one such ion is needed to balance the oppositely charged ion(s).
a. silver(I) perchlorate (usually called silver perchlorate)
b. cobalt(III) hydroxide
c. sodium hypochlorite
d. potassium dichromate
e. ammonium nitrite
f. iron(III) hydroxide
g. ammonium hydrogen carbonate
h. potassium perbromate

1 How many of the following compounds are named correctly?

I. Na_2SO_4 sodium sulfate

II. $CaCO_3$ calcium carbonate

III. PCl_5 phosphorus pentachloride

IV. CoO   cobalt(II) oxide

A   4

B   3

C   2

D   1

2 Which of the following chemical formulas is incorrect?

A   FeS   iron(II) sulfide

B SF_6 sulfur hexafluoride

C PbO_2 lead(IV) oxide

D NH_4SO_4 ammonium sulfate

3 Which of the following compounds is named incorrectly?

A PCl_3 phosphorus trichloride

B $MgCl_2$ magnesium dichloride

C   CuO   copper(II) oxide

D   At least two of the above (A–C) are named incorrectly.

4 Which of the following names is incorrect?

A   cobalt(II) chloride

B   magnesium oxide

C   aluminum(III) oxide

D   diphosphorus pentoxide

5 In which case is the polyatomic ion named incorrectly?

A NH_4^+ ammonium

B SO_3^{2-} sulfate

C CO_3^{2-} carbonate

D NO_2^- nitrite

6 What is the correct name for the compound Fe_2O_3?

A   iron oxide

B   iron(III) oxide

C   iron(II) oxide

D   diiron trioxide

7 Which of the following is the correct formula for chlorous acid?

A   HClO

B $HClO_2$

C $HClO_3$

D $HClO_4$

8 When dihydrogen sulfide is dissolved in water, it is called,

A   sulfuric acid.

B   sulfurous acid.

C   hydrosulfuric acid.

D   dihydrosulfuric acid.

9 Which of the following acids is named incorrectly?

A HNO_3 nitrous acid

B   HCl   hydrochloric acid

C $HC_2H_3O_2$ acetic acid

D H_3PO_4 phosphoric acid

10 Fill in the missing name or formula

Name	Formula
barium phosphate	
	N_2O
sulfuric acid	
	Cu_2O
boron trifluoride	

11 In naming binary compounds, you sometimes simply name the ions. In other cases, you need to use Roman numerals, or prefixes.

a. Explain why Roman numerals are sometimes needed in naming binary compounds, and provide an example name and formula.

b. Explain why prefixes are sometimes needed in naming binary compounds, and provide an example name and formula.

Chapter 4
Standardized Test Practice

1. A

2. D

3. B

4. C

5. B

6. B

7. B

8. C

9. A

10.

Name	Formula
barium phosphate	$Ba_3(PO_4)_2$
dinitrogen monoxide	N_2O
sulfuric acid	H_2SO_4
copper(I) oxide	Cu_2O
boron trifluoride	BF_3

11. a. Roman numerals are needed when the metal ion can have more than one possible positive charge in a compound. For example, FeO is iron(II) oxide and Fe_2O_3 is iron(III) oxide.

b. Prefixes are needed when naming compounds consisting of two nonmetals. For example, CO is carbon monoxide and CO_2 is carbon dioxide.

Test-Taking Strategy

Students may be confused when an *incorrect* answer is the *correct* choice for a problem. Explain that this method is used in test items, such as in questions 2–5, to assess the level of understanding of a concept. Advise students to respond slowly to these types of questions, carefully reading each answer choice before selecting the answer.

Assessment Resources
CHAPTER 4

For additional practice with standardized testing, see *Standardized Test Practice* located in the *Teacher Resources*.

Planning Guide

Section	Segment		Text Features and Components	Labs, Demonstrations, & Activities
5.1 Scientific Notation and Units **0.5 Block** pp. 126–132	A	Scientific Notation		
	B	Units	**SE** Chemistry in Your World: Critical Units! *p. 129*	
	C	Measurements of Length, Volume, and Mass		**TE** Mini-Demo *p. 131*
5.2 Uncertainty in Measurement and Significant Figures **1.5 Blocks** pp. 133–142	A	Uncertainty in Measurement	**SE** Chemistry Explorers: Cecile Hoover Edwards *p. 135*	**RP** Classroom Activities and Projects *TE p. 134* **LM** Experiment 18: Measurement and the SI System, Traditional Lab Manual Report Sheets Teacher's Lab Guide
	B	Significant Figures	**TE** Teaching Support: Background Information *p. 137* **SE** Chemistry in Your World: Measuring Changes *p. 141*	**RP** Classroom Activities and Projects *TE p. 135* **LM** Experiment 19: Measuring a Book? Precisely! Lab Manual Report Sheets Teacher's Lab Guide
		continued on next page		

Key				
SE Student Edition	**TE** Teacher Edition	**RP** Teacher Resource Package		
AR Additional Materials	**LM** Lab Materials	**🗎** Transparencies		
◉ DVD	**▭** CD-ROM	**🌐** classzone.com		

All Learners	Technology	Review & Assessment	Standards
TE Teaching Tips *pp. 126–127* **TE** Misconceptions *p. 127* **RP** MINT: Math Concepts *TE p. 126* **RP** MINT: Reading Concepts *TE p. 127*	⊙ EasyPlanner	**SE** Active Reading Question *p. 126* **SE** Active Reading Question *p. 128* **SE** Practice Problem *p. 128* **TE** More Examples *p. 128* **SE** Key Terms *p. 163* **SE** Questions and Problems *p. 164*	**TE** **NSES** UCP1, A1, A2, E2
TE Teaching Tips *pp. 129–130*	▭ Transparency: Table 5.2 ⊙ EasyPlanner	**SE** Active Reading Question *p. 129* **SE** Critical Thinking *p. 129* **SE** Key Terms *p. 163* **SE** Questions and Problems *p. 164*	
TE Meeting Individual Needs *p. 130* **TE** Meeting Individual Needs *p. 131* **TE** Teaching Tips *p. 132* **RP** Team Learning Worksheet (Sec. 5.1)	▭ Transparency: Figure 5.1 ▭ Transparency: Table 5.3 ⊙ EasyPlanner	**SE** Active Reading Question *p. 131* **SE** Review Questions (5.1.A–5.1.C) *p. 132* **SE** Key Terms *p. 163* **SE** Questions and Problems *pp. 164–165*	
TE Teaching Tip *p. 133* **RP** MINT: Math Concepts *TE p. 134*	▮ Lab Generator CD ⊙ EasyPlanner	**SE** Active Reading Question *p. 134* **SE** Key Terms *p. 163* **SE** Questions and Problems *p. 165*	**TE** **NSES** UCP1,UCP3, A1, A2, E1, E2, F4, F6, G3
TE Teaching Tips *pp. 135–137* **TE** Meeting Individual Needs *p. 138* **TE** Meeting Individual Needs *p. 139* **RP** MINT: Math Concepts *TE p. 136* **RP** Team Learning Worksheet (Sec. 5.2)	▮ Lab Generator CD ⊙ EasyPlanner	**SE** Active Reading Question *p. 136* **SE** Practice Problem *p. 137* **TE** More Examples *p. 137* **TE** More Examples *p. 139* **SE** Practice Problem *p. 140* **TE** More Examples *p. 140* **SE** Review Questions (5.2.A–5.2.B) *p. 142* **SE** Key Terms *p. 163* **SE** Questions and Problems *pp. 165–166*	

5 | Measurements and Calculations

Planning Guide

Section	Segment	Text Features and Components	Labs, Demonstrations, & Activities
5.3 Problem Solving and Unit Conversions 1.5 Blocks pp. 143–162	**A** Tools for Problem Solving		(SE) Hands-On Chemistry: Cooking in a Metric World *p. 146* (LM) Experiment 20: Conversion Factors, Traditional Lab Manual Report Sheets Teacher's Lab Guide
	B Temperature Conversions	(SE) Chemistry in Your World: Ersatz Fog *p. 154* (TE) Teaching Support: Graphing Temperature Scales *pp. 150–151*	(TE) Teaching Support: Demonstration *pp. 156–157*
	C Density	(SE) Top Ten Elements with Highest Densities *p. 161* (SE) Celebrity Chemical: Carvone *p. 162*	(TE) Group Activity *p. 157* (TE) Mini-Demos *p. 158* (SE) Hands-On Chemistry: The Density of Clay *p. 161* (TE) Group Activity *p. 161* (LM) Experiment 21: Measurement and Density, Traditional Lab Manual Report Sheets Teacher's Lab Guide

Key
(SE) Student Edition   (TE) Teacher Edition   (RP) Teacher Resource Package
(AR) Additional Materials   (LM) Lab Materials   (⊖) Transparencies
(⊙) DVD   CD-ROM   (ⓘ) classzone.com

124c

All Learners	Technology	Review & Assessment	Standards
TE Teaching Tips *pp. 144, 146* **TE** Misconceptions *p. 145* **TE** Meeting Individual Needs *p. 148* **RP** MINT: Math Concepts *TE p. 147*	**◻** Lab Generator CD **◉** EasyPlanner	**SE** Active Reading Questions *p. 146* **SE** Practice Problem *p. 147* **TE** More Examples *p. 147* **TE** More Examples *p. 148* **SE** Practice Problem *p. 149* **SE** Key Terms *p. 163* **SE** Questions and Problems *p. 166*	**TE** **NSES** UCP1, UCP3, A1, A2, E1, E2
TE Teaching Tips *pp. 149, 153* **TE** Meeting Individual Needs *p. 152* **TE** Meeting Individual Needs *p. 155*	**◻** Transparency: Figure 5.5 **◉** EasyPlanner	**SE** Active Reading Question *p. 150* **TE** More Examples *p. 151* **SE** Practice Problem *p. 152* **TE** More Examples *p. 152* **TE** More Examples *p. 154* **SE** Practice Problem *p. 155* **SE** Practice Problem *p. 156* **TE** More Examples *p. 156* **SE** Key Terms *p. 163* **SE** Questions and Problems *pp. 166–167*	
TE Misconception *p. 158* **TE** Meeting Individual Needs *p. 159* **TE** Teaching Tip *p. 161* **RP** Team Learning Worksheet (Sec. 5.3)	**◻** Lab Generator CD **◉** EasyPlanner	**SE** Active Reading Question *p. 157* **TE** More Examples *p. 157* **TE** More Examples *p. 159* **SE** Practice Problem *p. 160* **TE** More Examples *p. 160* **SE** Review Questions (5.3.A–5.3.C) *p. 162* **SE** Key Terms *p. 163* **SE** Questions and Problems *p. 167*	

Resource Materials for Chapter 5

SE Chapter Review *p. 163*

SE Critical Thinking *p. 168*

SE Standardized Test Practice *p. 169*

AR English/Spanish Summaries

◻ English Summaries Audio

◻ Spanish Summaries Audio

RP Meeting Individual Needs Toolkit (MINT)
    Reading Concepts
    Math Concepts
    Chapter Review Worksheets
    Chapter Summaries

RP Solutions Guide

RP Standardized Test Practice

RP Chapter Tests

RP Test Bank

◉ Test Generator

Chapter 5

Overview

In this chapter our goals are for students to:

- Show how numbers can be expressed in scientific notation

- Learn the English, metric, and SI systems of measurement

- Use the metric system to measure length, volume, and mass

- Learn how uncertainty in a measurement arises and express uncertainty using significant figures

- Learn to determine the number of significant figures in a calculated result

- Learn how dimensional analysis can be used to solve various types of problems

- Learn the three temperature scales and how to convert from one to another

- Define density and its units

Chapter 5

Measurements and Calculations

There are a variety of measuring devices that you can use to make a quantitative observation.

124

IN YOUR LIFE

As we pointed out in Chapter 1, making observations is a key part of the scientific process. Sometimes observations are *qualitative* ("the substance is a yellow solid") and sometimes they are *quantitative* ("the substance weighs 4.3 grams"). A quantitative observation is called a **measurement**. Measurements are very important in our daily lives. For example, we pay for gasoline by the gallon, so the gas pump must accurately measure the gas delivered to our fuel tank. The efficiency of the modern automobile engine depends on various measurements, including the amount of oxygen in the exhaust gases, the temperature of the coolant, and the pressure of the lubricating oil. In addition, cars with traction control systems have devices to measure and compare the rates of rotation of all four wheels.

As we will see in the "Chemistry in Your World" discussion in this chapter, measuring devices have become very sophisticated in dealing with our fast-moving and complicated society.

A gas pump measures the amount of gasoline delivered.

WHAT DO YOU KNOW?

Prereading Questions

1. What are some units that are used in the metric system?

2. A donut shop sells donuts only by the dozen. If you have to buy donuts for 63 people and want each person to get at least one donut, how many dozen do you need to buy?

3. How do you think the word *quantity* relates to the word *quantitative*?

Measurements and Calculations • Chapter 5 • **125**

Student Preparation

Assign students to read Section 5.1 and to answer the Review Questions at the end of the section before coming to class.

Active Learning
Team Learning Worksheet

After introducing the material in Section 5.1 in class, place students in groups and have them work together on **Section 5.1: Team Learning Worksheet**.

Active Reading Question

A qualitative observation describes something without numbers; a quantitative observation (or a measurement) describes the amount of something.

Homework

You may wish to assign these selected end-of-chapter problems as homework for this section: 1, 2, 3a–b, 4a–b, 5a–d, 6a–f, 7a–d, 8a–d, 9a–c, 10a–c, 12, 13, 15, 18, 19.

Additional end-of-chapter problems can be used for extra practice.

5.1.A Scientific Notation

Objective To show how very large and very small numbers can be expressed as the product of a number between 1 and 10 and a power of 10

TEACHING TIPS

- You will find that students have used scientific notation to some extent in their math classes. Point out that numbers in science are often very large or very small, so using scientific notation is an excellent shorthand way of writing numbers.

- Work out plenty of examples in class for each type of situation. This reinforcement will give students more confidence in doing problems on their own.

Scientific Notation and Units

Key Terms
- Measurement
- Scientific notation
- Units
- English system
- Metric system
- International System (SI)
- Volume
- Liter
- Milliliter
- Mass
- Gram

Objectives
- *To show how very large or very small numbers can be expressed in scientific notation*
- *To learn the English, metric, and SI systems of measurement*
- *To use the metric system to measure length, volume, and mass*

A measurement always consists of two parts: a number and a unit. Both parts are necessary to make the measurement meaningful. For example, suppose that a friend tells you that she saw a bug 5 long. This statement is meaningless as it stands. Five what? If it's 5 millimeters, the bug is quite small. If it's 5 centimeters, the bug is quite large. If it's 5 meters, run for cover!

The point is that for a measurement to be meaningful, it must consist of both a number and a unit that tells us the scale being used.

Active Reading Question

What is the difference between a qualitative observation and a quantitative observation?

A. Scientific Notation

The numbers associated with scientific measurements are often very large or very small. For example, the distance from Earth to the sun is approximately 93,000,000 (93 million) miles. Written out, this number is rather bulky. Scientific notation is a method for making very large or very small numbers more compact and easier to write.

To see how this is done, consider the number 125, which can be written as the product:

$$125 = 1.25 \times 100$$

Because $100 = 10 \times 10 = 10^2$, we can write:

$$125 = 1.25 \times 100 = 1.25 \times 10^2$$

Similarly, the number 1700 can be written:

$$1700 = 1.7 \times 1000$$

Because $1000 = 10 \times 10 \times 10 = 10^3$, we can write:

$$1700 = 1.7 \times 1000 = 1.7 \times 10^3$$

Scientific notation *expresses a number as a product of a number between 1 and 10 and the appropriate power of 10.*

Representing Large Numbers The distance from Earth to the sun is about 93 million miles. The number 93,000,000 can be expressed as:

$$93,000,000 = 9.3 \times 10 \times 10 \times 10 \times 10 \times 10 \times 10 \times 10$$
$$= 9.3 \times 10^7$$

Number between 1 and 10 | Appropriate power of 10 ($10,000,000 = 10^7$)

MATH

When writing a number in scientific notation, keep one digit to the left of the decimal point.

Meeting Individual Needs
MATH CONCEPTS

If students need extra math help, have them read *Scientific Notation* located in the *Teacher Resources*. A worksheet is available to go along with the handout.

The easiest way to determine the appropriate power of 10 for scientific notation is to start with the number being represented and count the number of places the decimal point must be moved to obtain a number between 1 and 10. For example, for the number

9 3 0 0 0 0 0 0
  7 6 5 4 3 2 1

we must move the decimal point seven places to the left to get 9.3 (a number between 1 and 10). To compensate for every move of the decimal point to the left, we must multiply by 10. That is, each time we move the decimal point to the left, we make the number smaller by one power of 10. So for each move of the decimal point to the left, we must multiply by 10 to restore the number to its original magnitude. Moving the decimal point seven places to the left means that we must multiply 9.3 by 10 seven times, which equals 10^7:

$93,000,000 = 9.3 \times 10^7$ We moved the decimal point seven places to the left, so we need to multiply by 10^7.

Remember: when the decimal point is moved to the *left*, the exponent of 10 is *positive*.

Representing Small Numbers We can represent numbers smaller than 1 by using the same convention, but in this case the power of 10 is negative. For example, for the number 0.010 we must move the decimal point two places to the right to obtain a number between 1 and 10:

0 . 0 1 0
    1 2

This requires an exponent of −2, so $0.010 = 1.0 \times 10^{-2}$. Remember: when the decimal point is moved to the *right*, the exponent of 10 is *negative*.

Next consider the number 0.000167. In this case we must move the decimal point four places to the right to obtain 1.67 (a number between 1 and 10):

0 . 0 0 0 1 6 7
     1 2 3 4

Moving the decimal point four places to the right requires an exponent of −4. Therefore,

$0.000167 = 1.67 \times 10^{-4}$ We moved the decimal point four places to the right.

Let's Review

Using Scientific Notation

- Any number can be represented as the product of a number between 1 and 10 and a power of 10 (either positive or negative).
- The power of 10 depends on the number of places the decimal point is moved and in which direction. The *number of places* the decimal point is moved determines the *power of 10*. The *direction* of the move determines whether the power of 10 is *positive* or *negative*. If the decimal point is moved to the left, the power of 10 is positive; if the decimal point is moved to the right, the power of 10 is negative.

MATH

Moving the decimal point to the *left* requires a *positive* exponent.

MATH

Moving the decimal point to the *right* requires a *negative* exponent.

i n f o r m a t i o n

Turn to the Appendix if you need a further discussion of exponents and scientific notation.

TEACHING TIP

When introducing scientific notation, use familiar numbers such as 1000 and 5000. Students will see more clearly that $1000 = 10 \times 10 \times 10 = 1 \times 10^3$, and $5000 = 5 \times 10 \times 10 \times 10 = 5 \times 10^3$.

MISCONCEPTIONS Math

- This chemistry course may be the first time a student is asked to report and manipulate numbers using scientific notation. While students may be familiar with exponents, they are often not comfortable using them. For example, many students will say that 1×10^{-7} is greater than 1×10^{-3} because 7 is larger than 3. Other students are likely to disregard the exponent entirely, so, for example, 2.3×10^3 is said to be larger than 1.8×10^6 because 2.3 is greater than 1.8.

- It is common for students to use their calculator incorrectly when using scientific notation so that they multiply by 10 twice. For example, when entering the number 2.1×10^7 into the calculator, a student may enter "2.1" "×" "10" "EE" "7", even though the "EE" button represents "× 10". The student has effectively entered 2.1×10^8 and will be incorrect by a factor of 10.

Meeting Individual Needs

READING CONCEPTS

For additional help with math in the text, have students read *Reading Math* located in the *Teacher Resources*. This handout discusses the math symbols students will encounter in the chemistry course.

Active Reading Question

A number with a positive exponent is greater than 1 (and the decimal has been moved to the left). A number with a negative exponent is less than 1 (and the decimal has been moved to the right).

EXAMPLE 5.1

More Examples

Express each number in scientific notation.

a. 12,500
1.25×10^4

b. 247
2.47×10^2

c. 10
1×10^1

d. 3,500,000
3.5×10^6

e. 1430
1.43×10^3

EXAMPLE 5.2

More Practice

Express each number in scientific notation.

1. 0.135
1.35×10^{-1}

2. 0.0024
2.4×10^{-3}

3. 0.104
1.04×10^{-1}

4. 0.0306
3.06×10^{-2}

5. 0.00000072
7.2×10^{-7}

 Answer to Practice Problem 5.2

$357 = 3.57 \times 10^2$

$0.0055 = 5.5 \times 10^{-3}$

Active Reading Question

What does it mean when a number written in scientific notation has a positive exponent? What does it mean when a number written in scientific notation has a negative exponent?

EXAMPLE 5.1

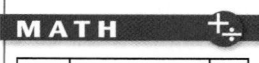
Scientific Notation: Powers of 10 (Positive)

Represent the following numbers in scientific notation.

    a. 238,000   b. 1,500,000

MATH $+\div$

1	1	10^0
10	10	10^1
100	10×10	10^2
1000	$10 \times 10 \times 10$	10^3
10000	$10 \times 10 \times 10 \times 10$	10^4

Solution

a. First we move the decimal point until we have a number between 1 and 10, in this case 2.38.

2 3 8 0 0 0
   5 4 3 2 1   The decimal point was moved five places to the left.

Because we moved the decimal point five places to the left, the power of 10 is positive 5. So, $238,000 = 2.38 \times 10^5$.

b. 1 5 0 0 0 0 0
   6 5 4 3 2 1   The decimal point was moved six places to the left, so the power of 10 is 6.

So $1,500,000 = 1.5 \times 10^6$.

EXAMPLE 5.2

Scientific Notation: Powers of 10 (Negative)

Represent the following numbers in scientific notation.

    a. 0.00043   b. 0.089

MATH $+\div$

1	1	10^0
0.1	$\frac{1}{10}$	10^{-1}
0.01	$\frac{1}{10 \times 10}$	10^{-2}
0.001	$\frac{1}{10 \times 10 \times 10}$	10^{-3}
0.0001	$\frac{1}{10 \times 10 \times 10 \times 10}$	10^{-4}

Solution

a. First we move the decimal point until we have a number between 1 and 10, in this case 4.3.

0 . 0 0 0 4 3
     1 2 3 4   The decimal point was moved four places to the right.

Because we moved the decimal point four places to the right, the power of 10 is negative 4. Therefore, $0.00043 = 4.3 \times 10^{-4}$.

b. 0 . 0 8 9   The power of 10 is negative 2 because the decimal point was moved
      1 2   two places to the right.

So $0.089 = 8.9 \times 10^{-2}$.

 Practice Problem • Exercise 5.2

Write the numbers 357 and 0.0055 in scientific notation. If you are having difficulty with scientific notation, read the Appendix.

B. Units

The **units** part of a measurement tells us what *scale* or *standard* is being used to represent the results of the measurement. From the earliest days of civilization, trade has required common units. For example, if a farmer from one region wanted to trade grain for the gold of a miner who lived in another region, the two people had to have common standards (units) for measuring the amount of the grain and the weight of the gold.

The need for common units also applies to scientists, who measure quantities such as mass, length, time, and temperature. If every scientist had her or his own personal set of units, complete chaos would result. Unfortunately, although standard systems of units did arise, different systems were adopted in different parts of the world. The two most widely used systems are the **English system** used in the United States and the **metric system** used in most of the rest of the industrialized world.

Active Reading Question

Why is a unit a necessary part of a measurement?

The metric system has long been preferred for most scientific work. In 1960 an international agreement set up a comprehensive system of units called the **International System** (*le Système Internationale* in French), or **SI**. The SI units are based on the metric system and units derived from the metric system. The most important fundamental SI units are listed in **Table 5.1.** Later in this chapter we will discuss how to manipulate some of these units.

> **Unit**
> The part of the measurement telling us the scale being used

CRITICAL THINKING

What if you were not allowed to use units for one day? How would it affect your life for that day?

CHEMISTRY IN YOUR WORLD

Science, Technology, and Society

Critical Units!

How important are conversions from one unit to another? If you ask the National Aeronautic and Space Administration (NASA), very important! In 1999, NASA lost a $125 million Mars Climate Orbiter because of a failure to convert from English to metric units.

The problem arose because two teams working on the Mars mission were using different sets of units. NASA's scientists at the Jet Propulsion Laboratory in Pasadena, California, assumed that the thrust data for the rockets on the Orbiter that they received from Lockheed Martin Astronautics in Denver, which built the spacecraft, were in metric units. In reality, the units were English. As a result, the Orbiter dipped 100 kilometers lower into the Mars atmosphere than planned and the friction from the atmosphere caused the craft to burn up.

NASA's mistake refueled the controversy over whether Congress should require the United States to

switch to the metric system. About 95% of the world now uses the metric system, and the United States is slowly switching from English to metric. For example, the automobile industry has adopted metric fasteners and we buy our soda in two liter bottles.

Units can be very important. In fact, they can mean the difference between life and death on some occasions. In 1983, for example, a Canadian jetliner almost ran out of fuel when someone pumped 22,300 pounds of fuel into the aircraft instead of 22,300 kilograms. Remember to watch your units!

Artist's conception of the lost Mars Climate Orbiter

5.1.B Units
Objective To learn the English, metric, and SI systems of measurement

 TEACHING TIPS

- Have students focus on learning only one conversion between English and metric for each parameter (e.g., length, volume, mass). This approach will permit students to switch between systems. They usually can convert successfully within a given system.

- Stress the need for including units with a measurement. Without units, we have no idea what is being measured. Use the Critical Thinking feature to bring this point through in a dramatic fashion.

- Some metric units are already meaningful to students. Bring in a 1-L water bottle (and show how it is equal to 1.05 qt). You can also show students an example of a packaged food, such as cereal, that lists weights in both grams and ounces. It is helpful if students have a feel for the size of a liter, gram, and meter.

Active Reading Question

Without a unit, we have no scale to justify the number. If we are told the volume of something is "4," we do not know if it is small (4 mL) or large (4 L).

CRITICAL THINKING

Students often complain about our emphasis on keeping track of units. However, the same students often do not realize that they use units all the time. For example, challenge students to go into their favorite sandwich shop and order "two" to see whether they get what they want.

Chemistry in Your World
Critical Units!

Students often discount the importance of units. However, a measurement is meaningless without both the number and the unit. Either part by itself is of no use to us. For example, if you say that you just saw a man with a nose 5 long, the statement conveys no useful information. If the units are millimeters, the man has a very short nose. If the units are centimeters, he has an

average nose. If the units are meters, we are talking Pinocchio!

"Critical Units!" shows just how important units are. Although incorrect use of units is usually just an annoyance, it can cause expensive or even fatal accidents.

TEACHING TIP

When introducing the metric system, ask students to give examples of the use of the metric system in their lives. This discussion should introduce the ideas of liter and meter in a more natural way. Some students are not familiar with the prefixes needed in the metric system. Use the transparency of Table 5.2 to introduce them.

5.1.C Measurements of Length, Volume, and Mass
Objective To use the metric system to measure length, volume, and mass

TECHNOLOGY

 Figure 5.1

TABLE 5.1
Common Fundamental SI Units

Physical Quality	Name of Unit	Abbreviation
mass	kilogram	kg
length	meter	m
time	second	s
temperature	kelvin	K

Because the fundamental units are not always a convenient size, the SI system uses prefixes to change the size of the unit. The most commonly used prefixes are listed in **Table 5.2.** Although the fundamental unit for length is the meter (m), we can also use the decimeter (dm), which represents one-tenth (0.1) of a meter; the centimeter (cm), which represents one one-hundredth (0.01) of a meter; the millimeter (mm), which represents one one-thousandth (0.001) of a meter; and so on. For example, it's much more convenient to specify the diameter of a certain contact lens as 1.0 cm than as 1.0×10^{-2} m.

TABLE 5.2
Commonly Used Prefixes in the Metric System

Prefix	Symbol	Meaning	Power of 10 for Scientific Notation
mega	M	1,000,000	10^6
kilo	k	1000	10^3
deci	d	0.1	10^{-1}
centi	c	0.01	10^{-2}
milli	m	0.001	10^{-3}
micro	μ	0.000001	10^{-6}
nano	n	0.000000001	10^{-9}

C. Measurements of Length, Volume, and Mass

The fundamental SI unit of length is the meter, which is a little longer than a yard (1 meter = 39.37 inches). In the metric system fractions of a meter or multiples of a meter can be expressed by powers of 10, as summarized in **Table 5.3.**

The English and metric systems are compared on the ruler shown in **Figure 5.1.** Note that:

1 inch = 2.54 centimeters

Other English-metric equivalences are given in Section 5.3.

Figure 5.1
Comparison of English and metric units for length on a ruler

130 • Chapter 5 • Measurements and Calculations

Meeting Individual Needs
VISUAL LEARNERS

In small groups, have students use various measuring devices for length to measure common classroom objects. Have students express each measure in inches, feet, yards, millimeters, centimeters, and meters.

TABLE 5.3

Metric System for Measuring Length

Unit	Symbol	Meter Equivalent
kilometer	km	1000 m or 10^3 m
meter	m	1 m or 1 m
decimeter	dm	0.1 m or 10^{-1} m
centimeter	cm	0.01 m or 10^{-2} m
millimeter	mm	0.001 m or 10^{-3} m
micrometer	μm	0.0000001 m or 10^{-6} m
nanometer	nm	0.000000000 m or 10^{-9} m

Active Reading Question

How does a kilometer compare with a meter? How does a milliliter compare with a liter?

Volume is the amount of three-dimensional space occupied by a substance. The fundamental unit of volume in the SI system is based on the volume of a cube that measures 1 meter in each of the three directions. That is, each edge of the cube is 1 meter in length. The volume of this cube is:

$$1 \text{ m} \times 1 \text{ m} \times 1 \text{ m} = (1 \text{ m})^3 = 1 \text{ m}^3$$

or, in words, one cubic meter. In **Figure 5.2** a cube is divided into 1000 smaller cubes. Each of these small cubes represents a volume of 1 dm^3, which is commonly called the **liter** (rhymes with "meter" and is slightly larger than a quart). Liter is abbreviated L.

The cube with a volume of 1 dm^3 (1 liter) can in turn be broken into 1000 smaller cubes, each representing a volume of 1 cm^3. Each liter contains 1000 cm^3. One cubic centimeter is called a **milliliter** (abbreviated mL), a unit of volume used very commonly in chemistry. This relationship is summarized in **Table 5.4.**

Figure 5.3
A 100-mL
graduated cylinder

TABLE 5.4

Relationship Between the Liter and Milliliter

Unit	Symbol	Equivalence
liter	L	1 L = 1000 mL
milliliter	mL	$\frac{1}{1000}$ L = 10^{-3} L = 1 mL

The *graduated cylinder* (see **Figure 5.3**), which is commonly used in chemical laboratories for measuring the volumes of liquids, is marked off in convenient units of volume (usually milliliters). The graduated cylinder is filled to the desired volume with the liquid, which then can be poured out.

Volume
The amount of three-dimensional space occupied by a substance

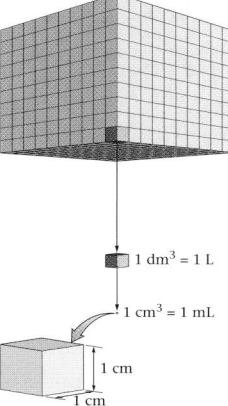

Figure 5.2
The largest drawing represents a cube that has sides 1 m in length and a volume of 1 m^3. The middle-size cube has sides 1 dm in length and a volume of 1 dm^3, or 1 L. The smallest cube has sides 1 cm in length and a volume of 1 cm^3, or 1 mL.

- Now is an excellent time to discuss the difference between mass and weight. In daily life, we often use these terms interchangeably. They have very different meanings to a chemist, however. Since our language does not have a verb for *mass*, we use the term *weigh* in chemistry to mean "finding the mass of the substance on a balance."

- Ask students to compare the relationship between a liter and a quart, a gram and a pound, and a kilometer and a mile. Try to get them to relate these ideas to familiar objects in everyday life without actually converting the units.

SECTION 5.1
ASSESS

 SECTION 5.1
Review Questions

1. positive, negative
2. a. 8.475×10^6
   b. 7.54×10^{-5}
   c. 1×10^3
   d. 3.5724×10^{-1}
3.

	English	Metric
Length	yard	meter
Volume	quart	liter
Mass	pound	kilogram

4. 500 mm
5. A liter is slightly larger than a quart.

Mass
The quantity of matter in an object

Figure 5.4
An electronic analytical balance used in chemistry labs

Another important measurable quantity is **mass**, which can be defined as the quantity of matter present in an object. The fundamental SI unit of mass is the kilogram. Because the metric system, which existed before the SI system, used the gram as the fundamental unit, the prefixes for the various mass units are based on the **gram**, as shown in **Table 5.5**.

TABLE 5.5
Most Commonly Used Metric Units for Mass

Unit	Symbol	Gram Equivalent
kilogram	kg	$1000 = 10^3 g = 1$ kg
gram	g	1 g
milligram	mg	$0.001\ g = 10^{-3} g = 1$ mg

In the laboratory we determine the mass of an object by using a balance. A balance compares the mass of the object to a set of standard masses (weights). For example, the mass of an object can be determined by using a single-pan balance (see **Figure 5.4**).

To help you get a feeling for the common units of length, volume, and mass, some familiar objects are described in **Table 5.6**.

TABLE 5.6
Examples of Commonly Used Units

length	A dime is 1 mm thick. A quarter is 2.5 cm in diameter. The average height of an adult man is 1.8 m.
mass	A nickel has a mass of about 5 g. A 120-lb woman has a mass of about 55 kg.
volume	A 12-oz can of soda has a volume of about 360 mL. A half gallon of milk is equal to about 2 L of milk.

SECTION 5.1
REVIEW QUESTIONS

❶ When writing numbers using scientific notation, numbers greater than one have _____ exponents and numbers less than one have _____ exponents.

❷ Change the following to scientific notation:
   a. 8,475,000   c. 1,000
   b. 0.0000754   d. 0.35724

❸ Copy and complete the table below.

	English unit	Metric unit
Length		meter
Volume	quart	
Mass	pound	

❹ How many millimeters are in 50 cm?

❺ Which is a larger, a liter or a quart?

 RESEARCH LINKS
CLASSZONE.COM

132 • Chapter 5 • Measurements and Calculations

Uncertainty in Measurement and Significant Figures

Objectives

- *To learn how uncertainty in a measurement arises*
- *To learn to indicate a measurement's uncertainty by using significant figures*
- *To learn to determine the number of significant figures in a calculated result*

Key Terms

- Significant figures
- Rounding off

A. Uncertainty in Measurement

Whenever a measurement is made with a device such as a ruler or a graduated cylinder, an estimate is required. We can illustrate this by measuring the pin shown.

We can see from the ruler that the pin is a little longer than 2.8 cm and a little shorter than 2.9 cm. Because there are no graduations on the ruler between 2.8 and 2.9, we must estimate the pin's length between 2.8 and 2.9 cm. We do this by *imagining* that the distance between 2.8 and 2.9 is broken into 10 equal divisions shown in blue and estimating to which division the end of the pin reaches.

The end of the pin appears to come about halfway between 2.8 and 2.9, which corresponds to 5 of our 10 imaginary divisions. So we estimate the pin's length as 2.85 cm. The result of our measurement is that the pin is approximately 2.85 cm in length, but we had to rely on a visual estimate, so it might actually be 2.84 or 2.86 cm.

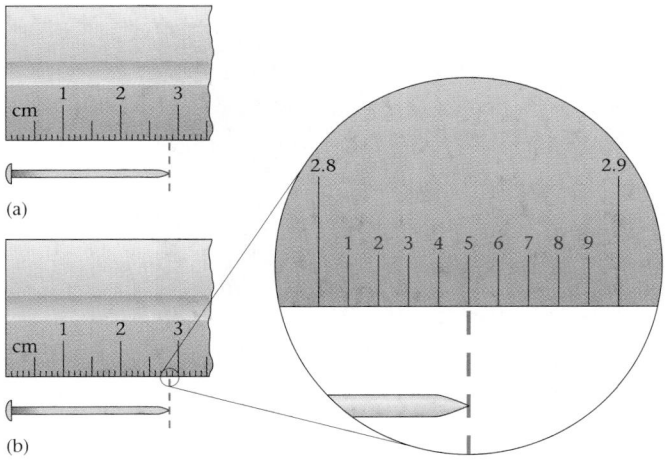

(a)

(b)

5.2 • Uncertainty in Measurement and Significant Figures • **133**

SECTION 5.2
INTRODUCE

Student Preparation

Assign students to read Section 5.2 and to answer the Review Questions at the end of the section before coming to class.

Active Learning
Team Learning Worksheet

After introducing the material in Section 5.2 in class, place students in groups and have them work together on **Section 5.2: Team Learning Worksheet.**

 LABORATORY
EXPERIMENT 18:
Measurement and the SI System, Traditional

SECTION 5.2
GUIDE THE LEARNING

Homework

You may wish to assign these selected end-of-chapter problems as homework for this section: 22, 23, 24a–d, 25, 27, 28, 30, 32a–b, 33a–b, 34a–b

Additional end-of-chapter problems can be used for extra practice.

5.2.A Uncertainty in Measurement

Objective To learn how uncertainty in measurement arises and to indicate a measurement's uncertainty by using significant figures

 TEACHING TIP

To illustrate uncertainty in measurements, bring to class several pieces of glassware used to measure volume. Show students the glassware. Draw the shape of a piece of glassware on the board, marking the drawing to show the meniscus of a liquid between two of the lines. Because the volume falls between the lines, there is uncertainty involved in the reading. Have students write the result of the measurement and then compare results. The number recorded for this measurement will vary from student to student only in the last digit. Thus there is only one uncertain digit.

For a project to help students better understand uncertainty in measurements, see *Precision, Accuracy, and Percent Error* located in the *Teacher Resources*.

Active Reading Question

When we record a measurement, we always include an estimated digit.

Because the last number is based on a visual estimate, it may be different when another person makes the same measurement. For example, if five different people measured the pin, the results might be

Person	Result of Measurement
1	2.85 cm
2	2.84 cm
3	2.86 cm
4	2.85 cm
5	2.86 cm

Note that the first two digits in each measurement are the same regardless of who made the measurement; these are called the *certain* numbers of the measurement. However, the third digit is estimated and can vary; it is called an *uncertain* number. When one is making a measurement, the custom is to record all of the certain numbers plus the *first* uncertain number. It would not make any sense to try to measure the pin to the third decimal place (thousandths of a centimeter), because this ruler requires an estimate of even the second decimal place (hundredths of a centimeter).

A measurement always has some degree of uncertainty.

The uncertainty of a measurement depends on the measuring device. For example, if our ruler had marks indicating hundredths of a centimeter, the uncertainty in the measurement of the pin would occur in the thousandths place rather than the hundredths place—but some uncertainty would still exist.

Active Reading Question

What do we mean when we say that a measurement always has a degree of uncertainty?

Students working on a lab project

Meeting Individual Needs
MATH CONCEPTS

If students need extra help with uncertainty in measurements, have them read *Significant Figures* located in the *Teacher Resources*. A worksheet is available to go along with the handout.

5.2.B Significant Figures
Objective To determine the number of significant figures in a calculated result

 LABORATORY
EXPERIMENT 19:
Measuring a Book? Precisely!

 Active Learning
Classroom Activities and Projects

See *Special Rulers for Measuring Lab* located in the *Teacher Resources*.

🍎 **TEACHING TIP**

Students have the most trouble determining whether zeros are significant. Make sure you show examples with zeros in various locations within the number.

CHEMISTRY EXPLORERS
Cecile Hoover Edwards • 1926–2005

Cecile Hoover Edwards was born in East St. Louis, Illinois, in 1926. She enrolled in college at the age of 15 and received a master's degree in chemistry from what is now Tuskegee University before she turned 21.
   After receiving a doctorate in nutrition from Iowa State University in 1950, she returned to Tuskegee as a faculty member and researcher and worked there for the next 20 years.
   In 1971 she joined the faculty of Howard University, served as a professor and dean, and established a doctoral program in nutrition. Much of her research focused on improving the nutritional value of the high-protein low-cost foods used by African-Americans eating a traditional southeastern American diet.
   In 1984, Illinois declared April 5 "Dr. Cecile Hoover Edwards Day."

The numbers recorded in a measurement (all the certain numbers plus the first uncertain number) are called **significant figures**. The number of significant figures for a given measurement is determined by the inherent uncertainty of the measuring device. For example, the ruler used to measure the pin can give results only to hundredths of a centimeter. So, when we record the significant figures for a measurement, we automatically give information about the uncertainty in a measurement. The uncertainty in the last number (the estimated number) is usually assumed to be ± 1 unless otherwise indicated.
   For example, the measurement 1.86 kilograms can be interpreted as 1.86 ± 0.01 kilograms, where the symbol ± means plus or minus. That is, it could be 1.86 kg − 0.01 kg = 1.85 kg or 1.86 kg + 0.01 kg = 1.87 kg.

> **Significant figures**
> The certain digits and the first uncertain digit of a measurement

B. Significant Figures

We have seen that any measurement involves an estimate and thus is uncertain to some extent. We signify the degree of certainty for a particular measurement by the number of significant figures we record.
   Because doing chemistry requires many types of calculations, we must consider what happens when we use numbers that contain uncertainties. It is important that we know the degree of uncertainty in the final result. Although we will not discuss the process here, mathematicians have studied how uncertainty accumulates and have designed a set of rules to determine how many significant figures the result of a calculation should have. You should follow these rules whenever you carry out a calculation. The first thing we need to do is learn how to count the significant figures in a given number. To do this we use the following rules:

CHEMISTRY EXPLORERS
Cecile Hoover Edwards

The Illinois House Resolution delaring April 5 to be "Dr. Cecile Hoover Edwards Day" lists many accomplishments. Dr. Edwards was Dean of the School of Human Ecology at Howard University. There she established the Ph.D. program in nutrition. She served two terms on the Secretary of Agriculture's Expert committee on Nitrates, Nitrites, and Nitrosamines and was a Panel Chairman of the White House Conference on Food, Nutrition, and Health. She is the author and coauthor of over 140 publications on nutrition and quality of life.

- Students often have trouble determining which numbers qualify as exact numbers. Discuss numbers that are exact as you encounter them in examples. Help students recognize numbers from definitions and from counting objects as exact.

- The easiest way to determine the number of significant figures in a number is to write the number in scientific notation. In this notation there are no leading zeros, all zeros in the middle of the number are significant, and trailing zeros are recorded only if they are significant.

Active Reading Question

The measurement 10.0 g implies that the mass is between 9.9 g and 10.1 g. The measurement 10 g implies that the mass is between 9 and 11 g.

 information

- Leading zeros are never significant figures.
- Captive zeros are always significant figures.
- Trailing zeros are sometimes significant figures.
- Exact numbers never limit the number of significant figures in a calculation.

Rules for Counting Significant Figures

1. **Nonzero integers.** Nonzero integers *always* count as significant figures. For example, the number 1457 has four nonzero integers, all of which count as significant figures.

2. **Zeros.** There are three classes of zeros:

   a. **Leading zeros** are zeros that *precede* all of the nonzero digits. They *never* count as significant figures. For example, in the number 0.0025, the three zeros simply indicate the position of the decimal point. The number has only two significant figures, the 2 and the 5.

   b. **Captive zeros** are zeros that fall *between* nonzero digits. They *always* count as significant figures. For example, the number 1.008 has four significant figures.

   c. **Trailing zeros** are zeros at the *right end* of the number. They are significant only if the number is written with a decimal point. The number one hundred written as 100 has only one significant figure, but written as 100., it has three significant figures.

3. **Exact numbers.** Often calculations involve numbers that were not obtained using measuring devices but were determined by counting: 10 experiments, 3 apples, 8 molecules. Such numbers are called *exact numbers*. They can be assumed to have an unlimited number of significant figures. Exact numbers can also arise from definitions. For example, 1 inch is defined as *exactly* 2.54 centimeters. Thus, in the statement 1 in. = 2.54 cm, neither 2.54 nor 1 limits the number of significant figures when it is used in a calculation.

Rules for counting significant figures also apply to numbers written in scientific notation. For example, the number 100. can be written as 1.00×10^2, and both versions have three significant figures. Scientific notation offers two major advantages: the number of significant figures can be indicated easily, and fewer zeros are needed to write a very large or a very small number. For example, the number 0.000060 is much more conveniently represented as 6.0×10^{-5}, and the number has two significant figures, written in either form.

 Active Reading Question

The numbers 10.0 and 10 are the same, but the measurements 10.0 g and 10 g are different. Why?

136 • Chapter 5 • Measurements and Calculations

Meeting Individual Needs
MATH CONCEPTS

Students who need extra help with numbers should read *Estimation* located in the *Teacher Resources*. A worksheet is available to go along with the handout.

EXAMPLE 5.3

Counting Significant Figures

Give the number of significant figures for each of the following measurements.

a. A sample of orange juice contains 0.0108 g of vitamin C.

b. A forensic chemist in a crime lab weighs a single hair and records its mass as 0.0050060 g.

c. The distance between two points was found to be 5.030×10^3 ft.

d. In yesterday's bicycle race, 110 riders started but only 60 finished.

Solution

a. The number contains three significant figures. The zeros to the left of the 1 are leading zeros and are not significant, but the remaining zero (a captive zero) is significant.

b. The number contains five significant figures. The leading zeros (to the left of the 5) are not significant. The captive zeros between the 5 and the 6 are significant, and the trailing zero to the right of the 6 is significant because the number contains a decimal point.

c. This number has four significant figures. Both zeros in 5.030 are significant.

d. Both numbers are exact (they were obtained by counting the riders). Thus these numbers have an unlimited number of significant figures.

 Practice Problem • Exercise 5.3

Give the number of significant figures for each of the following measurements.

a. 0.00100 m   b. 2.0800×10^2 L   c. 480 cars

Rounding Off Numbers

When you perform a calculation on your calculator, the number of digits displayed is usually greater than the number of significant figures that the result should possess. So you must "round off" the number (reduce it to fewer digits). The rules for **rounding off** follow.

Rules for Rounding Off

1. If the digit to be removed
   a. is less than 5, the preceding digit stays the same. For example, 1.33 rounds to 1.3.
   b. is equal to or greater than 5, the preceding digit is increased by 1. For example, 1.36 rounds to 1.4, and 3.15 rounds to 3.2.

2. In a series of calculations, carry the extra digits through to the final result and *then* round off.* This means that you should carry all of the digits that show on your calculator until you arrive at the final number (the answer) and then round off, using the procedures in rule 1.

> **i** **nformation**
>
> The rules for rounding off reflect the way calculators round off.

*This practice will not be followed in the worked-out examples in this text, because we want to show the correct number of significant figures in each step of the example.

EXAMPLE 5.3

More Examples

Give the number of significant figures for each measurement.

1. The mass of a single eyelash is 0.000304 g.
   (3)

2. The length of a skid mark is 1.270×10^2 m.
   (4)

3. A 125-g sample of chocolate chip cookies contains 10 g of chocolate.
   (3, 1)

4. The volume of soda remaining in a can after a spill is 0.09020 L.
   (4)

5. A dose of antibiotic is 4.0×10^{-1} cm^3.
   (2)

Answer to Practice Problem 5.3

a. 3 significant figures. The leading zeros (to the left of the 1) do not count, but the trailing zeros do.

b. 5 significant figures. The one captive zero and the two trailing zeros all count.

c. This is an exact number obtained by counting the cars. It has an unlimited number of significant figures.

🍎 TEACHING TIP

Students have had practice rounding off numbers in math class. Often, however, they do not know at what point in a problem to round off. Make sure you emphasize the second rule for rounding because students use calculators. In general, students should carry all calculator digits until the end of the problem and then round off to the correct number of significant figures.

Teaching Support

BACKGROUND INFORMATION

When constructing worksheet problems and exams, it is important to follow the steps used in "Rules for Rounding Off" when determining the answers and choices for answers. Otherwise, students' correct answer and your correct answer may differ, leading students to believe they have done the calculations incorrectly.

Students should pay attention to significant figures throughout the year, not just in this chapter. Throughout this text answers are rounded to correct significant figures. Having students be aware of the number of significant figures in their answers reminds them that in science, measurements have limitations. All atomic masses in the text have been rounded to four significant figures, so atomic masses will not limit the number of significant figures in the answer for a calculation.

We need to make one more point about rounding off to the correct number of significant figures. Suppose that the number 4.348 needs to be rounded to two significant figures. In doing this, we look at *only* the *first number* to the right of the 3:

4.348

↑

Look at this number to round off to two significant figures.

The number is rounded to 4.3 because 4 is less than 5. It is incorrect to round sequentially. For example, do *not* round the 4 to 5 to give 4.35 and then round the 3 to 4 to give 4.4.

When rounding off, *use only the first number to the right of the last significant figure.*

Determining Significant Figures in Calculations

Next we will learn how to determine the correct number of significant figures in the result of a calculation. To do this we will use the following rules.

> For multiplication and division, significant figures are counted.
> For addition and subtraction, the decimal places are counted.

Rules for Significant Figures in Multiplication and Division Calculations

For *multiplication* or *division,* the number of significant figures in the result is the same as that in the measurement with the *smallest number* of significant figures. We say this measurement is *limiting,* because it limits the number of significant figures in the result. For example, consider this calculation:

$$4.56 \times 1.4 = 6.384 \quad \text{Round off} \quad 6.4$$

Three significant figures / Limiting (two significant figures) / Two significant figures

Because 1.4 has only two significant figures, it limits the result to two significant figures. Thus the product is correctly written as 6.4, which has two significant figures.

Consider another example. In the division $\frac{8.315}{298}$, how many significant figures should appear in the answer?

Because 8.315 has four significant figures, the number 298 (with three significant figures) limits the result. The calculation is correctly represented as:

Four significant figures

$$\frac{8.315}{298} = 0.0279027 \quad \text{Round off} \quad 2.79 \times 10^{-2}$$

Limiting (three significant figures) / Result shown on calculator / Three significant figures

---

Meeting Individual Needs
ENGLISH LANGUAGE LEARNERS

It may be helpful when first introducing significant figures to relate the term *significant* to words like *important* or *meaningful.*

Rules for Significant Figures in Addition and Subtraction Calculations

For *addition* or *subtraction,* the limiting term is the one with the smallest number of decimal places. For example, consider the following sum:

```
 12.11
 18.0      Limiting term (has one decimal place)
  1.013
 31.123    Round off        31.1
                              ↑
                    One decimal place
```

The correct result is 31.1 (it is limited to one decimal place because 18.0 has only one decimal place). Consider another example:

```
  0.6875
 −0.1      Limiting term (one decimal place)

  0.5875   Round off        0.6
```

EXAMPLE 5.4

Counting Significant Figures in Calculations

Without performing the calculations, tell how many significant figures each answer should contain.

   a. 5.19
       1.9
   + 0.842

   b. $1081 - 7.25$

   c. 2.3×3.14

   d. the total cost of 3 boxes of candy at \$2.50 per box

Solution

   a. The answer will have one digit after the decimal place. The limiting number is 1.9, which has one decimal place, so the answer has two significant figures.

   b. The answer will have no digits after the decimal point. The number 1081 has no digits to the right of the decimal point and limits the result, so the answer has four significant figures.

   c. The answer will have two significant figures because the number 2.3 has only two significant figures (3.14 has three).

   d. The answer will have three significant figures. The limiting factor is 2.50 because 3 (boxes of candy) is an exact number.

EXAMPLE 5.4

More Examples

Without performing the calculations, determine the correct number of significant figures in each answer.

1. $17.1 + 0.77 + 241$
   (3)

2. $47.2 - 9$
   (2)

3. 1.27×3.1416
   (3)

4. $\dfrac{0.072}{4.36}$
   (2)

5. cost of 2 tickets to a concert at \$27.50 per ticket
   (4)

Meeting Individual Needs
INCLUSION STRATEGIES

Review the decimal place-value chart and verify that students can correctly read decimal notation by having them read aloud or write in expanded form numbers such as 1.325, 0.78, and 10.2.

EXAMPLE 5.5

More Examples

Give the correct power of 10 for each answer.

1. $(1.71 \times 10^3)(2.0 \times 10^2) =$
$3.4 \times$ ____
10^5

2. $\dfrac{1.64 \times 10^{-2}}{1.2 \times 10^{-2}} =$
$1.4 \times$ ____
10^0

3. Solve the following, giving the answer in scientific notation with the correct number of significant figures.

a. $(1.83 \times 10^{-4})(7.55 \times 10^7) =$
1.38×10^4

b. $3.3 \times 5280 =$
1.7×10^4

c. $\dfrac{(5.0 \times 10^{-4})(8.51 \times 10^{-2})}{2.92 \times 10^4} =$
1.5×10^{-9}

d. $1.842 + 45.2 + 87.55 =$
1.346×10^2

e. $714.3 - 18.56 =$
6.957×10^2

✔ Answer to Practice Problem 5.5

a. $12.6 \times 0.53 = 6.678 = 6.7$
$\uparrow$
Limiting

b. $12.6 \times 0.53 = 6.7$
$\uparrow$
Limiting

Limiting → 6.7
$\dfrac{-4.59}{2.11} = 2.1$

c. 25.36
$\dfrac{-4.15}{21.21}$
$21.21 \div 2.317 =$
$9.15408 = 9.154$

EXAMPLE 5.5

Calculations Using Significant Figures

Carry out the following mathematical operations, and give each result to the correct number of significant figures.

    a. 5.18×0.0208 **d.** $116.8 - 0.33$

    b. $(3.60 \times 10^{-3}) \times (8.123) \div 4.3$ **e.** $(1.33 \times 2.8) + 8.41$

    c. $21 + 13.8 + 130.3$

Solution

    Limiting terms   Round to this digit.

a. $5.18 \times 0.0208 = 0.107744 \Rightarrow 0.108$

The answer should contain three significant figures because each number being multiplied has three significant figures (rule 1). The 7 is rounded to 8 because the following digit is greater than 5.

    Round to this digit.

b. $\dfrac{(3.60 \times 10^{-3})(8.123)}{4.3} = 6.8006 \times 10^{-3} \Rightarrow 6.8 \times 10^{-3}$

    Limiting term

Because 4.3 has the least number of significant figures (two), the result should have two significant figures (rule 1).

c.
```
   21
   13.8
  130.36
  165.16 → 165
```
In this case 21 is limiting (there are no digits after the decimal point). Thus the answer must have no digits after the decimal point, in accordance with the rule for addition (rule 2).

d.
```
  116.8
  -0.33
  116.5 → 165.47
```
Because 116.8 has only one decimal place, the answer must have only one decimal place (rule 2). The 4 is rounded up to 5 because the digit to the right (7) is greater than 5.

e. $1.33 \times 2.8 = 3.724 \to 3.7$
```
    3.7
  +8.41
  12.11 → 12.1
```

Note that in this case we multiplied and then rounded the result to the correct number of significant figures before we performed the addition so that we would know the correct number of decimal places.

✔ Practice Problem • Exercise 5.5

Give the answer for each calculation to the correct number of significant figures.

    a. 12.6×0.53

    b. $(12.6 \times 0.53) - 4.59$

    c. $(25.36 - 4.15) \div 2.317$

CHEMISTRY IN YOUR WORLD

Measuring Changes

Measurement lies at the heart of doing science. We obtain the data for formulating laws and testing theories by doing measurements. Measurements also have very practical importance; they tell us whether our drinking water is safe, whether we are anemic, and the exact amount of gasoline we put in our cars at the filling station.

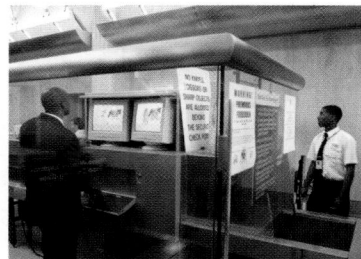

Engines in modern automobiles have oxygen sensors that analyze the oxygen content in the exhaust gases. This information is sent to the computer that controls the engine functions so that instantaneous adjustments can be made in spark timing and air-fuel mixtures to provide efficient power with minimum air pollution.

Scientists are now developing a screening procedure that bombards airline luggage with high-energy particles that cause any substance present to emit radiation characteristic of that substance. This radiation is monitored to identify luggage with unusually large quantities of nitrogen because most chemical explosives are based on compounds containing nitrogen.

Scientists are examining the natural world to find supersensitive detectors because many organisms are sensitive to tiny amounts of chemicals in their environments—for example, the sensitive noses of bloodhounds. One of these natural measuring devices uses the sensory hairs from Hawaiian red swimming crabs, which are connected to electrical analyzers and used to detect hormones at levels as low as 10^{-8} g/L.

Chemistry in Your World

Measuring Changes

"Measuring Changes" provides the background for students to discuss the implications of measuring things ever more precisely. The discussion can include the benefits and hazards of measuring such small amounts. We have been able to create faster and more accurate computers by reducing the sizes of microchips. We are now able to detect minute amounts of chemicals in our food supply. Does the fact that we can now measure these contaminants mean that our food is less safe than it was 10 years ago, when we couldn't detect them? What effect does this knowledge have on our society? Should we be worried about these tiny amounts of chemicals in our daily lives? This discussion can be used in conjunction with a writing class or social science class.

SECTION 5.2
Review Questions

1. All measurements are limited by the measuring device. Since these devices are not fully certain, neither are measurements made using them. Also, measurements are limited by our ability to accurately estimate the last digit.

2. The three classes are leading zeros, such as in 0.05, captive zeros, such as in 104, and trailing zeros, such as in 3.40 or in 10. Leading zeros are never significant, captive zeros are always significant, and trailing zeros are sometimes significant (the zero in 3.40 is significant, but the zero in 10 is not).

3. Significant zeros are

   a. between the 3 and 4

   b. between the 4 and 3 and the last digit on the right

   c. none

   d. the last digit on the right

   e. both are significant figures

   f. all are significant

   g. zero is significant

4. The number of significant figures in each case is

   a. 4   e. 3
   b. 5   f. 7
   c. 1   g. 3
   d. 2

5. The number of significant figures in each case is

   a. 2   d. 2
   b. 3   e. 1
   c. 2

6. a. 8.6   d. 2.3×10^{-5}
   b. 1.33   e. 50
   c. 16

7. a. 2 significant figures (14 is a sample measurement)

   b. 3 significant figures (3.14 is a sample measurement)

   c. 2 significant figures (4.6 is a sample measurement)

SECTION 5.2
REVIEW QUESTIONS

❶ Why are all measurements uncertain?

❷ What are the three types of zeros in a number? Which type is always significant? Which type is never significant? Which type is sometimes significant?

❸ Copy the following numbers, and mark each significant zero with an arrow.

   a. 0.003042
   b. 1.4030
   c. 1000
   d. 0.060
   e. 50.0
   f. 10.47020
   g. 250.

❹ How many significant figures are in each number below?

   a. 0.003042
   b. 1.4030
   c. 1000
   d. 0.060
   e. 50.0
   f. 10.47020
   g. 250.

❺ Without doing the calculation, tell how many significant figures should be in each result.

   a. $3.2 + 4.17 + 1.243$
   b. $1.3478 - 0.02$
   c. 4.6×3.435
   d. $(4.2 \times 10^{-5}) \times 3.74 \div 6.783$
   e. $50 - 0.00473$

❻ Perform the calculations, and determine the results from question 5.

❼ State the number of significant figures in a measurement made with each ruler:

a.

b.

c.

RESEARCH LINKS
CLASSZONE.COM

Problem Solving and Unit Conversions

Objectives

- *To learn how dimensional analysis can be used to solve problems*
- *To learn the three temperature scales*
- *To learn to convert from one temperature scale to another*
- *To practice using problem-solving techniques*
- *To define density and its units*

Key Terms

- Conversion factor
- Equivalence statement
- Dimensional analysis
- Fahrenheit scale
- Celsius scale
- Kelvin scale (absolute)
- Density
- Specific gravity

A. Tools for Problem Solving

Suppose that the boss at the store where you work on weekends asks you to pick up two dozen doughnuts on the way to work. However, you find that the doughnut shop sells by the doughnut. How many doughnuts do you need?

Problem-Solving Strategy

One of the most important things we do in life is solve problems. We confront problems constantly in school, at our jobs and in our personal lives. The more creative we are at solving these problems, the more successful we will be. It turns out that most of the problems we encounter can be attacked systematically. It is helpful to use the following steps when solving a problem:

Where do we want to go?

- To solve a problem, we need to be able to state the problem clearly— what exactly are we trying to do? What is the goal? Often drawing a picture can help.

What do we know?

- This represents the starting point. What facts do we know that relate to the problem?

How do we get there?

- How do we use the facts we know and the understanding we have of the relevant concepts to proceed from the starting point to the eventual goal—the solution to the problem. In many types of problems we will discuss the relevant fundamental ideas and a method (often in the form of steps) for solving the problem before you are asked to try a similar one on your own. You might think of these steps as the tools for solving the problem.

Does it make sense?

- After we have reached the solution, we need to evaluate it. Is the answer we have obtained reasonable? For example, if we are trying to calculate the volume of water in a certain glass and our answer is 65 L, that would be unreasonable. This number cannot be correct. We must have made a mistake somewhere. When we arrive at an answer to a problem, it is important to test the reasonableness of the answer.

SECTION 5.3
INTRODUCE

Student Preparation

Assign students to read Section 5.3 and to answer the Review Questions at the end of the section before coming to class.

 Active Learning
Team Learning Worksheet

After introducing the material in Section 5.3 in class, place students in groups and have them work together on **Section 5.3: Team Learning Worksheet.**

 LABORATORY
EXPERIMENT 20:
Conversion Factors, Traditional

SECTION 5.3
GUIDE THE LEARNING

Homework

You may wish to assign these selected end-of-chapter problems as homework for this section: 35, 36, 39a–d, 40a–d, 41, 45, 47a–c, 48a–c, 50, 51, 55, 57, 59, 60

Additional end-of-chapter problems can be used for extra practice.

5.3.A Tools for Problem Solving

Objective To learn how dimensional analysis can be used to solve various types of problems

- Make sure you help students understand how to use equivalence statements. An equivalence statement relates the same quantity in two different units. The statement can be used to generate two different conversion factors. Students must learn to use the correct conversion factor in setting up the problem. Their choice should indicate the unit they need or want on the top of the factor and the unit they are trying to eliminate on the bottom of the conversion factor.

- When doing examples in class, give both of the possible conversion factors. Ask students to choose the one that will produce the correct result. This approach reinforces the idea that all conversion factors can be written in two possible ways and that students must choose the appropriate one based on the desired units.

- Students often think they already know how to convert units. Frequently they do not use units on their conversion factors. As the problems become more complex, this omission becomes an increasing difficulty. Encourage all students to place proper units on the conversion factors. Ask students to set up problems and show how the units work out for the final result without actually doing the calculation.

- Discuss with students which conversions come from definitions (such as 1 in. = 2.54 cm) and which conversions are the results of measurements. Knowing the difference helps students decide which conversion limits the number of significant figures.

Cooking

3 cups = ? pints

Traveling

250 pesos = ? dollars

Sports

3215 km = ? miles

Conversion factor
A ratio used to convert from one unit to another

TABLE 5.7

English-Metric and English-English Equivalents

Length	1 m = 1.094 yd	
	2.54 cm = 1 in.	
	1 mi = 5280. ft	
	1 mi = 1760. yd	
Mass	1 kg = 2.205 lb	
	453.6 g = 1 lb	
Volume	1 L = 1.06 qt	
	1 ft³ = 28.32 L	

144 • Chapter 5 • Meaurements and Calculations

In doing problems in this text, we will use this general strategy where it fits. It usually works best for numerical problems such as the examples in the remainder of this chapter.

Converting Units of Measurement The "doughnut problem" mentioned previously is an example of something you encounter all the time: converting from one unit of measurement to another.

How do we convert from one unit of measurement to another? Let's explore this process by using the doughnut problem.

2 dozen doughnuts = ? individual doughnuts

The essential information you must have is the definition of a dozen:

1 dozen = 12

You can use this information to make the needed conversion as follows:

$$2 \text{ dozen doughnuts} \times \frac{12}{1 \text{ dozen}} = 24 \text{ doughnuts}$$

You need to buy 24 doughnuts.

Note two important things about this process.

1. The factor $\frac{12}{1 \text{ dozen}}$ is a conversion factor based on the definition of the term *dozen*. This conversion factor is a ratio of the two parts of the definition of a dozen given above.

2. The unit *dozen* itself cancels.

To change from one unit to another, we will use a conversion factor.

$$\text{Unit}_1 \times \text{conversion factor} = \text{Unit}_2$$

The **conversion factor** is a ratio of the two parts of the statement that relates the two units.

Choosing Conversion Factors Earlier in this chapter we considered a pin that measured 2.85 cm in length. What is the length of the pin in inches? We can represent this problem as

2.85 cm → ? in.

The question mark stands for the number we want to find. To solve this problem, we must know the relationship between inches and centimeters. In **Table 5.7,** which gives several equivalents between the English and metric systems, we find the relationship:

2.54 cm = 1 in.

This is called an **equivalence statement**. In other words, 2.54 cm and 1 in. stand for *exactly the same distance* (see **Figure 5.1** on page 130). The respective numbers are different because they refer to different *scales (units)* of distance.

The equivalence statement 2.54 cm = 1 in. can lead to either of two conversion factors:

$$\frac{2.54 \text{ cm}}{1 \text{ in.}} \quad \text{or} \quad \frac{1 \text{ in.}}{2.54 \text{ cm}}$$

Conversion factors are ratios of the two parts of the equivalence statement that relates the two units.

Which of the two possible conversion factors do we need? Recall our problem:

2.85 cm = ? in.

That is, we want to convert from units of centimeters to inches:

2.85 cm × conversion factor = ? in.

We choose a conversion factor that cancels the units we want to eliminate and leaves the units we want in the result.

Thus we do the conversion as follows:

$$2.85 \text{ cm} \times \frac{1 \text{ in.}}{2.54 \text{ cm}} = \frac{2.85 \text{ in.}}{2.54} = 1.12 \text{ in.}$$

Note two important facts about this conversion.

1. The centimeter units cancel to give inches for the result. This is exactly what we wanted to accomplish. Using the other conversion factor:

$$\left(2.85 \text{ cm} \times \frac{2.54 \text{ cm}}{1 \text{ in.}} \right)$$

would not work because the units would not cancel to give inches in the result.

2. As the units changed from centimeters to inches, the number changed from 2.85 to 1.12. Thus 2.85 cm has exactly the same value (is the same length) as 1.12 in. Notice that in this conversion, the number decreased from 2.85 to 1.12. This makes sense because the inch is a larger unit of length than the centimeter is. That is, it takes fewer inches to make the same length in centimeters.

The result in the previous conversion has three significant figures as required. Caution: Noting that the term *1* appears in the conversion, you might think that because this number appears to have only one significant figure, the result should have only one significant figure. That is, the answer should be given as 1 in. rather than 1.12 in. However, in the equivalence statement 1 in. = 2.54 cm, the 1 is an exact number (by definition). In other words, exactly 1 in. equals 2.54 cm. Therefore, the 1 does not limit the number of significant digits in the result.

We have seen how to convert from centimeters to inches. What about the reverse conversion? For example, if a pencil is 7.00 in. long, what is its length in centimeters? In this case, the conversion we want to make is:

7.00 in. → ? cm

What conversion factor do we need to make this conversion?

Remember that two conversion factors can be derived from each equivalence statement. In this case, the equivalence statement 2.54 cm = 1 in. gives

$$\frac{2.54 \text{ cm}}{1 \text{ in.}} \quad \text{or} \quad \frac{1 \text{ in.}}{2.54 \text{ cm}}$$

Again, we choose which to use by looking at the *direction* of the required change. For us to change from inches to centimeters, the inches must cancel. Thus the factor $\frac{2.54 \text{ cm}}{1 \text{ in.}}$ is used, and the conversion is done as follows:

$$7.00 \text{ in.} \times \frac{2.54 \text{ cm}}{1 \text{ in.}} = (7.00)(2.54) \text{ cm} = 17.8 \text{ cm}$$

Here the inch units cancel, leaving centimeters as required.

MATH

Units can cancel, just as numbers can.

information

When you finish a calculation, always check to make sure that the answer makes sense.

MATH

When exact numbers are used in a calculation, they never limit the number of significant digits.

MISCONCEPTIONS Math

- Dimensional analysis is a double-edged sword: It is both extremely useful and quite dangerous. It is useful because it allows students to solve problems by considering only the units. It is dangerous for the same reason; that is, it can allow students to solve problems they do not understand.

- It is important to differentiate between achieving the correct answer and understanding the concepts underlying the problem. As an example, you may wish to give students this problem:

  There are 2 igals in 1 odonku, and 6 odonkus in 4 falgers. If you have 3 igals, how many falgers is this?

  Most students eventually get the answer "1 falger." Once they have solved the problem, ask them questions such as "What is an igal? An odonku? A falger?" While we expect students to be able to do the mathematical mechanics illustrated by this problem, they should also strive to understand the problems they are solving.

- Even students who correctly use equivalence statements may not realize that when you multiply a given value by an equivalence statement, you are effectively multiplying that value by 1, since the values in the numerator and denominator are equivalent. This point should be emphasized.

- Students frequently interpret equivalence statements incorrectly. For example, consider 1 L = 1.0567 qt. While a student may be able to use this statement correctly to convert a given number of liters to the correct number of quarts, this same student may claim that a quart is larger than a liter because 1.0567 is greater than 1. It is useful to bring in two empty 1-L bottles and add 1 L of water to one and 1 quart of water to the other to show the difference.

Students are often reluctant to check their answers, which leads to many careless mistakes in calculations: Ask them to consider whether their answers make sense. They should check the magnitude and sign of the answers.

Active Reading Questions

1. To be able to multiply by a conversion factor we need to multiply by 1 and have the units cancel. This means the numerator and denominator must be equal.

2. We use the conversion factor that cancels the units we want to discard and leaves the units we want in the result.

Note that in this conversion, the number increased (from 7.00 to 17.8). This increase makes sense because the centimeter is a smaller unit of length than the inch. That is, it takes more centimeters to make the same length in inches.

> Always take a moment to think about whether your answer makes sense. It will help you avoid errors.

Changing from one unit to another via conversion factors (based on the equivalence statements between the units) is often called **dimensional analysis**. We will use this method throughout our study of chemistry.

We can now state some general steps for doing conversions by dimensional analysis. These steps are the tools for "How do we get there" in our problem-solving strategy.

Dimensional Analysis
The process of using conversion factors to change from one unit to another

 nformation

Consider the direction of the required change to select the correct conversion factor.

Tools for Converting from One Unit to Another

Step 1 To convert from one unit to another, use the equivalence statement that relates the two units. The conversion factor needed is a ratio of the two parts of the equivalence statement.

Step 2 Choose the appropriate conversion factor by looking at the direction of the required change (make sure that the unwanted units cancel).

Step 3 Multiply the quantity to be converted by the conversion factor to give the quantity with the desired units.

Step 4 Make sure that you have the correct number of significant figures.

Active Reading Questions

1. Why must a conversion factor come from an equivalence statement?

2. How can you decide which conversion factor to choose in a problem?

HANDS-ON CHEMISTRY • MINI-LAB •

Cooking in a Metric World

Materials
• recipe cards
• conversion table
• calculator

Procedure
1. Obtain a recipe card from your teacher.
2. Convert all of the measurements to metric units. Be careful in determining the number of significant figures in your answers.

Hands-On Chemistry
MINI-LAB

Cooking in a Metric World

Materials Each student/group needs one (or more) recipe card(s) and a calculator. Save recipe cards from magazines or have students bring them to class. If you choose to have students bring them, announce this fact early and set the due date for a few days before you plan to do this activity.

Purpose Students practice unit conversions and review rules for significant figures.

Discussion This activity can be adapted to fit varying time limits.

EXAMPLE 5.6

An Italian bicycle has its frame size given as 62 cm. What is the frame size in inches?

Solution

Where do we want to go?

The problem can be represented as:

62 cm = ? in.

What do we know?

• The frame size is 62 cm.

• 1 in. = 2.54 cm

How do we get there?

In this problem we want to convert from centimeters to inches.

62 cm × conversion factor = ? in.

Step 1 To convert from centimeters to inches, we need the equivalence statement 1 in. = 2.54 cm. This leads to two conversion factors:

$$\frac{1 \text{ in.}}{2.54 \text{ cm}} \text{ and } \frac{2.54 \text{ cm}}{1 \text{ in.}}$$

Step 2 In this case, the direction we want is

centimeters → inches

so we need the conversion factor $\frac{1 \text{ in.}}{2.54 \text{ cm}}$. We know that this is the one we want because using it will make the units of centimeters cancel, leaving units of inches.

Step 3 The conversion is carried out as follows:

$$62 \text{ c\cancel{m}} \times \frac{1 \text{ in.}}{2.54 \text{ c\cancel{m}}} = 24 \text{ in.}$$

Step 4 The result is limited to two significant figures by the number 62. The centimeters cancel, leaving inches as required.

Does it make sense?

Note that the number decreased in this conversion. This makes sense because the inch is a larger unit of length than the centimeter.

Practice Problem • Exercise 5.6

Water is often bottled in 0.750-L containers. Using the appropriate equivalence statement from Table 5.7, calculate the volume of such a water bottle in quarts.

We can also use dimensional analysis and this problem-solving plan to make multiple conversions.

EXAMPLE 5.6

More Examples

1. A new baby weighs 7.8 lb. What is its mass in kilograms?
   3.5 kg

2. A piece of lumber is 88.4 cm long. What is its length in millimeters? In inches?
   884 mm; 34.8 in.

3. A bottle of soda contains 2.0 L. What is the volume in quarts?
   2.12 qt

Answer to Practice Problem 5.6

$$0.75 \text{ L} \times \frac{1.06 \text{ qt}}{1 \text{ L}} = 0.795 \text{ qt}$$

Meeting Individual Needs
MATH CONCEPTS

If students need additional help with conversions, have them read *Dimensional Analysis* located in the *Teacher Resources*. A worksheet is available to go along with the handout.

EXAMPLE 5.7

More Examples

1. In the Olympics, one swimming event has a distance of 100 meters. How long is the race in feet?
   328 ft

2. How many seconds are in one day?
   86,400 s

3. Your car has a 5.00-L engine. What is the size of this engine in cubic inches?
   305 in^3

EXAMPLE 5.7

Conversion Factors: Multiple-Step Problems

The length of the marathon race is approximately 26.2 mi. What is this distance in kilometers?

Solution

Where do we want to go?

The problem can be represented as: 26.2 mi = ? km

What do we know?

- The race is 26.2 mi.
- 1 mi = 1760 yd
- 1 m = 1.094 yd

How do we get there?

Step 1 Because **Table 5.7** gives the equivalence statements 1 mi = 1760 yd and 1 m = 1.094 yd, we will proceed as follows:

Miles → yards → meters → kilometers

Step 2 and Step 3 for each conversion

Miles → Yards:

Result shown on calculator

$$26.2 \text{ mi} \times \frac{1760 \text{ yd}}{1 \text{ mi}} = 46,112 \text{ yd}$$

46,112 yd [Round off] 46,100 yd = 4.61×10^4 yd

Yards → Meters:

Result shown on calculator

$$4.61 \times 10^4 \text{ yd} \times \frac{1 \text{ m}}{1.094 \text{ yd}} = 4.213894 \times 10^4 \text{ m}$$

4.213894×10^4 m [Round off] 4.21×10^4 m

Meters → Kilometers:

$$4.21 \times 10^4 \text{ m} \times \frac{1 \text{ km}}{10^3 \text{ m}} = 4.21 \times 10^1 \text{ km}$$

$$= 42.1 \text{ km}$$

MATH

Remember that we are rounding off at the end of each step to show the correct number of significant figures. However, in doing a multistep calculation, you should retain the extra numbers that show on your calculator and round off only at the end of the calculation.

Thus the marathon (26.2 mi) is 42.1 km.

When you feel comfortable with the conversion process, you can combine the steps. The combined expression is miles → yards → meters → kilometers.

Step 4 Note that the answer has 3 significant figures. This matches the number of significant figures in the original measurement (26.2 mi).

Does it make sense?

The problem asked for the distance in kilometers. Our answer is given in kilometers and has 3 significant figures as required.

information

Units provide a very valuable check on the validity of your solution. Always use them.

Meeting Individual Needs
VISUAL LEARNERS

Encourage students to set up a table, like the one shown, to perform dimensional analysis.

Point out that vertical lines represent multiplication and horizontal lines represent division. Using this type of table will help students determine where to place a measure

to get the correct conversion. For instance, Example 5.7 could be set up in the following way:

26.2 mi	1760 yd	1 m	1 km
	1 mi	1.094 yd	1000 m

Practice Problem • Exercise 5.7

Racing cars at the Indianapolis Motor Speedway routinely travel around the track at an average speed of 225 mi/h. What is this speed in kilometers per hour?

Let's Review

Whenever you work problems, remember the following points:

- Always include the units (a measurement always has two parts: a number *and* a unit).
- Cancel units as you carry out the calculations.
- Check that your final answer has the correct units. If it doesn't, you have done something wrong.
- Check that your final answer has the correct number of significant figures.
- Think about whether your answer makes sense.

B. Temperature Conversions

When the doctor tells you that your temperature is 102 degrees and the meteorologist on TV says it will be 75 degrees tomorrow, they are using the **Fahrenheit scale**. Water boils at 212 °F and freezes at 32 °F, and normal body temperature is 98.6 °F (where °F signifies "Fahrenheit degrees"). This temperature scale is widely used in the United States and Great Britain, and it is the scale employed in most of the engineering sciences.

Another temperature scale, used in Canada and Europe and in the physical and life sciences in most countries, is the **Celsius scale**. In keeping with the metric system, which is based on powers of 10, the freezing and boiling points of water on the Celsius scale are assigned as 0 °C and 100. °C, respectively. On both the Fahrenheit and the Celsius scales, the unit of temperature is called a degree, and the symbol for it is followed by the capital letter representing the scale on which the units are measured: °C or °F.

Still another temperature scale used in the sciences is the **absolute** or **Kelvin scale**. On this scale water freezes at 273 K and boils at 373 K. On the Kelvin scale, the unit of temperature is called a kelvin and is symbolized by K. Thus, on the three scales, the boiling point of water is stated as 212 Fahrenheit degrees (212 °F), 100. Celsius degrees (100. °C), and 373 kelvins (373 K). The three temperature scales are compared in **Figure 5.5.**

MATH

Although 373 K is often stated as 373 degrees kelvin, it is more correct to say 373 kelvins.

Figure 5.5
The three major temperature scales

 Answer to Practice Problem 5.7

$$225 \frac{\text{mi}}{\text{h}} \times \frac{1760 \text{ yd}}{1 \text{ mi}} \times \frac{1 \text{ m}}{1.094 \text{ yd}} \times \frac{1 \text{ km}}{1000 \text{ m}} = 362 \frac{\text{km}}{\text{h}}$$

5.3.B Temperature Conversions

Objective To learn the three temperature scales, convert from one scale to another, and continue to develop problem-solving skills

 TEACHING TIPS

- This section provides an excellent opportunity to begin to emphasize relationships instead of simply memorizing formulas. The temperature scales can be related by graphing a straight line. See Teaching Support: Graphing Temperature Scales in this section. This idea relates to a student's math background. It is a good time for cross-curricular teaching with the math department.

- One way to assess how well students understand temperature scales is to invent a new scale and ask students to make conversions between this new scale and the others.

TECHNOLOGY

Figure 5.5

An increase of 1 °C or 1 K is equally larger than an increase of 1 °F.

- The size of each temperature unit (each degree) is the same for the Celsius and Kelvin scales. This follows from the fact that the *difference* between the boiling and freezing points of water is 100 units on both of these scales.

- The Fahrenheit degree is smaller than the Celsius and Kelvin unit. Note that on the Fahrenheit scale there are 180 Fahrenheit degrees between the boiling and freezing points of water, as compared with 100 units on the other two scales.

- The zero points are different on all three scales.

In your study of chemistry, you will sometimes need to convert from one temperature scale to another. We will consider in some detail how this conversion is done. In addition to learning how to change temperature scales, you should also use this section as an opportunity to further develop your skills in problem solving.

Converting Between the Kelvin and Celsius Scales

It is simple to convert between the Celsius and Kelvin scales because

- the temperature unit is the same size.
- the zero points are different. Look at **Figure 5.5.** To go from each Celsius temperature marked on the middle thermometer to the Kelvin temperature on the right thermometer, what do we need to do?

$$100. \ °C + 273 = 373 \ K$$
$$0 \ °C + 273 = 273 \ K$$
$$-18 \ °C + 273 = 255 \ K$$
$$-273 \ °C + 273 = \ \ \ 0 \ K$$

In each case we need to add 273 to the Celsius temperature. Because 0 °C corresponds to 273 K, this addition of 273 corrects for the difference in zero points.

$$T_{°C} + 273 = T_{K}$$

We will illustrate this procedure in Example 5.8.

Active Reading Question

Which change is the largest, a change of 1 °C, 1 °F, or 1 K?

Teaching Support

GRAPHING TEMPERATURE SCALES

To relate the temperature scales by graphing you can do the following:

Kelvin/Celsius Graph the freezing and boiling points of water on a graph with the x-axis as Celsius and the y-axis as Kelvin. Draw a line through the points and write the equation for the line in the form $y = mx + b$. Have students determine the slope and the y-intercept. Show them that this is the

equation for converting between the scales. Also, point out that the size of the degrees is the same (the slope is 1) and that the nonzero y-intercept indicates that the zero points of the two scales differ by 273.

Fahrenheit/Celsius Make a new graph relating the Celsius (x-axis) and Fahrenheit (y-axis) boiling and freezing points of water. Once again, draw a line through the points and have students write the $y = mx + b$ form for the equation of the line. Point out that the slope of the line is the relationship between

EXAMPLE 5.8

Temperature Conversion: Celsius to Kelvin

The boiling point of water at the top of Mt. Everest is 70. °C. Convert this temperature to the Kelvin scale.

Solution

Where do we want to go?
- 70. °C = ? K

What do we know?
- The boiling point is 70. °C.
- The relationship between the Celsius and Kelvin scales is:

$$T_{°C} + 273 = T_K$$

How do we get there?
Celsius-to-Kelvin conversions require us to adjust for different zero points by using the formula

$$T_{°C} + 273 = T_K$$

Using this formula to solve this problem gives

$$70. + 273 = 343$$

343 K is the correct answer. This conversion is summarized in **Figure 5.6.**

70. °C - - - - - - - - 343 K

70 Celsius   70
degrees   kelvins

0 °C - - - - - - - - 273 K

Figure 5.6
Converting 70. °C to units
measured on the Kelvin scale

Does it make sense?
The problem asked for the boiling point in kelvins. Our answer is given in kelvins. Note that the answer is to the units place as required by the original measurement (70. °C).

> ### MATH +÷
> The decimal point after the temperature reading indicates that the trailing zero is significant.

Let's Review

To convert from the Celsius to the Kelvin scale, we use the formula:

$$T_{°C} \quad + \quad 273 = T_K$$

Temperature   Temperature
in Celsius   in kelvins
degrees

EXAMPLE 5.8

More Examples

1. The temperature is a balmy 28.5 °C. Convert it to the Kelvin scale.

   301.5 K

2. The freezing point of nitrogen is 2210 °C. What is this temperature on the Kelvin scale?

   63 K

(continued)

the size of the degrees (how many degrees on each scale between boiling and freezing) and that the zero points on the scales differ by 32. The equation for converting between Celsius and Fahrenheit is shown on the graph.

Now invent a temperature scale and ask students to write an equation for converting from Celsius to your imaginary scale. The number of degrees between the boiling and freezing points of water should be different from the number of degrees for any of the common scales. The difference in the zero points should not be 273 or 32. If students understand the relationship between the imaginary scale and the Celsius scale, they should be able to write an equation for converting between the two.

EXAMPLE 5.9

More Examples

1. If your body temperature is 312 K, what is it on the Celsius scale?

   39 °C

2. If the outdoor thermometer reads 300. K, should you wear a jacket? What is the temperature on the Celsius scale?

   No; 27.0 °C

Answer to Practice Problem 5.9

The best way to solve this problem is to convert 172 K to Celsius degrees. To do so, we will use the formula

$T_{°C} = T_K - 273 = 172 - 273 = -101$

So 172 K = −101 °C, which is a lower temperature than −75 °C. Thus 172 K is colder than −75 °C.

EXAMPLE 5.9

Temperature Conversion: Kelvin to Celsius

Liquid nitrogen boils at 77 K. What is the boiling point of nitrogen on the Celsius scale?

Solution

Where do we want to go?

- 77 K = ? °C

What do we know?

- Liquid nitrogen boils at 77 K.
- The relationship between the Celsius and Kelvin scales is $T_{°C} + 273 = T_K$

How do we get there?

We solve this problem by using the formula $T_{°C} + 273 = T_K$

However, in this case we want to solve for the Celsius temperature $T_{°C}$. That is, we want to isolate $T_{°C}$ on one side of the equal sign. To do this, we use an important mathematical principle: doing *the same thing on both sides of the equal sign* preserves the equality. In other words, it's always okay to perform the same operation on both sides of the equal sign.

To isolate $T_{°C}$, we need to subtract 273 from both sides.

$$T_{°C} + 273 - 273 = T_K - 273$$

Sum is zero

to give $T_{°C} = T_K - 273$

Using this equation to solve the problem, we have

$$T_{°C} = T_K - 273 = 77 - 273 = -196$$

So we have shown that 77 K = −196 °C.

Does it make sense?

The problem asked for the boiling point in degrees Celsius. Our answer is given in degrees Celsius. Our answer (−196 °C) has the correct units. Note that the answer is to the units place as required by the original measurement (77 K).

Practice Problem • Exercise 5.9

Which temperature is colder, 172 K or −75 °C?

In summary, because the Kelvin and Celsius scales have the same size unit, to switch from one scale to the other we must simply account for the different zero points. We must add 273 to the Celsius temperature to obtain the temperature on the Kelvin scale:

$$T_K = T_{°C} + 273$$

To convert from the Kelvin scale to the Celsius scale, we must subtract 273 from the Kelvin temperature:

$$T_{°C} = T_K - 273$$

152 • Chapter 5 • Measurements and Calculations

Meeting Individual Needs
INCLUSION STRATEGIES

Review the addition and subtraction properties of equality before explaining the Kelvin to Celsius conversion.

Addition Property of Equality: For any numbers, *a*, *b*, and *c*, if *a* = *b*, then *a* + *c* = *b* + *c*.

Subtraction Property of Equality: For any numbers, *a*, *b*, and *c*, if *a* = *b*, then *a* − *c* = *b* − *c*.

Converting Between the Fahrenheit and Celsius Scales

The conversion between the Fahrenheit and Celsius temperature scales requires two adjustments:

- For the different size units
- For the different zero points

To see how to adjust for the different unit sizes, consider the diagram in **Figure 5.7**. Note that because 212 °F = 100. °C and 32 °F = 0 °C,

$$212 - 32 = 180. \text{ Fahrenheit degrees} = 100. - 0 = 100. \text{ Celsius degrees}$$

Thus

$$180. \text{ Fahrenheit degrees} = 100. \text{ Celsius degrees}$$

Dividing both sides of this equation by 100. gives

$$\frac{180.}{100.} \text{ Fahrenheit degrees} = \frac{\cancel{100.}}{\cancel{100.}} \text{ Celsius degrees}$$

or

$$1.80 \text{ Fahrenheit degrees} = 1.00 \text{ Celsius degree}$$

The factor 1.80 is used to convert from one degree size to the other.

Next we have to account for the fact that 0 °C is *not* the same as 0 °F. In fact, 32 °F = 0 °C.

212 F ———— 100. °C——— Boiling point
180. Fahrenheit degrees / 100. Celsius degrees
32 F ———— 0 C ———— Freezing point

Figure 5.7
Comparison of the Celsius and Fahrenheit scales

MATH

Note that because 180 and 100 here are both exact numbers obtained by counting the number of degrees, the ratio 180/100 has an unlimited number of significant digits. This ratio is typically shown as 1.80.

Celsius to Fahrenheit Although we will not show how to derive it, the equation to convert a temperature in Celsius degrees to the Fahrenheit scale is:

$$T_{°\text{F}} = 1.80(T_{°\text{C}}) + 32$$

↑ Temperature in °F   ↑ Temperature in °C

In this equation the term $1.80(T_{°\text{C}})$ adjusts for the difference in degree size between the two scales. The 32 in the equation accounts for the different zero points. We will now show how to use this equation.

To convert from Celsius to Fahrenheit, we have used the equation

$$T_{°\text{F}} = 1.80(T_{°\text{C}}) + 32)$$

5.3 • Problem Solving and Unit Conversions • **153**

EXAMPLE 5.10

More Examples

1. You're traveling in a metric country and don't feel well. Your temperature is 40.0 °C. What is it on the Fahrenheit scale?

    104 °F

2. Convert 32.0 °C to Fahrenheit degrees.

    89.6 °F

3. The boiling point of nitrogen is −196 °C. What is this temperature on the Fahrenheit scale?

    −321 °F

EXAMPLE 5.10

Temperature Conversion: Celsius to Fahrenheit

On a summer day the temperature in the laboratory, as measured on a lab thermometer, is 28 °C. Express this temperature on the Fahrenheit scale.

Solution

Where do we want to go?

- 28 °C = ? °F

What do we know?

- The temperature is 28 °C.
- The relationship between the Celsius and Kelvin scales is
  $T_{°F} + 1.80(T_{°C}) + 32$

How do we get there?

$$T_{°F} = 1.80(T_{°C}) + 32$$

In this case,

$$T_{°C}$$
$$\downarrow$$

$$T_{°F} = ?\ °F = 1.80(28) + 32 = 50.4 + 32$$

Rounds off to 50.

$$= 50. + 32 = 82$$

Thus 28 °C = 82 °F.

Does it make sense?

The problem asked for the temperature in degrees Fahrenheit. Our answer is given in degrees Fahrenheit. Our answer (82 °F) has the correct units. Note that the answer is to the units place as required by the original measurement (28 °C).

MATH

Note that 28 °C is approximately equal to 82 °F. Because the numbers are reversed, this is an easy reference point to remember for the two scales.

CHEMISTRY IN YOUR WORLD

Science, Technology, and Society

Ersatz Fog

Did you know that a knowledge of chemistry might win you an Academy Award? In fact, James F. Foley, Charles E. Converse, and F. Edward Gardner of Praxair Corporation were given Technical Achievement Awards by the Academy of Motion Picture Arts and Sciences for their fake fog concoction used in the movie "Batman and Robin." The Praxair employees created a special low-lying fog for scenes involving the villain Mr. Freeze, played by Arnold Schwarzenegger. The fog resulted from a special mixture of steam, liquid nitrogen, and liquid oxygen. About 27.5 million cubic feet of the mixture was used in making the film. The liquid oxygen and nitrogen were hauled to the studio daily from a nearby Praxair air liquefaction plant in a cryogenic tank truck. A patent is now pending for the fog recipe, which looks like it has a "bright" future in Hollywood.

Note the ersatz fog behind Mr. Freeze.

EXAMPLE 5.11

Temperature Conversion: Celsius to Fahrenheit

Express the temperature −40. °C on the Fahrenheit scale.

Solution

Where do we want to go?
- −40. °C = ? °F

What do we know?
- The temperature is −40. °C.
- The relationship between the Fahrenheit and Celsius scales is
  $T_{°F} = 1.80(T_{°C}) + 32$

How do we get there?

$T_{°F} = 1.80(T_{°C}) + 32$

In this case,

$$T_{°F} = ? \text{ °F} = 1.80(\overset{T_{°C}}{\underset{\downarrow}{-40.}}) + 32$$
$$= -72 + 32 = -40.$$

So −40. °C = −40. °F. This is a very interesting result and is another useful reference point.

Does it make sense?
The problem asked for the temperature in degrees Fahrenheit. Our answer is given in degrees Fahrenheit. Our answer (−40. °F) has the correct units. Note that the answer is to the units place as required by the original measurement (−40. °C).

✅ Practice Problem • Exercise 5.11

Hot tubs are often maintained at 41 °C. What is this temperature in Fahrenheit degrees?

Fahrenheit to Celsius To convert a Fahrenheit temperature to Celsius, we need to rearrange this equation to isolate Celsius degrees ($T_{°C}$). Remember that we can always do the same operation to both sides of the equation. First subtract 32 from each side:

$$T_{°F} - 32 = 1.80(T_{°C}) + \underset{\underset{\text{Sum is zero}}{\uparrow \qquad \uparrow}}{32 - 32}$$

to give

$$T_{°F} - 32 = 1.80(T_{°C})$$

Next divide both sides by 1.80

$$\frac{T_{°F} - 32}{1.80} = \frac{1.80\,(T_{°C})}{1.80} = T_{°C}$$

$$\text{Temperature in °C} = \quad T_{°C} = \frac{T_{°F} - 32}{180}$$

EXAMPLE 5.11

✅ Answer to Practice Problem 5.11

The problem is 41 °C = ? °F.

Using the formula

$$T_{°F} = 1.80(T_{°C}) + 32$$

we have

$$T_{°F} = ? \text{ °F} = 1.80(41) + 32$$
$$= 74 + 32 = 106$$

That is, 41 °C = 106 °F.

Meeting Individual Needs
INCLUSION STRATEGIES

Review the order of operations for math:

1. Perform all operations within parentheses.
2. Evaluate all exponents.
3. Perform multiplication and division from left to right.
4. Perform addition and subtraction from left to right.

EXAMPLE 5.12

More Examples

1. Ray Bradbury wrote a book titled *Fahrenheit 451*. What is this temperature on the Celsius scale?

   233 °C

2. Pork is considered to be cooked properly when its internal temperature reaches 160 °F. What is this temperature on the Celsius scale?

   71 °C

Answer to Practice Problem 5.12

This problem can be stated as 239 °F = ? °C.

Using the formula

$$T_{°C} = \frac{T_{°F} - 32}{1.80}$$

we have in this case

$$T_{°C} = ? \,°C = \frac{239 - 32}{1.80}$$

$$= \frac{207}{1.80} = 115$$

That is, 239 °F = 115 °C.

EXAMPLE 5.12

Temperature Conversion: Fahrenheit to Celsius

One of the body's responses to an infection or injury is to elevate its temperature. A certain flu victim has a body temperature of 101 °F. What is this temperature on the Celsius scale?

Solution

Where do we want to go?

- 101 °F = ? °C

What do we know?

- The temperature is 101 °F.

- The relationship between the Celsius and Fahrenheit scales is:

$$T_{°C} = \frac{T_{°F} - 32}{1.80}$$

How do we get there?

$$T_{°C} = \frac{T_{°F} - 32}{1.80}$$

yields $T_{°F}$

$$T_{°C} = ? \,°C = \frac{101 - 32}{1.80} = \frac{69}{1.80} = 38$$

That is, 101 °F = 38 °C.

Does it make sense?

The problem asked for the temperature in degrees Celsius. Our answer is given in degrees Celsius. Our answer (38 °C) has the correct units. Note that the answer is to the units place as required by the original measurement (101 °F).

Practice Problem • Exercise 5.12

An antifreeze solution in a car's radiator boils at 239 °F. What is this temperature on the Celsius scale?

Let's Review

Temperature Conversion Formulas

Celsius to Kelvin	$T_K = T_{°C} + 273$
Kelvin to Celsius	$T_{°C} = T_K - 273$
Celsius to Fahrenheit	$T_{°F} = 1.80(T_{°C}) + 32$
Fahrenheit to Celsius	$T_{°C} = \dfrac{T_{°F} - 32}{1.80}$

Teaching Support
DEMONSTRATION

Rainbow Density Column

Materials

- 300 g sucrose
- Separatory funnel
- Food coloring
- Rubber tubing
- 6 beakers or cups
- Large cylinder (1000-mL graduated)

Procedure The night before the demonstration, prepare six solutions of sugar water according to the table below.

Color	Dye	Sugar Concentration	Sugar Mass
Red	Red	0%	0 g
Orange	Red:Yellow (1:1)	10%	14 g
Yellow	Yellow	20%	28 g
Green	Green	30%	42 g
Blue	Blue	40%	56 g
Violet	Blue:Red (1:1)	60%	84 g

Make the colored water for each solution (140 mL) first, adjusting the colors to the desired shade to make a clear distinction between them before adding the sugar. Then dissolve the sugar in the water. A microwave can be used to warm the water to dissolve the sugar. The liquids can be transported to school in foam cups with lids.

Place the large cylinder on a ring stand. Connect the tubing to the bottom of the separatory funnel. Suspend the

C. Density

When you were in elementary school, you may have been embarrassed by your answer to the question, "Which is heavier, a pound of lead or a pound of feathers?" If you said lead, you were undoubtedly thinking about density, not mass. **Density** can be defined as the amount of matter present *in a given volume* of substance. That is, density is mass per unit volume, or the ratio of the mass of an object to its volume:

$$\text{Density} = \frac{\text{mass}}{\text{volume}}$$

It takes a much bigger volume to make a pound of feathers than to make a pound of lead. This is because lead has a much greater mass per unit volume—a greater density.

Density
The mass of a substance per a given volume of that substance

Active Reading Question

Which is heavier, a pound of lead or a pound of feathers? What is the "trick" about this question?

The density of a liquid can be determined easily by weighing a known volume of the substance as illustrated in Example 5.13.

EXAMPLE 5.13

Calculating Density

Suppose that a student finds that 23.50 mL of a certain liquid weighs 35.062 g. What is the density of this liquid?

Solution

Where do we want to go?
- Density of liquid = ? g/mL

What do we know?
- Volume = 23.50 mL
- Mass = 35.062 g
- Density $= \frac{\text{mass}}{\text{volume}}$

How do we get there?

We can calculate the density of this liquid simply by applying the definition.

$$\text{Density} = \frac{\text{mass}}{\text{volume}} = \frac{35.062 \text{ g}}{23.50 \text{ mL}} = 1.492 \text{ g/mL}$$

This result could also be expressed as 1.492 g/cm^3 because 1 mL = 1 cm^3.

Does it make sense?

Density is defined as $\frac{\text{mass}}{\text{volume}}$. Our units $(\frac{\text{g}}{\text{mL}})$ express mass (g) over volume (mL). Our answer has 4 significant figures as required by the 4 significant figures in the volume measurement (23.50 mL).

5.3.C Density
Objective To define density and its units

 LABORATORY
EXPERIMENT 21:
Measurement and Density, Traditional

 Active Reading Question

A pound of lead and a pound of feathers weigh the same (a pound). The trick is that lead is more dense, and therefore one may be more likely to think that a sample of lead always weighs more than a sample of feathers.

EXAMPLE 5.13

More Examples

A block has a volume of 25.3 cm^3. Its mass is 21.7 g. Calculate the density of the block.
0.858 g/cm^3

 Active Learning
Group Activity

Have each team predict what would happen if they dropped a few raisins or small pieces of spaghetti into a container of carbonated liquid. Would the items sink or float? What would happen after 30 seconds? Have students justify their predictions. Now have them test their predictions. Once the testing is complete, ask the teams if they want to change their thinking.

(continued)

separatory funnel in an iron ring above the large cylinder so that the tubing reaches very near to the bottom of the cylinder. With the stopcock closed, fill the separatory funnel with red solution. Add the red solution to the cylinder, being careful to close the stopcock just before all of the red solution drains out. Take the orange solution and slowly open the stopcock to add it to the column. Again, close the stopcock before

all of the solution is drained out of the separatory funnel. Add the remaining solutions in the same manner, in order of increasing concentration. You should end up with a rainbow column. The layers will remain visible for at least 24 hours if the column remains undisturbed. You can also stir the column at the end of the demonstration, which mixes the colors and shows students that the density was based on concentration, not miscibility.

Variation Students can construct their own columns by using 10-mL graduated cylinders and Beral pipets for the addition of the colors. They must add the solutions from most dense to least dense.

- Use a 1-L soda bottle to prepare a demonstration of density. Add 500 mL of vegetable oil and 500 mL of water (colored with food coloring) to the bottle. Tighten the top and shake. Allow liquids to settle. Ask students which liquid is more dense. You can extend your discussion to include an introduction to the immiscibility of oil and water. You can then ask students whether a density column could be made from different concentrations of the same substance. See Teaching Support: Rainbow Density Column in this section for the construction of such a column.

- You can use a large graduated cylinder filled with colored water to measure the density of an object. Use an object with a known density first (such as a cylinder of a pure metal) to show that the method works. Then use the method for an irregularly shaped object, such as a stone.

**MISCONCEPTION
Math**

Density calculations may be the first time students will deal with a ratio of measurements. Because of this, students often confuse mass and density. They often believe that a substance with a larger mass is also the more dense substance.

Figure 5.8
(a) Tank of water
(b) Person submerged in the tank, raising the level of the water

(a)   (b)

The volume of a solid object is often determined indirectly by submerging it in water and measuring the volume of water displaced. In fact, this is the most accurate method for measuring a person's percentage of body fat. The person is submerged momentarily in a tank of water, and the increase in volume is measured (see **Figure 5.8**). It is possible to calculate the body density by using the person's weight (mass) and the volume of the person's body determined by submersion. Fat, muscle, and bone have different densities (fat is less dense than muscle tissue, for example), so the fraction of the person's body that is fat can be calculated. The more muscle and the less fat a person has, the higher his or her body density. For example, a muscular person weighing 150 lb has a smaller body volume (and thus a higher density) than a non-muscular person weighing 150 lb. The densities of various common substances are given in **Table 5.8.**

TABLE 5.8

Densities of Various Common Substances at 20 °C

Substance	Physical State	Density (g/cm³)	Substance	Physical State	Density (g/cm³)
oxygen	gas	0.00133*	aluminum	solid	2.70
hydrogen	gas	0.0000084*	iron	solid	7.87
ethanol	liquid	0.78	copper	solid	8.96
benzene	liquid	0.880	silver	solid	10.5
water	liquid	1.000	lead	solid	11.34
magnesium	solid	1.74	mercury	liquid	13.6
salt (sodium chloride)	solid	2.16	gold	solid	19.32
*At 1 atmosphere pressure					

158 • Chapter 5 • Measurements and Calculations

EXAMPLE 5.14

Determining Density

At a local pawn shop, a student finds a medallion that the shop owner insists is pure platinum. However, the student suspects that the medallion may actually be silver and thus much less valuable. The student buys the medallion only after the shop owner agrees to refund the price if the medallion is returned within two days. The student, a chemistry student, then takes the medallion to her lab and measures the density as follows:

*   She weighs the medallion and finds that its mass is 55.64 g.
*   She places some water in a graduated cylinder and reads the volume as 75.2 mL.
*   She drops the medallion into the water in the cylinder and reads the new volume as 77.8 mL.

Is the medallion platinum (density = 21.4 g/cm^3) or silver (density = 10.5 g/cm^3)?

Solution

Where do we want to go?

*   We want to determine the density of the medallion to see whether it is platinum or silver.

What do we know?

*   Mass (medallion) = 55.64 g
*   Density (Pt) = 21.4 g/cm^3
*   Initial volume of water = 75.2 mL
*   Density (Ag) = 10.5 g/cm^3
*   Final volume (water + medallion) = 77.8 mL
*   1 g/mL = 1 g/cm^3
*   Density = $\dfrac{\text{mass}}{\text{volume}}$

How do we get there?

Calculating the density of the medallion

*   Density = $\dfrac{\text{mass}}{\text{volume}} = \dfrac{55.64 \text{ g}}{\text{volume}}$

*   The volume of medallion is obtained by finding the difference between the volume reading of the water in the graduated cylinder.

    Volume (medallion) = 77.8 mL − 75.2 mL = 2.6 mL

*   Density = mass/volume = $\dfrac{55.64 \text{ g}}{2.6 \text{ mL}} = 21\dfrac{\text{g}}{\text{mL}} = 21\dfrac{\text{g}}{\text{cm}^3}$

Comparing densities

*   Densities

    Density (medallion) = 21 g/cm^3

    Density (Pt) = 21.4 g/cm^3

    Density (Ag) = 10.5 g/cm^3

*   The medallion must be platinum because its density is the same as the platinum.

Does it make sense?

The density of the medallion is the same as platinum to two significant figures (as required by the volume measurement).

information

The most common units for density are g/mL = g/cm^3.

EXAMPLE 5.14

More Examples

A student fills a graduated cylinder to 25.0 mL with liquid. She then immerses a solid in the liquid. The volume of the liquid rises to 33.9 mL. The mass of the solid is 63.5 g. What is the density of the solid?

7.1 g/mL

Meeting Individual Needs
ADVANCED LEARNERS

Ask students to investigate the relationship between specific gravity and density. Have students research hydrometers, instruments used to measure the specific gravity of liquids.

We obtain the density of the cleaner by dividing its mass by its volume.

$$\text{Density} = \frac{\text{mass}}{\text{volume}}$$

$$= \frac{28.1 \text{ g}}{35.8 \text{ mL}}$$

$$= 0.785 \text{ g/mL}$$

This density identifies the liquid as isopropyl alcohol.

EXAMPLE 5.15

More Examples

1. Isopropyl alcohol has a density of 0.785 g/mL. What volume should be measured to obtain 20.0 g of the liquid?

   25.5 mL

2. A student needs 150 cm^3 of salt for an experiment. The density of salt is 2.16 g/cm^3. How many 1-lb boxes of salt should he buy at the grocery store?

   324 g; needs one 1-lb box

3. A beaker contains 725 mL of water. The density of water is 1.00 g/mL. Calculate the volume of water in liters. Find the mass of the water.

   0.725 L; 725 g

Practice Problem • Exercise 5.14

A student wants to identify the main component in a commercial liquid cleaner. He finds that 35.8 mL of the cleaner weighs 28.1 g. Of the following possibilities, which is the main component of the cleaner?

Substance	Density, g/cm^3
chloroform	1.483
diethyl ether	0.714
isopropyl alcohol	0.785
toluene	0.867

EXAMPLE 5.15

Using Density in Calculations

Spherical droplets of mercury, a very dense liquid

Mercury has a density of 13.6 g/mL. What volume of mercury must be taken to obtain 225 g of the metal?

Solution

Where do we want to go?

• volume of mercury → 225 g

What do we know?

• Mass (Hg) = 225 g

• Density (Hg) = 13.6 g/mL

• Density = $\frac{\text{mass}}{\text{volume}}$

How do we get there?

To solve this problem, start with the definition of density:

$$\text{Density} = \frac{\text{mass}}{\text{volume}}$$

Then rearrange this equation to isolate the required quantity. In this case we want to find the volume. Remember that we maintain an equality when we do the same thing to both sides. For example, if we multiply *both sides* of the density definition by volume,

$$\text{Volume} \times \text{density} = \frac{\text{mass}}{\cancel{\text{volume}}} \times \cancel{\text{volume}}$$

volume cancels on the right, leaving

$$\text{Volume} \times \text{density} = \text{mass}$$

We want the volume, so we now divide both sides by density:

$$\frac{\text{Volume} \times \cancel{\text{density}}}{\cancel{\text{density}}} = \frac{\text{mass}}{\text{density}}$$

to give

$$\text{Volume} = \frac{\text{mass}}{\text{density}}$$

Now we can solve the problem by substituting the given numbers:

$$\text{Volume} = \frac{225 \text{ g}}{13.6 \text{ g/mL}}$$

$$= 16.5 \text{ mL}$$

We must take 16.5 mL of mercury to obtain an amount that has a mass of 225 g.

Hands-On Chemistry
MINI-LAB

The Density of Clay

Materials Each student/group will need a piece of clay. Have water, balances, graduated cylinders, and rulers available for students to use.

Purpose Students should better understand the concept of density.

Discussion There are two common ways for students to determine the density of the clay. In both cases, they need to determine the mass of the clay by using a balance. To determine the volume, a student may use water displacement. In this method, place some water in a graduated cylinder and note the volume reading. Then put the piece of clay into the cylinder and determine the volume of water displaced. This is the volume of the clay. Another method is to mold the clay into an easily measured

Does it make sense?

The correct unit for volume is milliliters, which we have in our answer (16.5 mL). Our answer has 3 significant figures as required.

Besides being a tool for the identification of substances, density has many other uses. For example, the liquid in your car's lead storage battery (a solution of sulfuric acid) changes density because the sulfuric acid is consumed as the battery discharges. In a fully charged battery, the density of the solution is about 1.30 g/cm^3. When the density falls below 1.20 g/cm^3, the battery has to be recharged. Density measurement is also used to determine the amount of antifreeze, and thus the level of protection against freezing, in the cooling system of a car. Water and antifreeze have different densities, so the measured density of the mixture tells us how much of each is present. The device used to test the density of the solution—a hydrometer—is shown in **Figure 5.9.**

In certain situations, the term *specific gravity* is used to describe the density of a liquid. **Specific gravity** is defined as the ratio of the density of a given liquid to the density of water at 4 °C. Because it is a ratio of densities, specific gravity has no units.

> **Specific gravity**
> The ratio of the density of given liquid to the density of water at 4 °C

Figure 5.9
A hydrometer being used to determine the density of the antifreeze solution in a car's radiator

Top Ten Elements with Highest Densities		
Element	Year Discovered	Density (g/cm^3)
Osmium	1804	22.59
Iridium	1804	22.56
Platinum	1748	21.45
Rhenium	1925	21.01
Neptunium	1940	20.26
Plutonium	1940	20.26
Gold	prehistoric	19.32
Tungsten	1783	19.26
Uranium	1789	19.05
Tantalum	1802	16.67

HANDS-ON CHEMISTRY • MINI-LAB •

The Density of Clay

Materials
- clay
- student-determined materials

Procedure
1. Obtain a piece of clay from your teacher.
2. Develop a method to determine the density of clay. You will be able to use a balance, a graduated cylinder, and water. Discuss your method with your teacher.
3. Determine the density of your clay.

Results/Analysis
1. Does the amount of clay you use in your determination affect the density you calculate? Why or why not?
2. Does the shape of the clay used in your determination affect the density you calculate? Why or why not?
3. If you make a hollow ball out of clay, will it have the same density as you calculated? Explain.

5.3 • Problem Solving and Unit Conversions • 161

(continued)
geometric shape, such as a cube. The student can use a ruler, take the proper measurements, and calculate the volume. The density of the clay is the ratio of the mass to the volume.

For this activity, use modeling clay that does not readily absorb water. Students should see that neither the shape of the object nor its size affects the density of the clay, as long as their object is not hollow. Many students confuse density with mass, and it is good for

them to see that a large sample of clay has the same density as a small piece. When a piece of clay is formed with a cavity in its center, it has a much greater volume and essentially the same mass (although the mass of air adds a little to the total) and thus is less dense than a solid sample of clay.

Active Learning
Group Activity

Challenge students to create a density bottle with three layers using three liquids: baby oil, water containing food coloring, and 70% isopropyl alcohol solution (rubbing alcohol). The best containers for this activity are 18 × 150 mm test tubes with corks or stoppers.

Additional Information It is difficult to form layers with the alcohol and water because they are miscible. To form three layers, students must begin with water, add oil, and then add alcohol. Any shaking will make the third layer disappear, because the alcohol and water will mix.

TEACHING TIP

Specific gravity is used in measuring the density of solutions, such as measuring the sulfuric acid in a car battery to determine its state of charge, and testing whether an alcoholic beverage has completed its fermentation process. A hydrometer is the instrument used to find the specific gravity of a solution.

TOP TEN

Have students use the Internet or book resources (such as the *Handbook of Chemistry and Physics*) to find the 10 least dense elements. Are they all gases at room temperature? Have students compare the densities of the 10 least dense elements with the densities of the 10 most dense.

SECTION 5.3
Review Questions

1. An equivalence statement is an equation that shows that two measurements stand for the same thing. The numbers are different because the scales of the measurement are different. Two conversion factors can be created from each equivalence statement.

453.6 g = 1 lb

$$\frac{1 \text{ lb}}{453.6 \text{ g}} \text{ or } \frac{453.6 \text{ g}}{1 \text{ lb}}$$

2. a. $\dfrac{1 \text{ in.}}{2.54 \text{ cm}}$

   b. $\dfrac{1 \text{ L}}{1.06 \text{ qt}}$

   c. $\dfrac{2.205 \text{ lb}}{1 \text{ kg}}$

   d. $\dfrac{1760 \text{ yd}}{1 \text{ mi}} \times \dfrac{1 \text{ m}}{1.094 \text{ yd}}$

3. a. 15 in.   c. 4.9 lb
   b. 4.0 L   d. 5600 m

4. 21 mi/h

5. a. 86 °F   c. −259 °C
   b. 295 K   d. 156 °F

6. 19 mL

7. a. The orange block is more dense. It has more mass and has a smaller volume than the blue block (density is mass/volume, so with a higher mass and smaller volume, density must be greater).

   b. We cannot determine this since the orange block has a greater mass and volume, but we do not know the relative numbers.

   c. The blue block is more dense since it has the same mass, but a smaller volume (density is mass/volume).

   d. The blue block is more dense since the blocks have the same volume but the blue block has more mass (density is mass/volume).

CELEBRITY CHEMICAL   Carvone ($C_{10}H_{14}O$)

Carvone is the main component of spearmint oil. It occurs naturally in caraway seeds, dill seeds, gingergrass, and spearmint. A pleasant-smelling liquid at room temperature, this chemical is often used as a flavoring agent in liqueurs and chewing gum and is added to soaps and perfumes to improve their aromas. Carvone is one of the "essential oils" that have been used in spices, perfumes, and medicines for thousands of years.

Carvone is a member of a class of compounds called *terpenes* that are produced by plants, often to attract beneficial insects. For example, certain plants give off these compounds when they are attacked by caterpillars. The released terpenes attract the attention of parasitic wasps that kill the caterpillars and inject their eggs. The caterpillar bodies then serve as food for the developing wasp larvae.

A gulf fritillary caterpillar

SECTION 5.3
REVIEW QUESTIONS

1. What is an equivalence statement? How many conversion factors can be created from one equivalence statement? Choose an equivalence statement from Table 5.7, and write all the possible conversion factors from it.

2. Write a conversion factor or factors for these problems. Do not do the calculation.

   a. 37 cm × _____ = ? in.

   b. 4.2 qt × _____ = ? L

   c. 2.2 kg × _____ = ? pounds

   d. 3.5 mi × _____ = ? m

3. Complete the conversions for each of the problems in question 2.

4. You run a 100-yd dash in 9.8 seconds. What is your speed in miles per hour?

5. Convert the following temperatures.

   a. 30. °C to °F   c. 14 K to °C

   b. 72 °F to K   d. 342 K to °F

6. A certain liquid has a density of 0.79 g/mL. What volume of this liquid has a mass of 15.0 g?

7. For each of the following, decide which block is more dense: the orange block or the blue block, or state that it cannot be determined. Explain your answers.

a.

c.

b.

d.

RESEARCH LINKS
CLASSZONE.COM

CELEBRITY CHEMICAL

Carvone ($C_{10}H_{14}O$)

Carvone exists in two mirror-image forms (or enantiomers). While *R*-carvone smells like spearmint, *S*-carvone smells like caraway. You can bring in caraway seeds and spearmint to show students that, while the molecules have the same atoms and bonds, their 3-D shapes also determine their properties. You can also discuss this during Chapter 12.

Chapter 5 Review

Key Terms

5.1 Measurement
Scientific notation
Units
English system
Metric system
International System (SI)
Volume
Liter
Milliliter
Mass
Gram

5.2 Significant figures
Rounding off

5.3 Conversion factor
Equivalence statement
Dimensional analysis
Fahrenheit scale
Celsius scale
Kelvin scale (absolute)
Density
Specific gravity

Key Ideas

5.1 Scientific Notation and Units
- A quantitative observation is called a measurement and consists of a number and a unit.
- Very large or very small numbers are conveniently expressed by using scientific notation.
  - The number is expressed as a number between 1 and 10 multiplied by 10 and raised to a power.
- Units provide a scale on which to represent the results of a measurement. There are three commonly used unit systems.
  - English
  - Metric (uses prefixes to change the size of the unit)
  - SI (uses prefixes to change the size of the unit)

5.2 Uncertainty in Measurement and Significant Figures
- All measurements have some uncertainty, which is reflected by the number of significant figures used to express the number.
- Rules exist for rounding off to the correct number of significant figures in a calculated result.

5.3 Problem Solving and Unit Conversions
- We can convert from one system of units to another by a method called dimensional analysis using conversion factors.
- Conversion factors are built from an equivalence statement which shows the relationship between the units in different systems.

English-Metric and English-English Equivalents	
Length	1 m = 1.094 yd
	2.54 cm = 1 in.
	1 mi = 5280. ft
	1 mi = 1760. yd
Mass	1 kg = 2.205 lb
	453.6 g = 1 lb
Volume	1 L = 1.06 qt
	1 ft^3 = 28.32 L

- There are three commonly used temperature scales: Fahrenheit, Celsius, and Kelvin.
- We can convert among the temperature scales by adjusting the zero point and the size of the unit. Useful equations for conversions are:
  - $^\circ T_C + 273 = T_K$
  - $^\circ T_F = 1.80(^\circ T_C) + 32$
  - Density represents the amount of matter present in a given volume:
    $$\text{density} = \frac{\text{mass}}{\text{volume}}$$

RESEARCH LINKS
CLASSZONE.COM

Meeting Individual Needs	**Assessment Resources**
CHAPTER REVIEW	CHAPTER 5

Chapter 5 Review Worksheet at the appropriate level:
    Basic
    Standard
    Challenge
	Chapter 5 Test

CHAPTER SUMMARY	**TECHNOLOGY**
A **Chapter Summary** that includes additional Active Reading Questions for Chapter 5 is available.	Computerized Test Bank for Chapter 5

Chapter 5 Assessment

Chapter 5 Assessment

1. 4

2. 4512

3. (a) 0.06235
   (b) 7229
   (c) 0.000005001
   (d) 86,210

4. (a) −5
   (b) 6
   (c) −4
   (d) 4

5. (a) 9.367421×10^6
   (b) 7.241×10^3
   (c) 5.519×10^{-4}
   (d) 5.408×10^0
   (e) already in scientific notation
   (f) 6.319×10^{-1}
   (g) 7.215×10^{-9}
   (h) 7.21×10^{-1}

6. (a) 483
   (b) 0.0007221
   (c) 6.1
   (d) 0.0000000911
   (e) 4,221,000
   (f) 0.00122
   (g) 9999
   (h) 0.00001016
   (i) 101,600
   (j) 0.411
   (k) 97,100
   (l) 0.000971

7. (a) 1.423×10^5
   (b) 7.741×10^{-13}
   (c) 2.27×10^4
   (d) already in scientific notation
   (e) 2.51×10^2
   (f) 9.7522×10^1
   (g) 9.7752 (9.7752×10^0)
   (h) 4.4252×10^8

8. (a) 3.1×10^3
   (b) 1×10^6
   (c) 1 or 1×10^0
   (d) 1.8×10^{-5}
   (e) 1×10^7
   (f) 1.00×10^6
   (g) 1.00×10^{-7}
   (h) 1×10^1

9. (a) 10^3
   (b) 10^{-2}
   (c) 10^{-3}
   (d) 10^{-1}
   (e) 10^{-9}
   (f) 10^{-6}

10. (a) mega
    (b) milli
    (c) nano
    (d) mega
    (e) centi
    (f) micro

11. 100 miles

All exercises with blue numbers have answers in the back of this book.

5.1 Scientific Notation and Units

A. Scientific Notation

1. When the number 98,145 is written in standard scientific notation, the exponent indicating the power of 10 will be _____.

2. When the number 4.512×10^3 is written in ordinary decimal notation, it is expressed as _____.

3. Write each of the following as an "ordinary" decimal number.

   a. 6.235×10^{-2} c. 5.001×10^{-6}
   b. 7.229×10^3 d. 8.621×10^4

4. For each of the following numbers, if the number is rewritten in standard scientific notation, what will be the value of the exponent (for the power of 10)?

   a. 0.000067   c. 1/10,000
   b. 9,331,442   d. 163.1×10^2

5. Express each of the following numbers in *standard* scientific notation.

   a. 9,367,421   e. 6.24×10^2
   b. 7241   f. 6319×10^{-2}
   c. 0.0005519   g. 0.000000007215
   d. 5.408   h. 0.721

6. Express each of the following as an "ordinary" decimal number.

   a. 4.83×10^2 g. 9.999×10^3
   b. 7.221×10^{-4} h. 1.016×10^{-5}
   c. 6.1×10^0 i. 1.016×10^5
   d. 9.11×10^{-8} j. 4.11×10^{-1}
   e. 4.221×10^6 k. 9.71×10^4
   f. 1.22×10^{-3} l. 9.71×10^{-4}

7. Write each of the following numbers in *standard* scientific notation.

   a. 142.3×10^3 e. 0.0251×10^4
   b. 0.0007741×10^{-9} f. $97,522 \times 10^{-3}$
   c. 22.7×10^3 g. 0.0000097752×10^6
   d. 6.272×10^{-5} h. $44,252 \times 10^4$

---

8. Write each of the following numbers in standard scientific notation.

   a. $\dfrac{1}{0.00032}$ e. $\dfrac{(10^5)(10^4)(10^{-4})}{(10^{-2})}$

   b. $\dfrac{10^3}{10^{-3}}$ f. $\dfrac{43.2}{(4.32 \times 10^{-5})}$

   c. $\dfrac{10^3}{10^3}$ g. $\dfrac{(4.32 \times 10^{-5})}{432}$

   d. $\dfrac{1}{55,000}$ h. $\dfrac{1}{(10^5)(10^{-6})}$

B. Units

9. Indicate the meaning (as a power of 10) for each of the following metric prefixes.

   a. kilo   d. deci
   b. centi   e. nano
   c. milli   f. micro

10. Give the metric prefix that corresponds to each of the following:

    a. 1,000,000   d. 10^6
    b. 10^{-3} e. 10^{-2}
    c. 10^{-9} f. 0.000001

C. Measurements of Length, Volume, and Mass

11. Which distance is greater, 100 mi or 100 km?

12. One liter of volume in the metric system is approximately equivalent to one _____ in the English system.

13. The length 52.2 mm can also be expressed as _____ cm.

14. Who is taller, a man who is 1.62 m tall or a woman who is 5 ft 6 in. tall?

15. A 1-kg package of hamburger has a mass closest to which of the following?

    a. 8 oz   c. 2 lb
    b. 1 lb   d. 10 lb

16. A 2-L bottle of soda contains a volume closest to which of the following?

    a. 5 gal   c. 2 pt
    b. 1 qt   d. 2 qt

17. A recipe written in metric units calls for 250 mL of milk. Which of the following best approximates this amount?

    a. 1 qt   c. 1 cup
    b. 1 gal   d. 1 pt

---

12. quart

13. 5.22 cm

14. the woman

15. c

16. d

17. c

18. Which metric system unit is most appropriate for measuring the distance between two cities?

    a. meters   c. centimeters

    b. millimeters   d. kilometers

For exercises 19 and 20, some examples of simple approximate metric to English equivalents are given in the table.

Examples of Commonly Used Units	
length	A dime is 1 mm thick. A quarter is 2.5 cm in diameter. The average height of an adult man is 1.8 m.
mass	A nickel has a mass of about 5 g. A 120-lb woman has a mass of about 55 kg.
volume	A 12-oz can of soda has a volume of about 360 mL. A half gallon of milk is equal to about 2 L of milk.

19. What is the value in dollars of a stack of dimes that is 10 cm high?

20. How many quarters must be lined up in a row to reach a length of 1 meter?

5.2 Uncertainty in Measurement and Significant Figures

A. Uncertainty in Measurement

21. When a measuring scale is used properly to the limit of precision, the last significant digit recorded for the measurement is said to be *uncertain*. Explain.

22. For the pin shown below, why is the third digit determined for the length of the pin uncertain? Considering that the third digit is uncertain, explain why the length of the pin is indicated as 2.85 cm rather than, for example, 2.83 or 2.87 cm.

23. Why can the length of the pin shown below not be recorded as 2.850 cm?

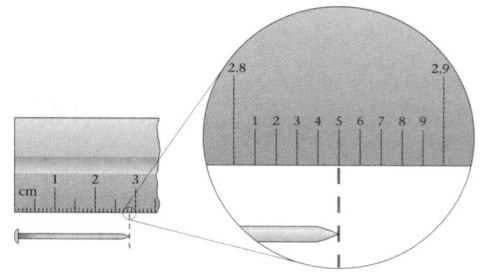

B. Significant Figures

24. Indicate the number of significant figures in each of the following:

    a. 1422   e. 200.

    b. 65,321   f. 2.00×10^2

    c. 1.004×10^5 g. 435.662

    d. 200   h. 56.341

25. Indicate the number of significant figures implied in each of the following statements:

    a. The population of the United States is 250 million.

    b. One hour is equivalent to 60 minutes.

    c. There are 5280 feet in 1 mile.

    d. Jet airliners fly at 500 mi/h.

    e. The Daytona 500 is a 500-mile race.

26. Round off each of the following numbers to three significant digits.

    a. 1,566,311   d. 0.0011672

    b. 2.7651×10^{-3} e. 0.07759

    c. 84,592

27. Round off each of the following numbers to the indicated number of significant digits, and write the answer in standard scientific notation.

    a. 0.00034159 to three digits

    b. 103.351×10^2 to four digits

    c. 17.9915 to five digits

    d. 3.365×10^5 to three digits

28. When the calculation (0.0043)(0.0821)(298) is performed, the answer should be reported to _____ significant figures.

18. d

19. $10

20. 40 quarters

21. We estimate measurements between the smallest divisions on the scale; since this is our best estimate, the last significant digit recorded is uncertain.

22. It is given as 2.85 cm (rather than any other number) to indicate that the point of the pin appears to the observer to be halfway between the smallest marked scale divisions.

23. The scale of the ruler is marked to the nearest tenth of a centimeter. Writing 2.850 would imply that the scale was marked to the nearest hundredth of a centimeter (and that the zero in the thousandths place had been estimated).

24. (a) four
(b) five
(c) four
(d) one
(e) three
(f) three
(g) six
(h) five

25. (a) probably only two
(b) infinite (definition)
(c) infinite (definition)
(d) probably only one
(e) three (the race is defined to be 500. miles)

26. (a) 1,570,000 or 1.57×10^6
(b) 2.77×10^{-3}
(c) 84,600 or 8.46×10^4
(d) 0.00117 or 1.17×10^{-3}
(e) 0.0776 or 7.76×10^{-2}

27. (a) 3.42×10^{-4}
(b) 1.034×10^4
(c) 1.7992×10^1
(d) 3.37×10^5

28. 2

29. 3

30. 1

31. none

32. (a) 641.0
    (b) 1.327
    (c) 77.34
    (d) 3215

33. (a) 124
    (b) 1.995×10^{-23}
    (c) 1.14×10^{-2}
    (d) 5.3×10^{-4}

34. (a) 2.045
    (b) 3.8×10^3
    (c) 5.19×10^{-5}
    (d) 3.8418×10^{-7}

35. infinite (definition)

36. 1 mi/1760 yd;
    1760 yd/1 mi

37. $0.79/1 lb

38. 1 lb/$0.79

39. (a) 2.44 yd
    (b) 42.2 m
    (c) 115 in
    (d) 2238 cm
    (e) 648.1 mi
    (f) 716.9 km
    (g) 0.0362 km
    (h) 5.01×10^4 cm

40. (a) 0.2543 kg
    (b) 2.75×10^3 g
    (c) 6.06 lb
    (d) 97.0 oz
    (e) 1.177 lb
    (f) 794 g
    (g) 2.5×10^2 g
    (h) 1.62 oz

41. 24.00 euros; $83.33

42. 3.1×10^2 km; 3.1×10^5 m;
    1.0×10^6 ft

43. The Boston–New York trains
    will be faster (the U.K. trains
    travel at a speed of 140. mi/h).

44. 212 °F; 100 °C

45. 100

29. The quotient $\dfrac{(2.3733 \times 10^2)}{(343)}$ should be written with _____ significant figures.

30. How many digits after the decimal point should be reported when the calculation (199.0354 + 43.09 + 121.2) is performed?

31. How many digits after the decimal point should be reported when the calculation (10,434 − 9.3344) is performed?

32. Evaluate each of the following, and write the answer to the appropriate number of significant figures.
    a. 212.2 + 26.7 + 402.09
    b. 1.0028 + 0.221 + 0.10337
    c. 52.331 + 26.01 − 0.9981
    d. $(2.01 \times 10^2) + (3.014 \times 10^3)$

33. Evaluate each of the following, and write the answer to the appropriate number of significant figures.
    a. (4.031)(0.08206)(373.1)/(0.995)
    b. $(12.011)/(6.022 \times 10^{23})$
    c. (0.500)/(44.02)
    d. (0.15)/(280.62)

34. Evaluate each of the following, and write the answer to the appropriate number of significant figures.
    a. (2.0944 + 0.0003233 + 12.22)/(7.001)
    b. $[(1.42 \times 10^2) + (1.021 \times 10^3)]/(3.1 \times 10^{-1})$
    c. $(9.762 \times 10^{-3})/[(1.43 \times 10^2) + (4.51 \times 10^1)]$
    d. $(6.1982 \times 10^{-4})^2$

5.3 Problem Solving and Unit Conversions

A. Tools for Problem Solving

35. How many significant figures are understood for the numbers in the following definition: 1 mi = 5280 ft?

36. Given that 1 mi = 1760 yd, determine what conversion factor is appropriate to convert 1849 yd to miles and to convert 2.781 mi to yards.

For exercises 37 and 38, apples cost $0.79 per pound.

37. What conversion factor is appropriate to express the cost of 5.3 lb of apples?

38. What conversion factor could be used to determine how many pounds of apples could be bought for $2.00?

39. Perform each of the following conversions, being sure to set up clearly the appropriate conversion factor in each case.
    a. 2.23 m to yards
    b. 46.2 yd to meters
    c. 292 cm to inches
    d. 881.2 in. to centimeters
    e. 1043 km to miles
    f. 445.5 mi to kilometers
    g. 36.2 m to kilometers
    h. 0.501 km to centimeters

40. Perform each of the following conversions, being sure to set up clearly the appropriate conversion factor in each case.
    a. 254.3 g to kilograms
    b. 2.75 kg to grams
    c. 2.75 kg to pounds
    d. 2.75 kg to ounces
    e. 534.1 g to pounds
    f. 1.75 lb to grams
    g. 8.7 oz to grams
    h. 45.9 g to ounces

41. If $1.00 is equivalent to 1.2 euros, what is $20.00 worth in euros? What is the value in dollars of 100 euros?

42. Boston and New York City are 190 miles apart. What is this distance in kilometers? In meters? In feet?

43. The United States will soon have high-speed trains running between Boston and New York capable of speeds up to 160 mi/h. Will these trains be faster or slower than the fastest trains in the United Kingdom, which reach speeds of 225 km/h?

B. Temperature Conversions

44. The normal boiling point of water is _____ °F, or _____ °C.

45. On both the Celsius and Kelvin temperature scales, there are _____ degrees between the normal freezing and boiling points of water.

46. On which temperature scale (°F, °C, or K) does 1 degree represent the smallest change in temperature?

47. Convert the following temperatures to kelvins.
- a. -155 °C
- d. 101 °F
- b. 200 °C
- e. -52 °F
- c. -52 °C
- f. -196 °F

48. Convert the following Kelvin temperatures to Celsius degrees.
- a. 275 K
- d. 77 K
- b. 445 K
- e. 10,000. K
- c. 0 K
- f. 2 K

49. Carry out the indicated temperature conversions.
- a. -40 °C to Fahrenheit degrees
- b. -40 °F to Celsius degrees
- c. 232 K to Celsius degrees
- d. 232 K to Fahrenheit degrees

50. Carry out the indicated temperature conversions.
- a. -201 °F to kelvins
- b. -201 °C to kelvins
- c. 351 °C to Fahrenheit degrees
- d. -150 °F to Celsius degrees

C. Density

51. The ratio of an object's mass to its _____ is called the *density* of the object.

52. A kilogram of lead occupies a much smaller volume than a kilogram of water because _____ has a much higher density.

53. Typically, gases have very (high/low) densities compared with those of solids and liquids (see Table 5.8).

54. What property of density makes it useful as an aid in identifying substances?

55. Referring to Table 5.8, determine whether air, water, ethanol, or aluminum is the most dense.

56. For the masses and volumes indicated, calculate the density in grams per cubic centimeter.
- a. mass = 4.53 kg; volume = 225 cm^3
- b. mass = 26.3 g; volume = 25.0 mL
- c. mass = 1.00 lb; volume = 500. cm^3
- d. mass = 352 mg; volume = 0.271 cm^3

57. If 89.2 mL of a liquid has a mass of 75.2 g, calculate the liquid's density.

58. A cube of metal weighs 1.45 kg and displaces 542 mL of water when immersed. Calculate the density of the metal.

59. A material will float on the surface of a liquid if the material has a density less than that of the liquid. Given that the density of water is approximately 1.0 g/mL, will a block of material having a volume of 1.2×10^4 in.^{3} and weighing 3.5 lb float or sink when placed in a reservoir of water?

60. The density of pure silver is 10.5 g/cm^3 at 20 °C. If 5.25 g of pure silver pellets is added to a graduated cylinder containing 11.2 mL of water, to what volume level will the water in the cylinder rise?

Use the information in the table for questions 61–62.

Densities of Various Common Substances at 20 °C		
Substance	Physical State	Density (g/cm^3)
benzene	liquid	0.880
salt (sodium chloride)	solid	2.16
iron	solid	7.87
silver	solid	10.5
mercury	liquid	13.6
gold	solid	19.32

61. Calculate the volume of 50.0 g of each of the following substances.
- a. sodium chloride
- c. benzene
- b. mercury
- d. silver

62. Calculate the mass of 50.0 cm^3 of each of the following substances.
- a. gold
- c. lead
- b. iron
- d. aluminum

46. Fahrenheit (°F)

47. (a) 118 K
(b) 473 K
(c) 221 K
(d) 311 K
(e) 226 K
(f) 77 K

48. (a) 2 °C
(b) 172 °C
(c) -273 °C
(d) -196 °C
(e) 9727 °C
(f) -271 °C

49. (a) -40 °F
(b) -40 °C
(c) -41 °C
(d) -42 °F

50. (a) 144 K
(b) 72 K
(c) 664 °F
(d) -101 °C

51. volume

52. lead

53. low

54. Density is a characteristic property of a pure substance.

55. $1.05/lb

56. (a) 20.1 g/cm^3
(b) 1.05 g/cm^3
(c) 0.907 g/cm^3
(d) 1.30 g/cm^3

57. 0.843 g/mL

58. 2.68 g/mL

59. float

60. 11.7 mL

61. (a) 23.1 cm^3
(b) 3.68 cm^3
(c) 56.8 cm^3
(d) 4.76 cm^3

62. (a) 966 g
(b) 394 g
(c) 567 g
(d) 135 g

63. (a) cm
   (b) m
   (c) km
   (d) cm
   (e) mm

64. highway: 19 km/L
   city: 16 km/L

65. Because $1 = 1.2 Euros and
   1 kg = 2.2 lbs, the peaches
   will cost $1.05/lb.

66. 24 capsules

67. The ball will sink
   ($d = 3.8$ g/cm^3).

68. 959 g

69. (a) 4, positive
   (b) 6, negative
   (c) 0, zero
   (d) 5, positive
   (e) 2, negative

70. 4.25 grams

71. (a) one
   (b) one
   (c) four
   (d) two
   (e) infinite (definition)
   (f) one

72. 38.2 mL

73. 3.8 g/mL

74. 7.853 g/mL

75. 81 feet

Critical Thinking

63. Which unit of length in the metric system would be most appropriate in size for measuring each of the following items?

   a. the dimensions of this page

   b. the size of the room in which you are sitting

   c. the distance from New York to London

   d. the diameter of a baseball

   e. the diameter of a common pin

64. Suppose that your car is rated at 45 mi/gal for highway use and 38 mi/gal for city driving. If you wanted to write to your friend in Spain about your car's mileage, what ratings in kilometers per liter would you report?

65. You are in Paris, and you want to buy some peaches for lunch. The sign in the fruit stand indicates that peaches are 2.76 Euros per kilogram. Given that there are approximately 11.2 Euros to the dollar, calculate what a pound of peaches will cost in dollars.

66. Suppose a sample of antibiotic pills has a mass of 15.6 g. If the average mass per pill is 0.65 g, determine how many pills are in the sample.

67. For a material to float on the surface of water, the material must have a density less than that of water (1.0 g/mL) and must not react with the water or dissolve in it. A spherical ball has a radius of 0.50 cm and weighs 2.0 g. Will this ball float or sink when placed in water?

   (Note: Volume of a sphere $= \frac{4}{3}\pi r^3$)

68. Ethanol and benzene dissolve in each other. When 100. mL of ethanol is dissolved in 1.00 L of benzene, what is the mass of the mixture? (See Table 5.8.)

69. For each of the following numbers, by how many places must the decimal point be moved to express the number in standard scientific notation? In each case, will the exponent be positive, negative, or zero?

   a. 55,651   d. 883,541

   b. 0.000008991   e. 0.09814

   c. 2.04

70. Which weighs more, 4.25 grams of gold or 425 milligrams of gold?

71. Indicate the number of significant figures in each of the following:

   a. This book contains over 500 pages.

   b. A mile is just over 5000 ft.

   c. A liter is equivalent to 1.059 qt.

   d. The population of the United States is approaching 250 million.

   e. A kilogram is 1000 g.

   f. The Boeing 747 cruises at around 600 mi/h.

72. An organic solvent has density 1.31 g/mL. What volume is occupied by 50.0 g of the liquid?

73. A sample containing 33.42 g of metal pellets is poured into a graduated cylinder initially containing 12.7 mL of water, causing the water level in the cylinder to rise to 21.6 mL. Calculate the density of the metal.

74. You place 10.00 mL of water in a graduated cylinder and add a 15.0 g sample of iron to the water. The new water level is 11.91 mL. What is the density of the iron?

75. You are a passenger in a car traveling at 55 mph (miles per hour). How many feet do you travel in 1 second? There are 5280 feet in a mile.

1 Express 1,870,000 in scientific notation.

A 5.49×10^{-8}

B 1.87×10^{-6}

C 1.87×10^{6}

D 187×10^{6}

2 The number 0.00003007 expressed in exponential notation is

A 3.007×10^{-5}

B 3.7×10^{-5}

C 3.007×10^{-5}

D 3.007×10^{-4}

3 The SI prefix that corresponds to a factor of 10^{-3} is

A kilo

B deci

C centi

D milli

4 The number of milliliters in 0.0367 liter is

A 3.67×10^{-5} mL

B 36.7 mL

C 3.67 mL

D 367 mL

5 Consider the numbers 23.68 and 4.12. The sum of these numbers has ____ significant figures, and the product of these numbers has ____ significant figures.

A 3, 3

B 4, 4

C 3, 4

D 4, 3

6 An equivalence statement is written so that on each side of the equal sign

A there are the same numbers and same units.

B there are the same numbers but different units.

C there are generally different numbers and different units.

D there are generally different numbers but the same units.

7 Which of the following statements is true?

A A change of 1 °C is larger than a change of 1 °F, but smaller than a change of 1 K.

B A change of 1 °F is larger than a change of 1 °C, but smaller than a change of 1 K.

C A change of 1 °C is larger than a change of 1 °F, and equal to a change of 1 K.

D A change of 1 °F is larger than a change of 1 °C, and equal to a change of 1 K.

8 A 15.0 mL sample of a liquid has a mass of 12.3 g. What is the density of the liquid?

A 0.820 g/mL

B 1.22 g/mL

C 185 g/mL

D 12.3 g/mL

9 The beakers shown below have different precisions as shown.

I   II   III

a. Report the volume of water in each beaker with the proper number of significant figures.

b. Label the digits in each measurement from part A as "certain" or "uncertain."

c. You pour the water from these three beakers into one container. What is the volume of liquid in the container reported to the correct number of significant figures?

Chapter 5

Standardized Test Practice

1. C

2. A

3. D

4. B

5. D

6. C

7. C

8. A

9. a. Beaker I: 26.4 mL
      Beaker II: 28 mL
      Beaker III: 26.42 mL

   b. Beaker I: 2 and 6 are certain, 4 is uncertain
      Beaker II: 2 is certain, 8 is uncertain
      Beaker III: The first 2, 6, and 4 are certain, the last 2 is uncertain

   c. 81 mL

Test-Taking Strategy

Encourage students to cross out obvious distracters, such as choice A in question 1 and choice C in question 6.

Planning Guide

Section	Segment		Text Features and Components	Labs, Demonstrations, & Activities
6.1 **Atoms and Moles** **1 Block** pp. 172–184	A	**Counting by Weighing**	**TE** Teaching Support: Background Information *pp. 172–173*	**TE** Group Activity *p. 173*
	B	**Atomic Masses: Counting Atoms by Weighing**		**SE** Hands-On Chemistry: Counting Pennies Without Counting *p. 177*

	C	**The Mole**	**TE** Teaching Support: Historical Note *p. 180*	**TE** Teaching Support: Demonstration *p. 178*
				TE Mini-Demo *p. 180*
				TE Group Activity *p. 181*
				RP Classroom Activities and Projects *TE p. 179*
				LM Experiment 22: Bean Lab, Traditional
				    Lab Manual
				    Report Sheets
				    Teacher's Lab Guide

6.2 **Molar Mass and Percent Composition** **1 Block** pp. 185–195	A	**Molar Mass**		**SE** Hands-On Chemistry: Relative Masses *p. 191*
	B	**Percent Composition of Compounds**		**SE** Hands-On Chemistry: And the Winner Is . . . *p. 194*
		continued on next page		

Key	**SE** Student Edition	**TE** Teacher Edition	**RP** Teacher Resource Package
	AR Additional Materials	**LM** Lab Materials	**⬛** Transparencies
	⦿ DVD	**▭** CD-ROM	**ⓘ** classzone.com

All Learners	Technology	Review & Assessment	Standards
TE Teaching Tips *pp. 172–173*	**⊙** EasyPlanner	**SE** Active Reading Question *p. 174* **SE** Questions and Problems *p. 210*	**TE** **NSES** UCP1, UCP2, UCP3, A1, A2, B1, B2, B3, E1, E2, G1, G2, G3
TE Teaching Tips *pp. 174–175, 177* **RP** MINT: Reading Concepts *TE p. 174* **RP** MINT: Math Concepts *TE p. 176*	**⊙** EasyPlanner	**SE** Practice Problem *p. 176* **TE** More Examples *p. 176* **SE** Practice Problem *p. 177* **TE** More Examples *p. 177* **SE** Key Terms *p. 209* **SE** Questions and Problems *p. 210*	
TE Teaching Tips *pp. 179–180, 182* **TE** Meeting Individual Needs *p. 182* **TE** Meeting Individual Needs *p. 183* **RP** MINT: Math Concepts *TE p. 179* **RP** Team Learning Worksheet (Sec. 6.1)	**▣** Lab Generator CD **⊙** EasyPlanner	**SE** Active Reading Question *p. 179* **SE** Critical Thinking *p. 180* **SE** Critical Thinking *p. 181* **TE** More Examples *p. 182* **TE** More Examples *p. 183* **SE** Practice Problem *p. 184* **SE** Review Questions (6.1.A–6.1.C) *p. 184* **SE** Key Terms *p. 209* **SE** Questions and Problems *pp. 210–211*	
TE Teaching Tips *pp. 185, 187* **TE** Misconceptions *p. 186*	**▤** Transparency: Figure 6.1 **⊙** EasyPlanner	**SE** Active Reading Question *p. 186* **TE** More Examples *p. 186* **SE** Practice Problem *p. 187* **TE** More Examples *p. 187* **SE** Practice Problem *p. 188* **TE** More Examples *p. 189* **TE** More Examples *p. 190* **SE** Practice Problem *p. 191* **SE** Key Terms *p. 209* **SE** Questions and Problems *p. 211*	**TE** **NSES** UCP1, UCP3, UCP5, A1, A2, B1, B2, B3, G1, G2
TE Teaching Tips *pp. 192* **RP** MINT: Math Concepts *TE p. 192* **RP** Team Learning Worksheet (Sec. 6.2)	**⊙** EasyPlanner	**SE** Active Reading Question *p. 193* **TE** More Examples *p. 193* **SE** Practice Problem *p. 194* **SE** Review Questions (6.2.A–6.2.B) *p. 195* **SE** Key Terms *p. 209* **SE** Questions and Problems *p. 212*	

Planning Guide

Section	Segment		Text Features and Components	Labs, Demonstrations, & Activities
6.3 Formulas of Compounds 1 Block pp. 196–208	**A**	**Empirical Formulas**		**TE** Mini-Demo *p. 197*
	B	**Calculation of Empirical Formulas**	**SE** Chemistry Explorers: William Perkin *p. 201*	**LM** Experiment 23: Decomposing Copper Oxide Lab Manual Report Sheets Teacher's Lab Guide
	C	**Calculation of Molecular Formulas**	**SE** Chemistry in Your World: Nutrition Facts *p. 208*	**LM** Experiment 24: Formula of a Hydrate, Traditional Lab Manual Report Sheets Teacher's Lab Guide

Key
SE Student Edition   **TE** Teacher Edition   **RP** Teacher Resource Package
AR Additional Materials   **LM** Lab Materials   Transparencies
DVD   CD-ROM   classzone.com

All Learners	Technology	Review & Assessment	Standards
TE Teaching Tips *pp. 196, 198*	**●** EasyPlanner	**SE** Active Reading Question *p. 198* **TE** More Examples *p. 198* **SE** Key Terms *p. 209* **SE** Questions and Problems *p. 212*	**TE** **NSES** UCP1, UCP3, UCP5, A1, A2, B2, B3, D3, F1, G1, G2, G3
TE Teaching Tips *pp. 198–200, 204* **TE** Meeting Individual Needs *p. 202* **TE** Meeting Individual Needs *p. 203*	**▮** Lab Generator CD **●** EasyPlanner	**TE** More Examples *p. 199* **TE** More Examples *p. 202* **SE** Practice Problem *p. 203* **TE** More Examples *p. 203* **SE** Practice Problem *p. 204* **SE** Practice Problem *p. 205* **SE** Questions and Problems *pp. 212–213*	
TE Teaching Tips *p. 205* **TE** Meeting Individual Needs *p. 207* **RP** MINT: Challenge Projects *TE p. 206* **RP** Team Learning Worksheet (Sec. 6.3)	**▮** Lab Generator CD **●** EasyPlanner	**TE** More Examples *p. 206* **SE** Practice Problem *p. 207* **SE** Active Reading Question *p. 207* **SE** Questions and Problems *p. 213* **SE** Review Questions (6.3.A–6.3.C) *p. 208*	

Resource Materials for Chapter 6

SE Chapter Review *p. 209*

SE Critical Thinking *pp. 213–214*

SE Standardized Test Practice *p. 215*

AR English/Spanish Summaries

▮ English Summaries Audio

▮ Spanish Summaries Audio

RP Meeting Individual Needs Toolkit (MINT)
    Reading Concepts
    Math Concepts
    Challenge Projects
    Chapter Review Worksheets
    Chapter Summaries

RP Solutions Guide

RP Standardized Test Practice

RP Chapter Tests

RP Test Bank

🛈 Test Generator

In this chapter our goals are for students to:

- Understand average mass and explore how counting can be done by weighing

- Understand atomic mass and its experimental determination

- Understand the mole concept and Avogadro's number and convert among moles, mass, and number of atoms in a sample

- Understand the definition of molar mass

- Learn to convert between moles and mass of a given sample of a chemical compound

- Learn to find the mass percent of an element in a compound

- Understand the meaning of empirical formulas

- Learn to calculate empirical formulas

- Learn to calculate the molecular formula of a compound, given its empirical formula and molar mass

Chapter 6
Chemical Composition

Pearls are made of layers of calcium carbonate. They can be measured by counting or by weighing.

LOOKING AHEAD

170

Prereading Questions

1. Add the numbers and divide by 7, the number of data points. The average is 4.43 (disregarding significant figures).

2. Students generally will use units of grams for mass measurements.

3. 314 pennies

4. 6.023×10^{23} carbon atoms

5. 56.67% of students are female.

IN YOUR LIFE

One very important chemical activity is the synthesis of new substances. Nylon, the artificial sweetener Splenda, Kevlar used in bulletproof vests and the body parts of exotic cars, polyvinyl chloride (PVC) for plastic water pipes, Teflon, and so many other materials that make our lives easier all originated in some chemist's laboratory. When a chemist makes a new substance, the first order of business is to identify it. What is its composition? What is its chemical formula?

The body of this sports car is made from new lightweight compounds to make it go faster on less fuel.

WHAT DO YOU KNOW?

Prereading Questions

1. Explain how to find the average of the following data set: 2, 8, 6, 4, 2, 4, 5.

2. What units are used for mass measurements?

3. Consider a sample of pennies with a mass of 857.2 g. The average mass of a penny is 2.73 g. How many pennies are in the sample?

4. Consider a 12.01 g sample of carbon. The average mass of a carbon atom is 1.994×10^{23} g. How many carbon atoms are in the sample?

5. In a class of 30 chemistry students, 17 of the students are female. What percentage of students is female?

Chemical Composition • Chapter 6 • **171**

TECHNOLOGY IN THE CLASSROOM

 Transparency
Figure: 6.1

 Power Presentation DVD
   PowerPoint Slides
   eEdition
   EasyPlanner

 Lab Generator CD
   English Summaries CD
   Spanish Summaries CD
   ML Test Generator

 classzone.com

Student Preparation

Assign students to read Section 6.1 and to answer the Review Questions at the end of the section before coming to class.

 Active Learning
Team Learning Worksheet

After introducing the material in Section 6.1 in class, place students in groups and have them work together on **Section 6.1: Team Learning Worksheet.**

SECTION 6.1
GUIDE THE LEARNING

Homework

You may wish to assign these selected end-of-chapter problems as homework for this section: 2, 4, 5a–c, 6a–c, 8, 10, 13, 14a–d, 15a–d, 16a–d

Additional end-of-chapter problems can be used for extra practice.

6.1.A Counting by Weighing

Objective To understand the concept of average mass and explore how counting can be done by weighing

 TEACHING TIPS

• Using analogies to cooking and daily life is helpful for beginning students.

• Students often spend so much time on the mechanics of solving these problems that they lose sight of the big picture of what they are trying to learn. Keep talking to them about the idea that we are determining chemical quantities to decide how much we will have or how much we may need of a particular substance.

SECTION 6.1
Atoms and Moles

Key Terms
• Atomic mass unit
• Average atomic mass
• Mole
• Avogadro's number

Objectives
• *To understand the concept of average mass*
• *To learn how counting can be done by weighing*
• *To understand atomic mass and learn how it is determined*
• *To understand the mole concept and Avogadro's number*
• *To learn to convert among moles, mass, and number of atoms*

A. Counting by Weighing

In this chapter we will learn to determine a compound's formula. Before we can do that, however, we need to think about counting atoms. How do we determine the number of each type of atom in a substance so that we can write its formula? Of course, atoms are too small to count individually. As we will see in this chapter, we typically count atoms by weighing them. So let us first consider the general principle of counting by weighing.

Suppose you work in a candy store that sells gourmet jelly beans by the bean. People come in and ask for 50 beans, 100 beans, 1000 beans, and so on, and you have to count them out—a tedious process at best. As a good problem solver, you try to come up with a better system. It occurs to you that it might be far more efficient to buy a scale and count the jelly beans by weighing them. How can you count jelly beans by weighing them? What information about the individual beans do you need to know?

Averaging the Mass of Similar Objects

Assume that all of the jelly beans are identical and that each has a mass of 5 g. If a customer asks for 1000 jelly beans, what mass of jelly beans would be required? Each bean has a mass of 5 g, so you would need 1000 beans × 5 g/bean, or 5000 g (5 kg). It takes just a few seconds to weigh out 5 kg of jelly beans. It would take much longer to count out 1000 of them.

In reality, jelly beans are not identical. For example, let's assume that you weigh 10 beans individually and get the following results:

Bean	1	2	3	4	5	6	7	8	9	10
Mass (g)	5.1	5.2	5.0	4.8	4.9	5.0	5.0	5.1	4.9	5.0

Jellybeans can be counted by weighing.

MATH
To find an average, add up all the individual measurements and divide by the total number of measurements.

Can we count these nonidentical beans by weighing? Yes. The key piece of information we need is the *average* mass of the jelly beans. Let's compute the average mass for our 10-bean sample.

$$\text{Average mass} = \frac{\text{total mass of beans}}{\text{number of beans}}$$

$$= \frac{5.1\,g + 5.2\,g + 5.0\,g + 4.8\,g + 4.9\,g + 5.0\,g + 5.0\,g + 5.1\,g + 4.9\,g + 5.0\,g}{10}$$

$$= \frac{50.0}{10}\,g = 5.0\,g$$

The average mass of a jelly bean is 5.0 g.

Teaching Support
BACKGROUND INFORMATION

The Chemistry of Jelly Beans

It takes up to seven days to make a jelly bean with a soft center and surprisingly, before now, candy-makers have not known why. Gregory Ziegler, Associate Professor of Food Science at Penn State University, decided to solve the mystery of how a jelly bean can have a soft center and a hard outer shell.

A jelly bean is made from the inside out. A mixture of corn syrup, sugar, and flavorings is cooked in a large kettle and then poured into a molding tray. Overnight the centers become hard. The next step involves "engrossing"—a sugar shell is added to surround the center. Then the candy-makers must wait two to four days for the center to soften.

Ziegler and his colleagues used MRI (magnetic resonance imaging) to study the softening process. They found that the moisture from the outer shell is drawn into the center. This

So, to count out 1000 beans, we need to weigh out 5000 g of beans. This sample of beans, in which the beans have an average mass of 5.0 g, can be treated exactly like a sample where all of the beans are identical.

> Objects do not need to have identical masses to be counted by weighing. We simply need to know the average mass of the objects.

For purposes of counting, the objects *behave as though they were all identical,* as though they each actually had the average mass.

Averaging the Mass of Different Objects

Suppose a customer comes into the store and says, "I want to buy a bag of candy for each of my kids. One of them likes jelly beans and the other one likes mints. Please put a scoopful of jelly beans in a bag and a scoopful of mints in another bag." Then the customer recognizes a problem. "Wait! My kids will fight unless I bring home exactly the same number of candies for each one. Both bags must have the same number of pieces because they'll definitely count them and compare. But I'm really in a hurry, so we don't have time to count them here. Is there a simple way you can be sure the bags will contain the same number of candies?"

You need to solve this problem quickly. Suppose you know the average masses of the two kinds of candy:

Jelly beans: average mass = 5 g

Mints: average mass = 15 g

You fill the scoop with jelly beans and dump them onto the scale, which reads 500 g. Now the key question:

What mass of mints do you need to give the same number of mints as there are jelly beans in 500 g of jelly beans?

Comparing the average masses of the mints (15 g) and jelly beans (5 g), you realize that each mint has three times the mass of each jelly bean:

$$\frac{\text{average mass of mints}}{\text{average mass of jelly beans}} = \frac{15\ g}{5g} = 3$$

This means that you must weigh out an amount of mints that is three times the mass of the jelly beans:

$$3 \times 500\ g = 1500\ g$$

You weigh out 1500 g of mints and put them in a bag. The customer leaves with your assurance that both the bag containing 500 g of jelly beans and the bag containing 1500 g of mints contain the same number of candies.

In solving this problem, you have discovered a principle that is very important in chemistry:

> Two samples containing different types of components, A and B, both contain the same number of components if the ratio of the sample masses is the same as the ratio of the masses of the individual components of A and B.

6.1 • Atoms and Moles • **173**

Active Learning
Group Activity

You can demonstrate the jelly bean concept of counting by weighing by using a balance and small candy packages (such as M&Ms). Place the candies from one package on the balance. Have students determine the average mass per candy. Next, give students/groups a package and have them use the mass per candy to predict the number of candies in their package based on the package's net weight. Write the results on the board. Have students open the package and count the candies. Record the actual counts next to the predicted counts. Compare and discuss the differences. Enjoy the candy!

 TEACHING TIP

The concept of counting atoms from the mass of a sample is difficult for students to understand. Develop the idea slowly. Many students learn to work the problems without really understanding this section. Lack of understanding leads to trouble later when students try to solve more complex problems. Return to the candy analogy to assist in developing this concept. You can also use a hardware store analogy of buying nails by weight or a banking analogy of gathering coins into rolls by weighing them.

(continued)

change softens the center and hardens the shell. The driving force for this movement of water to the center is osmosis. The water flows toward the center, which is a more concentrated "solution" than the shell, to try to equalize the two concentrations. Osmosis also explains how pickles are made. When cucumbers are placed in a brine [NaCl(*aq*)] solution, water flows out of the cucumber into the brine, shrinking the cucumber into

a pickle. Water flows from the more dilute to the more concentrated solution.

Now that the curing process is understood, candy-makers hope to find a way to speed up the jelly bean manufacturing process so that they do not have to store the jelly beans for several days before shipping them.

The total mass of the sample and the average mass of the objects are needed to count by weighing.

6.1.B Atomic Masses: Counting Atoms by Weighing

Objective To understand atomic mass and its experimental determination

 TEACHING TIPS

- Even though students understand counting candy by weighing, it may be difficult for them to transfer the idea to counting atoms or molecules by mass. This concept seems much more abstract and confusing for them.

- Refer back to the candy analogy or activity in part A of this section. The average mass of a candy does not represent the mass of a particular candy. Similarly, the average mass of an atom does not represent the mass of an individual atom. This reasoning allows you to introduce the idea that atoms are slightly different in mass without developing the idea of isotopes at this time.

- The relative values of coins can be used as an analogy to relative masses. A penny has a relative value of 1, a nickel has a relative value of 5, and so on. Inflation, however, keeps these values from being absolute (in the past, for example, you could actually buy something with a penny!). Suppose the government phases out pennies in circulation. Then we could think of the nickel as having a relative value of 1, a dime having a relative value of 2, and a quarter having a relative value of 5.

 Active Reading Question

What information is needed in order to count by weighing?

A Closer Look

Let's look at the relationship between mass and number of components more closely by using our candy example. The individual candies have the masses 15 g (mints) and 5 g (jelly beans). Consider several cases.

1 Candy	10 Candies	100 Candies
15 g =	150 g =	1500 g =
	10 mints	100 mints
$(1 \text{ mint}) \times \left(\frac{15 \text{ g}}{\text{mint}}\right) = 15 \text{ g}$	$(10 \text{ mints}) \times \left(\frac{15 \text{ g}}{\text{mint}}\right) = 150 \text{ g}$	$(100 \text{ mints}) \times \left(\frac{15 \text{ g}}{\text{mint}}\right) = 1500 \text{ g}$
5 g =	50 g =	500 g =
	10 jelly beans	100 jelly beans
$(1 \text{ jelly bean}) \times \left(\frac{5 \text{ g}}{\text{jelly bean}}\right) = 5 \text{ g}$	$(10 \text{ jelly beans}) \times \left(\frac{5 \text{ g}}{\text{jelly bean}}\right) = 50 \text{ g}$	$(100 \text{ jelly beans}) \times \left(\frac{5 \text{ g}}{\text{jelly bean}}\right) = 500 \text{ g}$

READING TIP

Reading Math The division sign is read aloud as "per." For example, $15 \frac{\text{g}}{\text{mint}}$ is read aloud as "15 grams per mint."

Note in each case that the ratio of the masses is always 3 to 1,

$$\frac{15}{5} = \frac{150}{50} = \frac{1500}{500} = \frac{3}{1}$$

which is the ratio of the masses of the individual components:

Mass of mint/mass of jelly bean $= \frac{15}{5} = \frac{3}{1}$

Any two samples, one of mints and one of jelly beans, that have a mass ratio of 15/5 = 3/1 will contain the same number of components. And these same ideas apply also to atoms, as we will see below.

B. Atomic Masses: Counting Atoms by Weighing

The balanced chemical equation for the reaction of solid carbon and gaseous oxygen to form gaseous carbon dioxide is as follows:

$$C(s) + O_2(g) \rightarrow CO_2(g)$$

Now suppose you have a small pile of solid carbon and want to know how many oxygen molecules are required to convert all of this carbon into carbon dioxide. The balanced equation tells us that one oxygen molecule is required for each carbon atom.

C(s)	+	$O_2(g)$	$\rightarrow$	$CO_2(g)$
1 atom of carbon	reacts with	1 molecule of oxygen	to yield	1 molecule of carbon dioxide

174 • Chapter 6 • Chemical Composition

To determine the number of oxygen molecules required, we must know how many carbon atoms are present in the pile of carbon. But individual atoms are far too small to see. We must learn to count atoms by weighing samples containing large numbers of them.

Earlier we saw that we can easily count things like jelly beans and mints by weighing. Exactly the same principles can be applied to counting atoms.

Because atoms are so tiny, the normal units of mass—the gram and the kilogram—are much too large to be convenient. For example, the mass of a single carbon atom is 1.99×10^{-23} g. To avoid using terms like 10^{-23} when describing the mass of an atom, scientists have defined a much smaller unit of mass called the **atomic mass unit**, which is abbreviated **amu.** In terms of grams,

$$1 \text{ amu} = 1.66 \times 10^{-24} \text{ g}$$

Atomic mass unit (amu)
A small unit of mass equal to 1.66×10^{-24} grams

Counting Carbon Atoms To count carbon atoms by weighing, we need to know the mass of individual atoms, just as we needed to know the mass of the individual jelly beans. We learned from Chapter 3 that the atoms of a given element exist as isotopes.

The isotopes of carbon are $^{12}_{6}$C, $^{13}_{6}$C, and $^{14}_{6}$C. Any sample of carbon contains a mixture of these isotopes, always in the same proportions. Each of these isotopes has a slightly different mass. Therefore, just as with the non-identical jelly beans, we need to use an average mass for the carbon atoms.

The **average atomic mass** for carbon atoms is 12.01 amu. This means that any sample of carbon from nature can be treated as though it were composed of identical carbon atoms, each with a mass of 12.01 amu.

Average atomic mass
The weighted average of the masses of all the isotopes of an element

Calculating Mass

Now that we know the average mass of the carbon atom (12.01 amu), we can count carbon atoms by weighing samples of natural carbon. For example, what mass of natural carbon must we take to have 1000 carbon atoms present?

$$\text{Mass of 1000 natural carbon atoms} = (1000 \text{ atoms}) \frac{12.01 \text{ amu}}{\text{atom}}$$
$$= 12{,}010 \text{ amu}$$
$$= 1.201 \times 10^{4} \text{ amu}$$

information

Remember that 1000 is an exact number here.

Using Mass to Count Atoms Now let's assume that when we weigh the pile of natural carbon mentioned earlier, the result is 3.00×10^{20} amu. How many carbon atoms are present in this sample?

We know that an average carbon atom has the mass 12.01 amu, so we can compute the number of carbon atoms by using the equivalence statement

$$1 \text{ carbon atom} = 12.01 \text{ amu}$$

to construct the appropriate conversion factor,

$$\frac{1 \text{ carbon atom}}{12.01 \text{ amu}}$$

 TEACHING TIPS

- We introduce counting atoms by weighing using atomic mass units. Students are not familiar with these units. It helps to reassure students that soon we will be working with more familiar units (grams).

- It is also helpful to point out to students that someone has already measured the masses of atoms and that we have a table for average atomic masses as a result of that work (the periodic table).

- The idea that different samples with identical mass ratios contain the same number of objects is a difficult one for students. Consider using the following example.

Suppose we have two blocks: a red block and a yellow block. The red block weighs 1.0 ounce, and the yellow block weighs 4.0 ounces. Now suppose we have 16 of each color block. What is the mass of each sample? The sample of red blocks weighs 16.0 ounces and the sample of yellow blocks weighs 64.0 ounces. Note, however, that 16.0 ounces is also 1.0 pound, so 64.0 ounces is 4.0 pounds. The relative masses of the blocks are

	1 Block	16 Blocks
Red	1.0 ounce	1.0 pound
Yellow	4.0 ounces	4.0 pounds

The relative masses stay the same (1:4) but the units change.

You can draw an analogy between ounces and pounds in this case and atomic mass units and grams in the case of the periodic table. In the blocks example, the number 16 is analogous to Avogadro's number.

EXAMPLE 6.1

More Examples

1. Calculate the mass (in amu) of a sample of carbon that contains 62 atoms.

   744.6 amu

2. Calculate the mass (in amu) of a sample of iron that contains 15 atoms.

   837.8 amu

✅ **Answer to Practice Problem 6.1**

The average mass of nitrogen is 14.01 amu. The appropriate equivalence statement is 1 N atom = 14.01 amu, which yields the conversion factor we need:

$$23 \text{ N atoms} \underset{\text{(exact)}}{} \times \frac{14.01 \text{ amu}}{\text{N atoms}} =$$

$$322.2 \text{ amu}$$

The calculation is carried out as follows:

$$\underset{\text{mass of sample}}{3.00 \times 10^{20} \text{ amu}} \times \underset{\substack{\text{conversion} \\ \text{factor}}}{\frac{1 \text{ carbon atom}}{12.01 \text{ amu}}} = \underset{\substack{\text{Number of} \\ \text{atoms in sample}}}{2.50 \times 10^{19} \text{ carbon atoms}}$$

The principles we have just discussed for carbon apply to all the other elements as well. All the elements as found in nature typically consist of a mixture of various isotopes. Values for the average masses of the atoms of the elements are listed in Appendix H of this book.

To count the atoms in a sample of a given element by weighing, we must know the mass of the sample and the average mass for that element.

EXAMPLE 6.1

Calculating Mass Using Atomic Mass Units (amu)

Calculate the mass, in amu, of a sample of aluminum that contains 75 atoms.

Solution

Where do we want to go?

75 atoms Al → ? amu

What do we know?

* Mass (Al) = 26.98 amu

* 75 atoms Al

How do we get there?

We set up the equivalence statement

   1 Al atom = 26.98 amu

which gives the conversion factor we need:

$$75 \text{ Al atoms} \times \frac{26.98 \text{ amu}}{\text{Al atom}} = 2024 \text{ amu}$$

Does it make sense?

The correct unit for mass in this case is amu which we have in our answer (2024 amu). Our answer has 4 significant figures as required since the mass is 26.98 and 75 is an exact number.

✅ **Practice Problem • Exercise 6.1**

Calculate the mass of a sample that contains 23 nitrogen atoms.

The opposite calculation can also be carried out. That is, if we know the mass of a sample, we can determine the number of atoms present. This procedure is illustrated in Example 6.2.

Meeting Individual Needs

MATH CONCEPTS

If students need extra help with dimensional analysis, have them read *Dimensional Analysis* located in the *Teacher Resources*. A worksheet of practice problems is available to go along with the handout.

EXAMPLE 6.2

Calculating the Number of Atoms from the Mass

Calculate the number of sodium atoms present in a sample that has a mass of 1172.49 amu.

Solution

Where do we want to go?

1172.49 amu → atoms Na

What do we know?

- Mass (Na) = 1172.49 amu
- Average atomic mass (Na) = 22.99 amu

How do we get there?

The appropriate equivalence statement is

1 Na atom = 22.99 amu

which gives the conversion factor we need:

$$1172.49 \; \text{amu} \times \left(\frac{\text{Na atom}}{22.99 \; \text{amu}} \right) = 51.00 \; \text{Na atoms}$$

Does it make sense?

The correct unit for our answer in this case is atoms. Our answer (51.00 atoms) has 4 significant figures as required by the average mass of 22.99.

 Practice Problem • Exercise 6.2

Calculate the number of oxygen atoms in a sample that has a mass of 288 amu.

HANDS-ON CHEMISTRY • MINI-LAB •

Counting Pennies Without Counting

Materials

- sealed container with pennies
- empty container similar to the sealed container
- ten pennies
- balance

Procedure

1. Obtain a sample of pennies in a sealed container. Do not count the pennies.

2. Obtain an empty container that is similar to the one containing the pennies. Obtain one additional penny. Devise a method using a balance to determine the number of pennies in the sealed container without opening it. Determine the number of pennies in the sealed container.

3. Repeat step 2 using ten additional pennies instead of one penny. Use your method to determine the number of pennies in the sealed container.

4. Open the sealed container and count the pennies.

Results/Analysis

1. Which method (using one penny or ten pennies) allowed you to more accurately determine the number of pennies in the sealed container? Why? How does this finding relate to counting atoms by weighing?

6.1 • Atoms and Moles • **177**

 TEACHING TIP

You can use the Hands-On Chemistry activity, "Counting Pennies Without Counting," for a class discussion. Show that if we weigh all of the pennies and divide the result by the mass of one penny, the calculation of the total number of pennies is close, but incorrect. We need to determine an average mass for the pennies. This leads to a good discussion of isotopes if you wish to introduce that concept at this time.

EXAMPLE 6.2

More Examples

1. Calculate the number of copper atoms present in a sample that has a mass of 1779.4 amu.

   28.00 atoms

2. Calculate the number of argon atoms present in a sample that has a mass of 3755.3 amu.

   94.00 atoms

Answer to Practice Problem 6.2

The average mass of oxygen is 16.00 amu, which gives the equivalence statement 1 oxygen atom = 16.00 amu. The number of oxygen atoms present is

$$288 \; \text{amu} \times \frac{1 \; \text{oxygen atom}}{16.00 \; \text{amu}} =$$

18.0 oxygen atoms

Hands-On Chemistry
MINI-LAB

Counting Pennies Without Counting

Materials Each group will need a sealed container with a certain number of pennies (greater than 10), an empty container similar to the sealed one, 10 additional pennies, and a balance. Butter or margarine tubs work well.

Purpose Students will better understand the idea of counting by weighing, which is crucial in understanding the mole concept.

Discussion To determine the number of pennies, students must find the mass of the pennies in the tub. They can do so by subtracting the mass of the empty tub from the mass of the sealed tub with pennies, assuming that the tubs are similar in mass. They also need to find the average mass of a penny (they should compare the mass of one penny and the average mass of a penny from the sample of 10). Students then divide the total mass of pennies in the sealed tub by the average mass of a penny to determine the number of pennies in the sealed tub.

Students should be able to determine the number of pennies in the tub quite accurately. They should notice that using the average mass of 10 pennies gives a more accurate number. It is a good idea to place more than 10 pennies in the tub because the masses of pennies vary.

Objective To understand the mole concept and Avogadro's number and to learn to convert among moles, mass, and number of atoms in a given sample

LABORATORY EXPERIMENT 22:
Bean Lab, Traditional

TEACHING TIP

This section provides a bridge between amu units and grams. The reasoning used to explain the relative atomic masses on the periodic table is the concept of mass ratios, which was introduced in part A of this section. Students can memorize the definitions, but to ensure that they get a real understanding of the ideas presented here, proceed slowly using many examples.

C. The Mole

Earlier we used atomic mass units for mass, because atoms are so tiny. In the laboratory, a much larger unit, the gram, is the convenient unit for mass. Now we will learn to count atoms in samples with masses given in grams.

Masses with the Same Number of Atoms

What mass of copper contains the same number of atoms as 26.98 g of aluminum?

Where do we want to go?

| 26.98 g aluminum | ←— Contains the same number of atoms —→ | ? grams copper |

What do we know?

• Our Al sample has a mass of 26.98 g.

• Atomic masses for the elements in this problem:

  Al   26.98 amu

  Cu   63.55 amu

How do we get there?

• Which atom has the greater atomic mass, aluminum or copper?

  Copper

• If we have 26.98 g of Al, do we need more or less than 26.98 g Cu to have the same number of copper atoms as aluminum atoms?

  Each copper atom has a greater mass than each aluminum atom. We will need more mass of copper than aluminum for the same number of atoms.

• How much copper do we need?

  The average atomic masses for the elements are:

  Al   26.98 g
  Cu   63.55 g

  These masses contain the same number of atoms.
  We need 63.55 g of copper.

Does it make sense?

The mass of copper found is greater than the mass of aluminum. This makes sense because a copper atom has a greater mass than an aluminum atom.

Earlier we learned that samples in which the ratio of the masses is the same as the ratio of the masses of the individual atoms always contain the same number of atoms. In the case just considered, the ratios are

$$\frac{26.98\text{g}}{63.55\text{g}} = \frac{26.98 \text{ amu}}{63.55 \text{ amu}}$$

Ratio of   =   Ratio of
sample masses   atomic masses

Moles and Molecules
Materials
• Four 500-mL beakers
• Sugar
• Sulfur
• Water

Procedure Place the following in separate, labeled beakers:

18 mL water (labeled 1 mol water)

342 g sugar (labeled 1 mol sugar)

256 g sulfur (labeled 1 mol sulfur)

342 mL water (labeled 342 g water)

Show students the beakers, each containing one mole. Note differences in mass and volume. Note that the number of molecules (6.022×10^{23}) is the same in each case.

Now use the beaker containing sugar and the one containing 342 g water.

Emphasize that they have the same mass. Ask students how the numbers of molecules in the beakers compare. The sugar contains 6.022×10^{23} molecules, and the water contains $19(6.022 \times 10^{23})$ = 1.14×10^{25} molecules of water.

Extending the Idea Ask students to determine the ratio of the number of molecules in the sugar beaker to the number of molecules in the water beaker (342 g). How does this ratio compare to the ratio of moles of sugar to water?

Therefore, 26.98 g of aluminum contains the same number of aluminum atoms as 63.55 g of copper contains copper atoms.

> **Active Reading Question**
>
> **What mass of copper has the same number of atoms as 40.47 g of aluminum?**

Defining the Mole

Now compare silver (average atomic mass, 107.9 amu) and lead (average atomic mass, 207.2 amu). A sample of 107.9 g of silver contains the same number of atoms as 207.2 g of lead.

	Silver (Ag)	Lead (Pb)
Average atomic mass of this element	107.9 amu	207.2 amu
Mass of this sample	107.9 g	207.2 g
Number of atoms in this sample	6.022×10^{23} atoms	6.022×10^{23} atoms

In fact, if we weigh out samples of all the elements such that each sample has a mass equal to that element's average atomic mass in grams, these samples all contain the same number of atoms. This number (the number of atoms present in all of these samples) assumes special importance in chemistry. It is called the mole, the unit all chemists use in describing numbers of atoms.

The **mole** (abbreviated **mol**) can be defined as *the number equal to the number of carbon atoms in 12.01 grams of carbon.*

Techniques for counting atoms very precisely have been used to determine this number to be 6.022×10^{23}. This number is called **Avogadro's number**.

> One mole of something consists of 6.022×10^{23} units of that substance.

Just as a dozen eggs is 12 eggs, a mole of eggs is 6.022×10^{23} eggs. And a mole of water contains 6.022×10^{23} H_2O molecules.

The magnitude of the number 6.022×10^{23} is very difficult to imagine. To give you some idea, 1 mol of seconds represents a span of time 4 million times as long as the earth has already existed! One mole of marbles is enough to cover the entire earth to a depth of 50 miles! However, because atoms are so tiny, a mole of atoms or molecules is a perfectly manageable quantity to use in a reaction.

> **Mole**
> The number equal to the number of carbon atoms in exactly 12 grams of pure ^{12}C: Avogadro's number. One mole represents 6.022×10^{23} units.
>
> **Avogadro's number**
> The number of atoms in exactly 12 grams of pure ^{12}C, equal to 6.022×10^{23}

Meeting Individual Needs
MATH CONCEPTS

Avogadro's number is written in scientific notation. If students need to review this, have them read *Scientific Notation* in the *Teacher Resources*. A worksheet of practice problems is available to go along with the handout.

 TEACHING TIPS

- It is important for students to realize that a mole describes the number of objects present, just as a dozen means 12. This connection between a mole as a number and the mass of a sample is essential because we count atoms by weighing samples containing large numbers of moles.

- The mole is a crucial concept in this chapter. An understanding of it is important for many topics later in the course.

- We define the mole differently than the following SI definition: *The mole is the amount of substance that contains as many entities as there are in exactly 0.012 kg of carbon 12.* Our definition is *the mole is the number equal to the number of carbon atoms in 12.01 g of carbon.* We believe that our definition is easier for students to understand at this point. It more strongly emphasizes both that the mole is a number and that the periodic table contains average atomic masses.

- Make sure students understand that *mol* means mole, not molecule.

- Some students memorize the equivalence statement as 1 mol = 6.022×10^{-23} presumably because chemistry deals with many small numbers (diameter of an atom, mass of a proton, etc.). Students must understand that Avogadro's number references the number of atoms or molecules in a sample; therefore, a mole must be larger than 1. Review scientific notation and emphasize that 1 mol = 6.022×10^{23}.

 Active Learning
Classroom Activities and Projects

Have students construct a "bean bag mole." See *Design a Mole* located in the *Teacher Resources*.

6×10^{23} seconds is about 2×10^{20} hours (keeping track of significant figures) or about 2×10^{16} years. Thus the hourly wage is approximately 5×10^{-15} dollars/hour. Earning a penny would require on the order of hundreds of millions of years. In short, it would be impossible. Calculations such as these should help students appreciate the magnitude of the mole.

MINI-DEMO

Bring a dozen eggs, a gross of pencils, and a ream of paper to class. Show students the eggs and ask students to determine how many eggs are in five dozen. Have a student explain how he or she got the answer. Do a similar thing with the pencils and the paper. Once students are familiar with calculating the number of objects of a given type, write the number of objects in a mole on the board. Ask students to determine how many atoms of aluminum are in a mole of aluminum. Repeat this idea with different elements and amounts. Make sure students understand that the process used is the same regardless of the unit.

 TEACHING TIPS

• Students do not need to memorize the average atomic masses of elements. These masses are given in the periodic table.

• Have students recall the jelly bean analogy from part A of this section.

What if you were offered $1 million to count from 1 to 6×10^{23} at a rate of one number each second? Determine your hourly wage. Would you do it?

Using the Mole

How do we use the mole in chemical calculations? Recall that Avogadro's number is defined such that a sample of *any* element that weighs a number of grams equal to the average atomic mass of that element contains 6.022×10^{23} atoms (1 mol) of that element. For example:

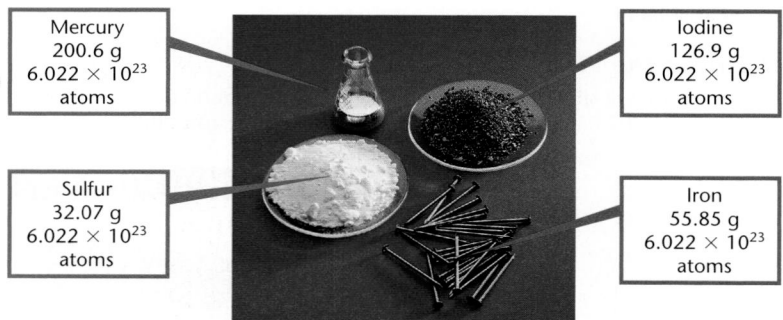

Mercury 200.6 g 6.022×10^{23} atoms

Iodine 126.9 g 6.022×10^{23} atoms

Sulfur 32.07 g 6.022×10^{23} atoms

Iron 55.85 g 6.022×10^{23} atoms

Table 6.1 shows the masses of several elements that contain 1 mol of atoms.

A sample of an element with a mass equal to that element's average atomic mass expressed in grams contains 1 mol of atoms.

ℹ️ nformation

Avogadro's number (to four significant figures) is 6.022×10^{23}. One mole of anything is 6.022×10^{23} units of that substance.

Table 6.1
Comparison of 1-Mol Samples of Various Elements

Element	Number of Atoms Present	Mass of Sample (g)
Aluminum	6.022×10^{23}	26.98
Gold	6.022×10^{23}	196.97
Iron	6.022×10^{23}	55.85
Sulfur	6.022×10^{23}	32.07
Boron	6.022×10^{23}	10.81
Xenon	6.022×10^{23}	131.3

A Closer Look

To do chemical calculations, you must

• understand what the mole means

• determine the number of moles in a given mass of a substance

However, before we do any calculations, let's be sure that the process of counting by weighing is clear.

Consider the "bag" of H atoms (symbolized by dots in the green circle), which contains 1 mol (6.022×10^{23}) of H atoms and has a mass of 1.008 g. Assume the bag itself has no mass (**Sample A).**

Teaching Support
HISTORICAL NOTE

Naming the number 6.022×10^{23} as Avogadro's number honors Amadeo Avogadro (1776–1856), the Italian chemist who first realized that equal volumes of gases at the same pressure and temperature contain equal numbers of particles (atoms or molecules). This idea, known as Avogadro's hypothesis, was advanced by Avogadro in 1811 but went unnoticed for about half a century. It was

not until 1860, after Avogadro's death, that another Italian chemist, Stanislao Cannizzaro, used Avogadro's hypothesis to determine the molar masses of several compounds and proved the correctness of Avogadro's idea.

Have students investigate the lives and careers of Avogadro and Cannizzaro to understand more fully their monumental contributions to chemistry.

Now consider another "bag" of hydrogen atoms in which the number of hydrogen atoms is unknown **(Sample B).**

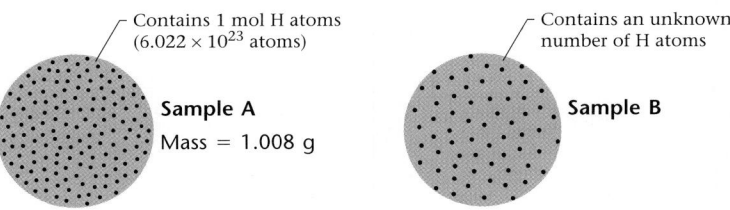

Contains 1 mol H atoms
(6.022×10^{23} atoms)

Sample A

Mass = 1.008 g

Contains an unknown
number of H atoms

Sample B

We want to find out how many H atoms are present in Sample ("bag") B. How can we do that? We can do it by weighing the sample. We find the mass of Sample B to be 0.500 g.

How does this measured mass help us determine the number of atoms in Sample B? We know that 1 mol of H atoms has a mass of 1.008 g. Sample B has a mass of 0.500 g, which is approximately half the mass of a mole of H atoms.

Sample A	
Mass = 1.008 g	

Contains 1 mol
of H atoms

Sample B	
Mass = 0.500 g	

Must contain about
1/2 mol of H atoms

We carry out the calculation by using the equivalence statement

1 mol H atoms = 1.008 g H

to construct the conversion factor we need:

$$0.500 \text{ g H} \times \frac{1 \text{ mol H}}{1.008 \text{ g H}} = 0.496 \text{ mol H in Sample B}$$

mass of   ×   conversion   =   number of moles
Sample B   factor   in Sample B

Let's summarize. We know the mass of 1 mol of H atoms, so we can determine the number of moles of H atoms in any other sample of pure hydrogen by weighing the sample and *comparing* its mass to 1.008 g (the mass of 1 mol of H atoms). We can follow this same process for any element, because we know the mass of 1 mol for each of the elements.

Also, because we know that 1 mol is 6.022×10^{23} units, once we know the *moles* of atoms present, we can easily determine the *number* of atoms present. In the case considered above, we have approximately 0.5 mol of H atoms in Sample B. This means that about $\frac{1}{2}$ of 6×10^{23}, or 3×10^{23}, H atoms are present. We carry out the actual calculation by using the equivalence statement

1 mol = 6.022×10^{23}

to determine the conversion factor we need:

$$0.496 \text{ mol H atoms} \times \frac{6.022 \times 10^{23} \text{ H atoms}}{1 \text{ mol H atoms}}$$

$$= 2.99 \times 10^{23} \text{ H atoms in Sample B}$$

These procedures are illustrated in Example 6.3.

CRITICAL THINKING ?

What if you discovered Avogadro's number was not 6.02×10^{23} but 3.01×10^{23}? Would your discovery affect the relative masses given on the periodic table? If so, how? If not, why not?

Active Learning
Group Activity

Bring a balance and samples of several elements to class. Weigh a sample of an element. Have students determine the number of moles and the number of atoms or molecules in the sample.

Remind students to express their answers in scientific notation with correct significant figures. This effort helps students remember that these considerations are important for every problem in chemistry.

CRITICAL THINKING ?

The value of Avogadro's number does not affect the relative masses of the atoms in elements. Regardless of the value of Avogadro's number, the mass of an average carbon atom is always approximately 12 times as great as the mass of an average hydrogen atom.

EXAMPLE 6.3

More Examples

1. Calculate the number of moles of atoms and the number of atoms in a 25.0-g sample of calcium.

   0.624 mol Ca;
   3.76×10^{23} Ca atoms

2. Calculate the number of moles of atoms and the number of atoms in a 57.7-g sample of sulfur.

   1.80 mol S;
   1.08×10^{24} S atoms

🍎 TEACHING TIP

Either Avogadro's number or atomic masses can limit the number of significant figures in a result. Make sure students recognize that these numbers are not exact.

EXAMPLE 6.3

Calculating Moles and Number of Atoms

A bicycle with an aluminum frame

Aluminum (Al), a metal with a high strength-to-weight ratio and a high resistance to corrosion, is often used for structures such as high-quality bicycle frames. Compute both the number of moles of atoms and the number of atoms in a 10.0-g sample of aluminum.

Solution
Where do we want to go?

| 10.0 g Al | $\Rightarrow$ | ? moles of Al atoms |

What do we know?
- The mass of 1 mol (6.022×10^{23} atoms) of aluminum is 26.98 g.
- The sample we are considering has a mass of 10.0 g.

How do we get there?

We calculate the number of moles of aluminum atoms in 10.0 g by using the equivalence statement

$$1 \text{ mol Al} = 26.98 \text{ g Al}$$

to construct the appropriate conversion factor,

$$10.0 \ \cancel{\text{g Al}} = \frac{1 \text{ mol Al}}{26.98 \ \cancel{\text{g Al}}} = 0.371 \text{ mol Al}$$

Next we convert from moles of atoms to the number of atoms, using the equivalence statement

$$6.022 \times 10^{23} \text{ Al atoms} = 1 \text{ mol Al atoms}$$

We have

$$0.371 \ \cancel{\text{mol Al}} \times \frac{6.022 \times 10^{23} \text{ Al atoms}}{1 \ \cancel{\text{mol Al}}} = 2.23 \times 10^{23} \text{ Al atoms}$$

We can summarize this calculation as follows:

| 10.0 g Al | $\times \frac{1 \text{ mol}}{26.98 \text{ g}}$ | $\Rightarrow$ | 0.371 mol Al |

| 0.371 mol Al | $\times \frac{6.022 \times 10^{23} \text{ Al atoms}}{\text{mol}}$ | $\Rightarrow$ | 2.23×10^{23} Al atoms |

Does it make sense?

Since 10 g is smaller than 26.98 g (the mass of 1 mol), we should have fewer than 6.022×10^{23} Al atoms. Our answer is 2.23×10^{23} Al atoms which makes sense.

Meeting Individual Needs
ENGLISH LANGUAGE LEARNERS

To help explain conversions, ask ELL students about the types of currency used in their native countries. Ask students to find a currency conversion chart for their currency type to U.S. dollars. Help students convert from their currency into U.S. dollars and vice versa.

EXAMPLE 6.4

Calculating the Number of Atoms

A silicon chip used in an integrated circuit of a computer has a mass of 5.68 mg. How many silicon (Si) atoms are present in this chip? The average atomic mass for silicon is 28.09 amu.

A silicon chip of the type used in electronic equipment

Solution

Where do we want to go?

Our strategy for doing this problem is to convert from milligrams of silicon to grams of silicon, then to moles of silicon, and finally to atoms of silicon:

| Milligrams of Si atoms | ⇨ | Grams of Si atoms | ⇨ | Moles of Si atoms | ⇨ | Number of Si atoms |

What do we know?

- Our sample has a mass of 5.68 mg.

- The atomic mass for silicon is 28.09 amu.

How do we get there?

Each arrow in the schematic represents a conversion factor. Using 1 g = 1000 mg, we can convert the mass to grams.

$$5.68 \text{ mg Si} \times \frac{1 \text{g Si}}{1000 \text{ mg Si}} = 5.68 \times 10^{-3} \text{ g Si}$$

Next, because the average mass of silicon is 28.09 amu, we know that 1 mol of Si atoms weighs 28.09 g. This leads to the equivalence statement

1 mol Si = 28.09 g Si

Thus,

$$5.68 \times 10^{-3} \text{ g Si} \times \frac{1 \text{ mol Si}}{28.09 \text{ g Si}} = 2.02 \times 10^{-4} \text{ mol Si}$$

Using the definition of a mole (1 mol = 6.022×10^{23}), we have

$$2.02 \times 10^{-4} \text{ mol Si} \times \frac{6.022 \times 10^{23} \text{ atoms}}{1 \text{ mol Si}} = 1.22 \times 10^{20} \text{ Si atoms}$$

We can summarize this calculation as follows:

| 5.68 mg Si $\times \dfrac{1 \text{ g}}{1000 \text{ mg}}$ | ➡ | 5.68×10^{-3} g Si |

| 5.68×10^{-3} g Si $\times \dfrac{1 \text{ mol}}{28.09 \text{ g}}$ | ➡ | 2.02×10^{-4} mol Si |

| 2.02×10^{-4} mol Si $\times \dfrac{6.022 \times 10^{23} \text{ Si atoms}}{\text{mol}}$ | ➡ | 1.22×10^{20} Si atoms |

Does it make sense?

Because 5.68 mg is much smaller than 28.09 g (the mass of 1 mol Si), we expect the number of atoms to be less than 6.022×10^{23}. So our answer 1.22×10^{20} Si atoms makes sense.

6.1 • Atoms and Moles • **183**

The sample of 5.00×10^{20} atoms of chromium contains less than 1 mol (6.022×10^{23} atoms) of chromium. The fraction of a mole that it represents can be determined as follows:

$$5.00 \times 10^{20} \; \text{atoms Cr} \times \frac{1 \; \text{mol Cr}}{6.022 \times 10^{23} \; \text{atoms Cr}} = 8.30 \times 10^{-4} \; \text{mol Cr}$$

Because the mass of 1 mol of chromium atoms is 52.00 g, the mass of 5.00×10^{20} atoms can be determined as follows:

$$8.30 \times 10^{-4} \; \text{mol Cr} \times \frac{52.00 \; \text{g Cr}}{1 \; \text{mol Cr}} = 4.32 \times 10^{-2} \; \text{g Cr}$$

SECTION 6.1
ASSESS

SECTION 6.1
Review Questions

1. Count out 10 nuts and 10 bolts. Weigh each sample and divide by 10 to find the average mass of a nut and the average mass of a bolt. Then multiply each average mass by 1200 to find the correct amount to be weighed out. Weigh out these amounts and deliver the nuts and bolts to the waiting customer.

2. Not all atoms of a given element have identical masses. Therefore the average atomic mass of an element is not a whole number.

3. a. 1 mol = 6.022×10^{23} units

   b. The possible conversion factors are

   $$\frac{1 \; \text{mol}}{6.022 \times 10^{23} \; \text{units}}$$

   and

   $$\frac{6.022 \times 10^{23} \; \text{units}}{1 \; \text{mol}}$$

   c. The correct conversion factors are

   $$\frac{6.022 \times 10^{23} \; \text{atoms Al}}{1 \; \text{mol}}$$

   and

   $$\frac{1 \; \text{mol}}{6.022 \times 10^{23} \; \text{atoms Au}}$$

Practice Problem • Exercise 6.4

Chromium (Cr) is a metal that is added to steel to improve its resistance to corrosion (for example, to make stainless steel). Calculate both the number of moles in a sample of chromium containing 5.00×10^{20} atoms and the mass of the sample.

information

The values for the average masses of the atoms of the elements are listed in the inside front cover of this book.

Using Units in Problem Solving When you finish a problem, always think about the "reasonableness" of your answer.

In Example 6.4, 5.68 mg of silicon is clearly much less than 1 mol of silicon (which has a mass of 28.09 g), so the final answer of 1.22×10^{20} atoms (compared to 6.022×10^{23} atoms in a mole) at least lies in the right direction. That is, 1.22×10^{20} atoms is a smaller number than 6.022×10^{23}.

Always include the units as you do calculations and make sure the correct units are obtained at the end. Paying careful attention to units and making this type of general check can help you find errors such as an inverted conversion factor or a number that was incorrectly entered into your calculator.

SECTION 6.1
REVIEW QUESTIONS

1. Suppose you work in a hardware store. The manager asks you to fill an order for an important customer who is waiting impatiently. You need 1200 matched sets of nuts and bolts. Unfortunately the nuts and bolts are not boxed—they are loose in big buckets. How can you earn a bonus from your boss and make the customer happy by filling the order in less than 2 minutes?

2. Why is the average atomic mass of any element not a whole number (for example, C, 12 amu; H, 1 amu; N, 14 amu)?

3. A mole of any substance contains Avogadro's number of units.

   a. Write an equivalence statement for this definition.

   b. Write the possible conversion factors from this relationship.

   c. To determine the following, tell which conversion factor you would need to use:
   • Moles Al from atoms Al
   • Atoms Au from mol Au

4. Copy and complete the following table.

Mass of Sample	Moles of Sample	Atoms in Sample
	0.250 mol Al	
25.4 g Fe		
		2.13×10^{24} atoms Au
	1.28 mol Ca	
4.28 mg Na		
		3.14×10^{23} atoms C

5. Which sample contains more atoms: 3.89 g of nickel or 6.61 g of silver? Defend your answer.

RESEARCH LINKS
CLASSZONE.COM

4.

Mass of Sample	Moles of Sample	Atoms in Sample
6.7 g Al	0.250 mol Al	1.51×10^{23} atoms Al
25.4 g Fe	0.455 mol Fe	2.74×10^{23} atoms Fe
697 g Au	3.54 mol Au	2.13×10^{24} atoms Au
51.3 g Ca	1.28 mol Ca	7.71×10^{23} atoms Ca
4.28 mg Na	1.86×10^{-4} mol Na	1.12×10^{20} atoms Na
6.26 g C	0.521 mol C	3.14×10^{23} atoms C

5. The nickel sample contains more atoms. There are 0.066 mol nickel atoms (3.89/58.69) and 0.062 mol silver atoms (6.61/107.9).

Molar Mass and Percent Composition

Objectives

- *To understand the definition of molar mass*
- *To learn to convert between moles and mass*
- *To learn to mass percent of an element in a compound*

Key Terms
- Molar mass
- Mass percent

A. Molar Mass

A chemical compound is, fundamentally, a collection of atoms. For example, methane (the major component of natural gas) consists of molecules each containing one carbon atom and four hydrogen atoms (CH_4).

1 CH_4 molecule → 1 C atom   4 H atoms

How can we calculate the mass of 1 mol of methane? That is, what is the mass of 6.022×10^{23} CH_4 molecules? Because each CH_4 molecule contains one carbon atom and four hydrogen atoms, 1 mol of CH_4 molecules consists of 1 mol of carbon atoms and 4 mol of hydrogen atoms (see **Figure 6.1**). The mass of 1 mol of methane can be found by summing the masses of carbon and hydrogen present:

$$
\begin{aligned}
\text{Mass of 1 mol of C} &= 1 \times 12.01 \text{ g} = 12.01 \text{ g}\\
\text{Mass of 4 mol of H} &= 4 \times 1.008 \text{ g} = \underline{4.032 \text{ g}}\\
\text{Mass of 1 mol of } CH_4 &= 16.04 \text{ g}
\end{aligned}
$$

> ### information
> Note that when we say 1 mol of methane, we mean 1 mol of methane *molecules.*

> ### MATH
> Remember that the least number of decimal places limits the number of significant figures in addition.

10 CH_4 molecules → 10 C atoms   40 H atoms

1 **mol** CH_4 molecules (6.022×10^{23} CH_4 molecules) →
- 1 **mol** C atoms (6.022×10^{23} C atoms)
- 4 **mol** H atoms $4 (6.022 \times 10^{23}$ H atoms)

Figure 6.1
Various numbers of methane molecules showing their constituent atoms

---

SECTION 6.2
INTRODUCE

Student Preparation

Assign students to read Section 6.2 and to answer the Review Questions at the end of the section before coming to class.

Active Learning
Team Learning Worksheet

After introducing the material in Section 6.2 in class, place students in groups and have them work together on **Section 6.2: Team Learning Worksheet.**

SECTION 6.2
GUIDE THE LEARNING

Homework

You may wish to assign these selected end-of-chapter problems as homework for this section: 18, 19a–c, 20a–c, 21, 23, 25a–c, 26a–c

Additional end-of-chapter problems can be used for extra practice.

6.2.A Molar Mass

Objective To understand the definition of molar mass and to learn to convert between moles and mass of a given sample of a chemical compound

TEACHING TIPS

- Some students find it difficult to translate a formula into moles at this point. For example, 1 mol of methane molecules contains 4 mol of hydrogen atoms. Make sure students practice this translation and justify their answers.

- Emphasize that molar mass is the mass per one mole of substance. For example, one mole of diatomic oxygen gas has a mass of 32.00 g. A sample containing two moles of oxygen gas has a mass of 64.00 g.

TECHNOLOGY
Figure 6.1

Active Reading Question

To calculate the molar mass, add together the masses of the atoms in the compound. For example, the molar mass of water (H_2O) is calculated by adding the masses of the two hydrogen atoms (2×1.008) to the mass of the oxygen atom (16.00) to get 18.016.

EXAMPLE 6.5

More Examples

Here are some additional examples to use for molar mass calculations. Each answer has been rounded to four significant figures.

Water	H_2O	18.02 g/mol
Ammonia	NH_3	17.03 g/mol
C_3H_8	propane	44.09 g/mol
$C_6H_{12}O_6$	glucose	180.2 g/mol

Molar mass
The mass in grams of 1 mole of the substance

The quantity 16.04 g is called the molar mass for methane: the mass of 1 mol of CH_4 molecules. The **molar mass** of any substance is the *mass (in grams) of 1 mol of the substance.*

The molar mass is obtained by summing the masses of the component atoms.

Active Reading Question

Explain how to calculate the molar mass of a compound and give an example.

EXAMPLE 6.5

Calculating Molar Mass

Calculate the molar mass of sulfur dioxide, a gas produced when sulfur-containing fuels are burned. Unless "scrubbed" from the exhaust, sulfur dioxide can react with moisture in the atmosphere to produce acid rain.

information

A substance's molar mass (in grams) is the mass of 1 mol of that substance.

Solution
Where do we want to go?

Molar mass (SO_2) → ? g/mol

What do we know?

• The formula for sulfur dioxide is SO_2

• Atomic masses
  S = 32.07 g/mol
  O = 16.00 g/mol

How do we get there?
We need to find the mass of 1 mol of SO_2 molecules—the molar mass for sulfur dioxide.

Mass of 1 mol of S = $1 \times 32.07 = 32.07$ g
Mass of 2 mol of O = $2 \times 16.00 = \underline{32.00}$ g

Mass of 1 mol of SO_2 = 64.07 g = molar mass = 64.07 g/mol

The molar mass of SO_2 is 64.07 g. It represents the mass of 1 mol of SO_2 molecules.

Does it make sense?
Note the units obtained here (g/mol) are correct for molar mass. The answer is given to two decimal places as required by the atomic masses.

Here are some additional examples to use for molar mass calculations for ionic compounds. They can also be used to review naming ionic compounds. Each answer has been rounded to four significant figures.

Calcium sulfate	$CaSO_4$	136.2 g/mol
Sodium carbonate	Na_2CO_3	106.0 g/mol
Barium hydroxide	$Ba(OH)_2$	171.3 g/mol

Practice Problem • Exercise 6.5

Polyvinyl chloride, called PVC, which is widely used for floor coverings ("vinyl") as well as for plastic pipes in plumbing systems, is made from a molecule with the formula C_2H_3Cl. Calculate the molar mass of this substance.

Some substances exist as a collection of ions rather than as separate molecules. For example, ordinary table salt, sodium chloride (NaCl), is composed of an array of Na^+ and Cl^- ions. There are no NaCl molecules present. In some books the term *formula weight* is used instead of *molar mass* for ionic compounds. However, in this book we will apply the term *molar mass* to both ionic and molecular substances.

To calculate the molar mass for sodium chloride, we must realize that 1 mol of NaCl contains 1 mol of Na^+ ions and 1 mol of Cl^- ions.

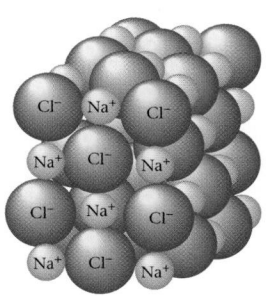

Therefore, the molar mass (in grams) for sodium chloride represents the sum of the mass of 1 mol of sodium ions and the mass of 1 mol of chloride ions.

Mass of 1 mol of Na^+ = 22.99 g
Mass of 1 mol of Cl^- = 35.45 g
Mass of 1 mol of NaCl = 58.44 g = molar mass

The molar mass of NaCl is 58.44 g. It represents the mass of 1 mol of sodium chloride.

EXAMPLE 6.6

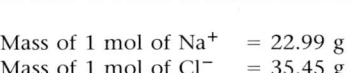

Calculating Mass from Moles

Calcium carbonate, $CaCO_3$ (also called calcite), is the principal mineral found in limestone, marble, chalk, pearls, and the shells of marine animals such as clams.

   a. Calculate the molar mass of calcium carbonate.

   b. A certain sample of calcium carbonate contains 4.86 mol. What is the mass in grams of this sample?

Solution
a. Where do we want to go?

   Molar mass ($CaCO_3$) = ? g/mol

   What do we know?

- The formula for calcium carbonate is $CaCO_3$.

- Atomic masses
    Ca = 40.08 g/mol
    C = 12.01 g/mol
    O = 16.00 g/mol

6.2 • Molar Mass and Percent Composition • **187**

Answer to Practice Problem 6.5

Each molecule of C_2H_3Cl contains two carbon atoms, three hydrogen atoms, and one chlorine atom. Thus 1 mol of C_2H_3Cl molecules contains 2 mol of C atoms, 3 mol of H atoms, and 1 mol of Cl atoms.

Mass of 2 mol of C atoms:
  $2 \times 12.01 = 24.02$ g

Mass of 3 mol of H atoms:
  $3 \times 1.008 = 3.024$ g

Mass of 1 mol of Cl atoms:
  $1 \times 35.45 = \underline{35.45\ g}$
          62.494 g

The molar mass of C_2H_3Cl is 62.49 g (rounding to the correct number of significant figures).

TEACHING TIP

Students should not round off atomic masses when calculating molar masses, for example, by using 1 for hydrogen and 12 for carbon. If students develop this habit now, they will have trouble obtaining the correct answer to stoichiometry problems later in the course.

EXAMPLE 6.6

More Examples

1. Calculate the mass of 1.48 mol of potassium oxide.
    139 g (K_2O)

2. Calculate the mass of 4.85 mol of acetic acid, $HC_2H_3O_2$. Vinegar is a dilute solution of acetic acid.
    291 g

i n f o r m a t i o n

The mass of the electron is so small that Na^+ and Na have the same mass for our purposes, even though Na^+ has one electron less than Na. Also, the mass of Cl virtually equals the mass of Cl^- even though it has one more electron than Cl.

Answer to Practice Problem 6.6

The formula for sodium sulfate is Na_2SO_4. One mol of Na_2SO_4 contains 2 mol of sodium ions and 1 mol of sulfate ions.

1 mol of $Na_2SO_4 \rightarrow$

Na^+ SO_4^{2-} Na^+

2 mol Na^+

1 mol SO_4^{2-}

Mass of 2 mol of Na^+ =

$2 \times 22.99 = 45.98$ g

Mass of 1 mol of SO_4^{2-} =

$32.07 + 4(16.00) = 96.07$ g

45.98 g $+ 96.07$ g $= 142.05$ g

The molar mass for sodium sulfate is 142.05 g.

A sample of sodium sulfate with a mass of 300.0 g represents more than 1 mol. (Compare 300.0 g to the molar mass of Na_2SO_4.) We calculate the number of moles of Na_2SO_4 present in 300.0 g as follows:

$3.00 \text{ g } Na_2SO_4 \times \dfrac{1 \text{ mol } Na_2SO_4}{142.05 \text{ g } Na_2SO_4} =$

$2.112 \text{ mol } Na_2SO_4$

How do we get there?

Calcium carbonate is an ionic compound composed of Ca^{2+} and CO_3^{2-} ions. One mole of calcium carbonate contains 1 mol of Ca^{2+} and 1 mol of CO_3^{2-} ions. We calculate the molar mass by summing the masses of the components.

Mass of 1 mol of Ca^{2+} $= 1 \times 40.08$ g $= 40.08$ g

Mass of 1 mol of CO_3^{2-} (contains 1 mol of C and 3 mol of O):

    1 mol of C $= 1 \times 12.01$ g $= 12.01$ g

    3 mol of O $= 3 \times 16.00$ g $= \underline{48.00 \text{ g}}$

              Mass of 1 mol of $CaCO_3 = 100.09$ g = molar mass

Does it make sense?

Note the units obtained here (g/mol) are correct for molar mass. The answer is given to two decimal places as required by the atomic masses.

b. **Where do we want to go?**

    Mass of 4.86 mol $CaCO_3$ = ? g

What do we know?

- Molar mass $CaCO_3 = 100.09$ g/mol
- Moles $CaCO_3 = 4.86$ mol

How do we get there?

We determine the mass of 4.86 mol of $CaCO_3$ by using the molar mass,

$$4.86 \text{ mol } CaCO_3 \times \frac{100.09 \text{ g } CaCO_3}{1 \text{ mol } CaCO_3} = 486 \text{ g } CaCO_3$$

which can be diagrammed as follows:

| 4.86 mol $CaCO_3$ | $\times$ | $\dfrac{100.09 \text{ g}}{\text{mol}}$ | $\Rightarrow$ | 486 g $CaCO_3$ |

Does it make sense?

Note that this sample contains nearly 5 mol and thus should have a mass of nearly 500 g (since the molar mass is about 100 g) so our answer makes sense. The number of significant figures in our answer (486 g) is three as required by the initial moles (4.86).

✔ Practice Problem • Exercise 6.6

Calculate the molar mass for sodium sulfate, Na_2SO_4. A sample of sodium sulfate with a mass of 300.0 g represents what number of moles of sodium sulfate?

ℹ nformation

For average atomic masses, look inside the front cover of this book.

Let's Review

- The molar mass of a substance can be obtained by summing the masses of the component atoms.

- The molar mass (in grams) represents the mass of 1 mol of the substance.

- Once we know the molar mass of a compound, we can compute the number of moles present in a sample of known mass.

EXAMPLE 6.7

Calculating Moles from Mass

Juglone, a dye known for centuries, is produced from the husks of black walnuts. It is also a natural herbicide (weed killer) that kills off competitive plants around the black walnut tree but does not affect grass and other noncompetitive plants. The formula for juglone is $C_{10}H_6O_3$.

a. Calculate the molar mass of juglone.

b. A sample of 1.56 g of pure juglone was extracted from black walnut husks. How many moles of juglone does this sample represent?

Juglone, a natural herbicide, is produced from the husks of black walnuts.

Solution

a. Where do we want to go?

Molar mass (juglone) = ? g/mol

What do we know?

• The formula for juglone is $C_{10}H_6O_3$.

• Atomic masses

C = 12.01 g/mol   H = 1.008 g/mol   O = 16.00 g/mol

How do we get there?

The molar mass is obtained by summing the masses of the component atoms.

$$\begin{matrix} 1\ \text{mol} \\ \text{juglone} \\ C_{10}H_6O_3 \end{matrix} \rightarrow \begin{matrix} 10\ \text{mol C} \\ 6\ \text{mol H} \\ 3\ \text{mol O} \end{matrix}$$

Mass of 10 mol C = 10 × 12.01 g = 120.1 g

Mass of 6 mol H = 6 × 1.008 g =   6.048 g

Mass of 3 mol O = 3 × 16.00 g = 48.00 g

Mass of 1 mol $C_{10}H_6O_3$ = 174.1 g = molar mass = 174.1 g/mol

Does it make sense?

Note the units obtained here (g/mol) are correct for molar mass. The answer is given to one decimal place as required by the mass of 10 mol of C (120.1 g).

b. Where do we want to go?

1.56 g juglone = ? mol juglone

What do we know?

• Molar mass (juglone) = 174.1 g/mol   • Mass of juglone sample = 1.56 g

How do we get there?

We can determine the exact fraction of a mole by using the equivalence statement

1 mol = 174.1 g juglone

$$1.56\ \cancel{\text{g juglone}} \times \frac{1\ \text{mol juglone}}{174.1\ \cancel{\text{g juglone}}} = 0.00896\ \text{mol juglone}$$

$$= 8.96 \times 10^{-3}\ \text{mol juglone}$$

 × $\frac{1\ \text{mol}}{174.1\ \text{g}}$ ⇨

EXAMPLE 6.7

More Examples

1. Formaldehyde, which in the past was used to preserve biological samples, has the formula H_2CO. How many moles of formaldehyde does a 7.55-g sample represent?

   0.251 mol formaldehyde

2. How many moles of tetraphosphorus decoxide does a 250.0-g sample represent?

   0.8805 mol tetraphosphorus decoxide (P_4O_{10})

EXAMPLE 6.8

More Examples

1. How many water molecules are in a 10.0-g sample of water?

   3.34×10^{23} water molecules

2. Sucrose, or table sugar, has the formula $C_{12}H_{22}O_{11}$. How many molecules of sugar are in a 5.00-lb bag of sugar?

   3.99×10^{24} sugar molecules

Does it make sense?

The mass of 1 mol of this compound is 174.1 g, so 1.56 g is much less than a mole. Our answer (8.96×10^{-3} mol) has units of mol as expected and has three significant figures as required by the original sample size (1.56 g).

EXAMPLE 6.8

Calculating Number of Molecules

Isopentyl acetate, $C_7H_{14}O_2$, the compound responsible for the scent of bananas, can be produced commercially. Interestingly, bees release about 1 mg (1×10^{-6} g) of this compound when they sting. This attracts other bees, which then join the attack. How many moles and how many molecules of isopentyl acetate are released in a typical bee sting?

Solution

Where do we want to go?

* 1×10^{-6} g $C_7H_{14}O_2$ $\rightarrow$? mol $C_7H_{14}O_2$

What do we know?

*   The formula for isopentyl acetate is $C_7H_{14}O_2$.
*   Atomic masses

    C = 12.01 g/mol   H = 1.008 g/mol   O = 16.00 g/mol
*   Sample size = 1×10^{-6} g

How do we get there?

*   We are given a mass of isopentyl acetate and want the number of molecules, so we must first compute the molar mass.

$$7 \text{ mol C} \times 12.01 \frac{\text{g}}{\text{mol}} = 84.07 \text{ g C}$$

$$14 \text{ mol H} \times 1.008 \frac{\text{g}}{\text{mol}} = 14.11 \text{ g H}$$

$$2 \text{ mol O} \times 16.00 \frac{\text{g}}{\text{mol}} = \underline{32.00 \text{ g O}}$$

Mass of 1 mol $C_7H_{14}O_2$ = 130.18 g = molar mass

This means that 1 mol of isopentyl acetate (6.022×10^{23} molecules) has a mass of 130.18 g. The molar mass is 130.18 g/mol.

*   Next we determine the number of moles of isopentyl acetate in 1μg, which is 1×10^{-6} g. To do this we use the equivalence statement

    1 mol isopentyl acetate = 130.18 g isopentyl acetate

    which yields the conversion factor we need:

$$1 \times 10^{-6} \text{ g } C_7H_{14}O_2 \times \frac{1 \text{ mol } C_7H_{14}O_2}{130.18 \text{ g } C_7H_{14}O_2} = 8 \times 10^{-9} \text{ mol } C_7H_{14}O_2$$

Hands-On Chemistry
MINI-LAB

Relative Masses

Materials Each student/group will need cotton balls (at least 20), paper clips (at least 10), rubber stoppers (all the same size, at least 5), a balance or scale, and a calculator.

Purpose Students will gain a better understanding of the concept of relative masses and the mole.

Discussion Students should notice that the numbers in the "Relative mass of one object" column and those in the "Mass of *n* objects" column are the same (and in the same ratio as the numbers in the "Mass of one object" column). This relationship shows that if we have equal numbers of different objects, the relative masses are the same as for single objects.

The relative mass of one object is analogous to relative atomic mass. The mass of *n* objects (in lb) is analogous to

molar mass. The mass of *n* objects tells us the mass of a certain number of objects (molar mass tells us the mass of one mole of atoms or molecules). The number *n* is analogous to Avogadro's number (the mole). It essentially converts a unitless number (like relative atomic mass) to a number with a mass (like molar mass). A sample table of answers is included on the next page. In this case, *n* = 1033.

Using the equivalence statement 1 mol = 6.022×10^{23} units, we can determine the number of molecules:

$$8 \times 10^{-9} \text{ mol } C_7H_{14}O_2 \times \frac{6.022 \times 10^{23} \text{ molecules}}{1 \text{ mol } C_7H_{14}O_2} = 5 \times 10^{15} \text{ molecules}$$

This very large number of molecules is released in each bee sting.

Does it make sense?

The mass of $C_7H_{14}O_2$ released in each sting (1×10^{-6} g) is much less than the mass of one mole of $C_7H_{14}O_2$ so the number of moles (8×10^{-9}) is much smaller than one and the number of molecules (5×10^{15}) is much smaller than 6×10^{23}. The number of significant figures in our answer is 1 as determined by the mass of $C_7H_{14}O_2$ given (1×10^{-6} g).

 Practice Problem • Exercise 6.8

The substance Teflon, the nonstick coating on many frying pans, is made from the C_2F_4 molecule. Calculate the number of C_2F_4 units present in 135 g of Teflon.

HANDS-ON CHEMISTRY   • MINI-LAB •

Relative Masses

Materials
- cotton balls
- paper clips
- rubber stoppers
- balance

Procedure
1. Obtain cotton balls, paper clips, and rubber stoppers from your teacher.
2. Devise a method to find the average mass of each of these objects. Discuss this method with your teacher.
3. Determine the average mass of each object.

Results/Analysis
1. Copy the table onto your paper.
2. Record the average masses of each of the objects in your table.

	Mass of one object	Relative mass of one object	Mass of *n* objects
Cotton balls	____ g		____ lb
Paper clips	____ g		____ lb
Rubber stoppers	____ g		____ lb

3. Give the lightest object a relative mass of 1.0 in your table. Determine the relative masses of the remaining objects and record these in your table.
4. How many of the lightest object would you need to have a pound of that object? Call this number *n*.
5. If you had *n* of each of the other objects, how much would each sample weigh? Fill these numbers into your table.
6. Determine which columns correspond to the chemical terms "atomic mass" and "molar mass."
7. Which number represents "Avogadro's number"?

(continued)

	Mass of one object	Relative mass of one object	Mass of *n* objects
Cotton balls	0.44 g	$\frac{0.44}{0.44} = 1.0$	1.0 lb
Paper clips	1.42 g	$\frac{1.42}{0.44} = 3.2$	3.2 lb
Rubber stoppers	88 g	$\frac{88}{0.44} = 200$	200 lb

Answer to Practice Problem 6.8

First we must compute the mass of 1 mol of C_2F_4 molecules (the molar mass). Because 1 mol of C_2F_4 contains 2 mol of C atoms and 4 mol of F atoms, we have

$$2 \text{ mol } C \times \frac{12.01 \text{ g}}{\text{mol}} = 24.02 \text{ g C}$$

$$4 \text{ mol } F \times \frac{19.00 \text{ g}}{\text{mol}} = 76.00 \text{ g F}$$

Mass of 1 mol of C_2F_4: 100.02 g = molar mass

Using the equivalence statement 100.02 g C_2F_4 = 1 mol C_2F_4, we calculate the moles of C_2F_4 units in 135 g of Teflon.

$$135 \text{ g } C_2F_4 \text{ units} \times \frac{1 \text{ mol } C_2F_4}{100.02 \text{ g } C_2F_4} = 1.35 \text{ mol } C_2F_4 \text{ units}$$

Next, using the equivalence statement 1 mol = 6.022×10^{23} units, we calculate the number of C_2F_4 units in 135 g of Teflon.

$$1.35 \text{ mol } C_2F_4 \times \frac{6.022 \times 10^{23} \text{ units}}{1 \text{ mol}} = 8.13 \times 10^{23} C_2F_4 \text{ units}$$

Objective To learn to find the mass percent of an element in a given compound

 TEACHING TIPS

- Bring a sample of a compound to class to use in discussing percent composition. Good examples include copper(II) nitrate, hydrogen peroxide, and potassium permanganate. Put the formula for the compound on the board and use it to illustrate mass percent calculations.

- Remind students that a percentage is just a fraction multiplied by 100—it represents a part of the whole. You may need to spend some time in class working with students on the concept of percentages.

- Use two simple ball-and-stick models of the same molecule (water is a good example) to make your discussion of percent composition more concrete. Show students one model and ask them how to determine the percent by mass of each of the different colored balls in the model. The model can be taken apart to illustrate the first step—that is, to determine the mass of all balls of the same color. After a discussion about percentages, display both models and ask students to determine the percent by mass in a sample consisting of two models. Give students time to calculate this answer if they do not recognize that the percent composition must be the same for a sample containing one model as it is for the sample containing two models. Use this discussion to explain that sample size does not influence percent composition.

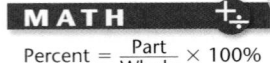

$$\text{Percent} = \frac{\text{Part}}{\text{Whole}} \times 100\%$$

The formula for ethanol is written C_2H_5OH, although you might expect it to be written simply as C_2H_6O.

B. Percent Composition of Compounds

So far we have discussed the composition of compounds in terms of the numbers of each type of atom. It is often useful to know a compound's composition in terms of the *masses* of its elements. We can obtain this information from the formula of the compound by comparing the mass of each element present in 1 mol of the compound to the total mass of 1 mol of the compound. The mass fraction for each element is calculated as follows:

$$\text{Mass fraction for a given element} = \frac{\text{mass of the element present in 1 mol of compound}}{\text{mass of 1 mol of compound}}$$

The mass fraction is converted to *mass percent* by multiplying by 100%.

We will illustrate this concept using the compound ethanol, an alcohol obtained by fermenting the sugar in grapes, corn, and other fruits and grains. Ethanol is often added to gasoline as an octane enhancer to form a fuel called gasohol. The added ethanol has the effect of increasing the octane of the gasoline and also lowering the carbon monoxide in automobile exhaust.

Note from its formula (C_2H_5OH) that each molecule of ethanol contains two carbon atoms, six hydrogen atoms, and one oxygen atom.

$$\boxed{\begin{array}{c}1 \text{ mol} \\ C_2H_5OH\end{array}} \longrightarrow \boxed{\begin{array}{c}2 \text{ mol C} \\ 6 \text{ mol H} \\ 1 \text{ mol O}\end{array}}$$

We calculate the mass of each element present and the molar mass for ethanol as follows:

$$\text{Mass of C} = 2 \text{ mol} \times 12.01 \frac{g}{\text{mol}} = 24.02 \text{ g}$$

$$\text{Mass of H} = 6 \text{ mol} \times 1.008 \frac{g}{\text{mol}} = 6.048 \text{ g}$$

$$\text{Mass of O} = 1 \text{ mol} \times 16.00 \frac{g}{\text{mol}} = 16.00 \text{ g}$$

$$\text{Mass of 1 mol of } C_2H_5OH = 46.07 \text{ g} = \text{molar mass}$$

The **mass percent** (sometimes called the weight percent) of carbon in ethanol can be computed by comparing the mass of carbon in 1 mol of ethanol with the total mass of 1 mol of ethanol and multiplying the result by 100%.

$$\text{Mass percent of C} = \frac{\text{mass of C in 1 mol } C_2H_5OH}{\text{mass of 1 mol } C_2H_5OH} \times 100\%$$

$$= \frac{24.02 \text{ g}}{46.07 \text{ g}} \times 100\% = 52.14\%$$

That is, ethanol contains 52.14% by mass of carbon. The mass percents of hydrogen and oxygen in ethanol are obtained in a similar manner.

$$\text{Mass percent of H} = \frac{\text{mass of H in 1 mol } C_2H_5OH}{\text{mass of 1 mol } C_2H_5OH} \times 100\%$$

$$= \frac{6.048 \text{ g}}{46.07 \text{ g}} \times 100\% = 13.13\%$$

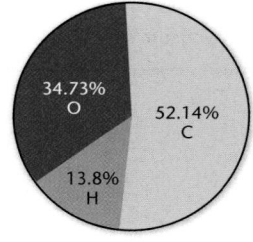

Meeting Individual Needs
MATH CONCEPTS

Students who need extra help with percents should read *Percent* located in the *Teacher Resources*. A worksheet of practice problems is available to go along with the handout.

Mass percent of O = $\dfrac{\text{mass of O in 1 mol C}_2\text{H}_5\text{OH}}{\text{mass of 1 mol C}_2\text{H}_5\text{OH}} \times 100\%$

$= \dfrac{16.00 \text{ g}}{46.07 \text{ g}} \times 100\% = 34.73\%$

The mass percentages of all the elements in a compound add up to 100%, although rounding-off effects may produce a small deviation. Adding up the percentages is a good way to check the calculations. In this case, the sum of the mass percents is 52.14% + 13.13% + 34.73% = 100.00%.

MATH

Sometimes, because of rounding-off effects, the sum of the mass percents in a compound is not exactly 100%.

 Active Reading Question

In the compound C_2H_5OH, the number of hydrogen atoms in a molecule is greater than the number of carbon atoms and oxygen atoms in the molecule. However, the mass percent of hydrogen is lower than the mass percent of carbon and the mass percent of oxygen. Why is this?

EXAMPLE 6.9

Calculating Mass Percent

Carvone is a substance that occurs in two forms, both of which have the same molecular formula ($C_{10}H_{14}O$) and molar mass. One type of carvone gives caraway seeds their characteristic smell; the other is responsible for the smell of spearmint oil. Compute the mass percent of each element in carvone.

Solution

Where do we want to go?

For carvone
- %C = ? %
- %H = ? %
- %O = ? %

What do we know?
- The formula for carvone is $C_{10}H_{14}O$.
- Atomic masses
  C = 12.01 g/mol   H = 1.008 g/mol   O = 16.00 g/mol

How do we get there?

Because the formula for carvone is $C_{10}H_{14}O$, the masses of the various elements in 1 mol of carvone are

Mass of C in 1 mol = 10 mol × 12.01 $\dfrac{\text{g}}{\text{mol}}$ = 120.1 g

Mass of H in 1 mol = 14 mol × 1.008 $\dfrac{\text{g}}{\text{mol}}$ = 14.11 g

Mass of O in 1 mol = 1 mol × 16.00 $\dfrac{\text{g}}{\text{mol}}$ = 16.00 g

Mass of 1 mol of $C_{10}H_{14}O$ = 150.21 g

Molar mass   = 150.2 g/mol
(rounding to the correct number of significant figures)

MATH

The 120.1 limits the sum to one decimal place. Remember, in addition the number with the fewest decimal places determines the number of significant figures in the answer.

 Active Reading Question

The hydrogen atom has a relative average mass of 1.008 compared to 12.01 for the carbon atom and 16.00 for the oxygen atom. There are 6 hydrogen atoms and 2 carbon atoms, so there are 3 times as many hydrogen atoms. However, because a carbon atom has a relative mass of about 12 times the mass of a hydrogen atom, the mass of carbon is greater than the mass of hydrogen. The same goes for oxygen.

EXAMPLE 6.9

More Examples

1. Determine the mass percent of each element in sulfuric acid (H_2SO_4).

   2.055% hydrogen by mass, 32.70% sulfur by mass, 65.25% oxygen by mass

2. Rubbing alcohol is an aqueous solution of isopropyl alcohol. Isopropyl alcohol has the formula C_3H_7OH. Determine the mass percent of each element in isopropyl alcohol.

   59.96% carbon by mass, 13.42% hydrogen by mass, 26.62% oxygen by mass

Answer to Practice Problem 6.9

The molar mass of penicillin F is computed as follows:

C: $14 \text{ mol} \times 12.01 \frac{g}{mol} = 168.1 \text{ g}$

H: $20 \text{ mol} \times 1.008 \frac{g}{mol} = 20.16 \text{ g}$

N: $2 \text{ mol} \times 14.01 \frac{g}{mol} = 28.02 \text{ g}$

S: $1 \text{ mol} \times 32.07 \frac{g}{mol} = 32.07 \text{ g}$

O: $4 \text{ mol} \times 16.00 \frac{g}{mol} = 64.00 \text{ g}$

Mass of 1 mol of $C_{14}H_{20}N_2SO_4$
$= 312.39 \text{ g} = 312.4 \text{ g}$

Mass percent of C =

$\frac{168.1 \text{ g C}}{312.4 \text{ g } C_{14}H_{20}N_2SO_4} \times 100\%$

$= 53.81\%$

Mass percent of H =

$\frac{20.16 \text{ g H}}{312.4 \text{ g } C_{14}H_{20}N_2SO_4} \times 100\%$

$= 6.453\%$

Mass percent of N =

$\frac{28.02 \text{ g N}}{312.4 \text{ g } C_{14}H_{20}N_2SO_4} \times 100\%$

$= 8.969\%$

Mass percent of S =

$\frac{32.07 \text{ g S}}{312.4 \text{ g } C_{14}H_{20}N_2SO_4} \times 100\%$

$= 10.27\%$

Mass percent of O =

$\frac{64.00 \text{ g O}}{312.4 \text{ g } C_{14}H_{20}N_2SO_4} \times 100\%$

$= 20.49\%$

Check: The percentages add up to 99.99%.

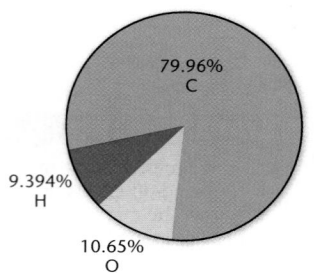

Next we find the fraction of the total mass contributed by each element and convert it to a percentage.

Mass percent of C $= \dfrac{120.1 \text{ g C}}{150.2 \text{ g } C_{10}H_{14}O} \times 100\% = 79.96\%$

Mass percent of H $= \dfrac{14.11 \text{ g H}}{150.2 \text{ g } C_{10}H_{14}O} \times 100\% = 9.394\%$

Mass percent of O $= \dfrac{16.00 \text{ g O}}{150.2 \text{ g } C_{10}H_{14}O} \times 100\% = 10.65\%$

Does it make sense?

Add the individual mass percent values—they should total 100% within a small range due to rounding off. In this case the percentages add up to 100.0%.

 Practice Problem • Exercise 6.9

Penicillin, an important antibiotic (antibacterial agent), was discovered accidentally by the Scottish bacteriologist Alexander Fleming in 1928, although he was never able to isolate it as a pure compound. This and similar antibiotics have saved millions of lives that would otherwise have been lost to infections. Penicillin, like many of the molecules produced by living systems, is a large molecule containing many atoms. One type of penicillin, penicillin F, has the formula $C_{14}H_{20}N_2SO_4$. Compute the mass percent of each element in this compound.

HANDS-ON CHEMISTRY • MINI-LAB •

And the Winner Is . . .

Materials
- three different types of sandwich cookies
- balance
- aluminum foil
- spoon

Procedure

1. Obtain three different types of sandwich cookies from your teacher.

2. Determine the percent composition of each cookie. Assume the cookie consists of two parts, the crunchy cookie and the cream filling. You will need a balance, foil, and a spoon. Place the foil on the balance before you place any part of the cookie or cream filling on the balance.

Results/Analysis

1. How does the percent composition of each cookie compare?
2. Which would you say was the best cookie? Why do you say this?
3. Your teacher will tell you the price per cookie for each of the three types. Use this information to decide which cookie is the best buy. Defend your answer.

Hands-On Chemistry
MINI-LAB

And the Winner Is . . .

Materials Each student/group will need three types of sandwich cookies, a balance, aluminum foil, a spoon, and a calculator.

Purpose Students will gain a better understanding of the concept of percent composition.

Discussion Students first should determine the mass of an intact sandwich cookie and then scrape all of the filling off the cookie. Have students determine the masses of the filling and the crunchy cookies, and then compare the sum of these values to the mass of the intact cookie. Multiplying the ratio of the filling to the intact cookie by 100 gives the percent filling in each cookie.

Students sometimes have difficulty with the concept of percent composition.

This activity should provide a concrete example that a percentage is a ratio of the part to the whole (multiplied by 100). The analogy can be made that finding percent composition is like taking apart an individual molecule, measuring the total mass of each type of atom, and then comparing this mass to the mass of the entire molecule.

The determination of the best cookie is a matter of personal preference.

SECTION 6.2
REVIEW QUESTIONS

1 Tell how many moles of each element are in the following amounts of each compound:

  a. 3 moles NH_3

  b. 0.25 moles H_2O

  c. 5.0 moles H_2SO_4

  d. 0.75 moles $Ca(NO_3)_2$

2 Determine the molar mass for each of the following:

  a. NH_3

  b. H_2O

  c. H_2SO_4

  d. $Ca(NO_3)_2$

3 Determine the mass of each sample in question 1.

4 Explain how you would find the mass percent of each element in water.

5 Copy and complete the following table.

Moles	Mass	Number of molecules
4.7 moles NH_3		
	1.80 g H_2O	
		5.21×10^{22} molecules CH_4

6 Use the graph to match compounds A, B, C, and D with the following choices: NaCN, HNO_3, NH_3, $Ca(NO_3)_2$.

RESEARCH LINKS
CLASSZONE.COM

SECTION 6.2
Review Questions

1.a. 3 mol N, 9 mol H

  b. 0.50 mol H, 0.25 mol O

  c. 10.0 mol H, 5.0 mol S, 20.0 mol O

  d. 0.75 mol Ca, 1.50 mol N, 4.50 mol O

2.a. 17.03 g/mol

  b. 18.02 g/mol

  c. 98.09 g/mol

  d. 164.1 g/mol

3.a. 50 g

  b. 4.5 g

  c. 490 g

  d. 120 g

4. To find the mass percent of each element in water, first you would need to determine the moles of each element in the formula. This means multiplying the atomic mass for hydrogen by 2, as there are two atoms of hydrogen in the formula. This mass of hydrogen in one mole of water should then be divided by the molar mass of water to determine the mass fraction of hydrogen in water. This value can be converted to a percentage by multiplying by 100%. The process could be repeated for oxygen (omitting the step of multiplying by 2, as there is only one mole of oxygen per mole of water). Alternatively, the percentage of oxygen could be obtained by subtracting the percentage of hydrogen from 100%.

5.

Moles	Mass	Number of molecules
4.7 mol NH_3	80. g NH_3	2.8×10^{24} molecules NH_3
0.0999 mol H_2O	1.80 g H_2O	6.02×10^{22} molecules H_2O
0.0865 mol CH_4	1.39 g CH_4	5.21×10^{22} molecules CH_4

6. compound A = NaCN, compound B = NH_3, compound C = $Ca(NO_3)_2$, compound D = HNO_3

SECTION 6.3
Formulas of Compounds

Key Terms
• Empirical formula
• Molecular formula

Objectives
• *To understand the meaning of empirical formula*
• *To learn to calculate empirical formulas*
• *To learn to calculate the molecular formula of a compound*

Assume that you have mixed two solutions, and a solid product forms. How can you find out what the solid is? What is its formula? Although an experienced chemist can often predict the product expected in a chemical reaction, the only sure way to identify the product is to perform experiments. Usually we compare the physical properties of the product to the properties of known compounds.

A. Empirical Formulas

Sometimes a chemical reaction gives a product that has never been obtained before. In such a case, a chemist determines what compound has been formed by determining which elements are present and how much of each is there. These data can be used to obtain the formula of the compound. Previously we used the formula of the compound to determine the mass of each element present in a mole of the compound. To obtain the formula of an unknown compound, we do the opposite. That is, we use the measured masses of the elements present to determine the formula.

A Closer Look

Recall that the formula of a compound represents the relative numbers of the various types of atoms present. For example, the molecular formula CO_2 tells us that for each carbon atom there are two oxygen atoms in each molecule of carbon dioxide. So to determine the formula of a substance we need to count the atoms. As we have seen in this chapter, we can do this by weighing.

Suppose we know that a compound contains only the elements carbon, hydrogen, and oxygen, and we weigh out a 0.2015-g sample. Using methods we will not discuss here, we find that this 0.2015-g sample of compound contains 0.0806 g of carbon, 0.01353 g of hydrogen, and 0.1074 g of oxygen. We have just learned how to convert these masses to numbers of atoms by using the atomic mass of each element.

Carbon

$$(0.0806 \text{ g C}) \times \frac{1 \text{ mol C atoms}}{12.01 \text{ g C}} = 0.00671 \text{ mol C atoms}$$

Hydrogen

$$(0.01353 \text{ g H}) \times \frac{1 \text{ mol H atoms}}{1.008 \text{ g H}} = 0.01342 \text{ mol H atoms}$$

Oxygen

$$(0.1074 \text{ g O}) \times \frac{1 \text{ mol O atoms}}{16.00 \text{ g O}} = 0.006713 \text{ mol O atoms}$$

Let's review what we have established. We now know that 0.2015 g of the compound contains 0.00671 mol of C atoms, 0.01342 mol of H atoms, and 0.006713 mol of O atoms.

Carbon

$$(0.00671 \text{ mol C atoms}) \times \frac{6.022 \times 10^{23} \text{ C atoms}}{1 \text{ mol C atoms}} = 4.04 \times 10^{21} \text{ C atoms}$$

Hydrogen

$$(0.01342 \text{ mol H atoms}) \times \frac{6.022 \times 10^{23} \text{ H atoms}}{1 \text{ mol H atoms}} = 8.08 \times 10^{21} \text{ H atoms}$$

Oxygen

$$(0.006713 \text{ mol O atoms}) \times \frac{6.022 \times 10^{23} \text{ O atoms}}{1 \text{ mol O atoms}} = 4.043 \times 10^{21} \text{ O atoms}$$

These are the numbers of the various atoms *in 0.2015 g of compound*. What do these numbers tell us about the formula of the compound? Note the following:

- The compound contains the same number of C and O atoms.
- There are twice as many H atoms as C atoms or O atoms.

Finding the Formula

We can represent this information by the formula CH_2O, which expresses the *relative* numbers of C, H, and O atoms present. Is this the true formula for the compound? In other words, is the compound made up of CH_2O molecules? It may be. However, it might also be made up of $C_2H_4O_2$ molecules, $C_3H_6O_3$ molecules, $C_4H_8O_4$ molecules, $C_5H_{10}O_5$ molecules, $C_6H_{12}O_6$ molecules, and so on. Note that each of these molecules has the required 1:2:1 ratio of carbon to hydrogen to oxygen atoms (the ratio shown by experiment to be present in the compound).

When we break a compound down into its separate elements and "count" the atoms present, we learn only the ratio of atoms—we get only the *relative* numbers of atoms. The formula of a compound that expresses the smallest whole-number ratio of the atoms present is called the **empirical formula** or *simplest formula*. A compound that contains the molecules $C_4H_8O_4$ has the same empirical formula as a compound that contains $C_6H_{12}O_6$ molecules. The empirical formula for both is CH_2O. The actual formula of a compound—the one that gives the composition of the molecules that are present—is called the **molecular formula**. The sugar called glucose is made of molecules with the molecular formula $C_6H_{12}O_6$ (see **Figure 6.2**). Note from the molecular formula for glucose that the empirical formula is CH_2O. We can represent the molecular formula as a multiple (by 6) of the empirical formula:

$$C_6H_{12}O_6 = (CH_2O)_6$$

Empirical formula
The formula of a compound expressing the smallest whole-number ratio of atoms in a compound

Molecular formula
The actual formula of a compound giving the types of atoms and numbers of each type of atom

Figure 6.2
The glucose molecule. The molecular formula is $C_6H_{12}O_6$, as can be verified by counting the atoms. The empirical formula for glucose is CH_2O.

6.3 • Formulas of Compounds • **197**

Answers will vary. Two examples when the empirical and molecular formulas are different include the empirical formula CH_3 and the molecular formula C_2H_6 (ethane), and the empirical formula HO and the molecular formula H_2O_2 (hydrogen peroxide). Two examples when the empirical formula and molecular formulas are the same include NH_3 (ammonia) and H_2O (water).

EXAMPLE 6.10

More Examples

Determine the empirical formula from each of the following molecular formulas.

1. H_2O_2, hydrogen peroxide, a substance commonly diluted with water and used as a disinfectant
   HO

2. C_4H_{10}, butane, commonly used in lighters
   C_2H_5

3. CCl_4, carbon tetrachloride, an organic solvent
   CCl_4

 TEACHING TIP

Remind students that subscripts outside the parentheses have an effect on the number of each atom inside the parentheses. You can relate this effect to the distributive property for multiplication over addition. This discussion will remind students to multiply subscripts to obtain the number of atoms.

6.3.B Calculation of Empirical Formulas

Objective To learn to calculate empirical formulas

LABORATORY
EXPERIMENT 23:
Decomposing Copper Oxide

 TEACHING TIP

The key concept in this section is that the mass of each element in a compound is an indicator of the number of atoms of that element in the compound, but only if the mass is converted to moles.

Provide two examples when empirical and molecular formulas are different. Provide two examples when empirical and molecular formulas are the same.

EXAMPLE 6.10

 Determining Empirical Formulas

information

When a subscript is outside of the parentheses, it applies to everything in the parentheses. Each subscript inside is multiplied by the subscript outside the parentheses.

In each case below, the molecular formula for a compound is given. Determine the empirical formula for each compound.

Compound	Use	Molecular Formula	Empirical Formula
Benzene	Starting material for organic chemicals	C_6H_6	?
Dioxin	Poison	$C_{12}H_4Cl_4O_2$	?

Solution

$C_6H_6 = (CH)_6$;   CH is the empirical formula. Each subscript in the empirical formula is multiplied by 6 to obtain the molecular formula.

$C_{12}H_4Cl_4O_2 = (C_6H_2Cl_2O)_2$; $C_6H_2Cl_2O$ is the empirical formula. Each subscript in the empirical formula is multiplied by 2 to obtain the molecular formula.

B. Calculation of Empirical Formulas

One of the most important things we can learn about a new compound is its chemical formula. To calculate the empirical formula of a compound, we first determine the relative masses of the various elements that are present.

One way to do this is to measure the masses of elements that react to form the compound. For example, suppose we weigh out 0.2636 g of pure nickel metal into a crucible and heat this metal in the air so that the nickel can react with oxygen to form a nickel oxide compound. After the sample has cooled, we weigh it again and find its mass to be 0.3354 g. The gain in mass is due to the oxygen that reacts with the nickel to form the oxide. Therefore, the mass of oxygen present in the compound is the total mass of the product minus the mass of the nickel:

Total mass of nickel oxide	−	Mass of nickel originally present	=	Mass of oxygen that reacted with the nickel
0.3354 g		0.2636 g		0.0718 g

Note that the mass of nickel present in the compound is the nickel metal origi-nally weighed out. So we know that the nickel oxide contains 0.2636 g of nickel and 0.0718 g of oxygen. What is the empirical formula of this compound?

To answer this question we must convert the masses to numbers of atoms, using atomic masses:

$$0.2636 \text{ g Ni} \times \frac{1 \text{ mol Ni atoms}}{58.69 \text{ g Ni}} = 0.004491 \text{ mol Ni atoms}$$

(Four significant figures allowed.)

$$0.0718 \text{ g O} \times \frac{1 \text{ mol O atoms}}{16.00 \text{ g O}} = 0.00449 \text{ mol O atoms}$$

(Three significant figures allowed.)

These mole quantities represent numbers of atoms (remember that a mole of atoms is 6.022×10^{23} atoms). It is clear from the moles of atoms that the compound contains an equal number of Ni and O atoms, so the formula is NiO. This is the *empirical formula*; it expresses the smallest whole-number ratio of atoms:

$$\frac{0.004491 \text{ mol Ni atoms}}{0.00449 \text{ mol O atoms}} = \frac{1 \text{ Ni}}{1 \text{ O}}$$

That is, this compound contains equal numbers of nickel atoms and oxygen atoms. We say the ratio of nickel atoms to oxygen atoms is 1:1 (1 to 1).

EXAMPLE 6.11

Calculating Empirical Formulas

An oxide of aluminum is formed by the reaction of 4.151 g of aluminum with 3.692 g of oxygen. Calculate the empirical formula for this compound.

Solution

Where do we want to go?

Empirical formula = Al_xO_y
- $x = ?$ • $y = ?$

What do we know?

- The compound contains:

  4.151 g Al   3.692 g O

- Atomic masses

  Al = 26.98 g/mol   O = 16.00 g/mol

How do we get there?

We need to know the relative numbers of each type of atom to write the formula, so we must convert the masses of the elements to moles of atoms to get the empirical formula. We carry out the conversion by using the atomic masses of the elements.

$$4.151 \text{ g Al} \times \frac{1 \text{ mol Al}}{26.98 \text{ g Al}} = 0.1539 \text{ mol Al atoms}$$

$$3.692 \text{ g O} \times \frac{1 \text{ mol O}}{16.00 \text{ g O}} = 0.2308 \text{ mol O atoms}$$

Al Group 3

O Group 6

EXAMPLE 6.11

More Examples

1. A 1.500-g sample of a compound containing only carbon and hydrogen is found to contain 1.198 g of carbon. Determine the empirical formula for this compound.
   CH_3

2. A 3.450-g sample of nitrogen reacts with 1.970 g of oxygen. Determine the empirical formula for this compound.
   N_2O

🍎 TEACHING TIP

Students often will divide the mass of oxygen or mass percent of oxygen by 32.00 instead of 16.00. Remind students that we are determining the ratio of oxygen atoms in the compound.

MATH +÷

Multiplying both the numerator and the denominator of a fraction (ratio) by the same number is just multiplying by 1:

$\frac{2}{2} = 1$, $\frac{3}{3} = 1$, and so on.

It does not change the value of the fraction but it can help us get whole numbers in the ratio.

Because chemical formulas use only whole numbers, we next find the whole-number ratio of the atoms. To do this we start by dividing both numbers by the smallest of the two. This converts the smallest number to 1.

$$\frac{0.1539 \text{ mol Al}}{0.1539} = 1.000 \text{ mol Al atoms}$$

$$\frac{0.2308 \text{ mol O}}{0.1539} = 1.500 \text{ mol O atoms}$$

Note that dividing both numbers of moles of atoms by the *same* number does not change the *relative* numbers of oxygen and aluminum atoms. That is,

$$\frac{0.2308 \text{ mol O}}{0.153 \text{ mol Al}} = \frac{1.500 \text{ mol O}}{1.000 \text{ mol Al}}$$

Thus we know that the compound contains 1.500 mol of O atoms for every 1.000 mol of Al atoms, or, in terms of individual atoms, we could say that the compound contains 1.500 O atoms for every 1.000 Al atom. However, because only *whole* atoms combine to form compounds, we must find a set of *whole numbers* to express the empirical formula. When we multiply both 1.000 and 1.500 by 2, we get the integers we need.

$$1.500 \text{ O} \times 2 = 3.000 = 3 \text{ O atoms}; \quad x = 3$$

$$1.000 \text{ Al} \times 2 = 2.000 = 2 \text{ Al atoms}; \quad y = 2$$

Therefore, this compound contains two Al atoms for every three O atoms, and the empirical formula is Al_2O_3. Note that the *ratio* of atoms in this compound is given by each of the following fractions:

$$\frac{0.2308 \text{ O}}{0.1539 \text{ Al}} = \frac{1.500 \text{ O}}{1.000 \text{ Al}} = \frac{\left(\frac{3}{2} \text{ O}\right)}{(1 \text{ Al})} \times \frac{2}{2} = \frac{3 \text{ O}}{2 \text{ Al}}$$

The smallest whole-number ratio corresponds to the subscripts of the empirical formula, Al_2O_3.

Sometimes the relative numbers of moles you get when you calculate an empirical formula will not turn out to be whole numbers, as is the case in Example 6.11. When this happens, you must convert to the appropriate whole numbers. This is done by multiplying all the numbers by the same smallest whole number, which can be found by trial and error. The multiplier needed is almost always between 1 and 6. We will now summarize what we have learned about calculating empirical formulas.

Tools for Determining the Empirical Formula of a Compound

Step 1 Obtain the mass of each element present (in grams).

Step 2 Determine the number of moles of each type of atom present.

Step 3 Divide the number of moles of each element by the smallest number of moles to convert the smallest number to 1. If all of the numbers so obtained are whole numbers, they are the subscripts in the empirical formula. If one or more of these numbers are not whole numbers, go on to step 4.

Step 4 Multiply the numbers from step 3 by the smallest whole number that will convert all of them to whole numbers. This set of whole numbers represents the subscripts in the empirical formula.

CHEMISTRY EXPLORER

William Perkin • 1838–1907

Sometimes a little chemical knowledge can lead to a new and profitable career—as happened to a young chemistry student named William Perkin. In one of his chemistry lectures, Perkin's professor said it would be wonderful to make quinine artificially (in 1856, the only source for quinine—a drug effective against malaria—was the bark of the cinchona tree). Perkin, who was only 18 at the time, decided to make quinine in his home laboratory as a project over Easter vacation.

In his attempts to make quinine Perkin started with materials obtained from coal tar. However, instead of getting quinine he got red-brown and black sludges. Fortunately Perkins noticed that one of these messes turned a beautiful purple color when dissolved in alcohol or water. Perkin liked the color so much that he was distracted from his original quest to make quinine. In testing the purple solutions, he found he could use them to dye silk and cotton.

Perkin decided to quit school, against the advice of his professors, and convinced his wealthy father to invest in him. He patented his dye and built a factory to produce it on a large scale. His dye became known as *mauve*.

Until Perkin's discovery, all permanent purple or lavender dyes were outrageously expensive. The only source for the natural dye was a mollusk in the Mediterranean Sea. It took 9000 mollusks for 1 g of dye! No wonder purple became the color for royalty. Perkin changed everything by producing a purple dye from coal tar that just about everyone could afford.

Perkin went on to develop another popular dye called alizarin in 1869. This red dye was being produced by the ton in his factory by 1871. Perkin sold his factory in 1874 (at the age of 36) and had enough money to spend the rest of his life doing pure research. He bought a new house and continued working in his old laboratory. Eventually he made coumarin, the first perfume from coal tar and cinnamic acid. Perkin's work started an explosion in the manufacture of organic chemicals.

6.3 • Formulas of Compounds • **201**

CHEMISTRY EXPLORERS
William Perkin

The 50th anniversary of the discovery of mauvene was commemorated by the establishment of the Perkin Medal, which is widely acknowledged as the highest honor in American industrial chemistry. This medal was first presented in New York to Perkin himself. Another notable winner of the Perkin Medal is Nobel laureate Glenn Seaborg.

EXAMPLE 6.12

More Examples

1. When a 2.000-g sample of iron metal is heated in air, it reacts with oxygen to achieve a final mass of 2.573 g. Determine the empirical formula for this iron oxide.

   FeO [iron(II) oxide]

2. A 4.550-g sample of cobalt reacts with 5.475 g chlorine to form a binary compound. Determine the empirical formula for this compound.

   $CoCl_2$ [cobalt(II) chloride]

EXAMPLE 6.12

Calculating Empirical Formulas for Binary Compounds

When a 0.3546-g sample of vanadium metal is heated in air, it reacts with oxygen to reach a final mass of 0.6330 g. Calculate the empirical formula of this vanadium oxide.

Solution

Where do we want to go?

Empirical formula = V_xO_y
- x = ?
- y = ?

What do we know?
- The sample of compound contains 0.3546 g V.
- Mass of the sample is 0.6330 g
- Atomic masses
  V = 50.94 g/mol   O = 16.00 g/mol

How do we get there?

Step 1 All the vanadium that was originally present will be found in the final compound, so we can calculate the mass of oxygen that reacted by taking the following difference:

Total mass of compound	−	Mass of vanadium in compound	=	Mass of oxygen in compound
0.6330 g	−	0.3546 g	=	0.2784 g

Step 2 Using the atomic masses (50.94 for V and 16.00 for O), we obtain

$$0.3546 \text{ g V} \times \frac{1 \text{ mol V atoms}}{50.94 \text{ g V}} = 0.006961 \text{ mol V atoms}$$

$$0.2784 \text{ g O} \times \frac{1 \text{ mol O atoms}}{16.00 \text{ g O}} = 0.01740 \text{ mol O atoms}$$

Step 3 Then we divide both numbers of moles by the smaller, 0.006961.

$$\frac{0.006961 \text{ mol V atoms}}{0.006961} = 1.000 \text{ mol V atoms}$$

$$\frac{0.01740 \text{ mol O atoms}}{0.006961} = 2.500 \text{ mol O atoms}$$

Because one of these numbers (2.500) is not a whole number, we go on to step 4.

Step 4 We note that $2 \times 2.500 = 5.000$ and $2 \times 1.000 = 2.000$, so we multiply both numbers by 2 to get whole numbers.

$$2 \times 1.000 \text{ V} = 2.000 \text{ V} = 2 \text{ V} \qquad x = 2$$
$$2 \times 2.500 \text{ O} = 5.000 \text{ O} = 5 \text{ O} \qquad y = 5$$

This compound contains 2 V atoms for every 5 O atoms, and the empirical formula is V_2O_5.

MATH

$V_{1.000}O_{2.500}$ becomes V_2O_5 when we multiply both subscripts by 2.

Meeting Individual Needs
AUDITORY LEARNERS

Read aloud Example 6.12 emphasizing the key words *reacts, reach,* and *final.* Have students describe how these key words help to set up the solution to the problem.

In a lab experiment it was observed that 0.6884 g of lead combines with 0.2356 g of chlorine to form a binary compound. Calculate the empirical formula of this compound.

The same procedures we have used for binary compounds also apply to compounds containing three or more elements, as Example 6.13 illustrates.

EXAMPLE 6.13

Calculating Empirical Formulas for Compounds Containing Three or More Elements

A sample of lead arsenate, an insecticide used against the potato beetle, contains 1.3813 g of lead, 0.00672 g of hydrogen, 0.4995 g of arsenic, and 0.4267 g of oxygen. Calculate the empirical formula for lead arsenate.

Solution

Where do we want to go?

Empirical formula = $Pb_aH_bAs_cO_d$

• $a = ?$ • $b = ?$ • $c = ?$ • $d = ?$

What do we know?

• The sample of compound contains:

1.3813 g Pb	0.00672 g H
0.4995 g As	0.4267 g O

• Atomic masses

Pb = 207.2 g/mol	H = 1.008 g/mol
As = 74.92 g/mol	O = 16.00 g/mol

How do we get there?

Step 1 The compound contains 1.3813 g Pb, 0.00672 g H, 0.4995 g As, and 0.4267 g O.

Step 2 We use the atomic masses of the elements present to calculate the moles of each.

$$1.3813 \text{ g Pb} \times \frac{1 \text{ mol Pb}}{207.2 \text{ g Pb}} = 0.006667 \text{ mol Pb}$$

$$0.00672 \text{ g H} \times \frac{1 \text{ mol H}}{1.008 \text{ g H}} = 0.00667 \text{ mol H}$$

$$0.4995 \text{ g As} \times \frac{1 \text{ mol As}}{74.92 \text{ g As}} = 0.006667 \text{ mol As}$$

$$0.4267 \text{ g O} \times \frac{1 \text{ mol O}}{16.00 \text{ g O}} = 0.02667 \text{ mol O}$$

 information

Only three significant figures are allowed because the mass of H has only three significant figures.

Answer to Practice Problem 6.12

Step 1

0.6884 g lead and 0.2356 g chlorine

Step 2

$$0.6884 \text{ g Pb} \times \frac{1 \text{ mol Pb}}{207.2 \text{ g Pb}} =$$

0.003322 mol Pb

$$0.2356 \text{ g Cl} \times \frac{1 \text{ mol Cl}}{35.45 \text{ g Cl}} =$$

0.006646 mol Cl

Step 3

$$\frac{0.003322 \text{ mol Pb}}{0.003322} = 1.000 \text{ mol Pb}$$

$$\frac{0.006646 \text{ mol Cl}}{0.003322} = 2.001 \text{ mol Cl}$$

These numbers are very close to integers, so step 4 is unnecessary. The empirical formula is $PbCl_2$.

EXAMPLE 6.13

More Examples

1. Phosphoric acid is found in some soft drinks. A sample of phosphoric acid contains 0.3086 g of hydrogen, 3.161 g of phosphorus, and 6.531 g of oxygen. Determine the empirical formula for phosphoric acid.

   H_3PO_4

2. *Para*-dichlorobenzene is often used in chemistry labs when studying melting points. A sample of *para*-dichlorobenzene contains 5.657 g of carbon, 0.3165 g of hydrogen, and 5.566 g of chlorine. Determine the empirical formula for this compound.

   C_3H_2Cl

Answer to Practice Problem 6.13

Step 1
0.8007 g C, 0.9333 g N, 0.2016 g H, and 2.133 g O

Step 2

$0.8007 \text{ g C} \times \dfrac{1 \text{ mol C}}{12.01 \text{ g C}} =$
0.06667 mol C

$0.9333 \text{ g N} \times \dfrac{1 \text{ mol C}}{14.01 \text{ g N}} =$
0.06662 mol N

$0.2016 \text{ g H} \times \dfrac{1 \text{ mol H}}{1.008 \text{ g H}} =$
0.2000 mol H

$0.8007 \text{ g O} \times \dfrac{1 \text{ mol O}}{16.00 \text{ g O}} =$
0.1333 mol O

Step 3

$\dfrac{0.06667 \text{ mol C}}{0.06662} = 1.001 \text{ mol C}$

$\dfrac{0.06662 \text{ mol N}}{0.06662} = 1.000 \text{ mol N}$

$\dfrac{0.2000 \text{ mol H}}{0.06662} = 3.002 \text{ mol H}$

$\dfrac{0.1333 \text{ mol O}}{0.06662} = 2.001 \text{ mol O}$

The empirical formula is CNH_3O_2.

TEACHING TIP

Point out that percent composition can be used to determine the empirical formula of a compound by using the percentages to determine the mass of each element present. Remind students that a percentage can be converted to grams if the size of the sample is known. If no sample size is given in the problem, students can assume a 100-g sample (for ease in doing the math) and find the mass of each element from its percentage. Then they can use the masses to find the formula as before.

EXAMPLE 6.14

More Examples

1. The simplest amino acid, glycine, has the following mass percents: 32.00% carbon, 6.714% hydrogen, 42.63% oxygen, and 18.66% nitrogen. Determine the empirical formula for glycine.

$C_2H_5O_2N$

2. A compound has been analyzed and found to have the following mass percent composition: 66.75% copper, 10.84% phosphorus, and 22.41% oxygen. Determine the empirical formula for this compound.

Cu_3PO_4

Step 3 Now we divide by the smallest number of moles.

$\dfrac{0.006667 \text{ mol Pb}}{0.006667} = 1.000 \text{ mol Pb} \quad a = 1$

$\dfrac{0.006667 \text{ mol H}}{0.006667} = 1.00 \text{ mol H} \quad b = 1$

$\dfrac{0.006667 \text{ mol As}}{0.006667} = 1.000 \text{ mol As} \quad c = 1$

$\dfrac{0.02667 \text{ mol O}}{0.006667} = 4.000 \text{ mol O} \quad d = 4$

The empirical formula is $PbHAsO_4$.

 Practice Problem • Exercise 6.13

Sevin, the commercial name for an insecticide used to protect crops such as cotton, vegetables, and fruit, is made from carbamic acid. A chemist analyzing a sample of carbamic acid finds 0.8007 g of carbon, 0.9333 g of nitrogen, 0.2016 g of hydrogen, and 2.133 g of oxygen. Determine the empirical formula for carbamic acid.

When a compound is analyzed to determine the relative amounts of the elements present, the results are usually given in terms of percentages by masses of the various elements. Previously we learned to calculate the percent composition of a compound from its formula. Now we will do the opposite. Given the percent composition, we will calculate the empirical formula.

To understand this procedure, you must understand the meaning of *percent*. Remember that percent means parts of a given component per 100 parts of the total mixture. For example, if a given compound is 15% carbon (by mass), the compound contains 15 g of carbon per 100 g of compound.

Calculation of the empirical formula of a compound when one is given its percent composition is illustrated in Example 6.14.

information

Percent by mass for a given element means the grams of that element in 100 g of the compound.

EXAMPLE 6.14

Calculating Empirical Formulas from Percent Composition

Cisplatin, the common name for a platinum compound that is used to treat cancerous tumors, has the composition (mass percent) 65.02% platinum, 9.34% nitrogen, 2.02% hydrogen, and 23.63% chlorine. Calculate the empirical formula for cisplatin.

Solution
Where do we want to go?
Empirical formula = $Pt_aN_bH_cCl_d$
- $a = ?$ • $b = ?$ • $c = ?$ • $d = ?$

What do we know?
- The sample of compound contains:

| 65.02% Pt | 9.34% N | 2.02% H | 23.63% Cl |

- Atomic masses

Pt = 195.1 g/mol	H = 1.008 g/mol
N = 14.01 g/mol	Cl = 35.45 g/mol

How do we get there?

Step 1 Determine how many grams of each element are present in 100 g of the compound. For 100 g of cisplatin:

- 65.02% Pt → 65.02 g Pt
- 2.02% H → 2.02 g H
- 9.34% N → 9.34 g N
- 23.63% Cl → 23.63 g Cl

Step 2 Determine the number of moles of each type of atom. We use the atomic masses to calculate moles.

$$65.02 \text{ g Pt} \times \frac{1 \text{ mol Pt}}{195.1 \text{ g Pt}} = 0.3333 \text{ mol Pt}$$

$$2.02 \text{ g H} \times \frac{1 \text{ mol H}}{1.008 \text{ g H}} = 2.00 \text{ mol H}$$

$$9.34 \text{ g N} \times \frac{1 \text{ mol N}}{14.01 \text{ g N}} = 0.667 \text{ mol N}$$

$$23.63 \text{ g Cl} \times \frac{1 \text{ mol Cl}}{35.45 \text{ g Cl}} = 0.6666 \text{ mol Cl}$$

Step 3 Divide through by the smallest number of moles.

$$\frac{0.3333 \text{ mol Pt}}{0.3333} = 1.000 \text{ mol Pt} \qquad a = 1$$

$$\frac{2.00 \text{ mol H}}{0.3333} = 6.01 \text{ mol H} \qquad c = 6$$

$$\frac{0.667 \text{ mol N}}{0.3333} = 2.00 \text{ mol N} \qquad b = 2$$

$$\frac{0.6666 \text{ mol Cl}}{0.3333} = 2.000 \text{ mol Cl} \qquad d = 2$$

The empirical formula for cisplatin is $PtN_2H_6Cl_2$. Note that the number for hydrogen is slightly greater than 6 because of rounding.

 Practice Problem • Exercise 6.14

The most common form of nylon (Nylon-6) is 63.68% carbon, 12.38% nitrogen, 9.80% hydrogen, and 14.4% oxygen. Calculate the empirical formula for Nylon-6.

C. Calculation of Molecular Formulas

If we know the composition of a compound in terms of the masses (or mass percentages) of the elements present, we can calculate the empirical formula but not the molecular formula. For reasons that will become clear as we consider Example 6.15, to obtain the molecular formula we must know the molar mass. Next we will consider compounds where both the percent composition and the molar mass are known.

Step 1
In 100.00 g of Nylon-6 the masses of elements present are 63.68 g C, 12.38 g N, 9.80 g H, and 14.14 g O.

Step 2
$$63.68 \text{ g C} \times \frac{1 \text{ mol C}}{12.01 \text{ g C}} = 5.302 \text{ mol C}$$

$$12.38 \text{ g N} \times \frac{1 \text{ mol N}}{14.01 \text{ g N}} = 0.8837 \text{ mol N}$$

$$9.80 \text{ g H} \times \frac{1 \text{ mol H}}{1.008 \text{ g H}} = 9.72 \text{ mol H}$$

$$14.14 \text{ g O} \times \frac{1 \text{ mol O}}{16.00 \text{ g O}} = 0.8838 \text{ mol O}$$

Step 3
$$\frac{5.302 \text{ mol C}}{0.8837} = 6.000 \text{ mol C}$$

$$\frac{0.8837 \text{ mol N}}{0.8837} = 1.000 \text{ mol N}$$

$$\frac{9.72 \text{ mol H}}{0.8837} = 11.0 \text{ mol H}$$

$$\frac{0.8838 \text{ mol O}}{0.8837} = 1.000 \text{ mol O}$$

The empirical formula for Nylon-6 is $C_6NH_{11}O$.

6.3.C Calculation of Molecular Formulas

Objective To learn to calculate the molecular formula of a compound, given its empirical formula and molar mass

 LABORATORY
EXPERIMENT 24:
Formula of a Hydrate, Traditional

TEACHING TIPS

- Students should understand that, unless they are given the molar mass of a compound, they can calculate only the empirical formula for the compound.

- Tell students that they must first calculate the empirical formula before they can determine the molecular formula for a compound. This idea leads to a discussion of how the molar mass of an empirical formula can be used.

EXAMPLE 6.15

More Examples

1. A compound containing carbon, hydrogen, and oxygen is found to be 40.00% carbon and 6.700% hydrogen by mass. The molar mass of this compound is between 115 g/mol and 125 g/mol. Determine the molecular formula for this compound.

   $C_4H_8O_4$

2. Caffeine is a compound containing carbon, hydrogen, nitrogen, and oxygen. The mass percent composition of caffeine is 49.47% carbon, 5.191% hydrogen, 28.86% nitrogen, and 16.48% oxygen. The molar mass of caffeine is approximately 194 g/mol. Determine the molecular formula for caffeine.

   $C_8H_{10}N_4O_2$

EXAMPLE 6.15

Calculating Molecular Formulas

A white powder is analyzed and found to have an empirical formula of P_2O_5. The compound has a molar mass of 283.88 g/mol. What is the compound's molecular formula?

Solution

Where do we want to go?

Molecular formula = P_xO_y

- $x = ?$
- $y = ?$

What do we know?

- Empirical formula = P_2O_5
- Molar mass = 283.88 g/mol
- Atomic masses

  P = 30.97 g/mol   O = 16.00 g/mol

How do we get there?

To obtain the molecular formula, we must compare the empirical formula mass to the molar mass. The empirical formula mass for P_2O_5 is the mass of 1 mol of P_2O_5 units.

$$
\begin{aligned}
&\overset{\text{Atomic mass of P}}{} \\
2 \text{ mol P: } &2 \times 30.97 \text{ g} = 61.94 \text{ g} \\
5 \text{ mol O: } &5 \times \underline{16.00 \text{ g}} = \underline{80.00 \text{ g}} \\
&\phantom{5 \times 16.00 \text{ g} = } 141.94 \text{ g} \quad \text{Mass of 1 mol of } P_2O_5 \text{ units} \\
&\underset{\text{Atomic mass of O}}{}
\end{aligned}
$$

Recall that the molecular formula contains a whole number of empirical formula units. That is,

Molecular formula = (empirical formula)$_n$

where n is a small whole number. Now, because

Molecular formula = $n \times$ empirical formula

then

Molar mass = $n \times$ empirical formula mass

Solving for n gives

$$n = \frac{\text{molar mass}}{\text{empirical formula mass}}$$

Thus, to determine the molecular formula, we first divide the molar mass by the empirical formula mass. This tells us how many empirical formula masses are present in one molar mass.

$$\frac{\text{Molar mass}}{\text{Empirical formula mass}} = \frac{283.88 \text{ g}}{141.94 \text{ g}} = 2$$

Meeting Individual Needs

CHALLENGE PROJECTS

For an advanced project on chemical formulas, see *Using Analogies to Explain Molecular and Empirical Formulas* located in the *Teacher Resources*.

This result means that $n = 2$ for this compound, so the molecular formula consists of two empirical formula units, and the molecular formula is $(P_2O_5)_2$, or P_4O_{10}. Thus $x = 4$, $y = 10$. The structure of this interesting compound is shown in **Figure 6.3.**

 Practice Problem • Exercise 6.15

A compound used as an additive for gasoline to help prevent engine knock shows the following percentage composition:

71.65% Cl   24.27% C   4.07% H

The molar mass is known to be 98.96 g. Determine the empirical formula and the molecular formula for this compound.

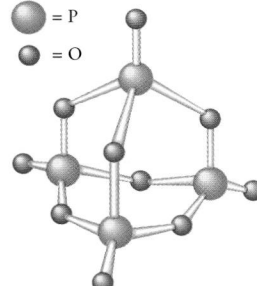

= P
= O

Figure 6.3
The structure of P_4O_{10} as a "ball-and-stick" model. This compound has a great affinity for water and is often used as a desiccant, or drying agent.

The molecular formula is always a whole number multiple of the empirical formula.

For example, the sugar glucose (see Figure 6.2) has the empirical formula CH_2O and the molecular formula $C_6H_{12}O_6$. In this case there are six empirical formula units in each glucose molecule:

$$(CH_2O)_6 = C_6H_{12}O_6$$

In general, we can represent the molecular formula in terms of the empirical formula as follows:

(Empirical formula)$_n$ = molecular formula

where n is a whole number. If $n = 1$, the molecular formula is the same as the empirical formula. For example, for carbon dioxide the empirical formula (CO_2) and the molecular formula (CO_2) are the same, so $n = 1$. On the other hand, for tetraphosphorus decoxide the empirical formula is P_2O_5 and the molecular formula is $P_4O_{10} = (P_2O_5)_2$. In this case $n = 2$.

 nformation

Molecular formula = (empirical formula)$_n$, where n is a whole number.

 Active Reading Question

What data are needed to determine the empirical formula of a compound? What additional information is needed to determine the molecular formula of this compound?

Step 1
Convert mass percents to mass in grams. In 100.0 g of the compound, there are 71.65 g of chlorine, 24.27 g of carbon, and 4.07 g of hydrogen.

Step 2
Use these masses to compute the moles of atoms present.

$71.65 \text{ g Cl} \times \dfrac{1 \text{ mol Cl}}{35.45 \text{ g Cl}} = 2.021 \text{ mol Cl}$

$24.27 \text{ g C} \times \dfrac{1 \text{ mol C}}{12.01 \text{ g C}} = 2.021 \text{ mol C}$

$4.07 \text{ g H} \times \dfrac{1 \text{ mol H}}{1.008 \text{ g H}} = 4.04 \text{ mol H}$

Step 3
Dividing each mole value by 2.021 (the smallest number of moles present), we obtain the empirical formula $ClCH_2$.

To determine the molecular formula, we must compare the empirical formula mass to the molar mass. The empirical formula mass is 49.48.

Cl:	35.45
C:	12.01
2 H:	2 × (1.008)
$ClCH_2$:	49.48 = empirical formula mass

The molar mass is known to be 98.96. We know that

Molar mass = n × (empirical formula mass)

So we can obtain the value of n as follows:

$$\dfrac{\text{Molar mass}}{\text{Empirical formula mass}} =$$

$$\dfrac{98.96}{49.48} = 2$$

Molecular formula = $(ClCH_2)_2$

$= Cl_2C_2H_4$

This substance is composed of molecules with the formula $Cl_2C_2H_4$.

 Active Reading Question

For an empirical formula, we need the relative number of each type of atom in the compound, which can be determined given each element's mass percent. For a molecular formula, we also need the molar mass of the compound.

SECTION 6.3
Review Questions

1 The empirical formula for a compound is the same as the molecular formula whenever the empirical molar mass is the same as the compound's molecular molar mass.

2. Because only whole numbers of atoms combine to form compounds, we use whole numbers to express the empirical formula.

3. To determine the molecular formula from the empirical formula, the molar mass of the compound must be known.

4. CuO

5. C_4H_{10}

6. $C_{12}H_{22}O_{11}$

CHEMISTRY IN YOUR WORLD

Consumer Connection

Nutrition Facts

The food you eat contains all kinds of nutrients. But how much of what things? And is it healthful or "junk food"? To help you make informed decisions about the food you choose to eat, the U.S. Food and Drug Administration requires manufacturers to place nutrition facts on the packages of processed foods. Look at the label shown here from a package of macaroni. Notice that the values of several substances are given as % Daily Value. Because it is important to know the percent composition for food, the labels must list the percentages of fat, trans fat, protein, carbohydrate, and other vital chemicals. You can use these guides to help you consume a healthy diet.

The law requires that the content of food (per serving) be printed on the label.

Nutrition Facts
Serving Size 1/2 cup (220g)
Servings Per Container about 2

Amount Per Serving	
Calories 320	Calories from Fat 80

	% Daily Value*
Total Fat 9g	14%
Saturated Fat 4g	20%
Trans Fat 0g	
Cholesterol 20mg	6%
Sodium 880mg	37%
Total Carbohydrate 45g	15%
Dietary Fiber 4g	16%
Sugars 5g	
Protein 14g	

Vitamin A 6%	•	Vitamin C 0%
Calcium 20%	•	Iron 10%

SECTION 6.3
REVIEW QUESTIONS

❶ Is the empirical formula for a compound ever the same as its molecular formula? Explain.

❷ Why are the subscripts in a chemical formula whole numbers (for example, N_2O_5 instead of $NO_{2.5}$)?

❸ What critical piece of information must be known (or given in the problem) in order to determine the molecular formula for a compound from its empirical compound?

❹ When 1.50 g of copper is heated in air, it reacts with oxygen to achieve a final mass of 1.88 g. Calculate the empirical formula of this copper oxide.

❺ A certain hydrocarbon (a compound consisting of carbon and hydrogen) is 82.66% carbon by mass and has a molar mass of 58.12 g. Determine the molecular formula of this hydrocarbon.

❻ The following graph shows the mass percent of the elements in sucrose (table sugar). Determine the empirical formula for sucrose.

Percent Composition of Sucrose

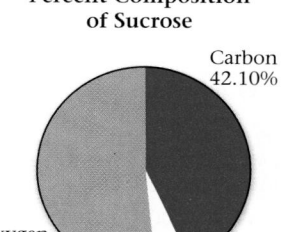

Carbon 42.10%
Oxygen 51.42%
Hydrogen 6.48%

RESEARCH LINKS
CLASSZONE.COM

Chemistry in Your World
Nutrition Facts

Additional Activity The nutrition labels on snack foods list the mass of sodium per serving. Have students choose a snack food or drink and record the mass of sodium per serving and the number of servings in the container. Have them determine the number of moles and atoms of sodium both per serving and for the whole container. Write the data on the board for all of the snacks. Which snacks contain the most sodium per serving? Which contain the least sodium?

Chapter 6 Review

Key Terms

Key Ideas

6.1 Atoms and Moles

- Objects do not need to have identical masses to be counted by weighing. All we need to know is the average mass of the objects.

- To count the atoms in a sample of a given element by weighing we must know the mass of the sample and the average mass for that element.

- Samples in which the ratio of the masses is the same as the ratio of the masses of the individual atoms always contain the same number of atoms.

- One mole of anything contains 6.022×10^{23} units of that substance.

- A sample of an element with a mass equal to that element's average atomic mass (expressed in g) contains one mole of atoms.

6.2 Molar Mass and Percent Composition

- The molar mass of any compound is the mass in grams of one mole of the compound.

- The molar mass of a compound is the sum of the masses of the component atoms.

- $$\text{Moles of a compound} = \frac{\text{mass of the sample (g)}}{\text{molar mass of the compound (g/mol)}}$$

- Mass of a sample (g) = (moles of sample) $\times$ (molar mass of compound)

- Percent composition consists of the mass percent of each element in a compound:

  $$\text{Mass percent} = \frac{\text{mass of a given element in 1 mol of a compound}}{\text{mass of 1 mol of compound}} \times 100\%$$

6.3 Formulas of Compounds

- The empirical formula of a compound is the simplest whole number ratio of the atoms present in the compound.

- The empirical formula can be found from the percent composition of the compound.

- The molecular formula is the exact formula of the molecules present in a substance.

- The molecular formula is always a whole number multiple of the empirical formula.

- The following diagram shows these different ways of expressing the same information.

RESEARCH LINKS
CLASSZONE.COM

Meeting Individual Needs
CHAPTER REVIEW

Chapter 6 Review Worksheet at the appropriate level:
   Basic
   Standard
   Challenge

CHAPTER SUMMARY

A **Chapter Summary** that includes additional Active Reading Questions for Chapter 6 is available.

Assessment Resources
CHAPTER 6

Chapter 6 Test

TECHNOLOGY

 Computerized Test Bank for Chapter 6

Chapter 6 Assessment

Chapter 6 Assessment (answers)

1. 11.0 g; 909 washers

2. 307 corks; 116 stoppers; 2640 g

3. The atomic mass unit (amu) is a unit of mass used to more simply describe relative masses on an atomic or molecular scale. One amu is equivalent to 1.66×10^{-24} g.

4. The average atomic mass is a weighted average including a contribution based on the mass of the individual isotopes of an element and their abundance in nature.

5. (a) 640. amu
   (b) 2.319×10^6 amu
   (c) 1642 amu
   (d) 1.011×10^{25} amu
   (e) 4.976×10^4 amu

6. (a) 1 B atom
   (b) 10 S atoms
   (c) 100 Au atoms
   (d) 150 Xe atoms
   (e) 133 Al atoms

7. 258 S atoms; 1.672×10^{26} amu

8. 1.205×10^{24}

9. Avogadro's number (6.022×10^{23})

10. 20.05 g Ca; 40.08 g

11. 177 g

12. 2.66×10^{-23} g

13. 0.50 mol O

14. (a) 0.133 mol Au
    (b) 1.04 mol Ca
    (c) 2.44×10^{-3} mol Ba
    (d) 1.33×10^{-5} mol Pd
    (e) 5.20×10^{-13} mol Ni
    (f) 8.12 mol Fe
    (g) 1.000 mol C

15. (a) 112 g Fe
    (b) 30.6 g Ni
    (c) 0.240 g Pt
    (d) 1.50×10^4 g Pb
    (e) 0.0248 g Mg
    (f) 1.31×10^5 g Al
    (g) 1468 g Li
    (h) 3.95×10^{-5} g Na

All exercises with blue numbers have answers in the back of this book.

6.1 Atoms and Moles

A. Counting by Weighing

1. Merchants usually sell small nuts, washers, and bolts by weight (like jelly beans!) rather than by individually counting the items. Suppose a particular type of washer weighs 0.110 g on the average. What would 100 such washers weigh? How many washers would there be in 100 g of washers?

2. A particular small laboratory cork weighs 1.63 g, whereas a rubber lab stopper of the same size weighs 4.31 g. How many corks would there be in 500 g of such corks? How many rubber stoppers would there be in 500 g of similar stoppers? How many grams of rubber stoppers would be needed to contain the same number of stoppers as there are corks in 1.00 kg of corks?

B. Atomic Masses: Counting Atoms by Weighing

3. Define the *amu*. What is one amu equivalent to in grams?

4. Why do we use the *average* atomic mass of the elements when performing calculations?

5. Using average atomic masses for each of the following elements (see the table in the inside front cover of this book), calculate the mass, in amu, of each of the following samples.
   a. 635 atoms of hydrogen
   b. 1.261×10^4 atoms of tungsten
   c. 42 atoms of potassium
   d. 7.213×10^{23} atoms of nitrogen
   e. 891 atoms of iron

6. Using average atomic masses for each of the following elements (see the table in the inside front cover of this book), calculate the number of atoms present in each of the following samples.
   a. 10.81 amu of boron
   b. 320.7 amu of sulfur
   c. 19,697 amu of gold
   d. 19,695 amu of xenon
   e. 3588.3 amu of aluminum

7. If an average atom of sulfur weighs 32.07 amu, how many sulfur atoms are contained in a sample with mass 8274 amu? What is the mass of 5.213×10^{24} sulfur atoms?

C. The Mole

8. In 24.02 g of carbon, there are _____ carbon atoms.

9. A sample equal to the atomic mass of an element in grams contains _____ atoms.

10. What mass of calcium metal contains the same number of atoms as 12.16 g of magnesium? What mass of calcium metal contains the same number of atoms as 24.31 g of magnesium?

11. What mass of cobalt contains the same number of atoms as 57.0 g of fluorine?

12. Calculate the average mass in grams of 1 atom of oxygen.

13. Which weighs more, 0.50 mol of oxygen atoms or 4 mol of hydrogen atoms?

14. Using the average atomic masses given in the inside front cover of this book, calculate the number of moles of each element in samples with the following masses.
    a. 26.2 g of gold
    b. 41.5 g of calcium
    c. 335 mg of barium
    d. 1.42×10^{23} g of palladium
    e. 3.05×10^{25} mg of nickel
    f. 1.00 lb of iron
    g. 12.01 g of carbon

15. Using the average atomic masses given in the inside front cover of this book, calculate the *mass in grams* of each of the following samples.
    a. 2.00 mol of iron
    b. 0.521 mol of nickel
    c. 1.23×10^{-3} mol of platinum
    d. 72.5 mol of lead
    e. 0.00102 mol of magnesium
    f. 4.87×10^3 mol of aluminum
    g. 211.5 mol of lithium
    h. 1.72×10^{-6} mol of sodium

210 • Chapter 6 • Chemical Composition

16. Using the average atomic masses given in the inside front cover of this book, calculate the indicated quantities.

    a. the number of cobalt atoms in 0.00103 g of cobalte

    b. the number of cobalt atoms in 0.00103 mol of cobalt

    c. the number of moles of cobalt in 2.75 g of cobalt

    d. the number of moles of cobalt represented by 5.99×10^{21} cobalt atoms

    e. the mass of 4.23 mol of cobalt

    f. the number of cobalt atoms in 4.23 mol of cobalt

    g. the number of cobalt atoms in 4.23 g of cobalt

6.2 Molar Mass and Percent Composition

A. Molar Mass

17. The _____ of a substance is the mass (in grams) of 1 mol of the substance.

18. The molar mass of a substance can be obtained by _____ the atomic masses of the component atoms.

19. Calculate the molar mass for each of the following substances.

    a. sodium nitride, Na_3N

    b. carbon disulfide, CS_2

    c. ammonium bromide, NH_4Br

    d. ethyl alcohol, C_2H_5OH

    e. sulfurous acid, H_2SO_3

    f. sulfuric acid, H_2SO_4

20. Calculate the molar mass for each of the following substances.

    a. barium perchlorate

    b. magnesium sulfate

    c. lead(II) chloride

    d. copper(II) nitrate

    e. tin(IV) chloride

    f. phenol, C_6H_6O

21. Calculate the number of moles of the indicated substance in each of the following samples.

    a. 49.2 mg of sulfur trioxide

    b. 7.44×10^4 kg of lead(IV) oxide

    c. 59.1 g of chloroform, $CHCl_3$

    d. 3.27 mg of trichloroethane, $C_2H_3Cl_3$

    e. 4.01 g of lithium hydroxide

22. Calculate the number of moles of the indicated substance in each of the following samples.

    a. 4.26×10^{-3} g of sodium dihydrogen phosphate

    b. 521 g of copper(I) chloride

    c. 151 kg of iron

    d. 8.76 g of strontium fluoride

    e. 1.26×10^4 g of aluminum

23. Calculate the *mass in grams* of each of the following samples.

    a. 1.50 mol of aluminum iodide

    b. 1.91×10^{-3} mol of benzene, C_6H_6

    c. 4.00 mol of glucose, $C_6H_{12}O_6$

    d. 4.56×10^5 mol of ethanol, C_2H_5OH

    e. 2.27 mol of calcium nitrate

24. Calculate the *mass in grams* of each of the following samples.

    a. 1.27×10^{-3} mol of carbon dioxide

    b. 4.12×10^3 mol of nitrogen trichloride

    c. 0.00451 mol of ammonium nitrate

    d. 18.0 mol of water

    e. 62.7 mol of copper(II) sulfate

25. Calculate the number of *molecules* present in each of the following samples.

    a. 6.37 mol of carbon monoxide

    b. 6.37 g of carbon monoxide

    c. 2.62×10^{-6} g of water

    d. 2.62×10^{-6} mol of water

    e. 5.23 g of benzene, C_6H_6

26. Calculate the number of *moles* of sulfur atoms present in each of the following samples.

    a. 2.01 g of sodium sulfate

    b. 2.01 g of sodium sulfite

    c. 2.01 g of sodium sulfide

    d. 2.01 g of sodium thiosulfate, $Na_2S_2O_3$

Chapter 6 • Assessment • **211**

16. (a) 1.05×10^{19} Co atoms
    (b) 6.20×10^{20} Co atoms
    (c) 0.0467 mol Co
    (d) 0.00995 mol Co
    (e) 249 g Co
    (f) 2.55×10^{24} Co atoms
    (g) 4.32×10^{22} Co atoms

17. molar mass

18. adding (summing)

19. (a) 82.98 g
    (b) 76.15 g
    (c) 97.94 g
    (d) 46.07 g
    (e) 82.09 g
    (f) 98.09 g

20. (a) 336.2 g
    (b) 120.38 g
    (c) 278.1 g
    (d) 187.57 g
    (e) 260.5 g
    (f) 94.11 g

21. (a) 6.14×10^{-4} mol SO_3
    (b) 3.11×10^5 mol PbO_2
    (c) 0.495 mol $CHCl_3$
    (d) 2.45×10^{-8} mol $C_2H_3Cl_3$
    (e) 0.167 mol LiOH

22. (a) 3.55×10^{-5} mol
    (b) 5.26 mol
    (c) 2700 mol
    (d) 0.0697 mol
    (e) 467 mol

23. (a) 612 g AlI_3
    (b) 0.149 g C_6H_6
    (c) 721 g $C_6H_{12}O_6$
    (d) 2.10×10^7 g C_2H_5OH
    (e) 373 g $Ca(NO_3)_2$

24. (a) 0.0559 g CO_2
    (b) 4.96×10^5 g NCl_3
    (c) 0.361 g NH_4NO_3
    (d) 324 g H_2O
    (e) 1.00×10^4 g $CuSO_4$

25. (a) 3.84×10^{24} molecules CO
    (b) 1.37×10^{23} molecules CO
    (c) 8.76×10^{16} molecules H_2O
    (d) 1.58×10^{18} molecules H_2O
    (e) 4.03×10^{22} molecules C_6H_6

26. (a) 0.0141 mol S
    (b) 0.0159 mol S
    (c) 0.0258 mol S
    (d) 0.0254 mol S

212 • Chapter 6 • Chemical Composition

27. (a) 32.37% Na, 22.58% S,
45.05% O
(b) 36.48% Na, 25.44% S,
38.08% O
(c) 58.91% Na, 41.09% S
(d) 29.08% Na, 40.56% S,
30.36% O
(e) 55.26% K, 14.59% P,
30.15% O
(f) 44.90% K, 0.5787% H,
17.78% P, 36.74% O
(g) 28.73% K, 1.481% H,
22.76% P, 47.03% O
(h) 79.10% K, 20.88% P

28. (a) 28.45% Cu
(b) 44.29% Cu
(c) 44.06% Fe
(d) 34.43% Fe
(e) 18.84% Co
(f) 13.41% Co
(g) 88.12% Sn
(h) 78.77% Sn

29. (a) 49.32% C
(b) 35.00% N
(c) 49.47% C
(d) 52.56% Cl
(e) 71.92% C
(f) 39.99% C
(g) 85.03% C
(h) 52.14% C

30. (a) 33.73% NH_4^+
(b) 39.81% Cu^{2+}
(c) 64.94% Au^{3+}
(d) 63.51% Ag^+

31. The mass composition
and the molar mass of a
compound must be known.

32. The empirical formula
represents the smallest whole-
number ratio of the elements
present in a compound. The
molecular formula indicates the
actual number of atoms of each
element found in a molecule of
the substance.

33. (a) NaO
(b) $C_4H_3O_2$
(c) $C_{12}H_{12}N_2O_3$
(d) C_2H_3Cl

34. (a) These have the same
empirical formulas.
(b) These do not have the same
empirical formulas.
(c) These have the same
empirical formulas.
(d) These do not have the same
empirical formulas.

35. C_3H_2OCl

36. CaO

37. $BaSO_4$

38. $AlCl_3$

39. Co_2S_3

6.3 Formulas of Compounds

A. Percent Composition of Compounds

27. Calculate the percent by mass of each element
in the following compounds.

    a. sodium sulfate

    b. sodium sulfite

    c. sodium sulfide

    d. sodium thiosulfate, $Na_2S_2O_3$

    e. potassium phosphate

    f. potassium hydrogen phosphate

    g. potassium dihydrogen phosphate

    h. potassium phosphide

28. Calculate the percent by mass of the element
listed *first* in the formulas for each of the
following compounds.

    a. copper(II) bromide, $CuBr_2$

    b. copper(I) bromide, $CuBr$

    c. iron(II) chloride, $FeCl_2$

    d. iron(III) chloride, $FeCl_3$

    e. cobalt(II) iodide, CoI_2

    f. cobalt(III) iodide, CoI_3

    g. tin(II) oxide, SnO

    h. tin(IV) oxide, SnO_2

29. Calculate the percent by mass of the element
listed first in the formulas for each of the
following compounds.

    a. adipic acid, $C_6H_{10}O_4$

    b. ammonium nitrate, NH_4NO_3

    c. caffeine, $C_8H_{10}N_4O_2$

    d. chlorine dioxide, ClO_2

    e. cyclohexanol, $C_6H_{11}OH$

    f. dextrose, $C_6H_{12}O_6$

    g. eicosane, $C_{20}H_{42}$

    h. ethanol, C_2H_5OH

30. For each of the following ionic substances,
calculate the percentage of the overall molar
mass of the compound that is represented by
the positive ions the compound contains.

    a. ammonium chloride

    b. copper(II) sulfate

    c. gold(III) chloride

    d. silver nitrate

B. Formulas of Compounds

31. What experimental evidence about a new
compound must be known before its formula
can be determined?

32. What does the *empirical* formula of a compound
represent? How does the *molecular* formula differ
from the empirical formula?

33. Give the empirical formula that corresponds to
each of the following molecular formulas.

    a. sodium peroxide, Na_2O_2

    b. terephthalic acid, $C_8H_6O_4$

    c. phenobarbital, $C_{12}H_{12}N_2O_3$

    d. 1,4-dichloro-2-butene, $C_4H_6Cl_2$

34. Which of the following pairs of compounds
have the same *empirical* formula?

    a. acetylene, C_2H_2, and benzene, C_6H_6

    b. ethane, C_2H_6, and butane, C_4H_{10}

    c. nitrogen dioxide, NO_2, and dinitrogen
    tetroxide, N_2O_4

    d. diphenyl ether, $C_{12}H_{10}O$, and phenol,
    C_6H_5OH

C. Calculation of Empirical Formulas

35. A new compound has been prepared. A 0.4791-g
sample was analyzed and was found to contain
the following masses of elements:
carbon, 0.1929 g
hydrogen, 0.01079 g
oxygen, 0.08566 g
chlorine, 0.1898 g
Determine the empirical formula of the new
compound.

36. In an experiment, a 2.514-g sample of calcium
was heated in a stream of pure oxygen, and was
found to increase in mass by 1.004 g. Calculate
the empirical formula of calcium oxide.

37. A compound has the following percentages
by mass: barium, 58.84%; sulfur, 13.74%;
oxygen, 27.43%. Determine the empirical
formula of the compound.

38. If a 1.271-g sample of aluminum metal is heated
in a chlorine gas atmosphere, the mass of aluminum chloride produced is 6.280 g. Calculate the
empirical formula of aluminum chloride.

39. If cobalt metal is mixed with excess sulfur and
heated strongly, a sulfide is produced that
contains 55.06% cobalt by mass. Calculate the
empirical formula of the sulfide.

40. If 2.461 g of metallic calcium is heated in a stream of chlorine gas, 4.353 g of Cl_2 is absorbed in forming the metal chloride. Calculate the empirical formula of calcium chloride.

41. If 10.00 g of copper metal is heated strongly in the air, the sample gains 2.52 g of oxygen in forming an oxide. Determine the empirical formula of this oxide.

42. A compound has the following percentage composition by mass: copper, 33.88%; nitrogen, 14.94%; oxygen, 51.18%. Determine the empirical formula of the compound.

43. Sodium and nitrogen form two binary compounds. The percentages of the elements in these compounds are:

Compound	Na	N
1	83.12%	16.88%
2	35.36%	64.64%

Calculate the empirical formula of each of the compounds.

D. Calculation of Molecular Formulas

44. How does the molecular formula of a compound differ from the empirical formula? Can a compound's empirical and molecular formulas be the same? Explain.

45. What information do we need to determine the molecular formula of a compound if we know only the empirical formula?

46. A compound with the empirical formula CH_2O was found to have a molar mass between 89 and 91 g. What is the molecular formula of the compound?

47. A compound with the empirical formula CH_2 was found to have a molar mass of approximately 84 g. What is the molecular formula of the compound?

48. A compound with the empirical formula CH_4O was found in a subsequent experiment to have a molar mass of approximately 192 g. What is the molecular formula of the compound?

49. A compound having an approximate molar mass of 165–170 g has the following percentage composition by mass: carbon, 42.87%; hydrogen, 3.598%; oxygen, 28.55%; nitrogen, 25.00%. Determine the empirical and molecular formulas of the compound.

50. A compound consists of 65.45% C, 5.492% H, and 29.06% O on a mass basis and has a molar mass of approximately 110. Determine the molecular formula of the compound.

Critical Thinking

51. Use the periodic table inside the back cover of this text to determine the atomic mass (per mole) or molar mass of each of the substances in column 1, and find that mass in column 2.

Column 1

(1) molybdenum
(2) lanthanum
(3) carbon tetrabromide
(4) mercury(II) oxide
(5) titanium(IV) oxide
(6) manganese(II) chloride
(7) phosphine, PH_3
(8) tin(II) fluoride
(9) lead(II) sulfide
(10) copper(I) oxide

Column 2

(a) 33.99 g
(b) 79.9 g
(c) 95.94 g
(d) 125.84 g
(e) 138.9 g
(f) 143.1 g
(g) 156.7 g
(h) 216.6 g
(i) 239.3 g
(j) 331.6 g

52. Copy and complete the following table.

Mass of Sample	Moles of Sample	Atoms in Sample
5.00 g Al		
	0.00250 mol Fe	
		2.6×10^{24} atoms Cu
0.00250 g Mg		
	2.7×10^{23} mol Na	
		1.00×10^4 atoms U

40. $CaCl_2$

41. CuO

42. CuN_2O_6 [$Cu(NO_3)_2$]

43. Na_3N; NaN_3

44. The empirical formula represents the smallest whole-number relationship between the number and types of atoms in a compound. The molecular formula represents the actual number of atoms of each type in a true molecule of the substance. Water is an example of a compound that has the same empirical and molecular formulas.

45. molar mass

46. $C_3H_6O_3$

47. C_6H_{12}

48. $C_6H_{24}O_6$

49. empirical formula: C_2H_2ON
molecular formula: $C_6H_6O_3N_3$

50. empirical formula: C_3H_3O
molecular formula: $C_6H_6O_2$

51. (1) c
(2) e
(3) j
(4) h
(5) b
(6) d
(7) a
(8) g
(9) i
(10) f

52. 5.00 g Al, 0.185 mol, 1.12×10^{23} atoms; 0.140 g Fe, 0.00250 mol, 1.51×10^{21} atoms; 270 g Cu, 4.3 mol, 2.6×10^{24} atoms; 0.00250 g Mg, 1.30×10^{-4} mol, 6.19×10^{19} atoms; 0.062 g Na, 2.7×10^{-3} mol, 1.6×10^{21} atoms; 3.95×10^{-18} g U, 1.66×10^{-20} mol, 1.00×10^4 atoms

53. 4.24 g C_6H_6, 0.0543 mol,
3.27×10^{22} molecules,
3.92×10^{23} atoms;
4.04 g H_2O, 0.224 mol,
1.35×10^{23} molecules,
4.05×10^{23} atoms;
1.98 g CO_2, 0.0450 mol,
2.71×10^{22} molecules,
8.13×10^{22} atoms;
45.9 g HCl, 1.26 mol,
7.59×10^{23} molecules,
1.52×10^{24} atoms;
126 g H_2O, 6.99 mol,
4.21×10^{24} molecules,
1.26×10^{25} atoms;
0.297 g CH_3OH,
0.00927 mol,
5.58×10^{21} molecules,
3.35×10^{22} atoms

54. Mg_3N_2; MgO

55. Cu_2O, CuO

56. empirical formula: $C_4H_8O_4S$
molecular formula: $C_4H_8O_4S$

57. 2.12 g Fe

58. 2.36 g Co

59. $CuSH_{10}O_9$ (usually written as
$CuSO_4 \cdot 5H_2O$)

60. $C_3H_7N_2O$

61. HgO

62. $BaCl_2$

63. HNO_3

64. carbon (C)

65. (1) g
(2) c
(3) b
(4) a
(5) j
(6) i
(7) f
(8) h
(9) e
(10) d

53. Copy and complete the following table.

Mass of Sample	Moles of Sample	Molecules in Sample	Atoms in Sample
4.24 g C_6H_6			
	0.224 mol H_2O		
		2.71×10^{22} molecules CO_2	
	1.26 mol HCl		
		4.21×10^{24} molecules H_2O	
0.297 g CH_3OH			

54. A binary compound of magnesium and nitrogen is analyzed, and 1.2791 g of the compound is found to contain 0.9240 g of magnesium. When a second sample of this compound is treated with water and heated, the nitrogen is driven off as ammonia, leaving a compound that contains 60.31% magnesium and 39.69% oxygen by mass. Calculate the empirical formulas of the two magnesium compounds.

55. When a 2.118-g sample of copper is heated in an atmosphere in which the amount of oxygen present is restricted, the sample gains 0.2666 g of oxygen in forming a reddish-brown oxide. However, when 2.118 g of copper is heated in a stream of pure oxygen, the sample gains 0.5332 g of oxygen. Calculate the empirical formulas of the two oxides of copper.

56. A molecule of an organic compound has twice as many hydrogen atoms as carbon atoms, the same number of oxygen atoms as carbon atoms, and one-eighth as many sulfur atoms as hydrogen atoms. The molar mass of the compound is 152 g/mol. What are the empirical and molecular formulas for this compound?

57. Calculate the number of grams of iron that contain the same number of atoms as 2.24 g of cobalt.

58. Calculate the number of grams of cobalt that contain the same number of atoms as 2.24 g of iron.

59. A strikingly beautiful copper compound with the common name "blue vitriol" has the following elemental composition: 25.45% Cu, 12.84% S, 4.036% H, 57.67% O. Determine the empirical formula of the compound.

60. A 0.7221-g sample of a new compound has been analyzed and found to contain the following masses of elements: carbon, 0.2990 g; hydrogen, 0.05849 g; nitrogen, 0.2318 g; oxygen, 0.1328 g. Calculate the empirical formula of the compound.

61. When 4.01 g of mercury is strongly heated in air, the resulting oxide weighs 4.33 g. Calculate the empirical formula of the oxide.

62. When barium metal is heated in chlorine gas, a binary compound forms that consists of 65.95% Ba and 34.05% Cl by mass. Calculate the empirical formula of the compound.

63. A particular compound in the chemistry laboratory is found to contain 7.2×10^{24} atoms of oxygen, 56.0 g of nitrogen, and 4.0 mol of hydrogen. What is its empirical formula?

64. The compound A_2O is 63.7% A (a mystery element) and 36.3% oxygen. What is the identity of element A?

65. Find the item in list B that best explains or completes the statement or question in list A.

List A

(1) 1 amu
(2) 1008 amu
(3) mass of the "average" atom of an element
(4) number of carbon atoms in 12.01 g of carbon
(5) 6.022×10^{23} molecules
(6) total mass of all atoms in 1 mol of a compound
(7) smallest whole-number ratio of atoms present in a molecule
(8) formula showing the actual number of atoms present in a molecule
(9) product formed when any carbon-containing compound is burned in O_2
(10) have the same empirical formulas, but different molecular formulas

List B

(a) 6.022×10^{23}
(b) atomic mass
(c) mass of 1000 hydrogen atoms
(d) benzene, C_6H_6, and acetylene, C_2H_2
(e) carbon dioxide
(f) empirical formula
(g) 1.66×10^{-24} g
(h) molecular formula
(i) molar mass
(j) 1 mol

1 You have been saving dimes for a long time and take all of them to the bank to exchange for dollar bills. The teller weighs the dimes and records a total mass of 3358 g. If a dime has an average mass of 2.30 g, how much money are you owed?

A $7723.40   C $2.30

B $1460   D $146

2 How many atoms of neon (Ne) are in a sample of neon with a mass of 1452.96 amu?

A   29,321   C   65

B   72   D 6.02×10^{23}

3 Consider a 20.0 g sample of silver (Ag) metal and a 20.0 g sample of another "mystery" metal. You are told that there are exactly four times as many atoms of the "mystery" metal as of silver metal. Identify the "mystery" metal.

A   Iron (Fe)   C   Platinum (Pt)

B   Lithium (Li)   D   Aluminum (Al)

4 Which of the following is the most accurate description of a mole?

A   The number of atoms in 55.85 grams of iron (Fe).

B   The mass of carbon in a measured sample of carbon.

C   The number of atoms in any given mass of a molecule.

D 6.022×10^{23} grams of a sample of any element.

5 The molar mass of calcium nitrate, $Ca(NO_3)_2$, is:

A   102.09 g/mol

B   70.09 g/mol

C   164.1 g/mol

D   100.1 g/mol

6 A single molecule of a particular compound has a mass of 4.65×10^{-23} g. Which of the following could be this compound?

A   CO

B H_2O

C NO_2

D NH_3

7 What is the percent by mass of carbon in table sugar (sucrose, $C_{12}H_{22}O_{11}$)?

A   27.80%   C   56.69%

B   42.10%   D   71.38%

8 Which of the following compounds have the same empirical formulas?

A H_2O and H_2O_2

B N_2O_4 and NO_2

C   CO   and CO_2

D CH_4 and C_2H_6

9 The percent by mass of nitrogen is 46.7% for a species containing only nitrogen and oxygen. Which of the following could be this species?

A N_2O_5 C   NO

B NO_2 D N_2O

10 A compound consisting of carbon, hydrogen, and oxygen is found to contain 40.00% carbon by mass, and 6.71% hydrogen by mass. A 0.0500 mol sample of the compound has a mass of 9.00 g. Determine the molecular formula for the compound.

A $C_8H_{16}O_4$

B C_6HO_8

C $C_6H_{14}O_6$

D $C_6H_{12}O_6$

11 You are given the percent by mass of the elements in a compound and wish to determine the empirical formula. Label each of the following statements as true or false and explain your answers.

a.   You must assume exactly 100.0 g of the compound.

b.   You must convert percent by mass to relative numbers of atoms.

c.   You must divide all of the percent by mass numbers by the smallest percent by mass.

d.   You cannot solve for the empirical formula without the molar mass.

12 An oxide with the formula MO_2 is 40.1% oxygen by mass. Determine the identity of M.

---

1. D
2. B
3. D
4. A
5. C
6. A
7. B
8. B
9. C
10. D
11. a. False. We can assume any mass of the compound, but 100.0 g makes sense because we are given data in terms of mass percents (which add up to 100%).

   b. True. The empirical formula gives the relative ratios of the number of atoms in a compound.

   c. False. This would give relative percent by mass values when we need the relative number of each type of atom in a compound. We need to divide the number of atoms (or mol of atoms) by the smallest number of atoms (or mol of atoms).

   d. False. We need the molar mass to determine the molecular formula.

12. M is titanium (Ti).

Test-Taking Strategy

Explain that test items may require multiple steps before arriving at the correct answer. Caution students about looking at the answer choices before they have completed all of the steps because intermediate answers often are given as distracters.

Planning Guide

Section	Segment	Text Features and Components	Labs, Demonstrations, & Activities

7.1 Evidence for a Chemical Reaction
0.5 Block
pp. 218–219
			TE Mini-Demo *p. 219*
			TE Teaching Support: Demonstration *p. 219*
			RP Classroom Activities and Projects *TE p. 218*
			LM Experiment 25: Recognizing Chemical Reactions, Microscale
			  Lab Manual
			  Report Sheets
			  Teacher's Lab Guide
			LM Experiment 26: Examples of Reactions
			  Lab Manual
			  Report Sheets
			  Teacher's Lab Guide

7.2 Chemical Equations **1 Block** pp. 220–223			**TE** Teaching Support: Demonstration *p. 220*

7.3 Balancing Chemical Equations
1.5 Blocks
pp. 224–232
		SE Chemistry in Your World: The Bombardier Beetle *p. 229*	**TE** Teaching Support: Demonstration *p. 225*
			SE Hands-On Chemistry: Modeling Equations *p. 229*
			LM Experiment 27: Interpreting Chemical Reactions, Microscale
			  Lab Manual
			  Report Sheets
			  Teacher's Lab Guide
			LM Experiment 28: Conservation of Mass, Traditional
			  Lab Manual
			  Report Sheets
			  Teacher's Lab Guide

Key			
SE Student Edition	**TE** Teacher Edition	**RP** Teacher Resource Package	
AR Additional Materials	**LM** Lab Materials	Transparencies	
DVD	CD-ROM	classzone.com	

All Learners	Technology	Review & Assessment	Standards
(TE) Teaching Tip *p. 218*	(•) Video: Barking Dogs: Reaction of Phosphorus (•) Video: Dry Ice and Magnesium (•) Video: Nickel(II) Complexes (•) Video: Reactions of Silver(I) (•) Video: Zinc and Iodine (•) Video: Oxygen, Hydrogen, Soap Bubbles, & Balloons (•) Video: Copper Metal in Nitric Acid (•) Video: Thermite Reaction (📁) Transparency: Table 7.1 (💽) Lab Generator CD (•) EasyPlannner	(SE) Review Questions (7.1) *p. 219*	(TE) **NSES** UCP1, UCP3, A1, A2, B3, C6, E1, E2, F1, F5, G3
(TE) Teaching Tip *p. 220* (TE) Meeting Individual Needs *p. 221* (TE) Meeting Individual Needs *p. 222*	(📁) Transparency: Figure 7.2 (•) EasyPlanner	(SE) Active Reading Question *p. 221* (TE) More Examples *p. 222* (SE) Practice Problem *p. 223* (SE) Review Questions (7.2) *p. 223* (SE) Key Terms *p. 233*	
(TE) Teaching Tips *pp. 224–226* (TE) Meeting Individual Needs *p. 226* (TE) Meeting Individual Needs *p. 227* (RP) MINT: Reading Concepts *TE p. 224* (RP) Team Learning Worksheet (Chapter 7)	(•) Animation: Conservation of Mass: Balancing Equations (💽) Lab Generator CD (•) EasyPlannner	(SE) Active Reading Question *p. 225* (SE) Critical Thinking *p. 225* (SE) Active Reading Question *p. 227* (SE) Active Reading Question *p. 227* (TE) More Examples *p. 228* (SE) Critical Thinking *p. 228* (TE) More Examples *p. 230* (SE) Practice Problem *p. 231* (TE) More Examples *p. 231* (SE) Practice Problem *p. 232* (SE) Review Questions (7.3) *p. 232* (SE) Key Terms *p. 233*	

Resource Materials for Chapter 7

(SE) Chapter Review *p. 233*

(SE) Critical Thinking *p. 236*

(SE) Standardized Test Practice *p. 237*

(AR) English/Spanish Summaries

(💽) English Summaries Audio

(💽) Spanish Summaries Audio

(RP) Meeting Individual Needs Toolkit (MINT)
    Reading Concepts
    Chapter Review Worksheets
    Chapter Summaries

(RP) Solutions Guide

(RP) Standardized Test Practice

(RP) Chapter Tests

(RP) Test Bank

(ℹ) Test Generator

Chapter 7

Overview

In this chapter our goals are for students to:

- Learn the signals that show a chemical reaction has occurred

- Learn to identify the characteristics of a chemical reaction and the information given by a chemical reaction

- Learn to write a balanced equation for a chemical reaction

Chapter 7

Chemical Reactions: An Introduction

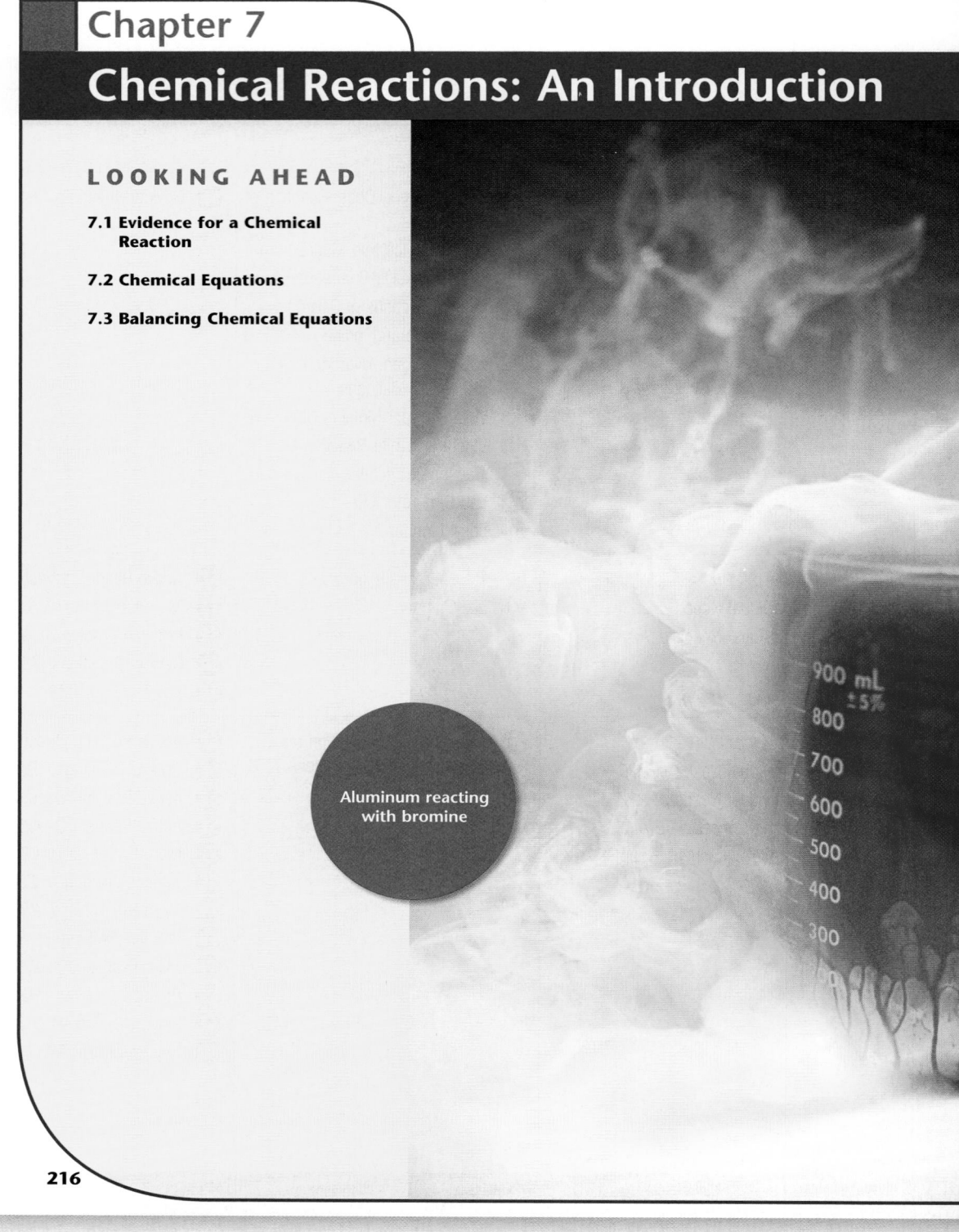

Aluminum reacting with bromine

900 mL
±5%
800
700
600
500
400
300

216

Prereading Questions

1. *Answers will vary.* Students may be aware of some clues, such as heat (or flames and smoke) or color changes.

2. $H_2(g) + O_2(g) \rightarrow H_2O(l)$ (unbalanced)

3. *Answers will vary,* but should convey that atoms are neither created nor destroyed in a chemical reaction.

IN YOUR LIFE

Chemistry is about change. Grass grows. Steel rusts. Hair is bleached, dyed, "permed," or straightened. Natural gas burns to heat houses. Nylon is produced for jackets, swimsuits, and pantyhose. Water is decomposed to hydrogen and oxygen gas by an electric current. The bombardier beetle concocts a toxic spray to shoot at its enemies.

These are just a few examples of chemical changes that affect each of us. Chemical reactions are the heart and soul of chemistry, and in this chapter we will discuss fundamental ideas about chemical reactions.

Nylon jackets are sturdy and dry quickly. These characteristics make them ideal for athletic wear.

WHAT DO YOU KNOW?

Prereading Questions

1. How can you tell that a chemical reaction has taken place?

2. Hydrogen gas reacts with oxygen gas to form water. Write a chemical equation for this reaction.

3. Write the law of conservation of matter in your own words.

Chemical Reactions: An Introduction • Chapter 7 • **217**

TECHNOLOGY IN THE CLASSROOM

 Transparencies
Figure: 7.2
Table: 7.1

 Power Presentation DVD
   PowerPoint Slides
   Animation
   Conservation of Mass: Balancing Equations
   Videos
   Barking Dogs: Reaction of Phosphorus
   Dry Ice and Magnesium
   Nickel(II) Complexes
   Reactions of Silver(I)

Zinc and Iodine
Oxygen, Hydrogen, Soap Bubbles, and Balloons
Copper Metal in Nitric Acid
Thermite Reaction
eEdition
EasyPlanner

 Lab Generator CD
English Summaries CD
Spanish Summaries CD
ML Test Generator

 classzone.com

Student Preparation

Assign students to read Sections 7.1 through 7.3 and to answer the Review Questions at the end of each section before coming to class.

 Active Learning
Team Learning Worksheet

After introducing the material in Chapter 7 in class, place students in groups and have them work together on **Chapter 7: Team Learning Worksheet.**

 Active Learning
Classroom Activities and Projects

Have students work together on *Evidence of a Chemical Reaction* located in the *Teacher Resources.*

SECTION 7.1
GUIDE THE LEARNING

Homework

You may wish to assign these selected end-of-chapter problems as homework for this section: 1, 2, 3, 4

Additional end-of-chapter problems can be used for extra practice.

 LABORATORY
EXPERIMENT 25:
Recognizing Chemical Reactions, Microscale

LABORATORY
EXPERIMENT 26:
Examples of Reactions

TEACHING TIP

Macroscopic clues are helpful but incomplete. We emphasize a microscopic perspective throughout the book because this model is a more powerful way to explain reactions. For example, if we rely on a color change as proof of a reaction, what about adding food coloring to water? Boiling water involves heat and results in the production of a gas, but it is not a chemical change. The production of a solid from the cooling of melted wax is also a physical change.

Objective

- *To learn the signals that show a chemical reaction has occurred*

How do we know when a chemical change (a reaction) has occurred? That is, what are the clues that a chemical change has taken place? A glance back at the processes in the introduction suggests that *chemical reactions often give a visual signal.* Steel changes from a smooth, shiny material to a reddish-brown, flaky substance when it rusts. Hair changes color when it is bleached. Solid nylon is formed when two particular liquid solutions are brought into contact. A blue flame appears when natural gas reacts with oxygen. Chemical reactions, then, often give *visual* clues:

- A color changes.
- A solid forms.
- Bubbles are produced.
- A flame occurs.

However, reactions are not always visible. Sometimes the only signal that a reaction is occurring is a change in temperature as heat is produced or absorbed (see **Figure 7.1**).

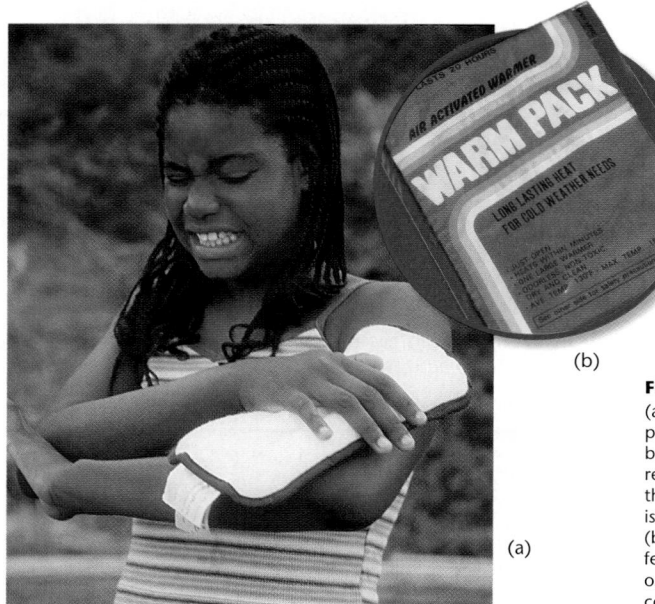

(b)

(a)

Figure 7.1
(a) An injured girl uses a cold pack to help prevent swelling. The pack is activated by breaking an ampule; which starts a chemical reaction that absorbs heat rapidly, lowering the temperature of the area to which the pack is applied.
(b) A hot pack is used to warm hands and feet in winter. When the package is opened, oxygen from the air penetrates a bag containing solid chemicals. The resulting reaction produces heat.

TECHNOLOGY

 Videos
Barking Dogs: Reaction of Phosphorus
Dry Ice and Magnesium
Nickel(II) Complexes
Reactions of Silver(I)
Zinc and Iodine
Oxygen, Hydrogen, Soap Bubbles, and Balloons
Copper Metal in Nitric Acid
Thermite Reaction

7

Evidence for a Chemical Reaction

color change

bubbles form

solid forms

heat or flame occurs

TABLE 7.1

Some Clues That a Chemical Reaction Has Occurred

1. The color changes.
2. A solid forms.
3. Bubbles form.
4. Heat and/or a flame is produced, or heat is absorbed.

SECTION 7.1
REVIEW QUESTIONS

❶ What types of evidence indicate that a chemical reaction has taken place?

❷ Give an example of each type of clue from Table 7.1 that a chemical reaction has taken place.

❸ Look at the following photographs and identify any clues that tell you a chemical reaction has taken place.

a.

b.

c.

d.

RESEARCH LINKS
CLASSZONE.COM

7.1 • Evidence for a Chemical Reaction • **219**

Homework

You may wish to assign these selected end-of-chapter problems as homework for this section: 5, 8, 9, 11, 12, 15, 16, 18, 21, 23, 26, 28, 30

Additional end-of-chapter problems can be used for extra practice.

 TEACHING TIP

In this section, students learn that a chemical reaction involves a rearrangement of the elements. It is very helpful to use simple models of the reactants that you can take apart and rearrange to show that atoms are conserved in a chemical reaction.

SECTION 7.2
Chemical Equations

Key Terms

- Chemical reaction
- Chemical equation
- Reactants
- Products
- Balancing the chemical equation

Objectives

- *To learn to identify the characteristics of a chemical reaction*
- *To learn the information given by a chemical equation*

Chemists have learned that a chemical change always involves a rearrangement of the ways in which the atoms are grouped. For example, when the methane, CH_4, in natural gas combines with oxygen, O_2, in the air and burns, carbon dioxide, CO_2, and water, H_2O, are formed. Such a chemical change is called a **chemical reaction**. We represent a chemical reaction by writing a **chemical equation** in which the chemicals present before the reaction, the **reactants**, are shown to the left of an arrow and the chemicals formed by the reaction, the **products**, are shown to the right of an arrow. The arrow indicates the direction of the change and is read as "yields" or "produces":

Reactants → Products

For the reaction of methane with oxygen, we have

Note from this equation that the products contain the same atoms as the reactants but that the atoms are associated in different ways. That is, *a chemical reaction involves changing the ways the atoms are grouped.*

In a chemical reaction, atoms are neither created nor destroyed. All atoms present in the reactants must be accounted for among the products.

In other words, there must be the same number of each type of atom on the product side as on the reactant side of the arrow. Making sure that the equation for a reaction obeys this rule is called **balancing the chemical equation** for a reaction.

The equation that we have shown for the reaction between CH_4 and O_2 is not balanced. We can see that it is not balanced by taking apart the reactants and products.

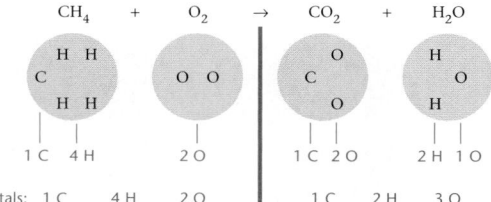

1 C 4 H	2 O	1 C 2 O	2 H 1 O

Totals: 1 C   4 H   2 O   1 C   2 H   3 O

The reaction cannot happen this way because, as it stands, this equation states that one oxygen atom is created and that two hydrogen atoms are destroyed. A reaction is only a rearrangement of the way the atoms are grouped; atoms are not created or destroyed. The total number of each type of atom must be

Chemical reaction
One or more substances are changed into one or more new substances by the reorganization of component atoms.

Chemical equation
A representation of a chemical reaction using the formulas of the starting substances that react and the new substances that are formed

Reactant
The starting substance of a chemical reaction, shown to the left of the reaction arrow

Product
The new substance formed by a chemical reaction, shown to the right of the reaction arrow

---

Teaching Support
DEMONSTRATION

Fire on Demand

Materials
- Potassium chlorate (*s*)
- Sugar (*s*)
- Evaporating dish or fire-resistant pad
- Concentrated sulfuric acid
- Dropper

Procedure Place equal amounts of potassium chlorate and sugar in a beaker. Mix well, but do not grind! For an evaporating dish, you will need about one teaspoon of each solid. Place the mixture in the center of the evaporating dish or in the center of the fire-resistant pad. Carefully add one drop of concentrated sulfuric acid to the pile of solid and step back.

Safety Notes This reaction produces sparks, so clear the area around the reaction site. It also produces smoke, so make sure you perform it in a well-ventilated area. Potassium chlorate is a dangerous chemical, and you should never grind it (it may explode). Do not make more of the mixture than you will need for that day.

HANDS-ON CHEMISTRY • MINI-LAB •

Modeling Equations

Materials
- four different colors of modeling clay
- toothpicks

Procedure

1. Obtain four different colors of modeling clay.

2. With the clay and toothpicks, make models of each of the reactants and products in the following equations, and use these models to balance the equations.

   a. $N_2 + H_2 \rightarrow NH_3$

   b. $C_2H_6 + O_2 \rightarrow CO_2 + H_2O$

   c. $H_2 + O_2 \rightarrow H_2O$

   d. $O_2 \rightarrow O_3$

Results/Analysis

1. How do your models show the difference between a subscript and a coefficient?

2. How do your models show why we cannot change a subscript to balance an equation?

CHEMISTRY IN YOUR WORLD

Connection to Biology

The Bombardier Beetle

If someone said to you, "Name something that protects itself by spraying its enemies," your answer would almost certainly be "a skunk." Of course, you would be correct, but there is another correct answer—the bombardier beetle. When threatened, this beetle shoots a boiling stream of toxic chemicals at its enemy. How does this clever beetle accomplish this? Obviously, the boiling mixture cannot be stored inside the beetle's body all the time. Instead, when endangered, the beetle mixes chemicals that produce the hot spray. The chemicals involved are stored in two compartments. One compartment contains the chemicals hydrogen peroxide (H_2O_2) and methylhydroquinone ($C_7H_8O_2$). The key reaction is the decomposition of hydrogen peroxide to form oxygen gas and water:

$$2H_2O_2(aq) \rightarrow 2H_2O(l) + O_2(g)$$

Hydrogen peroxide also reacts with the hydroquinones to produce other compounds that become part of the toxic spray.

However, none of these reactions occurs very fast unless certain enzymes are present. (Enzymes are natural substances that speed up biological reactions by means we will not discuss here.) When the beetle mixes the hydrogen peroxide and hydroquinones with the enzyme, the decomposition of H_2O_2 occurs rapidly, producing a hot mixture pressurized by the formation of oxygen gas. When the gas pressure becomes high enough, the hot spray is ejected in one long stream or in short bursts. The beetle has a highly accurate aim and can shoot several attackers with one batch of spray.

A bombardier beetle defending itself

7.3 • Balancing Chemical Equations • **229**

Chemistry in Your World

The Bombardier Beetle

"The Bombardier Beetle" emphasizes once again the many connections between chemistry and biology. In particular, insects are marvelous chemists. Bees and spiders manufacture venoms that they use to paralyze and kill their prey and defend against their enemies; insects synthesize pheromones used as danger signals, mating attractants, and means of recognition; spiders make silk to spin webs that are strong enough to capture large insects; bees make and store incredible quantities of wax and honey; silkworms make threads strong enough to construct clothes for humans as they spin their cocoons.

Have students think of more examples of how insects are skillful chemists.

EXAMPLE 7.3

More Examples

Write the balanced chemical equation for each of the following reactions.

1. Iron metal reacts with oxygen gas in the air to form iron(III) oxide.

   $4Fe(s) + 3O_2(g) \rightarrow 2Fe_2O_3(s)$

2. Diboron trioxide reacts with water to form boric acid, $B(OH)_3$.

   $B_2O_3(s) + 3H_2O(l) \rightarrow$
   $2B(OH)_3(aq)$

EXAMPLE 7.3

Balancing Chemical Equations II

Under appropriate conditions at 1000 °C, ammonia gas reacts with oxygen gas to produce gaseous nitrogen monoxide (common name, nitric oxide) and gaseous water.

- Write the unbalanced equation.
- Balance the equation for this reaction.

Solution

Step 1 The reactants are gaseous ammonia, $NH_3(g)$, and gaseous oxygen, $O_2(g)$. The products are gaseous nitrogen monoxide, $NO(g)$, and gaseous water, $H_2O(g)$.

Reactants	Products
1 N	1 N
3 H	2 H
2 O	1 O

Step 2 The unbalanced equation for the reaction is

$$NH_3(g) + O_2(g) \rightarrow NO(g) + H_2O(g)$$

Step 3 In this equation there is no molecule that is obviously the most complicated. Three molecules contain two elements, so we arbitrarily start with NH_3. We arbitrarily begin by looking at hydrogen. A coefficient of 2 for NH_3 and a coefficient of 3 for H_2O give six atoms of hydrogen on both sides.

$$2NH_3(g) + O_2(g) \rightarrow NO(g) + 3H_2O(g)$$
$$\underbrace{\qquad}_{6\,H} \qquad\qquad \underbrace{\qquad}_{6\,H}$$

We can balance the nitrogen by giving NO a coefficient of 2.

$$2NH_3(g) + O_2(g) \rightarrow 2NO(g) + 3H_2O(g)$$
$$\underbrace{\qquad}_{2\,N} \qquad\qquad \underbrace{\qquad}_{2\,N}$$

Finally, we note that there are two atoms of oxygen on the left and five on the right. The oxygen can be balanced with a coefficient of $\frac{5}{2}$ for O_2, because $\frac{5}{2} \times O_2$ gives five oxygen atoms.

$$2NH_3(g) + \tfrac{5}{2}O_2(g) \rightarrow 2NO(g) + 3H_2O(g)$$
$$\underbrace{\qquad}_{5\,O} \quad \underbrace{\qquad}_{2\,O} \quad \underbrace{\qquad}_{3\,O}$$

However, the convention is to have whole-number coefficients, so we multiply the entire equation by 2.

$$2 \times [2NH_3(g) + \tfrac{5}{2}O_2(g) \rightarrow 2NO(g) + 3H_2O(g)]$$

or

$$2 \times 2NH_3(g) + 2 \times \tfrac{5}{2}O_2(g) \rightarrow 2 \times 2NO(g) + 2 \times 3H_2O(g)$$

$$4NH_3(g) + 5O_2(g) \rightarrow 4NO(g) + 6H_2O(g)$$

Reactants	Products
4 N	4 N
12 H	12 H
10 O	10 O

Step 4

Check: There are 4 N, 12 H, and 10 O atoms on both sides, so the equation is balanced. These coefficients are the smallest whole numbers that give a balanced equation.

Practice Problem • Exercise 7.3

Propane, C_3H_8, a liquid at 25 °C under high pressure, is often used for gas grills and as a fuel in rural areas where there is no natural gas pipeline. When liquid propane is released from its storage tank, it changes to propane gas that reacts with oxygen gas (it "burns") to give gaseous carbon dioxide and gaseous water. Write and balance the equation for this reaction.

READING TIP

This description of a chemical process contains many words, some of which are crucial to solving the problem and some of which are not. First sort out the important information and use symbols to represent it.

EXAMPLE 7.4

Balancing Chemical Equations III

Glass is sometimes decorated by etching patterns on its surface. Etching occurs when hydrofluoric acid, an aqueous solution of HF, reacts with the silicon dioxide in the glass to form gaseous silicon tetrafluoride and liquid water.

- Write the equation for the reaction.
- Balance the equation.

Solution

Step 1 From the description of the reaction we can identify the reactants:

| hydrofluoric acid | HF(aq) |
| solid silicon dioxide | SiO_2(s) |

and the products:

| gaseous silicon tetrafluoride | SiF_4(g) |
| liquid water | H_2O(l) |

Step 2 The unbalanced equation is

$$SiO_2(s) + HF(aq) \rightarrow SiF_4(g) + H_2O(l)$$

Step 3 There is no clear choice here for the most complicated molecule. We arbitrarily start with the elements in SiF_4. The silicon is balanced (one atom on each side), but the fluorine is not. To balance the fluorine, we need a coefficient of 4 before the HF.

$$SiO_2(s) + 4HF(aq) \rightarrow SiF_4(g) + H_2O(l)$$

Hydrogen and oxygen are not balanced. Because we have four hydrogen atoms on the left and two on the right, we place a 2 before the H_2O:

$$SiO_2(s) + 4HF(aq) \rightarrow SiF_4(g) + 2H_2O(l)$$

This balances the hydrogen *and* the oxygen (two atoms on each side).

Step 4
Check:

$$SiO_2(s) + 4HF(aq) \rightarrow SiF_4(g) + 2H_2O(l)$$

Totals: 1 Si, 2 O, 4 H, 4 F → 1 Si, 4 F, 4 H, 2 O

All atoms check, so the equation is balanced.

Decorations on glass are produced by etching with hydrofluoric acid.

7.3 • Balancing Chemical Equations • **231**

Answer to Practice Problem 7.3

Step 1 The reactants are propane, $C_3H_8(g)$, and oxygen, $O_2(g)$; the products are carbon dioxide, $CO_2(g)$, and water, $H_2O(g)$.

Step 2 The unbalanced equation for the reaction is

$$C_3H_8(g) + O_2(g) \rightarrow CO_2(g) + H_2O(g)$$

Step 3 We start with C_3H_8 because it is the most complicated molecule. C_3H_8 contains three carbon atoms per molecule, so a coefficient of 3 is needed for CO_2:

$$C_3H_8(g) + O_2(g) \rightarrow 3CO_2(g) + H_2O(g)$$

Also, each C_3H_8 molecule contains eight hydrogen atoms, so a coefficient of 4 is required for H_2O:

$$C_3H_8(g) + O_2(g) \rightarrow 3CO_2(g) + 4H_2O(g)$$

The final element to be balanced is oxygen. Note that the left side of the equation now has two oxygen atoms, and the right side has ten. We can balance the oxygen by using a coefficient of 5 for O_2:

$$C_3H_8(g) + 5O_2(g) \rightarrow 3CO_2(g) + 4H_2O(g)$$

Step 4 Check:

3 C, 8 H, 10 O → 3 C, 8 H, 10 O

| Reactant atoms | Product atoms |

We cannot divide all coefficients by a given integer to give smaller integer coefficients.

EXAMPLE 7.4

More Examples

Write the balanced chemical equation for each of the following reactions.

1. Solid iron(III) oxide reacts with aqueous nitric acid to form aqueous iron(III) nitrate and water.

$$Fe_2O_3(s) + 6HNO_3(aq) \rightarrow 2Fe(NO_3)_3(aq) + 3H_2O(l)$$

2. Hydrogen sulfide gas reacts with aqueous lead(II) nitrate to form solid lead(II) sulfide and aqueous nitric acid.

$$H_2S(g) + Pb(NO_3)_2(aq) \rightarrow PbS(s) + 2HNO_3(aq)$$

Answer to Practice Problem 7.4

a. $NH_4NO_2(s) \rightarrow N_2(g) + H_2O(g)$
(unbalanced)

$NH_4NO_2(s) \rightarrow N_2(g) + 2H_2O(g)$
(balanced)

b. $NO(g) \rightarrow N_2O(g) + NO_2(g)$
(unbalanced)

$3NO(g) \rightarrow N_2O(g) + NO_2(g)$
(balanced)

c. $HNO_3(l) \rightarrow NO_2(g) + H_2O(l) + O_2(g)$
(unbalanced)

$4HNO_3(l) \rightarrow 4NO_2(g) + 2H_2O(l) + O_2(g)$ (balanced)

SECTION 7.3
ASSESS

SECTION 7.3
Review Questions

1. a. $Cl_2(aq) + 2KBr(aq) \rightarrow Br_2(l) + 2 KCl(aq)$

b. $2Al(s) + 3I_2(s) \rightarrow 2AlI_3(s)$

c. $Mg(s) + 2HCl(aq) \rightarrow 2MgCl_2(aq) + H_2(g)$

2. Only coefficients can be changed when balancing a chemical equation. If the subscripts are changed the identities of the compounds change.

3. We can multiply or divide all coefficients of the balanced equation by any number to give a new balanced equation. The preferred balanced equation is the one with the smallest possible integers.

4. The "+" means "reacts with"; the "2" in front of O_2 signifies that 2 mol of O_2 is required to react with 1 mol of CH_4, and the "2" in the formula for H_2O signifies that there are 2 atoms of hydrogen in each molecule of water.

5. While trial and error is a reasonable approach, some trials are better than others. In this case, it makes the most sense to start with C_2H_5OH because it is the most complex molecule (has the greatest number of different types of atoms). The balanced equation is $C_2H_5OH + 3O_2 \rightarrow 2CO_2 + 3H_2O$.

 Practice Problem • Exercise 7.4

Give the balanced equation for each of the following reactions.

a. When solid ammonium nitrite is heated, it produces nitrogen gas and water vapor.

b. Gaseous nitrogen monoxide (common name, nitric oxide) decomposes to produce dinitrogen monoxide gas (common name, nitrous oxide) and nitrogen dioxide gas.

c. Liquid nitric acid decomposes to reddish-brown nitrogen dioxide gas, liquid water, and oxygen gas. (This is why bottles of nitric acid become yellow upon standing.)

SECTION 7.3
REVIEW QUESTIONS

1 Write and balance each of the following chemical equations.

  a. Gaseous chlorine reacts with an aqueous solution of potassium bromide to form liquid bromine and an aqueous solution of potassium chloride.

  b. Solid aluminum reacts with solid iodine to produce solid aluminum iodide.

  c. Solid magnesium reacts with an aqueous solution of hydrochloric acid to form an aqueous solution of magnesium chloride bubbles of hydrogen gas.

2 Which can be changed when balancing a chemical equation, the coefficients or the subscripts? Why?

3 Why does each chemical reaction have many possible balanced equations? Of all possible balanced equations, which is preferred?

4 Explain what each of the following symbols (shown in red) represents:

$$CH_4(g) + 2O_2(g) \rightarrow CO_2(g) + 2H_2O(g)$$

5 When balancing the equation

$$C_2H_5OH(l) + O_2(g) \rightarrow CO_2(g) + H_2O(g),$$

which substance should you start with? Why? Balance the chemical equation.

 RESEARCH LINKS
CLASSZONE.COM

232 • Chapter 7 • Chemical Reactions: An Introduction

Chapter 7 Review

Key Terms

Key Ideas

7.1

7.1 Evidence for a Chemical Reaction

■ A chemical reaction produces a signal that it has occurred. These signals include

- Color change
- Solid formation
- Bubble formation
- Heat
- Flame

7.2
Chemical reaction
Chemical equation
Reactants
Products
Balancing the chemical equation

7.2 Chemical Equations

■ The physical states of reactants and products in a reaction are indicated by the following symbols.

Physical States	
Symbol	**State**
(s)	solid
(l)	liquid
(g)	gas
(aq)	dissolved in water (in aqueous solution)

■ Chemical reactions involve a rearrangement of the ways atoms are grouped together.

■ A chemical equation represents a chemical reaction.
- Reactants are shown to the left of an arrow.
- Products are shown to the right of the arrow.

■ In a chemical reaction atoms are neither created nor destroyed. A balanced chemical equation must have the same number of each type of atom on the reactant and product sides.

■ A balanced chemical equation uses numbers (coefficients) in front of the reactant and product formulas to show the relative numbers of each.

7.3 **Coefficients**

7.3 Balancing Chemical Equations

■ A chemical reaction is balanced by using a systematic approach.
- Write the formulas of the reactants and products to give the unbalanced chemical equation.
- Balance by trial and error, starting with the most complicated molecule(s).
- Check to be sure the equation is balanced (same numbers of all types of atoms on the reactant and product sides).

RESEARCH LINKS
CLASSZONE.COM

Meeting Individual Needs
CHAPTER REVIEW

Chapter 7 Review Worksheet at the appropriate level:
    Basic
    Standard
    Challenge

CHAPTER SUMMARY

A **Chapter Summary** that includes additional Active Reading Questions for Chapter 7 is available.

Assessment Resources
CHAPTER 7

Chapter 7 Test

TECHNOLOGY

 Computerized Test Bank for Chapter 7

Chapter 7 Assessment

All exercises with blue numbers have answers in the back of this book.

7.1 Evidence for a Chemical Reaction

1. Review how we defined *chemical change* in Chapter 3. Explain how the visual clues mentioned in this chapter are indicators of chemical change as defined in Chapter 3.

2. If a piece of blackboard chalk is heated strongly, the mass of the chalk decreases substantially, and the chalk is converted into a fine powder. What evidence is there for a chemical reaction having taken place when the chalk is heated?

3. If you have had a clogged sink drain at your home, your parents may have have tried using a commercial drain cleaner to dissolve the clog. What evidence is there that such drain cleaners work by chemical reaction?

4. If a bottle of aspirin is left open to the air, eventually one of the products is acetic acid (vinegar is a mixture of acetic acid and water). Is there evidence that this change represents a chemical reaction?

7.2 Chemical Equations

5. The substances present before a chemical reaction takes place are called the _____, and the substances present after the reaction takes place are called the _____.

6. In an ordinary chemical reaction, _____ are neither created nor destroyed.

7. The notation "(*g*)" after a substance's formula indicates it exists in the _____ state.

8. In a chemical equation for a reaction, the notation "(*aq*)" after a substance's formula means that the substance is dissolved in _____.

Note: In some of the following problems, you will need to write a chemical formula from the name of the compound. It may help to review Chapter 4.

9. If calcium carbonate is heated strongly, carbon dioxide gas is driven off, leaving a residue of calcium oxide. Write the unbalanced chemical equation for this process.

10. Liquefied propane gas is often used for cooking in rural areas away from natural gas lines. Propane (C_3H_8) burns in oxygen gas, producing carbon dioxide gas, water vapor, and heat. Write the unbalanced chemical equation for this process.

11. If a sample of pure hydrogen gas is ignited very carefully, the hydrogen burns gently, combining with the oxygen gas of the air to form water vapor. Write the unbalanced chemical equation for this reaction.

12. Solid ammonium carbonate, $(NH_4)_2CO_3$, is used as the active ingredient in "smelling salts." When solid ammonium carbonate is heated, it decomposes into ammonia gas, carbon dioxide gas, and water vapor. Write the unbalanced chemical equation for this process.

13. Silver oxide may be decomposed by strong heating into silver metal and oxygen gas. Write the unbalanced chemical equation for this process.

14. Methanol (CH_3OH, wood alcohol) is an important industrial chemical. Methanol may be synthesized from carbon monoxide gas and hydrogen gas under certain conditions of temperature and pressure. Write the unbalanced chemical equation for this process.

15. Elemental boron is produced in one industrial process by heating diboron trioxide with magnesium metal, also producing magnesium oxide. Write the unbalanced chemical equation for this process.

16. Calcium metal is moderately reactive. If pieces of calcium are added to water, the metal begins to bubble as hydrogen gas is formed. The water begins to turn cloudy as solid calcium hydroxide begins to form. Write the unbalanced chemical equation for the reaction of calcium metal with water.

17. Phosphorus trichloride is used in the manufacture of certain pesticides and may be synthesized directly from its elements. Write the unbalanced chemical equation for this process.

18. Magnesium hydroxide has been used for many years as an antacid ("milk of magnesia") because it reacts with the hydrochloric acid in the stomach, producing magnesium chloride and water. Write the unbalanced chemical equation for this process.

19. Nitrous oxide gas (systematic name: dinitrogen monoxide) is used by some dentists as an anesthetic. Nitrous oxide (and water vapor) can be produced in small amounts in the laboratory by careful heating of ammonium nitrate. Write the unbalanced chemical equation for this reaction.

Chapter 7 Assessment

1. In Chapter 3, we defined chemical change as a process in which a given substance (or substances) changes into a different substance (or substances). Evidence such as the formation of a solid or bubbles shows us that a new substance is being produced (a solid or a gaseous compound that was not present initially). If there is a color change, it is an indication that a new substance has formed. Also, when a substance changes into a new substance, an energy change is expected due to rearrangements of atoms in the molecules. Therefore, heat is absorbed or released.

2. decrease in mass; change in texture

3. The material in the drain does not dissolve in water until the drain cleaner is added. Heat may also be noticed.

4. yes; change in odor as acetic acid is produced

5. reactants, products

6. atoms

7. gaseous

8. water

9. $CaCO_3(s) \rightarrow CaO(s) + CO_2(g)$

10. $C_3H_8(g) + O_2(g) \rightarrow CO_2(g) + H_2O(g)$

11. $H_2(g) + O_2(g) \rightarrow H_2O(g)$

12. $(NH_4)_2CO_3(s) \rightarrow NH_3(g) + CO_2(g) + H_2O(g)$

13. $Ag_2O(s) \rightarrow Ag(s) + O_2(g)$

14. $CO(g) + H_2(g) \rightarrow CH_3OH(l)$

15. $B_2O_3(s) + Mg(s) \rightarrow B(g) + MgO(s)$

16. $Ca(s) + H_2O(l) \rightarrow Ca(OH)_2(s) + H_2(g)$

17. $P_4(s) + Cl_2(g) \rightarrow PCl_3(g)$

18. $Mg(OH)_2(s) + HCl(aq) \rightarrow MgCl_2(aq) + H_2O(l)$

19. $NH_4NO_3(s) \rightarrow N_2O(g) + H_2O(g)$

20. Hydrogen sulfide gas is responsible for the odor of rotten eggs. Hydrogen sulfide burns in air, producing sulfur dioxide gas and water vapor. Write the unbalanced chemical equation for this process.

21. Acetylene gas (C_2H_2) is often used by plumbers, welders, and glass blowers because it burns in oxygen with an intensely hot flame. The products of the combustion of acetylene are carbon dioxide and water vapor. Write the unbalanced chemical equation for this process.

22. If ferric oxide is heated strongly in a stream of carbon monoxide gas, it produces elemental iron and carbon dioxide gas. Write the unbalanced chemical equation for this process.

23. The Group 2 metals (Ba, Ca, Sr) can be produced in the elemental state by the reaction of their oxides with aluminum metal at high temperatures, also producing solid aluminum oxide. Write the unbalanced chemical equations for the reactions of barium oxide, calcium oxide, and strontium oxide with aluminum.

24. Ozone gas is a form of elemental oxygen containing molecules with *three* oxygen atoms, O_3. Ozone is produced from atmospheric oxygen gas, O_2, by the high-energy outbursts found in lightning storms. Write the unbalanced equation for the formation of ozone gas from oxygen gas.

25. Carbon tetrachloride may be prepared by the reaction of natural gas (methane, CH_4) and chlorine gas in the presence of ultraviolet light. Write the unbalanced chemical equation for this process. (HCl is also a product.)

26. Ammonium nitrate is used as a "high-nitrogen" fertilizer, despite the fact that it is quite explosive if not handled carefully. Ammonium nitrate can be synthesized by the reaction of ammonia gas and nitric acid. Write the unbalanced chemical equation for this process.

27. The principal natural ore of lead is galena, which is primarily lead(II) sulfide. Lead(II) sulfide can be converted to lead(II) oxide and sulfur dioxide gas by heating strongly in air. Write the unbalanced chemical equation for the reaction of lead(II) sulfide with oxygen gas.

28. At high temperatures, xenon gas will combine directly with fluorine gas to produce solid xenon tetrafluoride. Write the unbalanced chemical equation for this process.

29. Ammonium nitrate is highly explosive if not handled carefully, breaking down into nitrogen gas, oxygen gas, and water vapor. The expansion of the three gases produced yields the explosive force in this case. Write the unbalanced chemical equation for this process.

30. Silver nitrate is used in "styptic pencils," which help to cauterize small nicks and cuts that occur during shaving. Silver nitrate can be prepared by dissolving metallic silver in concentrated nitric acid, with hydrogen gas being an additional product of the reaction. Write the unbalanced chemical equation for this process.

7.3 Balancing Chemical Equations

31. When balancing a chemical equation, one must never change the _____ of any reactant or product.

32. After balancing a chemical equation, we ordinarily make sure that the coefficients are the smallest _____ possible.

33. Balance each of the following chemical equations.
   a. $H_2O_2(aq) \rightarrow H_2O(l) + O_2(g)$
   b. $Ag(s) + H_2S(g) \rightarrow Ag_2S(s) + H_2(g)$
   c. $FeO(s) + C(s) \rightarrow Fe(l) + CO_2(g)$
   d. $Cl_2(g) + KI(aq) \rightarrow KCl(aq) + I_2(s)$

34. Balance each of the following chemical equations.
   a. $CaF_2(s) + H_2SO_4(l) \rightarrow CaSO_4(s) + HF(g)$
   b. $KBr(s) + H_3PO_4(aq) \rightarrow K_3PO_4(aq) + HBr(g)$
   c. $TiCl_4(l) + Na(s) \rightarrow NaCl(s) + Ti(s)$
   d. $K_2CO_3(s) \rightarrow K_2O(s) + CO_2(g)$

35. Balance each of the following chemical equations.
   a. $SiI_4(s) + Mg(s) \rightarrow Si(s) + MgI_2(s)$
   b. $MnO_2(s) + Mg(s) \rightarrow Mn(s) + MgO(s)$
   c. $Ba(s) + S_8(s) \rightarrow BaS(s)$
   d. $NH_3(g) + Cl_2(g) \rightarrow NH_4Cl(s) + NCl_3(g)$

36. Balance each of the following chemical equations.
   a. $Ba(NO_3)_2(aq) + Na_2CrO_4(aq) \rightarrow$
      $BaCrO_4(s) + NaNO_3(aq)$
   b. $C_2H_5OH(l) + O_2(g) \rightarrow CO_2(g) + H_2O(l)$
   c. $CaC_2(s) + H_2O(l) \rightarrow Ca(OH)_2(s) + C_2H_2(g)$

34. (a) $CaF_2(s) + H_2SO_4(l) \rightarrow$
      $CaSO_4(s) + 2HF(g)$
   (b) $3KBr(s) + H_3PO_4(aq) \rightarrow$
      $K_3PO_4(aq) + 3HBr(g)$
   (c) $TiCl_4(l) + 4Na(s) \rightarrow$
      $4NaCl(s) + Ti(s)$
   (d) $K_2CO_3(s) \rightarrow$
      $K_2O(s) + CO_2(g)$ (already balanced)

35. (a) $SiI_4(s) + 2Mg(s) \rightarrow$
      $Si(s) + 2MgI_2(s)$
   (b) $MnO_2(s) + 2Mg(s) \rightarrow$
      $Mn(s) + 2MgO(s)$
   (c) $8Ba(s) + S_8(s) \rightarrow 8BaS(s)$
   (d) $4NH_3(g) + 3Cl_2(g) \rightarrow$
      $3NH_4Cl(s) + NCl_3(g)$

36. (a) $Ba(NO_3)_2(aq) + Na_2CrO_4(aq) \rightarrow$
      $BaCrO_4(s) + 2NaNO_3(aq)$
   (b) $C_2H_5OH(l) + 3O_2(g) \rightarrow$
      $2CO_2(g) + 3H_2O(l)$
   (c) $CaC_2(s) + 2H_2O(l) \rightarrow$
      $Ca(OH)_2(s) + C_2H_2(g)$

---

20. $H_2S(g) + O_2(g) \rightarrow$
      $SO_2(g) + H_2O(g)$

21. $C_2H_2(g) + O_2(g) \rightarrow$
      $CO_2(g) + H_2O(g)$

22. $Fe_2O_3(s) + CO(g) \rightarrow$
      $Fe(l) + CO_2(g)$

23. $BaO(s) + Al(s) \rightarrow$
      $Ba(s) + Al_2O_3(s)$;
      $CaO(s) + Al(s) \rightarrow$
      $Ca(s) + Al_2O_3(s)$;
      $SrO(s) + Al(s) \rightarrow$
      $Sr(s) + Al_2O_3(s)$

24. $O_2(g) \rightarrow O_3(g)$

25. $CH_4(g) + Cl_2(g) \rightarrow$
      $CCl_4(l) + HCl(g)$

26. $NH_3(g) + HNO_3(g) \rightarrow$
      $NH_4NO_3(aq)$

27. $PbS(s) + O_2(g) \rightarrow$
      $PbO(s) + SO_2(g)$

28. $Xe(g) + F_2(g) \rightarrow XeF_4(g)$

29. $NH_4NO_3(s) \rightarrow$
      $N_2(g) + O_2(g) + H_2O(g)$

30. $Ag(s) + HNO_3(aq) \rightarrow$
      $AgNO_3(aq) + H_2(g)$

31. formula (subscripts)

32. whole numbers

33. (a) $2H_2O_2(aq) \rightarrow$
      $2H_2O(l) + O_2(g)$
   (b) $2Ag(s) + H_2S(g) \rightarrow$
      $Ag_2S(s) + H_2(g)$
   (c) $2FeO(s) + C(s) \rightarrow$
      $2Fe(l) + CO_2(g)$
   (d) $Cl_2(g) + 2KI(aq) \rightarrow$
      $2KCl(aq) + I_2(s)$

37. $Al(s) + O_2(g) \rightarrow Al_2O_3(s)$

38. $KNO_3(s) + C(s) \rightarrow$
    $K_2CO_3(s) + CO(g) + H_2(g)$

39. $C_{12}H_{22}O_{11}(aq) + H_2O(l) \rightarrow$
    $4C_2H_5OH(l) + 4CO_2(g)$

40. $2H_2(g) + CO(g) \rightarrow CH_3OH(l)$

41. $2Al_2O_3(s) + 3C(s) \rightarrow$
    $4Al(s) + 3CO_2(g)$

42. $Fe_3O_4(s) + 4H_2(g) \rightarrow$
    $3Fe(s) + 4H_2O(g)$;
    $Fe_3O_4(s) + 4CO(g) \rightarrow$
    $3Fe(s) + 4CO_2(g)$

43. $2Li(s) + S(s) \rightarrow Li_2S(s)$;
    $2Na(s) + S(s) \rightarrow Na_2S(s)$;
    $2K(s) + S(s) \rightarrow K_2S(s)$;
    $2Rb(s) + S(s) \rightarrow Rb_2S(s)$;
    $2Cs(s) + S(s) \rightarrow Cs_2S(s)$;
    $2Fr(s) + S(s) \rightarrow Fr_2S(s)$

44. $2KClO_3(s) \rightarrow 2KCl(s) + 3O_2(g)$

45. $2H_2O_2(aq) \rightarrow H_2O(g) + O_2(g)$

46. $CaSiO_3(s) + 6HF(g) \rightarrow$
    $CaF_2(aq) + SiF_4(g) + 3H_2O(l)$

47. Carbon dioxide gas is released.

48. $K_2CrO_4(aq) + BaCl_2(aq) \rightarrow$
    $BaCrO_4(s) + 2KCl(aq)$

49. $Mg(s) + O_2(g) \rightarrow MgO(s)$

Critical Thinking

37. Many ships are built with aluminum superstructures to save weight. Aluminum, however, burns in oxygen if there is a sufficiently hot ignition source, which has led to several tragedies at sea. Write the unbalanced chemical equation for the reaction of aluminum with oxygen, producing aluminum oxide as the product.

38. Crude gunpowders often contain a mixture of potassium nitrate and charcoal (carbon). When such a mixture is heated until reaction occurs, a solid residue of potassium carbonate is produced. The explosive force of the gunpowder comes from the fact that two gases are also produced (carbon monoxide and nitrogen), which increase in volume with great force and speed. Write the unbalanced chemical equation for the process.

39. The sugar sucrose, which is present in many fruits and vegetables, reacts in the presence of certain yeast enzymes to produce ethyl alcohol (ethanol) and carbon dioxide gas. Balance the following equation for this reaction of sucrose.

$$C_{12}H_{22}O_{11}(aq) + H_2O(l) \rightarrow C_2H_5OH(aq) + CO_2(g)$$

40. Methanol (methyl alcohol), CH_3OH, is a very important industrial chemical. Today, methanol is synthesized from carbon monoxide and elemental hydrogen. Write the balanced chemical equation for this process.

41. The Hall process is an important method by which pure aluminum is prepared from its oxide (alumina, Al_2O_3) by indirect reaction with graphite (carbon). Balance the following equation, which is a simplified representation of this process.

$$Al_2O_3(s) + C(s) \rightarrow Al(s) + CO_2(g)$$

42. Iron oxide ores, commonly a mixture of FeO and Fe_2O_3, are given the general formula Fe_3O_4. They yield elemental iron when heated to a very high temperature with either carbon monoxide or elemental hydrogen. Balance the following equations for these processes.

$$Fe_3O_4(s) + H_2(g) \rightarrow Fe(s) + H_2O(g)$$
$$Fe_3O_4(s) + CO(g) \rightarrow Fe(s) + CO_2(g)$$

43. The elements of Group 1 all react with sulfur to form the metal sulfides. Write balanced chemical equations for the reactions of the Group 1 elements with sulfur.

44. A common experiment in chemistry classes involves heating a weighed mixture of potassium chlorate, $KClO_3$, and potassium chloride. Potassium chlorate decomposes when heated, producing potassium chloride and oxygen gas. By measuring the volume of oxygen gas produced in this experiment, students can calculate the relative percentage of $KClO_3$ and KCl in the original mixture. Write the balanced chemical equation for this process.

45. A common demonstration in chemistry classes involves adding a tiny speck of manganese(IV) oxide to a concentrated hydrogen peroxide, H_2O_2, solution. Hydrogen peroxide decomposes quite spectacularly under these conditions to produce oxygen gas and steam (water vapor). Manganese(IV) oxide speeds up the decomposition of hydrogen peroxide but is not consumed in the reaction. Write the balanced equation for the decomposition reaction of hydrogen peroxide.

46. Glass is a mixture of several compounds, but a major constituent of most glass is calcium silicate, $CaSiO_3$. Glass can be etched by treatment with hydrogen fluoride: HF attacks the calcium silicate of the glass, producing gaseous and water-soluble products that can be removed by washing the glass. For example, the volumetric glassware in chemistry laboratories is often graduated by using this process. Balance the following equation for the reaction of hydrogen fluoride with calcium silicate.

$$CaSiO_3(s) + HF(g) \rightarrow CaF_2(aq) + SiF_4(g) + H_2O(l)$$

47. If you had a "sour stomach," you might try an antacid tablet to relieve the problem. Can you think of evidence that the action of such an antacid is a chemical reaction?

48. If solutions of potassium chromate and barium chloride are mixed, a bright yellow solid (barium chromate) forms and settles out of the mixture, leaving potassium chloride in solution. Write a balanced chemical equation for this process.

49. When a strip of magnesium metal is heated in oxygen, it bursts into an intensely white flame and produces a finely powdered dust of magnesium oxide. Write the unbalanced chemical equation for this process.

1 Which of the following is not a clue that a chemical reaction has taken place?

A   A solid is formed when two clear solutions are mixed.

B   A clear solution is added to a red solution, and the result is a blue solution.

C   A solid is added to water, and bubbles form.

D   A pure solid is heated and turns into a pure liquid.

2 What does it mean for a chemical equation to be balanced?

A   The sums of the coefficients on each side of the equation are equal.

B   The same number of each type of atom appears on both sides of the equation.

C   The formulas of the reactants and the products are the same.

D   The sums of the subscripts on each side of the equation are equal.

3 Which of the following physical states is not used for H_2O in a chemical equation?

A (s)

B (l)

C (aq)

D (g)

4 Which of the following is the coefficient for O_2 when the equation is balanced?

$$C_4H_{10}(l) + O_2(g) \rightarrow CO_2(g) + H_2O(g)$$

A   4

B   8

C   10

D   13

5 What is the sum of the coefficients of the following equation when it is balanced?

$$FeS(s) + HCl(g) \rightarrow FeCl_2(s) + H_2S(g)$$

A   5

B   4

C   3

D   2

6 When the equation representing the reaction between iron(II) oxide and carbon to form iron and carbon dioxide is balanced, the coefficient for iron is

A   1

B   2

C   3

D   4

7 The reaction of an element X ($\triangle$) with element Y ($\bigcirc$) is represented in the following diagram. Which of the equations best describes this reaction?

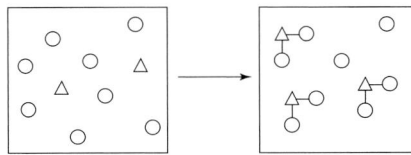

A $3X + 8Y \rightarrow X_3Y_8$

B $3X + 6Y \rightarrow X_3Y_6$

C $X + 2Y \rightarrow XY_2$

D $3X + 8Y \rightarrow 3XY_2 + 2Y$

8 Explain the law of conservation of mass and discuss how it applies to balancing a chemical equation.

For questions 9–12, write and balance the chemical equation as described. Include the state of each substance.

9 When magnesium metal is added to water, hydrogen gas is produced along with a solution of magnesium hydroxide.

10 When an aqueous solution of lead(II) nitrate is added to an aqueous solution of sodium iodide, the yellow solid lead(II) iodide is produced along with a solution of sodium nitrate.

11 Propane gas (C_3H_8) reacts with oxygen in the air to form carbon dioxide and water vapor.

12 Calcium metal reacts with oxygen gas to produce solid calcium oxide.

Chapter 7
Standardized Test Practice

1. D
2. B
3. C
4. D
5. A
6. B
7. C
8. The law of conservation of mass states that matter cannot be created or destroyed. When we balance a chemical equation, we make sure that there are the same numbers of each kind of atom on each side of the equation.
9. $Mg(s) + 2H_2O(l) \rightarrow H_2(g) + Mg(OH)_2(aq)$
10. $Pb(NO_3)_2(aq) + 2NaI(aq) \rightarrow PbI_2(s) + 2NaNO_3(aq)$
11. $C_3H_8(g) + 5O_2(g) \rightarrow 3CO_2(g) + 4H_2O(g)$
12. $2Ca(s) + O_2(g) \rightarrow 2CaO(s)$

Test-Taking Strategy

Advise students to spend time interpreting a diagram provided with a test item before attempting to answer the question. Tell students that they are allowed to mark or draw on any figure, table, or diagram and are encouraged to do so.

Assessment Resources
CHAPTER 7

For additional practice with standardized testing, see *Standardized Test Practice* located in the *Teacher Resources*.

Planning Guide

Section	Segment		Text Features and Components	Labs, Demonstrations, & Activities
8.1 Understanding Reactions in Aqueous Solutions **1.5 Blocks** pp. 240–253	A	**Predicting Whether a Reaction Will Occur**	🅣🅔 Teaching Support: Background Information *p. 241*	🅛🅜 Experiment 29: Precipitation Reaction, Microscale 　Lab Manual 　Report Sheets 　Teacher's Lab Guide
	B	**Reactions in Which a Solid Forms**	🅢🅔 Chemistry in Your World: Instant Cooking—On Demand *p. 242* 🅣🅔 Teaching Support: Background Information *pp. 244–245*	🅣🅔 Mini-Demo *p. 241* 🅣🅔 Group Activity *p. 245* 🅣🅔 Teaching Support: Demonstration *pp. 246–247* 🅣🅔 Teaching Support: Demonstration *pp. 249–251*
	C	**Describing Reactions in Aqueous Solutions**	🅢🅔 Celebrity Chemical: Ammonia *p. 252*	🅣🅔 Teaching Support: Demonstration *pp. 252–253* 🅢🅔 Hands-On Chemistry: Forecast: Precipitation *p. 253*
8.2 Other Reactions in Aqueous Solutions **1.5 Blocks** pp. 254–262	A	**Reactions That Form Water: Acids and Bases**	🅣🅔 Teaching Support: Background Information *p. 254* 🅢🅔 Celebrity Chemical: Calcium Carbonate *p. 257*	🅣🅔 Mini-Demo *p. 254*
	B	**Reactions of Metals with Nonmetals (Oxidation–Reduction)**		🅣🅔 Teaching Support: Demonstration *pp. 258–259* 🅣🅔 Teaching Support: Demonstration *pp. 260–261* 🅢🅔 Hands-On Chemistry: What's in Your Water? *p. 262*
	continued on next page			

Key			
🅢🅔 Student Edition	🅣🅔 Teacher Edition	🅡🅟 Teacher Resource Package	
🅐🅡 Additional Materials	🅛🅜 Lab Materials	🖨 Transparencies	
💿 DVD	💾 CD-ROM	🌐 classzone.com	

All Learners	Technology	Review & Assessment	Standards
TE Teaching Tip *p. 240*	▶ Lab Generator CD ◉ EasyPlanner	SE Active Reading Question *p. 240* SE Questions and Problems *p. 271*	TE **NSES** UCP3, UCP5, A1, A2, B3, D2, G1, G2
TE Teaching Tips *pp. 241–245*	◉ Animation: Dissolution of a Solid in a Liquid ◉ Animation: Electrolyte Behavior ◉ Video: Electrolytes ▣ Transparency: Table 8.1 ▣ Transparency: Figure 8.3 ◉ Video: Solubility Rules ◉ EasyPlanner	SE Active Reading Question *p. 244* TE More Examples *p. 246* TE More Examples *p. 248* SE Practice Problem *p. 249* SE Key Terms *p. 270* SE Questions and Problems *pp. 271–272*	
TE Teaching Tips *pp. 250–251* RP Team Learning Worksheet (Sec. 8.1)	◉ Animation: Precipitation Reactions ◉ EasyPlanner	SE Active Reading Questions *p. 250* SE Active Reading Question *p. 251* TE More Examples *p. 251* SE Practice Problem *p. 252* SE Review Questions (8.1.A–8.1.C) *p. 253* SE Key Terms *p. 270* SE Questions and Problems *p. 272*	
	◉ Animation: Proton Transfer ◉ Animation: Neutralization of a Strong Acid by a Strong Base ◉ EasyPlanner	SE Active Reading Question *p. 256* TE More Examples *p. 256* SE Key Terms *p. 270* SE Questions and Problems *p. 273*	TE **NSES** UCP3, UCP5, A1, A2, B3, D2, G2
TE Teaching Tips *pp. 258–259* RP Team Learning Worksheet (Sec. 8.2)	◉ Video: Barking Dogs: Reaction of Phosphorus ◉ Video: Dry Ice and Magnesium ◉ Video: Sugar and Potassium Chlorate ◉ Video: Zinc and Iodine ◉ Video: Thermite Reaction ◉ EasyPlanner	SE Active Reading Question *p. 258* TE More Examples *p. 260* SE Practice Problem *p. 261* SE Review Questions (8.2.A–8.2.B) *p. 262* SE Key Terms *p. 270* SE Questions and Problems *p. 273*	

Planning Guide

Section	Segment		Text Features and Components	Labs, Demonstrations, & Activities
8.3 Classifying Reactions **2 Blocks** pp. 263–269	**A**	**Ways to Classify Reactions**	**SE** Chemistry in Your World: Launching the Space Shuttle *p. 265*	**LM** Experiment 30: Activity Series for Metal, Microscale Lab Manual Report Sheets Teacher's Lab Guide **LM** Experiment 31: Unknown Solutions Lab Manual Report Sheets Teacher's Lab Guide
	B	**Other Ways to Classify Reactions**		**LM** Experiment 32: Qualitative Analysis: Anions, Microscale Lab Manual Report Sheets Teacher's Lab Guide **LM** Experiment 33: The Halide Family, Microscale Lab Manual Report Sheets Teacher's Lab Guide

Key	**SE** Student Edition	**TE** Teacher Edition	**RP** Teacher Resource Package
	AR Additional Materials	**LM** Lab Materials	**⊟** Transparencies
	◉ DVD	**▮** CD-ROM	**ⓘ** classzone.com

All Learners	Technology	Review & Assessment	Standards
TE Teaching Tips *pp. 263–264* **TE** Meeting Individual Needs *p. 264* **RP** MINT: Reading Concepts *TE p. 263*	**●** Lab Generator CD **◉** EasyPlanner	**SE** Active Reading Question *p. 263* **SE** Key Terms *p. 270* **SE** Questions and Problems *pp. 273–274*	**TE** **NSES** UCP3, UCP5, A1, A2, B3, C5, E1, E2, F1, F6
TE Teaching Tips *pp. 266–267* **TE** Meeting Individual Needs *p. 267* **RP** Team Learning Worksheet (Sec. 8.3)	**●** Transparency: Figure 8.8 **●** Lab Generator CD **◉** EasyPlanner	**SE** Practice Problem *p. 268* **TE** More Examples *p. 268* **SE** Critical Thinking *p. 269* **SE** Review Questions (8.3.A–8.3.B) *p. 269* **SE** Key Terms *p. 270* **SE** Questions and Problems *p. 274*	

Resource Materials for Chapter 8

SE Chapter Review *p. 270*

SE Critical Thinking *pp. 275–276*

SE Standardized Test Practice *p. 277*

AR English/Spanish Summaries

● English Summaries Audio

● Spanish Summaries Audio

RP Meeting Individual Needs Toolkit (MINT)
  Reading Concepts
  Chapter Review Worksheets
  Chapter Summaries

RP Solutions Guide

RP Standardized Test Practice

RP Chapter Tests

RP Test Bank

● Test Generator

In this chapter our goals are for students to:

- Learn about some of the factors that cause reactions to occur
- Learn to identify the solid that forms in a precipitation reaction
- Learn to describe reactions in solutions by writing molecular, complete ionic, and net ionic equations
- Learn the key characteristics of the reactions between strong acids and strong bases
- Learn the general characteristics of a reaction between a metal and a nonmetal
- Understand electron transfer as a driving force for a chemical reaction
- Learn various classification schemes for reactions

Chapter 8

Reactions in Aqueous Solutions

LOOKING AHEAD

Potassium metal reacts vigorously with water.

238

IN YOUR LIFE

The chemical reactions that are most important to us occur in water—in aqueous solutions. Virtually all of the chemical reactions that keep each of us alive and well take place in the aqueous medium present in our bodies. For example, the oxygen you breathe dissolves in your blood, where it associates with the hemoglobin in the red blood cells. While attached to the hemoglobin it is transported to your cells, where it reacts with fuel from the food you eat to provide energy for living. However, the reaction between oxygen and fuel is not direct—the cells are not tiny furnaces. Instead, electrons are transferred from the fuel to a series of molecules that pass them along (this is called the respiratory chain) until they eventually reach oxygen. Many other reactions are also crucial to our health and well-being. You will see numerous examples of these as you continue your study of chemistry.

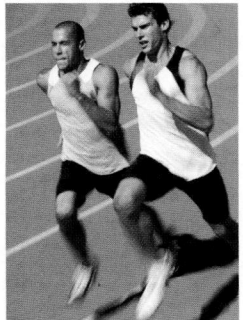

Oxygen is dissolved in the bloodstream of these runners to react with food chemicals to provide energy.

WHAT DO YOU KNOW?

Prereading Questions

1. If you could see an extremely magnified view of a solution of sodium chloride, what would it look like? What about a solution of barium nitrate?

2. Have you ever heard of *acid* or *base*? Give an example of each.

3. Have you heard of the terms *oxidation* or *reduction*? What do they mean?

1. Each of the solutions would contain ions. The sodium chloride solution would contain an equal number of sodium ions and chloride ions. The barium nitrate solution would contain two nitrate ions for every barium ion.

2. *Answers will vary.* Students may have heard of hydrochloric acid, nitric acid, or sulfuric acid. Students may have heard of sodium hydroxide.

3. *Answers will vary.* Students may be familiar with metals oxidizing (such as the formation of rust from iron).

TECHNOLOGY IN THE CLASSROOM

 Transparencies
Figures: 8.3, 8.8
Table: 8.1

 Power Presentation DVD
PowerPoint Slides
Animations
   Dissolution of a Solid in a Liquid
   Electrolyte Behavior
   Precipitation Reactions
   Neutralization of a Strong Acid by a Strong Base
   Proton Transfer
Videos
   Electrolytes
   Solubility Rules
   Barking Dogs: Reaction of Phosphorus
   Dry Ice and Magnesium
   Zinc and Iodine
   Sugar and Potassium Chlorate
   Thermite Reaction
eEdition
EasyPlanner

Lab Generator CD
English Summaries CD
Spanish Summaries CD
ML Test Generator

 classzone.com

SECTION 8.1
INTRODUCE

Student Preparation

Assign students to read Section 8.1 and to answer the Review Questions at the end of the section before coming to class.

 Active Learning
Team Learning Worksheet

After introducing the material in Section 8.1 in class, place students in groups and have them work together on **Section 8.1: Team Learning Worksheet**.

SECTION 8.1
GUIDE THE LEARNING

Homework

You may wish to assign these selected end-of-chapter problems as homework for this section:
2, 3, 6, 8a–d, 9a–b, 10, 11a–c, 14, 16

Additional end-of-chapter problems can be used for extra practice.

8.1.A Predicting Whether a Reaction Will Occur

Objective To learn about some of the factors that cause reactions to occur

 TEACHING TIP

Explain that chemists make predictions based on the driving forces in a reaction and their own databases (mostly in their memories) of chemical reactions. The more experience someone has, the easier it becomes to predict the correct products for a reaction.

 Active Reading Question

Answers will vary. Students can look through Chapter 7 to find examples.

8.1.B Reactions in Which a Solid Forms

Objective To learn to identify the solid that forms in a precipitation reaction

 LABORATORY
EXPERIMENT 29:
Precipitation Reaction, Microscale

Understanding Reactions in Aqueous Solutions

Key Terms
- Precipitation
- Precipitate
- Precipitation reaction
- Strong electrolyte
- Soluble solid
- Insoluble solid (slightly soluble solid)
- Molecular equation
- Complete ionic equation
- Spectator ions
- Net ionic equation

Objectives
- *To learn about some of the factors that cause reactions to occur*
- *To learn to identify the solid that forms in a precipitation reaction*
- *To learn to write molecular, complete ionic, and net ionic equations*

A. Predicting Whether a Reaction Will Occur

In this text we have already seen many chemical reactions. Now let's consider an important question: Why does a chemical reaction occur? What causes reactants to "want" to form products? As chemists have studied reactions, they have recognized several "tendencies" in reactants that drive them to form products. That is, there are several "driving forces" that pull reactants toward products—changes that tend to make reactions go in the direction of the arrow. The most common of these driving forces are

- Formation of a solid
- Transfer of electrons
- Formation of water
- Formation of a gas

When two or more chemicals are brought together, if any of these things can occur, a chemical change (a reaction) is likely to take place. Accordingly, when we are confronted with a set of reactants and want to predict whether a reaction will occur and what products might form, we will consider these driving forces. They will help us organize our thoughts as we encounter new reactions.

Figure 8.1
The precipitation reaction that occurs when yellow potassium chromate, $K_2CrO_4(aq)$, is mixed with a colorless barium nitrate solution, $Ba(NO_3)_2(aq)$

Precipitation
The formation of a solid in a chemical reaction

Precipitate
The solid that forms in a precipitation reaction

Precipitation reaction
A reaction in which a solid forms and separates from the solution

 Active Reading Question

Provide an example for each of the driving forces.

B. Reactions in Which a Solid Forms

One driving force for a chemical reaction is the formation of a solid, a process called **precipitation**. The solid that forms is called a **precipitate**, and the reaction is known as a **precipitation reaction**. For example, when an aqueous (water) solution of potassium chromate, $K_2CrO_4(aq)$, which is yellow, is added to a colorless aqueous solution containing barium nitrate, $Ba(NO_3)_2(aq)$, a yellow solid forms (see **Figure 8.1**). The fact that a solid forms tells us that a reaction—a chemical change—has occurred. That is, we have a situation where

Reactants → Products

What is the equation that describes this chemical change? To write the equation, we must decipher the identities of the reactants and products. The reactants have already been described: $K_2CrO_4(aq)$ and $Ba(NO_3)_2(aq)$. Is there some way in which we can predict the identities of the products? What is the yellow solid? The best way to predict the identity of this solid is to first *consider what products are possible*. To do this we need to know what chemical species are present in the solution that results when the reactant solutions are mixed. First, let's think about the nature of each reactant in an aqueous solution.

240 • Chapter 8 • Reactions in Aqueous Solutions

What Happens When an Ionic Compound Dissolves in Water?

The designation $Ba(NO_3)_2(aq)$ means that barium nitrate (a white solid) has been dissolved in water. Note from its formula that barium nitrate contains the Ba^{2+} and NO_3^- ions. *In virtually every case when a solid containing ions dissolves in water, the ions separate* and move around independently. We say that the ions of the solid *dissociate* when the solid dissolves in water. That is, $Ba(NO_3)_2(aq)$ does not contain $Ba(NO_3)_2$ units. Rather, it contains separated Ba^{2+} and NO_3^- ions. In the solution there are two NO_3^- ions for every Ba^{2+} ion. Chemists know that separated ions are present in this solution because it is an excellent conductor of electricity (see **Figure 8.2**). Pure water does not conduct an electric current. Ions must be present in water for a current to flow.

(a) Pure water does not conduct an electric current. The lamp does not light.

(b) When an ionic compound is dissolved in water, current flows and the lamp lights.

Figure 8.2
Electrical conductivity of aqueous solutions. The result of this experiment is strong evidence that ionic compounds dissolved in water exist in the form of separated ions.

When each unit of a substance that dissolves in water produces separated ions, the substance is called a **strong electrolyte**. Barium nitrate is a strong electrolyte in water, because each $Ba(NO_3)_2$ unit produces the separated ions $(Ba^{2+}, NO_3^-, NO_3^-)$.

$$Ba(NO_3)_2(s) \xrightarrow{H_2O} Ba^{2+}(aq) + 2NO_3^-(aq)$$

Similarly, aqueous K_2CrO_4 also behaves as a strong electrolyte. Potassium chromate contains the K^+ and CrO_4^{2-} ions, so an aqueous solution of potassium chromate (which is prepared by dissolving solid K_2CrO_4 in water) contains these separated ions.

$$K_2CrO_4(s) \xrightarrow{H_2O} 2K^+(aq) + CrO_4^{2-}(aq)$$

That is, $K_2CrO_4(aq)$ does not contain K_2CrO_4 units but instead contains K^+ cations and CrO_4^{2-} anions, which move around independently. (There are two K^+ ions for each CrO_4^{2-} ion.) The idea introduced here is very important:

> When ionic compounds dissolve, the resulting solution contains the separated ions.

Therefore, we can represent the mixing of $K_2CrO_4(aq)$ and $Ba(NO_3)_2(aq)$ in two ways. We usually write these reactants as:

$$K_2CrO_4(aq) + Ba(NO_3)_2(aq) \rightarrow \text{Products}$$

> **Strong electrolyte**
> A substance that dissolves in water by dissociating completely into ions

information

Note that the H_2O over the arrow here indicates that the substance is being dissolved in water.

8.1 • Understanding Reactions in Aqueous Solutions • **241**

- Review how ionic compounds are formed. Remind students that both positive and negative ions are needed to form a compound and that compounds must be electrically neutral.

- It is obvious to focus on the precipitate when discussing precipitation reactions. However, it is important to spend an equal amount of time discussing the reactants involved. Students should understand the nature of the reactant solutions to appreciate the reaction.

However, a more accurate representation of the situation is:

K$_2$CrO$_4$(aq)
Ions separate when
the solid dissolves.

Ba(NO$_3$)$_2$(aq)
Ions separate when
the solid dissolves.

We can express this information in equation form as follows:

$$2K^+(aq) + CrO_4^{2-}(aq) + Ba^{2+}(aq) + 2NO_3^-(aq) \rightarrow Products$$

The ions in
K$_2$CrO$_4$(aq)

The ions in
Ba(NO$_3$)$_2$(aq)

Thus the *mixed solution* contains four types of ions: K$^+$, CrO$_4^{2-}$, Ba^{2+}, and NO$_3^-$. Now that we know what the reactants are, we can make some educated guesses about the possible products.

How to Decide What Products Form

Which of these ions combine to form the yellow solid observed when the original solutions are mixed? This is not an easy question to answer. Even an experienced chemist is not sure what will happen in a new reaction. The chemist tries to think of the various possibilities, considers the likelihood of each possibility, and then makes a prediction (an educated guess). Only after identifying each product experimentally can the chemist be sure what reaction actually has taken place. However, an educated guess

CHEMISTRY IN YOUR WORLD

Consumer Connection

Instant Cooking—On Demand

Can you think of foods you've recently prepared that were ready to go—except for adding water? From breakfast through dessert, chemists have found ways to prepare mixes that stay unreacted and ready to use on our shelves. All we need to do is place them in a bowl, add water, and cook! Why don't the ingredients react in the box?

Most of the ingredients used in mixes are solids. We've already seen that solids don't usually react until they are dissolved in water. So as long as moisture is kept out of the mix, it will remain unreacted.

Sometimes manufacturers also dehydrate ingredients such as milk and eggs so they can be stored in unreactive form in the mix as well.

Flavored gelatin

Chemistry in Your World
Instant Cooking—On Demand

"Instant Cooking—On Demand" is a good place to remind students about the importance of water as a reaction medium. Water dissolves several important chemicals, which allows essential reactions in our everyday lives to occur. Have students make a list of some important reactions that occur in aqueous solutions.

is very useful because it indicates what kinds of products are most likely. It gives us a place to start. So the best way to proceed is first to think of the various possibilities and then to decide which of them is most likely.

Possible Products What are the possible products of the reaction between $K_2CrO_4(aq)$ and $Ba(NO_3)_2(aq)$ or, more accurately, what reaction can occur among the ions K^+, CrO_4^{2-}, Ba^{2+}, and NO_3^-? We already know some things that will help us decide.

> A solid compound must have a zero net charge. This means that the product of our reaction must contain both anions and cations (negative and positive ions).

For example, K^+ and Ba^{2+} could not combine to form the solid because such a solid would have a positive charge. Similarly, CrO_4^{2-} and NO_3^- could not combine to form a solid because that solid would have a negative charge.

Something else that will help us is an observation that chemists have made by examining many compounds: *most ionic materials contain only two types of ions*—one type of cation and one type of anion. This idea is illustrated by the following compounds (among many others):

Ionic Materials		
Compound	Cation	Anion
NaCl	Na^+	Cl^-
KOH	K^+	OH^-
Na_2SO_4	Na^+	SO_4^{2-}
NH_4Cl	NH_4^+	Cl^-
Na_2CO_3	Na^+	CO_3^{2-}

All the possible combinations of a cation and an anion to form uncharged compounds from among the ions K^+, CrO_4^{2-}, Ba^{2+}, and NO_3^- are shown below:

	NO_3^-	CrO_4^{2-}
K^+	KNO_3	K_2CrO_4
Ba^{2+}	$Ba(NO_3)_2$	$BaCrO_4$

So the compounds in red *might* be the solid.

Which of these possibilities is most likely to represent the yellow solid? We know it's not K_2CrO_4 or $Ba(NO_3)_2$; these are the reactants. They were present (dissolved) in the separate solutions that were mixed initially. The only real possibilities are KNO_3 and $BaCrO_4$. To decide which of these is more likely to represent the yellow solid, we need more facts. An experienced chemist, for example, knows that KNO_3 is a white solid. On the other hand, the CrO_4^{2-} ion is yellow. Therefore, the yellow solid must be $BaCrO_4$.

We have determined that one product of the reaction between $K_2CrO_4(aq)$ and $Ba(NO_3)_2(aq)$ is $BaCrO_4(s)$, but what happened to the K^+ and NO_3^- ions? The answer is that these ions are left dissolved in the solution. That is, KNO_3 does not form a solid when the K^+ and NO_3^- ions are present in water. In other words, if we took the white solid $KNO_3(s)$ and put it in water, it would

- To help students decide which products can form, list all possible combinations and then eliminate the unlikely ones.

- Students sometimes have trouble remembering that they must eliminate the starting reactants as possible products. Use molecular-level drawings to show why these substances cannot be products in the reaction.

Active Reading Question

K_2CrO_4 and $Ba(NO_3)_2$ are not the solids because they are the original reactants.

TEACHING TIP

Use at least one example in class in which two solutions are mixed and no solid forms (for example, Na_2SO_4 and KCl). Students should not develop the notion that a solid always forms when two solutions of ionic compounds are mixed.

totally dissolve (the white solid would "disappear," yielding a colorless solution). So when we mix $K_2CrO_4(aq)$ and $Ba(NO_3)_2(aq)$, $BaCrO_4(s)$ forms but KNO_3 is left behind in solution—we write it as $KNO_3(aq)$. If we poured the mixture through a filter to remove the solid $BaCrO_4$ and then evaporated all of the water, we would obtain the white solid KNO_3.

After all this thinking, we can finally write the unbalanced equation for the precipitation reaction.

$$K_2CrO_4(aq) + Ba(NO_3)_2(aq) \rightarrow BaCrO_4(s) + KNO_3(aq)$$

We can represent this reaction in pictures as follows:

Note that the K^+ and NO_3^- ions are not involved in the chemical change. They are present in the solution before and after the reaction.

Active Reading Question

How do we know that K_2CrO_4 and $Ba(NO_3)_2$ are not the solids?

Using Solubility Rules

In our example above we were finally able to identify the products of the reaction by using two types of chemical knowledge:

1. **Facts:** Knowing the colors of the compounds was very helpful.

2. **Concepts:** Knowing the concept that solids always have a net charge of zero was also important.

These two kinds of knowledge allowed us to make a good guess about the identity of the solid that formed. As you continue to study chemistry, you will see that a balance of factual and conceptual knowledge is always required. You must both *memorize* important facts and *understand* crucial concepts to succeed.

Solids must contain both anions and cations in the relative numbers necessary to produce zero net charge.

Does a Solid Always Form? In the present case we are dealing with a reaction in which an ionic solid forms—that is, a process in which ions that are dissolved in water combine to give a solid. We know that for a solid to form, both positive and negative ions must be present in relative numbers that give zero net charge. However, oppositely charged ions in water do not always react to form a solid, as we have seen for K^+ and NO_3^-. In addition, Na^+ and Cl^- can coexist in water in very large numbers with no formation of solid NaCl. In other words, when solid NaCl (common salt) is placed in water, it dissolves—the white solid "disappears" as the Na^+ and Cl^- ions are dispersed throughout the water. The following two statements, then, are really saying the same thing:

1. Solid NaCl is very soluble in water.

2. Solid NaCl does not form when one solution containing Na^+ is mixed with another solution containing Cl^-.

Teaching Support
BACKGROUND INFORMATION

One of the most valuable properties of water is its ability to dissolve many different substances. For example, salt "disappears" when you sprinkle it into the water used to cook vegetables, as does sugar when you add it to your iced tea. In each case, the "disappearing" substance is obviously still present—you can taste it. What happens when a solid dissolves? Liquid water consists

of a collection of H_2O molecules. An individual H_2O molecule is "bent" or V-shaped, with an H—O—H angle of approximately 105 degrees:

The O—H bonds in the water molecule are covalent bonds formed by electron sharing between the oxygen and hydrogen atoms. However, the electrons of the bond are not

Predicting Precipitates To predict whether a given pair of dissolved ions will form a solid when mixed, we must know some facts about the solubilities of various types of ionic compounds. In this text we will use the term **soluble solid** to mean a solid that readily dissolves in water; the solid "disappears" as the ions are dispersed in the water. The terms **insoluble solid** and **slightly soluble solid** are taken to mean the same thing: a solid where such a tiny amount dissolves in water that it is undetectable with the naked eye. The solubility information about common solids that is summarized in **Table 8.1** is based on observations of the behavior of many compounds. This is factual knowledge that you will need to predict what will happen in chemical reactions where a solid might form. This information is summarized in **Figure 8.3**.

> **Soluble solid**
> A solid that readily dissolves in water
>
> **Insoluble solid (slightly soluble solid)**
> A solid that dissolves to such a small degree that it is not detectable to the naked eye

---

Table 8.1

General Rules for Solubility of Ionic Compounds (Salts) in Water at 25 °C

1. Most nitrate (NO_3^-) salts are soluble.
2. Most salts of Na^+, K^+, and NH_4^+ are soluble.
3. Most chloride salts are soluble. Notable exceptions are $AgCl$, $PbCl_2$, and Hg_2Cl_2.
4. Most sulfate salts are soluble. Notable exceptions are $BaSO_4$, $PbSO_4$, and $CaSO_4$.
5. Most hydroxide compounds are only slightly soluble.* The important exceptions are $NaOH$ and KOH. $Ba(OH)_2$ and $Ca(OH)_2$ are moderately soluble.
6. Most sulfide (S^{2-}), carbonate (CO_3^{2-}), and phosphate (PO_4^{3-}) salts are only slightly soluble.*

*The terms *insoluble* and *slightly soluble* really mean the same thing: such a tiny amount dissolves that it is not possible to detect it with the naked eye.

(a) Soluble compounds

NO_3^- salts

Na^+, K^+, NH_4^+ salts

| Cl^-, Br^-, I^- salts | Except for those containing | Ag^+, Hg_2^{2+}, Pb^{2+} |

| SO_4^{2-} salts | Except for those containing | Ba^{2+}, Pb^{2+}, Ca^{2+} |

(b) Insoluble compounds

S^{2-}, CO_3^{2-}, PO_4^{3-} salts

| OH^- salts | Except for those containing | Na^+, K^+, Ca^{2+} |

Figure 8.3
Solubilities of common compounds

Notice that in Table 8.1 and Figure 8.3 the term *salt* is used to mean *ionic compound*. Many chemists use the terms *salt* and *ionic compound* interchangeably. In Example 8.1, we will illustrate how to use the solubility rules to predict the products of reactions among ions.

information

In predicting what reaction will occur when ions are mixed in water, focus on the ions that are in solution before any reaction occurs.

TEACHING TIPS

- Use the transparency for Figure 8.3 to help students decide on the identity of the precipitate.

- Compounds that are *slightly soluble* are virtually insoluble in water. Most of the compound remains as a solid in water.

TECHNOLOGY

📼 Table 8.1

📼 Figure 8.3

💿 **Video**
Solubility Rules

👤 **Active Learning**
Group Activity

Three-Bottle Puzzle

Give each student team a well tray and a set of three dropper bottles containing different numbered solutions. Give each team a list of the substances that are in their bottles. The goal is for the teams to correctly identify the substance in each bottle. Some possible combinations are:

Na_2S, $Ba(NO_3)_2$, K_2CO_3

KI, $Pb(NO_3)_2$, Na_2SO_4

KCl, $AgNO_3$, Na_2S

KOH, $Ni(NO_3)_2$, Na_2S

All solutions should be approximately 0.1 *M*. You may want to give some clues regarding color of the precipitates (sulfides are generally black, lead iodide is yellow, and so on).

(continued)

shared equally between these atoms. For reasons we will discuss in later chapters, oxygen has a greater attraction for electrons than does hydrogen. If the electrons were shared equally between the two atoms, both would be electrically neutral because, on average, the number of electrons around each would equal the number of protons in that nucleus. Because the oxygen atom has a greater attraction for electrons, the shared electrons tend to spend more time close to

the oxygen than to either of the hydrogens. Thus the oxygen atom gains a slight excess of negative charge, and the hydrogen atoms become slightly positive. Because of this unequal charge distribution, water is said to be a *polar molecule*. This polarity gives water its great ability to dissolve compounds.

EXAMPLE 8.1

More Examples

1. When an aqueous solution of barium nitrate is added to an aqueous solution of sodium sulfate, a white solid forms. Identify the white solid and write the balanced equation for the reaction that occurs.

$$Ba(NO_3)_2(aq) + Na_2SO_4(aq) \rightarrow BaSO_4(s) + 2NaNO_3(aq)$$

2. When an aqueous solution of lead(II) nitrate is added to an aqueous solution of potassium iodide, a yellow solid forms. Identify the yellow solid and write the balanced equation for the reaction that occurs.

$$Pb(NO_3)_2(aq) + 2KI(aq) \rightarrow PbI_2(s) + 2KNO_3(aq)$$

Students should deduce the identity of the solid by knowing that there is a solid (as given in the problem) and that potassium nitrate is not the solid (from the solubility rules).

EXAMPLE 8.1

Identifying Precipitates in Reactions Where a Solid Forms

When an aqueous solution of silver nitrate is added to an aqueous solution of potassium chloride, a white solid forms. Identify the white solid and write the balanced equation for the reaction that occurs.

ℹ information

$AgNO_3$ is usually called "silver nitrate" rather than "silver(I) nitrate" because silver forms only Ag^+.

Solution

First let's write the equation for the reaction:

$$AgNO_3(aq) + KCl(aq) \rightarrow \text{White solid}$$

To answer the question "What is the white solid?" we must decide what ions are present in the mixed solution. Remember that *when ionic substances dissolve in water, the ions separate*. So we can write the equation

$$\underbrace{Ag^+(aq) + NO_3^-(aq)}_{\substack{\text{Ions in} \\ AgNO_3(aq)}} + \underbrace{K^+(aq) + Cl^-(aq)}_{\substack{\text{Ions in} \\ KCl(aq)}} \rightarrow \text{Products}$$

or use pictures to represent the ions present in the mixed solution before any reaction occurs.

AgNO₃(aq)   KCl(aq)

ℹ information

Use a table like this to figure out the possible combinations.

	NO_3^-	Cl^-
Ag^+	$AgNO_3$	$AgCl$
K^+	KNO_3	KCl

Now we will consider what solid *might* form from this collection of ions. Because the solid must contain both positive and negative ions, the possible compounds that can be assembled from this collection of ions are

$$AgNO_3 \qquad AgCl \qquad KNO_3 \qquad KCl$$

$AgNO_3$ and KCl are the substances already dissolved in the reactant solutions, so we know that they do not represent the white solid product. We are left with two possibilities:

$$AgCl \qquad KNO_3$$

Another way to obtain these two possibilities is by *ion interchange*. This means that in the reaction of $AgNO_3(aq)$ and $KCl(aq)$, we take the cation from one reactant and combine it with the anion of the other reactant.

$$Ag^+ + NO_3^- + K^+ + Cl^- \rightarrow \text{Products}$$
$$\underbrace{\qquad\qquad\qquad\qquad}_{\text{Possible solid products}}$$

Ion interchange leads to the following possible solids:

$$AgCl \text{ or } KNO_3$$

Teaching Support
DEMONSTRATION

Lights Out!

Materials
- Saturated $Ba(OH)_2$
- 3 *M* H_2SO_4
- Beaker
- Stirring plate and stir bar
- Conductivity tester

Preparation Make saturated barium hydroxide by dissolving the maximum amount possible in distilled water. Decant the solution from the solid for use.

Presentation Place 25 mL distilled water and one drop of 3 *M* sulfuric acid in the beaker. Add the stirring bar and place the beaker on the stir plate. Place the conductivity tester in the beaker, out of the way of the spinning stir bar. Add the barium hydroxide solution dropwise,

observing the light. Continue adding barium hydroxide until the light goes out. Stop and discuss this result with your students. End the demonstration by asking for a prediction of what will happen if more barium hydroxide is added to the solution. Add more barium hydroxide and discuss the results with your students.

Teaching Notes This demonstration provides a practical connection between the macroscopic and microscopic

To decide whether AgCl or KNO_3 is the white solid, we need the solubility rules (Table 8.1).

Rule 2 states that most salts containing K^+ are soluble in water.

Rule 1 says that most nitrate salts (those containing NO_3^-) are soluble.

So the salt KNO_3 is water-soluble. That is, when K^+ and NO_3^- are mixed in water, a solid (KNO_3) does *not* form.

Rule 3 states that although most chloride salts (salts that contain Cl^-) are soluble, AgCl is an exception. That is, AgCl(s) is insoluble in water.

Thus the white solid must be AgCl. Now we can write

$$AgNO_3(aq) + KCl(aq) \rightarrow AgCl(s) + ?$$

What is the other product?

To form AgCl(s), we have used the Ag^+ and Cl^- ions:

$$Ag^+(aq) + NO_3^-(aq) + K^+(aq) + Cl^-(aq) \rightarrow AgCl(s)$$

This leaves the K^+ and NO_3^- ions. What do they do? Nothing. Because KNO_3 is very soluble in water (rules 1 and 2), the K^+ and NO_3^- ions remain separate in the water; the KNO_3 remains dissolved and we represent it as $KNO_3(aq)$. We can now write the full equation:

$$AgNO_3(aq) + KCl(aq) \rightarrow AgCl(s) + KNO_3(aq)$$

Figure 8.4 shows the precipitation of AgCl(s) that occurs when this reaction takes place. In graphic form, the reaction is

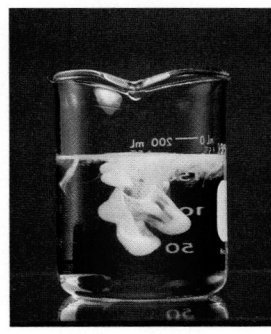

Figure 8.4
Precipitation of silver chloride occurs when solutions of silver nitrate and potassium chloride are mixed. The K^+ and NO_3^- ions remain in solution.

Let's Review

How to Predict Precipitates When Solutions of Two Ionic Compounds Are Mixed

Step 1 Write the reactants as they actually exist before any reaction occurs. Remember that when a salt dissolves, its ions separate.

Step 2 Consider the various solids that could form. To do this, simply *exchange the anions* of the added salts.

Step 3 Use the solubility rules (Table 8.1) to decide whether a solid forms and, if so, to predict the identity of the solid.

8.1 • Understanding Reactions in Aqueous Solutions • **247**

(continued)

worlds. Draw the solutions before the reaction on a molecular level. Discuss how conductivity tells us that ions are present in the solution. Proceed with the demonstration until the light goes out. Now discuss on a molecular level what is present in the beaker (water and solid $BaSO_4$) and explain how this situation is different from that before the reaction. After student predictions, explain that the

light comes on again as a result of the addition of more barium and hydroxide ions, which do not form a precipitate because all of the sulfate has been consumed.

EXAMPLE 8.2

More Examples

Using the solubility rules in Table 8.1, predict what will happen when the following solutions are mixed. Write the balanced equation for any reaction that occurs.

1. $Ba(NO_3)_2(aq) + K_3PO_4(aq)$

   $3Ba(NO_3)_2(aq) + 2K_3PO_4(aq) \rightarrow$
   $Ba_3(PO_4)_2(s) + 6KNO_3(aq)$

2. $Na_2SO_4(aq) + KCl(aq)$
   no reaction

EXAMPLE 8.2

Using Solubility Rules to Predict the Products of Reactions

Using the solubility rules in Table 8.1, predict what will happen when the following solutions are mixed. Write the balanced equation for any reaction that occurs.

  a. $KNO_3(aq)$ and $BaCl_2(aq)$ **c.** $KOH(aq)$ and $Fe(NO_3)_3(aq)$

  b. $Na_2SO_4(aq)$ and $Pb(NO_3)_2(aq)$

Solution

a. $KNO_3(aq)$ and $BaCl_2(aq)$

Step 1 $KNO_3(aq)$ represents an aqueous solution obtained by dissolving solid KNO_3 in water to give the ions $K^+(aq)$ and $NO_3^-(aq)$. Likewise, $BaCl_2(aq)$ is a solution formed by dissolving solid $BaCl_2$ in water to produce $Ba^{2+}(aq)$ and $Cl^-(aq)$. When these two solutions are mixed, the following ions will be present:

$$K^+, \quad NO_3^-, \qquad Ba^{2+}, \quad Cl^-$$
From $KNO_3(aq)$ From $BaCl_2(aq)$

Step 2 To get the possible products, we exchange the anions.

$$K^+ \quad NO_3^- \quad Ba^{2+} \quad Cl^-$$

This yields the possibilities KCl and $Ba(NO_3)_2$. These are the solids that *might* form. Notice that two NO_3^- ions are needed to balance the 2+ charge on Ba^{2+}.

Step 3 The rules listed in Table 8.1 indicate that both KCl and $Ba(NO_3)_2$ are soluble in water. So no precipitate forms when $KNO_3(aq)$ and $BaCl_2(aq)$ are mixed. All of the ions remain dissolved in the solution. This means that no reaction takes place. That is, no chemical change occurs.

b. $Na_2SO_4(aq)$ and $Pb(NO_3)_2(aq)$

Step 1 The following ions are present in the mixed solution before any reaction occurs:

$$Na^+, \quad SO_4^{2-}, \quad Pb^{2+}, \quad NO_3^-$$
From   From
$Na_2SO_4(aq)$ $Pb(NO_3)_2(aq)$

Step 2 Exchanging anions as follows:

$$Na^+ \quad SO_4^{2-} \quad Pb^{2+} \quad NO_3^-$$

yields the *possible* solid products $PbSO_4$ and $NaNO_3$.

248 • Chapter 8 • Reactions in Aqueous Solutions

Step 3 Using Table 8.1, we see that $NaNO_3$ is soluble in water (rules 1 and 2) but that $PbSO_4$ is only slightly soluble (rule 4). Thus, when these solutions are mixed, solid $PbSO_4$ forms. The balanced reaction is

$$Na_2SO_4(aq) + Pb(NO_3)_2(aq) \rightarrow PbSO_4(s) + 2NaNO_3(aq)$$

Remains dissolved

which can be represented as

Solid $PbSO_4$ forms.

c. $KOH(aq)$ and $Fe(NO_3)_3(aq)$

Step 1 The ions present in the mixed solution before any reaction occurs are

$$K^+, \quad OH^-, \quad Fe^{3+}, \quad NO_3^-$$

From $KOH(aq)$ From $Fe(NO_3)_3(aq)$

Step 2 Exchanging anions as follows:

$$K^+ \quad OH^- \quad Fe^{3+} \quad NO_3^-$$

yields the possible solid products KNO_3 and $Fe(OH)_3$.

Step 3 Rules 1 and 2 (Table 8.1) state that KNO_3 is soluble, whereas $Fe(OH)_3$ is only slightly soluble (rule 5). Thus, when these solutions are mixed, solid $Fe(OH)_3$ forms. The balanced equation for the reaction is

$$3KOH(aq) + Fe(NO_3)_3(aq) \rightarrow Fe(OH)_3(s) + 3KNO_3(aq)$$

which can be represented as

Solid $Fe(OH)_3$ forms.

⚗ Practice Problem • Exercise 8.2

Predict whether a solid will form when the following pairs of solutions are mixed. If so, identify the solid and write the balanced equation for the reaction.

   a. $Ba(NO_3)_2(aq)$ and $NaCl(aq)$

   b. $Na_2S(aq)$ and $Cu(NO_3)_2(aq)$

   c. $NH_4Cl(aq)$ and $Pb(NO_3)_2(aq)$

8.1 • Understanding Reactions in Aqueous Solutions • **249**

⚗ Answer to Practice Problem 8.2

a. The ions present are

$$Ba^{2+}(aq) + 2NO_3^-(aq) +$$
$$Na^+(aq) + Cl^-(aq) \rightarrow$$

Ions in   Ions in
$Ba(NO_3)_2(aq)$ $NaCl(aq)$

Exchanging the anions gives the possible solid products $BaCl_2$ and $NaNO_3$. Using Table 8.1, we see that both substances are very soluble (rules 1, 2, and 3). Thus no solid forms.

b. The ions present in the mixed solution before any reaction occurs are

$$2Na^+(aq) + S^{2-}(aq) +$$
$$Cu^{2+}(aq) + 2NO_3^-(aq) \rightarrow$$

Ions in   Ions in
$Na_2S(aq)$ $Cu(NO_3)_2(aq)$

Exchanging the anions gives the possible solid products CuS and $NaNO_3$ (soluble). By rule 6, CuS is insoluble, so it will precipitate. The balanced equation is

$$Na_2S(aq) + Cu(NO_3)_2(aq) \rightarrow$$
$$CuS(s) + 2NaNO_3(aq)$$

c. The ions present are

$$NH_4^+(aq) + Cl^-(aq) +$$
$$Pb^{2+}(aq) + 2NO_3^-(aq) \rightarrow$$

Ions in   Ions in
$NH_4Cl(aq)$ $Pb(NO_3)_2(aq)$

Exchanging the anions gives the possible solid products NH_4NO_3 and $PbCl_2$. NH_4NO_3 is soluble (rules 1 and 2) and $PbCl_2$ is insoluble (rule 3). Thus $PbCl_2$ will precipitate. The balanced equation is

$$2NH_4Cl(aq) + Pb(NO_3)_2(aq) \rightarrow$$
$$PbCl_2(s) + 2NH_4NO_3(aq)$$

Teaching Support		
DEMONSTRATION		

Colorful Precipitates

Materials
- 12 test tubes (18 × 150)
- Test tube rack
- Nickel(II) chloride
- Potassium iodide
- Sodium sulfate
- Sodium nitrate

- Sodium carbonate
- Lead(II) nitrate
- Barium chloride
- Copper(II) chloride
- Potassium chloride
- Silver nitrate
- Ammonium thiocyanate

Preparation Prepare dilute solutions of each of the listed compounds by adding 1 teaspoon of each to 500 mL of distilled water. Label the test tubes as follows:

1. $AgNO_3$	7. $NaNO_3$
2. NH_4SCN	8. KCl
3. $NiCl_2$	9. $BaCl_2$
4. Na_2CO_3	10. Na_2SO_4
5. $Pb(NO_3)_2$	11. $CuCl_2$
6. KI	12. Na_2CO_3

Fill each test tube one-third full of solution.

(continued on next page)

Objective To learn to describe reactions in solutions by writing molecular, complete ionic, and net ionic equations

 TEACHING TIPS

- Drawing molecular-level pictures when first discussing reactions in aqueous solutions is helpful for students.

- Molecular equations contain the complete formulas for all reactants and products. Complete ionic equations provide a window into the microscopic world. These equations show substances as they are in solution or at the molecular level.

- Remind students that a new product is often a solid and must not be written as ions if it is insoluble.

 Active Reading Questions

1. Molecular equation:
   $Pb(NO_3)_2(aq) + 2KI(aq) \rightarrow PbI_2(s) + 2KNO_3(aq)$

   Complete ionic equation:
   $Pb^{2+}(aq) + 2NO_3^{2-}(aq) + 2K^+(aq) + 2I^-(aq) \rightarrow PbI_2(s) + 2K^+(aq) + 2NO_3^-(aq)$

   Net ionic equation:
   $Pb^{2+}(aq) + 2I^-(aq) \rightarrow PbI_2(s)$

2. Nitrate ions, sodium ions, and potassium ions are generally spectator ions.

TECHNOLOGY

 Animation
Precipitation Reactions

Molecular equation
A chemical equation showing the complete (undissociated) forms of all reactants and products

Complete ionic equation
A chemical equation for a reaction in solution representing all strong electrolytes as ions

Spectator ion
An ion present in solution that does not participate in a reaction

Net ionic equation
A chemical equation for a reaction in solution showing only those components that are directly involved in the reaction. Strong electrolytes are represented as ions.

 nformation

A strong electrolyte is a substance that completely breaks apart into ions when dissolved in water. The resulting solution readily conducts an electric current.

C. Describing Reactions in Aqueous Solutions

Much important chemistry, including virtually all of the reactions that make life possible, occurs in aqueous solutions. We will now consider the types of equations used to represent reactions that occur in water. For example, as we saw earlier, when we mix aqueous potassium chromate with aqueous barium nitrate, a reaction occurs to form solid barium chromate and dissolved potassium nitrate. One way to represent this reaction is by the equation

$$K_2CrO_4(aq) + Ba(NO_3)_2(aq) \rightarrow BaCrO_4(s) + 2KNO_3(aq)$$

This is called the **molecular equation** for the reaction; it shows the complete formulas of all reactants and products. However, although this equation shows the reactants and products of the reaction, it does not give a very clear picture of what actually occurs in solution. As we have seen, aqueous solutions of potassium chromate, barium nitrate, and potassium nitrate contain the individual ions, not molecules as is implied by the molecular equation. Thus the **complete ionic equation**,

$$\overbrace{2K^+(aq) + CrO_4^{2-}(aq)}^{\text{Ions from } K_2CrO_4} + \overbrace{Ba^{2+}(aq) + 2NO_3^-(aq)}^{\text{Ions from } Ba(NO_3)_2} \rightarrow$$
$$BaCrO_4(s) + 2K^+(aq) + 2NO_3^-(aq)$$

better represents the actual forms of the reactants and products in solution. *In a complete ionic equation, all substances that are strong electrolytes are represented as ions.* Notice that $BaCrO_4$ is not written as the separate ions, because it is present as a solid; it is not dissolved.

The complete ionic equation reveals that only some of the ions participate in the reaction. Notice that the K^+ and NO_3^- ions are present in solution both before and after the reaction. Ions such as these, which do not participate directly in a reaction in solution, are called **spectator ions**. The ions that participate in this reaction are the Ba^{2+} and CrO_4^{2-} ions, which combine to form solid $BaCrO_4$:

$$Ba^{2+}(aq) + CrO_4^{2-}(aq) \rightarrow BaCrO_4(s)$$

This equation, called the **net ionic equation**, includes only those components that are directly involved in the reaction. Chemists usually write the net ionic equation for a reaction in solution, because it gives the actual forms of the reactants and products and includes only the species that undergo a change.

Active Reading Questions

1. A solution of lead(II) nitrate is reacted with a solution of potassium iodide. Write a molecular equation, complete ionic equation, and net ionic equation for this reaction.

2. According to the solubility rules, which ions are generally spectator ions?

(continued)

Presentation Pour the contents of test tube 1 into test tube 2. Ask students to make observations, write an ionic equation for the reaction, and name the precipitate. Repeat for the remaining test tubes, pairing 3 and 4, 5 and 6, 7 and 8, 9 and 10, and 11 and 12.

Teaching Notes Students can write the molecular, complete ionic, and net ionic equations for each reaction as you perform the demonstration.

Silver nitrate and ammonium thiocyanate produce a brown precipitate, silver thiocyanate [all ions are (aq)]:

$$Ag^+ + NO_3^- + NH_4^+ + SCN^- \rightarrow AgSCN(s) + NH_4^+ + NO_3^-$$

(Ions such as K^+ and NO_3^-, which do not enter the reaction, are called spectator ions.)

Nickel(II) chloride and sodium carbonate produce a pale blue precipitate, nickel(II) carbonate.

$$Ni^{2+} + 2Cl^- + 2Na^+ + CO_3^{2-} \rightarrow NiCO_3(s) + 2Cl^- + 2Na^+$$

Lead(II) nitrate and potassium iodide produce a yellow precipitate, lead(II) iodide.

$$Pb^{2+} + 2NO_3^- + 2K^+ + 2I^- \rightarrow PbI_2(s) + 2NO_3^- + 2K^+$$

Sodium nitrate and potassium chloride

Let's Review

Types of Equations for Reactions in Aqueous Solutions

Three types of equations are used to describe reactions in solutions.

- The *molecular equation* shows the overall reaction but not necessarily the actual forms of the reactants and products in solution.

- The *complete ionic equation* represents all reactants and products that are strong electrolytes as ions. All reactants and products are included.

- The *net ionic equation* includes only those components that undergo a change. Spectator ions are not included.

A Closer Look

In Example 8.2 we considered the reaction between aqueous solutions of lead nitrate and sodium sulfate. The molecular equation for this reaction is

$$Pb(NO_3)_2(aq) + Na_2SO_4(aq) \rightarrow PbSO_4(s) + 2NaNO_3(aq)$$

Because any ionic compound that is dissolved in water is present as the separated ions, we can write the complete ionic equation as follows:

$$Pb^{2+}(aq) + 2NO_3^-(aq) + 2Na^+(aq) + SO_4^{2-}(aq) \rightarrow$$
$$PbSO_4(s) + 2Na^+(aq) + 2NO_3^-(aq)$$

The $PbSO_4$ is not written as separate ions because it is present as a solid. The ions that take part in the chemical change are the Pb^{2+} and the SO_4^{2-} ions, which combine to form solid $PbSO_4$. Thus the net ionic equation is

$$Pb^{2+}(aq) + SO_4^{2-}(aq) \rightarrow PbSO_4(s)$$

The Na^+ and NO_3^- ions do not undergo any chemical change; they are spectator ions.

information

The net ionic equation includes only those components that undergo a change in the reaction.

Active Reading Question

What is the advantage of writing net ionic equations for chemical reactions?

EXAMPLE 8.3

Writing Equations for Reactions

For each of the following reactions, write the molecular equation, the complete ionic equation, and the net ionic equation.

a. Aqueous sodium chloride is added to aqueous silver nitrate to form solid silver chloride plus aqueous sodium nitrate.

b. Aqueous potassium hydroxide is mixed with aqueous iron(III) nitrate to form solid iron(III) hydroxide and aqueous potassium nitrate.

(continued)

produce no reaction.

$$Na^+ + NO_3^- + K^+ + Cl^- \rightarrow N.R.$$

Barium chloride and sodium sulfate produce a white precipitate, barium sulfate.

$$Ba^{2+} + 2Cl^- + 2Na^+ + SO_4^{2-} \rightarrow$$
$$BaSO_4(s) + 2Cl^- + 2Na^+$$

Copper(II) chloride and sodium carbonate produce a pale blue precipitate, copper(II) carbonate.

$$Cu^{2+} + 2Cl^- + 2Na^+ + CO_3^{2-} \rightarrow$$
$$CuCO_3(s) + 2Cl^- + 2Na^+$$

TEACHING TIP

Remind students that charges must be balanced in both ionic and net ionic equations.

Active Reading Question

Net ionic equations give the actual forms of the reactants and products and include only the species that undergo a change.

EXAMPLE 8.3

More Examples

For each of the following reactions, write the balanced molecular equation, complete ionic equation, and net ionic equation.

1. Aqueous silver nitrate is added to aqueous sodium chromate to form solid silver chromate and aqueous sodium nitrate.

   Molecular:
   $$2AgNO_3(aq) + Na_2CrO_4(aq) \rightarrow$$
   $$Ag_2CrO_4(s) + 2NaNO_3(aq)$$

   Complete ionic:
   $$2Ag^+(aq) + 2NO_3^-(aq) +$$
   $$2Na^+(aq) + CrO_4^{2-}(aq) \rightarrow$$
   $$Ag_2CrO_4(s) + 2Na^+(aq) +$$
   $$2NO_3^-(aq)$$

   Net ionic:
   $$2Ag^+(aq) + CrO_4^{2-}(aq) \rightarrow$$
   $$Ag_2CrO_4(s)$$

2. Aqueous nickel(II) nitrate is added to aqueous potassium carbonate to form solid nickel(II) carbonate and aqueous potassium nitrate.

   Molecular:
   $$Ni(NO_3)_2(aq) + K_2CO_3(aq) \rightarrow$$
   $$NiCO_3(s) + 2KNO_3(aq)$$

   Complete ionic:
   $$Ni^{2+}(aq) + 2NO_3^-(aq) +$$
   $$2K^+(aq) + CO_3^{2-}(aq) \rightarrow$$
   $$NiCO_3(s) + 2K^+(aq) +$$
   $$2NO_3^-(aq)$$

   Net ionic:
   $$Ni^{2+}(aq) + CO_3^{2-}(aq) \rightarrow$$
   $$NiCO_3(s)$$

a. Molecular:

$$Na_2S(aq) + Cu(NO_3)_2(aq) \rightarrow CuS(s) + 2NaNO_3(aq)$$

Complete ionic:

$$2Na^+(aq) + S^{2-}(aq) + Cu^{2+}(aq) + 2NO_3^-(aq) \rightarrow CuS(s) + 2Na^+(aq) + 2NO_3^-(aq)$$

Net ionic:

$$S^{2-}(aq) + Cu^{2+}(aq) \rightarrow CuS(s)$$

b. Molecular:

$$2NH_4Cl(aq) + Pb(NO_3)_2(aq) \rightarrow PbCl_2(s) + 2NH_4NO_3(aq)$$

Complete ionic:

$$2NH_4^+(aq) + 2Cl^-(aq) + Pb^{2+}(aq) + 2NO_3^-(aq) \rightarrow PbCl_2(s) + 2NH_4^+(aq) + 2NO_3^-(aq)$$

Net ionic:

$$2Cl^-(aq) + Pb^{2+}(aq) \rightarrow PbCl_2(s)$$

Solution

a. *Molecular equation:*

$$NaCl(aq) + AgNO_3(aq) \rightarrow AgCl(s) + NaNO_3(aq)$$

Complete ionic equation:

$$Na^+(aq) + Cl^-(aq) + Ag^+(aq) + NO_3^-(aq) \rightarrow AgCl(s) + Na^+(aq) + NO_3^-(aq)$$

Net ionic equation:

$$Cl^-(aq) + Ag^+(aq) \rightarrow AgCl(s)$$

b. *Molecular equation:*

$$3KOH(aq) + Fe(NO_3)_3(aq) \rightarrow Fe(OH)_3(s) + 3KNO_3(aq)$$

Complete ionic equation:

$$3K^+(aq) + 3OH^-(aq) + Fe^{3+}(aq) + 3NO_3^-(aq) \rightarrow Fe(OH)_3(s) + 3K^+(aq) + 3NO_3^-(aq)$$

Net ionic equation:

$$3OH^-(aq) + Fe^{3+}(aq) \rightarrow Fe(OH)_3(s)$$

 Practice Problem • Exercise 8.3

For each of the following reactions, write the molecular equation, the complete ionic equation, and the net ionic equation.

a. Aqueous sodium sulfide is mixed with aqueous copper(II) nitrate to produce solid copper(II) sulfide and aqueous sodium nitrate.

b. Aqueous ammonium chloride and aqueous lead(II) nitrate react to form solid lead(II) chloride and aqueous ammonium nitrate.

CELEBRITY CHEMICAL   Ammonia (NH₃)

Ammonia is a colorless gas with a strong odor that can be liquified at −34 °C. Ammonia (dissolved in water) is found in many household cleaning products.

Ammonia is manufactured by combining the elements nitrogen and hydrogen:

$$3H_2(g) + N_2(g) \rightarrow 2NH_3(g)$$

The major use of ammonia is as a fertilizer to furnish nitrogen atoms to growing plants. Approximately 30 *billion* pounds of ammonia are produced every year for this purpose. For use as a

fertilizer, the ammonia is liquified (at high pressures) and stored in mobile tanks that can be pulled through the fields by a tractor. It is then injected into the ground to serve as an additional source of nitrogen for the crop.

A cross section showing how ammonia is injected into the soil to act as a fertilizer

Teaching Support
DEMONSTRATION

Properties of Ammonia

Materials

- 10 g ammonium chloride
- 10 g sodium hydroxide pellets
- 250-mL Erlenmeyer flask
- One-holed rubber #5 stopper
- Glass tubing

- Two 500-mL flasks and rubber stopper to fit
- Red litmus paper
- Hot plate or Bunsen burner
- Shallow pan or baking dish

Preparation Before class, insert glass tubing through the #5 stopper. (Protect your hand. Use glycerin for lubrication.) In the hood, add the ammonium chloride and sodium hydroxide pellets to the 250-mL flask and cover with the

#5 stopper. Heat the solids gently and invert the 500-mL dry flask over the glass tube, filling the inverted flask with ammonia. (Test the mouth of the inverted flask with red litmus—when it turns blue, the flask is full of ammonia.) Stopper the larger flask and remove the smaller flask from the heat.

Presentation Unstopper the flask and place a piece of red litmus to the mouth of the flask. Restopper the flask and explain that moist red litmus turns blue when a

HANDS-ON CHEMISTRY • MINI-LAB •

Forecast: Precipitation

Materials
- index cards (or flashcards from the Chapter 4 activities if available)

Procedure
1. Make two sets of flashcards. Put the name of an ion on one side and its symbol and charge on the other (use the cards from the Chapter 4 activities if you did them).

    Set A: all of the alkali and alkaline earth metals, and iron(II), iron(III), lead(II), and silver.

    Set B: all of the nonmetals from Groups 5A, 6A, and 7A, and the polyatomic ions listed in Table 4.4

2. Randomly pick one card from Set A and one card from Set B. Write the proper formula for the ionic compound made from these two ions, and name the compound.

3. Repeat step 2. Are both ionic compounds soluble? If so, go to step 4, if not, go back to step 2.

4. Use the two soluble ionic compounds as reactants. Write the names and formulas for the possible products of the reaction, along with the molecular equation and complete ionic equation. Is at least one of the products insoluble? If so, go to step 5. If not, go back to step 2.

5. Write the net ionic equation for the reaction. Go back to step 2 and continue this process until you have 5 net ionic equations.

SECTION 8.1
REVIEW QUESTIONS

① What are the driving forces that indicate a chemical reaction is likely to occur?

② Use the solubility rules in Table 8.1 or the information in Figure 8.3 to predict which of the following will be soluble in water:

   a. potassium nitrate

   b. zinc hydroxide

   c. calcium carbonate

   d. ammonium chloride

③ Consider two separate beakers, one containing an aqueous solution of hydrochloric acid, the second an aqueous solution of lead(II) nitrate.

   a. Draw a picture of each solution showing the ions present.

   b. Draw a picture after the solutions are mixed showing what is present.

   c. Predict the products for any reaction that occurs.

   d. Write a net ionic equation for the reaction.

④ How is a molecular equation different from a complete ionic equation?

⑤ What is a spectator ion and what happens to it in a net ionic equation?

⑥ Consider the following reaction: aqueous sodium sulfate is added to aqueous barium bromide to form solid barium sulfate and aqueous sodium bromide.

   a. Write the molecular equation.

   b. Write the complete ionic equation.

   c. List the spectator ions.

   d. Write the net ionic equation.

RESEARCH LINKS
CLASSZONE.COM

8.1 • Understanding Reactions in Aqueous Solutions • **253**

SECTION 8.1
Review Questions

1. The driving forces for a reaction are formation of a solid, formation of water, transfer of electrons, and formation of a gas.

2. The following compounds are soluble in water: potassium nitrate, zinc hydroxide, and ammonium chloride.

3. a. The picture should contain H^+, Cl^-, and H_2O in one beaker and Pb^{2+}, NO_3^-, and H_2O in another beaker.

   b. The picture should contain $PbCl_2$, H^+, NO_3^-, and H_2O.

   c. The product is lead(II) chloride.

   d. $Pb(NO_3)_2(aq) + 2HCl(aq) \rightarrow PbCl_2(s) + 2HNO_3(aq)$

4. Molecular equations contain the complete formulas for all reactants and products. Complete ionic equations show substances as they are in solution.

5. A spectator ion is an ion that does not participate in the reaction in solution. Spectator ions are not shown in a net ionic equation.

6. a. $Na_2SO_4(aq) + BaBr_2(aq) \rightarrow BaSO_4(s) + 2NaBr(aq)$

   b. $2Na^+(aq) + SO_4^{2-}(aq) + Ba^{2+}(aq) + 2Br^-(aq) \rightarrow BaSO_4(s) + 2Na^+(aq) + 2Br^-(aq)$

   c. The spectator ions are sodium ions and bromide ions.

   d. $SO_4^{2-}(aq) + Ba^{2+}(aq) \rightarrow BaSO_4(s)$

(continued)

base is present. Repeat this process with a flask containing air to show the difference.

Place the flask containing air in an inverted position in the shallow pan containing water. Nothing happens. Repeat this process with the flask containing ammonia. Water will rush into the flask because ammonia dissolves easily in water, lowering the pressure inside the flask.

Soil's acidity is lowered by dissolved ammonia in the soil's water.

Hands-On Chemistry
MINI-LAB

Forecast: Precipitation

Materials Each student/group will need the flashcards from the Chapter 4 activities and access to the solubility rules.

Purpose Students will practice interpreting the solubility rules and writing molecular, complete ionic, and net ionic equations. In addition,

they will review writing formulas from ions.

Discussion This activity can be altered to fit any time limit. For example, you can have students write a different number of net ionic equations.

SECTION 8.2
INTRODUCE

Student Preparation

Assign students to read Section 8.2 and to answer the Review Questions at the end of the section before coming to class.

 Active Learning
Team Learning Worksheet

After introducing the material in Section 8.2 in class, place students in groups and have them work together on **Section 8.2: Team Learning Worksheet.**

SECTION 8.2
GUIDE THE LEARNING

Homework

You may wish to assign these selected end-of-chapter problems as homework for this section: 17, 18, 22a–b, 23a–b, 25, 26, 28

Additional end-of-chapter problems can be used for extra practice.

8.2.A Reactions That Form Water: Acids and Bases

Objective To learn the key characteristics of the reactions between strong acids and strong bases

MINI-DEMO

Use the conductivity apparatus to show that acids and bases in solution conduct electricity. You can also use litmus paper to test each solution. Test distilled water to show its lack of conductivity.

SECTION 8.2
Other Reactions in Aqueous Solutions

Key Terms
- Acid
- Strong acids
- Base
- Strong bases
- Salt
- Oxidation–reduction reaction

Objectives
- *To learn about the reactions between strong acids and strong bases*
- *To learn about the reaction between a metal and a nonmetal*
- *To understand how electron transfer produces a chemical reaction*

A. Reactions That Form Water: Acids and Bases

In this section we encounter two very important classes of compounds: acids and bases. Acids were first associated with the sour taste of citrus fruits. In fact, the word *acid* comes from the Latin word *acidus*, which means "sour." Vinegar tastes sour because it is a dilute solution of acetic acid; citric acid is responsible for the sour taste of a lemon. Bases, sometimes called *alkalis*, are characterized by their bitter taste and slippery feel, like wet soap. Most commercial preparations for unclogging drains are highly basic.

 information

Don't taste chemicals!

Acids have been known for hundreds of years. For example, the *mineral acids* sulfuric acid, H_2SO_4, and nitric acid, HNO_3, so named because they were originally obtained by the treatment of minerals, were discovered around 1300. However, it was not until the late 1800s that the essential nature of acids was discovered by Svante Arrhenius, then a Swedish graduate student in physics.

Arrhenius Acids and Bases Arrhenius, who was trying to discover why only certain solutions could conduct an electric current, found that conductivity arose from the presence of ions. In his studies of solutions, Arrhenius observed that when the substances HCl, HNO_3, and H_2SO_4 were dissolved in water, they behaved as strong electrolytes. He suggested that this was the result of ionization reactions in water.

 information

The Arrhenius definition of an acid: a substance that produces H^+ ions in aqueous solution.

$$HCl \xrightarrow{H_2O} H^+(aq) + Cl^-(aq)$$

$$HNO_3 \xrightarrow{H_2O} H^+(aq) + NO_3^-(aq)$$

$$H_2SO_4 \xrightarrow{H_2O} H^+(aq) + HSO_4^-(aq)$$

Arrhenius proposed that an **acid** *is a substance that produces H^+ ions (protons) when it is dissolved in water.*

254 • Chapter 8 • Reactions in Aqueous Solutions

Teaching Support
BACKGROUND INFORMATION

Svante Arrhenius

The basis for the conductivity properties of solutions was first correctly identified by Svante Arrhenius (1859–1927), a Swedish graduate student in physics who did research on the nature of solutions at the University of Uppsala in the early 1880s. Arrhenius believed that the conductivity of solutions arose from the presence of ions, an idea that was at first scorned by the majority of the scientific establishment. However, in the late 1890s when atoms were found to contain charged particles, the ionic theory suddenly made sense and became widely accepted.

As Arrhenius postulated, the extent to which a solution can conduct an electric current depends directly on the number of ions present. Some materials, such as sodium chloride, readily produce ions in aqueous solution and thus are strong electrolytes. Other substances, such as acetic acid, produce relatively few ions when dissolved in water and are weak electrolytes. A third class of materials, such as sugar, form virtually no ions when dissolved in water and are nonelectrolytes.

TECHNOLOGY

 Animations
Proton Transfer
Neutralization of a Strong Acid
by a Strong Base

Studies show that when HCl, HNO_3, and H_2SO_4 are placed in water, *virtually every molecule* dissociates to give ions. This means that when 100 molecules of HCl are dissolved in water, 100 H^+ ions and 100 Cl^- ions are produced. Virtually no HCl molecules exist in aqueous solution.

HCl

Water

Each HCl molecule dissociates when it dissolves in water.

Because these substances are strong electrolytes that produce H^+ ions, they are called **strong acids**.

Arrhenius also found that *aqueous solutions that exhibit basic behavior* always contain hydroxide ions. He defined a **base** as a *substance that produces hydroxide ions (OH^-) in water*. The base most commonly used in the chemical laboratory is sodium hydroxide, NaOH, which contains Na^+ and OH^- ions and is very soluble in water. Sodium hydroxide, like all ionic substances, produces separated cations and anions when it is dissolved in water.

$$NaOH(s) \xrightarrow{H_2O} Na^+(aq) + OH^-(aq)$$

Although dissolved sodium hydroxide is usually represented as NaOH(*aq*), you should remember that the solution really contains separated Na^+ and OH^- ions. In fact, for every 100 units of NaOH dissolved in water, 100 Na^+ ions and 100 OH^- ions are produced.

Potassium hydroxide (KOH) has properties markedly similar to those of sodium hydroxide. It is very soluble in water and produces separated ions.

$$KOH(s) \xrightarrow{H_2O} K^+(aq) + OH^-(aq)$$

Because these hydroxide compounds are strong electrolytes that contain OH^- ions, they are called **strong bases**.

> When strong acids and strong bases (hydroxides) are mixed, the fundamental chemical change that always occurs is that H^+ ions react with OH^- ions to form water.
> $$H^+(aq) + OH^-(aq) \rightarrow H_2O(l)$$

Water is a very stable compound, as evidenced by the abundance of it on the earth's surface. Therefore, when substances that can form water are mixed, there is a strong tendency for the reaction to occur. In particular, the hydroxide ion OH^- has a high affinity for the H^+ ion to produce water.

The tendency to form water is the second of the driving forces for reactions that we mentioned before. Any compound that produces OH^- ions in water reacts vigorously to form H_2O with any compound that can furnish H^+ ions. For example, the reaction between hydrochloric acid and aqueous sodium hydroxide is represented by the following molecular equation:

$$HCl(aq) + NaOH(aq) \rightarrow H_2O(l) + NaCl(aq)$$

Strong acid
An acid that completely dissociates to produce H^+ ions in solution.

Strong base
A base that completely dissociates to produce OH^- ions in solution.

DID YOU KNOW

The Nobel Prize in Chemistry was awarded to Arrhenius in 1903 for his studies of solution conductivity.

8.2 • Other Reactions in Aqueous Solutions • **255**

Water is the product.
The net ionic equation is
$H^+(aq) + OH^-(aq) \rightarrow H_2O(l)$.

EXAMPLE 8.4

More Examples

1. Hydrobromic acid is a strong acid. Write the balanced molecular, complete ionic, and net ionic equations for the reaction of aqueous hydrobromic acid and aqueous sodium hydroxide.

   Molecular:
   $HBr(aq) + NaOH(aq) \rightarrow$
   $H_2O(l) + NaBr(aq)$

   Complete ionic:
   $H^+(aq) + Br^-(aq) +$
   $Na^+(aq) + OH^-(aq) \rightarrow$
   $H_2O(l) + Na^+(aq) + Br^-(aq)$

   Net ionic:
   $H^+(aq) + OH^-(aq) \rightarrow H_2O(l)$

2. Sulfuric acid is a strong acid. Write the balanced molecular, complete ionic, and net ionic equations for the reaction of aqueous sulfuric acid and aqueous potassium hydroxide.

   Molecular:
   $H_2SO_4(aq) + 2KOH(aq) \rightarrow$
   $2H_2O(l) + K_2SO_4(aq)$

   Complete ionic:
   $2H^+(aq) + SO_4^{2-}(aq) +$
   $2K^+(aq) + 2OH^-(aq) \rightarrow$
   $2H_2O(l) + 2K^+(aq) +$
   $SO_4^{2-}(aq)$

   Net ionic:
   $H^+(aq) + OH^-(aq) \rightarrow H_2O(l)$

---

information

Hydrochloric acid is an aqueous solution that contains dissolved hydrogen chloride. It is a strong electrolyte.

Because HCl, NaOH, and NaCl exist as completely separated ions in water, the complete ionic equation for this reaction is

$$H^+(aq) + Cl^-(aq) + Na^+(aq) + OH^-(aq) \rightarrow H_2O(l) + Na^+(aq) + Cl^-(aq)$$

Notice that the Cl^- and Na^+ are spectator ions (they undergo no changes), so the net ionic equation is

$$H^+(aq) + OH^-(aq) \rightarrow H_2O(l)$$

Thus the only chemical change that occurs when these solutions are mixed is that water is formed from H^+ and OH^- ions.

 Active Reading Question

What is always a product of an acid–base reaction?

EXAMPLE 8.4

Writing Equations for Acid–Base Reactions

Nitric acid is a strong acid. Write the molecular, complete ionic, and net ionic equations for the reaction of aqueous nitric acid and aqueous potassium hydroxide.

Solution

Molecular equation:

$$HNO_3(aq) + KOH(aq) \rightarrow H_2O(l) + KNO_3(aq)$$

Complete ionic equation:

$$H^+(aq) + NO_3^-(aq) + K^+(aq) + OH^-(aq) \rightarrow H_2O(l) + K^+(aq) + NO_3^-(aq)$$

Net ionic equation:

$$H^+(aq) + OH^-(aq) \rightarrow H_2O(l)$$

Note that K^+ and NO_3^- are spectator ions and that the formation of water is the driving force for this reaction.

There are two important things to note as we examine the reaction of hydrochloric acid with aqueous sodium hydroxide and the reaction of nitric acid with aqueous potassium hydroxide:

1. The net ionic equation is the same in both cases; water is formed.
   $$H^+(aq) + OH^-(aq) \rightarrow H_2O(l)$$

2. Besides water, which is *always a product* of the reaction of an acid with OH^-, the second product is an ionic compound, which might precipitate or remain dissolved, depending on its solubility.
   $$HCl(aq) + NaOH(aq) \rightarrow H_2O(l) + NaCl(aq)$$
   $$HNO_3(aq) + KOH(aq) \rightarrow H_2O(l) + KNO_3(aq)$$
   Dissolved ionic compounds

Salt
An ionic compound

This ionic compound is called a **salt**. In the first case the salt is sodium chloride, and in the second case the salt is potassium nitrate. We can obtain these soluble salts in solid form (both are white solids) by evaporating the water.

256 • Chapter 8 • Reactions in Aqueous Solutions

Let's Review

Strong Acids and Strong Bases

The following points about strong acids and strong bases are particularly important.

- The common strong acids are aqueous solutions of HCl, HNO_3, and H_2SO_4.

- A strong acid is a substance that completely dissociates (ionizes) in water. (Each molecule breaks up into an H^+ ion plus an anion.)

- A strong base is a metal hydroxide compound that is very soluble in water. The most common strong bases are NaOH and KOH, which completely break up into separated ions (Na^+ and OH^- or K^+ and OH^-) when they are dissolved in water.

- The net ionic equation for the reaction of a strong acid and a strong base is always the same: it shows the production of water.

$$H^+(aq) + OH^-(aq) \rightarrow H_2O(l)$$

- In the reaction of a strong acid and a strong base, one product is always water and the other is always an ionic compound called a salt, which remains dissolved in the water. This salt can be obtained as a solid by evaporating the water.

- The reaction of H^+ and OH^- is often called an acid–base reaction, where H^+ is the acidic ion and OH^- is the basic ion.

information

Both strong acids and strong bases are strong electrolytes.

CELEBRITY CHEMICAL Calcium Carbonate ($CaCO_3$)

Calcium carbonate, which contains the Ca^{2+} and CO_3^{2-} ions, is very common in nature, occurring in eggshells, limestone, marble, seashells, and coral. The spectacular formations seen in limestone caves are also composed of calcium carbonate.

Limestone caves form when underground limestone deposits come in contact with water made acidic by dissolved carbon dioxide. When rainwater absorbs CO_2 from the atmosphere, the following reaction occurs:

$$CO_2(g) + H_2O(l) \rightarrow H^+(aq) + HCO_3^-(aq)$$

This reaction leads to the presence of H^+ in the groundwater. The acidic groundwater then causes the limestone (which is made of $CaCO_3$) to dissolve:

$$CaCO_3(s) + H^+(aq) \rightarrow Ca^{2+}(aq) + HCO_3^-(aq)$$

Underground caverns then form. In the process of dissolving the limestone and creating the cave, the water containing the dissolved $CaCO_3$ drips from the ceiling of the cave. As the water forms drops, it tends to lose some of the dissolved CO_2, which lowers the amount of H^+ present (by the reversal

of the first reaction). This in turn leads to the reversal of the second reaction, which then reforms the solid $CaCO_3$. This process causes stalactites to "grow" from the ceiling of the cave. Water that drips to the floor before losing its dissolved CO_2 forms stalagmites that build up from the floor of the cave.

Stalactites and stalagmites in Carlsbad Caverns, New Mexico

8.2 • Other Reactions in Aqueous Solutions • **257**

CELEBRITY CHEMICAL

Calcium Carbonate ($CaCO_3$)

An easy way to remember which way stalactites and stalagmites point (for those of us who do not understand the rather archaic language) is as follows: Stalactites hang tight to the ceiling, while stalagmites grow into a mound on the ground.

Objective To learn the general characteristics of a reaction between a metal and a nonmetal and to understand electron transfer as a driving force for a chemical reaction

TEACHING TIP

Discuss the importance of oxidation–reduction reactions in daily life. Batteries, corrosion, and combustion are all oxidation–reduction reactions.

Active Reading Question

Metals lose electrons (are oxidized) and nonmetals gain electrons (are reduced) in a reaction.

Oxidation–reduction reaction
A chemical reaction involving the transfer of electrons

B. Reactions of Metals with Nonmetals (Oxidation–Reduction)

In Chapter 3 we spent considerable time discussing ionic compounds—compounds formed in the reaction of a metal and a nonmetal. A typical example is sodium chloride, formed by the reaction of sodium metal and chlorine gas:

$$2Na(s) + Cl_2(g) \rightarrow 2NaCl(s)$$

Let's examine what happens in this reaction.

- Sodium metal is composed of sodium atoms, each of which has a net charge of zero. (The positive charges of the eleven protons in its nucleus are exactly balanced by the negative charges on the eleven electrons.)

- Similarly, the chlorine molecule consists of two uncharged chlorine atoms (each has seventeen protons and seventeen electrons).

- However, in the product (sodium chloride), the sodium is present as Na^+ and the chlorine as Cl^-.

By what process do the neutral atoms become ions? The answer is that one electron is transferred from each sodium atom to each chlorine atom.

$$Na + Cl \rightarrow Na^+ + Cl^-$$
$$e^-$$

After the electron transfer, each sodium atom has ten electrons and eleven protons (a net charge of $1+$), and each chlorine atom has eighteen electrons and seventeen protons (a net charge of $1-$).

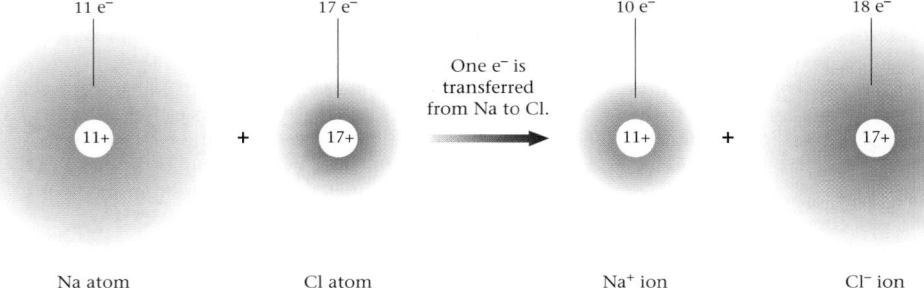

| Na atom | Cl atom | Na⁺ ion | Cl⁻ ion |

Thus the reaction of a metal with a nonmetal to form an ionic compound involves the transfer of one or more electrons from the metal (which forms a cation) to the nonmetal (which forms an anion). This tendency to transfer electrons from metals to nonmetals is the third driving force for reactions that we listed in Section 8.1. A reaction that *involves a transfer of electrons* is called an **oxidation–reduction reaction**.

Active Reading Question

Why can metal-nonmetal reactions always be assumed to be oxidation–reduction reactions?

There are many examples of oxidation–reduction reactions in which a metal reacts with a nonmetal to form an ionic compound. Consider the reaction of magnesium metal with oxygen,

$$2Mg(s) + O_2(g) \rightarrow 2MgO(s)$$

Note that the reactants contain uncharged atoms, but the product contains ions:

MgO

Contains Mg^{2+}, O^{2-}

Therefore, in this reaction, each magnesium atom loses two electrons ($Mg \rightarrow Mg^{2+} + 2e^-$) and each oxygen atom gains two electrons ($O + 2e^- \rightarrow O^{2-}$). We might represent this reaction as follows:

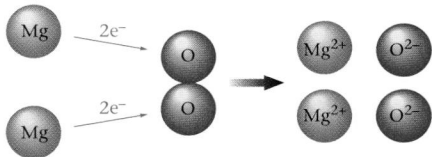

Another example is

$$2Al(s) + Fe_2O_3(s) \rightarrow 2Fe(s) + Al_2O_3(s)$$

which is a reaction (called the thermite reaction) that produces so much energy (heat) that the iron is initially formed as a liquid (see **Figure 8.5**). In this case the aluminum is originally present as the elemental metal (which contains uncharged Al atoms) and ends up in Al_2O_3, where it is present as Al^{3+} cations (the $2Al^{3+}$ ions just balance the charge of the $3O^{2-}$ ions). Therefore, in the reaction each aluminum atom loses three electrons.

$$Al \rightarrow Al^{3+} + 3e^-$$

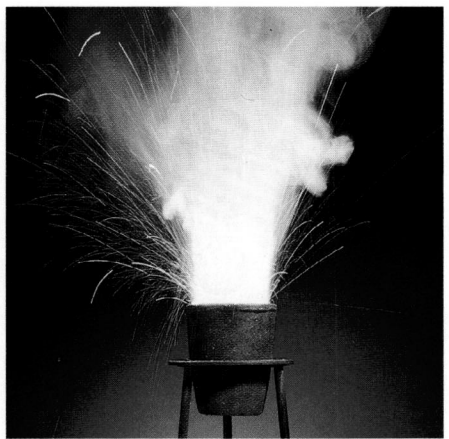

Figure 8.5
The thermite reaction gives off so much heat that the iron formed is molten.

8.2 • Other Reactions in Aqueous Solutions • **259**

TEACHING TIPS

- Point out that the loss or gain of electrons can take place only if another element is present to accept or donate electrons. If you do the demonstration "Making Salt," on the next page, point out that chlorine gas doesn't react alone, nor does sodium metal. Yet if you ignite the sodium and place it in the chlorine gas, the two elements react to form ions.

- It is easier for students to begin with oxidation–reduction reactions between two elements. Once they understand this type of reaction, move on to more complicated reactions such as:

  $$2NaBr + Cl_2 \rightarrow 2NaCl + Br_2.$$

  Reactions of this type are sometimes classified as single-displacement reactions. Students may be confused by how single displacement occurs when two elements are changing places. We choose to classify all oxidation–reduction reactions as reactions in which electrons are transferred between atoms. This terminology focuses students' attention on the driving force for the reaction. The term *single displacement* is discussed in Section 8.3.

TECHNOLOGY

 Videos
Barking Dogs: Reaction of Phosphorus
Dry Ice and Magnesium
Sugar and Potassium Chlorate
Zinc and Iodine
Thermite Reaction

(continued)

Solution D: 10 mL solution A and 3 drops phenolphthalein

Solution E: 10 mL solution A and 3 drops thymolphthalein

Presentation Place the large shallow dish and cups or beakers containing solutions A–E on the overhead projector. Add sodium silicate to the large shallow dish to a depth of $\frac{1}{4} - \frac{1}{2}$ inch. Have

students identify the color of solution A. Using a dropper or Beral pipet, add several drops of solution A to the sodium silicate solution in the large dish. Students should see a white circular-shaped solid immediately. Repeat this process with each of the solutions B–E. Each time make sure that students observe the color of the solution both before and after the addition.

Teaching Notes The crystals formed are a different color from the original solutions because the sodium silicate solution is basic and the original solutions were neutral. The color changes reflect the indicators used. The cobalt compound changes color because the chloride and silicates are different colors.

EXAMPLE 8.5

More Examples

For each of the following reactions, show how electrons are gained and lost.

1. $4Al(s) + 3O_2(g) \rightarrow 2Al_2O_3(s)$

Each Al atom loses 3 electrons (for a total of 12 electrons). Each oxygen atom gains 2 electrons (for a total of 12 electrons).

2. $4Na(s) + O_2(g) \rightarrow 2Na_2O(s)$

Each Na atom loses 1 electron (for a total of 4 electrons). Each oxygen atom gains 2 electrons (for a total of 4 electrons).

The opposite process occurs with the iron, which is initially present as Fe^{3+} ions in Fe_2O_3 and ends up as uncharged atoms in the elemental iron. Thus each iron cation gains three electrons to form an uncharged atom:

$$Fe^{3+} + 3e^- \rightarrow Fe$$

We can represent this reaction in schematic form as follows:

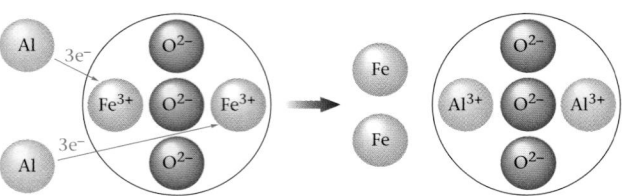

EXAMPLE 8.5

Identifying Electron Transfer in Oxidation–Reduction Reactions

Figure 8.6
When powdered aluminum and iodine (shown in the foreground) are mixed (and a little water added), they react vigorously.

For each of the following reactions, show how electrons are gained and lost.

a. $2Al(s) + 3I_2(s) \rightarrow 2AlI_3(s)$ (This reaction is shown in **Figure 8.6.** Note the purple "smoke," which is excess I_2 being driven off by the heat.)

b. $2Cs(s) + F_2(g) \rightarrow 2CsF(s)$

Solution

a. In AlI_3 the ions are Al^{3+} and I^- (aluminum always forms Al^{3+}, and iodine always forms I^-). In $Al(s)$ the aluminum is present as uncharged atoms. Thus aluminum goes from Al to Al^{3+} by losing three electrons ($Al \rightarrow Al^{3+} + 3e^-$). In I_2 each iodine atom is uncharged. Thus each iodine atom goes from I to I^- by gaining one electron ($I + e^- \rightarrow I^-$). A schematic for this reaction is

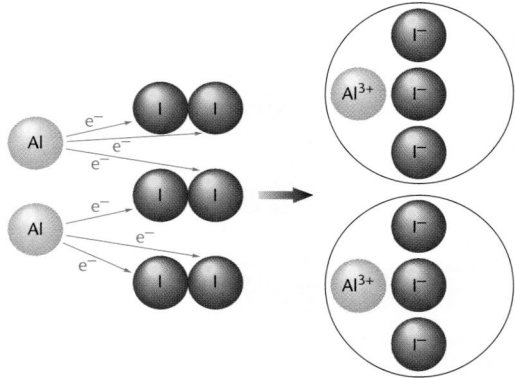

b. In CsF the ions present are Cs^+ and F^-. Cesium metal, $Cs(s)$, contains uncharged cesium atoms, and fluorine gas, $F_2(g)$, contains uncharged fluorine atoms. Thus in the reaction each cesium atom loses one

---

Teaching Support
DEMONSTRATION

Making Salt

Materials

- 1-L cylinder filled one-third full with dry sand
- Salt shaker filled with salt and with a wire attached long enough to reach out the top of the cylinder
- Deflagrating spoon
- Stopper to fit the cylinder
- Na metal
- Knife
- Cl_2 gas (lecture bottle)
- Tweezers
- Wash bottle/water

Preparation Bury the salt shaker completely in the sand in the cylinder, with the wire extending up and out the top of the cylinder. In the hood, fill the cylinder with Cl_2 gas and stopper it firmly, catching the wire between the stopper and the glass.

electron ($Cs \rightarrow Cs^+ + e^-$) and each fluorine atom gains one electron ($F + e^- \rightarrow F^-$). The schematic for this reaction is

Practice Problem • Exercise 8.5

For each reaction, show how electrons are gained and lost.

   a. $2Na(s) + Br_2(l) \rightarrow 2NaBr(s)$

   b. $2Ca(s) + O_2(g) \rightarrow 2CaO(s)$

So far we have emphasized electron transfer (oxidation–reduction) reactions that involve a metal and a nonmetal. Electron transfer reactions can also take place between two nonmetals. We will not discuss these reactions in detail here. All we will say at this point is that one sure sign of an oxidation–reduction reaction between nonmetals is the presence of oxygen, $O_2(g)$, as a reactant or product. In fact, oxidation got its name from oxygen. Thus the reactions

$$CH_4(g) + 2O_2(g) \rightarrow CO_2(g) + 2H_2O(g)$$

and

$$2SO_2(g) + O_2(g) \rightarrow 2SO_3(g)$$

are electron transfer reactions, even though it is not obvious at this point.

Let's Review

Characteristics of Oxidation–Reduction Reactions

- When a metal reacts with a nonmetal, an ionic compound is formed. The ions are formed when the metal transfers one or more electrons to the nonmetal, the metal atom becoming a cation and the nonmetal atom becoming an anion. *Therefore, a metal-nonmetal reaction can always be assumed to be an oxidation–reduction reaction, which involves electron transfer.*

- Two nonmetals can also undergo an oxidation–reduction reaction. At this point we can recognize these cases only by looking for O_2 as a reactant or product. When two nonmetals react, the compound formed is not ionic.

8.2 • Other Reactions in Aqueous Solutions • 261

SECTION 8.2
Review Questions

1. The products are a salt and water. The evidence for a reaction is heat.

2. A strong acid is a strong electrolyte that produces the H^+ ion. A strong base is a substance that dissolves in water to form OH^- ions.

3. The acid drawing should contain H^+, NO_3^-, and water molecules. The base drawing should contain K^+, OH^-, and water molecules.

4. An oxidation–reduction reaction involves the transfer of electrons. These reactions are typically reactions between metals and nonmetals or reactions between two nonmetals that have oxygen molecules as a reactant or a product.

5. The acid is HCl and the base is KOH. The reaction is
$HCl(aq) + KOH(aq) \rightarrow$
$\quad KCl(aq) + H_2O(l)$

6. Each magnesium atom loses two electrons to become Mg^{2+}. Each nitrogen atom gains three electrons to become N^{3-}. Sample graphics are located in Section 8.2.B.

HANDS-ON CHEMISTRY   • MINI-LAB •

What's in Your Water?

Materials
- various water samples
- dropper bottle of silver nitrate solution

Procedure

1. Obtain samples of water from your home faucet, bottled water, distilled water from school, water from the school drinking fountain, and a swimming pool (if available).

2. Get a dropper bottle of silver nitrate solution from your teacher. (**Caution:** Silver nitrate solution will stain your skin!). Add a few drops of the silver nitrate solution to your samples of water.

Results/Analysis

1. What do you notice when you add the silver nitrate solution to your water samples? Compare your results with your classmates.

2. Write the net ionic equation for any reaction.

3. What does this test tell you about the water samples?

SECTION 8.2
REVIEW QUESTIONS

❶ What are the products in a reaction between an acid and a base? How can you tell that a reaction has occurred?

❷ What is meant by the term *strong acid*? What is meant by the term *strong base*?

❸ Draw a picture (showing the ions) for a strong acid solution of HNO_3 and a strong base solution of KOH in separate beakers.

❹ What is an oxidation–reduction reaction? How can you identify this type of reaction?

❺ Write the formulas for the strong acid and strong base that must have reacted to form the solution shown to the right. Write the chemical equation for this reaction.

❻ Show how electrons are lost and gained in the reaction.
$3Mg(s) + N_2(g) \rightarrow Mg_3N_2(s)$

KCl(*aq*)

Hands-On Chemistry
MINI-LAB

What's in Your Water?

Materials Each student/group will need water samples and access to a solution of silver nitrate (~ 0.1 *M*). Empty film canisters work well for bringing in water samples (and drugstores will often give them to you in bulk).

Purpose Students will see that most water samples contain chloride ions. In addition, they will see an example of a precipitation reaction and write a net ionic equation.

Discussion Most likely, all of the water samples brought in by students will contain chloride ions to some extent (even bottled drinking water, which may surprise students). The distilled water from the school should be free of chloride ions. Before adding the silver nitrate, have students predict which samples will be high in chloride ions and which will be low. Then have them compare their predictions to the actual results.

The net ionic equation in all cases is
$Ag^+(aq) + Cl^-(aq) \rightarrow AgCl(s)$.

Classifying Reactions

Objective
• *To learn various classification schemes for reactions*

A. Ways to Classify Reactions

So far in our study of chemistry we have seen many, many chemical reactions—and this is just Chapter 8. In the world around us and in our bodies, literally millions of chemical reactions are taking place. Obviously, we need a system for putting reactions into meaningful classes that will make them easier to remember and easier to understand.

In Chapter 8 we have so far considered the following "driving forces" for chemical reactions:

• Formation of a solid
• Formation of water
• Transfer of electrons

Key Terms
• Double-displacement reaction
• Acid–base reactions
• Single-replacement reaction
• Combustion reactions
• Synthesis (combination) reaction
• Decomposition reactions

Active Reading Question

Write an example chemical equation for each of the driving forces listed.

Formation of a Solid In the following reaction, solid $BaCrO_4$ (a precipitate) is formed.

$$K_2CrO_4(aq) + Ba(NO_3)_2(aq) \rightarrow BaCrO_4(s) + 2KNO_3(aq)$$
Solution   Solution   Solid formed   Solution

Because the *formation of a solid when two solutions are mixed* is called *precipitation*, we call this a *precipitation reaction.*

Notice in this reaction that two anions (NO_3^- and CrO_4^{2-}) are simply exchanged. Note that CrO_4^{2-} was originally associated with K^+ in K_2CrO_4 and that NO_3^- was associated with Ba^{2+} in $Ba(NO_3)_2$. In the products these associations are reversed. Because of this double exchange, we sometimes call this reaction a double-exchange reaction or **double-displacement reaction**. We might represent such a reaction as

$$AB + CD \rightarrow AD + CB$$

So we can classify a reaction such as this one as a precipitation reaction or as a double-displacement reaction. Either name is correct, but precipitation is more commonly used by chemists.

Formation of Water In this chapter we have also considered reactions in which water is formed when a strong acid is mixed with a strong base. All of these reactions had the same net ionic equation:

$$H^+(aq) + OH^-(aq) \rightarrow H_2O(l)$$

The H^+ ion comes from a strong acid, such as $HCl(aq)$ or $HNO_3(aq)$, and the origin of the OH^- ion is a strong base, such as $NaOH(aq)$ or $KOH(aq)$. An example is

$$HCl(aq) + KOH(aq) \rightarrow H_2O(l) + KCl(aq)$$

We classify these reactions as **acid–base reactions**. You can recognize an acid–base reaction because it *involves an H^+ ion that ends up in the product water.*

information

A precipitation reaction is also called a double-displacement reaction.

8.3 • Classifying Reactions • **263**

- Remind students that once they have written the correct formulas for a chemical reaction, they still need to balance the chemical equation.

- Once students have been introduced to the three ways of classifying reactions, it is a good idea to have them practice as a class. Have students classify a series of reactions and then hold a class discussion in which they explain how they identified a given type of reaction.

Transfer of Electrons The third driving force is electron transfer. We see evidence of this driving force particularly in the "desire" of a metal to donate electrons to nonmetals. An example is

$$2Li(s) + F_2(g) \rightarrow 2LiF(s)$$

where each lithium atom loses one electron to form Li^+, and each fluorine atom gains one electron to form the F^- ion. The process of electron transfer is also called oxidation–reduction. Thus we classify the above reaction as an *oxidation–reduction reaction*.

Formation of a Gas An additional driving force for chemical reactions that we have not yet discussed is *formation of a gas*. A reaction in aqueous solution that forms a gas (which escapes as bubbles) is pulled toward the products by this event. An example is the reaction

$$2HCl(aq) + Na_2CO_3(aq) \rightarrow CO_2(g) + H_2O(l) + 2NaCl(aq)$$

for which the net ionic equation is

$$2H^+(aq) + CO_3^{2-}(aq) \rightarrow CO_2(g) + H_2O(l)$$

Note that this reaction forms carbon dioxide gas as well as water, so it illustrates two of the driving forces that we have considered. Because this reaction involves H^+ that ends up in the product water, we classify it as an acid–base reaction.

Consider another reaction that forms a gas:

$$Zn(s) + 2HCl(aq) \rightarrow H_2(g) + ZnCl_2(aq)$$

How might we classify this reaction? A careful look at the reactants and products shows the following:

$$Zn(s) + 2HCl(aq) \rightarrow H_2(g) + ZnCl_2(aq)$$

Contains uncharged Zn atoms | Really $2H^+(aq) + 2Cl^-(aq)$ | Contains uncharged H atoms | Really $Zn^{2+}(aq) + 2Cl^-(aq)$

Note that in the reactant zinc metal, Zn exists as uncharged atoms, whereas in the product it exists as Zn^{2+}. Thus each Zn atom loses two electrons. Where have these electrons gone? They have been transferred to two H^+ ions to form H_2. The schematic for this reaction is

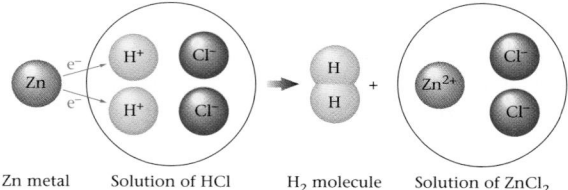

Zn metal · Solution of HCl · H_2 molecule · Solution of $ZnCl_2$

This is an electron transfer process, so the reaction can be classified as an oxidation–reduction reaction.

Another way this reaction is sometimes classified is based on the fact that a *single* type of anion (Cl^-) has been exchanged between H^+ and Zn^{2+}. That is, Cl^- is originally associated with H^+ in HCl and ends up associated with Zn^{2+} in the product $ZnCl_2$. We can call this a **single-replacement reaction** in contrast to double-displacement reactions, in which two types of anions are exchanged. We can represent a single replacement as

$$A + BC \rightarrow B + AC$$

Meeting Individual Needs

INCLUSION STRATEGIES

Have students create a summary chart listing the various types of reactions encountered in this chapter. Students should provide two to three examples of each type of reaction. Below each example, have students write characteristics of the reaction type. Encourage students to use the charts as a study aid.

CHEMISTRY IN YOUR WORLD

Launching the Space Shuttle

Launching into space a vehicle such as the space shuttle that weighs millions of pounds requires unimaginable quantities of energy—all furnished by oxidation–reduction reactions.

Notice that three cylindrical objects are attached to the shuttle orbiter. In the center is a tank about 28 feet in diameter and 154 feet long that contains liquid oxygen and liquid hydrogen (in separate compartments). These fuels are fed to the orbiter's main engines where they react to form water and release a huge quantity of energy.

$$2H_2 + O_2 \rightarrow 2H_2O + \text{energy}$$

Note that we can recognize this reaction as an oxidation–reduction reaction because O_2 is a reactant.

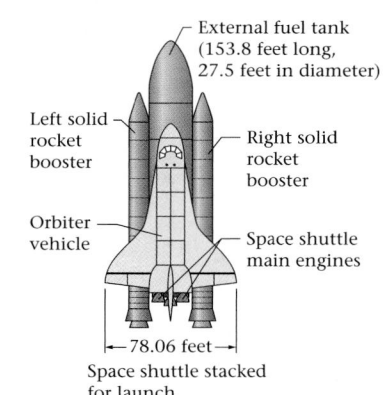

External fuel tank
(153.8 feet long,
27.5 feet in diameter)

Left solid rocket booster

Right solid rocket booster

Orbiter vehicle

Space shuttle main engines

←—— 78.06 feet ——→

Space shuttle stacked
for launch

Solid
propellant

149.16 feet long,
12.17 feet in diameter

Two solid-fuel rockets about 12 feet in diameter and 150 feet long are also attached to the orbiter. Each rocket contains 1.1 million pounds of fuel: ammonium perchlorate (NH_4ClO_4) and powdered aluminum mixed with a binder ("glue"). Because the rockets are so large, they are built in segments and assembled at the launch site as shown above. Each segment is filled with the syrupy propellant, which then solidifies to a consistency much like that of a hard rubber eraser.

The oxidation–reduction reaction between the ammonium perchlorate and the aluminum is

$$3NH_4ClO_4(s) + 3Al(s) \rightarrow$$
$$Al_2O_3(s) + AlCl_3(s) + 3NO(g) + 6H_2O(g) + \text{energy}$$

It produces temperatures of about 5700 °F (3150 °C) and 3.3 million pounds of thrust in each rocket.

Oxidation–reduction reactions furnish the energy to launch the space shuttle.

*Mixing the rocket
propellant*

Chemistry in Your World

Launching the Space Shuttle

"Launching the Space Shuttle" emphasizes the tremendous energy available from oxidation–reduction reactions. Virtually all of the reactions used in our society as energy sources are redox reactions. Examples include the reaction between the hydrocarbons in gasoline and the oxygen in the air used to power cars and trucks, the natural gas used to heat our homes (methane reacting with oxygen), and the decomposition of nitrogen- containing compounds such as TNT (trinitrotoluene) that act as explosives.

The solid-fuel rockets described in this Chemistry in Your World show that reactions can take place in the solid phase, although we almost always talk about reactions that occur in solutions.

8.3.B Other Ways to Classify Reactions

Objective To consider additional classes of chemical reactions

 LABORATORY

EXPERIMENT 32:
Qualitative Analysis: Anions, Microscale

LABORATORY

EXPERIMENT 33:
The Halide Family, Microscale

TEACHING TIP

Useful clues to help students identify combustion reactions are the presence of molecular oxygen and a carbon-containing molecule as reactants. The products of many combustion reactions are carbon dioxide and water. A good example to use is the combustion of ethyl alcohol:

$CH_3CH_2OH + 3O_2 \rightarrow 2CO_2 + 3H_2O$

B. Other Ways to Classify Reactions

So far in this chapter we have classified chemical reactions in several ways. The most commonly used of these classifications are:

- Precipitation reactions
- Acid–base reactions
- Oxidation–reduction reactions

However, there are still other ways to classify reactions that you may encounter in your future studies of chemistry. We will consider several of these in this section.

Combustion Reactions

Combustion reaction
A chemical reaction involving oxygen as one of the reactants that produces enough heat so that a flame results

Many chemical reactions that involve oxygen produce energy (heat) so rapidly that a flame results. Such reactions are called **combustion reactions**. We have considered some of these reactions previously. For example, the methane in natural gas reacts with oxygen according to the following balanced equation:

$$CH_4(g) + 2O_2(g) \rightarrow CO_2(g) + 2H_2O(g)$$

This reaction produces the flame of the common laboratory burner and is also used to heat most homes in the United States. Recall that we originally classified this reaction as an oxidation–reduction reaction. Thus we can say that the reaction of methane with oxygen is both an oxidation–reduction reaction and a combustion reaction. Combustion reactions, in fact, are a special class of oxidation–reduction reactions (see **Figure 8.7**).

There are many combustion reactions, most of which are used to provide heat or electricity for homes or businesses or energy for transportation. Some examples are:

- Combustion of propane (used to heat some rural homes)

  $C_3H_8(g) + 5O_2(g) \rightarrow 3CO_2(g) + 4H_2O(g)$

- Combustion of gasoline* (used to power cars and trucks)

  $2C_8H_{18}(l) + 25O_2(g) \rightarrow 16CO_2(g) + 18H_2O(g)$

- Combustion of coal* (used to generate electricity)

  $C(s) + O_2(g) \rightarrow CO_2(g)$

Figure 8.7
Classes of reactions—combustion reactions are a special type of oxidation–reduction reaction.

*This substance is really a complex mixture of compounds, but the reaction shown is representative of what takes place.

Synthesis (Combination) Reactions

One of the most important activities in chemistry is the synthesis of new compounds. Each of our lives has been greatly affected by synthetic compounds such as plastic, polyester, and aspirin. When a given compound is formed from simpler materials, we call this a **synthesis (combination) reaction**.

Examples of synthesis reactions starting with elements:

$2H_2(g) + O_2(g) \rightarrow 2H_2O(l)$

$C(s) + O_2(g) \rightarrow CO_2(g)$

Other ways to classify these reactions:

- Oxidation–reduction $\longrightarrow$ involves oxygen
- Combustion $\longrightarrow$ produces flames

Examples of synthesis reactions that do not involve oxygen:

$2Na(s) + Cl_2(g) \rightarrow 2NaCl(s)$

$Mg(s) + F_2(g) \rightarrow MgF_2(s)$

Another way to classify these reactions:

- Oxidation–reduction $\rightarrow$ uncharged atoms become ions in compounds

We have seen that synthesis reactions in which the reactants are elements are oxidation–reduction reactions as well. In fact, we can think of these synthesis reactions as another subclass of the oxidation–reduction class of reactions.

Decomposition Reactions

In many cases a compound can be broken down into simpler compounds or all the way to the component elements. This is usually accomplished by heating or by the application of an electric current. Such reactions are called **decomposition reactions**. Examples of decomposition reactions are

- $2H_2O(l) \xrightarrow{\text{Electric Current}} 2H_2(g) + O_2(g)$

- $2HgO(s) \xrightarrow{\text{Heat}} 2Hg(l) + O_2(g)$

Because O_2 is involved in the first reaction, we recognize it as an oxidation–reduction reaction. In the second reaction, HgO, which contains Hg^{2+} and O^{2-} ions, is decomposed to the elements, which contain uncharged atoms. In this process each Hg^{2+} gains two electrons and each O^{2-} loses two electrons, so this is both a decomposition reaction and an oxidation–reduction reaction.

A decomposition reaction, in which a compound is broken down into its elements, is just the opposite of the synthesis (combination) reaction, in which elements combine to form the compound. For example, we have just discussed the synthesis of sodium chloride from its elements. Sodium chloride can be decomposed into its elements by melting it and passing an electric current through it:

$2NaCl(l) \xrightarrow{\text{Electric Current}} 2Na(l) + Cl_2(g)$

Synthesis reaction (combination reaction)
A chemical reaction in which a compound is formed from simpler materials

Formation of the colorful plastics used in these zippers is an example of a synthesis reaction.

Decomposition reaction
A chemical reaction in which a compound is broken down into simpler compounds, or to the component elements

---

Meeting Individual Needs
ADVANCED LEARNERS

Have advanced learners investigate decomposition and synthesis reactions that occur within our bodies. This will give students a better idea of the relationship between chemistry and biology.

EXAMPLE 8.6

More Examples

Classify each of the following reactions in as many ways as possible.

1. $2C_2H_2(s) + 5O_2(g) \rightarrow 4CO_2(g) + 2H_2O(g)$
   Combustion, oxidation–reduction

2. $2Ni(s) + 4O_2(g) \rightarrow 2NiO(s)$
   Synthesis, oxidation–reduction

 Answer to Practice Problem 8.6

a. oxidation–reduction; combustion

b. synthesis; oxidation–reduction; combustion

c. synthesis; oxidation–reduction

d. decomposition; oxidation–reduction

e. precipitation (and double displacement)

f. synthesis; oxidation–reduction

g. acid–base (and double displacement)

h. combustion; oxidation–reduction

EXAMPLE 8.6
Classifying Reactions

Classify each of the following reactions in as many ways as possible.

a. $2K(s) + Cl_2(g) \rightarrow 2KCl(s)$
b. $Fe_2O_3(s) + 2Al(s) \rightarrow Al_2O_3(s) + 2Fe(s)$
c. $2Mg(s) + O_2(g) \rightarrow 2MgO(s)$
d. $HNO_3(aq) + NaOH(aq) \rightarrow H_2O(l) + NaNO_3(aq)$
e. $KBr(aq) + AgNO_3(aq) \rightarrow AgBr(s) + KNO_3(aq)$
f. $PbO_2(s) \rightarrow Pb(s) + O_2(g)$

Solution

a. This is both a synthesis reaction (elements combine to form a compound) and an oxidation–reduction reaction (uncharged potassium and chlorine atoms are changed to K^+ and Cl^- ions in KCl).

b. This is an oxidation–reduction reaction. Iron is present in $Fe_2O_3(s)$ as Fe^{3+} ions and in elemental iron, $Fe(s)$, as uncharged atoms. So each Fe^{3+} must gain three electrons to form Fe. The reverse happens to aluminum, which is present initially as uncharged aluminum atoms, each of which loses three electrons to give Al^{3+} ions in Al_2O_3. Note that this reaction might also be called a single-replacement reaction because O is switched from Fe to Al.

c. This is both a synthesis reaction (elements combine to form a compound) and an oxidation–reduction reaction (each magnesium atom loses two electrons to give Mg^{2+} ions in MgO, and each oxygen atom gains two electrons to give O^{2-} in MgO).

d. This is an acid–base reaction. It might also be called a double-displacement reaction because NO_3^- and OH^- "switch partners."

e. This is a precipitation reaction that might also be called a double-displacement reaction in which the anions Br^- and NO_3^- are exchanged.

f. This is a decomposition reaction (a compound breaks down into elements). It also is an oxidation–reduction reaction, because the ions in PbO_2 (Pb^{4+} and O^{2-}) are changed to uncharged atoms in the elements $Pb(s)$ and $O_2(g)$. That is, electrons are transferred from O^{2-} to Pb^{4+} in the reaction.

Practice Problems • Exercise 8.6

Classify each of the following reactions in as many ways as possible.

a. $4NH_3(g) + 5O_2(g) \rightarrow 4NO(g) + 6H_2O(g)$
b. $S_8(s) + 8O_2(g) \rightarrow 8SO_2(g)$
c. $2Al(s) + 3Cl_2(g) \rightarrow 2AlCl_3(s)$
d. $2AlN(s) \rightarrow 2Al(s) + N_2(g)$
e. $BaCl_2(aq) + Na_2SO_4(aq) \rightarrow BaSO_4(s) + 2NaCl(aq)$
f. $2Cs(s) + Br_2(l) \rightarrow 2CsBr(s)$
g. $KOH(aq) + HCl(aq) \rightarrow H_2O(l) + KCl(aq)$
h. $2C_2H_2(g) + 5O_2(g) \rightarrow 4CO_2(g) + 2H_2O(l)$

There are other schemes for classifying reactions that we have not considered. It should be apparent that many important reactions can be classified as oxidation–reduction reactions. As shown in **Figure 8.8,** various types of reactions can be viewed as subclasses of the overall oxidation–reduction category.

Figure 8.8
Summary of classes of reactions

CRITICAL **THINKING**

What if no ionic solids were soluble in water? Could reactions occur in aqueous solutions? Explain.

SECTION 8.3
REVIEW QUESTIONS

❶ What are the four driving forces for a chemical reaction?

❷ Why are precipitation reactions also called double displacement reactions?

❸ What are three other ways to classify oxidation–reduction reactions?

❹ Classify the following unbalanced equations as: precipitation, acid–base, or oxidation–reduction

  a. $Fe(s) + H_2SO_4\ (aq) \rightarrow Fe_3(SO_4)_2(aq) + H_2(g)$

  b. $HClO_4(aq) + RbOH(aq) \rightarrow RbClO_4(aq) + H_2O(l)$

  c. $K_2SO_4(aq) + CaCl_2(aq) \rightarrow KCl(aq) + CaSO_4(s)$

  d. $Ni(s) + Cl_2(g) \rightarrow NiCl_2(s)$

❺ One of the reactants in a combustion reaction must always be _____.

❻ Classify the reaction of hydrogen gas with oxygen gas to form water in three different ways.

❼ Balance the following equations and classify each in as many ways as possible.

  a. $Al(s) + O_2(g) \rightarrow Al_2O_3(s)$

  b. $Ba(OH)_2(aq) + H_2SO_4(aq) \rightarrow BaSO_4(s) + H_2O(l)$

  c. $H_2O_2(aq) \rightarrow H_2O(l) + O_2(g)$

RESEARCH LINKS
CLASSZONE.COM

Chapter 8 Review

Key Terms

8.1 Precipitation

Precipitate

Precipitation reaction

Strong electrolyte

Soluble solid

Insoluble solid (slightly soluble solid)

Molecular equation

Complete ionic equation

Spectator ions

Net ionic equation

8.2 Acid

Strong acids

Base

Strong bases

Salt

Oxidation–reduction reaction

8.3 Double-displacement reaction

Acid–base reactions

Single-replacement reaction

Combustion reactions

Synthesis (combination) reaction

Decomposition reactions

Key Ideas

8.1 Understanding Reactions in Aqueous Solution

■ Four driving forces favor chemical change.
   • Formation of a solid
   • Formation of water
   • Transfer of electrons
   • Formation of a gas

■ A reaction in which a solid forms is called a precipitation reaction.

■ Solubility rules help predict what solid (if any) will form when solutions are mixed.

■ Three types of equations are used to describe reactions in solution.
   • Molecular (formula) equation which shows the complete formulas of all reactants and products
   • Complete ionic equation in which all strong electrolytes are shown as ions
   • Net ionic equation which includes only those components of the solution that undergo a change
      ◆ Spectator ions (those that remain unchanged) are not shown in the net ionic equation.

8.2 Other Reactions in Aqueous Solutions

■ A strong acid is one in which virtually every molecule dissociates (ionizes) in water to an H^+ ion and an anion.

■ A strong base is a metal hydroxide that is completely soluble in water, giving separate OH^- ions and cations.

■ The products of the reaction of a strong acid and a strong base are water and a salt.

■ Reactions between metals and nonmetals involve a transfer of electrons from the metal to the nonmetal which is called an oxidation–reduction reaction.

8.3 Classifying Reactions

■ Reactions can be classified in various ways.
   • A synthesis reaction is one in which a compound forms from simpler substances, such as elements.
   • A decomposition reaction occurs when a compound is broken down into simpler substances.
   • A combustion reaction is an oxidation–reduction reaction that involves O_2.
   • A precipitation reaction can also be classified as a double displacement reaction.

RESEARCH LINKS
CLASSZONE.COM

Meeting Individual Needs	**Assessment Resources**
CHAPTER REVIEW	CHAPTER 8
Chapter 8 Review Worksheet at the appropriate level: **Basic** **Standard** **Challenge**	**Chapter 8 Test**
CHAPTER SUMMARY	**TECHNOLOGY**
A **Chapter Summary** that includes additional Active Reading Questions for Chapter 8 is available.	**Computerized Test Bank for Chapter 8**

All exercises with blue numbers have answers in the back of this book.

8.1 Understanding Reactions in Aqueous Solutions

A. Predicting Whether a Reaction Will Occur

1. Why is water an important solvent? Although you have not yet studied water in detail, can you think of some properties of water that make it so important?

2. What is a "driving force"? What are some of the driving forces discussed in this section that tend to make reactions likely to occur? Can you think of any other possible driving forces?

B. Reactions in Which a Solid Forms

3. When two solutions of ionic substances are mixed and a precipitate forms, what is the net charge of the precipitate? Why?

4. What does it mean to say that the ions of an electrolyte behave independently of one another when the electrolyte is dissolved in water?

5. What is meant by a *strong electrolyte*? Give two examples of substances that behave in solution as strong electrolytes.

6. When aqueous solutions of sodium chloride, NaCl, and silver nitrate, $AgNO_3$, are mixed, a precipitate forms, but this precipitate is *not* sodium nitrate. What does this reaction tell you about the solubility of $NaNO_3$ in water?

7. What do we mean when we say that a solid is "slightly" soluble in water? Is there a practical difference between *slightly* soluble and *insoluble*?

8. On the basis of the general solubility rules given in Table 8.1, predict which of the following substances are likely to be soluble in water.

    a. barium nitrate

    b. potassium carbonate

    c. sodium sulfate

    d. copper(II) hydroxide

    e. mercury(I) chloride

    f. ammonium phosphate

    g. chromium(III) sulfide

    h. lead(II) sulfate

9. On the basis of the general solubility rules given in Table 8.1, for each of the following compounds, indicate why the compound is *not* likely to be soluble in water. Indicate *which* of the solubility rules covers each substance's particular situation.

    a. iron(III) hydroxide

    b. calcium carbonate

    c. cobalt(III) phosphate

    d. silver chloride

10. On the basis of the general solubility rules given in Table 8.1, predict the identity of the precipitate that forms when aqueous solutions of the following substances are mixed. If no precipitate is likely, indicate which rules apply.

    d. sodium hydroxide, NaOH, and iron(III) chloride, $FeCl_3$

    e. potassium sulfate, K_2SO_4, and sodium nitrate, $NaNO_3$

    f. sodium carbonate, Na_2CO_3, and barium nitrate, $Ba(NO_3)_2$

is found in a water supply, for example, the difference could be crucial.

8. (a) soluble (most nitrate salts are soluble)
(b) soluble (most potassium salts are soluble)
(c) soluble (most sodium salts are soluble)
(d) insoluble (most hydroxide compounds are insoluble)
(e) insoluble (except for chloride salts)
(f) soluble (most ammonium salts are soluble)
(g) insoluble (most sulfide salts are only slightly soluble)
(h) insoluble (except for sulfate salts)

9. (a) rule 5: most hydroxide compounds are only slightly soluble
(b) rule 6: most carbonates are only slightly soluble
(c) rule 6: most phosphate salts are only slightly soluble
(d) rule 3: exception to the rule for chlorides

10. (a) calcium sulfate
(b) silver iodide
(c) lead(II) phosphate
(d) iron(III) hydroxide
(e) no precipitate: all potassium and sodium salts are soluble
(f) barium carbonate

Chapter 8 Assessment

1. Water has a relatively large liquid range. Thus it can absorb the heat generated by many reactions and remain a liquid. Water dissolves ionic compounds and other compounds in biological systems.

2. Driving forces are types of changes in a system that pull a reaction in the direction of product formation; driving forces include formation of a solid, formation of water, formation of a gas, and transfer of electrons.

3. The net charge of a precipitate must be zero. The total number of positive charges equals the total number of negative charges.

4. When an electrolyte dissolves in water, the resulting solution consists of separate individual cations and anions.

5. A substance is a strong electrolyte if each unit of the substance produces separated, distinct ions when the substance is dissolved in water. NaCl and KNO_3 are both strong electrolytes.

6. $NaNO_3$ must be soluble in water.

7. *Insoluble* and *slightly soluble* have roughly the same meanings. However, if a substance is highly toxic and

11. (a) no precipitate
(b) $(NH_4)_2S(aq) + CoCl_2(aq) \rightarrow$
$\underline{CoS(s)} + 2NH_4Cl(aq)$
(c) $H_2SO_4(aq) + Pb(NO_3)_2(aq) \rightarrow$
$\underline{PbSO_4(s)} + 2HNO_3(aq)$
(d) $CaCl_2(aq) + K_2CO_3(aq) \rightarrow$
$\underline{CaCO_3(s)} + 2KCl(aq)$
(e) no precipitate
(f) $Na_3PO_4(aq) + CrCl_3(aq) \rightarrow$
$\underline{CrPO_4(s)} + 3NaCl(aq)$

12. (a) $2AgNO_3(aq) + H_2SO_4(aq) \rightarrow$
$Ag_2SO_4(s) + 2HNO_3(aq)$
(b) $Ca(NO_3)_2(aq) + H_2SO_4(aq) \rightarrow$
$CaSO_4(s) + 2HNO_3(aq)$
(c) $Pb(NO_3)_2(aq) + H_2SO_4(aq) \rightarrow$
$PbSO_4(s) + 2HNO_3(aq)$

13. (a) $(NH_4)_2S(aq) + CoCl_2(aq) \rightarrow$
$CoS(s) + 2NH_4Cl(aq)$
(b) $FeCl_3(aq) + NaOH(aq) \rightarrow$
$Fe(OH)_3(s) + 3NaCl(aq)$
(c) $CuSO_4(aq) + Na_2CO_3(aq) \rightarrow$
$CuCO_3(s) + Na_2SO_4(aq)$

14. (a) $Ca^{2+}(aq) + SO_4^{2-}(aq) \rightarrow$
$CaSO_4(s)$
(b) $2Fe^{3+}(aq) + 3CO_3^{2-}(aq) \rightarrow$
$Fe_2(CO_3)_3(s)$
(c) $Ag^+(aq) + I^-(aq) \rightarrow AgI(s)$
(d) $3Co^{2+}(aq) + 2PO_4^{3-}(aq) \rightarrow$
$Co_3(PO_4)_2(s)$
(e) $Hg_2^{2+}(aq) + 2Cl^-(aq) \rightarrow$
$Hg_2Cl_2(s)$
(f) $Pb^{2+}(aq) + 2Br^-(aq) \rightarrow$
$PbBr_2(s)$

15. $Ag^+(aq) + Cl^-(aq) \rightarrow AgCl(s);$
$Pb^{2+}(aq) + 2Cl^-(aq) \rightarrow$
$PbCl_2(s);$ (e) $Hg_2^{2+}(aq) +$
$2Cl^-(aq) \rightarrow Hg_2Cl_2(s)$

16. $Ca^{2+}(aq) + C_2O_4^{2-}(aq) \rightarrow$
$C_2O_4(s)$

11. On the basis of the general solubility rules given in Table 8.1, write a balanced molecular equation for the precipitation reactions that take place when the following aqueous solutions are mixed. Underline the formula of the precipitate (solid) that forms. If no precipitation reaction is likely for the solutes given, so indicate.

a. nitric acid, HNO_3, and barium chloride, $BaCl_2$

b. ammonium sulfide, $(NH_4)_2S$, and cobalt(II) chloride, $CoCl_2$

c. sulfuric acid, H_2SO_4, and lead(II) nitrate, $Pb(NO_3)_2$

d. calcium chloride, $CaCl_2$, and potassium carbonate, K_2CO_3

e. sodium acetate, $NaC_2H_3O_2$, and ammonium nitrate, NH_4NO_3

f. sodium phosphate, Na_3PO_4, and chromium(III) chloride, $CrCl_3$

12. Balance each of the following equations that describe precipitation reactions.

a. $AgNO_3(aq) + H_2SO_4(aq) \rightarrow$
$Ag_2SO_4(s) + HNO_3(aq)$
b. $Ca(NO_3)_2(aq) + H_2SO_4(aq) \rightarrow$
$CaSO_4(s) + HNO_3(aq)$
c. $Pb(NO_3)_2(aq) + H_2SO_4(aq) \rightarrow$
$PbSO_4(s) + HNO_3(aq)$

13. For each of the following precipitation reactions, complete and balance the equation, indicating clearly which product is the precipitate.

a. $(NH_4)_2S(aq) + CoCl_2(aq) \rightarrow$?
b. $FeCl_3(aq) + NaOH(aq) \rightarrow$?
c. $CuSO_4(aq) + Na_2CO_3(aq) \rightarrow$?

C. Describing Reactions in Aqueous Solutions

14. Write balanced net ionic equations for the reactions that occur when the following aqueous solutions are mixed. If no reaction is likely to occur, so indicate.

d. ammonium phosphate and cobalt(II) sulfate

e. strontium chloride and mercury(I) nitrate

f. barium bromide and lead(II) nitrate

15. In the laboratory, students often learn to analyze mixtures of the common positive and negative ions, separating and confirming the presence of the particular ions in the mixture. One of the first steps in such an analysis is to treat the mixture with hydrochloric acid, which precipitates and removes silver ion, lead(II) ion, and mercury(I) ion from the aqueous mixture as the insoluble chloride salts. Write balanced net ionic equations for the precipitation reactions of these three cations with chloride ion.

16. Many plants are poisonous because their stems and leaves contain oxalic acid, $H_2C_2O_4$, or sodium oxalate, $Na_2C_2O_4$; when ingested, these substances cause swelling of the respiratory tract and suffocation. A standard analysis for determining the amount of oxalate ion, $C_2O_4^{2-}$, in a sample is to precipitate this species as calcium oxalate, which is insoluble in water. Write the net ionic equation for the reaction between sodium oxalate and calcium chloride, $CaCl_2$, in aqueous solution.

8.2 Other Reactions in Aqueous Solutions

A. Reactions That Form Water: Acids and Bases

17. What is meant by a *strong acid*? Are the strong acids also *strong electrolytes*? Explain.

18. What is meant by a *strong base*? Are the strong bases also *strong electrolytes*? Explain.

19. If 1000 NaOH units were dissolved in a sample of water, the NaOH would produce _____ Na^+ ions and _____ OH^- ions.

20. Along with the three strong acids emphasized in the chapter (HCl, HNO_3, and H_2SO_4), hydrobromic acid, HBr, and perchloric acid, $HClO_4$, are also strong acids. Write equations for the dissociation of each of these additional strong acids in water.

21. Along with the strong bases NaOH and KOH discussed in this chapter, the hydroxide compounds of other Group 1 elements also behave as strong bases when dissolved in water. Write equations for RbOH and CsOH that show which ions form when they dissolve in water.

22. Complete and balance each of the following molecular equations for strong acid/strong base reactions; circle the formula of the salt produced in each.

    a. $HCl(aq) + RbOH(aq) \rightarrow$?

    b. $HClO_4(aq) + NaOH(aq) \rightarrow$?

    c. $HBr(aq) + NaOH(aq) \rightarrow$?

    d. $H_2SO_4(aq) + CsOH(aq) \rightarrow$?

23. Below are indicated the formulas of some salts. Such salts could be formed by the reaction of the appropriate strong acid and strong base (with the other product of the reaction being, of course, water). For each salt, write an equation showing the formation of the salt from reaction of the appropriate strong acid and strong base.

    a. Na_2SO_4 c. $KClO_4$

    b. $RbNO_3$ d. KCl

B. Reactions of Metals with Nonmetals (Oxidation–Reduction)

24. What do we mean when we say that the transfer of electrons can be the "driving force" for a reaction? Give an example of a reaction where this happens.

25. If atoms of a metallic element (such as sodium) react with atoms of a nonmetallic element (such as sulfur), which element loses electrons and which element gains them?

26. If potassium atoms were to react with atoms of the nonmetal sulfur, how many electrons would each potassium atom lose? How many electrons would each sulfur atom gain? How many potassium atoms would have to react to provide enough electrons for one sulfur atom? What charges would the resulting potassium and sulfur ions have?

27. For the reaction $2Al(s) + 3Br_2(l) \rightarrow 2AlBr_3(s)$, show how electrons are gained and lost by the atoms.

28. Balance each of the following oxidation–reduction chemical reactions.

    a. $K(s) + F_2(g) \rightarrow KF(s)$

    b. $K(s) + O_2(g) \rightarrow K_2O(s)$

    c. $K(s) + N_2(g) \rightarrow K_3N(s)$

    d. $K(s) + C(s) \rightarrow K_4C(s)$

29. Balance each of the following oxidation–reduction chemical reactions.

    a. $Fe(s) + S(s) \rightarrow Fe_2S_3(s)$

    b. $Zn(s) + HNO_3(aq) \rightarrow Zn(NO_3)_2(aq) + H_2(g)$

    c. $Sn(s) + O_2(g) \rightarrow SnO(s)$

    d. $K(s) + H_2(g) \rightarrow KH(s)$

    e. $Cs(s) + H_2O(l) \rightarrow CsOH(s) + H_2(g)$

8.3 Classifying Reactions

A. Ways to Classify Reactions

30. What is a *double*-displacement reaction? What is a *single*-replacement reaction? Write balanced chemical equations showing two examples of each type.

31. Two "driving forces" for reactions discussed in this section are the formation of water in an acid–base reaction and the formation of a gaseous product. Write balanced chemical equations showing two examples of each type.

---

17. Strong acids are acids that completely ionize in water; thus strong acids are also strong electrolytes.

18. The strong bases are those hydroxide compounds that dissociate fully when dissolved in water. Strong bases that are highly soluble in water (NaOH, KOH) are also strong electrolytes.

19. 1000; 1000

20. $HBr(aq) \rightarrow H^+(aq) + Br^-(aq)$; $HClO_4(aq) \rightarrow H^+(aq) + ClO_4^-(aq)$

21. $RbOH(s) \rightarrow Rb^+(aq) + OH^-(aq)$; $CsOH(s) \rightarrow Cs^+(aq) + OH^-(aq)$

22. (a) $HCl(aq) + RbOH(aq) \rightarrow H_2O(l) +$ $\boxed{RbCl(aq)}$
(b) $HClO_4(aq) + NaOH(aq) \rightarrow H_2O(l) +$ $\boxed{NaClO_4(aq)}$
(c) $HBr(aq) + NaOH(aq) \rightarrow H_2O(l) +$ $\boxed{NaBr(aq)}$
(d) $H_2SO_4(aq) + CsOH(aq) \rightarrow$

$2H_2O(l) +$ $\boxed{Cs_2SO_4(aq)}$

23. (a) $H_2SO_4(aq) + 2NaOH(aq) \rightarrow 2H_2O(l) + Na_2SO_4(aq)$
(b) $HNO_3(aq) + RbOH(aq) \rightarrow H_2O(l) + RbNO_3(aq)$
(c) $HClO_4(aq) + KOH(aq) \rightarrow 2H_2O(l) + KClO_4(aq)$
(d) $HCl(aq) + KOH(aq) \rightarrow H_2O(l) + KCl(aq)$

24. A driving force tends to help convert reactants to products.

A transfer of electrons from atoms of a metal (like sodium) to atoms of a nonmetal (like chlorine) is favored because metals tend to lose electrons and nonmetals tend to gain electrons.

25. The metal loses electrons; the nonmetal gains electrons.

26. Each potassium atom would lose one electron to become a K^+ ion. Each sulfur atom would gain two electrons to become a S^{2-} ion. Two potassium ions would have to react for every one sulfur atom.

27. $AlBr_3$ is made up of Al^{3+} ions and Br^- ions. Aluminum atoms each lose three electrons and bromine atoms each gain one electron (Br_2 gains two electrons).

28. (a) $2K(s) + F_2(g) \rightarrow 2KF(s)$
(b) $4K(s) + O_2(g) \rightarrow K_2O(s)$
(c) $6K(s) + N_2(g) \rightarrow 2K_3N(s)$
(d) $4K(s) + C(s) \rightarrow K_4C(s)$

29. (a) $2Fe(s) + 3S(s) \rightarrow Fe_2S_3(s)$
(b) $Zn(s) + 2HNO_3(aq) \rightarrow Zn(NO_3)_2(aq) + H_2(g)$
(c) $2Sn(s) + O_2(g) \rightarrow 2SnO(s)$
(d) $2K(s) + H_2(g) \rightarrow 2KH(s)$
(e) $2Cs(s) + 2H_2O(l) \rightarrow 2CsOH(s) + H_2(g)$

30. In a double-displacement reaction, when two solutions of ionic solutes are mixed, the positive ions of the two solutes exchange anions. Two examples are

$AgNO_3(aq) + HCl(aq) \rightarrow AgCl(s) + HNO_3(aq)$

$Pb(NO_3)_2(aq) + Li_2CO_3(aq) \rightarrow PbCO_3(s) + 2LiNO_3(aq)$

In a single-displacement reaction, a new element replaces a less active element in the compound. Examples are

$Mg(s) + 2HCl(aq) \rightarrow MgCl_2(aq) + H_2(g)$

$Cu(s) + 2AgNO_3(aq) \rightarrow Cu(NO_3)_2(aq) + 2Ag(s)$

31. Examples of the formation of water:
$H_2SO_4(aq) + 2NaOH(aq) \rightarrow 2H_2O(l) + Na_2SO_4(aq)$;
$HClO_4(aq) + KOH(aq) \rightarrow 2H_2O(l) + KClO_4(aq)$
Examples of formation of a gaseous product:
$Mg(s) + 2HCl(aq) \rightarrow MgCl_2(aq) + H_2(g)$;
$2KClO_3(s) \rightarrow 2KCl(s) + 3O_2(g)$

32. (a) precipitation
(b) oxidation–reduction
(c) precipitation
(d) acid–base
(e) oxidation–reduction
(f) acid–base
(g) precipitation, acid–base
(h) oxidation–reduction
(i) precipitation

33. (a) oxidation–reduction
(b) oxidation–reduction
(c) acid–base
(d) acid–base, precipitation
(e) precipitation
(f) precipitation
(g) oxidation–reduction
(h) oxidation–reduction
(i) acid–base

34. A synthesis reaction represents the production of a given compound from simpler substances. An example is $C(s) + O_2(g) \rightarrow CO_2(g)$. This reaction can also be classified as an oxidation–reduction reaction and a combustion reaction. The reaction $2Fe(s) + 3Cl_2(g) \rightarrow 2FeCl_3(s)$ is a synthesis reaction that can also be classified as an oxidation–reduction reaction but not a combustion reaction.

35. A decomposition reaction is one in which a given compound is broken down into simpler compounds or constituent elements. These reactions may be classified in other ways. For example, $2HgO(s) \rightarrow 2Hg(l) + O_2(g)$ is both a decomposition reaction and an oxidation–reduction reaction.

36. (a) $C_2H_5OH(l) + 3O_2(g) \rightarrow 2CO_2(g) + 3H_2O(g)$
(b) $2C_6H_{14}(l) + 19O_2(g) \rightarrow 12CO_2(g) + 14H_2O(g)$
(c) $C_6H_{12}(l) + 9O_2(g) \rightarrow 6CO_2(g) + 6H_2O(g)$

37. (a) $2C_2H_6(g) + 7O_2(g) \rightarrow 4CO_2(g) + 6H_2O(g)$
(b) $C_2H_6O(l) + 3O_2(g) \rightarrow 2CO_2(g) + 3H_2O(g)$
(c) $2C_2H_6O_2(l) + 5O_2(g) \rightarrow 4CO_2(g) + 6H_2O(g)$

38. (a) $2Co(s) + 3S(s) \rightarrow Co_2S_3(s)$
(b) $2NO(g) + O_2(g) \rightarrow 2NO_2(g)$
(c) $FeO(s) + CO_2(g) \rightarrow FeCO_3(s)$
(d) $2Al(s) + 3F_2(g) \rightarrow 2AlF_3(s)$
(e) $2NH_3(g) + H_2CO_3(aq) \rightarrow (NH_4)_2CO_3(s)$

32. Identify each of the following unbalanced reaction equations as belonging to one or more of the following categories: precipitation, acid–base, or oxidation–reduction.

a. $K_2SO_4(aq) + Ba(NO_3)_2(aq) \rightarrow BaSO_4(s) + KNO_3(aq)$
b. $HCl(aq) + Zn(s) \rightarrow H_2(g) + ZnCl_2(aq)$
c. $HCl(aq) + AgNO_3(aq) \rightarrow HNO_3(aq) + AgCl(s)$
d. $HCl(aq) + KOH(aq) \rightarrow H_2O(l) + KCl(aq)$
e. $Zn(s) + CuSO_4(aq) \rightarrow ZnSO_4(aq) + Cu(s)$
f. $NaH_2PO_4(aq) + NaOH(aq) \rightarrow Na_3PO_4(aq) + H_2O(l)$
g. $Ca(OH)_2(aq) + H_2SO_4(aq) \rightarrow CaSO_4(s) + H_2O(l)$
h. $ZnCl_2(aq) + Mg(s) \rightarrow Zn(s) + MgCl_2(aq)$
i. $BaCl_2(aq) + H_2SO_4(aq) \rightarrow BaSO_4(s) + HCl(aq)$

33. Identify each of the following unbalanced reaction equations as belonging to one or more of the following categories: precipitation, acid–base, or oxidation–reduction.

a. $H_2O_2(aq) \rightarrow H_2O(l) + O_2(g)$
b. $H_2SO_4(aq) + Cu(s) \rightarrow CuSO_4(aq) + H_2(g)$
c. $H_2SO_4(aq) + NaOH(aq) \rightarrow Na_2SO_4(aq) + H_2O(l)$
d. $H_2SO_4(aq) + Ba(OH)_2(aq) \rightarrow BaSO_4(s) + H_2O(l)$
e. $AgNO_3(aq) + CuCl_2(aq) \rightarrow Cu(NO_3)_2(aq) + AgCl(s)$
f. $KOH(aq) + CuSO_4(aq) \rightarrow Cu(OH)_2(s) + K_2SO_4(aq)$
g. $Cl_2(g) + F_2(g) \rightarrow ClF(g)$
h. $NO(g) + O_2(g) \rightarrow NO_2(g)$
i. $Ca(OH)_2(s) + HNO_3(aq) \rightarrow Ca(NO_3)_2(aq) + H_2O(l)$

B. Other Ways to Classify Reactions

34. What is a *synthesis* or *combination* reaction? Give an example. Can such reactions also be classified in other ways? Give an example of a synthesis reaction that is also a *combustion* reaction. Give an example of a synthesis reaction that is also an *oxidation–reduction* reaction, but which does not involve combustion.

35. What is a *decomposition* reaction? Give an example. Can such reactions also be classified in other ways?

36. Balance each of the following equations that describe combustion reactions.

a. $C_2H_5OH(l) + O_2(g) \rightarrow CO_2(g) + H_2O(g)$
b. $C_6H_{14}(l) + O_2(g) \rightarrow CO_2(g) + H_2O(g)$
c. $C_6H_{12}(l) + O_2(g) \rightarrow CO_2(g) + H_2O(g)$

37. Balance each of the following equations that describe combustion reactions.

a. $C_2H_6(g) + O_2(g) \rightarrow CO_2(g) + H_2O(g)$
b. $C_2H_6O(l) + O_2(g) \rightarrow CO_2(g) + H_2O(g)$
c. $C_2H_6O_2(l) + O_2(g) \rightarrow CO_2(g) + H_2O(g)$

38. Balance each of the following equations that describe synthesis reactions.

a. $Co(s) + S(s) \rightarrow Co_2S_3(s)$
b. $NO(g) + O_2(g) \rightarrow NO_2(g)$
c. $FeO(s) + CO_2(g) \rightarrow FeCO_3(s)$
d. $Al(s) + F_2(g) \rightarrow AlF_3(s)$
e. $NH_3(g) + H_2CO_3(aq) \rightarrow (NH_4)_2CO_3(s)$

39. Balance each of the following equations that describe decomposition reactions.

a. $NI_3(s) \rightarrow N_2(g) + I_2(s)$
b. $BaCO_3(s) \rightarrow BaO(s) + CO_2(g)$
c. $C_6H_{12}O_6(s) \rightarrow C(s) + H_2O(g)$
d. $Cu(NH_3)_4SO_4(s) \rightarrow CuSO_4(s) + NH_3(g)$
e. $NaN_3(s) \rightarrow Na_3N(s) + N_2(g)$

39. (a) $2NI_3(s) \rightarrow N_2(g) + 3I_2(s)$
(b) $BaCO_3(s) \rightarrow BaO(s) + CO_2(g)$
(c) $C_6H_{12}O_6(s) \rightarrow 6C(s) + 6H_2O(g)$
(d) $Cu(NH_3)_4SO_4(s) \rightarrow CuSO_4(s) + 4NH_3(g)$
(e) $NaN_3(s) \rightarrow Na_3N(s) + 4N_2(g)$

Critical Thinking

40. Distinguish between the *molecular* equation, the *complete ionic* equation, and the *net ionic* equation for a reaction in solution. Which type of equation most clearly shows the substances that actually react with one another?

41. Using the general solubility rules given in Table 8.1, name three reactants that would form precipitates with each of the following ions in aqueous solution. Write the net ionic equation for each of your suggestions.

a. chloride ion

b. calcium ion

c. iron(III) ion

d. sulfate ion

e. mercury(I) ion, Hg_2^{2+}

f. silver ion

42. Without first writing a full molecular or ionic equation, write the net ionic equations for any precipitation reactions that occur when aqueous solutions of the following compounds are mixed. If no reaction occurs, so indicate.

c. lithium chloride and lead(II) nitrate

d. calcium nitrate and lithium carbonate

e. gold(III) chloride and sodium hydroxide

43. Complete and balance each of the following molecular equations for strong acid/strong base reactions. Underline the formula of the *salt* produced in each reaction.

a. $HNO_3(aq) + KOH(aq) \rightarrow$?

b. $H_2SO_4(aq) + Ba(OH)_2(aq) \rightarrow$?

c. $HClO_4(aq) + NaOH(aq) \rightarrow$?

d. $HCl(aq) + Ca(OH)_2(aq) \rightarrow$?

44. Copy and complete the following table with the formulas for the precipitates that would form. If no precipitate would form, write "No PPT."

	$C_2H_3O_2^-$	Cl^-	CO_3^{2-}	NO_3^-	OH^-	PO_4^{3-}	S^{2-}	SO_4^{2-}
Ag^+								
Ba^{2+}								
Ca^{2+}								
Fe^{3+}								
Hg_2^{2+}								
Na^+								
Ni^{2+}								
Pb^{2+}								

$SO_4^{2-}(aq) \rightarrow PbSO_4(s)$
(e) sulfide ion: $Hg_2^{2+}(aq) + S^{2-}(aq) \rightarrow Hg_2S(s)$;
carbonate ion: $Hg_2^{2+}(aq) + 2CO_3^{2-}(aq) \rightarrow Hg_2CO_3(s)$;
chloride ion: $Hg_2^{2+}(aq) + 2Cl^-(aq) \rightarrow Hg_2Cl_2(s)$
(f) chloride ion: $Ag^+(aq) + Cl^-(aq) \rightarrow AgCl(s)$;
sulfide ion: $2Ag^+(aq) + S^{2-}(aq) \rightarrow Ag_2S(s)$;
carbonate ion: $2Ag^+(aq) + 2CO_3^{2-}(aq) \rightarrow Ag_2CO_3(s)$

42. (a) no precipitate
(b) $Cu^{2+}(aq) + S^{2-}(aq) \rightarrow CuS(s)$
(c) $Pb^{2+}(aq) + 2Cl^-(aq) \rightarrow PbCl_2(s)$
(d) $Cu^{2+}(aq) + CO_3^{2-}(aq) \rightarrow CaCO_3(s)$
(e) $Au^{3+}(aq) + 3OH^-(aq) \rightarrow Au(OH)_3(s)$

43. (a) $HNO_3(aq) + KOH(aq) \rightarrow H_2O(l) + \underline{KNO_3}(aq)$
(b) $H_2SO_4(aq) + Ba(OH)_2(aq) \rightarrow 2H_2O(l) + \underline{BaSO_4}(aq)$
(c) $HClO_4(aq) + NaOH(aq) \rightarrow H_2O(l) + \underline{NaClO_4}(aq)$;
(d) $2HCl(aq) + Ca(OH)_2(aq) \rightarrow 2H_2O(l) + \underline{CaCl_2}(aq)$

44. Ag^+ ion: $AgCl$, Ag_2CO_3, $AgOH$, Ag_3PO_4, Ag_2S, Ag_2SO_4; Ba^{2+} ion: $BaCO_3$, $Ba(OH)_2$, $Ba_3(PO_4)_2$, BaS, $BaSO_4$; Ca^{2+} ion: $CaCO_3$, $Ca(OH)_2$, $Ca_3(PO_4)_2$, CaS, $CaSO_4$; Fe^{3+} ion: $Fe_2(CO_3)_3$, $Fe(OH)_3$, $FePO_4$, Fe_2S_3; Hg_2^{2+} ion: Hg_2Cl_2, Hg_2CO_3, $Hg_2(OH)_2$, $(Hg_2)_3(PO_4)_2$, Hg_2S; Na^+ ion: all common salts are soluble; Ni^{2+} ion: $NiCO_3$, $Ni(OH)_2$, $Ni_3(PO_4)_2$, NiS; Pb^{2+} ion: $PbCl_2$, $PbCO_3$, $Pb(OH)_2$, $Pb_3(PO_4)_2$, PbS, $PbSO_4$

40. A molecular equation uses the formulas for all reactants and products involved. The complete ionic equation shows the compounds broken into their respective ions (except for the product formed). The net ionic equation shows only those ions that form the product (an ionic solid, a gas, or water are the usual products). The net ionic equation most clearly shows the species that

actually react with each other.

41. (a) silver ion: $Ag^+(aq) + Cl^-(aq) \rightarrow AgCl(s)$;
lead(II) ion: $Pb^{2+}(aq) + 2Cl^-(aq) \rightarrow PbCl_2(s)$;
mercury(I) ion: $Hg_2^{2+}(aq) + 2Cl^-(aq) \rightarrow Hg_2Cl_2(s)$
(b) sulfate ion: $Ca^{2+}(aq) + SO_4^{2-}(aq) \rightarrow CaSO_4(s)$;
carbonate ion: $Ca^{2+}(aq) + CO_3^{2-}(aq) \rightarrow CaCO_3(s)$;
phosphate ion: $3Ca^{2+}(aq) +$

$2PO_4^{3-}(aq) \rightarrow Ca_3(PO_4)_2(s)$
(c) hydroxide ion:
$Fe^{3+}(aq) + 3OH^-(aq) \rightarrow Fe(OH)_3(s)$;
sulfide ion: $2Fe^{3+}(aq) + 3S^{2-}(aq) \rightarrow Fe_2S_3(s)$;
phosphate ion:
$Fe^{3+}(aq) + PO_4^{3-}(aq) \rightarrow FePO_4(s)$
(d) calcium ion: $Ca^{2+}(aq) + SO_4^{2-}(aq) \rightarrow CaSO_4(s)$;
barium ion: $Ba^{2+}(aq) + SO_4^{2-}(aq) \rightarrow BaSO_4(s)$;
lead(II) ion: $Pb^{2+}(aq) +$

45. (a) $AgNO_3(aq) + HCl(aq) \rightarrow$
$\underline{AgCl}(s) + HNO_3(aq)$
(b) $CuSO_4(aq) + (NH_4)_2CO_3(aq) \rightarrow$
$\underline{CuCO_3}(s) + (NH_4)_2SO_4(aq)$
(c) $FeSO_4(aq) + K_2CO_3(aq) \rightarrow$
$\underline{FeCO_3}(s) + K_2SO_4(aq)$
(d) no reaction
(e) $Pb(NO_3)_2(aq) + Li_2CO_3(aq)$
$\rightarrow \underline{PbCO_3}(s) + 2LiNO_3(aq)$
(f) $SnCl_4(aq) + 4NaOH(aq) \rightarrow$
$\underline{Sn(OH)_4}(s) + 4NaCl(aq)$

46. (a) $Ag^+(aq) + Cl^-(aq) \rightarrow AgCl(s)$
(b) $3Ca^{2+}(aq) + 2PO_4^{3-}(aq) \rightarrow$
$Ca_3(PO_4)_2(s)$
(c) $Pb^{2+}(aq) + 2Cl^-(aq) \rightarrow$
$PbCl_2(s)$
(d) $Fe^{3+}(aq) + 3OH^-(aq) \rightarrow$
$Fe(OH)_3(s)$

47. See the *Solutions Guide*.

48. (a) one
(b) one
(c) two
(d) two
(e) three

49. (a) two
(b) one
(c) three
(d) one
(e) two

50. (a) $2C_3H_8OH(l) + 9O_2(g) \rightarrow$
$6CO_2(g) + 8H_2O(g)$; oxidation–
reduction, combustion
(b) $HCl(aq) + AgC_2H_3O_2(aq) \rightarrow$
$AgCl(s) + HC_2H_3O_2(aq)$;
precipitation, double-
displacement
(c) $3HCl(aq) + Al(OH)_3(s) \rightarrow$
$AlCl_3(aq) + 3H_2O(l)$;
acid–base, double-displacement
(d) $2H_2O_2(aq) \rightarrow 2H_2O(l) + O_2(g)$;
oxidation–reduction,
decomposition
(e) $N_2H_4(l) + O_2(g) \rightarrow N_2(g) +$
$2H_2O(g)$; oxidation–reduction,
combustion

51. (a) acid–base
(b) precipitation
(c) oxidation–reduction,
combustion, synthesis
(d) oxidation–reduction,
decomposition

---

45. On the basis of the general solubility rules given in Table 8.1, write a balanced molecular equation for the precipitation reactions that take place when the following aqueous solutions are mixed. Underline the formula of the precipitate (solid) that forms. If no precipitation reaction is likely for the reactants given, so indicate.

  a. silver nitrate and hydrochloric acid

  b. copper(II) sulfate and ammonium carbonate

  c. iron(II) sulfate and potassium carbonate

  d. silver nitrate and potassium nitrate

  e. lead(II) nitrate and lithium carbonate

  f. tin(IV) chloride and sodium hydroxide

46. For each of the following *un*balanced molecular equations, write the corresponding *balanced net ionic equation* for the reaction.

  a. $HCl(aq) + AgNO_3(aq) \rightarrow$
    $AgCl(s) + HNO_3(aq)$

  b. $CaCl_2(aq) + Na_3PO_4(aq) \rightarrow$
    $Ca_3(PO_4)_2(s) + NaCl(aq)$

  c. $Pb(NO_3)_2(aq) + BaCl_2(aq) \rightarrow$
    $PbCl_2(s) + Ba(NO_3)_2(aq)$

  d. $FeCl_3(aq) + NaOH(aq) \rightarrow$
    $Fe(OH)_3(s) + NaCl(aq)$

47. Write a balanced oxidation–reduction equation for the reaction of each of the metals below

    Ba K Mg Rb Ca Li

with each of the nonmetals below.

    O_2 S Cl_2 N_2 Br_2

---

48. For each of the following metals, how many electrons will the metal atoms lose when the metal reacts with a nonmetal?

  a. sodium   d. barium

  b. potassium   e. aluminum

  c. magnesium

49. For each of the following nonmetals, how many electrons will each atom of the nonmetal gain in reacting with a metal?

  a. oxygen   d. chlorine

  b. fluorine   e. sulfur

  c. nitrogen

50. Classify the reactions represented by the following unbalanced equations by as many methods as possible. Balance the equations.

  a. $C_3H_8O(l) + O_2(g) \rightarrow CO_2(g) + H_2O(g)$

  b. $HCl(aq) + AgC_2H_3O_2(aq) \rightarrow$
    $AgCl(s) + HC_2H_3O_2(aq)$

  c. $HCl(aq) + Al(OH)_3(s) \rightarrow$
    $AlCl_3(aq) + H_2O(l)$

  d. $H_2O_2(aq) \rightarrow H_2O(l) + O_2(g)$

  e. $N_2H_4(l) + O_2(g) \rightarrow N_2(g) + H_2O(g)$

51. Classify each equation in one or more of the following categories:

- precipitation
- acid–base
- oxidation–reduction
- combustion
- synthesis
- decomposition

  a. $HNO_3(aq) + KOH(aq) \rightarrow$
    $H_2O(l) + KNO_3(aq)$

  b. $Ca(NO_3)_2(aq) + K_2SO_4(aq) \rightarrow$
    $CaSO_4(s) + 2KNO_3(aq)$

  c. $C(s) + O_2(g) \rightarrow CO_2(g)$

  d. $2H_2O(l) \rightarrow 2H_2(g) + O_2(g)$

1 Which of the following is the best microscopic representation of an aqueous solution of calcium chloride?

A

C

B

D

2 If two moles of sodium sulfate are dissolved in water, how many moles of ions are in solution?

A 2

B 3

C 6

D 15

For questions 3–5, use the solubility rules (Table 8.1).

3 Which of the following would result in the production of a solid?

A $NaCl(aq) + KNO_3(aq)$

B $AgNO_3(aq) + NaNO_3(aq)$

C $Ba(NO_3)_2(aq) + K_2SO_4(aq)$

D $HCl(aq) + NaOH(aq)$

4 When an aqueous solution of silver nitrate is mixed with an aqueous solution of potassium chloride, which are the spectator ions?

A nitrate ions and chloride ions

B nitrate ions and potassium ions

C silver ions and chloride ions

D silver ions and potassium ions

5 Choose the correct balanced complete ionic equation for the reaction of an aqueous solution of lead(II) nitrate with an aqueous solutions of potassium chloride.

A $Pb(NO_3)_2(aq) + KCl(aq) \rightarrow$
$PbCl(s) + KNO_3(aq)$

B $Pb^{2+}(aq) + 2NO_3^-(aq) + 2K^+(aq) + 2Cl^-(aq) \rightarrow$
$Pb^{2+}(aq) + 2Cl^-(aq) + 2K^+(aq) + 2NO_3^-(aq)$

C $Pb^{2+}(aq) + 2NO_3^-(aq) + 2K^+(aq) + 2Cl^-(aq)$
$\rightarrow Pb^{2+}(aq) + 2Cl^-(aq) + 2KNO_3(s)$

D $Pb^{2+}(aq) + 2NO_3^-(aq) + 2K^+(aq) + 2Cl^-(aq)$
$\rightarrow PbCl_2(s) + 2K^+(aq) + 2NO_3^-(aq)$

6 Which of the following types of reactions always has water as a product?

A precipitation reaction

B oxidation–reduction reaction

C combustion reaction

D strong acid-strong base reaction

7 Which of the following types of reactions is *not* an oxidation–reduction reaction?

A precipitation reaction

B synthesis reaction

C combustion reaction

D decomposition reaction

8 Aluminum reacts with oxygen in the air as an oxidation–reduction reaction. Which of the following best describes what happens?

A Each aluminum atom gains three electrons and each oxygen atom loses two electrons.

B Each aluminum atom loses two electrons and each oxygen atom gains two electrons.

C Each aluminum atom loses three electrons and each oxygen atom gains two electrons.

D Each aluminum atom gains two electrons and each oxygen atom loses two electrons

Chapter 8
Standardized Test Practice

1. B

2. C

3. C

4. B

5. D

6. D

7. A

8. C

Test-Taking Strategy

Encourage students to find out what reference materials will be provided with a test, prior to studying, so that they do not spend time trying to memorize unnecessary information. However, although students will not need to memorize such material, they will need to be familiar with the material and know how to use it. Direct students to review all necessary reference materials before a test, including those provided with the test.

Chapter 8 • Standardized Test Practice • **277**

Assessment Resources
CHAPTER 8

For additional practice with standardized testing, see *Standardized Test Practice* located in the *Teacher Resources*.

Planning Guide

Section	Segment		Text Features and Components	Labs, Demonstrations, & Activities
9.1 Using Chemical Equations **0.5 Block** pp. 280–287	A	Information Given by Chemical Equations		**SE** Hands-On Chemistry: The Nuts and Bolts of Stoichiometry *p. 282*
	B	Mole–mole Relationships		
9.2 Using Chemical Equations to Calculate Mass **2 Blocks** pp. 288–295	A	Mass Calculations		**LM** Experiment 34: Copper Wire in a Silver Nitrate Solution, Traditional Lab Manual Report Sheets Teacher's Lab Guide
	B	Mass Calculations Using Scientific Notation		**LM** Experiment 35: Mass Relationships in Chemical Compounds, Traditional Lab Manual Report Sheets Teacher's Lab Guide
	C	Mass Calculation: Comparing Two Reactions		**TE** Mini-Demo *p. 294* **LM** Experiment 36: Calcium Content of Milk, Microscale Lab Manual Report Sheets Teacher's Lab Guide
	continued on next page			

Key

SE Student Edition	**TE** Teacher Edition	**RP** Teacher Resource Package	
AR Additional Materials	**LM** Lab Materials	Transparencies	
⊙ DVD	CD-ROM	classzone.com	

Planning Guide

All Learners	Technology	Review & Assessment	Standards
TE Teaching Tips *pp. 280–281* **RP** MINT: Reading Concepts *TE p. 280*	**•** Video: Oxygen, Hydrogen, Soap Bubbles, and Balloons **•** EasyPlanner	**SE** Active Reading Question *p. 280* **TE** More Examples *p. 282* **SE** Questions and Problems *p. 310*	**TE** **NSES** UCP3, A1, A2, B2, B3
TE Teaching Tip *p. 283* **TE** Meeting Individual Needs *p. 284* **TE** Meeting Individual Needs *p. 285* **RP** Team Learning Worksheet (Sec. 9.1)	**•** EasyPlanner	**SE** Active Reading Question *p. 284* **TE** More Examples *p. 285* **SE** Practice Problem *p. 286* **TE** More Examples *p. 286* **TE** More Examples *p. 287* **SE** Review Questions (9.1.A–9.1.B) *p. 287* **SE** Key Terms *p. 309* **SE** Questions and Problems *p. 310*	
TE Teaching Tips *p. 289* **RP** MINT: Math Concepts *TE p. 289*	**•** Lab Generator CD **•** EasyPlanner	**SE** Critical Thinking *p. 288* **TE** More Examples *p. 290* **SE** Practice Problem *p. 291* **SE** Questions and Problems *pp. 310–312*	**TE** **NSES** UCP3, A1, A2, B2, B3, C5, C6, E1, E2, F1, F3, F5, F6, G3
RP MINT: Math Concepts *TE p. 291*	**•** Lab Generator CD **•** EasyPlanner	**TE** More Examples *p. 292* **SE** Practice Problem *p. 293* **SE** Key Terms *p. 309* **SE** Questions and Problems *p. 312*	
RP Team Learning Worksheet (Sec. 9.2)	**•** Lab Generator CD **•** EasyPlanner	**SE** Active Reading Question *p. 295* **SE** Review Questions (9.2.A–9.2.C) *p. 295* **SE** Questions and Problems *p. 312*	

Planning Guide

Section	Segment		Text Features and Components	Labs, Demonstrations, & Activities
9.3 Limiting Reactants and Percent Yield **2 Blocks** pp. 296–308	A	The Concept of Limitiing Reactants		**TE** Teaching Support: Demonstration *pp. 296–297*
	B	Calculations Involving a Limiting Reactant		**LM** Experiment 37: Stoichiometry Lab Manual Report Sheets Teacher's Lab Guide **LM** Experiment 38: Calorimetry and Limiting Reactants, CBL Lab Manual Report Sheets Teacher's Lab Guide
	C	Percent Yield	**SE** Chemistry in Your World: The "Golden" Dollar *p. 308*	**LM** Experiment 39: Synthesis of Manganese(II) Chloride, Microscale Lab Manual Report Sheets Teacher's Lab Guide

Key

SE Student Edition	**TE** Teacher Edition	**RP** Teacher Resource Package
AR Additional Materials	**LM** Lab Materials	Transparencies
DVD	CD-ROM	classzone.com

All Learners	Technology	Review & Assessment	Standards
TE Teaching Tips *pp. 296–297* **RP** MINT: Challenge Projects *TE p. 298*	Animation: Limiting Reactant EasyPlanner	**SE** Active Reading Question *p. 296* **SE** Active Reading Question *p. 299* **SE** Key Terms *p. 309* **SE** Questions and Problems *p. 312*	**TE** **NSES** UCP3, A1, A2, B2, B3, F6
TE Teaching Tips *pp. 299–301* **TE** Meeting Individual Needs *p. 302* **TE** Meeting Individual Needs *p. 303*	Transparency: Figure 9.1 Transparency: Steps for Solving Stoichiometry Problems Involving Limiting Reactants Lab Generator CD EasyPlanner	**TE** More Examples *p. 301* **TE** More Examples *p. 304* **SE** Practice Problem *p. 305* **SE** Active Reading Question *p. 305* **SE** Questions and Problems *pp. 312–313*	
TE Teaching Tips *p. 306* **TE** Meeting Individual Needs *p. 306* **RP** MINT: Math Concepts *TE p. 305* **RP** Team Learning Worksheet (Sec. 9.3)	Lab Generator CD EasyPlanner	**SE** Active Reading Question *p. 306* **TE** More Examples *p. 306* **SE** Practice Problem *p. 307* **SE** Review Questions (9.3.A–9.3.C) *p. 308* **SE** Key Terms *p. 309* **SE** Questions and Problems *pp. 313–314*	

Resource Materials for Chapter 9

SE Chapter Review *p. 309*

SE Critical Thinking *pp. 314–316*

SE Standardized Test Practice *p. 317*

AR English/Spanish Summaries

English Summaries Audio

Spanish Summaries Audio

RP Meeting Individual Needs Toolkit (MINT)
  Reading Concepts
  Math Concepts
  Challenge Projects
  Chapter Review Worksheets
  Chapter Summaries

RP Solutions Guide

RP Standardized Test Practice

RP Chapter Tests

RP Test Bank

Test Generator

Chapter 9
Overview

In this chapter our goals are for students to:

- Understand the molecular and mass information given in a balanced equation

- Learn to use a balanced equation to determine relationships between moles of reactants and moles of products

- Learn to relate masses of reactants and products in a chemical reaction

- Carry out mass calculations that involve scientific notation

- Understand the concept of limiting reactants

- Learn to recognize the limiting reactant in a reaction

- Learn to use the limiting reactant to do stoichiometric calculations

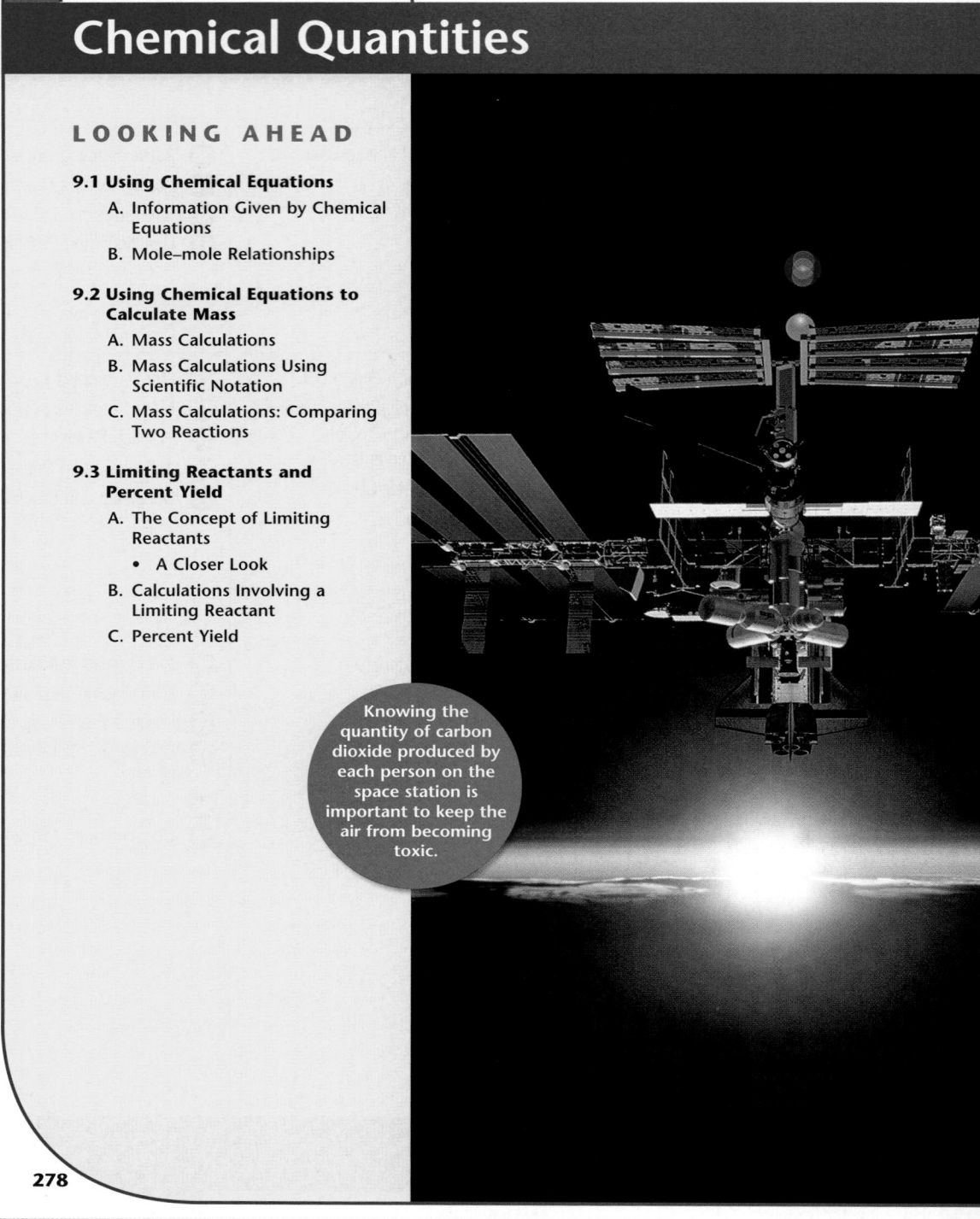

Chapter 9
Chemical Quantities

Knowing the quantity of carbon dioxide produced by each person on the space station is important to keep the air from becoming toxic.

278

IN YOUR LIFE

Suppose that you work for a consumer advocate organization and you want to test a company's advertising claims about the effectiveness of its antacid. The company claims that its product neutralizes ten times as much stomach acid per tablet as its nearest competitor. How would you test the validity of this claim?

Or suppose that some day you go to work for a chemical company that makes methanol (methyl alcohol), a substance used as a starting material for the manufacture of products such as antifreeze and aviation fuels and as a fuel in the cars that race in the Indianapolis 500. You are working with an experienced chemist who is trying to improve the company's process for making methanol from the reaction of gaseous hydrogen with carbon monoxide gas. The first day on the job, you are instructed to order enough hydrogen and carbon monoxide to produce 6.0 kg of methanol in a test run. How would you determine how much carbon monoxide and hydrogen to order?

After you study this chapter, you will be able to answer these questions.

WHAT DO YOU KNOW?

Prereading Questions

1. You are building model cars. Each car has four tires, two doors, and one body. If you have 16 tires, 10 doors, and 7 car bodies, how many model cars can you build? What is left over after you have built all of the cars?

2. Consider the reaction $N_2 + 3H_2 \rightarrow 2NH_3$. One mole of nitrogen gas requires how many moles of hydrogen gas? Two moles of nitrogen gas requires how many moles of hydrogen gas?

3. What is the molar mass of water?

4. Consider the reaction $2H_2(g) + O_2(g) \rightarrow 2H_2O(g)$. If there are two moles of each reactant, which reactant runs out first?

5. A certain recipe for chocolate chip cookies lists the yield as two dozen cookies. You make slightly larger cookies than recommended and make only 14 cookies. What percent of cookies did you make?

Chemical Quantities • Chapter 9 • **279**

Prereading Questions

1. You can build 4 cars from 16 tires. This would require 8 doors (2 left over) and 4 bodies (3 left over).

2. Three moles of hydrogen gas are required for every one mole of nitrogen gas. Two moles of nitrogen gas require six moles of hydrogen gas.

3. The molar mass of water is 18.016 g/mol ($2 \times 1.008 + 1 \times 16.00$).

4. Hydrogen gas runs out first. Since each mole of oxygen gas requires 2 moles of hydrogen gas, 2 moles of oxygen gas require 4 moles of hydrogen gas.

5. 58% ($14/24 \times 100\%$)

TECHNOLOGY IN THE CLASSROOM

 Transparencies
Figure: 9.1
Steps for Solving Stoichiometry Problems with Limiting Reactants

 Power Presentation DVD
PowerPoint Slides
Animation
Limiting Reactant
Video
Oxygen, Hydrogen, Soap Bubbles, and Balloons
eEdition
EasyPlanner

Lab Generator CD
English Summaries CD
Spanish Summaries CD
ML Test Generator

 classzone.com

Assign students to read Section 9.1 and to answer the Review Questions at the end of the section before coming to class.

 Active Learning
Team Learning Worksheet

After introducing the material in Section 9.1 in class, place students in groups and have them work together on **Section 9.1: Team Learning Worksheet.**

Homework

You may wish to assign these selected end-of-chapter problems as homework for this section: 2, 3, 6, 8, 9, 10

Additional end-of-chapter problems can be used for extra practice.

9.1.A Information Given by Chemical Equations
Objective To understand the molecular and mass information given in a balanced equation

 TEACHING TIP

Remind students that chemistry problems often require a balanced chemical equation. Remember to write the equation first, and then balance it before working the problem.

 Active Reading Question

The coefficients represent a ratio of reactants and products, not absolute numbers. We must multiply coefficients by the same amount because this ratio must stay the same.

Key Term
• Mole ratio

Objectives
• *To understand the information given in a balanced equation*
• *To use a balanced equation to determine relationships between moles of reactant and products*

A. Information Given by Chemical Equations

As we saw in the last two chapters, chemistry is really about reactions. Chemical changes involve rearrangements of atom groupings as one or more substances change to new substances. Recall that reactions are described by equations that give the identities of the reactants and products and show how much of each reactant and product participates in the reaction. It is the numbers (coefficients) in the balanced chemical equation that enable us to determine just how much product we can get from a given quantity of reactants.

To explore this idea, consider a nonchemical analogy. Assume that you are in charge of making deli sandwiches at a local fast-food restaurant. A particular type of sandwich requires 2 pieces of bread, 3 slices of meat, and 1 slice of cheese. You might represent making this sandwich by the following equation:

2 pieces bread + 3 slices meat + 1 slice cheese → 1 sandwich

Your boss sends you to the store to get enough ingredients to make 50 sandwiches. How do you figure out how much of each ingredient to buy? Because you need enough to make 50 sandwiches, you could multiply the preceding equation by 50.

50 (2 pieces bread) + 50 (3 slices meat) + 50 (1 slice cheese) →
    50 sandwiches

That is,

100 pieces bread + 150 slices meat + 50 slices cheese → 50 sandwiches

Notice that the numbers 100:150:50 correspond to the ratio 2:3:1, which represents the original numbers of bread, meat, and cheese ingredients in the equation for making a sandwich. If you needed the ingredients for 73 sandwiches, it would be easy to use the original sandwich equation to figure out what quantity of ingredients you need.

The equation for a chemical reaction gives you the same type of information. It indicates the relative numbers of reactant and product molecules required for the reaction to take place. Using the equation permits us to determine the amounts of reactants needed to give a certain amount of product or to predict how much product we can make from a given quantity of reactants.

A worker making sandwiches in a deli

 Active Reading Question

Why are we able to multiply coefficients in a chemical equation? Why must we multiply each coefficient by the same amount?

Meeting Individual Needs
READING CONCEPTS

A handout entitled *Reading Chemical Equations* is located in the *Teacher Resources* for students needing additional help with balancing chemical equations and understanding what the equations mean.

To illustrate how this idea works, consider the reaction between gaseous carbon monoxide and hydrogen to produce liquid methanol, $CH_3OH(l)$. The reactants and products are

Unbalanced: $CO(g) + H_2(g) \rightarrow CH_3OH(l)$
　　　　　　Reactants　　　　　Product

> Because atoms are just rearranged (not created or destroyed) in a chemical reaction, we must always balance a chemical equation.

That is, we must choose coefficients that give the same number of each type of atom on both sides. Using the smallest set of integers that satisfies this condition gives the balanced equation

$$CO(g) + 2H_2(g) \rightarrow CH_3OH(l)$$
1C 1O　　4H　　1C 1O 4H

> It is important to recognize that the coefficients in a balanced equation give the *relative* numbers of molecules.

That is, we could multiply this balanced equation by any number and still have a balanced equation. For example, we could multiply by 12,

$$12[CO(g) + 2H_2(g) \rightarrow CH_3OH(l)]$$

$$12 CO(g) + 24 H_2(g) \rightarrow 12 CH_3OH(l)$$

This is still a balanced equation (check to be sure). Because 12 represents a dozen, we could even describe the reaction in terms of dozens:

$$1 \text{ dozen } CO(g) + 2 \text{ dozen } H_2(g) \rightarrow 1 \text{ dozen } CH_3OH(l)$$

We could also multiply the original equation by a very large number, such as 6.022×10^{23},

$$(6.022 \times 10^{23}) [CO(g) + 2H_2(g) \rightarrow CH_3OH(l)]$$

which leads to the equation

$$(6.022 \times 10^{23}) CO(g) + 2(6.022 \times 10^{23}) H_2(g) \rightarrow (6.022 \times 10^{23}) CH_3OH(l)$$

Just as 12 is called a dozen, chemists call 6.022×10^{23} a *mole* (abbreviated mol). Our equation, then, can be written in terms of moles:

$$1 \text{ mol } CO(g) + 2 \text{ mol } H_2(g) \rightarrow 1 \text{ mol } CH_3OH(l)$$

 nformation

One mole is 6.022×10^{23} units.

Let's Review

Information Conveyed by the Balanced Equation for the Production of Methanol

$CO(g)$ +	$2H_2(g)$	$\rightarrow CH_3OH(l)$
1 molecule CO +	2 molecules H_2	$\rightarrow$ 1 molecule CH_3OH
1 dozen CO molecules +	2 dozen H_2 molecules	$\rightarrow$ 1 dozen CH_3OH molecules
(6.022×10^{23}) CO molecules +	$2(6.022 \times 10^{23})$ H_2 molecules	$\rightarrow (6.022 \times 10^{23})$ CH_3OH molecules
1 mol CO molecules +	2 mol H_2 molecules	$\rightarrow$ 1 mol CH_3OH molecules

9.1 • Using Chemical Equations • 281

 TEACHING TIPS

- Recipe analogies can help students relate to chemical equations and quantities. In a recipe (for chocolate chip cookies, for example) we need to know the ingredients, just as in a chemistry equation we need to know the reactants and products. An unbalanced chemical equation is like a recipe that lists the ingredients but not the amounts of each needed. Once a chemical equation is balanced, it is like a recipe that includes both the amounts and the identities of the ingredients. It can be increased or decreased by multiplying by the appropriate factor. For a cookie recipe, you can double or halve the recipe, just as you can multiply a chemical equation by 2 or by $\frac{1}{2}$.

- Emphasize that the coefficients in a balanced equation represent the mole *ratios*. An individual coefficient is meaningless (just as an amount of a single ingredient in a recipe is meaningless without the other amounts).

TECHNOLOGY

Video
Oxygen, Hydrogen, Soap Bubbles, and Balloons

EXAMPLE 9.1

More Examples

Give the balanced equation for each of the following, and state the meaning of the equation in terms of numbers of molecules and moles of molecules.

1. $NO(g) + H_2(g) \rightarrow N_2(g) + H_2O(l)$

   $2NO(g) + 2H_2(g) \rightarrow N_2(g) + 2H_2O(l);$
   2 molecules (or 2 moles) of NO react with 2 molecules (or 2 moles) of hydrogen gas to give 1 molecule (or 1 mole) of nitrogen gas and 2 molecules (or 2 moles) of water.

2. $SiH_4(g) + NH_3(g) \rightarrow Si_3N_4(s) + H_2(g)$

   $3SiH_4(g) + 4NH_3(g) \rightarrow Si_3N_4(s) + 12H_2(g);$
   3 molecules (or 3 moles) of SiH_4 react with 4 molecules (or 4 moles) of ammonia to give 1 molecule (or 1 mole) of Si_3N_4 and 12 molecules (or 12 moles) of hydrogen gas.

EXAMPLE 9.1

Relating Moles to Molecules in Chemical Equations

Propane is often used as a fuel for outdoor grills.

Propane, C_3H_8, is a fuel commonly used for cooking on gas grills and for heating in rural areas where natural gas is unavailable. Propane reacts with oxygen gas to produce heat and the products carbon dioxide and water. This combustion reaction is represented by the unbalanced equation

$$C_3H_8(g) + O_2(g) \rightarrow CO_2(g) + H_2O(g)$$

Give the balanced equation for this reaction, and state the meaning of the equation in terms of numbers of molecules and moles of molecules.

Solution

Using the techniques explained in Chapter 7, we can balance the equation.

$$C_3H_8(g) + 5O_2(g) \rightarrow 3CO_2(g) + 4H_2O(g)$$

Check: 3 C, 8 H, 10 O → 3 C, 8 H, 10 O

This equation can be interpreted in terms of molecules as follows:

1 molecule of C_3H_8 + 5 molecules of $O_2 \rightarrow$ 3 molecules of CO_2 + 4 molecules of H_2O

Alternatively, it can be stated in terms of moles (of molecules):

1 mol C_3H_8 + 5 mol $O_2 \rightarrow$ 3 mol of CO_2 + 4 mol H_2O

HANDS-ON CHEMISTRY • MINI-LAB •

The Nuts and Bolts of Stoichiometry

Materials
- a cup of nuts and bolts

Procedure
1. Obtain a cup of nuts and bolts from your teacher.
2. The nuts and bolts are the reactants. The product consists of 2 nuts on each bolt. Make as many products as possible.

Results/Analysis
1. Using N to symbolize a nut and B to symbolize a bolt, write an equation for the formation of the product. Pay attention to the difference between a subscript and a coefficient.
2. How many nuts did you have? How many bolts?
3. How many products could you make?
4. Which reactant (nut or bolt) was limiting? How did you make this determination?
5. The limiting reactant was the one that had (fewer/more) pieces.

6. An average mass of a bolt is 10.64 g and an average mass of a nut is 4.35 g. Suppose you are given "about 1500 g" of bolts and "about 1500 g" of nuts. Answer the following questions:
   a. How many bolts are in "about 1500 g"? How many nuts are in "about 1500 g"?
   b. Which reactant is limiting? Why is there a limiting reactant, given that you have equal masses of each?
   c. The limiting reactant was the one that had (fewer/more) pieces. Compare this answer to your answer in question 5. What does it tell you?
   d. What is the largest possible mass of product? How many products could you make?
   e. What is the mass of the leftover reactant?

Hands-On Chemistry
MINI-LAB

The Nuts and Bolts of Stoichiometry

Materials Each student/group will need a cup of nuts and bolts. The actual numbers do not matter, although it is a good idea to have more nuts than bolts, but fewer than twice as many.

Purpose Students will see a concrete example of the types of calculations involved in stoichiometry problems.

Discussion The equation for this "reaction" is $B + 2N \rightarrow BN_2$. Two nuts appear on each side, but the reactants are separate and the nuts are "bonded" together in the product. This activity should help students better understand the difference between a subscript and a coefficient.

The answers to 2 and 3 will vary depending on how many nuts and bolts you give to students. Give students quantities such that the answer to 4 is

the nut, and the answer to 5 is "more." This choice forces students to confront the common misconception that the limiting reactant is always the lesser quantity.

For 6, there are about 140 bolts (taking significant figures into account) and about 340 nuts. Using these numbers, the bolts are limiting. Having the same mass does not matter because the nuts and bolts "react" in terms of how many are present, not by mass (explicitly make

B. Mole–mole Relationships

Now that we have discussed the meaning of a balanced chemical equation in terms of moles of reactants and products, we can use an equation to predict the moles of products that a given number of moles of reactants will yield. For example, consider the decomposition of water to give hydrogen and oxygen, which is represented by the following balanced equation:

$$2H_2O(l) \rightarrow 2H_2(g) + O_2(g)$$

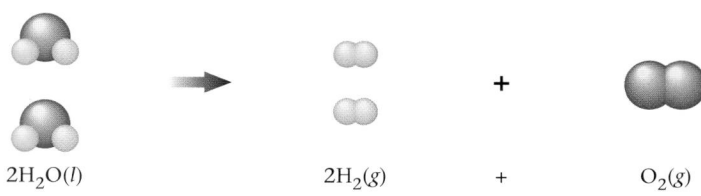

$2H_2O(l)$ $2H_2(g)$ $+$ $O_2(g)$

This equation tells us that 2 mol of H_2O yields 2 mol of H_2 and 1 mol of O_2.

Now suppose that we have 4 mol of water. If we decompose 4 mol of water, how many moles of products do we get?

One way to answer this question is to multiply the entire equation by 2; that will give us 4 mol of H_2O.

$$2[2H_2O(l) \rightarrow 2H_2(g) + O_2(g)]$$
$$4H_2O(l) \rightarrow 4H_2(g) + 2O_2(g)$$

$4H_2O(l)$ $4H_2(g)$ $+$ $2O_2(g)$

Now we can state that

4 mol of H_2O yields 4 mol of H_2 plus 2 mol of O_2

which answers the question of how many moles of products we get with 4 mol of H_2O.

Objective To learn to use a balanced equation to determine relationships between moles of reactants and moles of products

 TEACHING TIP

Students sometimes have difficulty understanding what a mole ratio represents. Spend some time explaining that a mole ratio relates the moles of one substance in the chemical equation to the moles of another substance through an equivalence statement. The confusion arises when students assume that equivalence means equality. The moles on either side of an equivalence statement are not equal; they are equivalent amounts.

For example, in Example 9.2 the equivalence statement between H_2O and O_2 is

2 mol H_2O = 1 mol O_2

Thus, if you begin with 2 mol water, you will produce 1 mol oxygen. The moles are not equal to each other but they are equivalent for this equation.

(continued)

the analogy to chemical reactions when discussing this point). In this case, the limiting reactant is the lesser quantity. This fact, along with the activity, shows us that we always have to think about which reactant is limiting. Depending on the circumstances, it may be the larger quantity or the smaller quantity.

Important points to make:

• We must know the ratio of the parts needed. In this case, it was 1 bolt:2 nuts. In chemistry we get this information from the balanced equation. For example, in the equation $2H_2 + O_2 \rightarrow 2H_2O$, we know that the ratio is 2:1:2.

• What we have is not the same as what we need. The ratio of bolts:nuts was 1:2. This is the ratio of what we need. It has no relation to what we are actually given.

• The calculations should make sense. For example, we did not calculate the number of products we could make from each component and then simply add those numbers together.

• It is not always true that the component present in the smallest numbers is used up first. It depends on how many of each component is needed. For example, with 7 bolts and 12 nuts we run out of nuts first, even though we have more nuts than bolts.

The mole ratio is a conversion factor using the coefficients from a balanced chemical equation. For example, in the equation $2Na(s) + Cl_2(g) \rightarrow 2NaCl(s)$, the mole ratio between sodium (Na) and chlorine (Cl_2) is 2:1.

Next, suppose that we decompose 5.8 mol of water. What numbers of moles of products are formed in this process?

$$2H_2O(l) \rightarrow 2H_2(g) + O_2(g)$$

We could answer this question by rebalancing the chemical equation as follows:

- First, we divide *all coefficients* of the balanced equation by 2 to give

$$H_2O(l) \rightarrow H_2(g) + \frac{1}{2}O_2(g)$$

- Now, because we have 5.8 mol of H_2O, we multiply this equation by 5.8.

$$5.8[H_2O(l) \rightarrow H_2(g) + \frac{1}{2}O_2(g)]$$

information

This equation with noninteger coefficients makes sense only if the equation means moles (of molecules) of the various reactants and products.

$$5.8H_2O(l) \rightarrow 5.8H_2(g) + 5.8(\tfrac{1}{2})O_2(g)$$

$$5.8H_2O(l) \rightarrow 5.8H_2(g) + 2.9O_2(g)$$

- Verify that this is a balanced equation.

Now we can state that

5.8 mol of H_2O yields 5.8 mol of H_2 plus 2.9 mol of O_2.

This procedure of rebalancing the equation to obtain the number of moles involved in a particular situation always works, but it can be cumbersome. In Example 9.2 we will develop a more convenient procedure, which uses conversion factors, or **mole ratios**, based on the balanced chemical equation.

Mole ratio
The ratio of moles of one substance to moles of another substance in a balanced chemical equation

Active Reading Question

What is meant by the term "mole ratio"? Give an example from an actual chemical equation.

Meeting Individual Needs
INCLUSION STRATEGIES

If students are having trouble understanding the relationship in a mole ratio, have them consider this example:
For every 3 school buses that arrive at the school, 2 will transport marching band members and 1 will transport chorus members.
3 buses → 2 marching band + 1 chorus
So, if 12 buses show up at the school, how many will transport chorus members? Lead students to see that the ratio to use is 3 buses:1 bus of chorus members.
12 buses → 8 marching band + 4 chorus

EXAMPLE 9.2

Determining Mole Ratios

What number of moles of O_2 will be produced by the decomposition of 5.8 mol of water?

Solution

Where do we want to go?

| 5.8 mol H_2O | yields ⟩ | ? mol of O_2 |

What do we know?

- $2H_2O(l) \rightarrow 2\,H_2(g) + O_2(g)$
- 5.8 mol H_2O

How do we get there?

To answer this question, we need to know the relationship between moles of H_2O and moles of O_2 in the balanced equation (conventional form):

$$2H_2O(l) \rightarrow 2H_2(g) + O_2(g)$$

From this equation we can state that

| 2 mol H_2O | yields ⟩ | 1 mol O_2 |

which can be represented by the following equivalence statement:

$$2 \text{ mol } H_2O = 1 \text{ mol } O_2$$

We now want to use this equivalence statement to obtain the conversion factor (mole ratio) that we need. Because we want to go from moles of H_2O to moles of O_2, we need the mole ratio

$$\frac{1 \text{ mol } O_2}{2 \text{ mol } H_2O}$$

so that mol H_2O will cancel in the conversion from moles of H_2O to moles of O_2.

$$5.8 \text{ mol } H_2O \times \frac{1 \text{ mol } O_2}{2 \text{ mol } H_2O} = 2.9 \text{ mol } O_2$$

So if we decompose 5.8 mol of H_2O, we will get 2.9 mol of O_2.

Does it make sense?

Note that this is the same answer we obtained earlier when we rebalanced the equation to give 5.8 $H_2O(l) \rightarrow$ 5.8 $H_2(g) + 2.9\,O_2(g)$.

ⓘ nformation

The statement
$2 \text{ mol } H_2O = 1 \text{ mol } O_2$
is obviously not true in a literal sense, but it correctly expresses the chemical equivalence between H_2O and O_2.

We saw in Example 9.2 that to determine the moles of a product that can be formed from a specified number of moles of a reactant, we can use the balanced equation to obtain the appropriate mole ratio. We will now extend these ideas in Example 9.3.

9.1 • Using Chemical Equations • 285

EXAMPLE 9.2

More Examples

Methane burns in oxygen to form carbon dioxide and water according to the balanced equation

$$CH_4(g) + 2O_2(g) \rightarrow CO_2(g) + 2H_2O(g)$$

1. What number of moles of oxygen gas is required to react with 7.4 mol of methane?

   14.8 mol $O_2(g)$

2. How many moles of carbon dioxide gas will be produced by reacting 2.6 mol of oxygen with excess methane?

   1.3 mol $CO_2(g)$

Meeting Individual Needs

ENGLISH LANGUAGE LEARNERS

Relate the word *decomposition* to the terms *breakdown* and *separate*. Try rereading the example using these terms so students can visualize what is happening with the water molecule.

EXAMPLE 9.3

More Examples

Hydrogen sulfide gas reacts with oxygen to produce sulfur dioxide gas and water according to the balanced equation

$$2H_2S(g) + 3O_2(g) \rightarrow 2SO_2(g) + 2H_2O(g)$$

1. How many moles of oxygen gas are required to react with 5.6 mol of hydrogen sulfide?

   8.4 mol $O_2(g)$

2. How many moles of sulfur dioxide gas will be produced by reacting 7.3 mol of hydrogen sulfide with excess oxygen?

   7.3 mol $SO_2(g)$

3. How many moles of sulfur dioxide gas will be produced by reacting 7.3 mol of oxygen with excess hydrogen sulfide?

   4.9 mol $SO_2(g)$

 Answer to Practice Problem 9.3

The problem can be stated as follows:

4.30 mol $C_3H_8 \rightarrow$? mol CO_2

From the balanced equation

$$C_3H_8(g) + 5O_2(g) \rightarrow 3CO_2(g) + 4H_2O(g)$$

we derive the equivalence statement

1 mol C_3H_8 = 3 mol CO_2

The appropriate conversion factor (moles of C_3H_8 must cancel) is 3 mol CO_2/1 mol C_3H_8, and the calculation is

$$4.3 \; \text{mol } C_3H_3 \times \frac{3 \text{ mol } CO_2}{1 \text{ mol } C_3H_8} = 12.9 \text{ mol } CO_2$$

Thus we can say

4.30 mol C_3H_8 yields 12.9 mol CO_2

EXAMPLE 9.3

 Using Mole Ratios in Calculations

Calculate the number of moles of oxygen required to react exactly with 4.30 mol of propane, C_3H_8, in the reaction described by the following balanced equation:

$$C_3H_8(g) + 5O_2(g) \rightarrow 3CO_2(g) + 4H_2O(g)$$

Solution
Where do we want to go?

4.30 mol of C_3H_8	requires	? mol of O_2

What do we know?

- $C_3H_8(g) + 5O_2(g) \rightarrow 3CO_2(g) + 4H_2O(g)$
- 4.30 mole C_3H_8

How do we get there?

To solve this problem, we need to consider the relationship between the reactants C_3H_8 and O_2. Using the balanced equation, we find that

1 mol of C_3H_8 requires 5 mol of O_2

which can be represented by the equivalence statement

1 mol C_3H_8 = 5 mol O_2

This leads to the required mole ratio

$$\frac{5 \text{ mol } O_2}{1 \text{ mol } C_3H_8}$$

for converting from moles of C_3H_8 to moles of O_2. We construct the conversion ratio this way so that mol C_3H_8 cancels:

$$4.30 \; \text{mol } C_3H_8 \times \frac{5 \text{ mol } O_2}{1 \text{ mol } C_3H_8} = 21.5 \text{ mol } O_2$$

We can now answer the original question:

4.30 mol of C_3H_8 requires 21.5 mol of O_2.

Practice Problem • Exercise 9.3

Calculate the moles of CO_2 formed when 4.30 mol of C_3H_8 reacts with the required 21.5 mol of O_2.

Hint: Use the moles of C_3H_8, and obtain the mole ratio between C_3H_8 and CO_2 from the balanced equation.

EXAMPLE 9.4

Using Mole Ratios

Ammonia (NH_3) is used in huge quantities as a fertilizer. It is manufactured by combining nitrogen and hydrogen according to the following equation:

$$N_2(g) + 3H_2(g) \rightarrow 2NH_3(g)$$

Calculate the number of moles of NH_3 that can be made from 1.30 mol $H_2(g)$ reacting with excess $N_2(g)$.

Solution

Where do we want to go?

| 1.30 mol H_2 | yields | ? mol NH_3 |

What do we know?

- $N_2(g) + 3H_2(g) \rightarrow 2NH_3(g)$ • 1.30 mol H_2

How do we get there?

The problem states that we have excess $N_2(g)$, which means that we have more than is needed to react with all of the H_2 (1.30 mol).

From the balanced equation we see that

3 mol H_2 yields 2 mol NH_3

which can be represented by the equivalence statement

3 mol H_2 = 2 mol NH_3

This leads to the required mole ratio $\dfrac{2 \text{ mol } NH_3}{3 \text{ mol } H_2}$ for converting moles of H_2 to moles of NH_3:

$$1.30 \text{ mol } H_2 \times \frac{2 \text{ mol } NH_3}{3 \text{ mol } H_2} = 0.867 \text{ mol } NH_3$$

Does it make sense?

Notice that the number of moles of NH_3 that can be produced is less than 1.30. This answer makes sense because it takes 3 moles of H_2 to yield 2 moles of NH_3. Thus the number of moles of NH_3 produced (0.867) should be smaller than the number of moles of H_2 consumed (1.30).

SECTION 9.1
REVIEW QUESTIONS

❶ What part of a chemical equation allows us to determine how much product we can get from a known amount of reactants?

❷ Why is it important to balance a chemical equation before proceeding to answer questions about it?

❸ Give at least three different ways to interpret the coefficient in a chemical equation.

❹ What number of moles of $O_2(g)$ is required to react with 3.6 mol $SO_2(g)$ in the following reaction?

$$2SO_2(g) + O_2(g) \rightarrow 2SO_3(g)$$

❺ Butane (C_4H_{10}) reacts with oxygen in the air to form carbon dioxide and water. How many moles of carbon dioxide can be formed from 1.25 mol butane and excess oxygen?

RESEARCH LINKS
CLASSZONE.COM

EXAMPLE 9.4

More Examples

Iron(II) oxide reacts with oxygen to form iron(III) oxide according to the balanced equation

$$4FeO(s) + O_2(g) \rightarrow 2Fe_2O_3(s)$$

1. What number of moles of oxygen gas is required to react with 2.4 mol of iron(II) oxide?

   0.60 mol $O_2(g)$

2. What number of moles of iron(III) oxide solid will be produced by reacting 9.2 mol of iron(II) oxide with excess oxygen?

   4.6 mol $Fe_2O_3(s)$

3. What number of moles of iron(III) oxide will be produced by reacting 9.2 mol of oxygen with excess iron(II) oxide?

   18.4 mol $Fe_2O_3(s)$

SECTION 9.1
ASSESS

SECTION 9.1
Review Questions

1. The mole ratio is the key to determining the amount of product produced from a given amount of reactant.

2. Balancing a chemical equation is necessary so that the mole quantities for the various substances are known. This information allows the mole ratios for different relationships in the chemical equation to be determined.

3. The coefficient in a chemical equation can represent the number of molecules, moles or dozens of molecules, atoms, or ions.

4. 1.8 mol $O_2(g)$

5. 5.00 mol $CO_2(g)$

Student Preparation

Assign students to read Section 9.2 and to answer the Review Questions at the end of the section before coming to class.

 Active Learning
Team Learning Worksheet

After introducing the material in Section 9.2 in class, place students in groups and have them work together on **Section 9.2: Team Learning Worksheet.**

Homework

You may wish to assign these selected end-of-chapter problems as homework for this section: 11, 13a–d, 14a–d, 15a–b, 16a–b, 17, 18, 21, 24, 25, 28

Additional end-of-chapter problems can be used for extra practice.

9.2.A Mass Calculations
Objective To learn to relate masses of reactants and products in a chemical reaction

 LABORATORY
EXPERIMENT 34:
Copper Wire in a Silver Nitrate Solution, Traditional

CRITICAL THINKING ?

Balancing in this way is not possible. Chemicals react by number. For example, each molecule of diatomic nitrogen requires three molecules of diatomic hydrogen to produce two molecules of ammonia. We do not use the masses as the coefficients (28 amu of nitrogen and 6 amu of hydrogen as reactants and products). We cannot balance equations using masses because this method does not conserve the atoms.

Using Chemical Equations to Calculate Mass

Key Term
• Stoichiometry

Objectives
• *To learn to relate masses of reactant and products in a chemical reaction*
• *To perform mass calculations that involve scientific notation*

A. Mass Calculations

Previously, we saw how to use the balanced equation for a reaction to calculate the numbers of moles of reactants and products for a particular case. However, moles represent numbers of molecules, and we cannot count molecules directly. In chemistry we count by weighing. Therefore, we need to review the procedures for converting between moles and masses and see how these procedures are applied to chemical calculations.

Let's consider the combustion of propane, C_3H_8. Propane, when used as a fuel, reacts with oxygen to produce carbon dioxide and water according to the following unbalanced equation:

$$C_3H_8(g) + O_2(g) \rightarrow CO_2(g) + H_2O(g)$$

What mass of oxygen will be required to react exactly with 44.1 g of propane?

Where do we want to go?

What do we know?
• $C_3H_8(g) + O_2(g) \rightarrow CO_2(g) + H_2O(g)$
• 44.1 g propane

How do we get there?
• Balance the equation:

$$C_3H_8(g) + 5O_2(g) \rightarrow 3CO_2(g) + 4H_2O(g)$$

 CRITICAL THINKING ?

Your lab partner has made the observation that we always measure the mass of chemicals but then use mole ratios to balance equations.

What if your lab partner decided to balance equations by using masses as coefficients? Is this possible? Why or why not?

• Our overall plan of attack is as follows:
1. We are given the number of grams of propane, so we must convert to moles of propane (C_3H_8) because the balanced equation deals in moles rather than grams.
2. Next, we can use the coefficients in the balanced equation to determine the moles of oxygen (O_2) required.
3. Finally, we will use the molar mass of O_2 to calculate grams of oxygen.

We can sketch this strategy as follows:

$$C_3H_8(g) \quad + \quad 5O_2(g) \quad \rightarrow \quad 3CO_2(g) + 4H_2O(g)$$

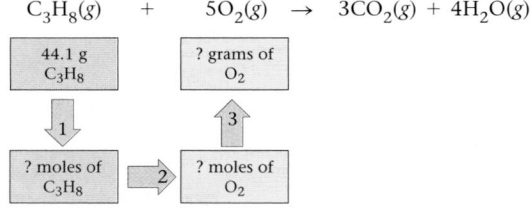

ℹ️ information

Always balance the equation for the reaction first.

288 • Chapter 9 • Chemical Quantities

The first question we must answer is, *How many moles of propane are present in 44.1 g of propane?*

The molar mass of propane is 44.09 g ($3 \times 12.01 + 8 \times 1.008$). The moles of propane present can be calculated as follows:

$$44.1 \text{ g C}_3\text{H}_8 \times \frac{1 \text{ mol C}_3\text{H}_8}{44.09 \text{ g C}_3\text{H}_8} = 1.00 \text{ mol C}_3\text{H}_8$$

Next, we recognize that each mole of propane reacts with 5 mol of oxygen. This gives us the equivalence statement

$$1 \text{ mol C}_3\text{H}_8 = 5 \text{ mol O}_2$$

from which we construct the mole ratio

$$\frac{5 \text{ mol O}_2}{1 \text{ mol C}_3\text{H}_8}$$

that we need to convert from moles of propane molecules to moles of oxygen molecules.

$$1.00 \text{ mol C}_3\text{H}_8 \times \frac{5 \text{ mol O}_2}{1 \text{ mol C}_3\text{H}_8} = 5.00 \text{ mol O}_2$$

Notice that the mole ratio is set up so that the moles of C_3H_8 cancel and the resulting units are moles of O_2.

Because the original question asked for the *mass* of oxygen needed to react with 44.1 g of propane, we must convert the 5.00 mol of O_2 to grams, using the molar mass of O_2 ($32.00 = 2 \times 16.00$).

$$5.00 \text{ mol O}_2 \times \frac{32.0 \text{ g O}_2}{1 \text{ mol O}_2} = 160. \text{ g O}_2$$

Therefore, 160 g of oxygen is required to burn 44.1 g of propane. The procedure we have followed is summarized at the right. This is a convenient way to make sure the final units are correct.

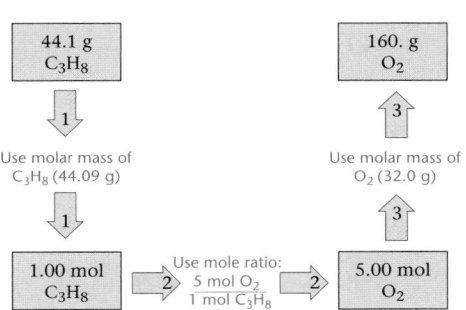

- Now is an excellent time to ensure that students use units when solving problems. Without units, solving stoichiometry problems is very difficult. Many students are unaccustomed to using units in mathematics and so do not see any reason to use them in chemistry. This chapter illustrates the importance of using units when solving problems.

- Remind students that conversion factors such as 44.01 g C_3H_8 = 1 mol C_3H_8 and 32.00 g O_2 = 1 mol O_2 come from the circulation of molar masses. We use the coefficients in the balanced equation when relating two different substances.

- Use diagrams and flowcharts to help students think through these problems. Try to be consistent in your approach. Begin with the balanced equation each time and write down what is known and what is being sought.

We can summarize this problem by writing out a "conversion string" that shows how the problem was done.

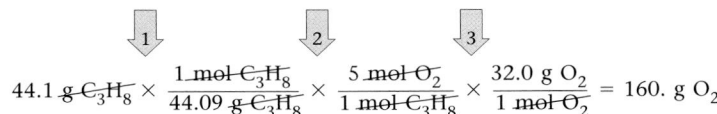

MATH ➗

Use units as a check to see that you have used the correct conversion factors (mole ratios).

$$44.1 \text{ g C}_3\text{H}_8 \times \frac{1 \text{ mol C}_3\text{H}_8}{44.09 \text{ g C}_3\text{H}_8} \times \frac{5 \text{ mol O}_2}{1 \text{ mol C}_3\text{H}_8} \times \frac{32.0 \text{ g O}_2}{1 \text{ mol O}_2} = 160. \text{ g O}_2$$

9.2 • Using Chemical Equations to Calculate Mass • **289**

| **Meeting Individual Needs** |
| MATH CONCEPTS |

For students who need additional help with mass calculations, have them read *Dimensional Analysis* located in the *Teacher Resources*. A worksheet is available to go along with the handout.

EXAMPLE 9.5

More Examples

Solutions of sodium hydroxide absorb carbon dioxide from the air, forming sodium carbonate according to the balanced equation

$$2NaOH(aq) + CO_2(g) \rightarrow Na_2CO_3(aq) + H_2O(l)$$

1. Calculate the mass of carbon dioxide gas that is required to react with a solution containing 10.0 g of sodium hydroxide.

   5.50 g $CO_2(g)$

2. Calculate the mass of sodium carbonate that is produced when 10.0 g of sodium hydroxide reacts with an excess of carbon dioxide.

   13.2 g $Na_2CO_3(aq)$

EXAMPLE 9.5

Mass Relationships in Chemical Reactions

Aluminum (left) and iodine (right) shown at the top, react vigorously to form aluminum iodide. The purple cloud results from excess iodine vaporized by the heat of the reaction.

Consider the reaction of powdered aluminum metal and finely ground iodine to produce aluminum iodide. The balanced equation for this vigorous chemical reaction is

$$2Al(s) + 3I_2(s) \rightarrow 2AlI_3(s)$$

Calculate the mass of $I_2(s)$ needed to just react with 35.0 g Al(s).

Solution

Where do we want to go?

   35.0 g Al(s)   requires   ? g $I_2(s)$

What do we know?

- $2Al(s) + 3I_2(s) \rightarrow 2AlI_3(s)$
- 35.0 g Al(s)

How do we get there?

Our plan

1. Convert 35.0 g Al to mol Al because the balanced equation deals in moles rather than grams.

2. Use the balanced equation to find the mol I_2 required to react with all of the Al.

3. Use the molar mass for iodine to calculate the mass of $I_2(s)$ required.

A schematic for this strategy is

$$2Al(s) \quad + \quad 3I_2(s) \quad \rightarrow \quad 2AlI_3(s)$$

| 35.0 g Al | → [1] → | ? moles of Al | → [2] → | ? moles of I_2 | → [3] → | ? grams I_2 |

[1] Using the molar mass of aluminum (26.98 g), we will first calculate the moles of aluminum present in 35.0 g Al:

$$35.0 \; \text{g Al} \times \frac{1 \; \text{mol Al}}{26.8 \; \text{g Al}} = 1.30 \; \text{mol Al}$$

[2] From the balanced equation for the reaction, we see that

   2 Al requires 3 I_2

Thus, the required conversion factor from Al to I_2 is:

$$\frac{3 \; \text{mol } I_2}{2 \; \text{mol Al}}$$

Now we can determine the moles of I_2 required by 1.30 moles of Al:

$$1.30 \; \text{mol Al} \times \frac{3 \; \text{mol } I_2}{2 \; \text{mol Al}} = 1.95 \; \text{mol } I_2$$

290 • Chapter 9 • Chemical Quantities

We know the moles of I_2 required to react with the 1.30 mol of Al (35.0 g). Convert 1.95 mol of I_2 to grams so we will know how much to weigh out. We do so by using the molar mass of I_2. The atomic mass of iodine is 126.9 g (for 1 mol of I atoms), so the molar mass of I_2 is

$$2 \times 126.9 \text{ g/mol} = 253.8 \text{ g/mol}$$

Now we convert the 1.95 mol of I_2 to grams of I_2.

$$1.95 \cancel{\text{mol } I_2} \times \frac{253.8 \text{ g } I_2}{\cancel{\text{mol } I_2}} = 495 \text{ g } I_2$$

We have solved the problem. We need to weigh out 495 g of iodine (contains I_2 molecules) to react exactly with the 35.0 g of aluminum.

This problem can be summarized as follows:

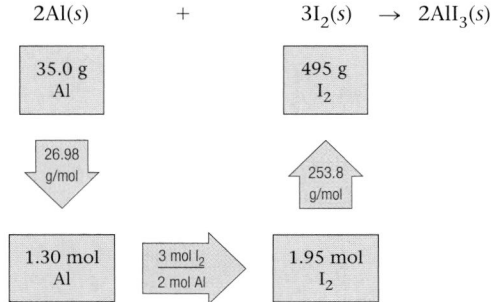

$$2Al(s) \quad + \quad 3I_2(s) \quad \rightarrow \quad 2AlI_3(s)$$

 Practice Problem • Exercise 9.5

Calculate the mass of $AlI_3(s)$ formed by the reaction of 35.0 g Al(s) with 495 g $I_2(s)$.

B. Mass Calculations Using Scientific Notation

So far in this chapter, we have spent considerable time "thinking through" the procedures for calculating the masses of reactants and products in chemical reactions.

Let's Review

Steps for Calculating the Masses of Reactants and Products in Chemical Reactions

Step 1 Balance the equation for the reaction.

Step 2 Convert the masses of reactants or products to moles.

Step 3 Use the balanced equation to set up the appropriate mole ratio(s).

Step 4 Use the mole ratio(s) to calculate the number of moles of the desired reactant or product.

Step 5 Convert from moles back to mass.

 Answer to Practice Problem 9.5

1.30 mol Al $\rightarrow$ 1.30 mol AlI_3

$$1.30 \cancel{\text{mol } AlI_3} \times \frac{407.7 \text{ g } AlI_3}{\cancel{\text{mol } AlI_3}} = 530. \text{ g } AlI_3$$

9.2.B Mass Calculations Using Scientific Notation

Objective To carry out mass calculations that involve scientific notation

 LABORATORY

EXPERIMENT 35:
Mass Relationships in Chemical Compounds, Traditional

Meeting Individual Needs

MATH CONCEPTS

For students who need additional help with scientific notation, have them read *Scientific Notation* located in the *Teacher Resources*. A worksheet is available to go along with the handout.

EXAMPLE 9.6

More Examples

Thionyl chloride, which is used as a drying agent in many synthetic chemistry experiments, reacts with water to form sulfur dioxide gas and hydrogen chloride gas:

$$SOCl_2(l) + H_2O(l) \rightarrow SO_2(g) + 2HCl(g)$$

1. Calculate the mass of water consumed by the complete reaction of 3.50×10^2 g of thionyl chloride.

   53.0 g $H_2O(l)$

2. Calculate the mass of hydrogen chloride produced by the complete reaction of 3.50×10^2 g of thionyl chloride.

   2.14×10^2 g $HCl(g)$

Stoichiometry
The process of using a balanced chemical equation to determine the relative masses of reactants and products involved in a reaction

The process of using a chemical equation to calculate the relative masses of reactants and products involved in a reaction is called **stoichiometry** (pronounced stoý·kē·om·ĕtry). Chemists say that the balanced equation for a chemical reaction describes the stoichiometry of the reaction.

EXAMPLE 9.6

Stoichiometric Calculations: Using Scientific Notation

Solid lithium hydroxide has been used in space vehicles to remove exhaled carbon dioxide from the living environment. The products are solid lithium carbonate and liquid water. What mass of gaseous carbon dioxide can 1.00×10^3 g of lithium hydroxide absorb?

Solution

Where do we want to go?

$$1.00 \times 10^3 \text{ g LiOH} \quad \text{absorbs} \quad ?\text{g CO}_2$$

***i*nformation**

For a review of writing formulas of ionic compounds, see Chapter 4.

What do we know?

- We can write an equation from the description in the problem:
$$LiOH(s) + CO_2(g) \rightarrow Li_2CO_3(s) + H_2O(l)$$
- 1.00×10^3 g LiOH

How do we get there?

Step 1 The balanced equation is
$$2LiOH(s) + CO_2(g) \rightarrow Li_2CO_3(s) + H_2O(l)$$

Step 2 We convert the given mass of LiOH to moles, using the molar mass of LiOH, which is 6.941 g + 16.00 g + 1.008 g = 23.95 g.

$$1.00 \times 10^3 \text{ g LiOH} \times \frac{1 \text{ mol LiOH}}{23.95 \text{ g LiOH}} = 41.8 \text{ mol LiOH}$$

Step 3 The appropriate mole ratio is
$$\frac{1 \text{ mol CO}_2}{2 \text{ mol LiOH}}$$

Step 4 Using this mole ratio, we calculate the moles of CO_2 needed to react with the given mass of LiOH.

$$41.8 \text{ mol LiOH} \times \frac{1 \text{ mol CO}_2}{2 \text{ mol LiOH}} = 20.9 \text{ mol CO}_2$$

Step 5 We calculate the mass of CO_2 by using its molar mass (44.01 g).

$$20.9 \text{ mol CO}_2 \times \frac{44.01 \text{ g CO}_2}{1 \text{ mol CO}_2} = 920. \text{ g CO}_2 = 9.20 \times 10^2 \text{ g CO}_2$$

Thus, 1.00×10^3 g of LiOH(s) can absorb 920. g of $CO_2(g)$.

We can summarize this problem as follows:

$$2LiOH(s) \quad + \quad CO_2(g) \quad \rightarrow \quad Li_2CO_3(s) + H_2O(l)$$

The conversion string is

$$1.00 \times 10^3 \text{ g LiOH} \times \frac{1 \text{ mol LiOH}}{23.95 \text{ g LiOH}} \times \frac{1 \text{ mol } CO_2}{2 \text{ mol LiOH}} \times \frac{44.01 \text{ g } CO_2}{1 \text{ mol } CO_2}$$

$$= 9.20 \times 10^2 \text{ g } CO_2$$

MATH

Carrying extra significant figures and rounding off only at the end gives an answer of 919 g CO_2.

✓ Practice Problem • Exercise 9.6

Hydrofluoric acid, an aqueous solution containing dissolved hydrogen fluoride, is used to etch glass by reacting with the silica, SiO_2, in the glass to produce gaseous silicon tetrafluoride and liquid water. The unbalanced equation is

$$HF(aq) + SiO_2(s) \rightarrow SiF_4(g) + H_2O(l)$$

a. Calculate the mass of hydrogen fluoride needed to react with 5.68 g of silica. *Hint:* Think carefully about this problem. What is the balanced equation for the reaction? What is given? What do you need to calculate? Sketch a map of the problem before you do the calculations.

b. Calculate the mass of water produced in the reaction described in part a.

C. Mass Calculations: Comparing Two Reactions

Let's consider the relative effectiveness of two antacids to illustrate how chemical calculations can be important in daily life. Baking soda, $NaHCO_3$, is often used as an antacid. It neutralizes excess hydrochloric acid secreted by the stomach. The balanced equation for the reaction is

$$NaHCO_3(s) + HCl(aq) \rightarrow NaCl(aq) + H_2O(l) + CO_2(g)$$

Milk of magnesia, which is an aqueous suspension of magnesium hydroxide, $Mg(OH)_2$, is also used as an antacid. The balanced equation for its reaction is

$$Mg(OH)_2(s) + 2HCl(aq) \rightarrow 2H_2O(l) + MgCl_2(aq)$$

Which antacid can consume the most stomach acid, 1.00 g of $NaHCO_3$ or 1.00 g of $Mg(OH)_2$?

Where do we want to go?

The question we must ask for each antacid is, *How many moles of HCl will react with 1.00 g of each antacid?*

Two antacid tablets containing HCO_3^- dissolve to produce CO_2 gas.

9.2.C Mass Calculations: Comparing Two Reactions

Objective To compare the stoichiometry of two reactions

🅐 **LABORATORY**
EXPERIMENT 36:
Calcium Content of Milk, Microscale

✓ Answer to Practice Problem 9.6

a. We first write the balanced equation.

$$SiO_2(s) + 4HF(aq) \rightarrow SiF_4(g) + 2H_2O(l)$$

The map of the steps required is

$$SiO_2(s) + 4HF(aq) \rightarrow SiF_4(g) + 2H_2O(l)$$

We convert 5.68 g of SiO_2 to moles as follows:

$$5.68 \text{ g } SiO_2 \times \frac{1 \text{ mol } SiO_2}{60.09 \text{ g } SiO_2} =$$
$$9.45 \times 10^{-2} \text{ mol } SiO_2$$

Using the balanced equation, we obtain the appropriate mole ratio and convert to mol HF.

$$9.45 \times 10^{-2} \text{ mol } SiO_2 \times$$
$$\frac{4 \text{ mol HF}}{1 \text{ mol } SiO_2} =$$
$$3.78 \times 10^{-1} \text{ mol HF}$$

Finally, we calculate the mass of HF by using its molar mass.

$$3.78 \times 10^{-1} \text{ mol HF} \times$$
$$\frac{20.01 \text{ g HF}}{\text{mol HF}} = 7.56 \text{ g HF}$$

b. The map for this problem is

$$SiO_2(s) + 4HF(aq) \rightarrow SiF_4(g) + 2H_2O(l)$$

We have already accomplished the first conversion in part a. Using the balanced equation, we obtain moles of H_2O as follows:

$$9.45 \times 10^{-2} \text{ mol } SiO_2 \times$$
$$\frac{2 \text{ mol } H_2O}{1 \text{ mol } SiO_2} =$$
$$1.89 \times 10^{-1} \text{ mol } H_2O$$

The mass of water formed is

$$1.89 \times 10^{-1} \text{ mol } H_2O \times$$
$$\frac{18.02 \text{ g } H_2O}{\text{mol } H_2O} =$$
$$3.41 \text{ g } H_2O$$

The reaction between baking soda and an acid is a quick, fun demonstration to illustrate a neutralization reaction. Use a 2-L soda bottle with a stopper to fit. Wrap a teaspoon of baking soda in a tissue in a tube shape with the ends twisted closed. Make the "tube" thin enough to fit through the opening in the soda bottle. Place 100 mL of vinegar in the soda bottle before the demonstration. When you are ready to do the demonstration, stuff the "tube" into the bottle and stopper it. Shake gently to mix and do not aim at any people. The stopper should shoot across the room. You might then discuss the reaction:

$NaHCO_3(s) + HC_2H_3O_2(aq) \rightarrow$
$NaC_2H_3O_2(aq) + H_2O(l) +$
$CO_2(g)$

You can also discuss what might happen to the carbon dioxide gas if this reaction were to occur in the stomach.

What do we know?
- $NaHCO_3(s) + HCl(aq) \rightarrow NaCl(aq) + H_2O(l) + CO_2(g)$
- $Mg(OH)_2(s) + 2\ HCl(aq) \rightarrow MgCl_2(aq) + 2\ H_2O(l)$
- $1.00\ g\ Mg(OH)_2$
- $1.00\ g\ NaHCO_3$

How do we get there?

The antacid that reacts with the larger number of moles of HCl is more effective because it will neutralize more moles of acid. A schematic for this procedure is

Notice that in this case, we do not need to calculate how many grams of HCl react; we can answer the question with moles of HCl. We will now solve this problem for each antacid.

Step 1 Both of the equations are balanced, so we can proceed with the calculations.

For $NaHCO_3$:

Step 2 Using the molar mass of $NaHCO_3$, which is

$$22.99\ g + 1.008\ g + 12.01\ g + 3(16.00\ g) = 84.01\ g,$$

we determine the moles of $NaHCO_3$ in 1.00 g of $NaHCO_3$.

$$1.00\ g\ \cancel{NaHCO_3} \times \frac{1\ mol\ NaCO_3}{84.01\ g\ \cancel{NaHCO_3}} = 0.0119\ mol\ NaHCO_3$$

$$= 1.19 \times 10^{-2}\ mol\ NaHCO_3$$

Step 3 Next, we determine the moles of HCl, using the mole ratio $\frac{1\ mol\ HCl}{1\ mol\ NaHCO_3}$.

$$1.19 \times 10^{-2}\ mol\ \cancel{NaHCO_3} \times \frac{1\ mol\ HCl}{1\ mol\ \cancel{NaHCO_3}}$$

$$= 1.19 \times 10^{-2}\ mol\ HCl$$

Step 4 Thus, 1.00 g of $NaHCO_3$ neutralizes 1.19×10^{-2} mol of HCl. We need to compare this to the number of moles of HCl that 1.00 g of $Mg(OH)_2$ neutralizes.

For $Mg(OH)_2$:

Step 2 Using the molar mass of $Mg(OH)_2$, which is 24.31 g + 2(16.00 g) + 2(1.008 g) = 58.33 g, we determine the moles of $Mg(OH)_2$ in 1.00 g of $Mg(OH)_2$.

$$1.00 \text{ g } \cancel{Mg(OH)_2} \times 1 \ \frac{\text{mol } Mg(OH)_2}{58.33 \text{ g } \cancel{Mg(OH)_2}} = 0.0171 \text{ mol } Mg(OH)_2$$
$$= 1.71 \times 10^{-2} \text{ mol } Mg(OH)_2$$

Step 3 To determine the moles of HCl that react with this amount of $Mg(OH)_2$, we use the mole ratio $\dfrac{2 \text{ mol HCl}}{1 \text{ mol } Mg(OH)_2}$.

$$1.71 \times 10^{-2} \text{ mol } \cancel{Mg(OH)_2} \times \frac{2 \text{ mol HCl}}{1 \text{ mol } \cancel{Mg(OH)_2}}$$
$$= 3.42 \times 10^{-2} \text{ mol HCl}$$

Step 4 1.00 g of $Mg(OH)_2$ neutralizes 3.42×10^{-2} mol of HCl. We have already calculated that 1.00 g of $NaHCO_3$ neutralizes only 1.19×10^{-2} mol of HCl. Therefore, $Mg(OH)_2$ is a more effective antacid than $NaHCO_3$ on a mass basis.

Active Reading Question

In the problem above, we added equal masses (1.0 g) of each antacid. Why would one antacid consume more stomach acid than the other?

SECTION 9.2
REVIEW QUESTIONS

❶ Why do we need to convert mass to moles in stoichiometry problems?

❷ Solutions of sodium hydroxide cannot be kept for very long because they absorb carbon dioxide from the air, forming sodium carbonate. The unbalanced equation is

$$NaOH(aq) + CO_2(g) \rightarrow Na_2CO_3(aq) + H_2O(l)$$

Calculate the number of grams of carbon dioxide that can be absorbed by complete reaction with a solution that contains 5.00 g of sodium hydroxide.

❸ Show how the steps in solving a stoichiometry problem are similar to a method that could be used in a supermarket to determine which of two products would be the best buy.

❹ You react 10.0 g of nitrogen gas with hydrogen gas according to the following reaction.

$$N_2(g) + 3H_2(g) \rightarrow 2NH_3(g)$$

a. What mass of hydrogen is required to completely react with 10.0 g sample of nitrogen gas?

b. What mass of ammonia is produced from 10.0 g of nitrogen gas and sufficient hydrogen gas?

❺ You react hydrogen gas with chlorine gas according to the following reaction.

$$H_2(g) + Cl_2(g) \rightarrow 2HCl(g)$$

What mass of $HCl(g)$ can be produced from 2.5×10^3 g of hydrogen gas with an excess of chlorine gas?

❻ Determine what mass of carbon monoxide and what mass of hydrogen are required to form 6.0 kg of methanol by the reaction

$$CO(g) + 2H_2(g) \rightarrow CH_3OH(l).$$

RESEARCH LINKS
CLASSZONE.COM

9.2 • Using Chemical Equations to Calculate Mass • **295**

9.2 • Using Chemical Equations to Calculate Mass • **295**

Active Reading Question

Since the antacids have different molar masses, 1.0 g of each represents a different number of moles of each.

SECTION 9.2
ASSESS

SECTION 9.2
Review Questions

1. A mole represents a huge number of molecules. Because we cannot count molecules directly, we count by weighing. The mass we determine must then be converted to moles so we can keep track of the number of molecules in the reaction.

2. 2.75 g CO_2 can be absorbed.

3. In a stoichiometry problem, the amount of a particular chemical needed to produce a certain amount of a second chemical is calculated by converting the mass of the first chemical to moles and using the mole ratio to find the moles of the second chemical and then its mass. In the supermarket, you might determine the best buy by taking the mass of each product and using the cost per package to find the cost per gram of the product. This calculation could be done for both products and then used to determine which package provides the most product per gram.

4. a. 2.16 g H_2
   b. 12.16 g NH_3

5. 9.0×10^4 g HCl

6. We need 5.3×10^3 g CO to react with 7.7×10^2 g H_2 to form 6.0×10^3 g (6.0 kg) of CH_3OH.

Student Preparation

Assign students to read Section 9.3 and to answer the Review Questions at the end of the section before coming to class.

Active Learning
Team Learning Worksheet

After introducing the material in Section 9.3 in class, place students in groups and have them work together on **Section 9.3: Team Learning Worksheet.**

SECTION 9.3
GUIDE THE LEARNING

Homework

You may wish to assign these selected end-of-chapter problems as homework for this section: 30, 31, 35, 37, 38, 40, 42, 44, 45

Additional end-of-chapter problems can be used for extra practice.

9.3.A The Concept of Limiting Reactants

Objective To understand the concept of limiting reactants

TEACHING TIP

Using a concrete analogy helps students better understand calculations, especially with problems involving a limiting reactant. Problems in which a reactant is limiting are conceptually very similar to cases in which no reactant is limiting. Nevertheless, students seem to have much more difficulty dealing with limiting reactants. Some students calculate the amount of product that could be made from each reactant and then add those amounts, or they may add the moles of each given reactant for the total. It is helpful to use analogies and be very explicit about these points.

Active Reading Question

More meat than bread or cheese is required per sandwich. For example, we need 3 times as much meat as cheese to make a sandwich, but we only have twice as much meat as bread.

Limiting Reactants and Percent Yield

Key Terms

- Limiting reactant (Limiting reagent)
- Theoretical yield
- Percent yield

Objectives

- *To understand the concept of limiting reactants*
- *To learn to recognize the limiting reactant in a reaction*
- *To learn to use the limiting reactant to do stoichiometric calculations*
- *To learn to calculate percent yield*

A. The Concept of Limiting Reactants

Earlier in this chapter, we discussed making sandwiches. Recall that the sandwich-making process could be described as follows:

2 pieces bread + 3 slices meat + 1 slice cheese → sandwich

In our earlier discussion, we always purchased the ingredients in the correct ratios so that we used all of the components, with nothing left over.

Now assume that you came to work one day and found the following quantities of ingredients:

20 slices of bread
24 slices of meat
12 slices of cheese

How many sandwiches can you make? What will be left over?

To solve this problem, let's see how many sandwiches we can make with each component.

Bread:

$$20 \text{ slices bread} \times \frac{1 \text{ sandwich}}{2 \text{ slices of bread}} = 10 \text{ sandwiches}$$

Meat:

$$24 \text{ slices meat} \times \frac{1 \text{ sandwich}}{3 \text{ slices of meat}} = 8 \text{ sandwiches}$$

Cheese:

$$12 \text{ slices cheese} \times \frac{1 \text{ sandwich}}{1 \text{ slice of cheese}} = 12 \text{ sandwiches}$$

How many sandwiches can you make? The answer is 8. When you run out of meat, you must stop making sandwiches. The meat is the limiting ingredient.

What do you have left over? Making 8 sandwiches requires 16 pieces of bread. You started with 20 pieces, so you have 4 pieces of bread left. You also used 8 pieces of cheese for the 8 sandwiches, so you have $12 - 8 = 4$ pieces of cheese left.

Active Reading Question

There are more slices of meat than of bread or cheese. So why does the meat limit the number of sandwiches you can make?

In this example, the ingredient present in the largest number (the meat) was actually the component that limited the number of sandwiches you could make. This situation arose because each sandwich required 3 slices of meat—more than the quantity required of any other ingredient.

Teaching Support	
DEMONSTRATION	

Limiting Reactants

Materials

- 5 test tubes (18 × 159 mm)
- Test tube rack
- Distilled water
- 10-mL graduated cylinders (2)

- 0.20 *M* NaI
- 0.10 *M* Pb(NO$_3$)$_2$

Preparation Add 10.0 mL of 0.10 *M* Pb(NO$_3$)$_2$ to each of the test tubes.

Presentation Add the following amounts of water to the respective test tubes: 8.0 mL, 6.0 mL, 4.0 mL, 2.0 mL, 0 mL. Add the following amounts of 0.20 *M* NaI to the respective test tubes: 2.0 mL, 4.0 mL, 6.0 mL, 8.0 mL, 10.0 mL. Note that the volume in each test tube is now the same. Let the test tubes stand for

---

TEACHING TIP
Use molecular diagrams like those shown in the text to make counting molecules more concrete (and similar to real-life experience).

A Closer Look

When molecules react with each other to form products, considerations very similar to those involved in making sandwiches arise. We can illustrate these ideas with the reaction of $N_2(g)$ and $H_2(g)$ to form $NH_3(g)$:

$$N_2(g) + 3H_2(g) \rightarrow 2NH_3(g)$$

Consider the following container of $N_2(g)$ and $H_2(g)$:

What will this container look like if the reaction between N_2 and H_2 proceeds to completion? To answer this question, you need to remember that each N_2 requires 3 H_2 molecules to form 2 NH_3. To make things clear, we will circle groups of reactants:

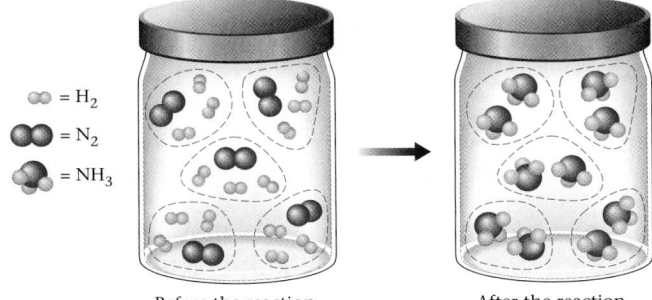

Before the reaction   After the reaction

In this case, the mixture of N_2 and H_2 contained just the number of molecules needed to form NH_3 with nothing left over. That is, the ratio of the number of H_2 molecules to N_2 molecules was

$$\frac{15 \ H_2}{5 \ N_2} = \frac{3 \ H_2}{1 \ N_2}$$

This ratio exactly matches the numbers in the balanced equation

$$3H_2(g) + N_2(g) \rightarrow 2NH_3(g).$$

This type of mixture is called a *stoichiometric mixture*—one that contains the relative amounts of reactants that matches the numbers in the balanced equation. In this case all reactants will be consumed to form products.

(continued)

several minutes and notice the amount of precipitate in each. There will be an increase in product in tubes 1 through 3, but this increase levels off for tubes 4 and 5.

Disposal Decant off the excess solution and dispose of it as required. Dry the precipitates and dispose of them as required.

Teaching Notes Have students predict what will happen before you add the NaI. It is important to explain to them that the water

is added to the test tubes to keep the volumes of the solutions constant. Ask students what is changing in the test tubes. Which reactant is the limiting reactant? How could students tell for sure? Since we have not yet discussed molarity, they cannot calculate the amounts of products unless you tell them the mass of each reactant in each test tube.

Now consider another container of $N_2(g)$ and $H_2(g)$:

∞ = H_2

$\bullet\!\bullet$ = N_2

What will the container look like if the reaction between $N_2(g)$ and $H_2(g)$ proceeds to completion? Remember that each N_2 requires 3 H_2. Circling groups of reactants we have

∞ = H_2

$\bullet\!\bullet$ = N_2

$\bullet$ = NH_3

Before the reaction   After the reaction

In this case, the hydrogen (H_2) is limiting. That is, the H_2 molecules are used up before all of the N_2 molecules are consumed. In this situation the amount of hydrogen limits the amount of product (ammonia) that can form—hydrogen is the limiting reactant. Some N_2 molecules are left over in this case because the reaction runs out of H_2 molecules first.

> To determine how much product can be formed from a given mixture of reactants, we have to look for the reactant that is limiting—the one that runs out first and thus limits the amount of product that can form.

In some cases, the mixture of reactants might be stoichiometric—that is, all reactants run out at the same time. In general, however, you cannot assume that a given mixture of reactants is a stoichiometric mixture, so you must determine whether one of the reactants is limiting.

> The reactant that runs out first and thus limits the amounts of products that can form is called the **limiting reactant (limiting reagent)**.

**Limiting reactant
(limiting reagent)**
The reactant that is
completely used up when
a reaction is run to
completion

To this point, we have considered examples where the numbers of reactant molecules could be counted. In "real life" you can't count the molecules directly—you can't see them and, even if you could, there would be far too many to count. Instead, you must count by weighing. We must therefore explore how to find the limiting reactant, given the masses of the reactants.

298 • Chapter 9 • Chemical Quantities

Meeting Individual Needs

CHALLENGE PROJECTS

For a research project dealing with extinguishing fires, see *Limiting Reactants in a Combustion Reaction* located in the *Teacher Resources*.

Active Reading Question

What is meant by the term "limiting reactant"?

B. Calculations Involving a Limiting Reactant

Manufacturers of cars, bicycles, and appliances order parts in the same proportion as they are used in their products. For example, auto manufacturers order four times as many wheels as engines and bicycle manufacturers order twice as many pedals as seats. Likewise, when chemicals are mixed together so that they can undergo a reaction, they are often mixed in stoichiometric quantities—that is, in exactly the correct amounts so that all reactants "run out" (are used up) at the same time.

Let's consider the production of hydrogen for use in the manufacture of ammonia. Ammonia, a very important fertilizer itself and a starting material for other fertilizers, is made by combining nitrogen from the air with hydrogen. The hydrogen for this process is produced by the reaction of methane with water according to the balanced equation

$$CH_4(g) + H_2O(g) \rightarrow 3H_2(g) + CO(g)$$

Let's consider the question, *What mass of water is required to react exactly with 249 g of methane?*

Where do we want to go?

How much water will just use up all of the 249 g of methane, leaving no water or methane remaining?

What do we know?

- $CH_4(g) + H_2O(g) \rightarrow 3\ H_2(g) + CO(g)$
- 249 g CH_4

How do we get there?

Drawing a map of the problem is helpful.

$$CH_4(g) \qquad + \qquad H_2O(g) \quad \rightarrow \quad 3H_2(g) + CO(g)$$

249 g CH_4		Grams of H_2O

⬇ Use molar mass of CH_4 ⬆ Use molar mass of H_2O

Moles of CH_4	⇨ Use mole ratio from balanced equation ⇨	Moles of H_2O

Ammonia being dissolved in irrigation water to provide fertilizer for a field of corn

Active Reading Question

The limiting reactant is the reactant that limits the amount of product formed. It is also the reactant that runs out first.

9.3.B Calculations Involving a Limiting Reactant

Objective To learn to recognize the limiting reactant in a reaction and to learn to use the limiting reactant to do stoichiometric calculations

 LABORATORY
EXPERIMENT 37:
Stoichiometry

 LABORATORY
EXPERIMENT 38:
Calorimetry and Limiting Reactants, CBL

TEACHING TIP

It may be useful to begin this section by introducing several examples that include simple equations and starting with moles rather than masses. A good example for beginning the discussion is

$$2Na + Cl_2 \rightarrow 2NaCl$$

Have students consider what occurs if we add 2 mol Na to 1 mol Cl_2 and the reaction goes to completion. The result is 0 mol Na, 0 mol Cl_2, and 2 mol NaCl. Next, ask what will be the result of mixing 0.5 mol Cl_2 and 2 mol Na. Students must now consider the limit that the 0.5 mol Cl_2 places on the system. They should find that the result would now be 1 mol NaCl, 0 mol Cl_2, and 1 mol Na. Once this idea is clear, move on to solving problems with more complex equations or problems beginning with mass.

TEACHING TIP

Another way of presenting a limiting reactant problem is presented below:

Sulfur and oxygen react to form sulfur trioxide:

$$2S + 3O_2 \rightarrow 2SO_3$$

Calculate the number of moles of SO_3 formed when 6.0 moles of each reactant is present initially and the reaction goes to completion.

Set up a table that includes all of the known information:

	$2S$	$+3O_2$	$\rightarrow 2SO_3$
Initial	6	6	0
Change	−?	−?	+?
End	?	?	?

Six moles of each reactant (and no product) are shown in the "Initial" row. The "Change" row shows the change in moles for each chemical. The "End" row shows the final reaction mixture. Because the reaction is complete, one (or possibly both) of the end values for sulfur or oxygen must be zero. But which one? We can decide by realizing a crucial point: *The ratio of the numbers in the "Change" row must be the same as the ratio of the coefficients in the balanced equation.* Consider the two possibilities:

	$2S$	$+3O_2$	$\rightarrow 2SO_3$
Initial	6	6	0
Change	−6	−9	+6
End	0	−3	6

	$2S$	$+3O_2$	$\rightarrow 2SO_3$
Initial	6	6	0
Change	−4	−6	+4
End	2	0	4

In the first table, we assume that all of the sulfur reacts. In the second table, we assume that all of the oxygen is consumed. We can see why sulfur is not limiting by looking at the first table—we need 3 more moles of oxygen than we actually have.

These tables give us all the needed information: which reactant is limiting, how much of the excess reactant is left over, and how much product is formed.

Step 1 The equation is already balanced.

Step 2 We first convert the mass of CH_4 to moles, using the molar mass of CH_4 (16.04 g/mol).

$$249 \text{ g CH}_4 \times \frac{1 \text{ mol CH}_4}{16.04 \text{ g CH}_4} = 15.5 \text{ mol CH}_4$$

Step 3 Because in the balanced equation 1 mol of CH_4 reacts with 1 mol of H_2O, we have

$$15.5 \text{ mol CH}_4 \times \frac{1 \text{ mol H}_2O}{1 \text{ mol CH}_4} = 15.5 \text{ mol H}_2O$$

Step 4 Therefore, 15.5 mol of H_2O will react exactly with the given mass of CH_4. Converting 15.5 mol of H_2O to grams of H_2O (molar mass = 18.02 g/mol) gives

$$15.5 \text{ mol H}_2O \times \frac{18.02 \text{ g H}_2O}{1 \text{ mol H}_2O} = 279 \text{ g H}_2O$$

This result means that if 249 g of methane is mixed with 279 g of water, both reactants will "run out" at the same time. The reactants have been mixed in stoichiometric quantities.

If, on the other hand, 249 g of methane is mixed with 300 g of water, the methane will be consumed before the water runs out. The water will be in *excess*. In this case, the quantity of products formed will be determined by the quantity of methane present. After the methane is consumed, no more products can be formed, even though some water still remains. In this situation, the amount of methane *limits* the amount of products that can be formed, and it is the limiting reactant.

In any stoichiometry problem, where reactants are not mixed in stoichiometric quantities, it is essential to determine which reactant is limiting to calculate correctly the amounts of products that will be formed. This concept is illustrated in **Figure 9.1.** Note from this figure that because there are fewer water molecules than CH_4 molecules, the water is consumed first. After the water molecules are gone, no more products can form. So in this case water is the limiting reactant.

> **information**
> The reactant that is consumed first limits the amounts of products that can form.

Figure 9.1
A mixture of $5CH_4$ and $3H_2O$ molecules undergoes the reaction $CH_4(g) + H_2O(g) \rightarrow 3H_2(g) + CO(g)$.
Note that the H_2O molecules are used up first, leaving two CH_4 molecules unreacted.

300 • Chapter 9 • Chemical Quantities

TECHNOLOGY

 Figure 9.1

EXAMPLE 9.7

Stoichiometric Calculations: Identifying the Limiting Reactant

Suppose that 25.0 kg (2.50×10^4 g) of nitrogen gas and
5.00 kg (5.00×10^3 g) of hydrogen gas are mixed and reacted
to form ammonia. Calculate the mass of ammonia produced when
this reaction is run to completion.

Solution

Where do we want to go?

How much ammonia will be produced when the reaction is complete?

What do we know?

- $N_2(g) + H_2(g) \rightarrow NH_3(g)$
- 2.5×10^4 g N_2
- 5.00×10^3 g H_2

How do we get there?

Step 1 The balanced equation for this reaction is

$$N_2(g) + 3H_2(g) \rightarrow 2NH_3(g)$$

This problem is different from the others we have done so far
in that we are mixing *specified amounts of two reactants*. To know
how much product forms, we must determine which reactant is
consumed first. That is, we must determine which is the limiting
reactant in this experiment. To do so, we must add a step to our
normal procedure. We can map this process as follows:

We will use the moles of the limiting reactant to calculate the
moles and then the grams of the product.

TEACHING TIPS

- Students have a great deal of trouble understanding that we cannot find the limiting reactant using mass. They should understand that comparisons in chemical reactions must be done using moles, not mass.

- Point out the clues that indicate a problem in which students should consider a limiting reactant. These clues include problems in which masses are given for two or more reactants and cases where one reactant is in excess (so the other becomes limiting).

EXAMPLE 9.7

More Examples

Aluminum reacts with chlorine gas to form aluminum chloride according to the balanced equation

$$2Al(s) + 3Cl_2(g) \rightarrow 2AlCl_3(s)$$

In a certain experiment, 10.0 g of aluminum is reacted with 35.0 g of chlorine gas.

1. What mass of aluminum chloride will be produced, assuming a complete reaction?

   43.9 g $AlCl_3(s)$

2. What mass of which reactant is left after the reaction?

   1.1 g $Al(s)$

Step 2 We first calculate the moles of the two reactants present:

$$2.50 \times 10^4 \ \cancel{g \ N_2} \times \frac{1 \ \text{mol} \ N_2}{28.02 \ \cancel{g \ N_2}} = 8.92 \times 10^2 \ \text{mol} \ N_2$$

$$5.00 \times 10^3 \ \cancel{g \ H_2} \times \frac{1 \ \text{mol} \ H_2}{2.016 \ \cancel{g \ H_2}} = 2.48 \times 10^3 \ \text{mol} \ H_2$$

Step 3 Now we must determine which reactant is limiting (will be consumed first). We have 8.92×10^2 mol of N_2. Let's determine *how many moles of H_2 are required to react with this much N_2*. Because 1 mol of N_2 reacts with 3 mol of H_2, the number of moles of H_2 we need to react completely with 8.92×10^2 mol of N_2 is determined as follows:

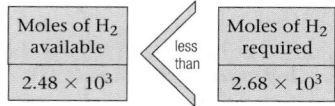

$$8.92 \times 10^2 \ \cancel{\text{mol} \ N_2} \times \frac{3 \ \text{mol} \ H_2}{1 \ \cancel{\text{mol} \ N_2}} = 2.68 \times 10^3 \ \text{mol} \ H_2$$

Is N_2 or H_2 the limiting reactant? The answer comes from the comparison

Moles of H_2 available		Moles of H_2 required
2.48×10^3	less than	2.68×10^3

We see that 8.92×10^2 mol of N_2 requires 2.68×10^3 mol of H_2 to react completely. However, only 2.48×10^3 mol of H_2 is present. This means that the hydrogen will be consumed before the nitrogen runs out, so hydrogen is the *limiting reactant* in this particular situation.

Note that in our effort to determine the limiting reactant, we could have started instead with the given amount of hydrogen and calculated the moles of nitrogen required.

$$2.48 \times 10^3 \ \cancel{\text{mol} \ H_2} \times \frac{1 \ \text{mol} \ N_2}{3 \ \cancel{\text{mol} \ H_2}} = 8.27 \times 10^2 \ \text{mol} \ N_2$$

Thus, 2.48×10^3 mol of H_2 requires 8.27×10^2 mol of N_2. Because 8.92×10^2 mol of N_2 is actually present, the nitrogen is in excess.

Moles of N_2 available		Moles of N_2 required
8.92×10^2	greater than	8.27×10^2

If nitrogen is in excess, hydrogen will "run out" first; again we find that hydrogen limits the amount of ammonia formed.

H_2 is limiting reactant.		N_2 is in excess.

Step 4 Because the moles of H_2 present are limiting, we must use this quantity to determine the moles of NH_3 that can form.

$$2.48 \times 10^3 \text{ mol } H_2 \times \frac{2 \text{ mol } NH_3}{3 \text{ mol } H_2} = 1.65 \times 10^3 \text{ mol } NH_3$$

Step 5 Next, we convert moles of NH_3 to mass of NH_3.

$$1.65 \times 10^3 \text{ mol } NH_3 \times \frac{17.03 \text{ g } NH_3}{1 \text{ mol } NH_3} = 2.81 \times 10^4 \text{ g } NH_3$$
$$= 28.1 \text{ kg } NH_3$$

Therefore, 25.0 kg of N_2 and 5.00 kg of H_2 can form 28.1 kg of NH_3.

The strategy used in Example 9.7 is summarized in **Figure 9.2.**

Figure 9.2
A map of the procedure used in Example 9.7

Let's Review

Steps for Solving Stoichiometry Problems Involving Limiting Reactants

Step 1 Write and balance the equation for the reaction.

Step 2 Convert known masses of reactants to moles.

Step 3 Using the numbers of moles of reactants and the appropriate mole ratios, determine which reactant is limiting.

Step 4 Using the amount of the limiting reactant and the appropriate mole ratios, compute the number of moles of the desired product.

Step 5 Convert from moles of product to grams of product, using the molar mass (if this is required by the problem).

Meeting Individual Needs
VISUAL LEARNERS

The following activity may help students better understand limiting reactants. Have students work in small groups. Pass out one piece of felt to each group, a small plastic bag of straight pins, and some pieces of yarn or ribbon. Give an excessive amount of straight pins to some of the groups and a limited amount of yarn. Give other groups an excess of yarn and limited amount of pins. With one pin and one piece of yarn each time, groups should pin the yarn to the felt. When finished, ask each group to display their finished felt designs. As a class, discuss why the felt pieces look different. Elicit what item limited each group's design and what item students had in excess.

EXAMPLE 9.8

More Examples

Iron(III) oxide reacts with carbon monoxide to form iron metal and carbon dioxide gas:

$$Fe_2O_3(s) + 3CO(g) \rightarrow 2Fe(s) + 3CO_2(g)$$

In a certain experiment, 5.0 g of iron(III) oxide is reacted with 5.0 g of carbon monoxide gas.

1. What mass of iron will be produced, assuming a complete reaction?

   3.5 g Fe(s)

2. What mass of carbon dioxide will be produced, assuming a complete reaction?

   4.1 g $CO_2(g)$

EXAMPLE 9.8

Stoichiometric Calculations: Reactions Involving the Masses of Two Reactants

Copper(II) oxide reacting with ammonia in a heated tube

Nitrogen gas can be prepared by passing gaseous ammonia over solid copper(II) oxide at high temperatures. The other products of the reaction are solid copper and water vapor. How many grams of N_2 are formed when 18.1 g of NH_3 is reacted with 90.4 g of CuO?

Solution

Where do we want to go?

How much nitrogen will be produced when the reaction is complete?

What do we know?

* $NH_3(g) + CuO(s) \rightarrow N_2(g) + Cu(s) + H_2O(g)$
*   18.1 g NH_3
*   90.4 g CuO

How do we get there?

Step 1 Balance the equation:

$$2NH_3(g) + 3CuO(s) \rightarrow N_2(g) + 3Cu(s) + 3H_2O(g)$$

Step 2 From the masses of reactants available, we must compute the moles of NH_3 (molar mass = 17.03 g) and of CuO (molar mass = 79.55 g).

$$18.1 \text{ g NH}_3 \times \frac{1 \text{ mol NH}_3}{17.03 \text{ g NH}_3} = 1.06 \text{ mol NH}_3$$

$$90.4 \text{ g CuO} \times \frac{1 \text{ mol CuO}}{79.55 \text{ g CuO}} = 1.14 \text{ mol CuO}$$

Step 3 To determine which reactant is limiting, we use the mole ratio between CuO and NH_3 to determine how CuO is required.

$$1.06 \text{ mol NH}_3 \times \frac{3 \text{ mol CuO}}{2 \text{ mol NH}_3} = 1.59 \text{ mol CuO}$$

Then we compare how much CuO we have with how much of it we need.

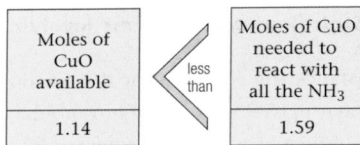

Therefore, 1.59 mol of CuO is required to react with 1.06 mol of NH_3, but only 1.14 mol of CuO is actually present. So the amount of CuO is limiting; CuO will run out before NH_3 does.

Note that CuO is limiting even though the original mass of CuO was much greater than the original mass of NH_3.

Step 4 CuO is the limiting reactant, so we must use the amount of CuO in calculating the amount of N_2 formed. Using the mole ratio between CuO and N_2 from the balanced equation, we have

$$1.14 \ \text{mol CuO} \times \frac{1 \ \text{mol N}_2}{3 \ \text{mol CuO}} = 0.380 \ \text{mol N}_2$$

Step 5 Using the molar mass of N_2 (28.02), we can now calculate the mass of N_2 produced.

$$0.380 \ \text{mol N}_2 \times \frac{28.02 \ \text{g N}_2}{1 \ \text{mol N}_2} = 10.6 \ \text{g N}_2$$

 Practice Problem • Exercise 9.8

Lithium nitride, an ionic compound containing the Li^+ and N^{3-} ions, is prepared by the reaction of lithium metal and nitrogen gas. Calculate the mass of lithium nitride formed from 56.0 g of nitrogen gas and 56.0 g of lithium in the unbalanced reaction:

$$Li(s) + N_2(g) \rightarrow Li_3N(s)$$

Active Reading Question

In the example, how can CuO be limiting if we started with a greater mass of CuO than NH_3?

C. Percent Yield

Previously, we calculated the amount of product formed when specified amounts of reactants were mixed together. In doing these calculations, we used the fact that the amount of product is controlled by the limiting reactant. Products stop forming when one reactant runs out.

The amount of product calculated in this way is called the **theoretical yield** of that product. It is the amount of product predicted from the amounts of reactants used. For instance, in Example 9.8, 10.6 g of nitrogen represents the theoretical yield. This is the *maximum amount* of nitrogen that can be produced from the quantities of reactants used. Actually, however, the amount of product predicted (the theoretical yield) is seldom obtained. One reason for this is the presence of side reactions (other reactions that consume one or more of the reactants or products).

The *actual yield* of product, which is the amount of product *actually obtained*, is often compared to the theoretical yield. This comparison, usually expressed as a percent, is called the **percent yield**.

$$\frac{\text{Actual yield}}{\text{Theoretical yield}} \times 100\% = \text{percent yield}$$

For example, *if* the reaction considered in Example 9.8 *actually* gave 6.63 g of nitrogen instead of the *predicted* 10.6 g, the percent yield of nitrogen would be

$$\frac{6.63 \ \text{g N}_2}{10.6 \ \text{g N}_2} \times 100\% = 62.5\%$$

Theoretical yield
The maximum amount of a given product that can be formed when the limiting reactant is completely consumed

Percent yield
The actual yield of a product as the percentage of the theoretical yield

information

Percent yield is important as an indicator of the efficiency of a particular reaction.

Meeting Individual Needs

MATH CONCEPTS

For students who need additional help with percent yield, have them read *Percent* located in the *Teacher Resources*. A worksheet is available to go along with the handout.

 Answer to Practice Problem 9.8

Step 1 The balanced equation for the reaction is

$$6Li(s) + N_2(g) \rightarrow 2Li_3N(s)$$

Step 2 To determine the limiting reactant, we must convert the masses of Li (atomic mass = 6.941 g) and N_2 (molar mass = 28.02 g) to moles.

$$56.0 \ \text{g Li} \times \frac{1 \ \text{mol Li}}{6.941 \ \text{g Li}} =$$

8.07 mol Li

$$56.0 \ \text{g N}_2 \times \frac{1 \ \text{mol N}_2}{28.02 \ \text{g N}_2} =$$

2.00 mol N_2

Step 3 Using the mole ratio from the balanced equation, we can calculate the moles of Li required to react with 2.00 mol of N_2.

$$2.00 \ \text{mol N}_2 \times \frac{6 \ \text{mol Li}}{1 \ \text{mol N}_2} =$$

12.0 mol Li

Therefore, 12.0 mol of Li are required to react with 2.00 mol of N_2. However, we have only 8.07 mol of Li, so lithium is limiting. It will be consumed before the nitrogen runs out.

Step 4 Because Li is the limiting reactant, we must use the 8.07 mol of Li to determine how many moles of Li_3N can be formed.

$$8.07 \ \text{mol Li} \times \frac{2 \ \text{mol Li}_3N}{6 \ \text{mol Li}} =$$

2.69 mol Li_3N

Step 5 We can now use the molar mass of Li_3N (34.83 g) to calculate the mass of Li_3N formed.

$$2.69 \ \text{mol Li}_3N \times \frac{34.83 \ \text{g Li}_3N}{1 \ \text{mol Li}_3N} =$$

93.7 g Li_3N

Active Reading Question

When converting to moles of each reactant we find we have just about an equal number of moles of each (1.06 mol NH_3 to 1.14 mol CuO). However, we need 3 mol CuO for every 2 mol NH_3, so we will run out of CuO first.

9.3.C Percent Yield

Objective To learn to calculate actual yield as a percentage of theoretical yield

LABORATORY
EXPERIMENT 39:
Synthesis of Manganese(II) Chloride, Microscale

- Students may find it difficult to understand that the answers to stoichiometry problems are actually theoretical yields. It is useful to draw a clear distinction between theoretical yield and actual yield. Point out that an actual yield must be determined by someone in the laboratory, whereas a theoretical yield can be determined by solving limiting reactant problems.

- Now is an excellent time to review the concept of percent composition. You may want to have students do some percent composition problems from Chapter 7 as part of the review.

 Active Reading Question

We calculate the theoretical yield.

EXAMPLE 9.9

More Examples

1. In a certain experiment, the expected yield is 1.352 g. The actual yield was 1.279 g. Determine the percent yield.
94.60%

2. Urea is formed by the reaction of ammonia and carbon dioxide:

$$2NH_3(g) + CO_2(g) \rightarrow CN_2H_4O(s) + H_2O(l)$$

In a certain experiment 100.0 g of ammonia is reacted with 100.0 g of carbon dioxide, and 120.0 g of urea is produced. Determine the percent yield for this reaction.
88.23%

 Active Reading Question

Which do we calculate by using stoichiometry, the actual or the theoretical yield?

EXAMPLE 9.9

Stoichiometric Calculations: Determining Percent Yield

MATH ➕

$$\text{Percent} = \frac{\text{Part}}{\text{Whole}} \times 100\%$$

Methanol can be produced by the reaction between carbon monoxide and hydrogen. Let's consider this process again. Suppose 68.5 kg (6.85×10^4 g) of $CO(g)$ is reacted with 8.60 kg (8.60×10^3 g) of $H_2(g)$.

- Calculate the theoretical yield of methanol.
- If 3.57×10^4 g of CH_3OH is actually produced, what is the percent yield of methanol?

Solution

Where do we want to go?

- theoretical yield of CH_3OH
- percent yield of CH_3OH

What do we know?

- $CO(g) + H_2(g) \rightarrow CH_3OH(l)$
- 8.60×10^3 g H_2
- 6.85×10^4 g CO
- 3.57×10^4 g CH_3OH produced

How do we get there?

Step 1 The balanced equation is
$$2H_2(g) + CO(g) \rightarrow CH_3OH(l).$$

Step 2 Next, we calculate the moles of reactants.

$$6.85 \times 10^4 \text{ g CO} \times \frac{1 \text{ mol CO}}{28.01 \text{ g CO}} = 2.45 \times 10^3 \text{ mol CO}$$

$$8.60 \times 10^3 \text{ g H}_2 \times \frac{1 \text{ mol H}_2}{2.016 \text{ g H}_2} = 4.27 \times 10^3 \text{ mol H}_2$$

Step 3 Now we determine which reactant is limiting. Using the mole ratio between CO and H_2 from the balanced equation, we have

$$2.45 \times 10^3 \text{ mol CO} \times \frac{2 \text{ mol H}_2}{1 \text{ mol CO}} = 4.90 \times 10^3 \text{ mol H}_2$$

Meeting Individual Needs

READING STRATEGIES

Remind students that a percent is a ratio that compares a number to 100. When reading a percent yield that is 52%, it means that there are 52 grams of that component out of 100 grams. Review that 52% can also be written as 0.52 or $\frac{13}{25}$.

We see that 2.45×10^3 mol of CO requires 4.90×10^3 mol of H_2. Because only 4.27×10^3 mol of H_2 is actually present, H_2 *is limiting*.

Step 4 We must therefore use the amount of H_2 and the mole ratio between H_2 and CH_3OH to determine the maximum amount of methanol that can be produced in the reaction.

$$4.27 \times 10^3 \text{ mol } H_2 \times \frac{1 \text{ mol } CH_3OH}{2 \text{ mol } H_2} = 2.14 \times 10^3 \text{ mol } CH_3$$

This represents the theoretical yield in moles.

Step 5 Using the molar mass of CH_3OH (32.04 g), we can calculate the theoretical yield in grams.

$$2.14 \times 10^3 \text{ mol } CH_3OH \times \frac{32.04 \text{ g } CH_3OH}{1 \text{ mol } CH_3OH} = 6.86 \times 10^4 \text{ g } CH_3OH$$

So, from the amounts of reactants given, the maximum amount of CH_3OH that can be formed is 6.85×10^4 g. This is the *theoretical yield*.

The percent yield is

$$\frac{\text{Actual yield (grams)}}{\text{Theoretical yield (grams)}} \times 100\%$$

$$= \frac{3.57 \times 10^4 \text{ g } CH_3OH}{6.86 \times 10^4 \text{ g } CH_3OH} \times 100\%$$

$$= 52.0\%$$

 Practice Problem • Exercise 9.9

Titanium(IV) oxide is a white compound used as a coloring pigment. In fact, the page you are now reading is white because of the presence of this compound in the paper. Solid titanium(IV) oxide can be prepared by reacting gaseous titanium(IV) chloride with oxygen gas. A second product of this reaction is chlorine gas.

$$TiCl_4(g) + O_2(g) \rightarrow TiO_2(s) + Cl_2(g)$$

a. Suppose that 6.71×10^3 g of titanium(IV) chloride is reacted with 2.45×10^3 g of oxygen. Calculate the maximum mass of titanium(IV) oxide that can form.

b. If the percent yield of TiO_2 is 75%, what mass is actually formed?

Step 4

We will now use the moles of $TiCl_4$ (the limiting reactant) to determine the moles of TiO_2 that would form if the reaction produced 100% of the expected yield (the theoretical yield).

$$3.54 \times 10^1 \text{ mol } TiCl_4 \times \frac{1 \text{ mol } TiO_2}{1 \text{ mol } TiCl_4} = 3.54 \times 10^1 \text{ mol } TiO_2$$

The mass of TiO_2 expected for 100% yield is

$$3.54 \times 10^1 \text{ mol } TiO_2 \times \frac{79.88 \text{ g } TiO_2}{1 \text{ mol } TiO_2} = 2.83 \times 10^3 \text{ g } TiO_2$$

This amount represents the theoretical yield.

b. Because the reaction is said to give only a 75.0% yield of TiO_2, we use the definition of percent yield,

$$\frac{\text{Actual yield}}{\text{Theoretical yield}} \times 100\% = \% \text{ yield}$$

to write the equation

$$\frac{\text{Actual yield}}{2.83 \times 10^3 \text{ g } TiO_2} \times 100\% = 75.0\% \text{ yield}$$

We now want to solve for the actual yield. First we divide both sides by 100%.

$$\frac{\text{Actual yield}}{2.83 \times 10^3 \text{ g } TiO_2} \times$$

$$\frac{100\%}{100\%} = \frac{75.0}{100} = 0.750$$

Then we multiply both sides by 2.83×10^3 g TiO_2.

$$2.83 \times 10^3 \text{ g } TiO_2 \times \frac{\text{Actual yield}}{2.83 \times 10^3 \text{ g } TiO_2} = 0.750 \times 2.83 \times 10^3 \text{ g } TiO_2$$

Actual yield =

$$0.750 \times 2.83 \times 10^3 \text{ g } TiO_2 = 2.12 \times 10^3 \text{ g } TiO_2$$

Thus 2.12×10^3 g of $TiO_2(s)$ is actually obtained in this reaction.

Answer to Practice Problem 9.9

a. Step 1
The balanced equation is

$$TiCl_4(g) + O_2(g) \rightarrow TiO_2(s) + 2Cl_2(g)$$

Step 2
The numbers of moles of reactants are

$$6.71 \times 10^3 \text{ g } TiCl_4 \times \frac{1 \text{ mol } TiCl_4}{189.68 \text{ g } TiCl_4} = 3.54 \times 10^1 \text{ mol } TiCl_4$$

$$2.45 \times 10^3 \text{ g } O_2 \times \frac{1 \text{ mol } O_2}{32.00 \text{ g } O_2} = 7.66 \times 10^1 \text{ mol } O_2$$

Step 3
In the balanced equation both $TiCl_4$ and O_2 have coefficients of 1, so

1 mol $TiCl_4$ = 1 mol O_2 and

$$3.54 \times 10^1 \text{ mol } TiCl_4 \times \frac{1 \text{ mol } O_2}{1 \text{ mol } TiCl_4} = 3.54 \times 10^1 \text{ mol } O_2 \text{ required}$$

We have 7.66×10^1 mol of O_2, so the O_2 is in excess and the $TiCl_4$ is limiting. This makes sense. $TiCl_4$ and O_2 react in a 1:1 mole ratio, so the $TiCl_4$ is limiting because fewer moles of $TiCl_4$ are present than moles of O_2.

SECTION 9.3
Review Questions

1. A stoichiometric mixture contains relative moles of reactants that just match the numbers in the balanced equation. It is recognizable because none of any reactant is left when the reaction is complete.

2. The lemons are limiting because they will all be used with 2 cups of sugar. One cup of sugar will be left.

3. A limiting reactant problem usually gives masses of more than one reactant. The other possible clue is that one reactant is given in excess. The other reactant is then the limiting reactant.

4. The theoretical yield is the maximum amount of product that can be produced in the reaction. The actual yield is the actual amount of product that is obtained in the laboratory. Differences occur between the theoretical and actual yields because side reactions may occur or the reaction conditions may not be optimal.

5. a. Cl_2 is limiting
   b. 27.1 g CCl_4
   c. 22.2 g CH_4

CHEMISTRY IN YOUR WORLD

Consumer Connection

The "Golden" Dollar

The dollar bill is very popular with U.S. consumers, but it has some problems—it has an average life of only 18 months and can be very frustrating to use in vending machines.

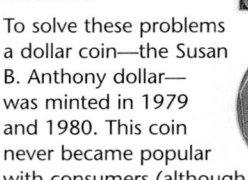

To solve these problems a dollar coin—the Susan B. Anthony dollar—was minted in 1979 and 1980. This coin never became popular with consumers (although 900 million are now in circulation) because it too closely resembled a quarter.

In the late 1990s, Congress decided to try again. The United States Dollar Coin Act of 1997 called for a new dollar coin to be golden in color, have a distinctive edge, and be the same size as the Anthony dollar. The idea was to mint a coin that looks and feels different from the quarter but that is enough like the Susan B. Anthony dollar to work in vending machines.

The new dollar coin, released in 2000, depicts Sacagawea, the young Native American (Shoshone) woman who guided the Lewis and Clark expedition, and her son, Jean Baptiste, on the front and a flying eagle on the back. The coin has the same color and luster as 14-carat gold, although it contains none of that precious metal.

The Sacagawea dollar is 88.5% copper, 6.0% zinc, 3.5% manganese, and 2% nickel. The copper core accounts for half of the coin's total thickness, with manganese brass, the surrounding golden-colored alloy of copper, zinc, manganese, and nickel making up the rest.

The coin costs 12 cents to manufacture, so the U.S. government makes 88 cents of every dollar minted. Such a deal!

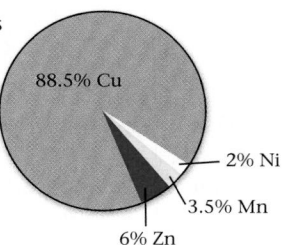

88.5% Cu
2% Ni
3.5% Mn
6% Zn

SECTION 9.3
REVIEW QUESTIONS

1. How do you recognize a stoichiometric mixture in a chemical reaction?

2. Suppose that a lemonade recipe calls for 1 cup of sugar for every 6 lemons. You have 12 lemons and 3 cups of sugar. Which ingredient is limiting? Why?

3. How is a limiting reactant problem different from other stoichiometry problems? (What is your clue that it is a limiting reactant problem?)

4. What is the difference between theoretical yield and the actual yield? Why is there a difference?

5. You react natural gas (methane, CH_4) with chlorine gas to produce carbon tetrachloride and hydrogen gas according to the following reaction:

$$CH_4(g) + 2Cl_2(g) \rightarrow CCl_4(l) + 2H_2(g)$$

Consider reacting 25.0 g of each reactant and answer the following.

   a. Which reactant is limiting?

   b. What mass of carbon tetrachloride should be produced (assuming 100% yield)?

   c. Determine the mass of leftover reactant.

RESEARCH LINKS
CLASSZONE.COM

Chemistry in Your World
The "Golden" Dollar

The "Golden" Dollar can be used to lead to a discussion of U.S. coins. Now might be a good time to discuss the alloys used for the various U.S. coins. You could also use this to review the percent composition ideas from Chapter 7.

Chapter 9 Review

Key Terms

Key Ideas

9.1 Mole ratio

9.1 Using Chemical Equations

- A balanced chemical equation gives relative numbers (or moles) of reactant and product molecules that participate in a chemical reaction.

- Stoichiometric calculations involve using a balanced chemical equation to determine the amounts of reactants needed or products formed in a reaction.

- To convert between moles of reactants and moles of products, we use mole ratios derived from the balanced chemical equation.

9.2 Stoichiometry

9.2 Using Chemical Equations to Calculate Mass

- To calculate masses from the moles of reactants needed or products formed, we can use the molar masses of substances for finding the masses (g) needed or formed.

9.3 Limiting reactant

Theoretical yield

Percent yield

9.3 Limiting Reactants and Percent Yield

- Often, reactants in a chemical reaction are not present in stoichiometric quantities (they do not "run out" at the same time).
  - In this case, we must determine which reactant runs out first and thus limits the amount of products that can form—this is called the limiting reactant.

- The actual yield (amount produced) of a reaction is usually less than the maximum expected (theoretical yield).

- The actual yield is often expressed as a percentage of the theoretical yield

$$\text{percent yield} = \frac{\text{actual yield (g)}}{\text{theoretical yield (g)}} \times 100\%$$

Meeting Individual Needs

CHAPTER REVIEW

Chapter 9 Review Worksheet at the appropriate level:
- **Basic**
- **Standard**
- **Challenge**

CHAPTER SUMMARY

A **Chapter Summary** that includes additional Active Reading Questions for Chapter 9 is available.

Assessment Resources

CHAPTER 9

Chapter 9 Test

TECHNOLOGY

 Computerized Test Bank for Chapter 9

Chapter 9 Assessment (left column continuation)

1. Atoms and molecules react on a particle-by-particle basis. We have to "count" these particles (by weighing) when doing chemical calculations.

2. Balanced chemical equations tell us in what proportions on a mole basis substances combine; as the molar masses of C(s) and $O_2(g)$ are different, 1 g of each reactant cannot represent the same number of moles of each reactant.

3. (a) $2NO(g) + O_2(g) \rightarrow 2NO_2(g)$. Two molecules (or two moles) of nitrogen monoxide gas combine with one molecule (or one mole) of oxygen gas, producing two molecules (or two moles) of nitrogen dioxide gas.
   (b) $2AgC_2H_3O_2(aq) + CuSO_4(aq) \rightarrow Ag_2SO_4(s) + Cu(C_2H_3O_2)_2(aq)$. Two formula units (or two moles) of silver acetate react with one formula unit (or one mole) of copper(II) sulfate, precipitating one formula unit (or one mole) of silver sulfate and leaving one formula unit (or one mole) of copper(II) acetate in solution.
   (c) $PCl_3(l) + 3H_2O(l) \rightarrow H_3PO_3(l) + 3HCl(g)$. One molecule (or one mole) of phosphorus trichloride reacts with three molecules (or three moles) of water, producing one molecule (or one mole) of phosphorous acid and three molecules (or three moles) of hydrogen chloride.
   (d) $C_2H_6(g) + Cl_2(g) \rightarrow C_2H_5Cl(g) + HCl(g)$. One molecule (or one mole) of ethane (C_2H_6) reacts with one molecule (or one mole) of chlorine, producing one molecule (or one mole) of chloroethane (C_2H_5Cl) and one molecule (or one mole) of hydrogen chloride.

4. (a) $3MnO_2(s) + 4Al(s) \rightarrow 3Mn(s) + 2Al_2O_3(s)$. Three formula units (or three moles) of manganese(IV) oxide react with four atoms (or four moles) of aluminum, producing three atoms (or three moles) of manganese and two formula units (or two moles) of aluminum oxide.
   (b) $B_2O_3(s) + 3CaF_2(s) \rightarrow 2BF_3(g) + 3CaO(s)$. One

---

Chapter 9 Assessment (center column)

All exercises with blue numbers have answers in the back of this book.

9.1 Using Chemical Equations
A. Information Given by Chemical Equations

1. Although *mass* is a property of matter we can conveniently measure in the laboratory, the coefficients of a balanced chemical equation are *not* directly interpreted on the basis of mass. Explain why.

2. Explain why, in the balanced chemical equation $C + O_2 \rightarrow CO_2$, we know that 1 g of C will *not* react exactly with 1 g of O_2.

3. For each of the following reactions, give the balanced equation for the reaction and state the meaning of the equation in terms of numbers of *individual molecules* and in terms of *moles* of molecules.
   a. $NO(g) + O_2(g) \rightarrow NO_2(g)$
   b. $AgC_2H_3O_2(aq) + CuSO_4(aq) \rightarrow Ag_2SO_4(s) + Cu(C_2H_3O_2)_2(aq)$
   c. $PCl_3(l) + H_2O(l) \rightarrow H_3PO_3(l) + HCl(g)$
   d. $C_2H_6(g) + Cl_2(g) \rightarrow C_2H_5Cl(g) + HCl(g)$

4. For each of the following reactions, give the balanced chemical equation for the reaction and state the meaning of the equation in terms of *individual molecules* and in terms of *moles* of molecules.
   a. $MnO_2(s) + Al(s) \rightarrow Mn(s) + Al_2O_3(s)$
   b. $B_2O_3(s) + CaF_2(s) \rightarrow BF_3(g) + CaO(s)$
   c. $NO_2(g) + H_2O(l) \rightarrow HNO_3(aq) + NO(g)$
   d. $C_6H_6(l) + H_2(g) \rightarrow C_6H_{12}(l)$

B. Mole–mole Relationships

5. True or false? For the reaction represented by the chemical equation
   $$2H_2O_2(aq) \rightarrow 2H_2O(l) + O_2(g)$$
   if 2.0 g of hydrogen peroxide decomposes, then 2.0 g of water and 1.0 g of oxygen gas will be produced.

6. Consider the balanced equation
   $$CH_4(g) + 2O_2(g) \rightarrow CO_2(g) + 2H_2O(g)$$
   What is the mole ratio that would enable you to calculate the number of moles of oxygen needed to react exactly with a given number of moles of $CH_4(g)$? What mole ratios would you use to calculate how many moles of each product form from a given number of moles of CH_4?

Chapter 9 Assessment (right column)

7. Consider the unbalanced chemical equation
   $$Ag(s) + H_2S(g) \rightarrow Ag_2S(s) + H_2(g)$$
   Balance the equation. Identify the mole ratios that you would use to calculate the number of moles of each product that would form for a given number of moles of silver reacting.

8. For each of the following *unbalanced* chemical equations, calculate how many *moles of each product* would be produced by the complete conversion of 0.125 mol of the reactant indicated in boldface. State clearly the mole ratio used for the conversion.
   a. **FeO**(s) + C(s) $\rightarrow$ Fe(l) + $CO_2(g)$
   b. $Cl_2(g)$ + **KI**(aq) $\rightarrow$ KCl(aq) + $I_2(s)$
   c. **$Na_2B_4O_7$**(s) + $H_2SO_4(aq)$ + $H_2O(l)$ $\rightarrow$ $H_3BO_3(s)$ + $Na_2SO_4(aq)$
   d. **CaC_2**(s) + $H_2O(l)$ $\rightarrow$ $Ca(OH)_2(s)$ + $C_2H_2(g)$

9. For each of the following balanced chemical equations, calculate how many *moles* and how many *grams* of each product would be produced by the complete conversion of 0.50 mol of the reactant indicated in boldface. State clearly the mole ratio used for each conversion.
   a. **NH_3**(g) + HCl(g) $\rightarrow$ $NH_4Cl(s)$
   b. $CH_4(g)$ + **4S**(s) $\rightarrow$ $CS_2(l)$ + $2H_2S(g)$
   c. **PCl_3**(l) + $3H_2O(l)$ $\rightarrow$ $H_3PO_3(aq)$ + $3HCl(aq)$
   d. **NaOH**(s) + $CO_2(g)$ $\rightarrow$ $NaHCO_3(s)$

10. For each of the following *unbalanced* equations, indicate how many *moles* of the *first product* are produced if 0.625 mol of the *second product* forms. State clearly the mole ratio used for each conversion.
   a. $KO_2(s)$ + $H_2O(l)$ $\rightarrow$ $O_2(g)$ + KOH(s)
   b. $SeO_2(g)$ + $H_2Se(g)$ $\rightarrow$ Se(s) + $H_2O(g)$
   c. $CH_3CH_2OH(l)$ + $O_2(g)$ $\rightarrow$ $CH_3CHO(aq)$ + $H_2O(l)$
   d. $Fe_2O_3(s)$ + Al(s) $\rightarrow$ Fe(l) + $Al_2O_3(s)$

9.2 Using Chemical Equations to Calculate Mass
A. Mass Calculations

11. What quantity serves as the conversion factor between the mass of a sample and the number of moles the sample contains?

12. What does it mean to say that the balanced chemical equation for a reaction describes the *stoichiometry* of the reaction?

(bottom row continuation)

molecule (or one mole) of diboron trioxide reacts with three formula units (or three moles) of calcium fluoride, producing two molecules (or two moles) of boron trifluoride.
(c) $3NO_2(g) + H_2O(l) \rightarrow 2HNO_3(aq) + NO(g)$. Three molecules (or three moles) of nitrogen dioxide react with one molecule (or one mole) of water, producing two

nitric acid and one molecule (or one mole) of nitrogen monoxide.
(d) $C_6H_6(g) + 3H_2(g) \rightarrow C_6H_{12}(g)$. One molecule (or one mole) of benzene (C_6H_6) reacts with three molecules (or three moles) of hydrogen gas, producing one molecule (or one mole) of cyclohexane (C_6H_{12}).

5. False; the coefficients represent the mole ratio, not the mass ratio.

6. 2 mol O_2/1 mol CH_4; 1 mol CO_2/1 mol CH_4; 2 mol H_2O/1 mol CH_4

7. $2Ag(s) + H_2S(g) \rightarrow Ag_2S(s) + H_2(g)$. For Ag_2S: 1 mol Ag_2S/2 mol Ag; for H_2: 1 mol H_2/2 mol Ag

13. Using the average atomic masses given inside the front cover of the text, calculate the number of *moles* of each substance contained in the following *masses*.

    a. 2.01×10^{-2} g of silver

    b. 45.2 mg of ammonium sulfide

    c. 61.7 μg of uranium

    d. 5.23 kg of sulfur dioxide

    e. 272 g of iron(III) nitrate

    f. 12.7 mg of iron(II) sulfate

    g. 6.91×10^3 g of lithium hydroxide

14. Using the average atomic masses given inside the front cover of the text, calculate the *mass in grams* of each of the following samples.

    a. 2.21×10^{-4} mol of calcium carbonate

    b. 2.75 mol of helium

    c. 0.00975 mol of oxygen gas

    d. 7.21×10^{-3} mol of carbon dioxide

    e. 0.835 mol of iron(II) sulfide

    f. 4.01 mol of potassium hydroxide

    g. 0.0219 mol of hydrogen gas

15. For each of the following *unbalanced* equations, calculate how many moles of the *second* reactant would be required to react completely with exactly 25.0 g of the *first* reactant. Indicate clearly the mole ratio used for each conversion.

    a. $Mg(s) + CuCl_2(aq) \rightarrow MgCl_2(aq) + Cu(s)$

    b. $AgNO_3(aq) + NiCl_2(aq) \rightarrow$
        $AgCl(s) + Ni(NO_3)_2(aq)$

    c. $NaHSO_3(aq) + NaOH(aq) \rightarrow$
        $Na_2SO_3(aq) + H_2O(l)$

    d. $KHCO_3(aq) + HCl(aq) \rightarrow$
        $KCl(aq) + H_2O(l) + CO_2(g)$

16. For each of the following *unbalanced* equations, calculate how many *milligrams of each product* would be produced by complete reaction of 10.0 mg of the reactant indicated in boldface. Indicate clearly the mole ratio used for the conversion.

    a. $\mathbf{FeSO_4}(aq) + K_2CO_3(aq) \rightarrow$
        $FeCO_3(s) + K_2SO_4(aq)$

    b. $\mathbf{Cr}(s) + SnCl_4(l) \rightarrow CrCl_3(s) + Sn(s)$

    c. $Fe(s) + \mathbf{S_8}(s) \rightarrow Fe_2S_3(s)$

    d. $Ag(s) + \mathbf{HNO_3}(aq) \rightarrow$
        $AgNO_3(aq) + H_2O(l) + NO(g)$

17. Although mixtures of hydrogen and oxygen are highly explosive, pure elemental hydrogen gas itself burns quietly in air with a pale blue flame, producing water vapor.

$$2H_2(g) + O_2(g) \rightarrow 2H_2O(g)$$

Calculate the mass (in grams) of water vapor produced when 56.0 g of pure hydrogen gas burns in air.

18. Given the information in Problem 17, calculate the mass of oxygen gas that would be necessary to burn 0.0275 mol of hydrogen gas.

19. When elemental carbon is burned in the open atmosphere, with plenty of oxygen gas present, the product is carbon dioxide.

$$C(s) + O_2(g) \rightarrow CO_2(g)$$

However, when the amount of oxygen present during the burning of the carbon is restricted, carbon monoxide is more likely to result.

$$2C(s) + O_2(g) \rightarrow 2CO(g)$$

What mass of each product is expected when a 5.00-g sample of pure carbon is burned under each of these conditions?

20. Although we usually think of substances as "burning" only in oxygen gas, the process of rapid oxidation to produce a flame may also take place in other strongly oxidizing gases. For example, when iron is heated and placed in pure chlorine gas, the iron "burns" according to the following (unbalanced) reaction:

$$Fe(s) + Cl_2(g) \rightarrow FeCl_3(s)$$

How many milligrams of iron(III) chloride result when 15.5 mg of iron is reacted with an excess of chlorine gas?

21. Small quantities of oxygen gas can be generated in the laboratory by the decomposition of hydrogen peroxide. The unbalanced equation for the reaction is

$$H_2O_2(aq) \rightarrow H_2O(l) + O_2(g)$$

Calculate the mass of oxygen produced when 10.00 g of hydrogen peroxide decomposes.

13. (a) 1.86×10^{-4} mol Ag
    (b) 6.63×10^{-4} mol $(NH_4)_2S$
    (c) 2.59×10^{-7} mol U
    (d) 81.6 mol SO_2
    (e) 1.12 mol $Fe(NO_3)_3$
    (f) 8.36×10^{-5} mol $FeSO_4$
    (g) 289 mol LiOH

14. (a) 0.0221 g $CaCO_3$
    (b) 11.0 g He
    (c) 0.312 g O_2
    (d) 0.317 g CO_2
    (e) 73.4 g FeS
    (f) 225 g KOH
    (g) 0.0442 g H_2

15. (a) 1.03 mol $CuCl_2$
    (b) 0.0735 mol $NiCl_2$
    (c) 0.240 mol NaOH
    (d) 0.250 mol HCl

16. (a) 7.36 mg $FeCO_3$
    11.5 mg K_2SO_4
    (b) 30.4 mg $CrCl_3$
    17.1 mg Sn
    (c) 21.6 mg Fe_2S_3
    (d) 20.3 mg $AgNO_3$
    1.43 mg H_2O; 1.19 mg NO

17. 500. g H_2O

18. 0.44 g O_2

19. 18.3 g CO_2; 11.7 g CO

20. 45.0 mg $FeCl_3$

21. 4.704 g O_2

8. (a) 0.125 mol Fe;
    0.0625 mol CO_2
    (b) 0.125 mol KCl;
    0.0625 mol I_2
    (c) 0.500 mol H_3BO_3;
    0.125 mol Na_2SO_4
    (d) 0.125 mol $Ca(OH)_2$;
    0.125 mol C_2H_2

9. (a) 0.50 mol NH_4Cl (27 g)
    (b) 0.125 mol CS_2 (9.5 g);
    0.25 mol H_2S (8.5 g)
    (c) 0.50 mol H_3PO_3 (41 g);
    1.5 mol HCl (55 g)
    (d) 0.50 mol $NaHCO_3$
    (42 g)

10. (a) 0.469 mol O_2
    (b) 0.938 mol Se
    (c) 0.625 mol CH_3CHO
    (d) 1.25 mol Fe

11. the molar mass of the substance

12. Stoichiometry is the process of using a chemical equation to calculate the relative masses of reactants and products involved in a reaction.

22. 0.631 g S

23. 0.437 g N_2; 0.250 g O_2;
0.562 g H_2O

24. 2.07 g MgO

25. 1.61×10^4 g I_2

26. 3.26×10^{-3} g Cl_2

27. The propane (C_3H_8) will require
more oxygen.

28. 1.42 g NH_3

29. The limiting reactant is the
reactant that limits the
amounts of products that can
form in a chemical reaction. All
reactants are necessary for a
reaction to continue.

30. The representation should have
four molecules of N_2 and four
molecules of NH_3.

31. First use the masses given to
calculate the number of moles
of each reactant present. Then
use the mole ratio in the
balanced equation to decide
which reactant is limiting.

32. Once the limiting reactant is
consumed, the reaction can no
longer proceed and no more
product can be formed.

33. A reactant is present in excess if
more of that reactant is present
than is required to react with
the limiting reactant. The
limiting reactant, by definition,
cannot be present in excess.
No.

22. An introductory chemistry experiment involves
heating finely divided copper metal with sulfur
to determine the proportions in which the
elements react to form copper(II) sulfide. The
experiment works well because any excess sulfur
beyond that required to react with the copper
may be simply boiled away from the reaction
container.

$$Cu(s) + S(s) \rightarrow CuS(s)$$

If 1.25 g of copper is heated with an excess of
sulfur, how many grams of sulfur will react?

23. Ammonium nitrate has been used as a high
explosive because it is unstable and decomposes
into several gaseous substances. The rapid
expansion of the gaseous substances produces
the explosive force.

$$NH_4NO_3(s) \rightarrow N_2(g) + O_2(g) + H_2O(g)$$

Calculate the mass of each product gas if 1.25 g
of ammonium nitrate reacts.

24. Magnesium metal burns in oxygen with an
intensely bright white flame. The balanced
equation for this reaction is

$$2Mg(s) + O_2(g) \rightarrow 2MgO(s)$$

How many grams of MgO(s) are produced by
complete reaction of 1.25 g of magnesium metal?

B. Mass Calculations Using Scientific Notation

25. If chlorine gas is bubbled through a potassium
iodide solution, elemental iodine is produced.
The *unbalanced* equation is

$$Cl_2(g) + KI(aq) \rightarrow I_2(s) + KCl(aq)$$

Calculate the mass of iodine produced when
4.50×10^3 g of chlorine gas is bubbled through
an excess amount of potassium iodide solution.

26. Elemental fluorine and chlorine gases are very
reactive. For example, they react with each other
to form chlorine monofluoride.

$$Cl_2(g) + F_2(g) \rightarrow 2ClF(g)$$

Calculate the mass of chlorine gas required to
produce 5.00×10^{-3} g of chlorine monofluoride
given an excess of fluorine gas.

C. Mass Calculations: Comparing Two Reactions

27. Both propane (C_3H_8) and butane (C_4H_{10}) react
with oxygen gas to form carbon dioxide and
water. If you have equal masses of each, which
will require a greater mass of oxygen to react?

28. Methane (CH_4) reacts with oxygen in the air to
produce carbon dioxide and water. Ammonia
(NH_3) reacts with oxygen in the air to produce
nitrogen monoxide and water. What mass of
ammonia is needed to react with excess oxygen
to produce the same amount of water as 1.00 g
of methane reacting with excess oxygen?

9.3 Limiting Reactants and Percent Yield

A. The Concept of Limiting Reactants

29. What is the *limiting reactant* for a process? Why
does a reaction stop when the limiting reactant
is consumed, even though there may be plenty
of the other reactants present?

30. Nitrogen (N_2) and hydrogen (H_2) react to
form ammonia (NH_3). Consider the mixture
of N_2 (⬤⬤) and H_2 (◯◯) in a closed container
as illustrated below:

Assuming the reaction goes to completion, draw
a representation of the product mixture. Explain
how you arrived at this representation.

B. Calculations Involving a Limiting Reactant

31. Explain how one determines which reactant in
a process is the limiting reactant. Does this
depend only on the masses of the reactant present? Is the mole ratio in which the reactants
combine involved?

32. How does the maximum *yield* of products for a
reaction depend on the limiting reactant?

33. What does it mean to say that a reactant is present "in excess" in a process? Can the *limiting
reactant* be present in excess? Does the presence
of an excess of a reactant affect the mass of
products expected for a reaction?

34. For each of the following *unbalanced* chemical equations, suppose that exactly 15.0 g of *each* reactant is taken. Determine which reactant is limiting, and calculate what mass of each product is expected. (Assume that the limiting reactant is completely consumed.)

   a. $Al(s) + HCl(aq) \rightarrow AlCl_3(aq) + H_2(g)$

   b. $NaOH(aq) + CO_2(g) \rightarrow$
          $Na_2CO_3(aq) + H_2O(l)$

   c. $Pb(NO_3)_2(aq) + HCl(aq) \rightarrow$
          $PbCl_2(s) + HNO_3(aq)$

   d. $K(s) + I_2(s) \rightarrow KI(s)$

35. For each of the following *unbalanced* chemical equations, suppose that exactly 50.0 g of *each* reactant is taken. Determine which reactant is limiting, and calculate what mass of the product in boldface is expected. (Assume that the limiting reactant is completely consumed.)

   a. $NH_3(g) + Na(s) \rightarrow \mathbf{NaNH_2}(s) + H_2(g)$

   b. $BaCl_2(aq) + Na_2SO_4(aq) \rightarrow$
          $\mathbf{BaSO_4}(s) + NaCl(aq)$

   c. $SO_2(g) + NaOH(s) \rightarrow \mathbf{Na_2SO_3}(s) + H_2O(l)$

   d. $Al(s) + H_2SO_4(aq) \rightarrow \mathbf{Al_2(SO_4)_3}(s) + H_2(g)$

36. For each of the following *unbalanced* chemical equations, suppose that 10.0 mg of *each* reactant is taken. Show by calculation which reactant is limiting. Calculate the mass of each product that is expected.

   a. $CO(g) + H_2(g) \rightarrow CH_3OH(l)$

   b. $Al(s) + I_2(s) \rightarrow AlI_3(s)$

   c. $Ca(OH)_2(aq) + HBr(aq) \rightarrow$
          $CaBr_2(aq) + H_2O(l)$

   d. $Cr(s) + H_3PO_4(aq) \rightarrow CrPO_4(s) + H_2(g)$

37. The more reactive halogen elements are able to replace the less reactive halogens from their compounds.

   $Cl_2(g) + NaI(aq) \rightarrow NaCl(aq) + I_2(s)$

   $Br_2(l) + NaI(aq) \rightarrow NaBr(aq) + I_2(s)$

Suppose that separate solutions, each containing 25.0 g of NaI, are available. If 5.00 g of Cl_2 gas is bubbled into one NaI solution, and 5.00 g of liquid bromine is added to the other, calculate the number of grams of elemental iodine produced in each case.

38. If steel wool (iron) is heated until it glows and is placed in a bottle containing pure oxygen, the iron reacts spectacularly to produce iron(III) oxide.

   $Fe(s) + O_2(g) \rightarrow Fe_2O_3(s)$

If 1.25 g of iron is heated and placed in a bottle containing 0.0204 mol of oxygen gas, what mass of iron(III) oxide is produced?

39. One method for chemical analysis involves finding some reagent that will precipitate the species of interest. The mass of the precipitate is then used to determine what mass of the species of interest was present in the original sample. For example, calcium ion can be precipitated from solution by addition of sodium oxalate. The balanced equation is

   $Ca^{2+}(aq) + Na_2C_2O_4(aq) \rightarrow$
          $CaC_2O_4(s) + 2Na^+(aq)$

Suppose that a solution is known to contain approximately 15 g of calcium ion. Show by calculation whether the addition of a solution containing 15 g of sodium oxalate will precipitate all of the calcium from the sample.

C. Percent Yield

40. What is the *actual yield* of a reaction? What is the *percent yield* of a reaction? How do the actual yield and the percent yield differ from the theoretical yield?

41. The text explains that one reason why the actual yield for a reaction may be less than the theoretical yield is side reactions. Suggest some other reasons why the percent yield for a reaction might not be 100%.

42. According to his prelaboratory theoretical yield calculations, a student's experiment should have produced 1.44 g of magnesium oxide. When he weighed his product after reaction, only 1.23 g of magnesium oxide was present. What is the student's percent yield?

40. The actual yield is the quantity of product actually isolated from the reaction vessel. The theoretical yield represents the maximum quantity of product possible if the reaction proceeds to completion. The percent yield represents the ratio of actual yield to theoretical yield.

41. If the reaction occurs in a solvent, the product may have a substantial solubility in the solvent; the reaction may come to equilibrium before the full yield of product is achieved (see Chapter 17); loss of product may occur to error.

42. 85.4%

---

34. (a) HCl is the limiting reactant; 18.3 g $AlCl_3$; 0.415 g H_2
(b) NaOH is the limiting reactant; 19.9 g Na_2CO_3; 3.38 g H_2O
(c) $Pb(NO_3)_2$ is the limiting reactant; 12.6 g $PbCl_2$; 5.71 g HNO_3
(d) I_2 is the limiting reactant; 19.6 g KI

35. (a) Na is the limiting reactant; 84.9 g $NaNH_2$

(b) $BaCl_2$ is the limiting reactant; 56.0 g $BaSO_4$
(c) NaOH is the limiting reactant; 78.8 g Na_2SO_3
(d) H_2SO_4 is the limiting reactant; 58.2 g $Al_2(SO_4)_3$

36. (a) CO is the limiting reactant; 11.4 mg CH_3OH
(b) I_2 is the limiting reactant; 10.7 mg AlI_3
(c) HBr is the limiting reactant; 12.4 mg $CaBr_2$; 2.23 mg H_2O

(d) H_3PO_4 is the limiting reactant; 15.0 mg $CrPO_4$; 0.309 mg H_2

37. 17.9 g I_2; 7.94 g I_2

38. 1.79 g Fe_2O_3

39. Not enough sodium oxalate has been added to precipitate all of the calcium ions in the sample.

43. 25.2 g $Na_2S_2O_3 \cdot 5H_2O$;
20.9% yield

44. $2LiOH(s) + CO_2(g) \rightarrow$
$Li_2CO_3(s) + H_2O(g)$.
142 g of CO_2 can be ultimately
absorbed; 102 g is 71.8% of
the canister's capacity.

45. 205 g XeF_4; 70.7% yield

46. 82.6%

47. 28.6 g $NaHCO_3$

48. 8.26 g FeS

43. The compound sodium thiosulfate pentahydrate, $Na_2S_2O_3 \cdot 5H_2O$, is important commercially to the photography business as "hypo," because it has the ability to dissolve unreacted silver salts from photographic film during development. Sodium thiosulfate pentahydrate can be produced by boiling elemental sulfur in an aqueous solution of sodium sulfite.

$$S_8(s) + Na_2SO_3(aq) + H_2O(l) \rightarrow$$
$$Na_2S_2O_3 \cdot 5H_2O(s) \text{ (unbalanced)}$$

What is the theoretical yield of sodium thiosulfate pentahydrate when 3.25 g of sulfur is boiled with 13.1 g of sodium sulfite? Sodium thiosulfate pentahydrate is very soluble in water. What is the percent yield of the synthesis if a student doing this experiment is able to isolate (collect) only 5.26 g of the product?

44. Alkali metal hydroxides are sometimes used to "scrub" excess carbon dioxide from the air in closed spaces (such as submarines and spacecraft). For example, lithium hydroxide reacts with carbon dioxide according to the unbalanced chemical equation

$$LiOH(s) + CO_2(g) \rightarrow Li_2CO_3(s) + H_2O(g)$$

Suppose that a lithium hydroxide cannister contains 155 g of LiOH(s). What mass of $CO_2(g)$ will the cannister be able to absorb? If it is found that after 24 hours of use the cannister has absorbed 102 g of carbon dioxide, what percentage of its capacity has been reached?

45. Although they were formerly called the inert gases, at least the heavier elements of Group 8 do form relatively stable compounds. For example, xenon combines directly with elemental fluorine at elevated temperatures in the presence of a nickel catalyst.

$$Xe(g) + 2F_2(g) \rightarrow XeF_4(s)$$

What is the theoretical mass of xenon tetrafluoride that should form when 130. g of xenon is reacted with 100. g of F_2? What is the percent yield if only 145 g of XeF_4 is actually isolated?

46. Anhydrous calcium chloride, $CaCl_2$, is frequently used in the laboratory as a drying agent for solvents because it absorbs 6 mol of water molecules for every mole of $CaCl_2$ used (forming a stable solid hydrated salt, $CaCl_2 \cdot 6H_2O$). Calcium chloride is typically prepared by treating calcium carbonate with hydrogen chloride gas.

$$CaCO_3(s) + 2HCl(g) \rightarrow$$
$$CaCl_2(s) + CO_2(g) + H_2O(g)$$

A large amount of heat is generated by this reaction, so the water produced from the reaction is usually driven off as steam. Some liquid water may remain, however, and it may dissolve some of the desired calcium chloride. What is the percent yield if 155 g of calcium carbonate is treated with 250. g of anhydrous hydrogen chloride and only 142 g of $CaCl_2$ is obtained?

Critical Thinking

47. One process for the commercial production of baking soda (sodium hydrogen carbonate) involves the following reaction, in which the carbon dioxide is used in its solid form ("dry ice") both to serve as a source of reactant and to cool the reaction system to a temperature low enough for the sodium hydrogen carbonate to precipitate:

$$NaCl(aq) + NH_3(aq) + H_2O(l) + CO_2(s) \rightarrow$$
$$NH_4Cl(aq) + NaHCO_3(s)$$

Because they are relatively cheap, sodium chloride and water are typically present in excess. What is the expected yield of $NaHCO_3$ when one performs such a synthesis using 10.0 g of ammonia and 15.0 g of dry ice, with an excess of NaCl and water?

48. A favorite demonstration among chemistry teachers, performed to show that the properties of a compound differ from those of its constituent elements, involves iron filings and powdered sulfur. If the teacher takes samples of iron and sulfur and simply mixes them together, the two elements can be separated from each other with a magnet (iron is attracted to a magnet, sulfur is not). If the teacher then combines and *heats* the mixture of iron and sulfur, a reaction takes place and the elements combine to form iron(II) sulfide (which is not attracted by a magnet).

$$Fe(s) + S(s) \rightarrow FeS(s)$$

Suppose that 5.25 g of iron filings is combined with 12.7 g of sulfur. What is the theoretical yield of iron(II) sulfide?

49. When the sugar glucose, $C_6H_{12}O_6$, is burned in air, carbon dioxide and water vapor are produced. Write the balanced chemical equation for this process, and calculate the theoretical yield of carbon dioxide when 1.00 g of glucose is burned completely.

50. The traditional method of analyzing the amount of chloride ion present in a sample was to dissolve the sample in water and then slowly add a solution of silver nitrate. Silver chloride is very insoluble in water, and by adding a slight excess of silver nitrate, it is possible to effectively remove all chloride ion from the sample.

$$Ag^+(aq) + Cl^-(aq) \rightarrow AgCl(s)$$

Suppose that a 1.054-g sample is known to contain 10.3% chloride ion by mass. What mass of silver nitrate must be used to completely precipitate the chloride ion from the sample? What mass of silver chloride will be obtained?

51. Consider the balanced equation

$$C_3H_8(g) + 5O_2(g) \rightarrow 3CO_2(g) + 4H_2O(g)$$

What mole ratio enables you to calculate the number of moles of oxygen needed to react exactly with a given number of moles of $C_3H_8(g)$? What mole ratios enable you to calculate how many moles of each product form from a given number of moles of C_3H_8?

52. For each of the following balanced reactions, calculate how many *moles of each product* would be produced by complete conversion of 0.50 mol of the reactant indicated in boldface. Indicate clearly the mole ratio used for the conversion.

   a. **$2H_2O_2(l)$** $\rightarrow 2H_2O(l) + O_2(g)$
   b. **$2KClO_3(s)$** $\rightarrow 2KCl(s) + 3O_2(g)$
   c. **$2Al(s)$** $+ 6HCl(aq) \rightarrow$
      $2AlCl_3(aq) + 3H_2(g)$
   d. **$C_3H_8(g)$** $+ 5O_2(g) \rightarrow 3CO_2(g) + 4H_2O(g)$

53. For each of the following balanced equations, indicate how many *moles of the product* could be produced by complete reaction of 1.00 g of the reactant indicated in boldface. Indicate clearly the mole ratio used for the conversion.

   a. **$NH_3(g)$** $+ HCl(g) \rightarrow NH_4Cl(s)$
   b. **$CaO(s)$** $+ CO_2(g) \rightarrow CaCO_3(s)$
   c. **$4Na(s)$** $+ O_2(g) \rightarrow 2Na_2O(s)$
   d. **$2P(s)$** $+ 3Cl_2(g) \rightarrow 2PCl_3(l)$

54. If sodium peroxide is added to water, elemental oxygen gas is generated:

$$Na_2O_2(s) + H_2O(l) \rightarrow NaOH(aq) + O_2(g)$$

Suppose that 3.25 g of sodium peroxide is added to a large excess of water. What mass of oxygen gas will be produced?

55. The gaseous hydrocarbon acetylene, C_2H_2, is used in welders' torches because of the large amount of heat released when acetylene burns with oxygen.

$$2C_2H_2(g) + 5O_2(g) \rightarrow 4CO_2(g) + 2H_2O(g)$$

How many grams of oxygen gas are needed for the complete combustion of 150 g of acetylene?

56. For each of the following *unbalanced* chemical equations, suppose that 25.0 g of each reactant is taken. Show by calculation which reactant is limiting. Calculate the theoretical yield in grams of the product in boldface.

   a. $C_2H_5OH(l) + O_2(g) \rightarrow$ **$CO_2(g)$** $+ H_2O(l)$
   b. $N_2(g) + O_2(g) \rightarrow$ **$NO(g)$**
   c. $NaClO_2(aq) + Cl_2(g) \rightarrow$
      $ClO_2(g) +$ **$NaCl(aq)$**
   d. $H_2(g) + N_2(g) \rightarrow$ **$NH_3(g)$**

57. Hydrazine, N_2H_4, emits a large quantity of energy when it reacts with oxygen, which has led to hydrazine's use as a fuel for rockets:

$$N_2H_4(l) + O_2(g) \rightarrow N_2(g) + 2H_2O(g)$$

How many moles of each of the gaseous products are produced when 20.0 g of pure hydrazine is ignited in the presence of 20.0 g of pure oxygen? How many grams of each product are produced?

58. Before going to lab, a student read in her lab manual that the percent yield for a difficult reaction to be studied was likely to be only 40.% of the theoretical yield. The student's prelab stoichiometric calculations predict that the theoretical yield should be 12.5 g. What is the student's actual yield likely to be?

59. When a certain element whose formula is X_4 combines with HCl, the results are XCl_3 and hydrogen gas. Write a balanced equation for the reaction. When 24.0 g of hydrogen gas results from such a reaction, it is noted that 248 g of X_4 are consumed. Identify element X.

49. $C_6H_{12}O_6(s) + 6O_2(g) \rightarrow$
$6CO_2(g) + 6H_2O(g)$;
1.47 g CO_2

50. 0.520 g $AgNO_3$ required,
0.439 g AgCl produced

51. for O_2, 5 mol O_2/1 mol C_3H_8;
for CO_2, 3 mol CO_2/1 mol
C_3H_8; for H_2O, 4 mol
H_2O/1 mol C_3H_8

52. (a) 0.50 mol H_2O,
0.25 mol O_2
(b) 0.50 mol KCl,
0.75 mol O_2
(c) 0.50 mol $AlCl_3$,
0.75 mol H_2
(d) 1.5 mol CO_2,
2.0 mol H_2O

53. (a) 0.0587 mol NH_4Cl;
$$\frac{1NH_4Cl}{1NH_3}$$
(b) 0.0178 mol $CaCO_3$;
$$\frac{1CaCO_3}{1CaO}$$
(c) 0.0217 mol Na_2O;
$$\frac{2Na_2O}{4Na}$$
(d) 0.0323 mol PCl_3; $\frac{2PCl_3}{2P}$

54. 0.667 g O_2

55. 4.6×10^2 g O_2

56. (a) 22.9 g CO_2
(b) 46.9 g NO
(c) 16.2 g NaCl
(d) 30.4 g NH_3

57. 0.624 mol N_2, 17.5 g N_2;
1.25 mol H_2O, 22.5 g H_2O

58. 5.0 g

59. $X_4 + 12HCl \rightarrow$
$4XCl_3 + 6H_2$;
X is phosphorus

60. X = 20 g/mol;
  Z = 40 g/mol

61. 54.4 g H_3PO_4

62. d

63. c

64. CaO is limiting. The mass of carbon left over is 23.2 g.

65. 73.3% yield

66. False. Amounts used can vary. However, according to the equation, for every 28.02 g of N_2 (2 mol) we need 6.048 g of H_2 (3 mol). So, for example, if we have 28.02 g of N_2 and 5.5 g of H_2, the H_2 is limiting. If we have 28.02 g of N_2 and 6.5 g of H_2, the N_2 is limiting.

67. (a) As we add more sodium, we get more product because sodium is the limiting reactant. However, eventually sodium is in excess (and chlorine is limiting), so the amount of product does not increase with an increase of sodium.
(b) 50.84 g NaCl
(c) 61.68 g Cl_2
(d) 101.68 g NaCl
(e) In part b, sodium is limiting, and 30.84 g Cl_2 is left over. In part d, Cl_2 is limiting and 10.00 g Na is left over.

60. When a 5.00-g sample of element X reacts completely with a 15.0-g sample of element Y, compound XY is formed. When a 3.00-g sample of element X reacts with an 18.0-g sample of element Z, compound XZ_3 is formed. The molar mass of Y is 60.0 g/mol. Find the molar masses of X and Z.

61. Phosphoric acid, H_3PO_4, can be synthesized from phosphorus, oxygen, and water according to the following reactions:

$$P_4(s) + O_2(g) \rightarrow P_4O_{10}(s)$$
$$P_4O_{10}(s) + H_2O(l) \rightarrow H_3PO_4(l)$$

If you start with 20.0 g of phosphorus, 30.0 g of oxygen gas, and 15.0 g of water, what is the maximum mass of phosphoric acid that can be formed?

62. Which of the following reaction mixtures would produce the greatest amount of product, assuming all went to completion? Each involves the reaction symbolized by the equation:

$$N_2 + 3H_2 \rightarrow 2NH_3$$

a. 1 mole of N_2 and 3 moles of H_2
b. 2 moles of N_2 and 3 moles of H_2
c. 3 moles of N_2 and 3 moles of H_2
d. Each would produce the same amount of product.

63. Which of the following statements is always true concerning a reaction represented by the following **balanced** chemical equation?

$$2C_2H_6(g) + 7O_2(g) \rightarrow 6H_2O(l) + 4CO_2(g)$$

a. If we react equal masses of C_2H_6 and O_2, there is no limiting reactant.
b. If we react an equal number of moles of C_2H_6 and O_2, there is no limiting reactant.
c. If we react a greater mass of C_2H_6 than of O_2, then O_2 must be limiting.
d. If we react a greater mass of O_2 than of C_2H_6, then C_2H_6 must be limiting.

64. Determine the limiting reactant and mass of left-over reactant when a 50.0 g sample of CaO is reacted with 50.0 g of carbon according to the balanced equation

$$2CaO(s) + 5C(s) \rightarrow 2CaC_2(s) + CO_2(g)$$

65. A sample of 13.97 g $KClO_3$ is decomposed according to the unbalanced equation

$$KClO_3(s) \rightarrow KCl(s) + O_2(g)$$

After the reaction 6.23 g KCl is collected. What is the percent yield of your experiment?

66. True or false? The limiting reactant is always the reactant that is present in the smallest amount (with respect to mass). Provide mathematical support for your answer using the chemical equation $N_2 + 3H_2 \rightarrow 2NH_3$.

67. You have seven closed containers each with equal masses of chlorine gas (Cl_2). You add 10.0 g of sodium to the first sample, 20.0 g of sodium to the second sample, and so on (adding 70.0 g of sodium to the seventh sample). Sodium and chlorine react to form sodium chloride according to the equation

$$2Na(s) + Cl_2(g) \rightarrow 2NaCl(s)$$

After each reaction is complete, you collect and measure the amount of sodium chloride formed. A graph of your results is shown below.

Answer the following questions:

a. Explain the shape of the graph.
b. Calculate the mass of NaCl formed when 20.0 g of sodium is used.
c. Calculate the mass of Cl_2 in each container.
d. Calculate the mass of NaCl formed when 50.0 g of sodium is used.
e. Identify the leftover reactant and determine its mass for parts b and d above.

1 Which of the following statements concerning balancing equations is **false**?

A There must always be a coefficient of 1 in an equation balanced in standard form.

B The ratio of coefficients in a balanced equation is much more meaningful than an individual coefficient in a balanced equation.

C The total number of atoms must be the same on the reactant side and the product side of the balanced equation.

D When there are two products in an equation, the order in which they are written does not matter.

2 When table sugar is burned in the air, carbon dioxide and water vapor are products as shown by the following balanced equation:

$$C_{12}H_{22}O_{11}(s) + 12O_2(g) \rightarrow$$
$$12CO_2(g) + 11H_2O(g)$$

How many moles of oxygen gas are required to react completely with 2.0 moles of sugar?

A 12

B 24

C 30

D 35

3 When ethane (C_2H_6) is reacted with oxygen in the air, the products are carbon dioxide and water. This process requires _____ mole(s) of oxygen for every one mole of ethane.

A 1

B 2.5

C 3.5

D 7

4 Consider the reaction represented by the following **un**balanced chemical equation

$$NH_3(g) + Cl_2(g) \rightarrow NH_4Cl(s) + NCl_3(g)$$

What mass of NH_4Cl can be produced from 10.0 g of NH_3 and an excess of Cl_2?

A 160.5 g

B 53.5 g

C 35.3 g

D 23.6 g

5 The flame of the Bunsen burner is caused by the reaction of methane (CH_4) and oxygen according to the following balanced equation

$$CH_4(g) + 2O_2(g) \rightarrow CO_2(g) + 2H_2O(g)$$

If 5.00 g of methane is burned, what mass of water can be produced? Assume the reaction goes to completion.

A 5.62 g

B 10.0 g

C 11.2 g

D 18.0 g

6 The maximum amount of a product that can be formed given the amounts of reactants used is called

A the actual yield.

B the theoretical yield.

C the percent yield.

D the limiting reactant.

7 Hydrogen gas (H_2) and oxygen gas (O_2) react to form water vapor according to the following unbalanced chemical equation:

$$H_2(g) + O_2(g) \rightarrow H_2O(g)$$

Consider the mixture of H_2 ⬤⬤ and O_2 ⬤⬤ in a closed container as illustrated:

= H_2

= O_2

Draw a molecular level picture of the product mixture, including any left over reactant.

Chapter 9

Standardized Test Practice

1. A

2. B

3. C

4. D

5. C

6. B

7. The picture should include 6 water molecules and 3 oxygen molecules.

Test-Taking Strategy

Students may be able to use the work backward strategy to answer a multiple choice question. Advise students to substitute an answer choice into the question to determine whether the choice seems reasonable or logical. If not, this choice can often be eliminated as a correct response. Encourage students to try this strategy before simply guessing an answer.

Assessment Resources

CHAPTER 9

For additional practice with standardized testing, see *Standardized Test Practice* located in the *Teacher Resources*.

Planning Guide

Section	Segment		Text Features and Components	Labs, Demonstrations, & Activities
10.1 **Energy,** **Temperature,** **and Heat** **1 Block** *pp. 320–325*	A	The Nature of Energy		(TE) Teaching Support: Demonstration *pp. 320–321* (TE) Mini-Demo *p. 321* (RP) Classroom Activities and Projects *TE p. 322*
	B	Temperature and Heat	(SE) Top Ten Lowest Temperatures Recorded by State *p. 323*	
	C	Exothermic and Endothermic Processes		(TE) Teaching Support: Demonstration *pp. 324–325*
10.2 **The Flow** **of Energy** **1 Block** *pp. 326–333*	A	Thermodynamics		(TE) Teaching Support: Demonstration *p. 326*

	B	Measuring Energy Changes	(SE) Chemistry in Your World: Nature Has Hot Plants *p. 331*
			(SE) Chemistry in Your World: Firewalking: Magic or Science? *p. 333*
				(TE) Teaching Support: Demonstration
				pp. 328–329
				(TE) Mini-Demo *p. 329*
				(TE) Teaching Support: Demonstration *p. 332*
				(LM) Experiment 40: Energy Value of Nuts, Traditional
				    Lab Manual
				    Report Sheets
				    Teacher's Lab Guide

	continued on next page			

Key	(SE) Student Edition	(TE) Teacher Edition	(RP) Teacher Resource Package
	(AR) Additional Materials	(LM) Lab Materials	Transparencies
	● DVD	CD-ROM	classzone.com

All Learners	Technology	Review & Assessment	Standards
TE Teaching Tips *pp. 320, 322* **RP** MINT: Reading Concepts *TE p. 322*	**●** Animation: Work vs. Energy Flow **●** EasyPlanner	**SE** Active Reading Question *p. 320* **SE** Critical Thinking *p. 321* **SE** Key Terms *p. 351* **SE** Questions and Problems *p. 353*	**TE** **NSES** A1, A2, B5, B6, C5
TE Teaching Tips *p. 323*	**●** Animation: Kinetic–Molecular Theory/Heat Transfer **●** EasyPlanner	**SE** Key Terms *p. 351* **SE** Questions and Problems *p. 353*	
TE Teaching Tip *p. 324* **RP** Team Learning Worksheet (Sec. 10.1)	**●** Video: Thermite Reaction **●** EasyPlanner	**SE** Active Reading Question *p. 325* **SE** Review Questions (10.1.A–10.1.C) *p. 325* **SE** Key Terms *p. 351* **SE** Questions and Problems *p. 353*	
TE Teaching Tips *p. 326*	**●** EasyPlanner	**SE** Key Terms *p. 352* **SE** Questions and Problems *p. 353*	**TE** **NSES** A1, A2, B5, B6, C5
TE Teaching Tips *pp. 327–329* **RP** MINT: Math Concepts *TE p. 327* **RP** Team Learning Worksheet (Sec. 10.2)	**■** Lab Generator CD **●** EasyPlanner	**SE** Practice Problem *p. 327* **TE** More Examples *p. 327* **TE** More Examples *p. 328* **SE** Practice Problem *p. 329* **SE** Active Reading Question *p. 329* **SE** Practice Problem *p. 330* **TE** More Examples *p. 330* **SE** Practice Problem *p. 332* **TE** More Examples *p. 332* **SE** Review Questions (10.2.A–10.2.B) *p. 333* **SE** Key Terms *p. 352* **SE** Questions and Problems *pp. 353–354*	

Planning Guide

Section	Segment		Text Features and Components	Labs, Demonstrations, & Activities
10.3 Energy and Chemical Reactions 3 Blocks pp. 334–338	A	Thermochemistry (Enthalpy)		**TE** Mini-Demo *p. 335* **LM** Experiment 41: Specific Heat of a Metal, CBL **LM** Experiment 42: Which Is Your Metal? **LM** Experiment 43: Stoichiometry and Calorimetry, CBL Lab Manual Report Sheets Teacher's Lab Guide
	B	Hess's Law	**TE** Teaching Support: Background Information *p. 336* **SE** Celebrity Chemical: Methane *p. 338*	**RP** Classroom Activities and Projects *TE p. 338* **LM** Experiment 44: Heat of Reaction, Traditional Lab Manual Report Sheets Teacher's Lab Guide **LM** Experiment 45: Hess's Law, CBL Lab Manual Report Sheets Teacher's Lab Guide
10.4 Using Energy in the Real World 0.5 Block pp. 339–350	A	Quality Versus Quantity of Energy		
	B	Energy and Our World	**SE** Chemistry in Your World: Veggie Power? *p. 345*	**TE** Group Activity *p. 341* **RP** Classroom Activities and Projects *TE p. 340*
	C	Energy as a Driving Force	**SE** Chemistry in Your World: Farming the Wind *p. 349*	**SE** Hands-On Chemistry: Distribution of Wealth *p. 350*

Key
SE Student Edition **TE** Teacher Edition **RP** Teacher Resource Package
AR Additional Materials **LM** Lab Materials ⬛ Transparencies
🔘 DVD ▭ CD-ROM ⓘ classzone.com

All Learners	Technology	Review & Assessment	Standards
	🎞 Transparency: Figure 10.5 💿 Lab Generator CD 💿 EasyPlanner	TE More Examples *p. 334* SE Practice Problem *p. 335* SE Key Terms *p. 352* SE Questions and Problems *p. 354*	TE **NSES** A1, A2, B5, B6, C6, D2, F3, F4, F6
TE Teaching Tips *pp. 335–336* RP Team Learning Worksheet (Sec. 10.3)	💿 Animation: Hess's Law 💿 Lab Generator CD 💿 EasyPlanner	SE Active Reading Question *p. 336* SE Practice Problem *p. 337* TE More Examples *p. 337* SE Review Questions (10.3.A–10.3.B) *p. 338* SE Key Terms *p. 352* SE Questions and Problems *p. 354*	
TE Teaching Tip *p. 339*	💿 EasyPlanner	SE Questions and Problems *p. 354*	TE **NSES** A1, A2, B5, B6, E1, E2, F1, F3, F4, F6
TE Teaching Tip *p. 340* TE Meeting Individual Needs *p. 341* TE Meeting Individual Needs *p. 342* TE Meeting Individual Needs *p. 343* TE Meeting Individual Needs *p. 344*	🎞 Transparency: Figure 10.6 🎞 Transparency: Figure 10.7 💿 EasyPlanner	SE Active Reading Question *p. 344* SE Critical Thinking *p. 346* SE Key Terms *p. 352* SE Questions and Problems *p. 354*	
TE Teaching Tips *pp. 346, 348* TE Meeting Individual Needs *p. 348* RP Team Learning Worksheet (Sec. 10.4)	💿 EasyPlanner	SE Active Reading Question *p. 348* SE Critical Thinking *p. 349* SE Review Questions (10.4.A–10.4.C) *p. 350* SE Key Terms *p. 352* SE Questions and Problems *p. 355*	

Resource Materials for Chapter 10

SE Chapter Review *pp. 351–352*

SE Critical Thinking *pp. 355–356*

SE Standardized Test Practice *p. 357*

AR English/Spanish Summaries

🔊 English Summaries Audio

🔊 Spanish Summaries Audio

RP Meeting Individual Needs Toolkit (MINT)
   Reading Concepts
   Math Concepts
   Chapter Review Worksheets
   Chapter Summaries

RP Solutions Guide

RP Standardized Test Practice

RP Chapter Tests

RP Test Bank

💿 Test Generator

Chapter 10

Overview

In this chapter our goals are for students to:

- Understand the general properties of energy

- Understand the concepts of temperature and heat

- Consider the direction of energy flow as heat

- Understand how energy flow affects internal energy

- Understand how heat is measured

- Consider the heat (enthalpy) of chemical reactions

- Understand Hess's law

- See how the quality of energy changes as it is used

- Consider the energy resources of our world

- Understand energy as a driving force for natural processes

Energy

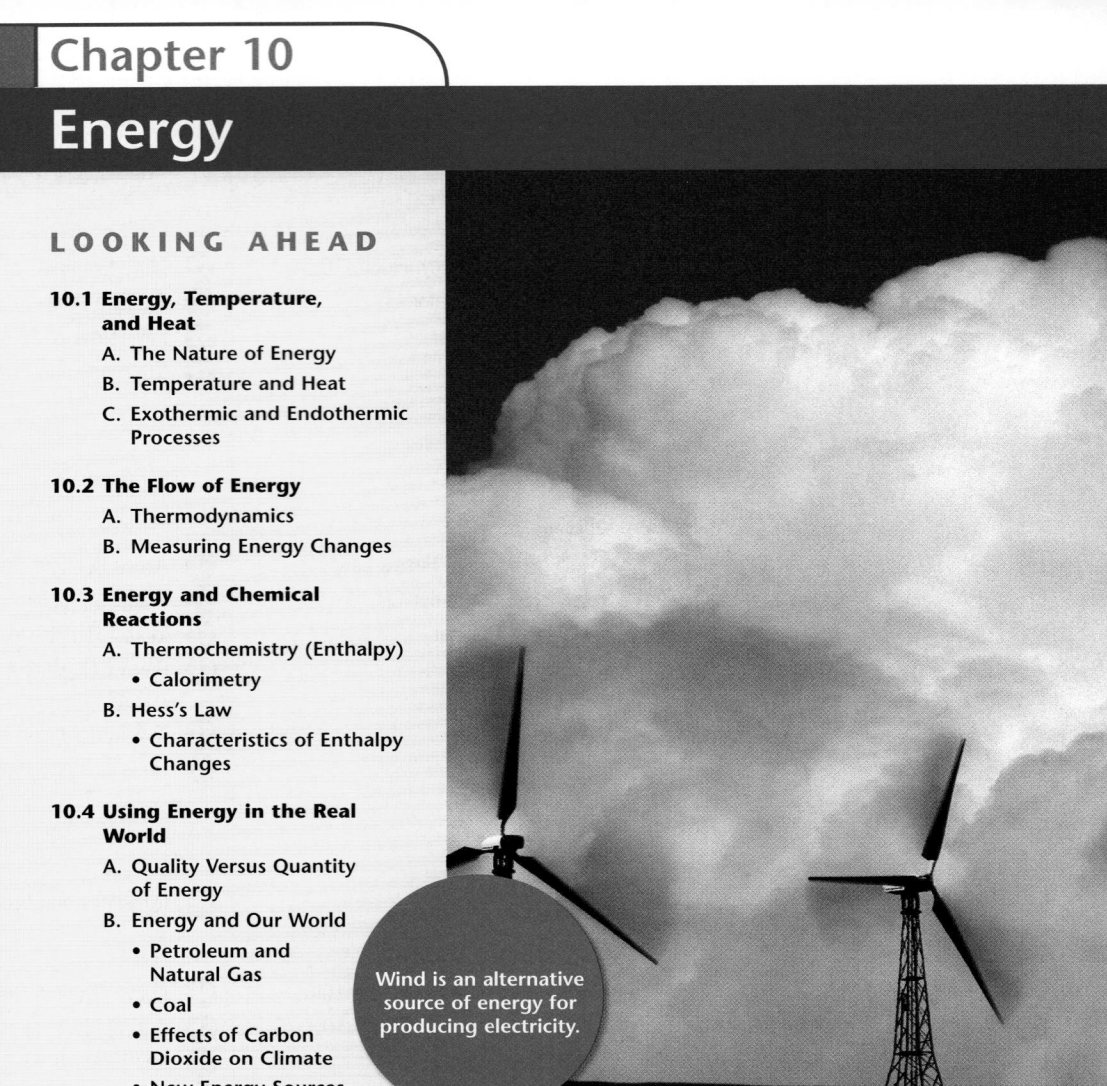

Wind is an alternative source of energy for producing electricity.

318

IN YOUR LIFE

Energy is the essence of our very existence as individuals and as a society. The food that we eat furnishes the energy to live, work, and play, just as the coal and oil consumed by manufacturing and transportation systems power our modern industrialized civilization.

Huge quantities of carbon-based fossil fuels have been available for the taking. This abundance of fuels has led to a world society with a voracious appetite for energy, consuming millions of barrels of petroleum every day. We are now dangerously dependent on the dwindling supplies of oil, and this dependence is an important source of tension among nations in today's world. In an incredibly short time we have moved from a period of ample and cheap supplies of petroleum to one of high prices and uncertain supplies. If our present standard of living is to be maintained, we must find alternatives to petroleum. To do this, we need to know the relationship between chemistry and energy, which we explore in this chapter.

WHAT DO YOU KNOW?

Prereading Questions

1. What first comes to mind when you hear the term *energy*?

2. What do calories measure?

3. List three sources of energy.

4. Have you heard of the term *entropy*? What does it mean?

Energy • Chapter 10 • **319**

Prereading Questions

1. *Answers will vary.* Energy is the ability to do work or produce heat.

2. Calories measure energy as heat.

3. *Answers will vary.* Sources include fossil fuels, wind, the sun, water, and nuclear power.

4. *Answers will vary.* Entropy is a measure of disorder.

TECHNOLOGY IN THE CLASSROOM

 Transparencies
Figures: 10.5, 10.6, 10.7

 Power Presentation DVD
 PowerPoint Slides
 Animations
 Work vs. Energy Flow
 Hess's Law
 Kinetic Molecular Theory/Heat
  Transfer
 Video
 Thermite Reaction

eEdition
EasyPlanner

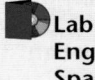**Lab Generator CD**
English Summaries CD
Spanish Summaries CD
ML Test Generator

 classzone.com

Student Preparation

Assign students to read Section 10.1 and to answer the Review Questions at the end of the section before coming to class.

 Active Learning
Team Learning Worksheet

After introducing the material in Section 10.1 in class, place students in groups and have them work together on **Section 10.1: Team Learning Worksheet**.

Homework

You may wish to assign these selected end-of-chapter problems as homework for this section: 1, 4, 5, 6, 8, 10, 11, 13, 14

Additional end-of-chapter problems can be used for extra practice.

10.1.A The Nature of Energy
Objective To understand the general properties of energy

 TEACHING TIP

It is helpful to use practical examples when introducing the concept of energy. Students can relate to examples from everyday life.

 Active Reading Question

Kinetic energy is energy due to motion (and related to mass and velocity by the formula $\frac{1}{2}mv^2$). Potential energy is energy due to position or composition.

Energy, Temperature, and Heat

Key Terms

- Energy
- Potential energy
- Kinetic energy
- Law of conservation of energy
- Work
- State function
- Temperature
- Heat
- System
- Surroundings
- Exothermic
- Endothermic

Objectives

- *To understand the general properties of energy*
- *To understand the concepts of temperature and heat*
- *To understand the direction of energy flow as heat*

A. The Nature of Energy

Although energy is a familiar concept, it is difficult to define precisely. For our purposes we will define **energy** as *the ability to do work or produce heat.* We will define these terms below.

Energy can be classified as either potential or kinetic energy. **Potential energy** is energy due to position or composition. For example, water behind a dam has potential energy that can be converted to work when the water flows down through turbines, thereby creating electricity. Attractive and repulsive forces also lead to potential energy. The energy released when gasoline is burned results from differences in attractive forces between the nuclei and electrons in the reactants and products. The **kinetic energy** of an object is energy due to the motion of the object and depends on the mass of the object m and its velocity v: $KE = \frac{1}{2}mv^2$.

 Active Reading Question

Explain the difference between kinetic energy and potential energy.

One of the most important characteristics of energy is that it is conserved. The **law of conservation of energy** states *that energy can be converted from one form to another but can be neither created nor destroyed.* That is, the energy of the universe is constant.

Although the energy of the universe is constant, it can be converted from one form to another. Consider the two balls as shown.

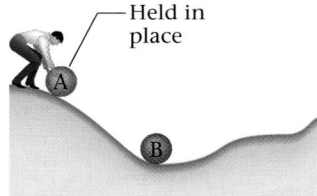

— Held in place

Ball A, because of its initially higher position, has more potential energy than ball B.

Energy
The ability to do work or to produce heat

Potential energy
Energy due to position or composition

Kinetic energy
Energy due to the motion of the object

Law of conservation of energy
Energy cannot be created or destroyed, but it can be converted from one form to another.

Teaching Support
DEMONSTRATION

Chemiluminescence: Seeing the Light!

Materials
- Several lightsticks of any color
- Knife
- 3 clear plastic cups
- Funnel and clear tubing
- 3% hydrogen peroxide solution (drugstores carry it)

Preparation Attach tubing to the funnel. Possible arrangements include a random curve, a spiral, or a zigzag pattern. Use clamps and a ringstand to achieve the desired effect. Use the knife to slice through one end of a lightstick. Pour the contents of the lightstick into one of the plastic cups. The main liquid is thick and colored. A small glass vial is found inside the lightstick as well. Separate the small glass vial (containing hydrogen peroxide) from the rest of the contents and discard it. Place about 5 mL of hydrogen peroxide into a small container (a film canister works well). You can use additional lightsticks in the same manner to make a longer demonstration.

Presentation Discuss different forms of energy with students. We most often "see" energy changes in chemical reactions as heat. Light is another form of energy observed in some chemical

When ball A is released, it moves down the hill and strikes ball B, giving this arrangement.

What has happened in going from the initial to the final arrangement? The potential energy of A has decreased because its position was lowered. However, this energy cannot disappear. Where is the energy lost by A?

Initially, the potential energy of A is changed to kinetic energy as the ball rolls down the hill. Part of this energy is transferred to B, causing it to be raised to a higher final position. Thus the potential energy of B has been increased, which means that **work** (force acting over a distance) has been performed on B. Because the final position of B is lower than the original position of A, however, some of the energy is still unaccounted for. Both balls in their final positions are at rest, so the missing energy cannot be attributed to their motions. What has happened to the remaining energy?

The answer lies in the interaction between the hill's surface and ball A. As ball A rolls down the hill, some of its kinetic energy is transferred to the surface of the hill as heat.

This transfer of energy is called *frictional heating*. The temperature of the hill increases very slightly as the ball rolls down. Thus the energy stored in A in its original position (potential energy) is distributed to B through work and to the surface of the hill by heat.

Imagine that we perform this same experiment several times, varying the surface of the hill from very smooth to very rough.

Rough surface	Smooth surface

| Less work | **More** work |
| **More** heat | Less heat |

In rolling to the bottom of the hill, A always loses the same amount of energy because its position always changes by exactly the same amount. The way that this energy transfer is divided between work and heat, however, depends on the specific conditions—the *pathway*.

Work
Force acting over a distance

10.1 • Energy, Temperature, and Heat • **321**

For example,

* On rough surface
    * Energy of A ⟶ frictional heating
    * No work is done on B.
* On smooth surface
    * Energy of A ⟶ frictional heating
      ⟶ Work done on B.
      (B moves to a higher level absorbing energy.)

Regardless of the condition of the hill's surface, the *total energy* transferred will be constant, although the amounts of heat and work will differ.

> Energy change is independent of the pathway, whereas work and heat are both dependent on the pathway.

State function
A property of a system that does not depend on the pathway

This brings us to a very important idea, the state function. A **state function** is a property of the system that changes independently of its pathway. Let's consider a nonchemical example. Suppose you are traveling from Chicago to Denver. Which of the following are state functions?

Distance traveled or Change in elevation

Distance traveled from Denver to Chicago

Because the distance traveled depends on the route taken (that is, the *pathway* between Chicago and Denver), it is *not* a state function.

Change in elevation from Denver to Chicago

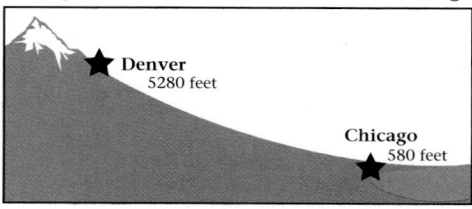

On the other hand, the change in elevation depends only on the difference between Denver's elevation (5280 ft) and Chicago's elevation (580 ft). It does not depend on the route taken between the two cities.

We can also learn about state functions from the ball example. Because ball A always goes from its initial position on the hill to the bottom of the hill, its energy change is always the same, regardless of whether the hill is smooth or bumpy. This energy is a state function—a given change in energy is independent of the pathway of the process. In contrast, work and heat are *not* state functions. For a given change in the position of A, a smooth hill produces more work and less heat than a rough hill does. That is, for a given change in the position of A, the change in energy is always the same (state function) but the way the resulting energy is distributed as heat or work depends on the nature of the hill's surface (heat and work are not state functions).

322 • Chapter 10 • Energy

B. Temperature and Heat

What does the temperature of a substance tell us about that substance? Put another way, how is warm water different from cold water? The answer lies in the motions of the water molecules. **Temperature** is a *measure of the random motions of the components of a substance.* That is, the H_2O molecules in warm water are moving around more rapidly than the H_2O molecules in cold water.

Consider an experiment in which we place 1.00 kg of hot water (90. °C) next to 1.00 kg of cold water (10. °C) in an insulated box. The water samples are separated from each other by a thin metal plate (see **Figure 10.1**). You already know what will happen: the hot water will cool down and the cold water will warm up.

Assuming that no energy is lost to the air, can we determine the final temperature of the two samples of water? Let's consider how to think about this problem.

First picture what is happening. Remember that the H_2O molecules in the hot water are moving faster than those in the cold water (see **Figure 10.2**). As a result, energy will be transferred through the metal wall from the hot water to the cold water. This energy transfer will cause the H_2O molecules in the hot water to slow down and the H_2O molecules in the cold water to speed up.

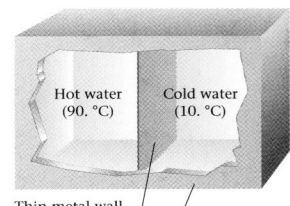
Thin metal wall
Insulated box

Figure 10.1
Equal masses of hot water and cold water separated by a thin metal wall in an insulated box

Temperature
Measure of the random motions (average kinetic energy) of the components of a substance

Heat
Flow of energy due to a temperature difference

Figure 10.2
The H_2O molecules in hot water have much greater random motions than the H_2O molecules in cold water.

Hot water (90. °C)   Cold water (10. °C)

Thus we have a transfer of energy from the hot water to the cold water. This flow of energy is called heat. **Heat** can be defined as a *flow of energy due to a temperature difference.* What will eventually happen? The two water samples will reach the same temperature (see **Figure 10.3**). At this point, how does the energy lost by the hot water compare to the energy gained by the cold water? They must be the same (remember that energy is conserved).

Figure 10.3
The water samples now have the same temperature (50. °C) and have the same random motions.

Water (50. °C)   Water (50. °C)

Top Ten Lowest Temperatures Recorded by State		
Temperature (°C)	State	Date
−62.2	Alaska	1/23/71
−56.7	Montana	1/20/54
−56.1	Utah	2/1/85
−54.4	Wyoming	2/9/33
−51.7	Colorado	2/1/85
−51.1	Idaho	1/18/43
−51.1	North Dakota	2/15/36
−51.1	Minnesota	2/2/96
−50.0	South Dakota	2/17/36
−47.8	Oregon	2/10/33

10.1 • Energy, Temperature, and Heat • **323**

 TEACHING TIPS

• We take a molecular perspective to discuss temperature and heat. This approach allows students to have a better understanding of the difference between these concepts.

• Some students have difficulty distinguishing between temperature and heat. It is important to talk about heat as a flow of energy and temperature as a measure of the "vigor" of the random motions of the components of a substance. Thermal energy is the energy that a substance contains due to the random motions of its components. Heat is the way that thermal energy is transferred from one object to another. Use Figures 10.1–10.3 to illustrate this point. Have students focus on the motion of the molecules in the compartments. Note that the molecules never mix, yet energy is transferred from one compartment to the other. The temperature in one compartment goes down and the temperature in the other compartment goes up. The energy flows from the higher-temperature compartment to the lower-temperature compartment.

TOP TEN

These temperatures can be used to review conversions among the various temperature scales. Have students convert to the Fahrenheit scale and to the Kelvin scale.

You can also use this information to initiate a discussion of global warming. Have students check the dates for the lowest temperatures and decide whether the data support the idea of global warming. What data do students need to make a better decision about whether the earth is warming?

Animation
Kinetic–Molecular Theory/Heat Transfer

10.1.C Exothermic and Endothermic Processes

Objective To consider the direction of energy flow as heat

 TEACHING TIP

To check comprehension, ask students to label the following as endothermic or exothermic.

1. Your hand gets cold when you touch ice. (exothermic)

2. Ice melts when you touch it. (endothermic)

3. Ice cream melts. (endothermic)

4. Propane burns in a propane torch. (exothermic)

5. After swimming, water drops on your skin evaporate. (endothermic)

6. Two chemicals mixing in a beaker give off heat. (exothermic)

 Video
Thermite Reaction
The thermite reaction is a very exothermic reaction.

We conclude that the final temperature is the average of the original temperatures:

$$T_{final} = \frac{T_{initial}^{hot} + T_{initial}^{cold}}{2} = \frac{90.\ °C + 10.\ °C}{2} = 50.\ °C$$

For the hot water, the temperature change is

Change in temperature (hot) = ΔT_{hot} = 90. °C − 50. °C = 40. °C

The temperature change for the cold water is

Change in temperature (cold) = ΔT_{cold} = 50. °C − 10. °C = 40. °C

In this example, the masses of hot water and cold water are equal. If they were unequal, this problem would be more complicated.

 Let's Review

Temperature and Heat

- Temperature is a measure of the random motions of the components of an object.

- Heat is a *flow* of energy due to a temperature difference.

- The random motions of the components of an object constitute the *thermal energy* of that object.

- The flow of energy called heat is the way in which thermal energy is transferred from a hot object to a colder object.

C. Exothermic and Endothermic Processes

Next we will consider the energy changes that accompany chemical reactions. To explore this idea, let's consider the striking and burning of a match. Energy is clearly released through heat as the match burns. To discuss this reaction, we divide the universe into two parts: the system and the surroundings. The **system** is the part of the universe on which we wish to focus attention; the **surroundings** include everything else in the universe. In this case we define the system as the reactants and products of the reaction. The surroundings consist of the air in the room and anything else other than the reactants and products.

When a process results in the evolution of heat, it is said to be **exothermic** (*exo-* is a prefix meaning "out of"); that is, energy flows *out of the system*. For example, in the combustion of a match, energy flows out of the system as heat. Processes that absorb energy from the surroundings are said to be **endothermic**. When the heat flow moves *into a system*, the process is endothermic. Boiling water to form steam is a common endothermic process.

Exothermic
Refers to a process in which energy (as heat) flows out of the system into the surroundings

Endothermic
Refers to a process in which energy (as heat) flows from the surroundings into the system

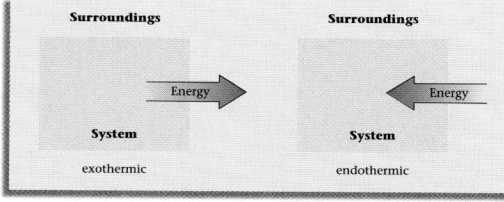

DEMONSTRATION

An Endothermic Reaction

Materials
- 250-mL beaker
- Second smaller beaker
- Wooden splint or tongue depressor
- Wooden board
- Wash bottle and water

- Barium hydroxide hydrate
- Ammonium thiocyanate

Preparation Measure about 20 g of Ba(OH)$_2$•8H$_2$O crystals into the 250-mL beaker. Place about 10 g of ammonium thiocyanate in the smaller beaker.

Presentation Place a small pool of water on the board. Place the 250-mL beaker on the board. Add the ammonium thiocyanate to the barium

hydroxide in the 250-mL beaker. Stir the two solids together with the wooden splint. After 2–3 minutes, the substances will be liquid and the beaker will be frozen to the board. When you lift the beaker, the board will stick to the bottom of it quite tightly.

Teaching Notes Ammonium chloride (7 g) or ammonium nitrate (10 g) can be substituted for the ammonium thiocyanate. The smell of ammonia is evident during the reaction. The

Define *exothermic* and *endothermic* using the term *surroundings* instead of *system*.

Where does the energy, released as heat, come from in an exothermic reaction? The answer lies in the difference in potential energies between the products and the reactants. Which has lower potential energy, the reactants or the products? We know that total energy is conserved and that energy flows from the system into the surroundings in an exothermic reaction. Thus *the energy gained by the surroundings must be equal to the energy lost by the system.* In the combustion of a match, the burned match has lost potential energy (in this case potential energy stored in the bonds of the reactants), which was transferred through heat to the surroundings (see **Figure 10.4**). The heat flow into the surroundings results from a lowering of the potential energy of the reaction system. *In any exothermic reaction, some of the potential energy stored in the chemical bonds is converted to thermal energy (random kinetic energy) via heat.*

A burning match releases energy.

Figure 10.4
The energy changes accompanying the burning of a match

SECTION 10.1
REVIEW QUESTIONS

❶ Explain why energy is a state function, and why heat and work are not.

❷ What is the significance of the law of conservation of energy?

❸ Explain the difference between potential energy and kinetic energy.

❹ Write a paragraph explaining what happens to the balls using the terms *potential energy, kinetic energy, work,* and *heat.*

❺ What is the difference between temperature and heat?

❻ Provide an example of an endothermic process and an exothermic process different from the examples in the book.

❼ Draw a picture of an endothermic reaction similar to the one for an exothermic reaction shown in Figure 10.4.

RESEARCH LINKS
CLASSZONE.COM

10.1 • Energy, Temperature, and Heat • **325**

(continued)

reaction is unusual because two solids actually react without being dissolved in a solvent.

If you do not have access to these chemicals, you can use the following chemicals to create a demonstration of endothermic and exothermic reactions. For an endothermic process, dissolve about 15 g of ammonium nitrate in about 100 mL of water (many ammonium compounds dissolve

endothermically). For an exothermic process, dissolve calcium chloride or sodium hydroxide. Allow students to touch the beaker before and after dissolution.

In an exothermic process, energy is released into the surroundings. In an endothermic process, energy is absorbed from the surroundings.

SECTION 10.1
ASSESS

SECTION 10.1
Review Questions

1. The amount of energy transferred in a chemical reaction is independent of the pathway. Heat and work change depending on the pathway. The energy change is always independent of the pathway.

2. The energy of the universe is constant. Energy is never lost or gained, but converted from one form to another.

3. Potential energy depends on the position or composition of the system. Kinetic energy depends on the motion of the object.

4. Ball A in the first figure has potential energy at the top of the hill. Ball B has zero potential energy. As ball A rolls down the hill, its potential energy decreases, but its kinetic energy increases because the velocity of the ball increases. Ball A does work on ball B because ball A hitting ball B causes ball B to roll up the hill. Ball B ends up with more potential energy due to its higher ending position. However, the potential energy of ball B is less than the initial potential energy of ball A because heat was transferred to the hill.

5. Heat is a flow of energy; temperature is a measure of the random motions of the particles in the system.

6. *Answers will vary.* Melting ice to form water is an endothermic process. A log burning in a fireplace is an exothermic process.

7. The picture should look like Figure 10.4 except the reactants are lower than the products. The ΔPE arrow should point up. The large arrow should point from the surroundings to the system and state that energy is absorbed from the surroundings as heat.

Student Preparation

Assign students to read Section 10.2 and to answer the Review Questions at the end of the section before coming to class.

 Active Learning
Team Learning Worksheet

After introducing the material in Section 10.2 in class, place students in groups and have them work together on **Section 10.2: Team Learning Worksheet**.

Homework

You may wish to assign these selected end-of-chapter problems as homework for this section: 15, 17, 19, 21, 22, 23, 24, 25a–b, 27, 28

Additional end-of-chapter problems can be used for extra practice.

10.2.A Thermodynamics

Objective To understand how energy flow affects internal energy

 TEACHING TIPS

- It is important that students think of energy from the system's point of view. Now is an excellent time to reinforce the idea that numbers representing thermodynamic quantities have two parts: the magnitude and the sign. It will be a new idea for many students to think about sign as a representation of direction.

- Emphasize that the sign convention is arbitrary. That is, because chemists chose to take the system's point of view, all signs are determined relative to the system.

The Flow of Energy

Key Terms

- Thermodynamics
- First law of thermodynamics
- Internal energy
- Calorie
- Joule

Objectives

- *To understand how energy flow affects internal energy*
- *To understand how heat is measured*

A. Thermodynamics

The study of energy is called **thermodynamics**. The law of conservation of energy is often called the **first law of thermodynamics**.

> The energy of the universe is constant.

The **internal energy**, E, of a system can be defined most precisely as the sum of the kinetic and potential energies of all "particles" in the system. The internal energy of a system can be changed by a flow of work, heat, or both.
That is,

$$\Delta E = q + w$$

where

Δ (delta) means a change in the function that follows,

q represents heat,

w represents work.

Thermodynamic quantities always consist of two parts:
- a *number*, giving the magnitude of the change
- a *sign*, indicating the direction of the flow. *The sign reflects the system's point of view.*

For example, if a quantity of energy flows *into* the system via heat (an endothermic process), q is equal to $+x$, where the *positive* sign indicates that the *system's energy is increasing*. On the other hand, when energy flows *out* of the system via heat (an exothermic process), q is equal to $-x$, where the *negative* sign indicates that the *system's energy is decreasing*.

Thermodynamics
The study of energy

First law of thermodynamics
The energy of the universe is constant.

Internal energy
Sum of the kinetic and potential energies of all particles in the system

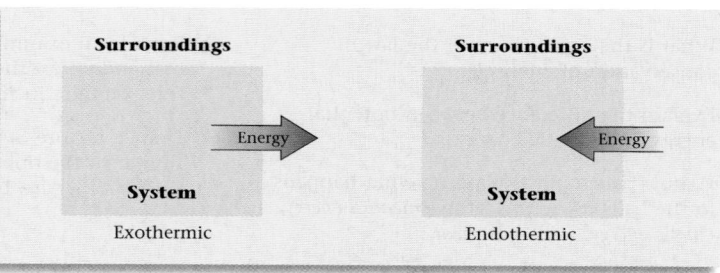

- $q = -x$
- negative $q \rightarrow$ system's energy decreases
- $\Delta E < 0$

- $q = +x$
- positive $q \rightarrow$ system's energy increases
- $\Delta E > 0$

Teaching Support
DEMONSTRATION

Spontaneous Combustion

Materials
- Potassium permanganate
- Fireproof pad or evaporating dish
- Glycerine
- Spatula

Presentation Pile 5.0 g of potassium permanganate on the fireproof pad or in the evaporating dish. With a spatula, form a depression in the center of the pile. Add about 1 mL of glycerine to the pile and step back. After a few seconds, a white puff of smoke is produced, followed by a purplish flame.

In this text the same conventions apply to the flow of work. If the system does work on the surroundings (energy flows out of the system), w is negative. If the surroundings do work on the system (energy flows into the system), w is positive. We define work from the system's point of view to be consistent for all thermodynamic quantities. That is, in this convention the signs of both q and w reflect what happens to the system; thus we use $\Delta E = q + w$.

B. Measuring Energy Changes

Earlier in this chapter we saw that when we heat a substance to a higher temperature, we increase the motions of the components of the substance—that is, we increase the thermal energy of the substance. Different materials respond differently to being heated. To explore this idea we need to introduce the common units of energy: the *calorie* and the *joule* (pronounced *jewel*).

In the metric system the **calorie** is defined as the amount of energy (heat) required to raise the temperature of one gram of water by one Celsius degree. The "calorie" with which you are probably familiar is used to measure the energy content of food and is actually a kilocalorie (1000 calories), written with a capital C (Calorie) to distinguish it from the calorie used in chemistry. The **joule** (an SI unit) can be most conveniently defined in terms of the calorie:

1 calorie = 4.184 joules

or using the normal abbreviations

1 cal = 4.184 J

You need to be able to convert between calories and joules. We will consider that conversion process in Example 10.1.

EXAMPLE 10.1

Converting Calories to Joules

Express 60.1 cal of energy in units of joules.

Solution
Where do we want to go?

| 60.1 cal | ⇨ | ? J |

What do we know?
- 60.1 cal of energy
- 1 cal = 4.184 J

How do we get there?
The conversion factor needed is $\dfrac{4.184\ \text{J}}{1\ \text{cal}}$. The result is $(60.1\ \cancel{\text{cal}})\left(\dfrac{4.184\ \text{J}}{1\ \cancel{\text{cal}}}\right) = 251\ \text{J}$.

Does it make sense?
Note that the 1 in the denominator is an exact number by definition and so does not limit the number of significant figures. The answer 251 J has the same number of significant figures as the original quantity (60.1 cal).

 Practice Problem • Exercise 10.1
How many calories of energy correspond to 28.4 J?

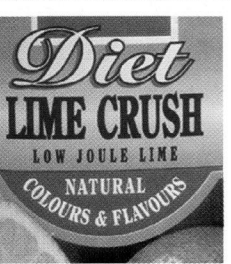

Diet drinks are now labeled as "low joule" instead of "low calorie" in European countries.

Calorie
The amount of energy needed to raise the temperature of one gram of water by one Celsius degree

---

10.2.B Measuring Energy Changes
Objective To understand how heat is measured

 LABORATORY
EXPERIMENT 40:
Energy Value of Nuts, Traditional

TEACHING TIPS

- In this section, students learn the difference between calories in real life and calories for a chemist. It offers an opportunity to talk about the differences in the way scientists use language and the way we use language in our daily lives. Point out the relationship between the calorie used in chemistry and the more familiar food Calorie, which really is a kilocalorie. Students can better understand this difference by completing the Calorie Value of Nuts experiment in the laboratory manual.

- This section also provides an excellent opportunity to review the process of unit conversion and to remind students that units should always be part of calculations and answers in chemistry.

EXAMPLE 10.1

More Examples

1. Express 34.8 cal of energy in units of joules.
   146 J

2. Express 47.3 J of energy in units of calories.
   11.3 cal

 Answer to Practice Problem 10.1

The conversion factor needed is $\dfrac{1\ \text{cal}}{4.184\ \text{J}}$, and the conversion is
$28.4\ \cancel{\text{J}} \times \dfrac{1\ \text{cal}}{4.184\ \cancel{\text{J}}} = 6.79\ \text{cal}$

Meeting Individual Needs
MATH CONCEPTS

For students who need additional help with conversions, have them read *Dimensional Analysis* located in the *Teacher Resources*. A worksheet is available to accompany the handout.

Using a molecular perspective enables us to explain why the amount of energy required to raise the temperature of water by 1 °C is directly related to the amount of water.

EXAMPLE 10.2

More Examples

1. Determine the amount of energy as heat that is required to raise the temperature of 1.0 L of water from 25.0 °C to boiling (100.0 °C). Answer in joules and calories. (1.0 L of water has a mass of 1.0 kg.)

   314,000 J (314 kJ);
   7.50×10^4 cal (75.0 kcal)

2. If 455 J of heat is transferred to 25.0 g of water at 45.0 °C, what is the final temperature of the water?

   49.3 °C

Now think about heating a substance from one temperature to another. How does the amount of substance heated affect the energy required? In 2 g of water there are twice as many molecules as in 1 g of water. It takes twice as much energy to change the temperature of 2 g of water by 1 °C, because we must change the motions of twice as many molecules in a 2-g sample as in a 1-g sample. Also, as we would expect, it takes twice as much energy to raise the temperature of a given sample of water by 2 degrees as it does to raise the temperature by 1 degree.

EXAMPLE 10.2

Calculating Energy Requirements

Determine the amount of energy (heat) in joules required to raise the temperature of 7.40 g water from 29.0 °C to 46.0 °C.

Solution

Where do we want to go?

What do we know?

- Mass of water = 7.40 g
- Initial temperature = 29.0 °C
- Final temperature = 46.0 °C
- 1 cal = 4.184 J

How do we get there?

From the discussion in the text, we know that 4.184 J of energy is required to raise the temperature of *one* gram of water by *one* Celsius degree.

Because in our case we have 7.40 g of water instead of 1.00 g, it will take 7.40 × 4.184 J to raise the temperature by one degree.

However, we want to raise the temperature of our sample of water by more than 1 °C. In fact, the temperature change required is from 29.0 °C to 46.0 °C. This is change of 17.0 °C (46.0 °C − 29.0 °C = 17.0 °C). Thus we will have to supply 17.0 times the energy necessary to raise the temperature of 7.40 g of water by 1 °C.

MATH ＋÷

The result you will get on your calculator is 526.3472, which rounds to 526.

This calculation is summarized as follows:

$$4.184 \, \frac{J}{g \, °C} \quad \times \quad 7.40 \, g \quad \times \quad 17.0 \, °C \quad = \quad 526 \, J$$

| Energy per gram of water per degree of temperature | × | Actual grams of water | × | Actual temperature change | = | Energy required |

Teaching Support

DEMONSTRATION

Heat Up or Chill Out?

Materials

- Ammonium chloride (50 g)
- Calcium chloride anhydrous (30 g)
- 2 small resealable storage bags
- Graduated cylinder
- Water

Preparation Measure 30 g calcium chloride and place it in a small resealable bag, label it "hot," and seal it. Measure 50 g ammonium chloride and place it into a second resealable bag, label it "cold," and seal it.

Presentation Introduce the idea that dissolving a solid can be an exothermic or endothermic process. Explain that common hot or cold packs used to relieve sore muscles are often based on this idea. Pour about 25 mL of water into the graduated cylinder. Open one of the plastic bags and pour in the water. Reseal the bag and shake it to mix the contents well. Repeat the process with the other plastic bag. Pass both bags around the class so that students can directly observe the temperature change associated with dissolving the solids.

Does it make sense?

The original measurements for mass and temperature have 3 significant figures which means our answer should have 3 significant figures. We are asked for the energy (heat) required. The units in our answer are J, which are energy units.

 Practice Problem • Exercise 10.2

Calculate the joules of energy required to heat 454 g of water from 5.4 °C to 98.6 °C.

Let's Review

The energy (heat) required to change the temperature of a substance depends on:

- The amount of substance being heated (number of grams)
- The temperature change (number of degrees)

There is, however, another important factor: the identity of the substance.

Different substances respond differently to being heated. We have seen that 4.184 J of energy raises the temperature of 1 g of water 1 °C. In contrast, this same amount of energy applied to 1 g of gold raises its temperature by approximately 32 °C! The point is that some substances require relatively large amounts of energy to change their temperatures, whereas others require relatively little. Chemists describe this difference by saying that substances have different heat capacities. *The amount of energy required to change the temperature of one gram of a substance by one Celsius degree* is called its **specific heat capacity** or, more commonly, its *specific heat*.

The specific heat capacities for several substances are listed in **Table 10.1.** You can see from the table that the specific heat capacity for water is very high compared to those of the other substances listed. This is why lakes and seas are much slower to respond to cooling or heating than are the surrounding land masses.

 Active Reading Question

Do metals have relatively high or low heat capacities? When in your life have you noticed this?

Specific heat capacity
The amount of energy needed to raise the temperature of one gram of a substance by one Celsius degree

Table 10.1

The Specific Heat Capacities of Some Common Substances

Substance	Specific Heat Capacity (J/g °C)
water (*l*)* (liquid)	4.184
water (*s*) (ice)	2.03
water (*g*) (steam)	2.0
aluminum (*s*)	0.89
iron (*s*)	0.45
mercury (*l*)	0.14
carbon (*s*)	0.71
silver (*s*)	0.24
gold (*s*)	0.13
copper (*s*)	0.385

*The symbols (*s*), (*l*), and (*g*) indicate the solid, liquid, and gaseous states, respectively.

Answer to Practice Problem 10.2

We know that it takes 4.184 J of energy to change the temperature of each gram of water by 1 °C, so we must multiply 4.184 by the mass of water (454 g) and the temperature change (98.6 °C − 5.4 °C = 93.2 °C).

$$4.184 \; \frac{J}{g \cdot °C} \times 454 \; g \times 93.2 \; °C$$
$$= 1.77 \times 10^5 \; J$$

TEACHING TIP

Students often do many problems involving water. Make sure you include some examples in which the specific heat capacities for other substances are needed.

MINI-DEMO

Use a heat conductivity apparatus (the apparatus looks like a star with a central circle of metal and spokes emanating from it) to demonstrate the specific heat capacities for various metals. Different metal spheres (shot) are attached to the ends of the spokes with paraffin. The apparatus is then heated at the center with a Bunsen burner. The heat travels out the spokes and the paraffin melts, causing the metal spheres to drop off at different times according to their specific heat capacities.

Active Reading Question

Metals have relatively low heat capacities. Students may have noticed that metals get hot rather quickly upon heating them (such as stirring soup with a metal spoon).

(continued)

Teaching Notes The heats of dissolution for the packs are

$$NH_4Cl(s) \rightarrow NH_4^+(aq) + Cl^-(aq)$$
$$\Delta H = 15.2 \; kJ$$
$$CaCl_2(s) \rightarrow Ca^{2+}(aq) + 2Cl^-(aq)$$
$$\Delta H = -82.8 \; kJ$$

Be sure that students do not hold the hot pack too long—it generates enough heat to produce discomfort. Dispose of the contents

according to regulations. You may also want to bring in commercial hot and cold packs to demonstrate their uses.

EXAMPLE 10.3

More Examples

1. Determine the amount of energy as heat that is required to raise the temperature of a 10.0-g sample of aluminum from 25 °C to 58 °C. Answer in joules and calories.
   294 J; 70. cal

2. If 294 J of heat is transferred to a 10.0-g sample of silver at 25 °C, what is the final temperature of the silver?
   148 °C

 Answer to Practice Problem 10.3

From Table 10.1, the specific heat capacity for solid gold is 0.13 J/g °C. Because it takes 0.13 J to change the temperature of *one* gram of gold by *one* Celsius degree, we must multiply 0.13 by the sample size (5.63 g) and the change in temperature (32 °C − 21 °C = 11 °C).

$$0.13 \, \frac{J}{g \cdot °C} \times 5.63 \, g \times 11 \, °C$$

$$= 8.1 \, J$$

We can change this energy to units of calories as follows:

$$8.1 \, J \times \frac{1 \, cal}{4.184 \, J} = 1.9 \, cal$$

EXAMPLE 10.3

Calculations Involving Specific Heat Capacity

What quantity of energy (in joules and in calories) is required to heat a piece of iron weighing 1.3 g from 25 °C to 46 °C?

Solution
Where do we want to go?

1.3 g iron		1.3 g iron
T = 25 °C	⟹ ? joules	T = 46 °C

What do we know?

- Mass of iron sample = 1.3 g
- Initial temperature = 25 °C
- Final temperature = 46 °C
- Specific heat of iron = 0.45 J/g °C
- 1 cal = 4.184 J

How do we get there?

Our task is to determine how much energy is required (J and cal). It takes 0.45 J to raise the temperature of a 1-g piece of iron by 1 °C.

1.0 g iron		1.0 g iron
T = 25 °C	⟹ 0.45 J	T = 26 °C

In this case our sample is 1.3 g, so 1.3 × 0.45 J is required for *each* degree of temperature increase.

1.3 g iron		1.3 g iron
T = 25 °C	⟹ 1.3 × 0.45 J	T = 26 °C

Because the temperature increase is 21 °C (46 °C − 25 °C = 21 °C), the total amount of energy required is

$$0.45 \, \frac{J}{g \cdot °C} \times 1.3 \, g \times 21 \, °C = 12 \, J$$

1.3 g iron		1.3 g iron
T = 25 °C	⟹ 21 × 1.3 × 0.45 J	T = 46 °C

To calculate this energy in calories, we construct the appropriate conversion factor. We want to change from joules to calories, so cal must be in the numerator and J in the denominator, where it cancels:

$$12 \, J \times = \frac{1 \, cal}{4.184 \, J} = 2.9 \, cal$$

Does it make sense?

The final units of J and cal are energy units as required. The answers have 2 significant figures because all of the measurements are given with 2 significant figures.

 Practice Problem • Exercise 10.3

A 5.63-g sample of solid gold is heated from 21 °C to 32 °C. How much energy (in joules and calories) is required?

CHEMISTRY IN YOUR WORLD

Nature Has Hot Plants

The voodoo lily is a beautiful and seductive plant. The exotic-looking lily features an elaborate reproductive mechanism—a purple spike that can reach nearly 3 feet in length and is cloaked by a hoodlike leaf. But approach to the plant reveals bad news—it smells terrible!

Despite its antisocial odor, this putrid plant has fascinated biologists for many years because of its ability to generate heat. At the peak of its metabolic activity, the plant's blossom can be as much as 15 °C above its surrounding temperature. To generate this much heat, the metabolic rate of the plant must be close to that of a flying hummingbird!

What's the purpose of this intense heat production? For a plant faced with limited food supplies in the very competitive tropical climate where it grows, heat production seems like a great waste of energy. The answer to this mystery is that the voodoo lily is pollinated mainly by carrion-loving insects. Thus the lily prepares a malodorous mixture of chemicals

characteristic of rotting meat, which it then "cooks" off into the surrounding air to attract flesh-feeding beetles and flies. Then, once the insects enter the pollination chamber, the high temperatures there (as high as 110 °F) cause the insects to remain very active to better carry out their pollination duties.

The voodoo lily is only one of many thermogenic (heat-producing) plants. These plants are of special interest to biologists because they provide opportunities to study metabolic reactions that are quite subtle in "normal" plants.

Titan Arum is reputedly the largest flower in the world.

Note that in Example 10.3, to calculate the energy (heat) required, we took the product of the specific heat capacity, the sample size in grams, and the change in temperature in Celsius degrees.

Energy (heat) required (Q)	=	Specific heat capacity (s)	×	Mass (m) in grams of sample	×	Changes in temperature (ΔT) in °C

We can represent this by the following equation:

$$Q = s \times m \times \Delta T$$

where

Q = energy (heat) required
s = specific heat capacity
m = mass of the sample in grams
ΔT = change in temperature in Celsius degrees

This equation always applies when a substance is being heated (or cooled) and no change of state occurs. Before you begin to use this equation, however, make sure you understand what it means.

MATH

The symbol Δ (the Greek letter delta) is shorthand for "change in."

Chemistry in Your World

Nature Has Hot Plants

"Nature Has Hot Plants" points out how plants use chemistry to enhance their existence. Some plants, such as walnut trees, produce a natural herbicide to kill grass around their roots to lower the competition for water. Others produce insect alarm pheromones to scare off invaders. Still others, such as the voodoo lily, produce a mixture of chemicals that attract insects to aid in pollination. Some plants produce chemicals that attract predators, such as wasps, that kill caterpillars attacking the plant. Many other examples exist as well. This topic would be a good choice for a student paper that would connect chemistry and biology.

EXAMPLE 10.4

More Examples

1. A 2.6-g sample of a metal requires 15.6 J of energy to change its temperature from 21 °C to 34 °C. Use the information in Table 10.1 to identify this metal.

   iron (Fe)

2. A sample of gold requires 3.1 J of energy to change its temperature from 19 °C to 27 °C. What is the mass of this sample of gold?

   3.0 g

 Answer to Practice Problem 10.4

Table 10.1 lists the specific heat capacities of several metals. We want to calculate the specific heat capacity (s) for this metal and then use Table 10.1 to identify the metal. Using the equation

$$Q = s \times m \times \Delta T$$

we can solve for s by dividing both sides by m (the mass of the sample) and by ΔT:

$$\frac{Q}{m \times \Delta T} = s$$

In this case,

Q = energy (heat) required
= 10.1 J

m = 2.8 g

ΔT = temperature change
= 36 °C − 21 °C = 15 °C

so

$$s = \frac{Q}{m \times \Delta T}$$

$$= \frac{10.1 \text{ J}}{(2.8 \text{ g})(15 \text{ °C})} = 0.24 \text{ J/g °C}$$

Table 10.1 shows that silver has a specific heat capacity of 0.24 J/g °C. The metal is silver.

EXAMPLE 10.4

Specific Heat Capacity Calculations: Using the Equation

A 1.6-g sample of a metal that has the appearance of gold requires 5.8 J of energy to change its temperature from 23 °C to 41 °C. Is the metal pure gold?

Solution

Where do we want to go?

Is the metal sample pure gold?

What do we know?

| 1.6 g metal |
| T = 23 °C |

⟹ 5.8 J

| 1.6 g metal |
| T = 41 °C |

$$\Delta T = 41 \text{ °C} - 23 \text{ °C} = 18 \text{ °C}$$

How do we get there?

We can calculate the value of the specific heat capacity for the metal and compare this value to the one for gold given in Table 10.1. We know that

$$Q = s \times m \times \Delta T$$

or, pictorially,

| 1.6 g metal |
| T = 23 °C |

⟹ 5.8 J = ? × 1.6 × 18

| 1.6 g metal |
| T = 41 °C |

When we divide both sides of the equation

$$Q = s \times m \times \Delta T$$

by $m \times \Delta T$, we get

$$\frac{Q}{m \times \Delta T} = \frac{s \times m \times \Delta T}{m \times \Delta T}$$

$$\frac{Q}{m \times \Delta T} = s$$

Now, we can calculate the value of s.

Q = energy (heat) required = 5.8 J

m = mass of the sample = 1.6 g

ΔT = change in temperature = 18 °C   (41 °C − 23 °C = 18 °C)

Thus

$$s = \frac{Q}{m \times \Delta T} = \frac{5.8 \text{ J}}{(1.6 \text{ g})(18 \text{ °C})} = 0.20 \text{ J/g °C}$$

As shown in Table 10.1, the specific heat capacity for gold is 0.13 J/g °C. Thus the metal must not be pure gold.

MATH

The result you will get on your calculator is 0.2013889, which rounds to 0.20.

✓ **Practice Problem • Exercise 10.4**

A 2.8-g sample of pure metal requires 10.1 J of energy to change its temperature from 21 °C to 36 °C. What is this metal? (Use Table 10.1.)

Teaching Support

DEMONSTRATION

The Fireproof Balloon

Materials

- Black balloons (9-in. diameter)
- Candle
- Medium-size beaker or plastic cup

Preparation Place 25 mL of water into one balloon. Place this balloon along with several additional balloons into the beaker, making sure that the water balloon is easy to remove.

Presentation Place a lighted candle on a level surface. Have a volunteer take a balloon, blow it up, and tie the end with a knot. Demonstrate the process yourself by picking up the water balloon and blowing it up. (*Note:* Be careful to keep your hand in front of the balloon to conceal the mass of water in the balloon.) Hold your balloon over the flame, making sure the flame is over the bottom of the balloon where the water is. Ask the volunteer to repeat the experiment with his/her balloon. At the end of the demonstration, heat the water balloon on its side while holding it over a trash can.

Teaching Notes The water in the balloon will absorb heat from the candle flame and prevent the balloon from breaking. Make sure you do not set the water balloon down because it will then be evident that it contains water.

CHEMISTRY IN YOUR WORLD

Science, Technology, and Society

Firewalking: Magic or Science?

For millennia people have been amazed at the ability of Eastern mystics to walk across beds of glowing coals without any apparent discomfort. Even in the United States, thousands of people have performed feats of firewalking as part of motivational seminars. How can this be possible? Do firewalkers have supernatural powers?

Actually, there are good scientific explanations of why firewalking is possible. First, human tissue is mainly composed of water, which has a relatively large specific heat capacity. This means that a large amount of energy must be transferred from the coals to change significantly the temperature of the feet. During the brief contact between feet and coals involved in firewalking, there is relatively little time for energy flow, so the feet do not reach a high enough temperature to cause damage.

Also, although the surface of the coals has a very high temperature, the red-hot layer is very thin. Therefore, the quantity of energy available to heat the feet is smaller than might be expected.

(Don't try this on your own!)

A group of firewalkers in Japan

SECTION 10.2
REVIEW QUESTIONS

① In our study of thermodynamics we look at changes in the internal energy of systems. To do this we consider thermodynamic quantities to consist of two parts. What are they? Why do we take the system's point of view?

② How is a food calorie different from the calorie we use in chemistry?

③ Copy and complete the following table.

Mass of water	Change in temperature	Energy (cal)	Energy (J)
100.0 g	24.2 °C		
75.0 g		1.29×10^3 cal	
	18.4 °C		59.6 J

④ Suppose you wanted to heat a mug of water (250 mL) from room temperature 25 °C to 100 °C to make a cup of tea. How much energy (in units of calories and joules) would you need from your microwave?

⑤ We apply the same amount of energy to 10.0-g samples of aluminum, iron, and silver which begin at the same temperature. Rank the metals from highest to lowest temperature after the heat is applied. (See Table 10.1.)

⑥ Determine the final temperature of a 10.0-g aluminum block originally at 25.0 °C if you apply 435 J of energy to it. (See Table 10.1.)

RESEARCH LINKS
CLASSZONE.COM

10.2 • The Flow of Energy • **333**

Chemistry in Your World

Firewalking: Magic or Science?

"Firewalking: Magic or Science?" illustrates some important points about energy transfer and the special ability of water to absorb large amounts of heat energy with a relatively small change in temperature. One of water's most useful properties is its ability to act as a coolant. Automobiles use an aqueous solution of ethylene glycol to absorb the heat produced by the engine. Likewise, many industries use water from nearby lakes and rivers as a coolant. Also, nuclear power plants use vast quantities of water to carry away the excess heat of the nuclear fission process.

This Chemistry in Your World also points out that phenomena that appear to be "magical" have logical explanations. Magicians' tricks are just that—clever manipulations of our senses that never violate the laws of nature.

SECTION 10.2
Review Questions

1. Thermodynamic quantities consist of a number and a sign. We take the system's point of view because then all thermodynamic quantities are consistent.

2. A food calorie is 1000 times larger than the calorie we use in chemistry.

3.

Mass of water	Change in temperature	Energy (cal)	Energy (J)
100.0 g	24.2 °C	2.42×10^3 cal	1.01×10^4 J
75.0 g	17.2 °C	1.29×10^3 cal	5.40×10^3 J
0.774 g	18.4 °C	14.2 cal	59.6 J

4. 1.9×10^2 cal or 7.8×10^4 J

5. Silver > iron > aluminum. The smaller the specific heat capacity, the greater the change in temperature for a given mass and amount of heat.

6. 35.4 °C

SECTION 10.3

SECTION 10.3
INTRODUCE

Student Preparation

Assign students to read Section 10.3 and to answer the Review Questions at the end of the section before coming to class.

 Active Learning
Team Learning Worksheet

After introducing the material in Section 10.3 in class, place students in groups and have them work together on **Section 10.3: Team Learning Worksheet.**

SECTION 10.3
GUIDE THE LEARNING

Homework

You may wish to assign these selected end-of-chapter problems as homework for this section: 29, 30, 31, 32, 33, 34, 35

Additional end-of-chapter problems can be used for extra practice.

10.3.A Thermochemistry (Enthalpy)

Objective To consider the enthalpy of chemical reactions

LABORATORY
EXPERIMENT 41:
Specific Heat of a Metal, CBL

LABORATORY
EXPERIMENT 42:
Which Is Your Metal?

LABORATORY
EXPERIMENT 43:
Stoichiometry and Calorimetry, CBL

EXAMPLE 10.5

More Examples

1. When 1 mol of sulfur dioxide reacts with excess oxygen to form sulfur trioxide at constant pressure, 198.2 kJ of energy is released as heat. Calculate ΔH for a process in which a 12.8-g sample of sulfur dioxide reacts with excess oxygen at constant pressure.
   39.6 kJ

SECTION 10.3
Energy and Chemical Reactions

Key Terms
• Enthalpy
• Calorimeter
• Hess's law

Objectives
• *To consider the heat (enthalpy) of chemical reactions*
• *To understand Hess's law*

A. Thermochemistry (Enthalpy)

We have seen that some reactions are exothermic (produce heat energy) and other reactions are endothermic (absorb heat energy). Chemists also like to know exactly how much energy is produced or absorbed by a given reaction. To make that process more convenient, we have invented a special energy function called **enthalpy**, which is designated by *H*. For a reaction occurring under conditions of constant pressure, the change in enthalpy (ΔH) is equal to the energy that flows as heat. That is,

$$\Delta H_p = \text{heat}$$

where the subscript *p* indicates that the process has occurred under conditions of constant pressure and Δ means "a change in." Thus the enthalpy change for a reaction (that occurs at constant pressure) is the same as the heat for that reaction.

> **Enthalpy**
> At constant pressure, a change in enthalpy (ΔH) is equal to the energy flow as heat.

EXAMPLE 10.5

Enthalpy

When 1 mol of methane (CH_4) is burned at constant pressure, 890 kJ of energy is released as heat. Calculate ΔH for a process in which a 5.8-g sample of methane is burned at constant pressure.

Solution
Where do we want to go?

| 5.8g methane burned | $\Rightarrow$ | $\Delta H = ? \text{ J}$ |

What do we know?
• 1 mol CH_4
• molar mass (CH_4) = 12.01 g/mol + 4(1.008 g/mol) = 16.04 g/mol
• constant pressure
• energy released per mol = 890 kJ
• $\Delta H = -890$ kJ/mol (CH_4) = q_p

How do we get there?
The actual value can be calculated as follows:

$$5.8 \text{ g CH}_4 \times \frac{1 \text{ mol CH}_4}{16.04 \text{ g CH}_4} = 0.36 \text{ mol CH}_4$$

$$0.36 \text{ mol CH}_4 \times \frac{-890 \text{ kJ}}{\text{mol CH}_4} = -320 \text{ kJ}$$

---

2. When 1 mol of hydrogen gas reacts with excess oxygen to form water at constant pressure, 241.8 kJ of energy is released as heat. Calculate ΔH for a process in which a 15.0-g sample of hydrogen gas reacts with excess oxygen at constant pressure.
   1.80×10^3 kJ

Thus, when a 5.8-g sample of CH_4 is burned at constant pressure,

$$\Delta H = \text{heat flow} = -320 \text{ kJ}$$

Does it make sense?

Since the mass of CH_4 burned is smaller than 1 mol, less than 890 kJ will be released as heat. The answer has 2 significant figures as required by the given quantities.

 Practice Problem • Exercise 10.5

The reaction that occurs in the heat packs used to treat sports injuries is

$$4Fe(s) + 3O_2(g) \rightarrow 2Fe_2O_3(s) \qquad \Delta H = -1652 \text{ kJ}$$

How much heat is released when 1.00 g of Fe(s) is reacted with excess $O_2(g)$?

Calorimetry

A **calorimeter** (see **Figure 10.5**) is a device used to determine the heat associated with a chemical reaction. The reaction is run in the calorimeter and the temperature change of the calorimeter is observed. Knowing the temperature change that occurs in the calorimeter and the heat capacity of the calorimeter enables us to calculate the heat energy released or absorbed by the reaction. Thus we can determine ΔH for the reaction.

Once we have measured the ΔH values for various reactions, we can use these data to *calculate* the ΔH values of other reactions. We will see how to carry out these calculations in the next section.

B. Hess's Law

One of the most important characteristics of enthalpy is that it is a state function. That is, the change in enthalpy for a given process is independent of the pathway for the process.

> In going from a particular set of reactants to a particular set of products, the change in enthalpy is the same whether the reaction takes place in one step or in a series of steps.

This principle, which is known as **Hess's law**, can be illustrated by examining the oxidation of nitrogen to produce nitrogen dioxide. The overall reaction can be written in one step, where the enthalpy change is represented by ΔH_1.

$$N_2(g) + 2O_2(g) \rightarrow 2NO_2(g) \qquad \Delta H_1 = 68 \text{ kJ}$$

This reaction can also be carried out in two distinct steps, with the enthalpy changes being designated as ΔH_2 and ΔH_3:

$$
\begin{array}{lll}
N_2(g) + O_2(g) & \rightarrow 2NO(g) & \Delta H_2 = 180 \text{ kJ} \\
2NO(g) + O_2(g) & \rightarrow 2NO_2(g) & \Delta H_3 = -112 \text{ kJ} \\
\hline
\text{Net reaction: } N_2(g) + 2O_2(g) & \rightarrow 2NO_2(g) & \Delta H_2 + \Delta H_3 = 68 \text{ kJ}
\end{array}
$$

Note that the sum of the two steps gives the net, or overall, reaction and that

$$\Delta H_1 = \Delta H_2 + \Delta H_3 = 68 \text{ kJ}$$

10.3 • Energy and Chemical Reactions • **335**

Calorimeter
A device used to determine the heat associated with a chemical or physical change

Hess's law
The change in enthalpy in going from a given set of reactants to a given set of products does not depend on the number of steps in the reaction.

Figure 10.5
A coffee-cup calorimeter made of two Styrofoam cups

Thermometer

Styrofoam cover

Styrofoam cups

Stirrer

TEACHING TIPS

- Hess's law problems relate well to the mathematics of equations. As students are already familiar with manipulating algebraic equations, this section is a good place to show the overlap of math and science. The two characteristics of enthalpy changes are easily related to algebraic concepts.

- An analogy you can use with Hess's law is paying for something at a store. If the net result is to pay the store $8, this goal can be achieved in many ways. For example, you can give the store one $5 bill and three $1 bills, or you can pay with a $10 bill and get $2 in change. No matter how many steps are involved in the process, the payment is the same.

TECHNOLOGY

 Animation
Hess's Law

 Active Reading Question

The sign tells us the direction of the energy. If a reaction is endothermic as written (heat is a *reactant*, denoted with a positive sign), reversing the reaction makes it exothermic (heat is a *product*, denoted with a negative sign).

The importance of Hess's law is that it allows us to *calculate* heats of reaction that might be difficult or inconvenient to measure directly in a calorimeter.

Characteristics of Enthalpy Changes

To use Hess's law to compute enthalpy changes for reactions, it is important to understand two characteristics of ΔH for a reaction:

Characteristics of ΔH

- If a reaction is reversed, the sign of ΔH is also reversed.
- The magnitude of ΔH is directly proportional to the quantities of reactants and products in a reaction. If the coefficients in a balanced reaction are multiplied by an integer, the value of ΔH is multiplied by the same integer.

Both these rules follow in a straightforward way from the properties of enthalpy changes. The first rule can be explained by recalling that the *sign* of ΔH indicates the *direction* of the heat flow at constant pressure. If the direction of the reaction is reversed, the direction of the heat flow also will be reversed. To see this, consider the preparation of xenon tetrafluoride, which was the first binary compound made from a noble gas:

$$Xe(g) + 2F_2(g) \rightarrow XeF_4(s) \qquad \Delta H = -251 \text{ kJ}$$

This reaction is exothermic, and 251 kJ of energy flows into the surroundings as heat. On the other hand, if the colorless XeF_4 crystals are decomposed into the elements, according to the equation

$$XeF_4(s) \rightarrow Xe(g) + 2F_2(g)$$

the opposite energy flow occurs because 251 kJ of energy must be added to the system to produce this endothermic reaction. Thus, for this reaction, $\Delta H = +251$ kJ.

The second rule comes from the fact that ΔH depends on the amount of substances reacting. For example, since 251 kJ of energy is evolved for the reaction

$$Xe(g) + 2F_2(g) \rightarrow XeF_4(s)$$

then for a preparation involving twice the quantities of reactants and products, or

$$2Xe(g) + 4F_2(g) \rightarrow 2XeF_4(s)$$

twice as much heat would be evolved:

$$\Delta H = 2(-251 \text{ kJ}) = -502 \text{ kJ}$$

Crystals of xenon tetrafluoride, the first reported binary compound containing a noble gas element

 Active Reading Question

Why is the sign of ΔH reversed if the reaction is reversed?

Teaching Support
BACKGROUND INFORMATION

The bombardier beetle (see the Chemistry in Your World feature in Chapter 7) is an insect "knowledgeable" about thermochemistry and Hess's law. The beetle protects itself from predators by mixing chemicals within its abdomen and spraying its enemy with the resulting concoction. The chemicals are hydroquinone [$C_6H_4(OH)_2(aq)$] and

hydrogen peroxide (H_2O_2). As these chemicals are mixed with a catalyst (enzyme), a fast exothermic reaction takes place that produces quinone ($C_6H_4O_2$) and water. The heat of reaction for this process is −204 kJ. This heat raises the entire solution to its boiling point and the resulting vapor is shot out in spurts (up to 30) as a hot mist with appropriate sound effects!

The appropriate steps for illustrating Hess's law follow.

$$C_6H_4(OH)_2(aq) \rightarrow C_6H_4O_2(aq) + H_2(g)$$
$$\Delta H = 177 \text{kJ}$$

$$H_2O_2(aq) \rightarrow H_2O(l) + \frac{1}{2} O_2(g)$$
$$\Delta H = -95 \text{ kJ}$$

$$H_2(g) + \frac{1}{2} O_2(g) \rightarrow H_2O(l)$$
$$\Delta H = -286 \text{ kJ}$$

$$C_6H_4(OH)_2(aq) + H_2O_2(aq) \rightarrow$$
$$C_6H_4O_2(aq) + 2H_2O(l)$$
$$\Delta H = -204 \text{ kJ}$$

EXAMPLE 10.6

Hess's Law

Two forms of carbon are graphite, the soft, black, slippery material used in "lead" pencils and as a lubricant for locks, and diamond, the brilliant, hard gemstone. Using the enthalpies of combustion for graphite (-394 kJ/mol) and diamond (-396 kJ/mol), calculate ΔH for the conversion of graphite to diamond:

$$C_{graphite}(s) \rightarrow C_{diamond}(s)$$

Solution

Where do we want to go?

$$\Delta H = ?$$

 graphite ⇨ diamond

What do we know?

- $\Delta H_{graphite}^{combustion} = -394$ kJ/mol
- $\Delta H_{diamond}^{combustion} = -396$ kJ/mol

How do we get there?

The combustion reactions are

$$C_{graphite}(s) + O_2(g) \rightarrow CO_2(g) \qquad \Delta H = -394 \text{ kJ}$$

$$C_{diamond}(s) + O_2(g) \rightarrow CO_2(g) \qquad \Delta H = -396 \text{ kJ}$$

Note that if we reverse the second reaction (which means we must change the sign of ΔH) and sum the two reactions, we obtain the desired reaction:

$$C_{graphite}(s) + O_2(g) \rightarrow CO_2(g) \qquad \Delta H = -394 \text{ kJ}$$

$$CO_2(g) \rightarrow C_{diamond}(s) + O_2(g) \qquad \Delta H = -(-396 \text{ kJ})$$

$$\overline{C_{graphite}(s) \rightarrow C_{diamond}(s) \qquad \Delta H = 2 \text{ kJ}}$$

Thus 2 kJ of energy is required to change 1 mol graphite to diamond. This process is endothermic.

✔ Practice Problem • Exercise 10.6

From the following information

$$S(s) + \tfrac{3}{2}O_2(g) \rightarrow SO_3(g) \qquad \Delta H = -395.2 \text{ kJ}$$

$$2SO_2(g) + O_2(g) \rightarrow 2SO_3(g) \qquad \Delta H = -198.2 \text{ kJ}$$

calculate ΔH for the reaction:

$$S(s) + O_2(g) \rightarrow SO_2(g)$$

EXAMPLE 10.6

More Examples

Given the following data

$$4CuO(s) \rightarrow 2Cu_2O(s) + O_2(g)$$
$$\Delta H = 288 \text{ kJ}$$

$$Cu_2O(s) \rightarrow Cu(s) + CuO(s)$$
$$\Delta H = 11 \text{ kJ}$$

calculate ΔH for the following reaction:

$$2Cu(s) + O_2(g) \rightarrow 2CuO(s)$$
$$-310. \text{ kJ}$$

✔ Answer to Practice Problem 10.6

Noting the reactants and products in the desired reaction

$$S(s) + O_2(g) \rightarrow SO_2(g)$$

we need to reverse the second equation and multiply it by $\tfrac{1}{2}$. This action reverses the sign and cuts the amount of energy by a factor of 2:

$$\tfrac{1}{2}[2SO_3(g) \rightarrow 2SO_2(g) + O_2(g)]$$
$$\Delta H = \frac{198.2 \text{ kJ}}{2}$$

or

$$SO_3(g) \rightarrow SO_2(g) + \tfrac{1}{2}O_2(g)$$
$$\Delta H = 99.1 \text{ kJ}$$

Now we add this reaction to the first reaction:

$$S(s) + \tfrac{3}{2}O_2(g) \rightarrow SO_3(g)$$
$$\Delta H = -395.2 \text{ kJ}$$

$$SO_3(g) \rightarrow SO_2(g) + \tfrac{1}{2}O_2(g)$$
$$\Delta H = 99.1 \text{ kJ}$$

$$\overline{S(s) + O_2(g) \rightarrow SO_2(g)}$$
$$\Delta H = -296.1 \text{ kJ}$$

SECTION 10.3
Review Questions

1. The sign for enthalpy in an exothermic reaction is negative because from the system's point of view, energy as heat is leaving the system.

2. To find the heat of reaction, the mass (5.0 g) must be multiplied by the specific heat capacity and the result should be multiplied by the change in temperature (9 °C).

3. Hess's law states that the change in enthalpy for a reaction is the same whether the reaction occurs in one step or in a series of steps. It is important because it allows us to calculate heats of reaction that are difficult or inconvenient to measure in a calorimeter.

4. −220.8 kJ

5. −58.0 kJ

Active Learning
Classroom Activities and Projects

For an activity to go with the Celebrity Chemical feature, see *Methane Hydrate Model* located in the *Teacher Resources*.

CELEBRITY CHEMICAL Methane (CH$_4$)

Methane is the main component of natural gas, a valuable fossil fuel. It is such a good fuel because the combustion of methane with oxygen

$$CH_4(g) + 2O_2(g) \rightarrow CO_2(g) + 2H_2O(g)$$

produces 55 kJ of energy per gram of methane. Natural gas, which is associated with petroleum deposits and contains as much as 97% methane, originated from the decomposition of plants in ancient forests that became buried in natural geological processes.

Although the methane in natural gas represents a tremendous source of energy for our civilization, an even more abundant source of methane lies in the depths of the ocean. The U.S. Geological Survey estimates that 320,000 trillion cubic feet of methane is trapped in the deep ocean near the United States. This amount is 200 times the amount of methane contained in the natural gas deposits in the United States. In the ocean, the methane is trapped in cavities formed by water molecules that are arranged very much like the water molecules in ice. These structures are called methane hydrates.

Although extraction of methane from the ocean floor offers tremendous potential benefits, it also carries risks. Methane is a "greenhouse gas"—its presence in the atmosphere helps to trap the heat from the sun. As a result, any accidental release of the methane from the ocean could produce serious warming of the earth's climate. As usual, environmental trade-offs accompany human activities.

Flaming pieces of methane hydrate

SECTION 10.3
REVIEW QUESTIONS

❶ If enthalpy is the heat for a reaction, it must have a sign as well as a magnitude. What sign should the enthalpy for an exothermic reaction have? Why?

❷ Suppose you ran a chemical reaction in the calorimeters shown in Figure 10.5. If the temperature of the solution goes from 27 °C to 36 °C for a sample of mass 5.0 g, how would you determine the energy produced by the reaction?

❸ What is Hess's law and why is it useful?

❹ The enthalpy of combustion of solid carbon to form carbon dioxide is −393.7 kJ/mol carbon, and the enthalpy of combustion of carbon monoxide to form carbon dioxide is −283.3 kJ/mol CO. Using these data calculate the change in enthalpy for the reaction

$$2C(s) + O_2(g) \rightarrow 2CO(g)$$

❺ Given the following data

$N_2(g) + 2O_2(g) \rightarrow 2NO_2(g)$	$\Delta H = 67.7$ kJ
$N_2(g) + 2O_2(g) \rightarrow N_2O_4(g)$	$\Delta H = 9.7$ kJ

calculate ΔH for $2NO_2(g) \rightarrow N_2O_4(g)$.

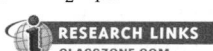
RESEARCH LINKS
CLASSZONE.COM

CELEBRITY CHEMICAL

Methane (CH$_4$)

In connection with your discussion of methane, a good student project would be to explore the topic of methane hydrates, the huge quantity of methane in the deep ocean trapped in "shells" of water molecules. Several articles about this topic have appeared recently, and it would make a particularly good web-based research project.

Using Energy in the Real World

Objectives

- *To understand how the quality of energy changes as it is used*
- *To consider the energy resources of our world*
- *To understand energy as a driving force for natural processes*

Key Terms

- Fossil fuels
- Petroleum
- Natural gas
- Coal
- Greenhouse effect
- Energy spread
- Matter spread
- Entropy
- Second law of thermodynamics

A. Quality Versus Quantity of Energy

One of the most important characteristics of energy is that it is conserved. Thus the total energy content of the universe will always be what it is now. If that is the case, why are we concerned about energy? For example, why should we worry about conserving our petroleum supply? Surprisingly, the "energy crisis" is not about the *quantity* of energy, but rather about the *quality* of energy.

To understand this idea, consider an automobile trip from Chicago to Denver. Along the way you would put gasoline into the car to get to Denver. What happens to that energy? The energy stored in the bonds of the gasoline and of the oxygen that reacts with it is changed to thermal energy, which is spread along the highway to Denver. The total quantity of energy remains the same as before the trip but the energy concentrated in the gasoline becomes widely distributed in the environment:

$$gasoline(l) + O_2(g) \rightarrow CO_2(g) + H_2O(l) + energy$$

↑ C_8H_{18} and other similar compounds

↓ Spread along the highway, heating the road and the air

Which energy is easier to use to do work: the concentrated energy in the gasoline or the thermal energy spread from Chicago to Denver? Of course, the energy concentrated in the gasoline is more convenient to use. This example illustrates a very important general principle:

> When we use energy to do work, we degrade its usefulness.

In other words, when we use energy the *quality* of that energy (its ease of use) is lowered.

In summary,

Concentrated Energy → Use the energy to do work → sPREAD ENERGy

You may have heard someone mention the "heat death" of the universe. Eventually (many eons from now), all energy will be spread evenly throughout the universe and everything will be at the same temperature. At this point it will no longer be possible to do any work. The universe will be "dead."

10.4 • Using Energy in the Real World • **339**

Objective To consider the energy resources of our world

TEACHING TIP

This section offers an excellent opportunity for students to work on a cross-curricular project with the Social Science department. Have students research energy resources in the news and on the web. They can make classroom presentations on alternative resources, have a debate about the advantages and disadvantages of different fuels, or discuss the implications of our energy use for the future.

TECHNOLOGY

 Figure 10.6

 Active Learning
Classroom Activities and Projects

For a group project dealing with Energy and Our World, see *Environmental Aspects of Energy Use* located in the *Teacher Resources*.

We don't have to worry about the heat death of the universe anytime soon, of course, but we do need to think about conserving "quality" energy supplies. The energy stored in petroleum molecules got there over millions of years through plants and simple animals absorbing energy from the sun and using this energy to construct molecules. As these organisms died and became buried, natural processes changed them into the petroleum deposits we now access for our supplies of gasoline and natural gas.

Petroleum is highly valuable because it furnishes a convenient, concentrated source of energy. Unfortunately, we are using this fuel at a much faster rate than natural processes can replace it, so we are looking for new sources of energy. The most logical energy source is the sun. *Solar energy* refers to using the sun's energy directly to do productive work in our society. We will discuss energy supplies next.

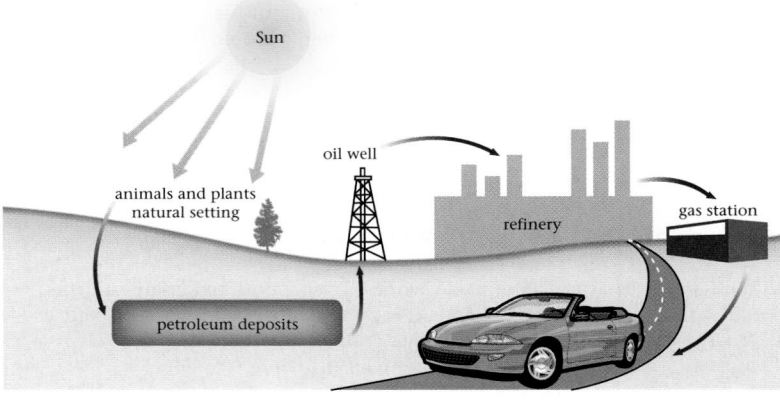

Fossil fuel
Fuel that consists of carbon-based molecules derived from the decomposition of once-living organisms

B. Energy and Our World

Woody plants, coal, petroleum, and natural gas provide a vast resource of energy that originally came from the sun. By the process of photosynthesis, plants store energy that can be claimed by burning the plants themselves or the decay products that have been converted over millions of years to **fossil fuels**. Although the United States currently depends heavily on petroleum for energy, this dependency is a relatively recent phenomenon, as shown in **Figure 10.6.** Now we will discuss some sources of energy and their effects on the environment.

■ Wood ■ Coal ▨ Petroleum/natural gas ▨ Hydro and nuclear

Figure 10.6
Energy sources used in the United States

Petroleum and Natural Gas

Although how they were produced is not completely understood, petroleum and natural gas were most likely formed from the remains of marine organisms that lived approximately 500 million years ago. **Petroleum** is a thick, dark liquid composed mostly of compounds called *hydrocarbons* that contain carbon and hydrogen. (Carbon is unique among elements in the extent to which it can bond to itself to form chains of various lengths.) **Table 10.2** gives the formulas and names for several common hydrocarbons. **Natural gas**, usually associated with petroleum deposits, consists mostly of methane, but it also contains significant amounts of ethane, propane, and butane.

The composition of petroleum varies somewhat, but it includes mostly hydrocarbons having chains that contain from 5 to more than 25 carbons. To be used efficiently, the petroleum must be separated into fractions by boiling. The lighter molecules (having the lowest boiling points) can be boiled off, leaving the heavier ones behind. The commercial uses of various petroleum fractions are shown in **Table 10.3.**

Petroleum
A thick, dark liquid composed mostly of hydrocarbon compounds

Natural gas
A gaseous fossil fuel, mostly consisting of methane (with some ethane, propane, and butane) and usually associated with petroleum deposits

Table 10.2
Names and Formulas for Some Common Hydrocarbons

Formula	Name
CH_4	Methane
C_2H_6	Ethane
C_3H_8	Propane
C_4H_{10}	Butane
C_5H_{12}	Pentane
C_6H_{14}	Hexane
C_7H_{16}	Heptane
C_8H_{18}	Octane

Table 10.3
Uses of the Various Petroleum Fractions

Petroleum Fraction in Terms of Numbers of Carbon Atoms	Major Uses
C_5-C_{10}	Gasoline
$C_{10}-C_{18}$	Kerosene Jet fuel
$C_{15}-C_{25}$	Diesel fuel Heating oil Lubricating oil
$>C_{25}$	Asphalt

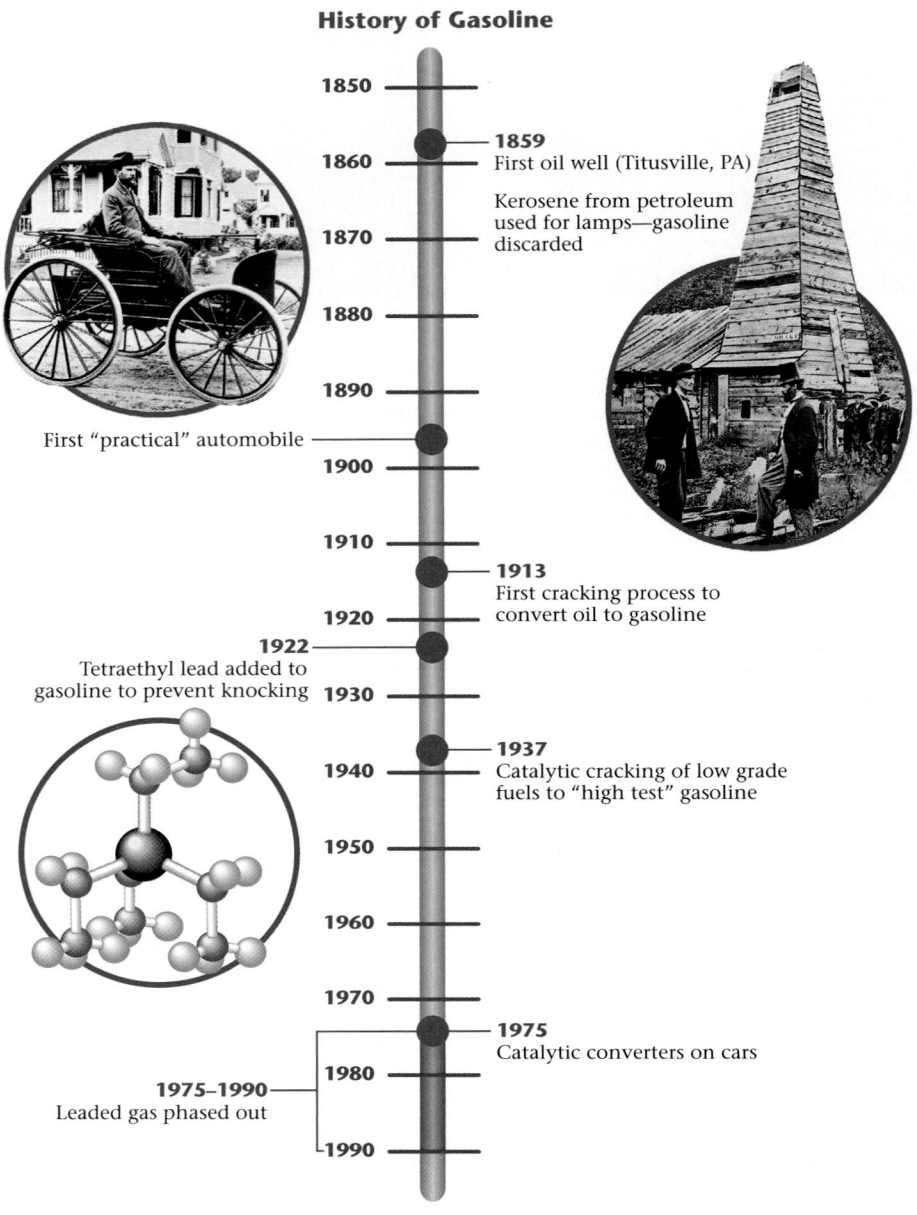

History of Gasoline

1850

1859
First oil well (Titusville, PA)

1860

Kerosene from petroleum used for lamps—gasoline discarded

1870

1880

1890

First "practical" automobile

1900

1910

1913
First cracking process to convert oil to gasoline

1920

1922
Tetraethyl lead added to gasoline to prevent knocking

1930

1937
Catalytic cracking of low grade fuels to "high test" gasoline

1940

1950

1960

1970

1975
Catalytic converters on cars

1980

1975–1990
Leaded gas phased out

1990

Coal being strip-mined

Coal

Coal was formed from the remains of plants that were buried and subjected to high pressure and heat over long periods of time. Plant materials have a high content of cellulose, a complex molecule whose empirical formula is CH_2O but whose molar mass is approximately 500,000 g/mol. After the plants and trees that grew on the earth at various times and places died and were buried, chemical changes gradually lowered the oxygen and hydrogen content of the cellulose molecules. Coal "matures" through four stages: lignite, subbituminous, bituminous, and anthracite. Each stage has a higher carbon-to-oxygen and carbon-to-hydrogen ratio; that is, the relative carbon content gradually increases. Typical elemental compositions of the various coals are given in **Table 10.4.** The energy available from the combustion of a given mass of coal increases as the carbon content increases. Anthracite is the most valuable coal, and lignite is the least valuable.

> **Coal**
> A solid fossil fuel mostly consisting of carbon

Table 10.4
Element Composition of Various Types of Coal

Type of Coal	Mass Percent of Each Element				
	C	H	O	N	S
Lignite	71	4	23	1	1
Subbituminous	77	5	16	1	1
Bituminous	80	6	8	1	5
Anthracite	92	3	3	1	1

Coal is an important and plentiful fuel in the United States, currently furnishing approximately 20% of our energy. As the supply of petroleum decreases, the share of the energy supply from coal could eventually increase to as high as 30%. However, coal is expensive and dangerous to mine underground, and the strip-mining of fertile farmland in the Midwest or of scenic land in the West causes obvious problems. In addition, the burning of coal, especially high-sulfur coal, yields air pollutants such as sulfur dioxide, which, in turn, can lead to acid rain. However, even if coal were pure carbon, the carbon dioxide produced when it was burned would still have significant effects on the earth's climate.

> **DID YOU KNOW**
>
> Coal has variable composition depending on both its age and location.

Effects of Carbon Dioxide on Climate

The earth receives a tremendous quantity of radiant energy from the sun, about 30% of which is reflected back into space by the earth's atmosphere. The remaining energy passes through the atmosphere to the earth's surface. Some of this energy is absorbed by plants for photosynthesis and some by the oceans to evaporate water, but most of it is absorbed by soil, rocks, and water, increasing the temperature of the earth's surface. This energy is, in turn, radiated from the heated surface mainly as *infrared radiation*, often called *heat radiation*.

10.4 • Using Energy in the Real World • **343**

Greenhouse effect
The process by which an atmosphere warms a planet

Greenhouse Effect The atmosphere, like window glass, is transparent to visible light but does not allow all the infrared radiation to pass back into space. Molecules in the atmosphere, principally H_2O and CO_2, strongly absorb infrared radiation and radiate it back toward the earth, as shown in **Figure 10.7**. A net amount of thermal energy is retained by the earth's atmosphere, causing the earth to be much warmer than it would be without its atmosphere. In a way, the atmosphere acts like the glass of a greenhouse, which is transparent to visible light but absorbs infrared radiation, thus raising the temperature inside the building. This **greenhouse effect** is seen even more spectacularly on Venus, where the dense atmosphere is thought to be responsible for the high surface temperature of that planet.

Thus the temperature of the earth's surface is controlled to a significant extent by the carbon dioxide and water content of the atmosphere. The effect of atmospheric moisture (humidity) is readily apparent in the Midwest, for example. In summer, when the humidity is high, the heat of the sun is retained well into the night, giving very high nighttime temperatures. In winter, the coldest temperatures always occur on clear nights, when the low humidity allows efficient radiation of energy back into space.

Active Reading Question

How does carbon dioxide act as a "greenhouse gas"?

Figure 10.7
The earth's atmosphere is transparent to visible light from the sun. This visible light strikes the earth, and part of it is changed to infrared radiation. The infrared radiation from the earth's surface is strongly absorbed by CO_2, H_2O, and other molecules present in smaller amounts (for example, CH_4 and N_2O) in the atmosphere. In effect, the atmosphere traps some of the energy, acting like the glass in a greenhouse and keeping the earth warmer than it would otherwise be.

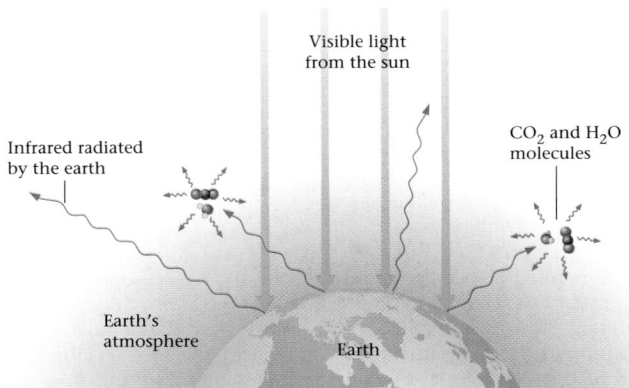

Atmospheric CO_2 The atmosphere's water content is controlled by the water cycle (evaporation and precipitation), and the average has remained constant over the years. However, as fossil fuels have been used more extensively, the carbon dioxide concentration has increased—up about 20% from 1880 to the present. Projections indicate that the carbon dioxide content of the atmosphere may be double in the twenty-first century what it was in 1880. This trend *could* increase the earth's average temperature by as much as 10 °C, causing dramatic changes in climate and greatly affecting the growth of food crops.

How well can we predict the long-term effects of carbon dioxide? Because weather has been studied for a period of time that is minuscule compared with the age of the earth, the factors that control the earth's climate in the long range are not clearly understood. For example, we do not understand what causes the earth's periodic ice ages. So it is difficult to estimate the effects of the increasing carbon dioxide levels.

Although the exact relationship between the carbon dioxide concentration in the atmosphere and the earth's temperature is not known at present, one thing is clear: The increase in the atmospheric concentration of carbon dioxide is quite dramatic (see **Figure 10.8**). We must consider the implications of this increase as we consider our future energy needs.

Figure 10.8
The atmospheric CO_2 concentration over the past 1000 years, based on ice core data and direct readings (since 1958). Note the dramatic increase in the past 100 years.

CHEMISTRY IN YOUR WORLD

Consumer Connection

Veggie Power?

Gasoline usage is as high as ever, and world petroleum supplies will eventually run out. One possible alternative to petroleum as a source of fuels and lubricants is vegetable oil—the same vegetable oil we now use to cook french fries. Researchers believe that the oils from soybeans, corn, canola, and sunflowers all have the potential to be used in cars as well as on salads.

The use of vegetable oil for fuel is not a new idea. Rudolf Diesel reportedly used peanut oil to run one of his engines at the Paris Exposition in 1900. In addition, ethyl alcohol has been used widely as a fuel in South America and as a fuel additive in the United States.

Biodiesel, a fuel made from vegetable oil, has some real advantages over regular diesel fuel. Biodiesel produces fewer pollutants. Also, because vegetable oils have no sulfur, there is no noxious sulfur dioxide in the exhaust gases. Biodiesel can run in existing engines with little modification. In addition, it is much more biodegradable than petroleum-based fuels, so spills cause less environmental damage.

Of course, biodiesel has some drawbacks. Biodiesel produces more nitrogen oxides in the exhaust than conventional diesel fuel and is less stable in storage. It can leave more gummy deposits in engines and

engines must be "winterized" by removing components that tend to solidify at low temperatures.

The best solution may be to use biodiesel as an additive to regular diesel fuel. One such fuel is known as B20 because it is 20% biodiesel and 80% conventional diesel fuel. B20 is especially attractive because of the higher lubricating ability of vegetable oils, which reduces diesel engine wear.

Vegetable oils are also being considered as replacements for motor oils and hydraulic fluids. Veggie oil fuels and lubricants seem to have a growing market as petroleum supplies decrease and as environmental laws become more severe. In Germany's Black Forest region, for example, environmental protection laws require that farm equipment use only vegetable oil fuels and lubricants. In the near future there may be veggie oil in your garage as well as in your kitchen.

This promotion bus both advertises biodiesel and demonstrates its usefulness.

Adapted from "Fill 'Er Up . . . with Veggie Oil," by Corinna Wu, as appeared in Science News, *Vol 154, December 5, 1998, p. 364.*

(continued)

This chapter also presents the opportunity to discuss the true nature of the "energy crisis." It's really not about supplies of energy. Because energy is conserved, there is always the same amount. The energy crisis is about the *quality* of energy, not the *quantity* of energy. As we "use" energy, we degrade its quality. For example, petroleum is high-quality energy because it contains lots of stored energy in a very compact

form. It took millions of years to form. When we burn petroleum to power our cars and heat our houses, we spread this energy throughout the environment via heat. This spread energy is much lower quality and is much more difficult to use. To power our society, we need concentrated sources of energy such as petroleum, coal, alcohol from corn, and oil from plants. Of course, the eventual hope is that we will learn to harness solar energy directly. Much research is

being done to find devices that can transform solar power directly into electrical power.

CRITICAL THINKING

This resolution would not solve all of our pollution problems. Most likely it would just shift the pollution to where the batteries are produced. Energy is required to make batteries and electricity is required to charge them, so the pollution would be concentrated there.

10.4.C Energy as a Driving Force

Objective To understand energy as a driving force for natural processes

TEACHING TIP

In this section, we discuss the "why" of energy. Energy is a driving force in chemical reactions. We discuss why this driving force arises and use the "why" as a basis for introducing the concept of entropy on a qualitative level.

CRITICAL THINKING

A government study concludes that burning fossil fuels to power our automobiles causes too much pollution.

What if Congress decided that all cars and trucks must be powered by batteries? Would this change solve the air pollution problems caused by transportation?

New Energy Sources

As we search for the energy sources of the future, we need to consider economic, climatic, and supply factors. There are several potential energy sources: the sun (solar), nuclear processes (fission and fusion), biomass (plants), wind, and synthetic fuels. Direct use of the sun's radiant energy to heat our homes and run our factories and transportation systems seems a sensible long-term goal. But what can we do now? Conservation of fossil fuels is one obvious step, but substitutes for fossil fuels also must be found. There is much research going on now to solve this problem.

C. Energy as a Driving Force

A major goal of science is to understand why things happen as they do. In particular, we are interested in the driving forces of nature. Why do things occur in a particular direction? For example, consider a log that has burned in a fireplace, producing ashes and heat energy. If you are sitting in front of the fireplace, you would be very surprised to see the ashes begin to absorb heat from the air and reconstruct themselves into the log. It just doesn't happen. That is, the process that always occurs is

$$\text{log} + O_2(g) \rightarrow CO_2(g) + H_2O(g) + \text{ashes} + \text{heat}$$

The reverse of this process

$$CO_2(g) + H_2O(g) + \text{ashes} + \text{heat} \rightarrow \text{log} + O_2(g)$$

never happens.

Consider another example. A gas is trapped in one end of a vessel as shown below.

When the valve is opened, what always happens? The gas spreads evenly throughout the entire container.

You would be very surprised to see the following process occur spontaneously:

So, why does this process

occur spontaneously but the reverse process never occur?

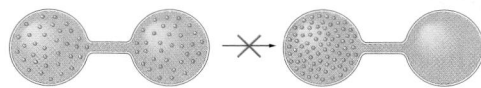

In many years of analyzing these and many other processes, scientists have discovered two very important driving forces:

- Energy spread
- Matter spread

Energy spread means that in a given process, concentrated energy is dispersed widely. This distribution happens every time an exothermic process occurs. For example, when a Bunsen burner burns, the energy stored in the fuel (natural gas—mostly methane) is dispersed into the surrounding air:

Heat

Methane

The energy that flows into the surroundings through heat increases the thermal motions of the molecules in the surroundings. In other words, this process increases the random motions of the molecules in the surroundings. *This always happens in every exothermic process.*

Matter spread means exactly what it says: the molecules of a substance are spread out and occupy a larger volume.

Ideal gas   Vacuum

Active Reading Question

The driving force for liquid water to freeze is that freezing is an exothermic process, so energy is spread from the system (water/ice) to the surroundings. The driving force for ice to melt is that liquid water has more disorder (a higher entropy) than ice, so matter is spread.

TEACHING TIP

Another everyday example of a process in which energy spread and matter spread are in opposition is when ice melts. The process of ice melting (solid to liquid) increases matter spread, but is endothermic. Ice will spontaneously melt above a certain temperature (0 °C) and water will spontaneously freeze below that temperature (assuming 1 atm). This shows that spontaneity is often temperature dependent.

After looking at thousands of processes, scientists have concluded that these two factors are the important driving forces that cause events to occur. That is, processes are favored if they involve energy spread and matter spread.

Do these driving forces ever occur in opposition? Yes, they do—in many, many processes. For example, consider ordinary table salt dissolving in water.

This process occurs spontaneously. You observe it every time you add salt to water to cook potatoes or pasta. Surprisingly, dissolving salt in water is *endothermic*. This process seems to go in the wrong direction—it involves energy concentration, not energy spread. Why does the salt dissolve? Because of matter spread. The Na^+ and Cl^- that are closely packed in the solid NaCl become spread around randomly in a much larger volume in the resulting solution. Salt dissolves in water because the favorable matter spread overcomes an unfavorable energy change.

Entropy

Entropy is a function we have invented to keep track of the natural tendency for the components of the universe to become disordered. Entropy (designated by the letter S) is a measure of disorder or randomness. As randomness increases, S increases. Which has lower entropy, solid water (ice) or gaseous water (steam)? Remember that ice contains closely packed, ordered H_2O molecules, and steam has widely dispersed, randomly moving H_2O molecules (see **Figure 10.9**). Thus ice has more order and a lower value of S.

Solid (Ice)   Gas (Steam)

Figure 10.9 Comparing the entropies of ice and steam

Active Reading Question

What is the driving force for water to freeze below 0 °C? What is the driving force for ice to melt above 0 °C?

348 • Chapter 10 • Energy

Meeting Individual Needs
VISUAL LEARNERS

To visually convey the meaning of entropy, empty a bag of marbles onto the floor. Then empty a bag of dough, or something similar, onto the floor. Compare the way in which the materials disperse on the floor. Point out how the marbles randomly scatter throughout the room, representing much disorder, or a high entropy. Explain that the dough simply clumps in one small space, representing a higher degree of order, or a low entropy. Discuss other real-world situations that are likely to have a natural tendency to become disordered. Examples include a student's bedroom and a backyard after a windstorm.

CHEMISTRY IN YOUR WORLD

Chemical Impact

Farming the Wind

In the Midwest the wind blows across fields of corn, soybeans, wheat, and wind turbines—wind turbines? It turns out that the wind that seems to blow almost continuously across the plains is now becoming the latest cash crop.

There is plenty of untapped wind power in the United States. Wind mappers rate regions on a scale of 1 to 6 (with 6 being the best) to indicate the quality of the wind resource. Wind farms are now being developed in areas rated from 4 to 6. The farmers who own the land welcome the increased income derived from the wind blowing across their land. Economists estimate that each acre devoted to wind turbines can pay royalties to the farmers of as much as $8000 per year, or many times the revenue from growing corn on that same land. Globally, wind generation of electricity has nearly quadrupled in the last five years and is expected to increase by about 60% per year in the United States. The economic feasibility of wind-generated electricity has greatly improved in the last 30 years as the wind turbines have become more efficient. Today's

turbines can produce electricity that costs about the same as that from other sources. The most impressive thing about wind power is the magnitude of the supply. According to the American Wind Energy Association in Washington, D.C., the wind power potential in the United States is comparable to or larger than the energy resources under the sands of Saudi Arabia.

Within a few years wind power could be a major source of electricity. There could be a fresh wind blowing across the energy landscape of the United States in the near future.

This State Line Wind Project along the Oregon-Washington border uses approximately 399 wind turbines to create enough electricity to power about 70,000 households.

What do you suppose happens to the disorder of the universe as energy spread and matter spread occur during a process?

 Energy spread → Faster random motions of the molecules in surroundings

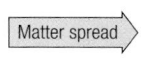 Matter spread → Components of matter are dispersed—they occupy a larger volume

It seems clear that both energy spread and matter spread lead to greater entropy (greater disorder) in the universe. This idea leads to a very important conclusion that is summarized in the **second law of thermodynamics**:

The entropy of the universe is always increasing.

That is, all processes that occur in the universe lead to a net increase in the disorder of the universe. As the universe "runs," it is always heading toward more disorder. We are plunging slowly but inevitably toward total randomness—the heat death of the universe. But don't despair, it will not happen soon.

10.4 • Using Energy in the Real World • **349**

CRITICAL THINKING

The first law of thermodynamics tells us that energy is conserved. The second law gives us some indication of the natural direction of energy flow (the second law is often described as "time's arrow"). For example, the first law cannot explain why we cannot uncook an egg by putting a cooked egg in the refrigerator, or why a ball that has just rolled down a hill (and has transferred energy to the hill) cannot roll up the hill by spontaneously gathering the newly transferred energy from the hill. The second law informs us that these phenomena are impossible.

CRITICAL THINKING

What if the first law of thermodynamics were true, but the second law were not? How would the world be different?

Hands-On Chemistry
MINI-LAB

Distribution of Wealth

Materials Each student/group will need 20 pennies.

Purpose Students will better understand the concept of a distribution.

Discussion While individual groups may have graphs that look different from a Boltzmann distribution (bell

curve), data from the entire class should give a rather smooth distribution. This activity shows students that anything could happen, but that there is also a most likely, expected configuration (10 heads and 10 tails). This idea is the main point in understanding entropy—from a probability perspective, there is a driving force in the way matter and energy spread. For example, a sample of a gas will spread to fill its container because this state has the greatest number of

configurations. It is not impossible for all of the gas molecules to gather into one corner of the room, just very improbable (so improbable we will never see it).

With 20 coins and 30 repetitions (flipping all 20 coins each time), you can expect the following (approximate) distribution. The top row is number of heads and the bottom row is the number of times that this number of heads will likely occur in the 30 repetitions.

10.4 • Using Energy in the Real World • **349**

SECTION 10.4
Review Questions

1. The amount of *useful* energy in the world is changing. As energy is used it is transformed into less useful forms. This situation creates the energy crisis—a constant quantity of energy is available but of lower quality.

2. a. bituminous

   b. lignite

   c. nitrogen

3. The quality of energy always decreases as the energy is used to do work. The energy goes from being concentrated to being spread. The "heat death" of the universe will occur when the energy is spread throughout the universe so that everything is at the same temperature and work cannot be done.

4. gasoline, kerosene, jet fuel, diesel fuel, heating oil, lubricating oil, and asphalt

5. The greenhouse effect is the trapping of infrared radiation by molecules within the atmosphere, which raises the temperature of the earth. The key molecules in this process are water and carbon dioxide.

6. The driving force of matter spread must be predominant for an endothermic reaction to occur. The matter spread must overcome an energy change that occurs in opposition to it (energy concentration).

7. Entropy is a measure of the disorder of the system. A gas has higher entropy because it consists of relatively widely spaced, randomly moving particles. A solid contains particles that are closely packed and ordered.

HANDS-ON CHEMISTRY   • MINI-LAB •

Distribution of Wealth

Materials
- 20 pennies
- Graph paper

Procedure

1. Use 20 pennies. Flip each penny and record the number of heads (head count). Do this 30 times.

2. Determine the frequency of each head count by counting the number of times each different head count appears.

Results/Analysis

1. Construct a bar graph of frequency versus head count.

2. Obtain data from the other groups in your class and make a bar graph of frequency versus head count for all of the data.

3. How can these graphs be related to probability?

SECTION 10.4
REVIEW QUESTIONS

❶ If energy is conserved how can there be an "energy crisis"?

❷ Use the charts below to answer the following questions.

Lignite

1%
1%
23%
4%
71%

- sulfur
- nitrogen
- oxygen
- hydrogen
- carbon

Bituminous

5%
1%
8%
6%
80%

- sulfur
- nitrogen
- oxygen
- hydrogen
- carbon

a. Which type of coal contains the larger percent mass of carbon?

b. Which type of coal contains the larger percent mass of sulfur?

c. Which element is present in equal amounts in both types of carbon?

❸ What does the "heat death" of the universe have to do with quality of energy?

❹ What are three uses of petroleum fractions?

❺ What is the greenhouse effect and what are the key molecules which cause it?

❻ What driving force must be predominant in order for an endothermic reaction to occur? Why?

❼ What is meant by the term *entropy*? Which has higher entropy, a solid or a gas of a particular compound at the same temperature? Why?

RESEARCH LINKS
CLASSZONE.COM

(continued)

0	1	2	3	4	5	6	7	8	9	10	11	12	13	14	15	16	17	18	19	20
0	0	0	0	0	0	0	1	2	4	5	5	5	4	2	1	0	0	0	0	0

With 15 groups (450 repetitions), we can expect the following (approximate) distribution (the top row is number of heads).

0	1	2	3	4	5	6	7	8	9	10	11	12	13	14	15	16	17	18	19	20
0	0	0	0	2	7	17	33	54	72	79	72	54	33	17	7	2	0	0	0	0

Chapter 10 Review

Key Terms

10.1 Energy

Potential energy

Kinetic energy

Law of conservation of energy

Work

State function

Temperature

Heat

System

Surroundings

Exothermic

Endothermic

Key Ideas

10.1 Energy, Temperature, and Heat

- Energy is conserved.
- The law of conservation of energy states that energy is neither created or destroyed in any process.
- In a process, energy can be changed from one form to another but the amount of energy remains constant.
- Thermodynamics is the study of energy and its changes.
- Energy is classified as one of the following:
  - Kinetic energy—energy due to the motion of an object
  - Potential energy—energy due to the position or composition of an object
- Some functions, called state functions, depend only on the beginning and final states of the system, not on the specific pathway followed.
  - Energy is a state function.
  - Heat and work are not state functions.
- Temperature indicates the vigor of the random motions of the components of that substance.
- Thermal energy is the sum of the energy produced by the random motions of the components.
- Heat is a flow of energy between two objects due to a temperature difference between the objects.
  - An exothermic process is one in which energy as heat flows out of the system into the surroundings.
  - An endothermic process is one in which energy as heat flows into the system from the surroundings.
  - The common units for heat are calories and joules.

RESEARCH LINKS
CLASSZONE.COM

Meeting Individual Needs
CHAPTER REVIEW
Chapter 10 Review Worksheet at the appropriate level: **Basic**   **Standard**   **Challenge**
CHAPTER SUMMARY
A **Chapter Summary** that includes additional Active Reading Questions for Chapter 10 is available.

Assessment Resources
CHAPTER 10
Chapter 10 Test
TECHNOLOGY
Computerized Test Bank for Chapter 10

10.2 Thermodynamics

First law of thermodynamics

Internal energy

Calorie

Joule

10.2 The Flow of Energy

■ Internal energy (E) is the sum of the kinetic and potential energy associated with an object.

    • Internal energy (E) can be changed by two types of energy flow:

        ◆ Heat (q)

        ◆ Work (w)

    • $\Delta E = q + w$

■ Specific heat capacity is the energy required to change the temperature of a mass of one gram of a substance by one Celsius degree.

10.3 Enthalpy

Calorimeter

Hess's law

10.3 Energy and Chemical Reactions

■ For a process carried out at constant pressure, the change in enthalpy (ΔH) of that process is equal to the heat.

Characteristics of ΔH

• If a reaction is reversed, the sign of ΔH is also reversed.

• The magnitude of ΔH is directly proportional to the quantities of reactants and products in a reaction. If the coefficients in a balanced reaction are multiplied by an integer, the value of ΔH is multiplied by the same integer.

■ Hess's law enables the calculation of the heat for a given reaction from known heats of related reactions.

■ A calorimeter is a device used to measure the heat associated with a given chemical reaction.

10.4 Fossil fuels

Petroleum

Natural gas

Coal

Greenhouse effect

Energy spread

Matter spread

Entropy

Second law of
    thermodynamics

10.4 Using Energy in the Real World

■ Although energy is conserved in every process, the quality (usefulness) of the energy decreases in every real process.

■ Natural processes occur in the direction that leads to an increase in the disorder (increase in entropy) of the universe.

    • The principal driving forces for natural processes can be described in terms of "matter spread" and "energy spread."

■ Our world has many sources of energy. The use of this energy affects the environment in various ways.

RESEARCH LINKS
CLASSZONE.COM

All exercises with blue numbers have answers in the back of this book.

10.1 Energy, Temperature, and Heat

A. The Nature of Energy

1. Explain the difference between kinetic and potential energy.

2. Why isn't all energy available for work?

3. Explain what is meant by the term *state function*. Provide examples of state functions.

4. Which ball has the higher potential energy? Explain.

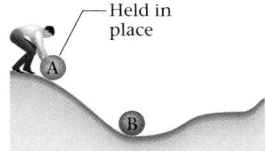
Held in place
A
B

5. The law of conservation of energy means that energy is a state function. Explain why.

B. Temperature and Heat

6. Explain the differences among heat, temperature, and thermal energy.

7. Do each of the following depend on the amount of substance you have? Explain.

    a. temperature

    b. thermal energy

8. Provide a molecular-level explanation of why the temperatures of a cold soft drink and hot coffee in the same room will eventually be the same.

9. In which case is more heat involved: mixing 100.0-g samples of 90 °C water and 80 °C water or mixing 100.0-g samples of 60 °C water and 10 °C water? Assume no heat is lost to the environment.

10. If 100.0 g of water at 90 °C is added to 50.0 g of water at 10 °C, estimate the final temperature of the water. Explain your reasoning.

C. Exothermic and Endothermic Processes

11. What is meant by potential energy in a chemical reaction? Where is it located?

12. What does it mean for a chemical to have a low potential energy?

13. In an endothermic reaction, do the reactants or the products have the lower potential energy?

14. Are the following processes exothermic or endothermic?

    a. When solid KBr is dissolved in water, the solution gets colder.

    b. Natural gas (CH_4) is burned in a furnace.

    c. When concentrated sulfuric acid is added to water, the solution gets very hot.

    d. Water is boiled in a teakettle.

10.2 The Flow of Energy

A. Thermodynamics

15. What does it mean when energy is reported with a negative sign? A positive sign?

16. What does it mean when work is reported with a negative sign? A positive sign?

17. In thermodynamics, the chemist takes the system's point of view. Explain.

18. How do engineers define *energy* and *work* differently from chemists? Why do engineers take this approach?

19. Calculate ΔE for each of the following cases.

    a. $q = +51$ kJ, $w = -15$ kJ

    b. $q = +100.$ kJ, $w = -65$ kJ

    c. $q = -65$ kJ, $w = -20.$ kJ

20. A gas absorbs 45 kJ of heat and does 29 kJ of work. Calculate ΔE.

21. A system releases 125 kJ of heat, and 104 kJ of work is done on it. Calculate ΔE.

B. Measuring Energy Changes

22. Describe what happens to the molecules in a sample of ice as the sample is slowly heated until it liquefies and then vaporizes.

23. Metallic substances tend to have (lower/higher) specific heat capacities than nonmetallic substances.

24. If it takes 526 J of energy to warm 7.40 g of water by 17 °C, how much energy would be needed to warm 7.40 g of water by 55 °C?

25. Convert the following numbers of calories or kilocalories into joules or kilojoules.

    a. 7845 cal

    b. 4.55×10^4 cal

    c. 62.142 kcal

    d. 43,024 cal

Chapter 10 Assessment

1. Kinetic energy is energy of motion. Potential energy is energy of position.

2. Some energy is given off in other forms such as heat or light.

3. A state function is a function that is not dependent on the pathway. Energy is an example of a state function; heat and work are not state functions.

4. Ball A has higher potential energy because of its higher position initially.

5. Because energy is conserved in any process, the pathway of the process does not matter. Thus energy is a state function.

6. Heat is a flow of energy due to a temperature difference; temperature is a measure of the average kinetic energy of a substance; thermal energy comes from the random motion of the components of the substance.

7. (a) No; temperature is a measure of average kinetic energy. (b) Yes; the thermal energy is from the random motions of the components of an object.

8. The particles in the hot coffee are moving faster than the particles in the cold soft drink. Because they are in the same room, they are both in contact with air at the same temperature. The particles in the coffee will slow down (a decrease in temperature) and the particles in the soft drink will speed up (an increase in temperature). Eventually the kinetic energy of the two samples will be the same.

9. There is more heat involved in mixing 100.0-g samples of 60 °C and 10 °C water because there is a larger temperature difference.

10. The final temperature should be less than 90 °C and greater than 50 °C. If the water samples had equal mass, the final temperature would be the average of the two (50 °C). Because we have more of the warmer water, the final temperature will be higher than the average of the two temperatures. (*Note:* The actual temperature would be 63 °C).

11. The potential energy is the energy available to do work. Potential energy in a chemical reaction is stored in the chemical bonds.

12. The chemical is stable; the bonds holding the atoms in the molecule are strong.

13. the reactants

14. (a) endothermic
(b) exothermic
(c) exothermic
(d) endothermic

15. The process is exothermic; the process is endothermic.

16. The system does work on the surroundings; the surroundings do work on the system.

17. The chemist chooses the sign based on whether energy flows from the system (negative sign) or into the system (positive sign).

18. Engineers make machines that do work (the machine is the system and work is done on the surroundings). Thus they define work from the surroundings' point of view. Work done by the system has a positive sign (which is opposite from the way a chemist thinks).

19. (a) 36 kJ
(b) 35 kJ
(c) −85 kJ

20. 16 kJ

21. −21 kJ

22. In ice, the water molecules are held together rigidly in fixed positions. As the sample is heated, the molecules vibrate but stay in their positions until the melting point is reached. Once the melting point is reached, the molecules move around much more freely (although they are still held together). As more heat is applied, the molecules move more quickly and freely until the boiling point is reached. When the individual molecules are moving quickly enough to overcome the forces holding them together, they escape from the liquid. As the molecules of the vapor are heated, they move more and more quickly.

23. lower

24. 1.70×10^3 J

25. (a) 32,820 J; 32.82 kJ
(b) 1.90×10^5 J; 190. kJ
(c) 2.600×10^5 J; 260. kJ
(d) 1.80×10^5 J; 180. kJ

26. 0.711 J/g °C

27. Gold (it has the smallest specific heat capacity)

28. 1.42 J/g °C

29. The reaction is exothermic; energy (in the form of heat) is released.

30. (a) 2.54×10^3 kJ
(b) 7.4×10^3 kJ
(c) 693 kJ

31. −55.5 kJ

32. −296.1 J

33. 226 kJ

34. −233 J

35. −11 kJ

36. The quality of energy tells us the form of the energy (potential or kinetic). The quantity of energy tells us how much is present. The total amount (or quantity) is conserved. When potential energy is converted to kinetic energy, we say that the quality is decreasing.

37. If there is no temperature difference, there can be no flow of energy.

• Chapter 10 • Energy

26. If 7.24 kJ of heat is applied to a 952-g block of metal, the temperature increases by 10.7 °C. Calculate the specific heat capacity of the metal in J/g °C.

27. Three 75.0-g samples of copper, silver, and gold are available. Each of these samples is initially at 24.0 °C, and then 2.00 kJ of heat is applied to each sample. Which sample will end up at the highest temperature?

28. A 35.2-g sample of metal X requires 1251 J of energy to heat the sample by 25.0 °C. Calculate the specific heat capacity of this metal.

10.3 Energy and Chemical Reactions

A. Thermochemistry (Enthalpy)

29. The equation for the fermentation of glucose to alcohol and carbon dioxide is

$$C_6H_{12}O_6(aq) \rightarrow 2C_2H_5OH(aq) + 2CO_2(g)$$

The enthalpy change for the reaction is −67 kJ. Is the reaction endothermic or exothermic? Is energy, in the form of heat, absorbed or released as the reaction occurs?

30. For the reaction

$$S(s) + O_2(g) \rightarrow SO_2(g) \quad \Delta H = -296 \text{ kJ/mol}$$

a. How much heat is released when 275 g of sulfur is burned in excess oxygen?

b. How much heat is released when 25 mol of sulfur is burned in excess oxygen?

c. How much heat is released when 150. g of sulfur dioxide is produced?

31. Calculate the enthalpy change when 1.00 g of methane is burned in excess oxygen according to the reaction

$$CH_4(g) + 2O_2(g) \rightarrow CO_2(g) + H_2O(l)$$
$$\Delta H = -891 \text{ kJ/mol}$$

B. Hess's Law

32. Given the following data:

$$S(s) + \tfrac{3}{2}O_2(g) \rightarrow SO_3(g) \qquad \Delta H = -395.2 \text{ kJ}$$
$$2SO_2(g) + O_2(g) \rightarrow 2SO_3(g) \qquad \Delta H = -198.2 \text{ kJ}$$

calculate ΔH for the reaction

$$S(s) + O_2(g) \rightarrow SO_2(g)$$

• Chapter 10 • Energy

33. Given the following data:

$$C_2H_2(g) + \tfrac{5}{2}O_2(g) \rightarrow 2CO_2(g) + H_2O(l)$$
$$\Delta H = -1300. \text{ kJ}$$
$$C(s) + O_2(g) \rightarrow CO_2(g) \quad \Delta H = -394 \text{ kJ}$$
$$H_2(g) + \tfrac{1}{2}O_2(g) \rightarrow H_2O(l) \quad \Delta H = -286 \text{ kJ}$$

calculate ΔH for the reaction

$$2C(s) + H_2(g) \rightarrow C_2H_2(g)$$

34. Given the following data:

$$2O_3(g) \rightarrow 3O_2(g) \qquad \Delta H = -427 \text{ kJ}$$
$$O_2(g) \rightarrow 2O(g) \qquad \Delta H = +495 \text{ kJ}$$
$$NO(g) + O_3(g) \rightarrow NO_2(g) + O_2(g)$$
$$\Delta H = -199 \text{ kJ}$$

calculate ΔH for the reaction

$$NO(g) + O(g) \rightarrow NO_2(g)$$

35. Given the following data:

$$Fe_2O_3(s) + 3CO(g) \rightarrow 2Fe(s) + 3CO_2(g)$$
$$\Delta H° = -23 \text{ kJ}$$
$$3Fe_2O_3(s) + CO(g) \rightarrow 2Fe_3O_4(s) + CO_2(g)$$
$$\Delta H° = -39 \text{ kJ}$$
$$Fe_3O_4(s) + CO(g) \rightarrow 3FeO(s) + CO_2(g)$$
$$\Delta H° = -18 \text{ kJ}$$

calculate $\Delta H°$ for the reaction

$$FeO(s) + CO(g) \rightarrow Fe(s) + CO_2(g)$$

10.4 Using Energy in the Real World

A. Quality Versus Quantity of Energy

36. What is the difference between the quality of energy and the quantity of energy? Which is decreasing?

37. Why can no work be done when everything in the universe is at the same temperature?

B. Energy and Our World

38. What was the advantage of using tetraethyl lead in gasoline? What were two disadvantages?

39. Why do we need some greenhouse gases? What is the problem with having too much of the greenhouse gases?

40. Which energy sources used in the United States have declined the most in the last 150 years? Which have increased the most?

• Chapter 10 • Energy

38. Tetraethyl lead reduces engine "knocking." It also lowers the effectiveness of catalytic converters (which lower air pollution) and increases the amount of lead in the environment.

39. If it were not for greenhouse gases, the surface temperature of the earth would be much colder. Having too large a quantity of greenhouse gases may cause the surface

temperature of the earth to rise to dangerous levels.

40. Wood has decreased the most. Nuclear and petroleum/natural gas have increased the most (see Figure 10.6).

• Chapter 10 • Energy

C. Energy as a Driving Force

41. Why can't the first law of thermodynamics explain why a ball doesn't spontaneously roll up a hill?

42. What is meant by the term *driving force*?

43. What is the driving force of an exothermic reaction—matter spread or energy spread? Explain.

44. Exothermic reactions have a driving force. Nevertheless, water melting into a liquid is endothermic and this process occurs at room conditions. Explain why.

Critical Thinking

45. Consider a sample of *steam* (water in the gaseous state) at 150 °C. Describe what happens to the molecules in the sample as the sample is slowly cooled until it liquefies and then solidifies.

46. Convert the following numbers of kilojoules into kilocalories. (Remember: kilo means 1000.)

    a. 462.4 kJ

    b. 18.28 kJ

    c. 1.014 kJ

    d. 190.5 kJ

47. Perform the indicated conversions.

    a. 45.62 kcal into kilojoules

    b. 72.94 kJ into kilocalories

    c. 2.751 kJ into calories

    d. 5.721 kcal into joules

48. Calculate the amount of energy required (in calories) to heat 145 g of water from 22.3 °C to 75.0 °C.

49. It takes 1.25 kJ of energy to heat a certain sample of pure silver from 12.0 °C to 15.2 °C. Calculate the mass of the sample of silver.

50. If 50. J of heat is applied to 10. g of iron, by how much will the temperature of the iron increase? (See Table 10.1.)

51. The specific heat capacity of gold is 0.13 J/g °C. Calculate the specific heat capacity of gold in cal/g °C.

52. Calculate the amount of energy required (in joules) to heat 2.5 kg of water from 18.5 °C to 55.0 °C.

53. If 10. J of heat is applied to 5.0-g samples of each of the substances listed in Table 10.1, which substance's temperature will increase the most? Which substance's temperature will increase the least?

54. A 50.0-g sample of water at 100. °C is poured into a 50.0-g sample of water at 25 °C. What will be the final temperature of the water?

55. A 25.0-g sample of pure iron at 85 °C is dropped into 75 g of water at 20. °C. What is the final temperature of the water–iron mixture?

56. If it takes 4.5 J of energy to warm 5.0 g of aluminum from 25 °C to a certain higher temperature, then it will take _____ J to warm 10. g of aluminum over the same temperature interval.

57. For each of the substances listed in Table 10.1, calculate the quantity of heat required to heat 150. g of the substance by 11.2 °C.

58. Suppose you have 10.0-g samples of each of the substances listed in Table 10.1 and that 1.00 kJ of heat is applied to each of these samples. By what amount would the temperature of each sample be raised?

59. Calculate ΔE for each of the following.

    a. $q = -47$ kJ, $w = +88$ kJ

    b. $q = +82$ kJ, $w = +47$ kJ

    c. $q = +47$ kJ, $w = 0$

    d. In which of these cases do the surroundings do work on the system?

60. Are the following processes exothermic or endothermic?

    a. the combustion of gasoline in a car engine

    b. water condensing on a cold pipe

    c. $CO_2(s) \rightarrow CO_2(g)$

    d. $F_2(g) \rightarrow 2F(g)$

---

constant during this process). As the liquid water cools, the molecules move more slowly and are interacting. At 0 °C the liquid water freezes.

46. (a) 110.5 kcal
(b) 4.369 kcal
(c) 0.2424 kcal
(d) 45.53 kcal

47. (a) 190.9 kJ
(b) 17.43 kJ
(c) 657.5 cal
(d) 2.394×10^4 J

48. 7.64×10^3 cal

49. 1.6×10^3 g silver

50. 11 °C

51. 0.031 cal/g °C

52. 3.8×10^5 J

53. For a given mass of substance, the substance with the smallest specific heat capacity (gold, 0.13 J/g °C) will undergo the largest increase in temperature. Conversely, the substance with the largest specific heat capacity (water, 4.184 J/g °C) will undergo the smallest increase in temperature.

54. 63 °C

55. 22 °C

56. 9.0 J

57.

Substance	Heat Required
water (l)	7.03×10^3 J
water (s)	3.41×10^3 J
water (g)	3.4×10^3 J
aluminum	1.5×10^3 J
iron	7.6×10^3 J
mercury	2.4×10^3 J
carbon	1.2×10^3 J
silver	4.0×10^3 J
gold	2.2×10^3 J

58.

Substance	Temperature Change
water (l)	23.9 °C
water (s)	49.3 °C
water (g)	50. °C
aluminum	1.1×10^2 °C
iron	2.2×10^2 °C
mercury	7.1×10^2 °C
carbon	1.4×10^2 °C
silver	4.2×10^2 °C
gold	7.7×10^2 °C

---

41. The first law of thermodynamics tells us that the total amount of energy is constant. It does not tell us anything about direction or energy transfer.

42. A driving force tends to make a process occur. For example, when we open a pressurized tank of gas, the gas will move from the tank to the surroundings. Moving from high to low pressure is a driving force for a gas.

43. The driving force of an exothermic reaction is energy spread. In an exothermic reaction energy is transferred from the system to the surroundings.

44. The energy of the surroundings is used to melt solid water. The temperature of the water will eventually reach that of the room, and room temperature is higher than the melting point of water. In addition, liquid water has greater entropy than solid water, so entropy is the driving force in this process.

45. As the steam is cooled, the molecules of vapor gradually slow down (decrease in kinetic energy). At 100 °C, the vapor condenses into a liquid (the temperature is

59. (a) 41 kJ
    (b) 129 kJ
    (c) 47 kJ
    (d) a and b

60. (a) exothermic
    (b) exothermic
    (c) endothermic
    (d) endothermic

61. (a) 1652 kJ released (1650 kJ
    with 3 significant figures)
    (b) 826 kJ released
    (c) 7.39 kJ released
    (d) 34.4 kJ released

62. $(\frac{1}{2})C \rightarrow A + B + D + F$;
    47 kJ/mol

63. 4.9×10^3 g, 4.9 L

64. About 9 hours at 4.0 mi/h

65. (a) 1460 J
    (b) We assume these to be the
    same.
    (c) The initial temperature is
    100.0 °C and the final
    temperature is 21.31 °C.
    (d) 0.388 J/g °C
    (e) The metal is zinc.

61. The overall reaction in commercial heat packs
    can be represented as

    $$4Fe(s) + 3O_2(g) \rightarrow 2Fe_2O_3(s) \quad \Delta H = -1652 \text{ kJ}$$

    a. How much heat is released when 4.00
       mol iron is reacted with excess O_2?

    b. How much heat is released when 1.00
       mol Fe_2O_3 is produced?

    c. How much heat is released when 1.00 g
       iron is reacted with excess O_2?

    d. How much heat is released when 10.0 g
       Fe and 2.00 g O_2 are reacted?

62. Consider the following equations:

    $$3A + 6B \rightarrow + 3D \qquad \Delta H = -403 \text{ kJ/mol}$$
    $$E + 2F \rightarrow A \qquad \Delta H = -105.2 \text{ kJ/mol}$$
    $$C \rightarrow E + 3D \qquad \Delta H = +64.8 \text{ kJ/mol}$$

    Suppose the first equation is reversed and multi-
    plied by $\frac{1}{6}$, the second and third equations are
    divided by 2, and the three adjusted equations
    are added. What is the net reaction and what is
    the overall heat of this reaction?

63. It has been determined that the body can
    generate 5500 kJ of energy during one hour
    of strenuous exercise. Perspiration is the body's
    mechanism for eliminating this heat. How many
    grams and how many liters of water would have
    to be evaporated through perspiration to rid the
    body of the heat generated during two hours of
    exercise? (The heat of vaporization of water is
    40.6 kJ/mol.)

64. One way to lose weight is to exercise. Walking
    briskly at 4.0 miles per hour for an hour
    consumes about 400 kcal of energy. How many
    miles would you have to walk at 4.0 miles per
    hour to lose one pound of body fat? One gram
    of body fat is equivalent to 7.7 kcal of energy.
    There are 454 g in 1 lb.

65. You are given a metal and asked to determine its
    identity. You are to do this by determining the
    specific heat of the metal. You place the metal
    in a boiling water bath for a few minutes and
    then transfer the metal to a 100.0 g sample of
    water at a measured temperature. You then
    record the highest temperature of the water.
    The data are given in the table below.

	Data
Mass water	100.0 g
Initial temperature of the water	21.31 °C
Final temperature of the water	24.80 °C
Mass metal	50.0 g

    a. Given that the specific heat capacity
       of water is 4.184 J/g °C, calculate the
       amount of heat that is absorbed by
       the water.

    b. How does the heat absorbed by the
       water compare to the heat lost by
       the metal?

    c. What is the initial temperature of
       the "hot" metal? What is the final
       temperature of the metal?

    d. Calculate the specific heat capacity
       of the metal.

    e. Given the following specific heat
       capacities, determine the identity
       of your metal.

    Tin: 0.227 J/g °C

    Zinc: 0.388 J/g °C

    Aluminum: 0.891 J/g °C

1 Energy of position is also called

A kinetic energy

B potential energy

C heat energy

D enthalpy

2 Temperature is

A a measure of the potential energy stored in a substance.

B the same as heat.

C a measure of the random motions of the particles in a system.

D a state function.

3 Of energy, enthalpy, heat, and work, how many are state functions?

A 1

B 2

C 3

D 4

4 Which of the following processes is exothermic?

A Candle wax melting

B A puddle evaporating

C Dry ice (solid carbon dioxide) subliming to form gaseous carbon dioxide

D Water freezing to form ice

5 Metals generally have relatively _____ specific heat capacities, meaning they respond rather _____ to cooling or heating.

A low, quickly

B low, slowly

C high, slowly

D high, quickly

6 Calculate the heat change when 45.0 g of water cools from 45 °C to 22 °C. The specific heat capacity of water is 4.184 J/g °C.

A 1.04 kJ

B 4.33 kJ

C −4.33 kJ

D −1.04 kJ

7 Given the following data:

$C(s) + O_2(g) \rightarrow CO_2(g)$ $\Delta H = -393.7$ kJ

$2CO(g) + O_2(g) \rightarrow 2CO_2(g)$ $\Delta H = -566.6$ kJ

calculate ΔH for the reaction

$2C(s) + O_2(g) \rightarrow 2CO(g)$

A 172.9 kJ

B −172.9 kJ

C 960.3 kJ

D −220.8 kJ

8 Why is there an energy crisis in the world?

A Because the law of conservation of energy states that energy cannot be created nor destroyed.

B Because the quantity of energy in the world is always decreasing.

C Because the quality of energy in the world is always decreasing.

D Because energy is a state function.

9 Given that the releasing of heat is a driving force for reactions, why do endothermic reactions take place at all?

A Because in an endothermic reaction, heat is released.

B In order for an endothermic reaction to occur, matter spread must occur as well.

C Endothermic reactions are always spontaneous.

D Endothermic reactions never occur naturally.

For questions 10 and 11, use the following graph on energy usage.

10 Which source of energy has had the largest increase in usage since 1900?

11 Which source of energy is no longer used to a great extent?

1. B

2. C

3. B

4. D

5. A

6. C

7. D

8. C

9. B

10. petroleum/natural gas

11. wood

Test-Taking Strategy

When trying to answer a multiple-choice reasoning question, such as #8, advise students to read each answer choice carefully and select the choice that is the most accurate and complete. Warn students that more than one choice may be true, but students need to choose the best answer.

Assessment Resources

CHAPTER 10

For additional practice with standardized testing, see *Standardized Test Practice* located in the *Teacher Resources*.

Planning Guide

Section	Segment	Text Features and Components	Labs, Demonstrations, & Activities
11.1 **Atoms and Energy** **1.5 Blocks** pp. 358–365	**A** **Rutherford's Atom**		

	B **Energy and Light**	**SE** Chemistry in Your World: Plants Seeing Red *p. 363*	**TE** Mini-Demo *p. 362*
			SE Hands-On Chemistry: Making Waves *p. 364*
			LM Experiment 46: Sunprint Paper, Traditional
			    Lab Manual
			    Report Sheets
			    Teacher's Lab Guide

	C **Emission of Energy by Atoms**		**TE** Teaching Support: Demonstration *p. 365*
			LM Experiment 47: Flame Tests, Traditional
			    Lab Manual
			    Report Sheets
			    Teacher's Lab Guide

11.2 **The Hydrogen Atom** **1 Block** pp. 366–370	**A** **The Energy Levels of Hydrogen**		**TE** Teaching Support: Demonstration *pp. 366–367*
	B **The Bohr Model of the Atom**	**SE** Chemistry Explorers: Niels Hendrik David Bohr *p. 369*	

	C **The Wave Mechanical Model of the Atom**		**LM** Experiment 48: Electron Probability
			    Lab Manual
			    Report Sheets
			    Teacher's Lab Guide

	continued on next page		

Key	**SE** Student Edition	**TE** Teacher Edition	**RP** Teacher Resource Package
	AR Additional Materials	**LM** Lab Materials	Transparencies
	DVD	CD-ROM	classzone.com

All Learners	Technology	Review & Assessment	Standards
TE Teaching Tip *p. 360*	⊙ Animation: Gold Foil Experiment ⊙ EasyPlanner	SE Questions and Problems *p. 392*	TE **NSES** UCP1, UCP2, A1, A2, B1, B2, B6, E1, E2, F6, G1, G2
TE Teaching Tips *pp. 361–362*	⊡ Transparency: Figure 11.4 ⊙ Animation: Electromagnetic Waves ⊙ Animation: Refraction of White Light ⊡ Lab Generator CD ⊙ EasyPlanner	SE Active Reading Question *p. 362* SE Active Reading Question *p. 362* SE Key Terms *p. 391* SE Questions and Problems *p. 392*	
RP Team Learning Worksheet (Sec. 11.1)	⊙ Video: Flame Tests ⊙ Video: Electrified Pickle ⊡ Transparency: Figure 11.7 ⊡ Lab Generator CD ⊙ EasyPlanner	SE Active Reading Question *p. 365* SE Review Questions (11.1.A–11.1.C) *p. 365* SE Questions and Problems *p. 392*	
TE Teaching Tips *pp. 366–368*	⊡ Transparency: Figure 11.8 ⊙ Animation: The Line Spectrum of Hydrogen ⊡ Transparency: Figure 11.11 ⊡ Transparency: Figure 11.12 ⊙ EasyPlanner	SE Active Reading Question *p. 368* SE Key Terms *p. 391* SE Questions and Problems *p. 392*	TE **NSES** UCP2, A1, A2, B6, G1, G2, G3
TE Teaching Tip *p. 368*	⊙ EasyPlanner	SE Questions and Problems *p. 392*	
TE Teaching Tips *pp. 369–370* RP Team Learning Worksheet (Sec. 11.2)	⊡ Lab Generator CD ⊙ EasyPlanner	SE Critical Thinking *p. 369* SE Review Questions (11.2.A–11.2.C) *p. 370* SE Key Terms *p. 391* SE Questions and Problems *p. 392*	

Planning Guide

Section	Segment		Text Features and Components	Labs, Demonstrations, & Activities
11.3 Atomic Orbitals 0.5 Block pp. 371–376	A	The Hydrogen Orbitals	**TE** Teaching Support: Background Information *pp. 373–375*	
	B	The Wave Mechanical Model: Further Development		**TE** Mini-Demo *p. 375*
11.4 Electron Configurations and Atomic Properties 0.5 Block pp. 377–390	A	Electron Arrangements in the First 18 Atoms on the Periodic Table	**TE** Teaching Support: Historical Note *p. 377* **TE** Teaching Support: Background Information *pp. 378–379*	
	B	Electron Configurations and the Periodic Table	**SE** Chemistry in Your World: A Magnetic Moment *p. 382*	**TE** Teaching Support: Demonstration *pp. 380–381* **TE** Mini-Demo *p. 382*
	C	Atomic Properties and the Periodic Table	**TE** Teaching Support: Background Information *pp. 386–388* **SE** Chemistry in Your World: Fireworks *p. 389* **SE** Celebrity Chemical: Hydrogen *p. 390*	**SE** Hands-On Chemistry: Which Element Is It? *p. 385* **RP** Classroom Activities and Projects *TE p. 388*

Key
SE Student Edition	**TE** Teacher Edition	**RP** Teacher Resource Package	
AR Additional Materials	**LM** Lab Materials	**🖻** Transparencies	
💿 DVD	**💾** CD-ROM	**ⓘ** classzone.com	

All Learners	Technology	Review & Assessment	Standards
TE Meeting Individual Needs *p. 371* **TE** Teaching Tip *p. 372* **TE** Meeting Individual Needs *p. 373*	**Transparency:** Figure 11.14 **Transparency:** Figure 11.18 **Animation:** $1s$ Orbital **Animation:** $2p_x$ Orbital **Animation:** $2p_y$ Orbital **Animation:** $2p_z$ Orbital **Transparency:** Figure 11.20 **Animation:** $3d_{x^2-y^2}$ Orbital **Animation:** $3d_{xy}$ Orbital **Animation:** $3d_{xz}$ Orbital **Animation:** $3d_{yz}$ Orbital **Animation:** $3d_{z^2}$ Orbital **EasyPlanner**	**SE** Active Reading Question *p. 372* **SE** Key Terms *p. 391* **SE** Questions and Problems *p. 393*	**TE** **NSES** UCP1, UCP2, A1, A2, B6, E1, E2, F3, F4, F6
TE Teaching Tip *p. 374* **RP** Team Learning Worksheet (Sec. 11.3)	**EasyPlanner**	**SE** Practice Problem *p. 376* **TE** More Examples *p. 376* **SE** Review Questions (11.3.A–11.3.B) *p. 376* **SE** Key Terms *p. 391* **SE** Questions and Problems *p. 393*	
TE Teaching Tips *pp. 378, 380*	**Transparency:** Figure 11.21 **EasyPlanner**	**SE** Practice Problem *p. 379* **TE** More Examples *p. 379* **SE** Key Terms *p. 391* **SE** Questions and Problems *p. 393*	**TE** **NSES** UCP1, UCP3, A1, A2, B2, B6, E1, E2, G1, G2, G3
TE Teaching Tips *pp. 380–381*	**Transparency:** Figure 11.23 **Animation:** Orbital Energies **Transparency:** Figure 11.26 **EasyPlanner**	**SE** Active Reading Question *p. 382* **SE** Practice Problem *p. 383* **TE** More Examples *p. 383* **SE** Critical Thinking *p. 384* **SE** Key Terms *p. 391* **SE** Questions and Problems *pp. 393–394*	
TE Teaching Tips *pp. 385–388* **RP** Team Learning Worksheet (Sec. 11.4)	**Transparency:** Figure 11.28 **Animation:** Periodic Table Trends **Video:** Oxygen, Hydrogen, Soap Bubbles, and Balloons **EasyPlanner**	**SE** Review Questions (11.4.A–11.4.C) *p. 390* **SE** Key Terms *p. 391* **SE** Questions and Problems *p. 394*	

Resource Materials for Chapter 11

SE Chapter Review *p. 391*

SE Critical Thinking *pp. 395–396*

SE Standardized Test Practice *p. 397*

AR English/Spanish Summaries

English Summaries Audio

Spanish Summaries Audio

RP Meeting Individual Needs Toolkit (MINT)
 Chapter Review Worksheets
 Chapter Summaries

RP Solutions Guide

RP Standardized Test Practice

RP Chapter Tests

RP Test Bank

Test Generator

Chapter 11

Overview

In this chapter our goals are for students to:

- Describe Rutherford's model of the atom
- Explore the nature of electromagnetic radiation
- See how atoms emit light
- Understand how the emission spectrum of hydrogen demonstrates the quantized nature of energy
- Learn about Bohr's model of the hydrogen atom
- Understand how the electron's position is represented in the wave mechanical model
- Learn about the shapes of orbitals designated by *s*, *p*, and *d*
- Learn about electron spin
- Understand how the principal energy levels fill with electrons in atoms beyond hydrogen
- Learn about valence electrons and core electrons
- Learn about the electron configurations of atoms with *Z* greater than 18
- Understand the general trends in atomic properties in the periodic table

Chapter 11

Modern Atomic Theory

LOOKING AHEAD

The colors in this fireworks display are the result of electron transfers between atomic energy levels.

IN YOUR LIFE

A fireworks display gives us a dramatic example of chemistry in action. Chemical reactions are used to provide the energy to propel the fireworks into the air, and other reactions are used for the explosions in the air. Of course, what most people remember are the beautiful and various colors that go along with the smoke and the sounds. But where do these colors come from?

It turns out that many are due to the positively charged ions (cations) of ionic solids (salts). For example, sodium salts give us yellow colors, strontium salts give us red colors, and barium salts give us green colors. But why do these ions display colors at all? And why do they display different colors? The answers have to do with the unique arrangement of the electrons in a given atom.

Until now we have dealt with rather simple models of the atom. For example, Dalton's model did not include electrons at all. In order to answer our questions about the colors of fireworks, we need to develop a more complicated model of the atom, and especially of the electrons in the atom. We have not yet looked deeply at the structure of an atom, but that is what this chapter is all about.

WHAT DO YOU KNOW?

Prereading Questions

1. What particles make up an atom?

2. Recall Rutherford's experiment from Chapter 3. What was the experiment and what did it show?

3. What does the term *quantum leap* mean?

Modern Atomic Theory • Chapter 11 • **359**

Prereading Questions

1. Protons and neutrons are in the nucleus of the atom. Electrons are outside the nucleus in the atom.

2. Rutherford shot α-particles at a thin sheet of gold foil. He noticed that while most α-particles went right through the foil, some α-particles were deflected and reflected. Rutherford took this to mean there must be a rather heavy, positively charged mass in the atom, which he termed the nucleus.

3. *Answers will vary.* A quantum leap is an abrupt change or a dramatic advance. Students often will link it to time travel. It will be applied in this chapter to quantized energy levels in an atom; that is, electrons can exist only at certain energy levels.

TECHNOLOGY IN THE CLASSROOM

 Transparencies
Figures: 11.4, 11.7, 11.8, 11.11, 11.12, 11.14, 11.18, 11.20, 11.21, 11.23, 11.26, 11.28

Power Presentation DVD
PowerPoint Slides
Animations
Gold Foil
   Experiment
Electromagnetic Waves
Refraction of White
   Light
The Line Spectrum of
   Hydrogen
$1s \ldots 3d_{z^2}$ Orbitals
Orbital Energies
Periodic Table Trends
Videos
Flame Tests
Electrified Pickle
Oxygen, Hydrogen,
   Soap Bubbles, and
   Balloons
eEdition
EasyPlanner

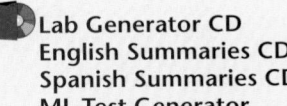Lab Generator CD
English Summaries CD
Spanish Summaries CD
ML Test Generator

 classzone.com

Student Preparation

Assign students to read Section 11.1 and to answer the Review Questions at the end of the section before coming to class.

 Active Learning
Team Learning Worksheet

After introducing the material in Section 11.1 in class, place students in groups and have them work together on **Section 11.1: Team Learning Worksheet**.

SECTION 11.1
GUIDE THE LEARNING

Homework

You may wish to assign these selected end-of-chapter problems as homework for this section:
1, 2, 3, 5, 6, 7, 8, 9

Additional end-of-chapter problems can be used for extra practice.

11.1.A Rutherford's Atom
Objective To describe Rutherford's model of the atom

 TEACHING TIP

This section is a review of the basic components of the atom. It offers an opportunity to reteach these components and to emphasize models and how they change over time.

TECHNOLOGY

 Animation
Gold Foil Experiment

SECTION 11.1
Atoms and Energy

Key Terms
- Electromagnetic radiation
- Wavelength
- Frequency
- Photons

Objectives
- *To describe Rutherford's model of the atom*
- *To explore the nature of electromagnetic radiation*
- *To see how atoms emit light*

The concept of atoms is a very useful one. It explains many important observations, such as why compounds always have the same composition (a specific compound always contains the same types and numbers of atoms) and how chemical reactions occur (they involve a rearrangement of atoms).

Once chemists came to "believe" in atoms, logical questions followed: What are atoms like? What is the structure of an atom? In Chapter 3 we learned to picture the atom with a positively charged nucleus composed of protons and neutrons at its center and electrons moving around the nucleus in a space very large compared to the size of the nucleus.

In this chapter, we will look at atomic structure in more detail. In particular, we will develop a picture of the electron arrangements in atoms—a picture that allows us to account for the chemistry of the various elements. Recall from our discussion of the periodic table in Chapter 3 that, although atoms exhibit a great variety of characteristics, certain elements can be grouped together because they behave similarly. For example, fluorine, chlorine, bromine, and iodine (the halogens) show great chemical similarities. Likewise lithium, sodium, potassium, rubidium, and cesium (the alkali metals) exhibit many similar properties, and helium, neon, argon, krypton, xenon, and radon (the noble gases) are all very nonreactive. Although the members of each of these groups of elements show great similarity *within* the group, the differences in behavior *between* groups are striking. In this chapter we will see that it is the way the electrons are arranged in various atoms that accounts for these facts. However, before we examine atomic structure, we must consider the nature of electromagnetic radiation, which plays a central role in the study of the atom's behavior.

Alkali metals   Halogens   Noble gases

A. Rutherford's Atom

Remember that in Chapter 3 we discussed the idea that an atom has a small positive core (called the nucleus) with negatively charged electrons moving around the nucleus in some way (see **Figure 11.1**). This concept of a *nuclear atom* resulted from Ernest Rutherford's experiments in which he bombarded metal foil with α particles.

Neon signmaker and artist Jess Baird shows off a few of the items he has made in his Weatherford, Texas, shop.

11.1.B Energy and Light

Objective To explore the nature of electromagnetic radiation

🔬 **LABORATORY**
EXPERIMENT 46:
Sunprint Paper, Traditional

🍎 **TEACHING TIPS**

• Students often consider the forms of electromagnetic radiation outside the visible range (radio, X rays, infrared, microwaves) to be entirely different from light. Use a transparency of the electromagnetic spectrum to show the range of frequencies for each type of radiation.

• Some insects use other forms of electromagnetic radiation to navigate. Students can investigate the travels of bees and migratory birds to find out how other animals perceive the electromagnetic spectrum.

Let's Review

Nuclear Model of the Atom

• The atom has a small dense nucleus which
  – is positively charged
  – contains protons (+1 charge)
  – contains neutrons (no charge)

• The remainder of the atom
  – Is mostly empty space
  – Contains electrons (–1 charge)

Figure 11.1
The Rutherford atom. The nuclear charge (*n*+) is balanced by the presence of *n* electrons moving in some way around the nucleus.

A major question left unanswered by Rutherford's work was, "What are the electrons doing?" That is, how are the electrons arranged and how do they move? Rutherford suggested that electrons might revolve around the nucleus like the planets revolve around the sun in our solar system. He couldn't explain, however, why the negative electrons aren't attracted into the positive nucleus, causing the atom to collapse.

At this point it became clear that more observations of the properties of atoms were needed to understand the structure of the atom more fully. To help us understand these observations, we need to discuss the nature of light and how it transmits energy.

B. Energy and Light

If you hold your hand a few inches from a brightly glowing light bulb, what do you feel? Your hand gets warm. The "light" from the bulb somehow transmits energy to your hand. The same thing happens if you move close to the glowing embers of wood in a fireplace—you receive energy that makes you feel warm. The energy you feel from the sun is a similar example.

In all three of these instances, energy is being transmitted from one place to another by light—more properly called **electromagnetic radiation**. Many kinds of electromagnetic radiation exist. Examples include

• X rays used to make images of bones
• "white" light from a light bulb
• microwaves used to cook hot dogs and other food
• radio waves that transmit voices and music.

How do these various types of electromagnetic radiation differ from one another? To answer this question we need to talk about waves. To explore the characteristics of waves, let's think about ocean waves. In **Figure 11.2** a seagull is shown floating on the ocean and being raised and lowered by the motion of the water surface as waves pass by. Notice that the gull just moves up and down as the waves pass—it is not moved forward. A particular wave is characterized by three properties: *wavelength, frequency,* and *speed.*

> **Electromagnetic radiation**
> Radiant energy that exhibits wavelike behavior and travels through space at the speed of light in a vacuum

Figure 11.2
A seagull floating on the ocean moves up and down as waves pass.

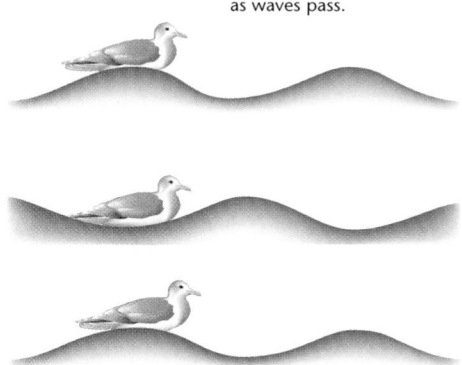

11.1 • Atoms and Energy • **361**

Figure 11.3
The wavelength of a wave is the distance between peaks.

Wavelength
The distance between two consecutive peaks or troughs in a wave

Frequency
The number of waves (cycles) per second that pass a given point in space

Photon
A particle of electromagnetic radiation

Figure 11.4
The different wavelengths of electromagnetic radiation

The **wavelength** (symbolized by the Greek letter lambda, λ) is the distance between two consecutive wave peaks (see **Figure 11.3**). The **frequency** of the wave (symbolized by the Greek letter nu, ν) indicates how many wave peaks pass a certain point per a given time period. This idea can best be understood by thinking about how many times the seagull in Figure 11.2 goes up and down per minute. The *speed* of a wave indicates how fast a given peak travels through the water.

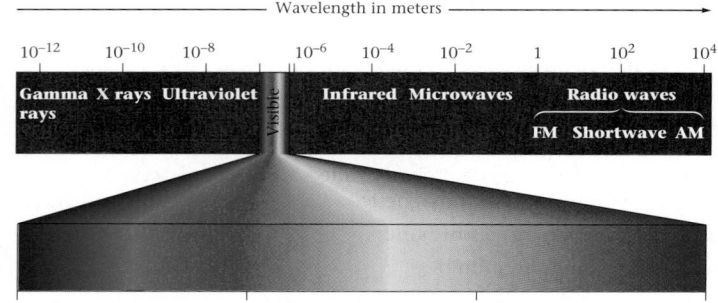 **Active Reading Question**

Describe the relationship between *wavelength* and *frequency*.

Although it is more difficult to picture than water waves, light (electromagnetic radiation) also travels as waves. The various types of electromagnetic radiation (X rays, microwaves, and so on) differ in their wavelengths. The classes of electromagnetic radiation are shown in **Figure 11.4.** Notice that X rays have very short wavelengths, whereas radiowaves have very long wavelengths.

Radiation provides an important means of energy transfer. For example, the energy from the sun reaches the earth mainly in the forms of visible and ultraviolet radiation. The glowing coals of a fireplace transmit heat energy by infrared radiation. In a microwave oven, the water molecules in food absorb microwave radiation, which increases their motions; this energy is then transferred to other types of molecules by collisions, thus increasing the food's temperature.

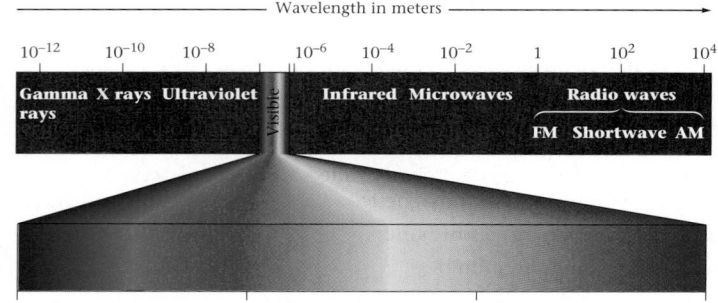 **Active Reading Question**

Which has the longer wavelength: blue light or red light?

Dual Nature of Light Thus we visualize electromagnetic radiation ("light") as a wave that carries energy through space. Sometimes, however, light doesn't behave as though it were a wave. That is, electromagnetic radiation can sometimes have properties that are characteristic of particles. (You will learn more about this idea in a physics course.) Another way to think of a beam of light traveling through space, then, is as a stream of tiny packets of energy called **photons**.

What is the exact nature of light? Does it consist of waves or is it a stream of particles of energy? It seems to be both (see **Figure 11.5**). This situation is often referred to as the wave–particle nature of light.

Light as a wave

○ ○ ○ ○ ○

Light as a stream of photons
(packets of energy)

Figure 11.5
Electromagnetic radiation (a beam of light) can be pictured in two ways: as a wave and as a stream of individual packets of energy called photons.

CHEMISTRY IN YOUR WORLD

Connection to Biology

Plants Seeing Red

Vegetable growers have long used plastic sheeting (mulch) in the rows between plants to retain moisture, retard weeds, and provide warmth for the roots of young plants. It is now becoming apparent that the color of the plastic used has a significant effect on the plants. How can this be? Why does the color of their mulch matter to plants?

Michael J. Kasperbauer of the Department of Agriculture's Coastal Plains Soil, Water, and Plant Research Laboratory in Florence, South Carolina, has spent most of his 40-year career studying the responses of plants to various colors of light. Plants use proteins called phytochromes to sense light in the red (640–670 nm) and the far red (700–750 nm) ranges. Although far red light is not photosynthetically active—it does not provide energy for plant growth—this light gives plants important information about their environment. For example, green leaves reflect a lot of light in the far red region. Therefore, when a given plant's phytochromes sense a high ratio of far red to red light wavelengths, the plant knows that it has many neighbors—many other plants around it are reflecting red light. Because these neighbors are competitors for the lifegiving light from the sun—their leaves will shade neighboring plants—a plant sensing this situation tends to direct its growth above ground, producing a taller, thinner structure that can compete more successfully for sunlight. In fact, Kasperbauer and his colleagues have

found that by using a red plastic mulch they can fool tomatoes into "thinking" they are crowded, leading to faster seedling growth and eventually producing earlier, larger fruit.

Since the opposite effect should benefit root crops, the Department of Agriculture scientists have grown turnips in soil covered by an orange mulch. These turnips proved much bigger than those mulched with black or red plastic, presumably because of increased reflection of red light by the orange plastic. The increased red light signaled no significant competition for light from other plants, encouraging growth of roots rather than above-ground foliage.

Besides affecting the plant's structure, the type of reflected light influences the nature of the waxy coating on the leaves and the taste of the plant product. Surprisingly, the color of the reflected light also seems to affect the plant's response to insect damage.

This research shows that plants are very sensitive to the type of red light that bathes them. Our plants may benefit from rose-colored glasses as much as we do.

Red plastic mulch being used in an experimental plot

Chemistry in Your World

Plants Seeing Red

Students may have studied the effect of light on photosynthesis in biology. Have them research the effect of the wavelength of light on photosynthesis. One common biology experiment involves growing plants in small cartons. Once the seedlings are growing, the cartons get covered in various colors of cellophane.

Observations of plant condition over time give an excellent indication of the light required for photosynthesis.

Students may also have an interest in why leaves change color in autumn. *ChemMatters*, October 1986, has an excellent article on this process.

As days get shorter and temperatures drop, the production of chlorophyll in leaves stops. Once the chlorophyll disappears, the yellow pigments—carotene and xanthophylls—become

visible, making the leaves appear yellow. The reds and purples are the result of bright light and cool nights. Bright daylight promotes sugar production in the leaves, and cool nights trap the sugar there, creating a red pigment called anthocyanin. Orange leaves result from combinations of the red and yellow pigments in the leaves. The best fall colors are observed when the days are sunny, nights are cool, and plenty of moisture is available.

Objective To see how atoms emit light

 LABORATORY
EXPERIMENT 47:
Flame Tests, Traditional

TECHNOLOGY

Videos
Flame Tests
Electrified Pickle

HANDS-ON CHEMISTRY • MINI-LAB •

Making Waves

Materials
• Graph paper

Procedure

1. On a sheet of graph paper, draw three waves with a small wavelength (3–4 cm).

2. Draw two more waves, the first with wavelength 2 times the original wave and the second with wavelength 4 times the original wave.

3. Order the wavelengths from lowest to highest frequency.

4. Order the wavelengths from lowest to highest energy.

Results/Analysis

1. Explain your answers for steps 2 and 3.

Different wavelengths of electromagnetic radiation carry different amounts of energy. For example, the photons that correspond to red light carry less energy than the photons that correspond to blue light. In general, the longer the wavelength of light, the lower the energy of its photons (see **Figure 11.6**).

Figure 11.6
A photon of red light (relatively long wavelength) carries less energy than a photon of blue light (relatively short wavelength) does.

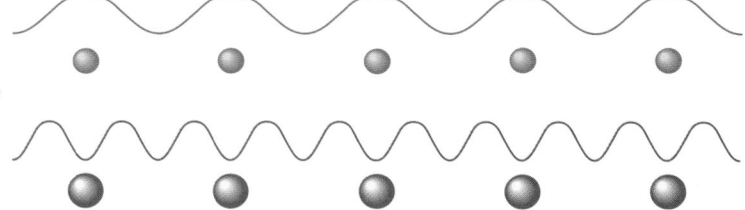

C. Emission of Energy by Atoms

Consider the results of the experiment shown in **Figure 11.7.** This experiment is run by dissolving compounds containing the Li^+ ion, the Cu^{2+} ion, and the Na^+ ion in separate dishes containing methyl alcohol (with a little water added to help dissolve the compounds). The solutions are then set on fire. The brilliant colors that result are shown below.

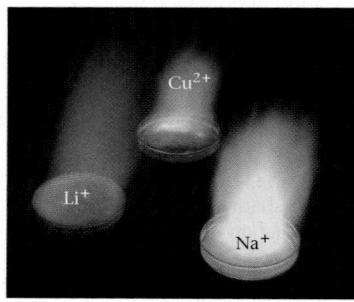

As we will see in more detail in the next section, the colors of these flames result from atoms in these solutions releasing energy by emitting visible light of specific wavelengths (that is, specific colors). The heat from the flame causes the atoms to absorb energy; we say that the atoms become *excited*.

Hands-On Chemistry
MINI-LAB

Making Waves

Materials Each student/group will need a sheet of graph paper.

Purpose Students will better understand the relationships among wavelength, frequency, and energy.

Discussion By drawing waves and comparing them with each other, students understand why a wave with a short wavelength has a higher frequency (and higher energy) than a wave with a longer wavelength. Have students imagine an object being hit by each of the three waves, and have them decide which object would be affected the most. In this way, the concept becomes more concrete. By having students draw the waves, you can get a better feeling for their understanding of wavelength.

Some of this excess energy is then released in the form of light. The atom moves to a lower energy state as it emits a photon of light.

Lithium emits red light because its energy change corresponds to photons of red light (see **Figure 11.7**). Copper emits green light because it undergoes a different energy change than lithium; the energy change for copper corresponds to the energy of a photon of green light. Likewise, the energy change for sodium corresponds to a photon with a yellow–orange color.

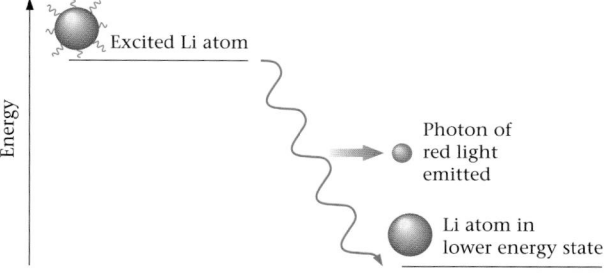

Figure 11.7
An excited lithium atom emitting a photon of red light to drop to a lower energy state

Active Reading Question

Why do we see colors when salt solutions in methanol are burned?

To summarize, we have the following situation. When atoms receive energy from some source—when they become excited—they can release this energy by emitting light. The emitted energy is carried away by a photon. Thus the energy of the photon corresponds exactly to the energy change experienced by the emitting atom. High-energy photons correspond to short-wavelength light and low-energy photons correspond to long-wavelength light. The photons of red light therefore carry less energy than the photons of blue light because red light has a longer wavelength than blue light does.

SECTION 11.1
REVIEW QUESTIONS

❶ Copy and label the atom showing the locations of the *electrons*, *protons*, *neutrons*, and *nucleus*.

❷ What is wrong with Rutherford's model of the atom? Why did it need to be modified?

❸ What is *electromagnetic radiation*? Provide three examples.

❹ How is the frequency of a wave different from its speed?

❺ What is a *photon*?

❻ What is the relationship between wavelength of light and the energy of its photons?

RESEARCH LINKS
CLASSZONE.COM

11.1 • Atoms and Energy • **365**

TECHNOLOGY

 Figure 11.7

Active Reading Question

The energy from the fire causes the electrons in the metals to go from a ground state to an excited state. When the electrons fall back to the ground state, certain photons of light are emitted and certain colors are seen.

SECTION 11.1
ASSESS

**SECTION 11.1
Review Questions**

1. The protons and neutrons are in the nucleus (blue circle). The electrons are the red circles.

2. Rutherford did not explain how electrons are arranged or how they move. He could not explain why atoms do not collapse when the negative electrons revolve about the nucleus. Modifications were needed in Rutherford's model to clear up these flaws and to better elucidate the structure of the atom.

3. Electromagnetic radiation is light. Examples include gamma rays, X rays, ultraviolet radiation, visible light, infrared radiation, microwaves, and radio waves.

4. The frequency is the number of waves passing a particular point in a given time. The speed is how fast the wave travels through the medium.

5. A photon is a "packet" of energy. Light can be thought of as a stream of photons.

6. The relationship is inverse. The longer the wavelength, the less energy in its photons.

Teaching Support
DEMONSTRATION

Burning Rainbows
Materials
- Several evaporating dishes
- Nitrate salts of various metals (Li, Sr, Cu, Ba, K, Na)
- Methanol in a labeled wash bottle
- Water in a wash bottle
- Stirring rods   • Matches

Presentation Place a pea-sized amount of each salt in separate evaporating dishes. Add a small amount of water to just begin dissolution. Add 10 mL of methanol, using the wash bottle. Stir each mixture with a different stirring rod. Light each dish with a match and dim the lights.

Teaching Notes The amount of methanol added will determine how long each dish burns. Be careful to plan for this variation. Initially the methanol

will burn as blue to colorless. Stirring may be necessary to produce color.

Variation Build a trough $\frac{1}{2} \times \frac{1}{2} \times 10$ from aluminum foil. Make sure that the narrow ends are folded up and are leakproof. Add 1.0 g of the metal salts in the order Sr, Li, Na, boric acid, Cu, K. Add a drop of water to each salt pile to aid in dissolution. Add enough methanol to cover the salts. Light the trough with a match.

Student Preparation

Assign students to read Section 11.2 and to answer the Review Questions at the end of the section before coming to class.

 Active Learning
Team Learning Worksheet

After introducing the material in Section 11.2 in class, place students in groups and have them work together on **Section 11.2: Team Learning Worksheet**.

Homework

You may wish to assign these selected end-of-chapter problems as homework for this section: 11, 12, 14, 15, 17, 20, 21, 22

Additional end-of-chapter problems can be used for extra practice.

11.2.A The Energy Levels of Hydrogen

Objective To understand how the emission spectrum of hydrogen demonstrates the quantized nature of energy

 TEACHING TIP

Use the example in this section to discuss the ramifications of seeing only certain colors. Also consider discussing white light.

Key Terms
- Quantized
- Wave mechanical model

Objectives
- *To understand how the emission spectrum of hydrogen demonstrates the quantized nature of energy*
- *To learn about Bohr's model of the hydrogen atom*
- *To understand how the electron's position is represented in the wave mechanical model*

A. The Energy Levels of Hydrogen

As we learned in the last section, an atom with excess energy is said to be in an *excited state*. An excited atom can release some or all of its excess energy by emitting a photon (a "particle" of electromagnetic radiation) and thus move to a lower energy state. The lowest possible energy state of an atom is called its *ground state*.

We can learn a great deal about the energy states of hydrogen atoms by observing the photons they emit.

Different wavelengths of light carry different amounts of energy per photon.

Recall that a beam of red light has lower-energy photons than a beam of blue light.

When a hydrogen atom absorbs energy from some outside source, it uses this energy to enter an excited state.

information

An atom can lose energy by *emitting* a photon.

Each photon of blue light carries a larger quantity of energy than a photon of red light.

= H atom

= Excited state H atom

Some H atoms absorb energy and become excited.

It can release this excess energy (go back to a lower state) by emitting a photon of light.

The excited atoms emit photons of light and return to the ground state.

Photon

Photon

Photon

Atomic Spectra

Materials
- Several gas discharge tubes of various elements and an apparatus to power them, or samples of metal salts and evaporating dishes as used in the Burning Rainbows demonstration earlier in the chapter.
- Diffraction spectroscopes or small pieces of diffraction grating (one per student)

Preparation You can make simple spectroscopes from a piece of diffraction grating and small black film canisters. Use a one-hole punch to punch a hole in the center of the gray top of the film canister. Then use an Exacto craft knife to cut a slit in the bottom of the film canister. Cut the diffraction grating into small pieces that are larger than the hole

punched in the top of the film canister. Using a small amount of superglue, affix the diffraction grating to the inside of the top of the film canister, covering the hole. Snap the top back onto the bottom and test the spectroscope.

Presentation Distribute a spectroscope or diffraction grating to each student. Have students use the spectroscopes to look at an incandescent light and find the rainbow on either side of the slit in the tube. (*Note:* Students often look

We can picture this process in terms of the energy-level diagram.

i **nformation**

A particular color (wavelength) of light carries a particular amount of energy per photon.

The energy contained in the photon corresponds to the change in energy that the atom experiences in going from the excited state to the lower state.

Consider the following experiment. Suppose we take a sample of H atoms and put a lot of energy into the system. When we study the photons of visible light emitted, we see only certain colors (see **Figure 11.8**). That is, *only certain types of photons* are produced. We don't see all colors, which would add up to give "white light;" we see only selected colors. This is a very significant result. Let's discuss carefully what it means.

410 nm 434 nm 486 nm   656 nm

Figure 11.8
When excited hydrogen atoms return to lower energy states, they emit photons of certain energies, and thus certain colors. Shown here are the colors and wavelengths (in nanometers) of the photons in the visible region that are emitted by excited hydrogen atoms.

Quantized Energy Levels Because only certain photons are emitted, we know that only certain energy changes are occurring (see **Figure 11.9**). This means that the hydrogen atom must have *certain discrete energy levels* (see **Figure 11.10**). Excited hydrogen atoms *always* emit photons with the same discrete colors (wavelengths) as those shown in Figure 11.8. They *never* emit photons with energies (colors) in between those shown.

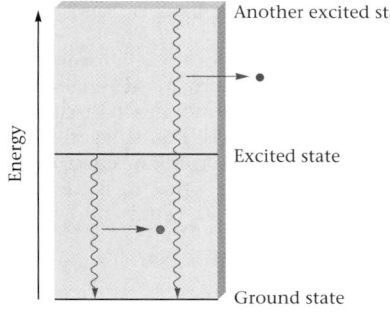

Figure 11.9
Hydrogen atoms have several excited-state energy levels. The color of the photon emitted depends on the energy change that produces it. A larger energy change may correspond to a blue photon, whereas a smaller change may produce a red photon.

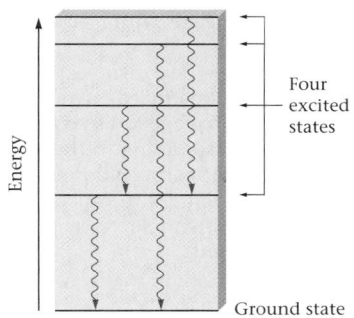

Figure 11.10
Each photon emitted by an excited hydrogen atom corresponds to a particular energy change in the hydrogen atom. In this diagram the horizontal lines represent discrete energy levels present in the hydrogen atom. A given H atom can exist in any of these energy states and can undergo energy changes to the ground state as well as to other excited states.

11.2 • The Hydrogen Atom • **367**

TECHNOLOGY

 Figure 11.8

 Animation
The Line Spectrum of Hydrogen

 TEACHING TIPS

• Make sure that you distinguish between an emission spectrum for an atom and light emitted by an atom. To see an emission spectrum, the light must be separated into its component parts. This separation is accomplished by using a prism or a diffraction grating.

• Discuss how hydrogen can have multiple lines even though it has only one electron. Students often forget that they are observing many thousands of atoms simultaneously when observing a line emission spectrum.

• Now is an excellent time to discuss the colors of streetlights. Mercury vapor lights have a blue cast, sodium lights are yellow, and neon lights are more orange. You may also want to discuss the difference between an incandescent light and a vapor light. Many students do not realize that lights differ. An incandescent lamp produces a continuous spectrum because the tiny filament is radiating all wavelengths of visible light, whereas vapor lamps (like many street lights) are similar to gas discharge tubes in their operation.

(continued)
through the wrong end of the spectroscope. They should look through the end containing the diffraction grating, not the slit end.) You can also have students observe the fluorescent lights in the classroom with the spectroscopes. Once students are proficient at using the spectroscopes, place a gas discharge tube at the front of the room. Darken the room and have students observe the spectrum from the

tube. They should see a line emission spectrum such as the one shown for hydrogen in Figure 11.8. Change the gas discharge tube to a different element and repeat the process. (*Note:* The gas discharge apparatus uses high voltage; make sure you unplug it before changing the tube.) Have students compare the emission spectra from different elements.

Variation If you do not have access to the gas discharge apparatus and tubes,

you can use the solutions from the Burning Rainbows demonstration to do the same thing. Make sure you use only one evaporating dish at a time and add a little extra salt to obtain good color.

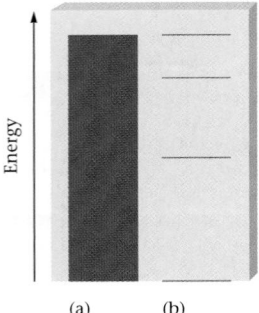

Figure 11.11
(a) Continuous energy levels. Any energy value is allowed.
(b) Discrete (quantized) energy levels. Only certain energy states are allowed.

So we can conclude that all hydrogen atoms have the same set of discrete energy levels. We say the energy levels of hydrogen are **quantized**. That is, only *certain values are allowed*. Scientists have found that the energy levels of *all* atoms are quantized.

Active Reading Question

What does the term *quantized* mean?

The quantized nature of the energy levels in atoms was a surprise when scientists discovered it. It had been assumed previously that an atom could exist at any energy level. That is, everyone had assumed that atoms could have a continuous set of energy levels rather than only certain discrete values (see **Figure 11.11**). A useful analogy here is the contrast between the elevations allowed by a ramp, which vary continuously, and those allowed by a set of steps, which are discrete (see **Figure 11.12**). The discovery of the quantized nature of energy has radically changed our view of the atom, as we will see in the next few sections.

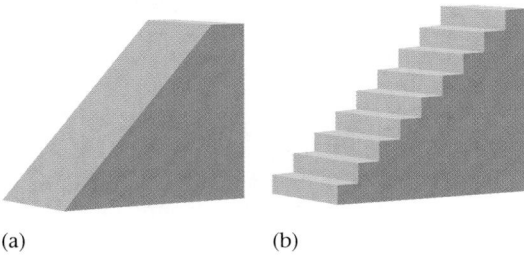

Figure 11.12
The difference between continuous and quantized energy levels can be illustrated by comparing a flight of stairs with a ramp.
(a) A ramp varies continuously in elevation.
(b) A flight of stairs allows only certain elevations; the elevations are quantized.

(a)   (b)

B. The Bohr Model of the Atom

In 1911 at the age of twenty-five, Niels Bohr received his Ph.D. in physics. He was convinced that the atom could be pictured as a small positive nucleus with electrons orbiting around it as the planets orbit the sun.

Over the next two years, Bohr constructed a model of the hydrogen atom with quantized energy levels that agreed with the hydrogen emission results we have just discussed. He pictured the electron moving in circular orbits corresponding to the various allowed energy levels. Bohr suggested that the electron could jump to a different orbit by absorbing or emitting a photon of light with exactly the correct energy content. Thus, in the Bohr atom, the energy levels in the hydrogen atom represented certain allowed circular orbits.

DID YOU KNOW

Although Bohr's model is consistent with the energy levels for hydrogen, it is fundamentally incorrect.

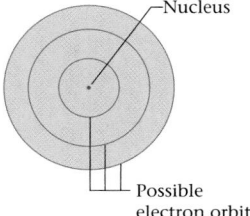

—Nucleus

Possible electron orbits

CHEMISTRY EXPLORERS

Niels Hendrik David Bohr • 1885–1962

Niels Hendrik David Bohr as a boy lived in the shadow of his younger brother Harald, who played on the 1908 Danish Olympic Soccer Team and later became a distinguished mathematician. In school, Bohr received his poorest marks in composition and struggled with writing his entire life. In fact, he wrote so poorly that he was forced to dictate his Ph.D. thesis to his mother. He is one of the very few people who felt the need to write rough drafts of postcards. Nevertheless, Bohr was a brilliant physicist. After receiving his Ph.D. in Denmark, he constructed a quantum model for the hydrogen atom by the time he was 27. Even though his model later proved to be incorrect, Bohr remained a central figure in the drive to understand the atom. He was awarded the Nobel Prize in Physics in 1922.

At first Bohr's model appeared very promising. It fit the hydrogen atom very well. However, when this model was applied to atoms other than hydrogen, it did not work. In fact, further experiments showed that the Bohr model is fundamentally incorrect. Although the Bohr model paved the way for later theories, it is important to realize that the current theory of atomic structure is not the same as the Bohr model. Electrons do *not* move around the nucleus in circular orbits like planets orbiting the sun. Surprisingly, as we shall see later in this chapter, we do not know exactly how the electrons move in an atom.

C. The Wave Mechanical Model of the Atom

By the mid-1920s it had become apparent that the Bohr model was incorrect. Scientists needed to pursue a totally new approach. Two young physicists, Louis Victor de Broglie from France and Erwin Schrödinger from Austria, suggested that because light seems to have both wave and particle characteristics (it behaves simultaneously as a wave and as a stream of particles), the electron might also exhibit both of these characteristics. Although everyone had assumed that the electron was a tiny particle, these scientists said it might be useful to find out whether it could be described as a wave.

When Schrödinger carried out a mathematical analysis based on this idea, he found that it led to a new model for the hydrogen atom that seemed to apply equally well to other atoms—something Bohr's model failed to do. We will now explore a general picture of this model, which is called the **wave mechanical model** of the atom.

Orbitals In the Bohr model, the electron was assumed to move in circular orbits. In the wave mechanical model, on the other hand, the electron states are described by orbitals. *Orbitals are nothing like orbits.* To approximate the idea of an orbital, picture a single male firefly in a room in the center of which is suspended an open vial of a chemical which attracts fireflies. The room is extremely dark and in one corner there is a camera with an open shutter. Every time the firefly "flashes," the camera records a pinpoint of light and thus the firefly's position in the room at that particular moment. The firefly senses the attractant and, as you can imagine, it spends a lot of time at the vial or close to it. However, now and then the insect flies randomly around the room.

DID YOU KNOW

There is now much experimental evidence suggesting that all matter exhibits both wave and particle properties.

CRITICAL THINKING

We now have evidence that electron energy levels in atoms are quantized.

What if energy levels in atoms were not quantized? What are some differences we would notice?

11.2.C The Wave Mechanical Model of the Atom

Objective To understand how the electron's position is represented in the wave mechanical model

 LABORATORY
EXPERIMENT 48:
Electron Probability

TEACHING TIP

This section introduces the idea of probability as a model for understanding nature. This concept will be new to all students, and most will find it confusing. Students tend to think of orbitals as physical structures and find it difficult to think of them as probability distributions. In the next section, we describe the orbital as a *potential space* for an electron. This idea presents a good way for students to think about orbitals initially.

CRITICAL THINKING

If energy levels were not quantized, there would be no characteristic colors in the flame tests. In fact, the most probable "color" in the flame tests would be white (depending on the amount of energy put into the solutions).

CHEMISTRY EXPLORERS
Niels Hendrik David Bohr

Neils Bohr is often mentioned in chemistry only as "the man who came up with the wrong model." This is quite misleading, as Bohr was one of the leading physicists of his time. One of the most famous debates in science was between Bohr and Albert Einstein concerning the probabilistic nature of quantum mechanics. As it turns out, history has thus far declared Bohr the winner of that debate. Bohr also contributed greatly to the (then new) field of nuclear physics. It is fitting that the element bohrium is named in his honor.

TEACHING TIP

The firefly experiment offers a way for students to understand the difference between an orbit and an orbital. Many students confuse orbitals and orbits. An orbit describes a particular path that an object follows as it travels around another object. For example, the Moon has an orbit about the Earth. Electrons do not follow a particular path around the nucleus. Instead, an orbital describes the areas around the nucleus where an electron is likely to be found. The exact path of an electron in this area is not known, in the same way that the exact path of a firefly is not known.

SECTION 11.2
ASSESS

 SECTION 11.2
Review Questions

1. The lines produced in an emission spectrum are the lines from thousands of atoms of hydrogen. Each line represents a single electron transition. Because we are observing thousands of transitions simultaneously, however, we see multiple lines corresponding to the allowed transitions in the visible spectrum.

2. When energy is put into a sample of hydrogen, color is emitted as energy is released. However, only certain colors are emitted, meaning only certain energy changes are occurring. Therefore, hydrogen must have discrete (or quantized) energy levels.

3. The ground state is the state of lowest energy. The excited state is a state of higher energy. When energy is absorbed by an atom, the electron goes from its ground state to an excited state.

4. The Bohr model of the atom cannot adequately explain the energy levels in any multielectron atoms and incorrectly assumes that the hydrogen electron travels in fixed orbits.

5. Electron motions are described by orbitals which give a probability map of the

Louis Victor de Broglie

When the film is taken out of the camera and developed, the picture will probably look like this. Because a picture is brightest where the film has been exposed to the most light, the color intensity at any given point tells us how often the firefly visited that point in the room. Notice that, as we might expect, the firefly spent the most time near the room's center.

Now suppose you are watching the firefly in the dark room. You see it flash at a given point far from the center of the room. Where do you expect to see it next? There is really no way to be sure. The firefly's flight path is not precisely predictable. However, if you had seen the time-exposure picture of the firefly's activities, you would have some idea of where to look next. Your best chance would be to look toward the center of the room. The picture suggests there is the highest probability (the highest odds, the greatest likelihood) of finding the firefly at any particular moment near the center of the room. You *can't be sure* the firefly will fly toward the center of the room, but it *probably* will. So the time-exposure picture is a kind of "probability map" of the firefly's flight pattern.

According to the wave mechanical model, the electron in the hydrogen atom can be pictured as being something like this firefly. Schrödinger found that he could not precisely describe the electron's path. His mathematics enabled him only to predict the probabilities of finding the electron at given points in space around the nucleus. In its ground state the hydrogen electron has a probability map like that shown here.

The more intense the color at a particular point, the more probable it is that the electron will be found at that point at a given instant. The model gives *no information about when* the electron occupies a certain point in space or *how it moves*. In fact, we have good reasons to believe that we can *never know* the details of electron motion, no matter how sophisticated our models may become. But we do feel confident that the electron *does not* orbit the nucleus in circles as Bohr suggested.

SECTION 11.2
REVIEW QUESTIONS

❶ In Figure 11.8 there are four different colored lines. You already know that hydrogen has only one electron. How can we get four lines from one electron?

❷ What evidence leads us to believe that energy levels in the hydrogen atom are quantized?

❸ Explain the terms *ground state* and *excited state*. When a photon of energy is absorbed by an atom, does the electron go from the ground state to an excited state or from an excited state to the ground state?

❹ What is wrong with the Bohr model of the atom?

❺ How does the wave mechanical model of the atom differ from Bohr's model?

❻ What does the wave mechanical model of the atom tell us about how the electron moves around the nucleus?

RESEARCH LINKS
CLASSZONE.COM

electron position. Electrons do not travel in orbits around the nucleus of an atom, a fact that contrasts with Bohr's model.

6. In the wave mechanical model of the atom, the paths of the electrons are unknown. This model tells us nothing about how the electron moves around the nucleus.

Atomic Orbitals

Objectives

- *To learn about the shapes of the* s, p *and* d *orbitals*
- *To review the energy levels and orbitals of the wave mechanical model of the atom*
- *To learn about electron spin*

Key Terms
- Orbital
- Principal energy levels
- Sublevels
- Pauli exclusion principle

A. The Hydrogen Orbitals

The probability map for the hydrogen electron on the previous page is called an **orbital**. Although the probability of finding the electron decreases at greater distances from the nucleus, the probability of finding it at even great distances from the nucleus never becomes exactly zero. A useful analogy might be the lack of a sharp boundary between the earth's atmosphere and "outer space." The atmosphere fades away gradually, but there are always a few molecules present. Because the edge of an orbital is "fuzzy," an orbital does not have an exactly defined size. Chemists arbitrarily define its size as the sphere that contains 90% of the total electron probability. This definition means that the electron spends 90% of the time inside this surface and 10% somewhere outside this surface. (Note that we are *not* saying the electron travels only on the *surface* of the sphere.) The orbital represented in the diagram to the right is named the 1*s* orbital, and it describes the hydrogen electron's lowest energy state (the ground state).

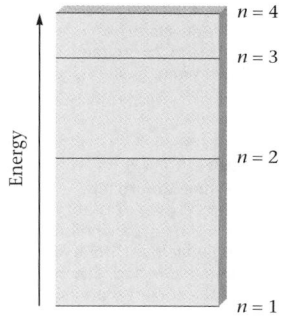

We saw earlier that the hydrogen atom can absorb energy to transfer the electron to a higher energy state (an excited state). In terms of the obsolete Bohr model, this meant the electron was transferred to an orbit with a larger radius. In the wave mechanical model, these higher energy states correspond to different kinds of orbitals with different shapes.

Orbital
The three-dimensional region in which there is a high probability of finding an electron in an atom

Hydrogen Energy Levels

At this point we need to stop and consider how the hydrogen atom is organized. Remember, we showed earlier that the hydrogen atom has discrete energy levels. We call these levels **principal energy levels** and label them with whole numbers (see **Figure 11.13**). Next we find that each of these levels is subdivided into **sublevels**. The following analogy should help you understand this. Picture an inverted triangle (see **Figure 11.14**). We divide the principal levels into various numbers of sublevels. Principal level 1 consists of one sublevel, principal level 2 has two sublevels, principal level 3 has three sublevels, and principal level 4 has four sublevels.

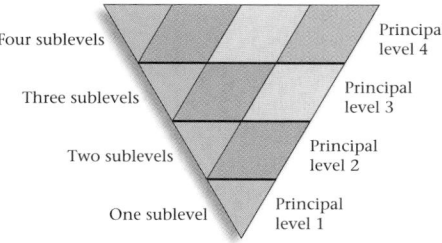

Figure 11.14
An illustration of how principal levels can be divided into sublevels

$n = 4$
$n = 3$
$n = 2$
$n = 1$

Energy

Figure 11.13
The first four principal energy levels in the hydrogen atom. Each level is assigned an integer, *n*.

Student Preparation

Assign students to read Section 11.3 and to answer the Review Questions at the end of the section before coming to class.

 Active Learning
Team Learning Worksheet

After introducing the material in Section 11.3 in class, place students in groups and have them work together on **Section 11.3: Team Learning Worksheet.**

SECTION 11.3
GUIDE THE LEARNING

Homework

You may wish to assign these selected end-of-chapter problems as homework for this section: 24, 26, 27, 28, 30, 32, 33

Additional end-of-chapter problems can be used for extra practice.

11.3.A The Hydrogen Orbitals

Objective To learn about the shapes of orbitals designated by *s*, *p*, and *d*

TECHNOLOGY

 Figure 11.14

Meeting Individual Needs
VISUAL LEARNERS

You can use solid models (usually foam) to demonstrate the shapes of the *s, p,* and *d* orbitals. Remind students that the electron probability is high within the shape but the electron does not follow a set path.

Students can easily become confused about the meanings of the following terms: principal energy level, sublevel, and orbital. Point out that the *principal energy level* gives the region of energy for the electrons. It also turns out that a given principal quantum number indicates the number of *sublevels* available for that energy level. The sublevels are lettered *s, p, d,* and *f* based on the shapes of the orbitals within them. An *orbital* represents a specific region of probability that can contain at most two electrons.

Active Reading Question

As the principal energy level increases, the number of sublevels increases. For each consecutive energy level, there is one more sublevel.

Like our triangle, the principal energy levels in the hydrogen atom contain sublevels. As we will see presently, these sublevels contain spaces for the electron that we call orbitals. Principal energy level 1 consists of just one sublevel, or one type of orbital. This orbital is spherical in shape. We label this orbital 1*s*. The number 1 is for the principal energy level, and *s* is a shorthand way to label a particular sublevel (type of orbital).

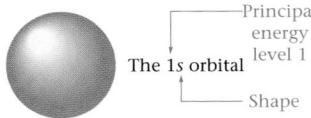

Principal energy level 2 has two sublevels. (Note the correspondence between the principal energy level number and the number of sublevels.) These sublevels are labeled 2*s* and 2*p*. The 2*s* sublevel consists of one orbital (called the 2*s*), and the 2*p* sublevel consists of three orbitals (called 2p_x, 2p_y, and 2p_z). Let's return to the inverted triangle to illustrate this. **Figure 11.15** shows principal level 2 divided into the sublevels 2*s* and 2*p* (which is subdivided into 2p_x, 2p_y, and 2p_z). The orbitals have the shapes shown in **Figures 11.16** and **11.17**. The 2*s* orbital is spherical like the 1*s* orbital but larger in size (see Figure 11.16). The three 2*p* orbitals are not spherical but have two "lobes." These orbitals are shown in Figure 11.17 both as electron probability maps and as surfaces that contain 90% of the total electron probability. Notice that the label *x, y,* or *z* on a given 2*p* orbital tells along which axis the lobes of that orbital are directed.

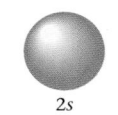

Figure 11.15
Principal level 2 shown divided into the 2*s* and 2*p* sublevels

Active Reading Question

What is the relationship between the principal level and the number of sublevels?

What we have learned so far about the hydrogen atom is summarized in **Figure 11.18.**

- Principal energy level 1 has one sublevel, which contains the 1*s* orbital.
- Principal energy level 2 contains two sublevels, one of which contains the 2*s* orbital and one of which contains the 2*p* orbitals (three of them).
- Note that each orbital is designated by a symbol or label.

Figure 11.16
The relative sizes of the 1*s* and 2*s* orbitals of hydrogen

Figure 11.17
The three 2*p* orbitals: (a) 2p_x, (b) 2p_z, (c) 2p_y. The *x, y,* or *z* label indicates along which axis the two lobes are directed. Each orbital is shown both as a probability map and as a surface that encloses 90% of the electron probability.

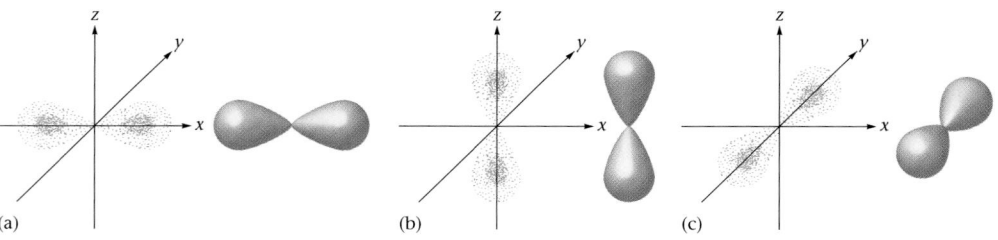

(a)   (b)   (c)

Meeting Individual Needs
ADVANCED LEARNERS

Point out that the relationship between the level number of the orbital and the average distance of the electron in that orbital is a *direct relationship*. Ask students to explain *direct relationships*. Then have them list three real-world situations and three situations related to chemistry that have direct relationships. For example: temperature and number of people swimming; pressure and temperature.

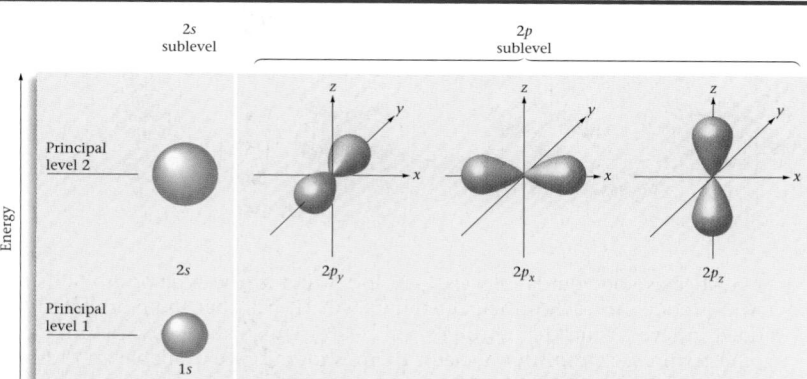

Figure 11.18
A diagram of principal energy levels 1 and 2 showing the shapes of orbitals that compose the sublevels

TECHNOLOGY

Figure 11.18

Animations
1s Orbital
2p$_x$ Orbital
2p$_y$ Orbital
2p$_z$ Orbital

Let's Review

Orbital Labels

- The number tells the principal energy level.
- The letter tells the shape. The letter *s* means a spherical orbital; the letter *p* means a two-lobed orbital. The *x*, *y*, or *z* subscript on a *p* orbital label tells along which of the coordinate axes the two lobes lie.

One important characteristic of orbitals is that as the level number increases, the average distance of the electron in that orbital from the nucleus also increases. That is, when the hydrogen electron is in the 1*s* orbital (the ground state), it spends most of its time much closer to the nucleus than when it occupies the 2*s* orbital (an excited state).

Hydrogen Orbitals

You may be wondering at this point why hydrogen, which has only one electron, has more than one orbital. It is best to think of an orbital as a *potential space* for an electron. The hydrogen electron can occupy only a single orbital at a time, but the other orbitals are still available should the electron be transferred into one of them. For example, when a hydrogen atom is in its ground state (lowest possible energy state), the electron is in the 1*s* orbital. By adding the correct amount of energy (for example, a specific photon of light), we can excite the electron to the 2*s* orbital or to one of the 2*p* orbitals.

So far we have discussed only two of hydrogen's energy levels. There are many others. For example, level 3 has three sublevels (see Figure 11.14), which we label 3*s*, 3*p*, and 3*d*. The 3*s* sublevel contains a single 3*s* orbital, a spherical orbital larger than 1*s* and 2*s* (see **Figure 11.19**). Sublevel 3*p* contains three orbitals: 3*p$_x$*, 3*p$_y$*, and 3*p$_z$*, which are shaped like the 2*p* orbitals except that they are larger. The 3*d* sublevel contains five 3*d* orbitals with the shapes and labels shown in **Figure 11.20.** (You do not need to memorize the 3*d* orbital shapes and labels. They are shown for completeness.)

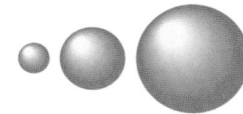

Figure 11.19
The relative sizes of the spherical 1*s*, 2*s*, and 3*s* orbitals of hydrogen

information

Think of orbitals as ways of dividing up the space around a nucleus.

11.3 • Atomic Orbitals • **373**

Teaching Support
BACKGROUND INFORMATION

Polyelectronic Atoms

The quantum mechanical model gives a description of the hydrogen atom that agrees very well with experimental data. However, it would not be very useful if it did not account for the properties of all other atoms as well.

To see how the model applies to polyelectronic atoms, let's consider helium. Three energy contributions must be considered in the

description of the helium atom: (1) the kinetic energy of the electrons as they move around the nucleus; (2) the potential energy of attraction between the nucleus and the electrons; and (3) the potential energy of repulsion between the two electrons.

Although the helium atom can be readily described in terms of the quantum mechanical model, the resulting Schrödinger equation cannot be solved exactly. The difficulty arises in dealing with the repulsions between the

(continued on next page)

Figure 11.20

Animations
3$d_{x^2-y^2}$ Orbital
3d_{xy} Orbital
3d_{xz} Orbital
3d_{yz} Orbital
3d_{z^2} Orbital

11.3.B The Wave Mechanical Model: Further Development

Objective To review the energy levels and orbitals of the wave mechanical model of the atom and to learn about electron spin

TEACHING TIP

The idea of electron spin is abstract and difficult for many students to grasp. Focus your discussion on the important point that for two electrons to occupy the same orbital, they must have opposite spins. An analogy to a magnet is often useful.

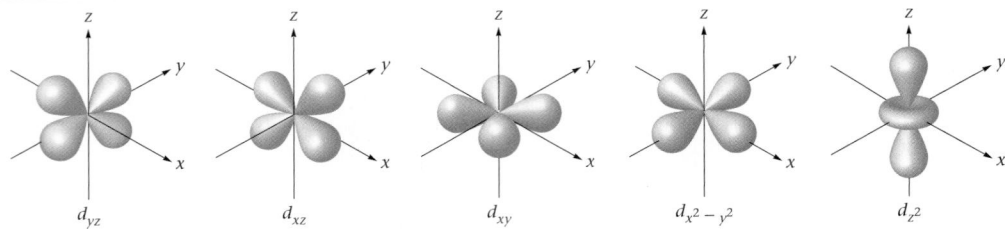

d_{yz} d_{xz} d_{xy} $d_{x^2-y^2}$ d_{z^2}

Figure 11.20
The shapes and labels of the five 3d orbitals

Notice as you compare levels 1, 2, and 3 that a new type of orbital (sublevel) is added in each principal energy level. (Recall that the p orbitals are added in level 2 and the d orbitals in level 3.) This makes sense because in going farther out from the nucleus, there is more space available and thus room for more orbitals.

It might help you to understand that the number of orbitals increases with the principal energy level if you think of a sports stadium. Picture a tennis court with circular rows of seats surrounding it. The farther from the court a row of seats is, the more seats it contains because the circle is larger. Orbitals divide up the space around a nucleus somewhat like the seats in this stadium. The greater the distance from the nucleus, the more space there is and the more orbitals we find.

The pattern of increasing numbers of orbitals continues with level 4. Level 4 has four sublevels labeled 4s, 4p, 4d, and 4f. The 4s sublevel has a single 4s orbital. The 4p sublevel contains three orbitals (4p_x, 4p_y, and 4p_z). The 4d sublevel has five 4d orbitals. The 4f sublevel has seven 4f orbitals.

The 4s, 4p, and 4d orbitals have the same shapes as the earlier s, p, and d orbitals, respectively, but are larger. We will not be concerned here with the shapes of the f orbitals.

A circular tennis stadium

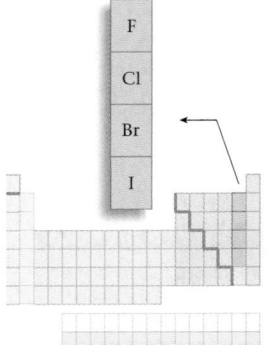

Group 7

F
Cl
Br
I

B. The Wave Mechanical Model: Further Development

A model for the atom is of little use if it does not apply to all atoms. The Bohr model was discarded because it could be applied only to hydrogen. The wave mechanical model can be applied to all atoms in basically the same form as we have just used it for hydrogen. In fact, the major triumph of this model is its ability to explain the periodic table of the elements. Recall that the elements on the periodic table are arranged in vertical groups, which contain elements that typically show similar chemical properties. For example, the halogens shown to the left are chemically similar. The wave mechanical model of the atom allows us to explain, based on electron arrangements, why these similarities occur. We will see later how this is done.

Atoms Beyond Hydrogen Remember that an atom has as many electrons as it has protons to give it a zero overall charge. Therefore, all atoms beyond hydrogen have more than one electron. Before we can consider the atoms beyond hydrogen, we must describe one more property of electrons that determines how they can be arranged in an atom's orbitals. This property is spin. Each electron appears to be spinning as a top spins on

374 • Chapter 11 • Modern Atomic Theory

(continued)

electrons. Because the electron pathways are unknown, the electron repulsions cannot be calculated exactly. This issue is called the *electron correlation problem*.

The electron correlation problem occurs with all polyelectronic atoms. To treat these systems using the quantum mechanical model, we must make approximations. Most commonly, the approximation used to treat each

electron assumes that the electron is moving in a *field of charge that is the net result of the nuclear attraction and the average repulsions of all other electrons*.

Let's single out the outermost electron and consider the forces that this electron feels. The electron is attracted to the highly charged nucleus. It also feels the repulsions caused by the other 10 electrons. The net effect is that the electron is not bound nearly as tightly to the nucleus as it would be if the other

electrons were not present. We say that the electron is *screened* or *shielded* from the nuclear charge by the repulsions of the other electrons.

This picture leads to *hydrogen-like orbitals* for polyelectronic atoms. They have the same general shapes as the orbitals for hydrogen, but their sizes and energies are different. The differences occur because of the interplay between the nuclear attraction and the electron repulsions.

its axis. Like the top, an electron can spin in only one of two directions. We often represent spin with an arrow: ↑ or ↓. One arrow represents the electron spinning in the one direction, and the other represents the electron spinning in the opposite direction. For our purposes, what is most important about electron spin is that two electrons must have *opposite* spins to occupy the same orbital. That is, two electrons that have the same spin cannot occupy the same orbital.

Pauli exclusion principle: An atomic orbital can hold a maximum of two electrons, and those two electrons must have opposite spins.

Pauli exclusion principle
In a given atom, no two electrons can occupy the same atomic orbital and have the same spin.

Let's Review

Principal Components of the Wave Mechanical Model of the Atom

- Atoms have a series of energy levels called **principal energy levels**, which are designated by whole numbers symbolized by n; n can equal 1, 2, 3, 4, . . . Level 1 corresponds to $n = 1$, level 2 corresponds to $n = 2$, and so on.

- The energy of the level increases as the value of n increases.

- Each principal energy level contains one or more *types* of orbitals, called **sublevels**.

- The number of sublevels present in a given principal energy level equals n. For example, level 1 contains one sublevel ($1s$); level 2 contains two sublevels (two types of orbitals), the $2s$ orbital and the three $2p$ orbitals; and so on. These are summarized in the following table. The number of each type of orbital is shown in parentheses.

n	Sublevels (Types of Orbitals) Present
1	$1s(1)$
2	$2s(1)\ 2p(3)$
3	$3s(1)\ 3p(3)\ 3d(5)$
4	$4s(1)\ 4p(3)\ 4d(5)\ 4f(7)$

- The n value is always used to label the orbitals of a given principal level and is followed by a letter that indicates the type (shape) of the orbital. For example, the designation $3p$ means an orbital in level 3 that has two lobes (a p orbital always has two lobes).

- An orbital can be empty or it can contain one or two electrons, but never more than two. If two electrons occupy the same orbital, they must have opposite spins.

- The shape of an orbital does not indicate the details of electron movement. It indicates the probability distribution for an electron residing in that orbital.

Use two bar magnets or cow magnets (available from Educational Innovations or local farm supply resources) to illustrate electron spin. Suspend both magnets with separate pieces of fishing line wrapped around their middles. Bring the magnets together and illustrate how they twist apart when the same poles are close to each other. Explain that electrons with the same spin repel each other in a similar manner, so electrons in the same orbital have opposite spins.

(continued)

An important difference between polyelectronic atoms and the hydrogen atom is that for hydrogen, all orbitals in a given principal quantum level have the same energy (they are said to be *degenerate*). This is not the case for polyelectronic atoms. In these atoms, for a given principal level the orbitals vary in energy as follows:

$$E_{ns} < E_{np} < E_{nd} < E_{nf}$$

In other words, when electrons are placed in a particular quantum level, they "prefer" the orbitals in the order s, p, d, f. Although an electron in the $2s$ orbital spends most of its time a little farther from the nucleus than does an electron in the $2p$ orbital, it spends a small but very significant amount of time very near the nucleus. We say that the $2s$ electron *penetrates* to the nucleus more than the electron in the $2p$ orbital. This *penetration effect* causes an electron

in a $2s$ orbital to be attracted to the nucleus more strongly than an electron in a $2p$ orbital. That is, the $2s$ orbital is lower in energy than the $2p$ orbitals in a polyelectronic atom. The same thing happens in the other principal quantum levels.

EXAMPLE 11.1

More Examples

Indicate whether each of the following statements about atomic structure is true or false.

a. The shape of a given type of orbital changes as n increases.

False. The shape of a given orbital stays the same while the size increases.

b. The number of types of orbitals in a given energy level is the same as the value of n.

True. For example, in $n = 2$ there are two types of orbitals (s and p).

c. The hydrogen atom has a 3s orbital.

True. There are no electrons in the 3s orbital for a hydrogen atom in its lowest energy state; however, the orbital is a potential space, not a physical structure.

Answer to Practice Problem 11.1

a. Circular pathways for electrons in the Bohr model

b. Three-dimensional probability maps that represent the likelihood that the electron will occupy a given point in space. The details of electron motion are not described by an orbital.

c. The surface that contains 90% of the total electron probability. That is, the electron is found somewhere inside this surface 90% of the time.

d. A set of orbitals of a given type of orbital within a principal energy level. For example, there are three sublevels in principal level 3; they consist of the 3s orbital, the three 3p orbitals, and the five 3d orbitals.

SECTION 11.3
ASSESS

**SECTION 11.3
Review Questions**

1. An orbit is a particular path for an electron in motion about the nucleus; an orbital describes a region of probability for finding an electron.

EXAMPLE 11.1

Understanding the Wave Mechanical Model of the Atom

Indicate whether each of the following statements about atomic structure is true or false.

    a. An s orbital is always spherical in shape.

    b. The 2s orbital is the same size as the 3s orbital.

    c. The number of lobes on a p orbital increases as n increases. That is, a 3p orbital has more lobes than a 2p orbital.

    d. Level 1 has one s orbital, level 2 has two s orbitals, level 3 has three s orbitals, and so on.

    e. The electron path is indicated by the surface of the orbital.

Solution

    a. True. The size of the sphere increases as n increases, but the shape is always spherical.

    b. False. The 3s orbital is larger (the electron is farther from the nucleus on average) than the 2s orbital.

    c. False. A p orbital always has two lobes.

    d. False. Each principal energy level has only one s orbital.

    e. False. The electron is *somewhere inside* the orbital surface 90% of the time. The electron does not move around *on* this surface.

Practice Problem • Exercise 11.1

Define the following terms.

    a. Bohr orbits

    b. orbitals

    c. orbital size

    d. sublevel

SECTION 11.3
REVIEW QUESTIONS

❶ What is the difference between an orbit and an orbital in atomic theory?

❷ Draw Figure 11.14 and fill in the different types of sublevels for each principal energy levels.

❸ Label each of the following orbitals as s, p, or d.

a.   b.   c.

❹ Tell how many orbitals are found in each type of sublevel: s, p, d, f.

❺ How do the shapes of s orbitals in different energy levels of a hydrogen atom compare? How do the sizes of these orbitals compare?

❻ What is the Pauli exclusion principle and how does it help us determine where an electron is within the atom?

RESEARCH LINKS
CLASSZONE.COM

---

2. Use the transparency for Figure 11.14 to assist students in placing the sublevels correctly.

3. **a.** p orbital

    b. s orbital

    c. d orbital

4. Orbitals in a given sublevel: $s = 1$; $p = 3$; $d = 5$; $f = 7$

5. The shapes of s orbitals in different energy levels of a hydrogen atom are the same (they are spheres). The s orbitals increase in size as the energy level increases (a 2s orbital is larger than a 1s orbital, and so on).

6. The Pauli exclusion principle states that an orbital can hold a maximum of two electrons and those two electrons must have opposite spins.

Electron Configurations and Atomic Properties

Objectives

- *To understand how the principal energy levels fill with electrons in atoms beyond hydrogen*
- *To learn about valence electrons and core electrons*
- *To learn about the electron configurations of atoms with $Z \leq 18$*
- *To understand the general trends in properties in the periodic table*

Key Terms

- Electron configuration
- Orbital diagram (box diagram)
- Valence electrons
- Core electrons
- Lanthanide series
- Actinide series
- Main-group elements (representative elements)
- Metals
- Nonmetals
- Metalloids
- Atomic size
- Ionization energy

A. Electron Arrangements in the First 18 Atoms on the Periodic Table

We will now describe the electron arrangements in atoms with $Z = 1$ to $Z = 18$ by placing electrons in the various orbitals in the principal energy levels, starting with $n = 1$, and then continuing with $n = 2$, $n = 3$, and so on. For the first 18 elements, the individual sublevels fill in the following order: $1s$, then $2s$, then $2p$, then $3s$, and then $3p$.

The most attractive orbital to an electron in an atom is always the $1s$, because in this orbital the negatively charged electron is closer to the positively charged nucleus than in any other orbital. That is, the $1s$ orbital involves the space around the nucleus that is closest to the nucleus. As n increases, the orbital becomes larger—the electron, on average, occupies space farther from the nucleus.

Electron Configurations In its ground state, hydrogen has its lone electron in the $1s$ orbital. This is commonly represented in two ways. First, we say that hydrogen has the electron arrangement, or **electron configuration**, $1s^1$. This means there is one electron in the $1s$ orbital. We can also represent this configuration by using an **orbital diagram**, also called a **box diagram**, in which orbitals are represented by boxes grouped by sublevel with small arrows indicating the electrons. For *hydrogen*, the electron configuration and box diagram are

Electron configuration
The arrangement of electrons in an atom

The arrow represents an electron spinning in a particular direction. The next element is *helium*, $Z = 2$. It has two protons in its nucleus and so has two electrons. Because the $1s$ orbital is the most desirable, both electrons go there but with opposite spins. For helium, the electron configuration and box diagram are

The opposite electron spins are shown by the opposing arrows in the box.

Lithium ($Z = 3$) has three electrons, two of which go into the $1s$ orbital. That is, two electrons fill that orbital. The $1s$ orbital is the only orbital for

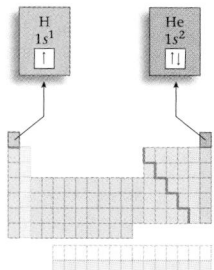

SECTION 11.4

Student Preparation

Assign students to read Section 11.4 and to answer the Review Questions at the end of the section before coming to class.

 Active Learning
Team Learning Worksheet

After introducing the material in Section 11.4 in class, place students in groups and have them work together on **Section 11.4: Team Learning Worksheet**.

SECTION 11.4
GUIDE THE LEARNING

Homework

You may wish to assign these selected end-of-chapter problems as homework for this section: 34, 35, 36, 37, 39, 40, 41, 43, 45, 46, 47, 48, 52, 53, 54, 55a–c, 56a–c, 57

Additional end-of-chapter problems can be used for extra practice.

11.4.A Electron Arrangements in the First 18 Atoms on the Periodic Table

Objective To understand how the principal energy levels fill with electrons in atoms beyond hydrogen and to learn about valence and core electrons

---

Teaching Support
HISTORICAL NOTE

Dmitri Ivanovich Mendeleev (1834–1907) Mendeleev was born in Siberia as the youngest of 17 children, and he taught chemistry at the University of St. Petersburg. In 1860, Mendeleev heard the Italian chemist Cannizzaro lecture on a reliable method for determining the atomic masses of the elements. This important development paved the way

for Mendeleev's own brilliant contribution to chemistry—the periodic table. In 1861, Mendeleev wrote a book on organic chemistry. Later, when he wrote a book on inorganic chemistry, he was struck by the fact that the systematic approach for characterizing organic chemistry was lacking in inorganic chemistry. In attempting to systematize inorganic chemistry, Mendeleev eventually arranged the elements in the form of the periodic table.

Mendeleev was a versatile genius who was interested in many fields of science. He worked on many problems associated with Russia's natural resources, such as coal, salt, and various metals. Being particularly interested in the petroleum industry, he visited the United States in 1876 to study the Pennsylvania oil fields. His interests also included meteorology and hot-air balloons. In 1887, he made an ascent in a balloon to study a total eclipse of the sun.

• Encourage students to use the periodic table to assist in figuring out electron configurations. Once they see that they can just move across the rows, placing electrons into the *s* and *p* orbitals, electron configurations will become much easier to write.

• For polyelectronic atoms, the third electron goes to the 2*s* orbital. In the hydrogen atom, the 2*s* and 2*p* orbitals have the same energy. Multiple electrons change this situation, however. With multiple electrons, in a given energy level the *s* orbitals are lower in energy (and thus are filled first) than the *p* orbitals, which in turn are lower in energy than the *d* orbitals.

• When explaining the filling of the *p* orbitals, it may be helpful to use the analogy of a restaurant with three tables that each seat two diners. When three strangers take seats, they usually occupy tables by themselves. Only when all three tables have an occupant will the next diner need to sit at a table that is already occupied.

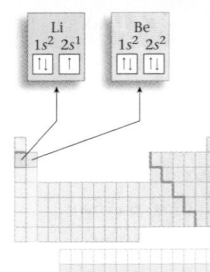

$n = 1$, so the third electron must occupy an orbital with $n = 2$—in this case the 2*s* orbital. This gives a $1s^2 2s^1$ configuration. The electron configuration and box diagram are

$$\text{Li:} \quad 1s^2 2s^1 \qquad \begin{array}{cc} 1s & 2s \\ \uparrow\downarrow & \uparrow \end{array}$$

The next element, *beryllium*, has four electrons, which occupy the 1*s* and 2*s* orbitals with opposite spins.

$$\text{Be:} \quad 1s^2 2s^2 \qquad \begin{array}{cc} 1s & 2s \\ \uparrow\downarrow & \uparrow\downarrow \end{array}$$

Boron has five electrons, four of which occupy the 1*s* and 2*s* orbitals. The fifth electron goes into the second type of orbital with $n = 2$, one of the 2*p* orbitals.

$$\text{B:} \quad 1s^2 2s^2 2p^1 \qquad \begin{array}{ccc} 1s & 2s & 2p \\ \uparrow\downarrow & \uparrow\downarrow & \uparrow\ \ \ \ \end{array}$$

Because all the 2*p* orbitals have the same energy, it does not matter which 2*p* orbital the electron occupies.

Carbon, the next element, has six electrons: two electrons occupy the 1*s* orbital, two occupy the 2*s* orbital, and two occupy 2*p* orbitals. There are three 2*p* orbitals, so each of the mutually repulsive electrons occupies a different 2*p* orbital. For reasons we will not consider, in the separate 2*p* orbitals the electrons have the same spin.

The configuration for carbon could be written $1s^2 2s^2 2p^1 2p^1$ to indicate that the electrons occupy separate 2*p* orbitals. However, the configuration is usually given as $1s^2 2s^2 2p^2$, and it is understood that the electrons are in different 2*p* orbitals.

information

Because electrons have the same charge, they repel each other.

$$\text{C:} \quad 1s^2 2s^2 2p^2 \qquad \begin{array}{ccc} 1s & 2s & 2p \\ \uparrow\downarrow & \uparrow\downarrow & \uparrow\uparrow\ \ \end{array}$$

Note the like spins for the unpaired electrons in the 2*p* orbitals.

The configuration for *nitrogen*, which has seven electrons, is $1s^2 2s^2 2p^3$. The three electrons in 2*p* orbitals occupy separate orbitals and have like spins.

$$\text{N:} \quad 1s^2 2s^2 2p^3 \qquad \begin{array}{ccc} 1s & 2s & 2p \\ \uparrow\downarrow & \uparrow\downarrow & \uparrow\uparrow\uparrow \end{array}$$

The configuration for *oxygen*, which has eight electrons, is $1s^2 2s^2 2p^4$. One of the 2*p* orbitals is now occupied by a pair of electrons with opposite spins, as required by the Pauli exclusion principle.

$$\text{O:} \quad 1s^2 2s^2 2p^4 \qquad \begin{array}{ccc} 1s & 2s & 2p \\ \uparrow\downarrow & \uparrow\downarrow & \uparrow\downarrow\uparrow\uparrow \end{array}$$

The electron configurations and orbital diagrams for *fluorine* (nine electrons) and *neon* (ten electrons) are

$$\text{F:} \quad 1s^2 2s^2 2p^5 \qquad \begin{array}{ccc} 1s & 2s & 2p \\ \uparrow\downarrow & \uparrow\downarrow & \uparrow\downarrow\uparrow\downarrow\uparrow \end{array}$$

$$\text{Ne:} \quad 1s^2 2s^2 2p^6 \qquad \begin{array}{ccc} 1s & 2s & 2p \\ \uparrow\downarrow & \uparrow\downarrow & \uparrow\downarrow\uparrow\downarrow\uparrow\downarrow \end{array}$$

With neon, the orbitals with $n = 1$ and $n = 2$ are completely filled.

378 • Chapter 11 • Modern Atomic Theory

Teaching Support

BACKGROUND INFORMATION

History of the Periodic Table

The periodic table was originally constructed to highlight the patterns observed in the chemical properties of the elements. As chemistry progressed, it became evident that the earth is composed of a great many elements with very different properties. At first, the array of elements and properties was bewildering. Gradually, however, patterns were noticed.

The first chemist to recognize patterns was Johann Dobereiner (1780–1849), who found several groups of three elements that have similar properties. As Dobereiner attempted to expand this model of *triads* to the rest of the known elements, it became clear that this idea was severely limited.

The next notable attempt was made by the English chemist John Newlands, who in 1864 suggested that elements should be arranged in *octaves,* based on the idea that certain properties seemed to repeat for every eighth tone. Although this model managed to group several elements with similar properties, it was not completely successful.

The present form of the periodic table was conceived independently by two chemists: the German Julius Lothar Meyer (1830–1895) and Dmitri Ivanovich Mendeleev (1834–1907),

For *sodium*, which has eleven electrons, the first ten electrons occupy the 1s, 2s, and 2p orbitals, and the eleventh electron must occupy the first orbital with $n = 3$, the 3s orbital. The electron configuration for sodium is $1s^2 2s^2 2p^6 3s^1$. To avoid writing the inner-level electrons, we often abbreviate the configuration $1s^2 2s^2 2p^6 3s^1$ as $[Ne]3s^1$, where [Ne] represents the electron configuration of neon, $1s^2 2s^2 2p^6$.

The orbital diagram for sodium is

i **nformation**

[Ne] is shorthand for $1s^2 2s^2 2p^6$.

1s	2s	2p	3s
↑↓	↑↓	↑↓ ↑↓ ↑↓	↑

The next element, *magnesium*, $Z = 12$, has the electron configuration $1s^2 2s^2 2p^6 3s^2$, or $[Ne]3s^2$.

The next six elements, *aluminum* through *argon*, have electron configurations obtained by filling the 3p orbitals one electron at a time. **Figure 11.21** summarizes the electron configurations of the first eighteen elements by giving the number of electrons in the type of orbital (sublevel) occupied last.

Figure 11.21
The electron configurations in the sublevel last occupied for the first eighteen elements

EXAMPLE 11.2

Writing Orbital Diagrams

Write the orbital diagram for magnesium.

Solution

Magnesium ($Z = 12$) has twelve electrons that are placed successively in the 1s, 2s, 2p, and 3s orbitals to give the electron configuration $1s^2 2s^2 2p^6 3s^2$. The orbital diagram is

1s	2s	2p	3s
↑↓	↑↓	↑↓ ↑↓ ↑↓	↑↓

Only occupied orbitals are shown here.

Practice Problem • Exercise 11.2

Write the complete electron configuration and the orbital diagram for each of the elements aluminum through argon.

TECHNOLOGY

🖥 Figure 11.21

EXAMPLE 11.2

More Examples

1. Write the orbital diagram for sodium.

1s	2s	2p	3s
↑↓	↑↓	↑↓ ↑↓ ↑↓	↑

2. Write the orbital diagram for silicon.

1s	2s	2p	3s	3p
↑↓	↑↓	↑↓ ↑↓ ↑↓	↑↓	↑ ↑

✓ Answer to Practice Problem 11.2

Al $1s^2 2s^2 2p^6 3s^2 3p^1$
$[Ne]3s^2 3p^1$

1s	2s	2p	3s	3p
↑↓	↑↓	↑↓ ↑↓ ↑↓	↑↓	↑

Si $[Ne]3s^2 3p^2$

1s	2s	2p	3s	3p
↑↓	↑↓	↑↓ ↑↓ ↑↓	↑↓	↑ ↑

P $[Ne]3s^2 3p^3$

1s	2s	2p	3s	3p
↑↓	↑↓	↑↓ ↑↓ ↑↓	↑↓	↑ ↑ ↑

S $[Ne]3s^2 3p^4$

1s	2s	2p	3s	3p
↑↓	↑↓	↑↓ ↑↓ ↑↓	↑↓	↑↓ ↑ ↑

Cl $[Ne]3s^2 3p^5$

1s	2s	2p	3s	3p
↑↓	↑↓	↑↓ ↑↓ ↑↓	↑↓	↑↓ ↑↓ ↑

Ar $[Ne]3s^2 3p^6$

1s	2s	2p	3s	3p
↑↓	↑↓	↑↓ ↑↓ ↑↓	↑↓	↑↓ ↑↓ ↑↓

(continued)

a Russian. Mendeleev is usually given most of the credit because it was he who emphasized how useful the table could be in predicting the existence and properties of still unknown elements. When Mendeleev first published his table in 1872, the elements gallium, scandium, and germanium were unknown. Mendeleev correctly predicted the existence and properties of these elements from gaps in his periodic table.

Using the table, Mendeleev also was able to correct several values for atomic masses. For example, the original atomic mass of 76 for indium was based on the assumption that indium oxide had the formula InO. This atomic mass placed indium, which has metallic properties, among the nonmetals. Mendeleev assumed that the atomic mass was probably incorrect and proposed that the formula of indium oxide was really In_2O_3. Based on this correct formula,

indium has an atomic mass of approximately 113, placing it among the metals. Mendeleev also corrected the atomic masses of beryllium and uranium. Because of its obvious usefulness, Mendeleev's periodic table was almost universally adopted, and it remains one of the most valuable tools at a chemist's disposal.

- Students are often confused about using core notation when writing electron configurations. It may be easier to have them use only the long form for electron configurations until Chapter 12, when an explanation of bonding makes core notation a useful form for writing the configurations. The major advantage of core notation is the emphasis it places on the outer electrons used in bonding. Make sure that students understand that in core notation, the last noble gas is used and the outer electrons are written after it.

- Point out that the periodic table (developed by considering the chemical properties of the elements) was created before the discovery of electrons. The wave mechanical model is consistent with the positions on the periodic table. This consistency presents strong support for the model.

11.4.B Electron Configurations and the Periodic Table

Objective To learn about the electron configurations of atoms with Z greater than 18

 TEACHING TIP

Encourage students to use the periodic table as a guide in writing electron configurations. Understanding the structure of the table can be much more useful to students than memorizing an order of filling. Each row guides them through an energy level; each block guides them through a sublevel. Use the transparency for Figure 11.23 to discuss this process.

Valence electron
The electron in the outermost principal energy level of an atom

Core electron
An inner electron; an electron not in the outermost principal energy level of an atom

---

i nformation

[Ar] is shorthand for $1s^22s^22p^63s^23p^6$.

Classifying Electrons At this point it is useful to introduce the concept of **valence electrons**—that is, *the electrons in the outermost (highest) principal energy level of an atom*. For example, nitrogen, which has the electron configuration $1s^22s^22p^3$, has electrons in principal levels 1 and 2. Therefore, level 2 (which has $2s$ and $2p$ sublevels) is the valence level of nitrogen, and the $2s$ and $2p$ electrons are the valence electrons. For the sodium atom (electron configuration $1s^22s^22p^63s^1$, or $[Ne]3s^1$) the valence electron is the electron in the $3s$ orbital, because in this case principal energy level 3 is the outermost level that contains an electron. The valence electrons are the most important electrons to chemists because, being the outermost electrons, they are the ones involved when atoms attach to each other (form bonds), as we will see in the next chapter. The inner electrons, which are known as **core electrons**, are not involved in bonding atoms to each other.

Note in Figure 11.21 that a very important pattern is developing: except for helium, *the atoms of elements in the same group (vertical column of the periodic table) have the same number of electrons in a given type of orbital (sublevel), except that the orbitals are in different principal energy levels*. Remember that the elements were originally organized into groups on the periodic table on the basis of similarities in chemical properties. Now we understand the reason behind these groupings.

Elements with the same valence electron arrangement show very similar chemical behavior.

B. Electron Configurations and the Periodic Table

We have seen that we can describe the atoms beyond hydrogen by simply filling the atomic orbitals starting with level $n = 1$ and working outward in order. This works fine until we reach the element *potassium* ($Z = 19$), which is the next element after argon. Because the $3p$ orbitals are fully occupied in argon, we might expect the next electron to go into a $3d$ orbital (recall that for $n = 3$ the sublevels are $3s$, $3p$, and $3d$). However, experiments show that the chemical properties of potassium are very similar to those of lithium and sodium.

Because we have learned to associate similar chemical properties with similar valence-electron arrangements, we predict that the valence-electron configuration for potassium is $4s^1$, resembling sodium ($3s^1$) and lithium ($2s^1$). That is, we expect the last electron in potassium to occupy the $4s$ orbital instead of one of the $3d$ orbitals. This means that the principal energy level 4 begins to fill before level 3 has been completed. This conclusion is confirmed by many types of experiments. So the electron configuration of potassium is

K: $1s^22s^22p^63s^23p^64s^1$, or $[Ar]4s^1$

The next element is *calcium*, with an additional electron that also occupies the $4s$ orbital.

Ca: $1s^22s^22p^63s^23p^64s^2$, or $[Ar]4s^2$

The $4s$ orbital is now full.

After calcium the next electrons go into the $3d$ orbitals to complete principal energy level 3. The elements that correspond to filling the $3d$ orbitals are called transition metals. Then the $4p$ orbitals fill. **Figure 11.22** gives partial electron configurations for the elements potassium through krypton.

Teaching Support
DEMONSTRATION

Roman Candle

Materials
- Test tube (200×24 cm)
- 600-mL beaker
- Sand
- Dropper
- Copper(II) chloride
- Potassium chlorate

- Granulated sugar
- Powdered iron
- Strontium nitrate
- Sulfuric acid (concentrated)

Preparation Measure 35.0 g potassium chlorate and 10.00 g granulated sugar separately and then mix them uniformly.

Caution Do not grind this mixture together. An explosion may result. Prepare a fresh mixture for each demonstration. Do not store the mixture.

Figure 11.22
Partial electron configurations for the elements potassium through krypton. The transition metals shown in green (scandium through zinc) have the general configuration [Ar]$4s^2 3d^n$, except for chromium and copper.

| K
$4s^1$ | Ca
$4s^2$ | Sc
$3d^1$ | Ti
$3d^2$ | V
$3d^3$ | Cr
$4s^1 3d^5$ | Mn
$3d^5$ | Fe
$3d^6$ | Co
$3d^7$ | Ni
$3d^8$ | Cu
$4s^1 3d^{10}$ | Zn
$3d^{10}$ | Ga
$4p^1$ | Ge
$4p^2$ | As
$4p^3$ | Se
$4p^4$ | Br
$4p^5$ | Kr
$4p^6$ |

Note from Figure 11.22 that all of the transition metals have the general configuration [Ar]$4s^2 3d^n$ except chromium ($4s^1 3d^5$) and copper ($4s^1 3d^{10}$). The reasons for these exceptions are complex and will not be discussed here.

Instead of continuing to consider the elements individually, we will now look at the overall relationship between the periodic table and orbital filling. **Figure 11.23** shows which type of orbital is filling in each area of the periodic table.

- Point out that Cu and Cr are notable exceptions to the expected electron configurations. The reasons for these exceptions are quite complicated.

- Students should realize that with an understanding of the structure of the periodic table, they can figure out the expected electron configuration of any element. They need not memorize these configurations.

Figure 11.23

ℹ️ nformation

- The $(n + 1)s$ orbital fills before the nd orbitals fill.

- Lanthanides are elements in which the $4f$ orbitals are being filled.

- Actinides are elements in which the $5f$ orbitals are being filled.

Figure 11.23
The orbitals being filled for elements in various parts of the periodic table. Note that in going along a horizontal row (a period), the $(n + 1)s$ orbital fills before the nd orbital. The group label indicates the number of valence electrons (the number of s plus the number of p electrons in the highest occupied principal energy level) for the elements in each group.

Rules for Orbital Filling

1. In a principal energy level that has d orbitals, the s orbital from the *next* level fills before the d orbitals in the current level. That is, the $(n + 1)s$ orbitals always fill before the nd orbitals. For example, the $5s$ orbitals fill for rubidium and strontium before the $4d$ orbitals fill for the second row of transition metals (yttrium through cadmium).

2. After lanthanum, which has the electron configuration [Xe]$6s^2 5d^1$, a group of fourteen elements called the **lanthanide series**, or the lanthanides, occurs. This series of elements corresponds to the filling of the seven $4f$ orbitals.

3. After actinium, which has the configuration [Rn]$7s^2 6d^1$, a group of fourteen elements called the **actinide series**, or the actinides, occurs. This series corresponds to the filling of the seven $5f$ orbitals.

4. Except for helium, the group numbers indicate the sum of electrons in the ns and np orbitals in the highest principal energy level that contains electrons (where n is the number that indicates a particular principal energy level). These electrons are the valence electrons, the electrons in the outermost principal energy level of a given atom.

11.4 • Electron Configurations and Atomic Properties • 381

(continued)

Starting at the bottom, prepare four zones of chemicals in the test tube as follows: (1) mixture of 3.0 g strontium nitrate and 9.0 g potassium chlorate/sugar (**red color**); (2) mixture of 2.0 g copper(II) chloride and 10.0 g potassium chlorate/sugar (**blue color**); (3) mixture of 3.0 g powdered iron and 9.0 g potassium chlorate/sugar (**yellow sparks**); (4) 12.0 g potassium chlorate/sugar (**white color**). Imbed the test tube upright in the beaker containing the sand.

Performance Note This demonstration **produces a lot of smoke. Perform it in a well-ventilated area or outside. Use a safety shield to protect the audience.** Add 1 or 2 drops of concentrated sulfuric acid to the test tube and *step back*. The test tube sometimes begins to melt in this demonstration. Make sure you wait for it to cool after the demonstration. The test tube can be discarded.

Teaching Notes You can use this demonstration as a review of the colors produced in the flame test. Ask students what chemical produces each color.

Elements in the same vertical columns (groups) on the periodic table generally have the same valence electron configurations.

MINI-DEMO

Place two Petri dishes on an overhead projector. Cover the bottom of each dish to a depth of 1 cm with water. Cut small samples of Na and K metals. Dry each with a paper towel. Add the Na to one dish and the K to the other. Observe the results and compare the reactions. Both metals skate around on the surface of the water, and they may burst into flames or smoke.

TECHNOLOGY

Animation
Orbital Energies

Order of filling of orbitals

6d ⬜⬜⬜⬜⬜
5f** ⬜⬜⬜⬜⬜⬜⬜
7s ⬜
6p ⬜⬜⬜
5d ⬜⬜⬜⬜⬜
4f* ⬜⬜⬜⬜⬜⬜⬜
6s ⬜
5p ⬜⬜⬜
4d ⬜⬜⬜⬜⬜
5s ⬜
4p ⬜⬜⬜
3d ⬜⬜⬜⬜⬜
4s ⬜
3p ⬜⬜⬜
3s ⬜
2p ⬜⬜⬜
2s ⬜
1s ⬜

To help you further understand the connection between orbital filling and the periodic table, **Figure 11.24** shows the orbitals in the order in which they fill.

A periodic table is almost always available to you. If you understand the relationship between the electron configuration of an element and its position on the periodic table, you can figure out the expected electron configuration of any atom.

 Active Reading Question

How does an electron configuration for an atom relate to the atom's placement on the periodic table?

Figure 11.24

A box diagram showing the order in which orbitals fill to produce the atoms in the periodic table. Each box can hold two electrons.
*After the $6s$ orbital is full, one electron goes into a $5d$ orbital. This corresponds to the element lanthanum ([Xe]$6s^2 5d^1$). After lanthanum, the $4f$ orbitals fill with electrons.
**After the $7s$ orbital is full, one electron goes into $6d$. This is actinium ([Rn]$7s^2 6d^1$). The $5f$ orbitals then fill.

CHEMISTRY IN YOUR WORLD

Science, Technology, and Society

A Magnetic Moment

An anesthetized frog lies in the hollow core of an electromagnet. As the current in the coils of the magnet is increased, the frog magically rises and floats in midair (see photo). How can this happen? Is the electromagnet an antigravity machine? In fact, there is no magic going on here. This phenomenon demonstrates the magnetic properties of all matter. We know that iron magnets attract and repel each other depending on their relative orientations. Is a frog magnetic like a piece of iron? If a frog lands on a steel manhole cover, will it be trapped there by magnetic attractions? Of course not. The magnetism of the frog, as with most objects, shows up only in the presence of a strong inducing magnetic field. In other words, the powerful electromagnet surrounding the frog in the experiment described above *induces* a magnetic field in the frog that opposes the inducing field. The opposing magnetic field in the frog repels the inducing field, and the frog lifts up until the magnetic force is balanced by the gravitational pull on its body. The frog then "floats" in air.

How can a frog be magnetic if it is not made of iron? It's the electrons. Frogs are composed of cells containing many kinds of molecules. Of course, these molecules are made of atoms—carbon atoms, nitrogen atoms, oxygen atoms, and other types. Each of these atoms contains electrons that are moving around the atomic nuclei. When these electrons sense a strong magnetic field, they respond by moving in a fashion that produces magnetic fields aligned to oppose the inducing field. This phenomenon is called *diamagnetism*.

All substances, animate and inanimate, because they are made of atoms, exhibit diamagnetism. Andre Geim and his colleagues at the University of Nijmegan, the Netherlands, have levitated frogs, grasshoppers, plants, and water droplets, among other objects. Geim says that, given a large enough electromagnet, even humans can be levitated. He notes, however, that constructing a magnet strong enough to float a human would be very expensive, and he sees no point in it. Geim does point out that inducing weightlessness with magnetic fields may be a good way to pretest experiments on weightlessness intended as research for future space flights—to see if the ideas fly as well as the objects.

A live frog being levitated in a magnetic field

Chemistry in Your World

A Magnetic Moment

Magnets have a useful application in human medicine in the form of MRI. A magnetic resonance imaging (MRI) scanner consists of a magnet large enough to accommodate an entire patient, along with additional coils (to excite hydrogen atoms, modify the magnetic field, and receive signals). Different tissues in the body give off different signals. These signals are separated into components that are then attributed to the site of origin in the body. A cross-sectional image of a patient can then be constructed on the screen. Most of the signals in an MRI scan originate from the hydrogen atoms in water. The difference in the way water is bound in different tissues produces the signal variations between healthy and diseased tissue.

MRI has become an important diagnostic tool for several reasons. An MRI scan does not expose the patient to X rays. Also, the image can be constructed irrespective of the patient's position in the machine. Diseased tissue produces a distinctive MRI image. MRI can also produce clear images of blood vessels.

Your students may want to investigate the use of magnetic fields in alternative medicine to treat sports injuries or arthritis. This topic would be an excellent choice for a web-based research project.

EXAMPLE 11.3

EXAMPLE 11.3

Determining Electron Configurations

Using the periodic table inside the back cover of the text, give the electron configurations for sulfur (S), gallium (Ga), hafnium (Hf), and radium (Ra).

Solution

Sulfur is element 16 and resides in Period 3, where the $3p$ orbitals are being filled (see **Figure 11.25**). Because sulfur is the fourth among the "$3p$ elements," it must have four $3p$ electrons. Sulfur's electron configuration is

S: $1s^2 2s^2 2p^6 3s^2 3p^4$, or [Ne]$3s^2 3p^4$

Gallium is element 31 in Period 4 just after the transition metals (see Figure 11.25). It is the first element in the "$4p$ series" and has a $4p^1$ arrangement. Gallium's electron configuration is

Ga: $1s^2 2s^2 2p^6 3s^2 3p^6 4s^2 3d^{10} 4p^1$, or [Ar]$4s^2 3d^{10} 4p^1$

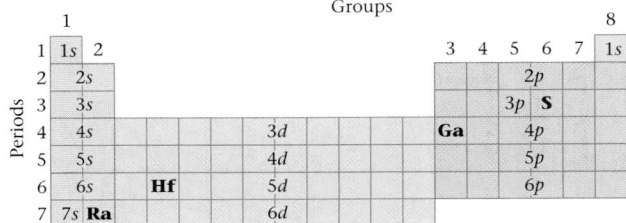

Groups

			1					3	4	5	6	7	8	

Figure 11.25
The positions of the elements considered in Example 11.3

Hafnium is element 72 and is found in Period 6, as shown in Figure 11.25. Note that it occurs just after the lanthanide series (see Figure 11.23). Thus the $4f$ orbitals are already filled. Hafnium is the second member of the $5d$ transition series and has two $5d$ electrons. Its electron configuration is

Hf: $1s^2 2s^2 2p^6 3s^2 3p^6 4s^2 3d^{10} 4p^6 5s^2 4d^{10} 5p^6 6s^2 4f^{14} 5d^2$,

or [Xe]$6s^2 4f^{14} 5d^2$

Radium is element 88 and is in Period 7 (and Group 2), as shown in Figure 11.25. Thus radium has two electrons in the 7s orbital, and its electron configuration is

Ra: $1s^2 2s^2 2p^6 3s^2 3p^6 4s^2 3d^{10} 4p^6 5s^2 4d^{10} 5p^6 6s^2 4f^{14} 5d^{10} 6p^6 7s^2$,

or [Rn]$7s^2$

Molten lead being poured into a mold to make toy soldiers

Practice Problem • Exercise 11.3

Using the periodic table inside the back cover of the text, predict the electron configurations for fluorine, silicon, cesium, lead, and iodine. If you have trouble, use Figure 11.23.

More Examples

Give the electron configuration for the following elements:

1. Bromine (Br)
   $1s^2 2s^2 2p^6 3s^2 3p^6 4s^2 3d^{10} 4p^5$
   or [Ar]$4s^2 3d^{10} 4p^5$

2. Tin (Sn)
   $1s^2 2s^2 2p^6 3s^2 3p^6 4s^2 3d^{10} 4p^6$
   $5s^2 4d^{10} 5p^2$ or [Kr]$5s^2 4d^{10} 5p^2$

3. Pollonium (Po)
   $1s^2 2s^2 2p^6 3s^2 3p^6 4s^2 3d^{10} 4p^6$
   $5s^2 4d^{10} 5p^6 6s^2 4f^{14} 5d^{10} 6p^4$ or
   [Xe]$6s^2 4f^{14} 5d^{10} 6p^4$

Answer to Practice Problem 11.3

Fluorine (F): In Group 7 and Period 2, it is the fifth $2p$ element. The configuration is $1s^2 2s^2 2p^5$, or [He]$2s^2 2p^5$.

Silicon (Si): In Group 4 and Period 3, it is the second of the $3p$ elements. The configuration is $1s^2 2s^2 2p^6 3s^2 3p^2$, or [Ne]$3s^2 3p^2$.

Cesium (Cs): In Group 1 and Period 6, it is the first of the $6s$ elements. The configuration is $1s^2 2s^2 2p^6 3s^2 3p^6 4s^2 3d^{10} 4p^6 5s^2$ $4d^{10} 5p^6 6s^1$, or [Xe]$6s^1$.

Lead (Pb): In Group 4 and Period 6, it is the second of the $6p$ elements. The configuration is [Xe]$6s^2 4f^{14} 5d^{10} 6p^2$.

Iodine (I): In Group 7 and Period 5, it is the fifth of the $5p$ elements. The configuration is [Kr]$5s^2 4d^{10} 5p^5$.

CRITICAL THINKING

There would be 3 elements in the s block, 9 elements in the p block, 15 elements in the d block, and 21 elements in the f block. The first few noble gases would have atomic numbers 3, 15, 27, and 54.

TECHNOLOGY

 Figure 11.26
This figure can help tie together the information presented in this chapter. It leads naturally to a discussion of the periodic trends.

CRITICAL THINKING

You have learned that each orbital can hold two electrons and that this pattern is evident in the periodic table.

What if each orbital could hold three electrons? How would it change the appearance of the periodic table? For example, what would be the atomic numbers of the noble gases?

Summary of the Wave Mechanical Model and Valence-Electron Configurations

The concepts we have discussed in this chapter are very important. They allow us to make sense of a good deal of chemistry. When it was first observed that elements with similar properties occur periodically as the atomic number increases, chemists wondered why. Now we have an explanation. The wave mechanical model pictures the electrons in an atom as arranged in orbitals, with each orbital capable of holding two electrons. As we build up the atoms, the same types of orbitals recur in going from one principal energy level to another. This means that particular valence-electron configurations recur periodically.

For reasons we will explore in the next chapter, elements with a particular type of valence configuration all show very similar chemical behavior. Thus groups of elements, such as the alkali metals, show similar chemistry because all the elements in that group have the same type of valence-electron arrangement. This concept, which explains so much chemistry, is the greatest contribution of the wave mechanical model to modern chemistry.

For reference, the valence-electron configurations for all the elements are shown on the periodic table in **Figure 11.26.**

Figure 11.26
The periodic table with atomic symbols, atomic numbers, and partial electron configurations

384 • Chapter 11 • Modern Atomic Theory

🍎 **TEACHING TIP**

Now is an excellent time to review the classification of the elements into metals, metalloids, and nonmetals.

Periodic Table and Electron Configurations

1. The group labels for Groups 1, 2, 3, 4, 5, 6, 7, and 8 indicate the *total number* of valence electrons for the atoms in these groups. For example, all the elements in Group 5 have the configuration ns^2np^3. (Any *d* electrons present are always in the next lower principal energy level than the valence electrons and so are not counted as valence electrons.)

2. The elements in Groups 1, 2, 3, 4, 5, 6, 7, and 8 are often called the **main-group elements**, or **representative elements**. Remember that every member of a given group (except for helium) has the same valence-electron configuration, except that the electrons are in different principal energy levels.

ℹ️ **information**

The group label gives the total number of valence electrons for that group.

C. Atomic Properties and the Periodic Table

With all of this talk about electron probability and orbitals, we must not lose sight of the fact that chemistry is still fundamentally a science based on the observed properties of substances. We know that wood burns, steel rusts, plants grow, sugar tastes sweet, and so on because we *observe* these phenomena. The atomic theory is an attempt to help us understand why these things occur. If we understand why, we can hope to better control the chemical events that are so crucial in our daily lives.

In the next chapter we will see how our ideas about atomic structure help us understand how and why atoms combine to form compounds. As we explore this topic, and as we use theories to explain other types of chemical behavior later in the text, it is important that we distinguish the observation (steel rusts) from the attempts to explain why the observed event occurs (theories). The observations remain the same over the decades, but the theories (our explanations) change as we gain a clearer understanding of how nature operates. A good example of this is the replacement of the Bohr model for atoms by the wave mechanical model.

Because the observed behavior of matter lies at the heart of chemistry, you need to understand thoroughly the characteristic properties of the

Gold leaf being applied to the dome of the courthouse in Huntington, West Virginia

HANDS-ON CHEMISTRY • MINI-LAB •

Which Element Is It?

Materials
- *World of Chemistry* textbook

Procedure
1. Work in a group of three or four students.

2. Have one person write down one of the representative elements without showing it to the other group members.

3. Take turns asking this person yes/no questions about the element. The person who chose the element must answer these questions (he or she can look through Chapter 3 or 11 for the information).

4. If the element is not identified after each person has asked three questions, the person choosing the element "wins" and identifies the element.

5. Continue until each group member has chosen an element.

Results/Analysis
1. Think about which questions were best to determine the element. What was it about these questions that made them good? How is the periodic table set up so that these questions worked well?

Hands-On Chemistry
MINI-LAB

Which Element Is It?

Materials Each group will need a periodic table and a textbook.

Purpose Students will better understand that chemical properties are similar in elements in the same period of the periodic table.

GROUP

Discussion Questions asked should focus on the properties of the elements (not, for example, "Does the name of the element begin with a *C*?"). Questions should resemble the following: "Does the element have a higher electronegativity than bromine?" or "Is the element the smallest in its group?" You may wish to change the number of questions that each student is allowed to ask after students become more adept at answering questions.

After a couple of rounds, students should see that asking about the properties narrows down their choices considerably.

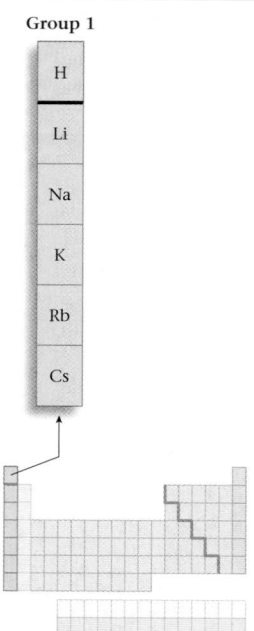

Group 1

| H |
| Li |
| Na |
| K |
| Rb |
| Cs |

various elements and the trends (systematic variations) that occur in those properties. To that end, we will now consider some especially important properties of atoms and see how they vary, horizontally and vertically, on the periodic table.

Metals and Nonmetals

The most fundamental classification of the chemical elements is into metals and nonmetals. **Metals** typically have the following physical properties: a lustrous appearance, the ability to change shape without breaking (they can be pulled into a wire or pounded into a thin sheet), and excellent conductivity of heat and electricity. **Nonmetals** typically do not have these physical properties, although there are some exceptions. (For example, solid iodine is lustrous; the graphite form of carbon is an excellent conductor of electricity; and the diamond form of carbon is an excellent conductor of heat.) However, it is the *chemical* differences between metals and nonmetals that interest us the most:

> Metals tend to lose electrons to form positive ions, and nonmetals tend to gain electrons to form negative ions.

When a metal and a nonmetal react, a transfer of one or more electrons from the metal to the nonmetal often occurs.

Most of the elements are classed as metals, as is shown in **Figure 11.27.** Note that the metals are found on the left side and at the center of the periodic table. The relatively few nonmetals are in the upper right corner of the table. A few elements exhibit both metallic and nonmetallic behavior; they are classed as **metalloids** or semimetals.

It is important to understand that simply being classified as a metal does not mean that an element behaves exactly like all other metals. For example, some metals can lose one or more electrons much more easily than others. In particular, cesium can give up its outermost electron (a $6s$ electron) more easily than can lithium (a $2s$ electron). In fact, for the alkali metals (Group 1) the ease of giving up an electron varies as follows:

$$Cs \quad > \quad Rb \quad > \quad K \quad > \quad Na \quad > \quad Li$$

Loses an electron most easily

Least likely to lose an electron

Figure 11.27
The classification of elements as metals, nonmetals, and metalloids

---

Atomic Radius

Just as the size of an orbital cannot be specified exactly, neither can the size of an atom be determined with certainty. We must make some arbitrary choices to obtain values for atomic radii. These values can be obtained by measuring the distances between atoms in chemical compounds. For example, in the bromine molecule, the distance between the two nuclei is known to be 229 pm. The bromine atomic radius is assumed to be half this distance, or 114 pm. These radii are often called *covalent atomic radii* because they are determined from distances between atoms in covalent bonds.

For nonmetallic atoms that do not form diatomic molecules, the atomic radii are estimated from their various covalent compounds. *Metallic radii* are obtained by taking half the distance between metal atoms in solid metal crystals.

The values of the atomic radii for representative elements are shown in Figure 11.28. These values are significantly smaller than might be expected from the 90% electron density volumes of isolated atoms because when atoms form bonds, their electron "clouds" penetrate one another.

Note from Figure 11.28 that atomic radii decrease in going from left to right

Note that as we go down the group, the metals become more likely to lose an electron. This makes sense because as we go down the group, the electron being removed resides, on average, farther and farther from the nucleus. That is, the 6s electron lost from Cs is much farther from the attractive positive nucleus—and so is easier to remove—than the 2s electron that must be removed from a lithium atom.

The same trend is also seen in the Group 2 metals (alkaline earth metals): the farther down in the group the metal resides, the more likely it is to lose an electron.

Just as metals vary somewhat in their properties, so do nonmetals. In general, the elements that can most effectively pull electrons from metals occur in the upper right corner of the periodic table.

As a general rule, we can say that the

- most chemically active metals appear in the lower left region of the periodic table
- most chemically active nonmetals appear in the upper right region
- properties of the semimetals, or metalloids, lie between the metals and the nonmetals

Atomic Size

The sizes of atoms vary as shown in **Figure 11.28**. Notice that atoms get larger as we go down a group on the periodic table and that they get smaller as we go from left to right across a period.

We can understand the increase in size that we observe as we go down a group by remembering that as the principal energy level increases, the average distance of the electrons from the nucleus also increases. So atoms get bigger as electrons are added to larger principal energy levels.

Group 2

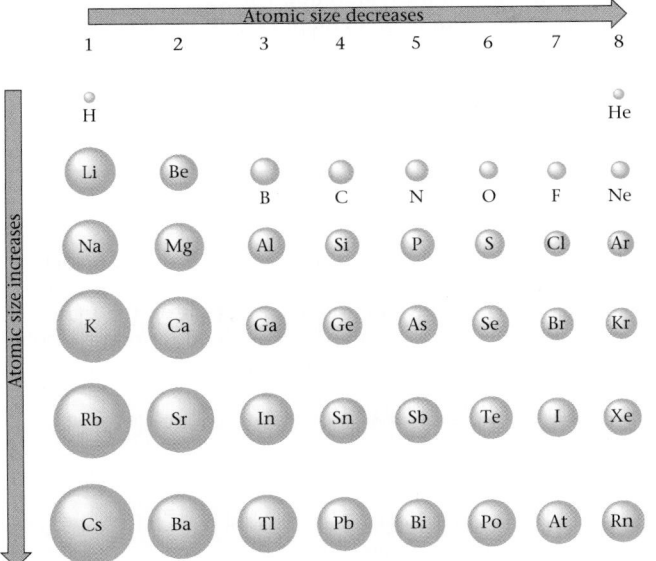

Figure 11.28
Relative atomic sizes for selected atoms. Note that atomic size increases down a group and decreases across a period.

(continued)

across a period. This decrease can be explained in terms of the increasing effective nuclear charge (decreasing shielding) in going from left to right. As a result, the valence electrons are drawn closer to the nucleus, decreasing the size of the atom.

Atomic radius increases down a group because of the increases in the orbital sizes in successive principal quantum levels.

Ionization Energy

In general, *as we go across a period from left to right, the first ionization energy increases*. This trend is consistent with the idea that electrons added in the same principal quantum level do not completely shield the increasing nuclear charge caused by the added protons. Thus electrons in the same principal quantum level are generally more strongly bound as we move to the right on the periodic table, and a general

increase in ionization energy values occurs as electrons are added to a given principal quantum level.

On the other hand, *first ionization energy decreases as we go down a group*. This trend can be seen most clearly by focusing on the Group 1A elements and the Group 8A elements. The decrease in ionization energy going down a group largely occurs because the electrons being removed are, on average, farther from

(continued on next page)

Explaining the decrease in **atomic size** across a period requires some thought about the atoms in a given row (period) of the periodic table. Recall that the atoms in a particular period all have their outermost electrons in a given principal energy level. That is, the atoms in Period 1 have their outer electrons in the 1s orbital (principal energy level 1), the atoms in Period 2 have their outermost electrons in principal energy level 2 (2s and 2p orbitals), and so on (see Figure 11.23). Because all the orbitals in a given principal energy level are expected to be the same size, we might expect the atoms in a given period to be the same size. However, remember that the number of protons in the nucleus increases as we move from atom to atom in the period.

The resulting increase in positive charge on the nucleus tends to pull the electrons closer to the nucleus. So instead of remaining the same size across a period as electrons are added in a given principal energy level, the atoms get smaller as the electron "cloud" is drawn in by the increasing nuclear charge.

Ionization Energies

Ionization energy
The amount of energy required to remove an electron from a gaseous atom or ion

The **ionization energy** of an atom is the energy required to remove an electron from an individual atom in the gas phase:

$$M(g) \Rightarrow M^+(g) + e^-$$

Ionization energy

As we have noted, the most characteristic chemical property of a metal atom is losing electrons to nonmetals. Another way of saying this is that *metals have relatively low ionization energies*—a relatively small amount of energy is needed to remove an electron from a typical metal.

Recall that metals at the bottom of a group lose electrons more easily than those at the top. In other words, ionization energies tend to decrease in going from the top to the bottom of a group.

In contrast to metals, nonmetals have relatively large ionization energies. Nonmetals tend to gain, not lose, electrons. Recall that metals appear on the left side of the periodic table and nonmetals appear on the right side. Thus it is not surprising that ionization energies tend to increase from left to right across a given period on the periodic table.

(continued)

the nucleus. As *n* increases, the size of the orbital increases, and the electron becomes easier to remove.

Some discontinuities in ionization energy appear in going across a period. In Period 2, boron has a lower ionization energy than beryllium, and oxygen has a lower value than nitrogen. These exceptions can be explained in terms of electron repulsions. The decrease in ionization energy in going from beryllium to boron reflects the fact that

the electrons in the filled 2s orbital shield electrons in the 2p orbital from the nuclear charge to some extent. The decrease in ionization energy in going from nitrogen to oxygen reflects the extra electron repulsions in the doubly occupied oxygen 2p orbital.

In general, the elements in the

- Lower left region of the periodic table have the lowest ionization energies (are the most chemically active metals)
- Upper right region of the periodic table have the highest ionization energies (are the most chemically active nonmetals).

CHEMISTRY IN YOUR WORLD

Science, Technology, and Society

Fireworks

The art of using mixtures of chemicals to produce explosives is an ancient one. Black powder—a mixture of potassium nitrate, charcoal, and sulfur—was being used in China well before A.D. 1000, and it has been used through the centuries in military explosives, in construction blasting, and for fireworks.

Before the nineteenth century, fireworks were confined mainly to rockets and loud bangs. Orange and yellow colors came from the presence of charcoal and iron filings. However, with the great advances in chemistry in the nineteenth century, new compounds found their way into fireworks. Salts of copper, strontium, and barium added brilliant colors. Magnesium and aluminum metals gave a dazzling white light.

How do fireworks produce their brilliant colors and loud bangs? Actually, only a handful of different chemicals are responsible for most of the spectacular effects. To produce the noise and flashes, an oxidizer (something with a strong affinity for electrons) is reacted with a metal such as magnesium or aluminum mixed with sulfur. The resulting reaction produces a brilliant flash, which is due to the aluminum or magnesium burning, and a loud report is produced by the rapidly expanding gases. For a color effect, an element with a colored flame is included.

Yellow colors in fireworks are due to sodium. Strontium salts give the red color familiar from highway safety flares. Barium salts give a green color.

Although you might think that the chemistry of fireworks is simple, achieving the vivid white flashes and the brilliant colors requires complex combinations of chemicals. For example, because the white flashes

produce high flame temperatures, the colors tend to wash out. Another problem arises from the use of sodium salts. Because sodium produces an extremely bright yellow color, sodium salts cannot be used when other colors are desired. In short, the manufacture of fireworks that produce the desired effects and are also safe to handle requires very careful selection of chemicals.*

---

*The chemical mixtures in fireworks are very dangerous. *Do not experiment with chemicals on your own.*

Brightly colored fireworks

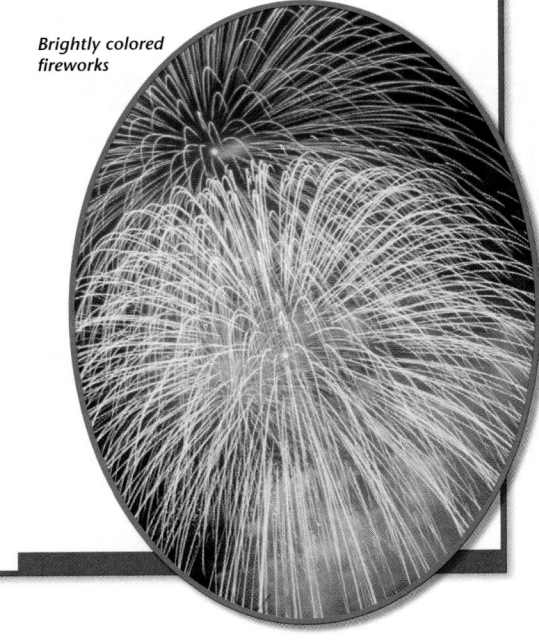

Chemistry in Your World

Fireworks

One interesting aspect of fireworks is the difficulty in making certain colors. For example, blue is an extremely difficult color to make. Shades of blue-violet and purple are not as difficult to produce. Ask students to hypothesize why true blue would be such a difficult color to create. The energy required to produce true blue lies between the energy levels of the atoms.

SECTION 11.4
Review Questions

1.

	1s	2s	2p	2p	2p	3s
Li	↑↓	↑				
C	↑↓	↑↓	↑	↑		
Mg	↑↓	↑↓	↑↓	↑↓	↑↓	↑↓

2. A valence electron is in the outermost level for the atom; a core electron is in one of the inner levels for the atom. Mg: $1s^2 2s^2 2p^6$ core; $3s^2$ valence

3. The valence electron configurations of atoms in the same families are the same but on different energy levels.

4. a. Hf, $6s^2 4f^{14} 5d^2$
b. Ra, $7s^2$
c. Sb, $5s^2 4d^{10} 5p^3$
d. Pb, $6s^2 4f^{14} 5d^{10} 6p^2$

5. Metals tend to lose electrons; nonmetals tend to gain electrons.

6. Metals have relatively few valence electrons. In contrast, nonmetals have a large number of electrons in the outer shell and a small size, making the attractive forces higher in these elements.

7. Atomic size decreases across a row because there is a greater pull on the electrons as atomic number increases. Atomic size increases down a group because valence electrons are farther from the nucleus. Ionization energy increases across a row because electrons are held more tightly and are harder to remove. Ionization energy decreases down the table because electrons are farther away and are easier to remove from an atom.

CELEBRITY CHEMICAL Hydrogen (H₂)

Hydrogen is the most abundant element in the universe, being the major constituent of all stars. Most of the hydrogen found on earth is in the combined state—in compounds with other elements. The amount of elemental hydrogen (H₂) found on earth is actually very small. The atmosphere contains only 0.00005% H₂ gas. Therefore, when H₂ gas is required to produce a substance such as NH₃ in the reaction

$$N_2(g) + 3 H_2(g) \rightarrow 2NH_3(g)$$

the H₂ must be obtained by decomposing a compound such as water.

Hydrogen is a colorless, odorless, and tasteless gas that reacts explosively with oxygen gas. In fact, the energetic reaction of $H_2(g)$ with $O_2(g)$ makes it a good candidate as a fuel. Hydrogen actually delivers four times as much energy per gram as does gasoline. The other advantage to using hydrogen as a fuel is that the combustion product is water, which is not harmful to the environment. Currently, hydrogen is too expensive to produce to be competitive as a fuel compared to gasoline or natural gas. However, if cheaper ways are found to produce it, hydrogen could prove a valuable fuel in the future.

Liquid hydrogen is used to power the space shuttle.

SECTION 11.4
REVIEW QUESTIONS

1 Write the orbital diagram for the elements listed below:

Li $\quad 1s^2 2s^1$
C $\quad 1s^2 2s^2 2p^2$
Mg $\quad 1s^2 2s^2 2p^6 3s^2$

2 What is the difference between a valence electron and a core electron? Select an element from row 3 of the periodic table and label both a valence electron and a core electron using its electron configuration.

3 Elements in vertical columns (groups) show similar chemical behavior. How are their electron configurations similar?

4 For each of the following elements, refer to its position on the periodic table and write its valence shell electron configuration.

a. hafnium, $Z = 72$
b. radium, $Z = 88$
c. antimony, $Z = 51$
d. lead, $Z = 82$

5 What chemical property distinguishes a metal from a nonmetal?

6 How can the property in question 5 be explained by using ionization energy trends?

7 Explain the general trends of atomic size and ionization energies across rows and down columns of the periodic table.

RESEARCH LINKS
CLASSZONE.COM

CELEBRITY CHEMICAL

Hydrogen (H₂)

 Video
Oxygen, Hydrogen, Soap Bubbles, and Balloons

Soap Bubbles

This demonstrtation shows the difference between bubbles of pure hydrogen, pure oxygen, and a mixture of hydrogen and oxygen. It can lead to a discussion of the use of hydrogen in dirigibles and hydrogen's safety and environmental friendliness as an alternative fuel for cars.

Because of hydrogen's low molar mass, it provides lots of energy per gram and it gives only H₂O as a combustion product. However, there are two major problems with using hydrogen as a fuel. First, virtually no free hydrogen exists, so energy must be expended to free it from compounds such as water. Second, hydrogen has a very low boiling point and requires very low temperatures and very high pressures to store as a liquid. Some metals, such as palladium, absorb large amounts of hydrogen; attempts have been made to use such systems for hydrogen storage in hydrogen-powered automobiles.

Researchers are attempting to adapt H₂/O₂ fuel cells similar to those used in the U.S. space program for use in automobiles. Several automobile companies are studying fuel cells that use reformers to break down gasoline into hydrogen.

Chapter 11 Review

Key Terms

Electromagnetic radiation

Wavelength

Frequency

Photons

11.2 Quantized

Wave mechanical model

11.3 Orbital

Principal energy levels

Sublevels

Pauli exclusion principle

11.4 Electron configuration

Orbital diagram (box diagram)

Valence electrons

Core electrons

Lanthanide series

Actinide series

Main-group elements (representative elements)

Metals

Nonmetals

Metalloids

Atomic size

Ionization energy

RESEARCH LINKS
CLASSZONE.COM

Key Ideas

11.1 Atoms and Energy

- Rutherford's atom consists of a tiny, dense nucleus at the center and electrons which occupy most of the volume of the atom.
- Electromagnetic radiation
  - Characterized by its wavelength and frequency
  - Can be thought of as a stream of packets of energy called photons
  - Atoms can gain energy by absorbing a photon or lose energy by emitting a photon.

11.2 The Hydrogen Atom

- The hydrogen atom can emit only certain energies as it changes from a higher to a lower energy.
- Hydrogen has quantized energy levels.

11.3 Atomic Orbitals

- The Bohr model assumed electrons travel around the nucleus in circular orbits which is incorrect.
- The wave mechanical model assumes the electron has both particle and wave properties and describes electrons as occupying orbitals.
  - The orbitals are different from the Bohr orbits.
  - Probability maps indicate the likelihood of finding the electron at a given point in space.
  - The size of an atom can be described by a surface that contains 90% of the total electron probability.

11.4 Electron Configurations and Atomic Properties

- Atomic energy levels are broken down into principal levels (n) which contain various numbers of sublevels.
  - The sublevels represent various types of orbitals (s, p, d, f) which have different shapes.
  - The number of sublevels increases as n increases.
- A given atom has Z protons in its nucleus and Z electrons surrounding the nucleus.
- The electrons occupy atomic orbitals starting with the lowest energy (the orbital closest to the nucleus).
- The Pauli exclusion principle states that an orbital can hold only two electrons with opposite spins.
- The electrons in the highest energy level are called valence electrons.
- The electron arrangement for a given atom explains its position on the periodic table.
- Atomic size generally increases down a group of the periodic table and decreases across a period.
- Ionization energy generally decreases down a group and increases across a period.

Chapter 11 Assessment

1. This experiment is explained in Chapter 3.

2. See Figure 11.1 for a sketch of Rutherford's atom. Rutherford could not answer questions such as, "Why are the negative electrons not attracted into the positive nucleus, causing atoms to collapse?"

3. Electromagnetic radiation is radiant energy that travels through space with wavelike behavior. Examples include visible light, radio and television signals, microwaves, infrared, and X rays.

4. The different forms of electromagnetic radiation all exhibit the same wavelike behavior and move through space at the same speed (the speed of light). The types of electromagnetic radiation differ in their frequency and wavelength and in the resulting amount of energy carried per photon.

5. The wavelength represents the distance between two corresponding points on successive cycles of a wave (see Figure 11.3). The frequency represents the number of complete cycles of the wave that pass a given point per second.

6. The speed of electromagnetic radiation represents how fast energy is transferred through space; the frequency of the radiation tells us how many waves pass a given point in a certain amount of time.

7. photon

8. The wave-particle nature of light refers to the fact that a beam of electromagnetic energy can be considered not only as a continuous wave, but also as a stream of discrete packets of energy moving through space.

9. The colors are due to the release of energy.

10. Higher-energy photons are released with Cu^{2+} because green light is emitted (red light is emitted from Li^+). Green light is of higher energy than red light.

All exercises with blue numbers have answers in the back of this book.

11.1 Atoms and Energy
A. Rutherford's Atom

1. Describe the experiment that allowed Rutherford to conclude that the atom consists of a relatively heavy positively charged nucleus surrounded by electrons.

2. Sketch a picture of the model of the atom that Rutherford developed. What questions were left unanswered by Rutherford's model?

B. Energy and Light

3. What do we mean by *electromagnetic radiation*? Give several examples of different sorts of electromagnetic radiation.

4. How are the different types of electromagnetic radiation similar? How do they differ?

5. What does the *wavelength* of electromagnetic radiation represent? Sketch a representation of a wave and indicate the *wavelength* on your graph. How does the *wavelength* of electromagnetic radiation differ from its *frequency*?

6. What do we mean by the *speed* of electromagnetic radiation? How do the *frequency* and the *speed* of electromagnetic radiation differ?

7. What is a "packet" of electromagnetic energy called?

8. What is meant by the *wave–particle* nature of light?

C. Emission of Energy by Atoms

9. Do the colors of flame tests result from taking in energy or releasing energy?

10. In which case are higher-energy photons released, with Li^+ or with Cu^{2+}? How do you know?

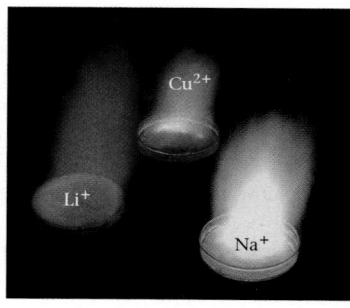

392 • Chapter 11 • Modern Atomic Theory

11.2 The Hydrogen Atom
A. The Energy Levels of Hydrogen

11. What does it mean to say that an atom is in an "excited state"?

12. When an atom in an excited state returns to its ground state, what happens to the excess energy of the atom?

13. Describe briefly why the study of electromagnetic radiation has been important to our understanding of the arrangement of electrons in atoms.

14. What does it mean to say that the hydrogen atom has *discrete energy levels*? How is this fact reflected in the radiation that excited hydrogen atoms emit?

15. What experimental evidence do scientists have that the energy levels of hydrogen are *quantized*?

16. What is meant by the *ground state* of an atom?

B. The Bohr Model of the Atom

17. What are the essential points of Bohr's theory of the structure of the hydrogen atom?

18. According to Bohr, what types of motions do electrons have in an atom, and what happens when energy is applied to the atom?

19. How does the Bohr theory account for the observed phenomenon of the emission of discrete wavelengths of light by excited atoms?

20. Why was Bohr's theory for the hydrogen atom initially accepted, and why was it ultimately discarded?

C. The Wave Mechanical Model of the Atom

21. What major assumption (that was analogous to what had already been demonstrated for electromagnetic radiation) did de Broglie and Schrödinger make about the motion of tiny particles?

22. Discuss briefly the difference between an orbit (as described by Bohr for hydrogen) and an orbital (as described by the more modern, wave mechanical picture of the atom).

23. We cannot *exactly* specify the location of an electron in an atom but can discuss only where an electron is *most likely* to be at any given time. How does the concept of an orbital show this?

---

11. An atom is in an excited state when it possesses more than its minimum energy (ground state energy).

12. It is emitted as a photon.

13. Excited atoms emit light (which we can measure) because of changes in their microscopic structure. By studying emissions of atoms, we can trace back to what happened inside the atom.

14. When excited hydrogen atoms emit their excess energy, the photons of radiation released always have exactly the same wavelength and energy. Thus the hydrogen atom possesses only certain allowed energy states.

15. Hydrogen always transmits light at exactly the same wavelengths, which correspond to transitions of the electron between the fixed energy states of the atom.

16. The ground state of an atom is its lowest possible energy state.

17. Bohr pictured electrons moving in circular orbits that corresponded to the various allowed energy levels. He suggested that the electrons could jump to a different orbit by absorbing or

11.3 Atomic Orbitals

A. The Hydrogen Orbitals

24. Why are the orbitals of the hydrogen atom described as "probability maps"? Why are the edges of the hydrogen orbitals sometimes drawn to appear "fuzzy"?

25. When we draw a picture of an orbital, we are indicating that the probability of finding the electron within this region of space is greater than 90%. Why is this probability never 100%?

26. What are the differences between the $2s$ orbital and the $1s$ orbital of hydrogen? How are they similar?

27. How is the *distance* of an electron from the nucleus related to the *principal energy level*? Does a *higher* principal energy level mean that the electron is *closer* to or *farther* away from the nucleus?

28. If an electron moves from the $1s$ orbital to the $2s$ orbital, its energy (increases/decreases).

29. Although a hydrogen atom has only one electron, the hydrogen atom possesses a complete set of available orbitals. What purpose do these additional orbitals serve?

B. The Wave Mechanical Model: Further Development

30. What is the *Pauli exclusion principle*? How many electrons can occupy an orbital, according to this principle? Why?

31. How does the *energy* of a principal energy level depend on the value of *n*? Does a higher value of *n* mean a higher or lower energy?

32. The number of sublevels in a principal energy level (increases/decreases) as *n* increases.

33. Which of the following orbital designations is (are) not correct?
- a. $2p$
- b. $1d$
- c. $3f$
- d. $4s$

11.4 Electron Configurations and Atomic Properties

A. Electron Arrangements in the First 18 Atoms on the Periodic Table

34. Which orbital is the *first* to be filled in any atom? Why?

35. Which electrons of an atom are the *valence* electrons? Why are these electrons especially important?

36. How are the electron arrangements in a given group (vertical column) of the periodic table related? How is this relationship shown in the properties of the elements in the given group?

37. Write the full electron configuration ($1s^2 2s^2$, etc.) for each of the following elements.
- a. strontium, $Z = 38$
- b. zinc, $Z = 30$
- c. helium, $Z = 2$
- d. bromine, $Z = 35$

38. Write the full electron configuration ($1s^2 2s^2$, etc.) for each of the following elements.
- a. calcium, $Z = 20$
- b. potassium, $Z = 19$
- c. fluorine, $Z = 9$
- d. krypton, $Z = 36$

39. Write the complete orbital diagram for each of the following elements, using boxes to represent orbitals and arrows to represent electrons.
- a. aluminum, $Z = 13$
- b. phosphorus, $Z = 15$
- c. bromine, $Z = 35$
- d. argon, $Z = 18$

40. How many valence electrons does each of the following atoms possess?
- a. sodium, $Z = 11$
- b. calcium, $Z = 20$
- c. iodine, $Z = 53$
- d. nitrogen, $Z = 7$

B. Electron Configurations and the Periodic Table

41. Why do we believe that the valence electrons of calcium and potassium reside in the $4s$ orbital rather than in the $3d$ orbital?

42. Would you expect the valence electrons of rubidium and strontium to reside in the $5s$ or the $4d$ orbitals? Why?

emitting a photon of light with exactly the correct energy content (corresponding to the difference in energy between the orbits).

18. According to Bohr, electrons move in fixed circular orbits around the nucleus. An electron can move to a larger orbit if a photon of applied energy equals the difference in energy between the two orbits.

19. According to Bohr, the energy levels were definite and fixed, so the atom should always emit energy at the same wavelength.

20. Bohr's theory explained the line spectrum of hydrogen exactly. It did not explain measurements made for atoms other than hydrogen.

21. As light has both wave and particle characteristics, then perhaps the electron might exhibit both of these characteristics. Thus perhaps an electron has wavelike properties along with particle-like properties.

22. An orbit refers to an exact circular pathway for the electron around the nucleus. An orbital represents a region in space in which there is a high probability of finding an electron.

23. Trying to measure the exact location of an electron (for example, by shooting a beam of light at it) would cause the electron to move. Measurement requires an energy change, which moves the electron.

24. Chemists arbitrarily define an orbital as representing 90% of the probability of finding an electron in this region. Orbitals represent mathematical functions and have no distinct outer edge (so they are drawn to appear fuzzy). They represent the most likely region in which an electron might be found.

25. Pictures representing orbitals are probability maps. They do not imply that the electron moves on the surface of, or within, the region of the picture. The mathematical probability of finding an electron never becomes zero moving out from the nucleus (the electron could be "anywhere").

26. The $2s$ orbital is similar in shape to the $1s$ orbital, but the $2s$ orbital is larger.

27. The higher the principal energy level (*n*), the farther from the nucleus (on average) the electron will be.

28. increases

29. The other orbitals serve as the excited states of the hydrogen atom. When energy of the appropriate frequency is applied to the hydrogen atom, the electron can move from its ground state to an excited state. The electron can move back if it releases the absorbed energy.

30. The Pauli exclusion principle states that an orbital can hold a maximum of two electrons, and that those two electrons must have opposite spin.

31. The higher the value of the principal quantum number (*n*), the higher the energy of the principal energy level.

32. increases

33. b and c are incorrect; a and d are correct

34. The $1s$ orbital is closest to the nucleus and lowest in energy, so it is always filled first.

35. Valence electrons are those electrons in the outermost energy level. These electrons can interact with the (valence) electrons of another atom in a chemical reaction.

36. The elements in a given column of the periodic table have the same valence electron configuration. Having the same valence electron configuration causes the elements in a given group to have similar chemical properties.

37. (a) $1s^2 2s^2 2p^6 3s^2 3p^6 4s^2\ 3d^{10} 4p^6 5s^2$
(b) $1s^2 2s^2 2p^6 3s^2 3p^6 4s^2 3d^{10}$
(c) $1s^2$
(d) $1s^2 2s^2\ 2p^6 3s^2 3p^6 4s^2 3d^{10} 4p^5$

38. (a) $1s^2 2s^2 2p^6 3s^2 3p^6 4s^2$
(b) $1s^2 2s^2 2p^6 3s^2 3p^6 4s^1$
(c) $1s^2 2s^2 2p^5$
(d) $1s^2 2s^2 2p^6\ 3s^2 3p^6 4s^2 3d^{10} 4p^6$

39. (a) (↑↓) (↑↓) (↑↓)(↑↓)(↑↓) (↑↓)
　　　1s　2s　　2p　　　3s

　　(↑)( )( )
　　　3p

(b) (↑↓) (↑↓) (↑↓)(↑↓)(↑↓) (↑↓)
　　　1s　2s　　2p　　　3s

　　(↑)(↑)(↑)
　　　3p

(c) (↑↓) (↑↓) (↑↓)(↑↓)(↑↓) (↑↓)
　　　1s　2s　　2p　　　3s

　　(↑↓)(↑↓)(↑↓) (↑↓)
　　　3p　　　　4s

　　(↑↓)(↑↓)(↑↓)(↑↓)(↑↓) (↑↓)(↑↓)(↑)
　　　　　3d　　　　　　　4p

(d) (↑↓) (↑↓) (↑↓)(↑↓)(↑↓) (↑↓)
　　　1s　2s　　2p　　　3s

　　(↑↓)(↑↓)(↑↓);
　　　3p

40. (a) 1
(b) 2
(c) 7
(d) 5

41. The physical and chemical properties of potassium are like those of the other Group 1 elements; calcium's properties are similar to those of the other Group 2 elements.

42. The properties of Rb and Sr suggest that they are members of Groups 1 and 2, respectively. Thus the outer electrons are filling the 5s orbital. The 5s orbital, then, must be lower in energy and fills before the 4d orbitals.

43. (a) $[Ar]4s^2$
(b) $[Rn]7s^1$
(c) $[Kr]5s^2 4d^1$
(d) $[Xe]6s^2 4f^1\ 5d^1$

43. Using the symbol of the previous noble gas to indicate the core electrons, write the valence-electron configuration for each of the following elements.
　　a. calcium, $Z = 20$
　　b. francium, $Z = 87$
　　c. yttrium, $Z = 39$
　　d. cerium, $Z = 58$

44. Using the symbol of the previous noble gas to indicate the core electrons, write the valence-electron configuration for each of the following elements.
　　a. phosphorus, $Z = 15$
　　b. chlorine, $Z = 17$
　　c. magnesium, $Z = 12$
　　d. zinc, $Z = 30$

45. How many 4d electrons are found in each of the following elements?
　　a. yttrium, $Z = 39$
　　b. zirconium, $Z = 40$
　　c. strontium, $Z = 38$
　　d. cadmium, $Z = 48$

46. For each of the following elements, indicate which set of orbitals is being filled last.
　　a. plutonium, $Z = 94$
　　b. nobelium, $Z = 102$
　　c. praeseodymium, $Z = 59$
　　d. radon, $Z = 86$

47. Write the shorthand valence-electron configuration of each of the following elements, basing your answer on the element's location on the periodic table.
　　a. uranium, $Z = 92$
　　b. manganese, $Z = 25$
　　c. mercury, $Z = 80$
　　d. francium, $Z = 87$

C. Atomic Properties and the Periodic Table

48. What types of ions do the metals and the nonmetallic elements form? Do the metals lose or gain electrons in doing this? Do the nonmetallic elements gain or lose electrons in doing this?

49. Give some similarities that exist among the elements of Group 1.

50. Give some similarities that exist among the elements of Group 7.

51. Where are the most nonmetallic elements located on the periodic table? Why do these elements pull electrons from metallic elements so effectively during a reaction?

52. Why do the metallic elements of a given period (horizontal row) typically have much lower ionization energies than do the nonmetallic elements of the same period?

53. Explain why the atoms of the elements at the bottom of a given group (vertical column) of the periodic table are *larger* than the atoms of the elements at the top of the same group.

54. Though all the elements in a given period (horizontal row) of the periodic table have their valence electrons in the same types of orbitals, the sizes of the atoms decrease from left to right within a period. Explain why.

55. In each of the following sets of elements, which element shows the least ability to gain or lose electrons?
　　a. Cs, Rb, Na
　　b. Ba, Ca, Be
　　c. F, Cl, Br
　　d. O, Te, S

56. In each of the following sets of elements, which element would be expected to have the highest ionization energy?
　　a. Cs, K, Li
　　b. Ba, Sr, Ca
　　c. I, Br, Cl
　　d. Mg, Si, S

57. Arrange the following sets of elements in order of increasing atomic size.
　　a. Sn, Xe, Rb, Sr
　　b. Rn, He, Xe, Kr
　　c. Pb, Ba, Cs, At

44. (a) $[Ne]3s^2 3p^3$
(b) $[Ne]3s^2 3p^5$
(c) $[Ne]3s^2$
(d) $[Ar]4s^2 3d^{10}$

45. (a) 1
(b) 2
(c) 0
(d) 10

46. (a) 5f
(b) 5f
(c) 4f
(d) 6p

47. (a) $[Rn]7s^2 6d^1 5f^3$
(b) $[Ar]4s^2 3d^5$
(c) $[Xe]6s^2 4f^{14} 5d^{10}$
(d) $[Rn]7s^1$

48. The metallic elements lose electrons and form positive ions (cations); the nonmetallic elements gain electrons and form negative ions (anions).

49. Group 1 metals are highly reactive, and all form 1+ ions almost exclusively when they react. Physically these metals are all soft and relatively low in density. They tend to be found with a layer of metal oxide coating, but appear shiny if a fresh surface is exposed.

50. All exist as diatomic molecules; all are nonmetals; all have relatively high electronegativities; all form 1− ions in reacting with metallic elements.

Critical Thinking

58. The distance in meters between two consecutive peaks (or troughs) in a wave is called the _____.

59. The speed at which electromagnetic radiation moves through a vacuum is called the _____.

60. The energy levels of hydrogen (and other atoms) are _____, which means that only certain values of energy are allowed.

61. In the modern theory of the atom, a(n) _____ represents a region of space in which there is a high probability of finding an electron.

62. Without referring to your textbook or a periodic table, write the full electron configuration, the orbital box diagram, and the noble gas shorthand configuration for the elements with the following atomic numbers.

    a. $Z = 19$

    b. $Z = 22$

    c. $Z = 14$

    d. $Z = 26$

    e. $Z = 30$

63. Write the general valence configuration (for example, ns^1 for Group 1) for the group in which each of the following elements is found.

    a. barium, $Z = 56$

    b. bromine, $Z = 35$

    c. tellurium, $Z = 52$

    d. potassium, $Z = 19$

    e. sulfur, $Z = 16$

64. How many valence electrons does each of the following atoms have?

    a. titanium, $Z = 22$

    b. iodine, $Z = 53$

    c. radium, $Z = 88$

    d. manganese, $Z = 25$

65. How do we know that the energy levels of the hydrogen atom are not *continuous*, as physicists originally assumed?

66. Why do the two electrons in the $2p$ sublevel of carbon occupy *different* $2p$ orbitals?

67. Write the full electron configuration ($1s^2 2s^2$, etc.) for each of the following elements.

    a. bromine, $Z = 35$

    b. xenon, $Z = 54$

    c. barium, $Z = 56$

    d. selenium, $Z = 34$

68. Metals have relatively (low/high) ionization energies, whereas nonmetals have relatively (high/low) ionization energies.

69. In each of the following sets of elements, indicate which element has the smallest atomic size.

    a. Ba, Ca, Ra

    b. P, Si, Al

    c. Rb, Cs, K

70. A 2+ ion of a particular element has an atomic mass of 203 and 123 neutrons in its nucleus.

    a. What is the nuclear charge in this element?

    b. What are the symbol and name of this element?

    c. How many valence electrons does a neutral atom of this element have?

    d. How many levels of electrons are occupied when this element is in its ground state?

51. The nonmetallic elements are found in the upper-right corner of the periodic table. They tend to be small in size, so the electrons are held in tightly by the nucleus.

52. The elements of a given period (horizontal row) have valence electrons in the same subshells. Nuclear charge increases across a period going from left to right.

Atoms at the left side have smaller nuclear charges and bind their valence electrons less tightly.

53. All atoms within a given group have the same number of valence electrons, and these valence electrons occur in the same type of subshell. At the bottom of the group, however, the valence electrons are in a higher principal energy level.

54. The nuclear charge increases from left to right within a period. The greater the nuclear charge, the more tightly the valence electrons are "pulled."

55. (a) Na
    (b) Be
    (c) Br
    (d) Te

56. (a) Li
    (b) Ca
    (c) Cl
    (d) S

57. (a) Xe < Sn < Sr < Rb
    (b) He < Kr < Xe < Rn
    (c) At < Pb < Ba < Cs

58. wavelength

59. speed of light

60. quantized

61. orbital

62. (a) (↑↓) (↑↓) (↑↓)(↑↓)(↑↓) (↑↓)
        1s   2s   2p   3s

    (↑↓)(↑↓)(↑↓) (↑)
       3p   4s

    $1s^2 2s^2 2p^6 3s^2 3p^6 4s^1$; $[Ar]4s^1$

    (b) (↑↓) (↑↓) (↑↓)(↑↓)(↑↓) (↑↓)
        1s   2s   2p   3s

    (↑↓)(↑↓)(↑↓) (↑↓)
       3p   4s

    (↑)(↑)( )( )( );
         3d

    $1s^2 2s^2 2p^6 3s^2 3p^6 4s^2 3d^2$;
    $[Ar]4s^2 3d^2$;

    (c) (↑↓) (↑↓) (↑↓)(↑↓)(↑↓) (↑↓)
        1s   2s   2p   3s

    (↑)(↑)( );
       3p

    $1s^2 2s^2 2p^6 3s^2 3p^2$; $[Ne]3s^2 3p^2$;

    (d) (↑↓) (↑↓) (↑↓)(↑↓)(↑↓) (↑↓)
        1s   2s   2p   3s

    (↑↓)(↑↓)(↑↓) (↑↓) (↑↓)(↑) (↑)(↑)(↑);
       3p   4s   3d

    $1s^2 2s^2 2p^6 3s^2 3p^6 4s^2 3d^6$;
    $[Ar]4s^2 3d^6$;

    (e) (↑↓) (↑↓) (↑↓)(↑↓)(↑↓) (↑↓)
        1s   2s   2p   3s

    (↑↓)(↑↓)(↑↓) (↑↓) (↑↓)(↑↓)(↑↓)(↑↓)(↑↓);
       3p   4s   3d

    $1s^2 2s^2 2p^6 3s^2 3p^6 4s^2 3d^{10}$;
    $[Ar]4s^2 3d^{10}$

63. (a) ns^2
    (b) $ns^2 np^5$
    (c) $ns^2 np^4$
    (d) ns^1
    (e) $ns^2 np^4$

64. (a) 2 (*d* electrons are not counted as valence electrons)
    (b) 7
    (c) 2
    (d) 2 (*d* electrons are not counted as valence electrons)

65. Light is emitted from the hydrogen atom only at certain wavelengths. If the energy levels of hydrogen were continuous, a hydrogen atom would emit energy at all possible wavelengths.

66. The three $2p$ orbitals of the carbon atoms are of the same energy; by occupying different orbitals of the same energy, repulsion between electrons is minimized.

67. (a) $1s^2 2s^2 2p^6 3s^2 3p^6 4s^2 3d^{10} 4p^5$
(b) $1s^2 2s^2 2p^6 3s^2 3p^6 4s^2 3d^{10} 4p^6 5s^2 4d^{10} 5p^6$
(c) $1s^2 2s^2 2p^6 3s^2 3p^6 4s^2 3d^{10} 4p^6 5s^2 4d^{10} 5p^6 6s^2$
(d) $1s^2 2s^2 2p^6 3s^2 3p^6 4s^2 3d^{10} 4p^4$

68. low; high

69. (a) Ca
(b) P
(c) K

70. (a) 80
(b) Hg, mercury
(c) 2
(d) 6

71. (a) iv
(b) ii
(c) ii
(d) v
(e) i
(f) NaN_3
(g) Mg_2N_3
(h) ii < i < vi < iv < v < iii

72. (a) F
(b) Lu
(c) Po
(d) Fr
(e) At
(f) Xe
(g) Lr

73. Element 120 would be a solid and a metal. It would be highly reactive with water and have a tendency to form ions with a 2+ charge.

74. *Answers may vary.* See the *Solutions Guide* for more detail.

71. Given elements with the following electron configurations, specify which meet the following conditions.

   i. $1s^2 2s^2 2p^6 3s^2$

   ii. $1s^2 2s^2 2p^6 3s^1$

   iii. $1s^2 2s^2 2p^6$

   iv. $1s^2 2s^2 2p^4$

   v. $1s^2 2s^2 2p^3$

   vi. $1s^2 2s^2 2p^1$

   a. Which will normally form a negative ion in solution?

   b. Which will have the lowest ionization energy?

   c. Which would be the most reactive metal?

   d. Which has the greatest number of unpaired electrons?

   e. Which metal would combine with oxygen in a one-to-one ratio?

   f. Predict the formula for the compound that would form between (ii) and (v).

   g. Predict the formula for the compound that would form between (i) and (v).

   h. List the six elements in order of increasing ionization energy.

72. Identify the following elements.

   a. the most reactive nonmetal (not a noble gas) on the periodic table

   b. the smallest lanthanide

   c. the largest metalloid

   d. the metal with the lowest ionization energy

   e. the least reactive halogen

   f. the least reactive member of the fifth period

   g. the actinide with the highest nuclear charge

73. Suppose that element 120 has just been discovered. Identify four chemical or physical properties expected of this element.

74. Suppose that in another universe there is a completely different set of elements from the ones we know. The inhabitants assign symbols of A, B, C, and so on in order of increasing atomic number, using all of the letters of our alphabet. They find that the following elements closely resemble one another in terms of their properties:

   A, C, G, K, Q, and Y

   B, F, J, P, and X

   V is its own family

Sketch a periodic table, similar to ours, using this information.

1 The form of electromagnetic radiation that has less energy per photon than infrared rays but more energy per photon than radio waves is

A microwaves   C gamma rays

B ultraviolet   D X rays

2 How many electrons can be contained in all of the orbitals with a principal energy level of 3 ($n = 3$)?

A 8   C 18

B 10   D 32

3 In general, the rows on the periodic table correspond to _____ and the columns numbered 1A, 2A, . . . 8A correspond to _____.

A the orbital of the valence electrons; the number of total electrons

B the energy level of the valence electrons; the number of valence electrons

C the energy level for the core electrons; the orbital of the valence electrons

D the number of valence electrons: the energy level of the valence electrons

4 An orbital is best described as

A the pathway for an electron.

B a region of probability of finding an electron.

C the space in which only valence electrons exist.

D a physical structure which holds the electrons.

5 Which of the following is true about the trend of ionization energy across a row on the periodic table?

A Ionization energy generally increases to the right because the number of protons increases from left to right.

B Ionization energy generally decreases to the right because the number of electrons increases from left to right.

C Ionization energy generally decreases to the right because the number of protons increases from left to right.

D Ionization energy is constant since all atoms in a row have the same valence energy level.

6 Which of the following is a representation of a *p* orbital?

7 For the atoms Li, N, F, and Na, which of the following is the correct order from smallest to largest atomic radius?

A Na, F, N, Li

B Na, Li, N, F

C N, F, Na, Li

D F, N, Li, Na

8 Which of the following correctly ranks the ionization energies of O, F, Na, S, and Cs from smallest to largest?

A Cs, Na, S, O, F

B Cs, S, Na, O, F

C F, O, Na, S, Cs

D F, O, S, Na, Cs

9 Write the expected electron configuration for the ground state of iron.

10 Fill in the following orbital diagram for a ground state oxygen atom

11 Fill in the following orbital diagram for a boron atom in an excited state.

12 True or false? Across a row of the periodic table, smaller atoms generally have smaller ionization energies. If true, provide an example and explain your answer. If false, provide a counterexample and explain your answer.

Chapter 11

Standardized Test Practice

1. A
2. C
3. B
4. B
5. A
6. C
7. D
8. A
9. $1s^2 2s^2 2p^6 3s^2 3p^6 4s^2 3d^6$
10.

1s	2s	2p			3s	3p		
↑↓	↑↓	↑↓	↑	↑				

11. *Answers can vary.* A possible answer is

1s	2s	2p			3s	3p		
↑↓	↑↓				↑			

12. False. In general, atoms tend to get smaller (have smaller radii) across a row because the number of protons increases, thus increasing the pull on the electrons. Because of this, smaller atoms in the same row tend to have larger ionization energies (more energy is required to remove an electron). For example, fluorine (F) is smaller than lithium (Li) and has a higher ionization energy.

Test-Taking Strategy

Point out that when a question asks you to determine which choice is true, you can eliminate answer choices once you have proven them to be false. Caution students about the words *always* and *never*. In a standard test question, statements including these words are often false.

Planning Guide

Section	Segment	Text Features and Components	Labs, Demonstrations, & Activities
12.1 Characteristics of Chemical Bonds **1 Block** pp. 400–406	**A** Types of Chemical Bonds	**TE** Teaching Support: Background Information *pp. 400–401*	
	B Electronegativity		
	C Bond Polarity and Dipole Moments	**SE** Chemistry Explorers: Linus Pauling *p. 406*	**LM** Experiment 49: Dyes and Dying, Traditional Lab Manual Report Sheets Teacher's Lab Guide
12.2 Characteristics of Ions and Ionic Compounds **0.5 Block** pp. 407–412	**A** Stable Electron Configurations and Charges on Ions		**TE** Group Activity *p. 410*
	B Ionic Bonding and Structures of Ionic Compounds	**TE** Teaching Support: Background Information *pp. 410–411*	
	continued on next page		

Key
SE Student Edition	**TE** Teacher Edition	**RP** Teacher Resource Package
AR Additional Materials	**LM** Lab Materials	**◨** Transparencies
◉ DVD	**▰** CD-ROM	**ⓘ** classzone.com

All Learners	Technology	Review & Assessment	Standards
TE Teaching Tips *pp. 400–401*	**Transparency:** Figure 12.2 **Animation:** Bonding in H_2 **Animation:** Covalent Bonding **EasyPlanner**	**SE** Active Reading Question *p. 402* **SE** Key Terms *p. 434* **SE** Questions and Problems *p. 435*	**TE** **NSES** UCP2, UCP5, A1, A2, B1, B2
TE Teaching Tips *pp. 402–404*	**Animation:** Polar Molecules **Transparency:** Figure 12.4 **Transparency:** Figure 12.5 **Transparency:** Table 12.1 **EasyPlanner**	**SE** Critical Thinking *p. 403* **SE** Active Reading Question *p. 403* **SE** Practice Problem *p. 404* **TE** More Examples *p. 404* **SE** Key Terms *p. 434* **SE** Questions and Problems *p. 435*	
TE Teaching Tips *p. 405* **RP** Team Learning Worksheet (Sec. 12.1)	**Lab Generator CD** **EasyPlanner**	**SE** Review Questions (12.1.A–12.1.C) *p. 406* **SE** Key Terms *p. 434* **SE** Questions and Problems *p. 435*	
TE Teaching Tips *pp. 407–409*	**Transparency:** Table 12.2 **Transparency:** Table 12.3 **EasyPlanner**	**SE** Active Reading Question *p. 408* **SE** Active Reading Question *p. 410* **SE** Questions and Problems *p. 436*	**TE** **NSES** UCP1, UCP2, UCP3, UCP5, A1, A2, B1, B2, E1, E2, F6
TE Teaching Tip *p. 412* **RP** Team Learning Worksheet (Sec. 12.2)	**Transparency:** Figure 12.8 **Animation:** Ionic Radii **EasyPlanner**	**SE** Critical Thinking *p. 412* **SE** Review Questions (12.2.A–12.2.B) *p. 412* **SE** Questions and Problems *p. 436*	

Planning Guide

Section	Segment		Text Features and Components	Labs, Demonstrations, & Activities
12.3 Lewis Structures 0.5 Block pp. 413–422	A	**Writing Lewis Structures**	**TE** Teaching Support: Background Information *p. 414*	
	B	**Lewis Structures of Molecules with Multiple Bonds**	**SE** Celebrity Chemical: Iron *p. 418* **TE** Teaching Support: Background Information *pp. 420–421*	
12.4 Structures of Molecules 1 Block pp. 423–433	A	**Molecular Structure**	**SE** Chemistry in Your World: Taste—It's the Structure That Counts *p. 424*	
	B	**The VSEPR Model**		**SE** Hands-On Chemistry: Geometric Balloons *p. 427*
	C	**Molecules with Double Bonds**		**LM** Experiment 50: Models of Molecules Lab Manual Report Sheets Teacher's Lab Guide

Key **SE** Student Edition   **TE** Teacher Edition   **RP** Teacher Resource Package
AR Additional Materials   **LM** Lab Materials   **▣** Transparencies
◉ DVD   **▮** CD-ROM   **ⓘ** classzone.com

All Learners	Technology	Review & Assessment	Standards
(TE) Teaching Tips pp. 413–414, 416 (TE) Meeting Individual Needs p. 415	(◉) EasyPlanner	(SE) Active Reading Question p. 413 (TE) More Examples p. 416 (SE) Practice Problem p. 417 (SE) Key Terms p. 434 (SE) Questions and Problems p. 436	(TE) **NSES** UCP2, UCP5, A1, A2, B1, B2, E1, E2, F6, G1, G2, G3
(TE) Teaching Tips pp. 417–419, 421 (TE) Meeting Individual Needs p. 417 (TE) Misconception p. 418 (RP) Team Learning Worksheet (Sec. 12.3)	(◉) EasyPlanner	(SE) Active Reading Question p. 419 (SE) Practice Problem p. 419 (TE) More Examples p. 419 (TE) More Examples p. 420 (SE) Practice Problem p. 421 (SE) Active Reading Question p. 422 (SE) Review Questions (12.3.A–12.3.B) p. 422 (SE) Key Terms p. 434 (SE) Questions and Problems pp. 436–437	
(TE) Teaching Tips p. 423	(◉) EasyPlanner	(SE) Key Terms p. 434 (SE) Questions and Problems p. 437	(TE) **NSES** UCP2, UCP5, A1, A2, B1, B2, E1, E2, F6
(TE) Teaching Tips p. 425	(◉) Animation: VSEPR: Two Electron Pair (◉) Animation: VSEPR: Three Electron Pair (◉) Animation: VSEPR: Four Electron Pair (◉) Animation: VSEPR (◉) EasyPlanner	(SE) Active Reading Question p. 426 (SE) Critical Thinking p. 427 (TE) More Examples p. 428 (SE) Critical Thinking p. 429 (SE) Practice Problem p. 429 (TE) More Examples p. 429 (SE) Active Reading Question p. 430 (SE) Key Terms p. 434 (SE) Questions and Problems p. 437	
(RP) Team Learning Worksheet (Sec. 12.4)	(⊟) Transparency: Table 12.4 (◼) Lab Generator CD (◉) EasyPlanner	(TE) More Examples p. 433 (SE) Review Questions (12.4.A–12.4.C) p. 433 (SE) Questions and Problems p. 437	

Resource Materials for Chapter 12

(SE) Chapter Review p. 434

(SE) Critical Thinking p. 438

(SE) Standardized Test Practice p. 439

(AR) English/Spanish Summaries

(◼) English Summaries Audio

(◼) Spanish Summaries Audio

(RP) Meeting Individual Needs Toolkit (MINT)
    Chapter Review Worksheets
    Chapter Summaries

(RP) Solutions Guide

(RP) Standardized Test Practice

(RP) Chapter Tests

(RP) Test Bank

(🛈) Test Generator

Chapter 12
Overview

In this chapter our goals are for students to:

- Learn about ionic and covalent bonds and explain how they are formed
- Learn about polar covalent bonds
- Understand the nature of bonds and their relationship to electronegativity
- Understand bond polarity and how it is related to molecular polarity
- Learn about ionic structures
- Understand factors governing ionic size
- Learn to write Lewis structures
- Understand molecular structure and bond angles
- Learn to apply the VSEPR model

Chemical Bonding

The atomium in Brussels, Belgium, is a giant-sized model of a crystal of iron in which the atoms are bound to each other.

IN YOUR LIFE

The world around us is composed almost entirely of compounds and mixtures of compounds. Rocks, coal, soil, petroleum, trees, and human beings are complex mixtures of chemical compounds in which different kinds of atoms are bound together. Most of the pure elements found in the earth's crust also contain many atoms bound together. In a gold nugget, each gold atom is bound to many other gold atoms; and in a diamond, many carbon atoms are bonded very strongly to each other. Substances composed of unbound atoms do exist in nature, but they are very rare. (Examples include the argon atoms in the atmosphere and the helium atoms found in natural gas reserves.)

The manner in which atoms are bound together has a profound effect on the chemical and physical properties of substances. For example, both graphite and diamond are composed solely of carbon atoms. However, graphite is a soft, slippery material used as a lubricant in locks; and diamond is one of the hardest materials known, valuable both as a gemstone and in industrial cutting tools. Why do these materials, both composed solely of carbon atoms, have such different properties? The answer lies in the different ways in which the carbon atoms are bound to each other in these substances.

Diamond, composed of carbon atoms bonded together to produce one of the hardest materials known, makes a beautiful gemstone.

WHAT DO YOU KNOW?

Prereading Questions

1. When representing a water molecule as H—O—H, what do the lines between the letters symbolize?

2. Write the electron configurations for fluorine, neon, and sodium.

3. Why is the term *sodium chloride molecule* incorrect?

Chemical Bonding • Chapter 12 • **399**

Characteristics of Chemical Bonds

Student Preparation

Assign students to read Section 12.1 and to answer the Review Questions at the end of the section before coming to class.

 Active Learning
Team Learning Worksheet

After introducing the material in Section 12.1 in class, place students in groups and have them work together on **Section 12.1: Team Learning Worksheet.**

Homework

You may wish to assign these selected end-of-chapter problems as homework for this section: 1, 2, 4, 5, 7, 8, 11, 14, 15, 17

Additional end-of-chapter problems can be used for extra practice.

12.1.A Types of Chemical Bonds
Objective To learn about ionic, covalent, and polar covalent bonds and explain how they are formed

 TEACHING TIPS

- Ionic and covalent bonding are the extremes of types of bonding. Students should understand that attractive forces in molecules lie on a continuum.

- Many of the terms used in bonding, such as *sharing, unequal sharing,* and *transfer,* can be related to human experience. This helps students begin to understand bonding at the molecular level.

Key Terms
- Bond
- Bond energy
- Ionic bonding
- Ionic compound
- Covalent bonding
- Polar covalent bond
- Electronegativity
- Dipole moment

Objectives
- *To learn about ionic and covalent bonds and explain how they are formed*
- *To learn about the polar covalent bond*
- *To understand the nature of bonds and their relationship to electronegativity*
- *To understand bond polarity and how it is related to molecular polarity*

Molecular bonding and structure play the central role in determining the course of chemical reactions, many of which are vital to our survival. Most reactions in biological systems are very sensitive to the structures of the participating molecules; in fact, very subtle differences in shape sometimes serve to channel the chemical reaction one way rather than another. Molecules that act as drugs must have exactly the right structure to perform their functions correctly. Structure also plays a central role in our senses of smell and taste. Substances have a particular odor because they fit into the specially shaped receptors in our nasal passages, and taste is also dependent on molecular shape.

To understand the behavior of natural materials, we must understand the nature of chemical bonding and the factors that control the structures of compounds. In this chapter, we will present various classes of compounds that illustrate the different types of bonds. We will then develop models to describe the structure and bonding that characterize the materials found in nature.

A. Types of Chemical Bonds

What is a chemical bond? Although there are several ways to answer this question, we will define a **bond** as a force that holds groups of two or more atoms together and makes them function as a unit. For example, in water the fundamental unit is the H—O—H molecule, which we describe as being held together by the two O—H bonds. We can obtain information about the strength of a bond by measuring the energy required to break the bond, the **bond energy.**

Atoms can interact with one another in several ways to form aggregates. We will consider specific examples to illustrate the various types of chemical bonds.

Ionic Bonding In Chapter 8 we saw that when solid sodium chloride is dissolved in water, the resulting solution conducts electricity, a fact that convinces chemists that sodium chloride is composed of Na^+ and Cl^- ions. Thus, when sodium and chlorine react to form sodium chloride, electrons are transferred from the sodium atoms to the chlorine atoms to form Na^+ and Cl^- ions, which then aggregate to form solid sodium chloride. The resulting solid sodium chloride is a very sturdy material; it has a melting point of approximately 800 °C. See **Figure 12.1.**

A water molecule

Bond (chemical bond)
The force that holds two or more atoms together and makes them function as a unit

Bond energy
The energy required to break a given chemical bond

(a)   (b)

Figure 12.1
(a) Sodium chloride contains ions closely packed together in the solid. (b). When dissolved in water, these ions become free to move around

---

Teaching Support
BACKGROUND INFORMATION

Models originate from our observations of the properties of nature. For example, the concept of bonds arose from the observations that most chemical processes involve collections of atoms and that chemical reactions involve rearrangements of the ways the atoms are grouped. To understand reactions, we must understand the forces that bind atoms together.

Natural processes have a tendency toward lower energy. Collections of atoms therefore occur because the aggregated state has lower energy than the separated atoms. Why? The best explanations for the energy change involve atoms sharing electrons or atoms transferring electrons to become ions. In the case of electron sharing, we find it convenient to assume that individual bonds occur between pairs of atoms.

The bonding model provides a framework to systematize chemical behavior by enabling

The strong bonding forces present in sodium chloride result from the attractions among the closely packed, oppositely charged ions. This is an example of **ionic bonding**. Ionic substances are formed when an atom that loses electrons relatively easily reacts with an atom that has a high affinity for electrons. In other words, an **ionic compound** results when a metal reacts with a nonmetal.

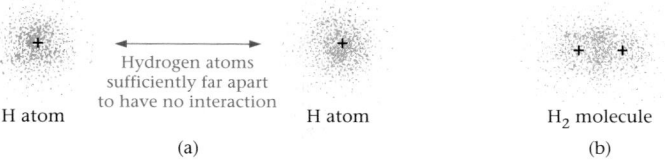

Ionic bonding
The attraction between oppositely charged ions

Ionic compound
A compound that results when a metal reacts with a nonmetal to form cations and anions

We have seen that a bonding force develops when two very different types of atoms react to form oppositely charged ions. But how does a bonding force develop between two identical atoms? Let's explore this situation by considering what happens when two hydrogen atoms are brought close together, as shown in **Figure 12.2.** When hydrogen atoms are close together, the two electrons are simultaneously attracted to both nuclei. Note in Figure 12.2b how the electron probability increases between the two nuclei, indicating that the electrons are shared by the two nuclei.

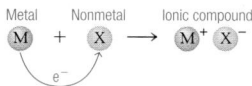

Hydrogen atoms sufficiently far apart to have no interaction

H atom   H atom H_2 molecule

(a)   (b)

Figure 12.2
The formation of a bond between two hydrogen atoms. (a) Two separate hydrogen atoms. (b) When two hydrogen atoms come close together, the two electrons are attracted simultaneously by both nuclei. This produces the bond. Note the relatively large electron probability between the nuclei, indicating sharing of the electrons.

Covalent bonding The type of bonding we encounter in the hydrogen molecule and in many other molecules where *electrons are shared by nuclei* is called **covalent bonding**. Note that in the H_2 molecule, the electrons reside primarily in the space between the two nuclei, where they are attracted simultaneously by both protons. Although we will not go into detail about it here, the increased attractive forces in this area lead to the formation of the H_2 molecule from the two separated hydrogen atoms. When we say that a bond is formed between the hydrogen atoms, we mean that the H_2 molecule is more stable than two separated hydrogen atoms by a certain quantity of energy (the bond energy).

Covalent bonding
A type of bonding in which atoms share electrons

So far we have considered two extreme types of bonding. In ionic bonding, the participating atoms are so different that one or more electrons are transferred to form oppositely charged ions. The bonding results from the attractions between these ions. In covalent bonding, two identical atoms share electrons equally. The bonding results from the mutual attraction of the two nuclei for the shared electrons. Between these extremes are intermediate cases in which the atoms are not so different that electrons are completely transferred but are different enough so that unequal sharing

12.1 • Characteristics of Chemical Bonds • 401

us to think of molecules as a collection of common fundamental components. For example, a typical biomolecule, such as a protein, contains hundreds of atoms and might seem discouragingly complex. However, thinking of a protein as constructed of individual bonds, such as C—C, C—H, C—N, C—O, and N—H, helps tremendously in predicting and understanding the protein's behavior. The essential idea is that we expect a given bond

to behave in roughly the same way in any molecular environment. This model of the chemical bond has helped chemists to systematize the reactions of the millions of existing compounds.

TEACHING TIPS

• Focus students' attention on where the electrons spend more time. Are they equally shared between two atoms or do they spend more time closer to one atom in the bond? This focus will help students understand bond polarity.

• While the electrons are simultaneously attracted to both nuclei, the nuclei of the hydrogen atoms repel each other.

TECHNOLOGY

 Figure 12.2

 Animations
Bonding in H_2
Covalent Bonding

An ionic bond is a bond between ions in an ionic compound, such as in NaCl. A polar covalent bond is a bond between different atoms, such as in H_2O. A covalent bond is a bond between the same type of atom, such as in O_2.

12.1.B Electronegativity

Objective To understand the nature of bonds and their relationship to electronegativity

 TEACHING TIPS

- This section develops the concept of electronegativity and its trends on the periodic table. Focus students' attention on how electronegativity relates to ionization energy.

- Students can memorize electronegativity trends, but it is important that they understand the reasons behind these trends (just as they should understand trends for atomic radius and ionization energy).

- Students should be able to compare the electronegativities of two elements in the same group or same period. They should not memorize the actual electronegativity numbers but rather be able to predict which is greater.

TECHNOLOGY

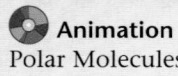 **Animation**
Polar Molecules

Polar covalent bond
A covalent bond in which the electrons are not shared equally because one atom attracts the shared electrons more than the other atom

Electronegativity
The tendency of an atom in a molecule to attract shared electrons to itself

---

of electrons results, forming what is called a **polar covalent bond**. The hydrogen fluoride (HF) molecule contains this type of bond, which produces the charge distribution

$$\underset{\delta^+ \quad \delta^-}{\text{H—F}}$$

where δ (delta) is used to indicate a partial or fractional charge.

The most logical explanation for the development of *bond polarity* (the partial positive and negative charges on the atoms in such molecules as HF) is that the electrons in the bonds are not shared equally. For example, we can account for the polarity of the HF molecule by assuming that the fluorine atom has a stronger attraction than the hydrogen atom for the shared electrons (see **Figure 12.3**). Because bond polarity has important chemical implications, we find it useful to assign a number that indicates an atom's ability to attract shared electrons.

(a)   (b)

Figure 12.3
Probability representations of the electron sharing in HF. (a) What the probability map would look like if the two electrons in the H—F bond were shared equally. (b) The actual situation, where the shared pair spends more time close to the fluorine atom than to the hydrogen atom. This gives fluorine a slight excess of negative charge and the hydrogen a slight deficit of negative charge (a slight positive charge).

 Active Reading Question

Provide an example of an ionic bond, an example of a polar covalent bond, and an example of a covalent bond.

B. Electronegativity

We have seen that when a metal and a nonmetal react, one or more electrons are transferred from the metal to the nonmetal to give ionic bonding. On the other hand, two identical atoms react to form a covalent bond in which electrons are shared equally. When *different* nonmetals react, a bond forms in which electrons are shared *unequally*, giving a polar covalent bond. The unequal sharing of electrons between two atoms is described by a property called **electronegativity**: *the relative ability of an atom in a molecule to attract shared electrons to itself.*

Chemists determine electronegativity values for the elements (see **Figure 12.4**) by measuring the polarities of the bonds between various atoms.

Electronegativity generally
- increases going from left to right across a period
- decreases going down a group for the representative elements.

The range of electronegativity values goes from 4.0 for fluorine to 0.7 for cesium and francium. Remember, the higher the atom's electronegativity value, the closer the shared electrons tend to be to that atom when it forms a bond.

Increasing electronegativity →

				H 2.1													
Li 1.0	Be 1.5											B 2.0	C 2.5	N 3.0	O 3.5	F 4.0	
Na 0.9	Mg 1.2											Al 1.5	Si 1.8	P 2.1	S 2.5	Cl 3.0	
K 0.8	Ca 1.0	Sc 1.3	Ti 1.5	V 1.6	Cr 1.6	Mn 1.5	Fe 1.8	Co 1.9	Ni 1.9	Cu 1.9	Zn 1.6	Ga 1.6	Ge 1.8	As 2.0	Se 2.4	Br 2.8	
Rb 0.8	Sr 1.0	Y 1.2	Zr 1.4	Nb 1.6	Mo 1.8	Tc 1.9	Ru 2.2	Rh 2.2	Pd 2.2	Ag 1.9	Cd 1.7	In 1.7	Sn 1.8	Sb 1.9	Te 2.1	I 2.5	
Cs 0.7	Ba 0.9	La-Lu 1.0-1.2	Hf 1.3	Ta 1.5	W 1.7	Re 1.9	Os 2.2	Ir 2.2	Pt 2.2	Au 2.4	Hg 1.9	Tl 1.8	Pb 1.9	Bi 1.9	Po 2.0	At 2.2	
Fr 0.7	Ra 0.9	Ac 1.1	Th 1.3	Pa 1.4	U 1.4	Np-No 1.4-1.3											

(left axis label: Decreasing electronegativity ↓)

Key
- [ ] < 1.5
- [ ] 1.5–1.9
- [ ] 2.0–2.9
- [ ] 3.0–4.0

Figure 12.4
Electronegativity values for selected elements. Note that metals have relatively low electronegativity values and that nonmetals have relatively high values.

The polarity of a bond depends on the *difference* between the electronegativity values of the atoms forming the bond.

If the atoms have very similar electronegativities, the electrons are shared almost equally and the bond shows little polarity. If the atoms have very different electronegativity values, a very polar bond is formed. In extreme cases one or more electrons are actually transferred, forming ions and an ionic bond. For example, when an element from Group 1 (electronegativity values of about 0.8) reacts with an element from Group 7 (electronegativity values of about 3), ions are formed and an ionic substance results. In general, if the *difference* between the electronegativities of two elements is about 2.0 or greater, the bond is considered to be ionic.

The relationship between electronegativity and bond type is shown in **Table 12.1**. The various types of bonds are summarized in **Figure 12.5**.

CRITICAL THINKING ?

We use differences in electronegativity to account for certain properties of bonds.

What if all atoms had the same electronegativity values? How would bonding between atoms be affected? What are some differences we would notice?

  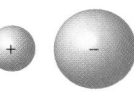

(a)   (b)   (c)

Figure 12.5
The three possible types of bonds are (a) a covalent bond formed between identical atoms; (b) a polar covalent bond, with both ionic and covalent components; and (c) an ionic bond, with no electron sharing.

Active Reading Question

In general, how do electronegativity trends compare to trends of atomic size?

TECHNOLOGY

 Figure 12.4

 Figure 12.5

 TEACHING TIP

Remind students that the electronegativity values of the lightest noble gases are assumed to be zero since they do not form chemical bonds. When we say that elements in the upper-right corner of the periodic table are the most electronegative, we do not include the noble gases. Have students explain why this statement is true.

CRITICAL THINKING ?

All bonds would be perfectly covalent. As a result, no polar molecules would exist (only London dispersion forces would be present). All small, light molecules (most notably water) would be gaseous. Only relatively large and heavy molecules would be solids (disregarding metallic bonding). Salts and ionic compounds could not exist. These facts have serious implications. Without aqueous solutions of soluble ionic compounds, life would be impossible.

 Active Reading Question

In general, the smaller the atomic size, the greater the electronegativity of the atoms.

TEACHING TIP

The relationship between the difference in electronegativity and bond type is rather arbitrary and serves only as a rough guide.

EXAMPLE 12.1

More Examples

On the basis of the electronegativity values given in Figure 12.4, indicate which is the more polar bond in each of the following pairs.

1. H—S or H—F
   H—F

2. O—S or O—F
   O—S

3. N—S or N—Cl
   N—Cl

4. C—S or C—Cl
   C—Cl

Answer to Practice Problem 12.1

Using the electronegativity values given in Figure 12.4, we choose the bond in which the atoms exhibit the largest difference in electronegativity. (Electronegativity values are shown in parentheses.)

a. H—C   >   H—P
   (2.1)(2.5)   (2.1)(2.1)

b. O—I   >   O—F
   (3.5)(2.5)   (3.5)(4.0)

c. S—O   >   N—O
   (2.5)(3.5)   (3.0)(3.5)

d. N—H   >   Si—H
   (3.0)(2.1)   (1.8)(2.1)

Table 12.1

The Relationship Between Electronegativity and Bond Type

Electronegativity Difference Between the Bonding Atoms	Bond Type	Covalent Character	Ionic Character
Zero	Covalent		
↓	↓	Increases ↑	Increases ↓
Intermediate	Polar covalent		
↓	↓		
Large	Ionic		

EXAMPLE 12.1

Using Electronegativity to Determine Bond Polarity

Using the electronegativity values given in Figure 12.4, arrange the following bonds in order of increasing polarity: H—H, O—H, Cl—H, S—H, and F—H.

Solution

The polarity of the bond increases as the difference in electronegativity increases. From the electronegativity values in Figure 12.4, the following variation in bond polarity is expected (the electronegativity value appears in parentheses below each element).

Bond	Electronegativity Value	Difference in Electronegativity Values	Bond Type	Polarity
H—H	(2.1) (2.1)	2.1 − 2.1 = 0	Covalent	
S—H	(2.5) (2.1)	2.5 − 2.1 = 0.4	Polar covalent	increasing ↓
Cl—H	(3.0) (2.1)	3.0 − 2.1 = 0.9	Polar covalent	
O—H	(3.5) (2.1)	3.5 − 2.1 = 1.4	Polar covalent	
F—H	(4.0) (2.1)	4.0 − 2.1 = 1.9	Polar covalent	

Therefore, in order of increasing polarity, we have

H—H   S—H   Cl—H   O—H   F—H

Least polar   Most polar

Practice Problem • Exercise 12.1

For each of the following pairs of bonds, choose the bond that is more polar.

   a. H—P, H—C   c. N—O, S—O

   b. O—F, O—I   d. N—H, Si—H

C. Bond Polarity and Dipole Moments

We have seen that hydrogen fluoride has a positive end and a negative end. A molecule such as HF that has a center of positive charge and a center of negative charge is said to have a **dipole moment**. The dipolar character of a molecule is often represented by an arrow. This arrow points toward the negative charge center, and its tail indicates the positive center of charge:

$$\delta^+ \qquad\qquad \delta^-$$

Any diatomic (two-atom) molecule that has a polar bond has a dipole moment. Some polyatomic (more than two atoms) molecules also have dipole moments. For example, because the oxygen atom in the water molecule has a greater electronegativity than the hydrogen atoms, the electrons are not shared equally. This results in a charge distribution that causes the molecule to behave as though it had two centers of charge—one positive and one negative. So the water molecule has a dipole moment.

The fact that the water molecule is polar (has a dipole moment) has a profound effect on its properties. In fact, it is not overly dramatic to state that the polarity of the water molecule is crucial to life as we know it on earth. Because water molecules are polar, they can surround and attract both positive and negative ions (see **Figure 12.6**). These attractions allow ionic materials to dissolve in water. Also, the polarity of water molecules causes them to attract each other strongly.

This means that much energy is required to change water from a liquid to a gas (the molecules must be separated from each other to undergo this change of state). Therefore, it is the polarity of the water molecule that causes water to remain a liquid at the temperatures on the earth's surface. If it were nonpolar, water would be a gas and the oceans would be empty.

Dipole moment
A property of a molecule in which the charge distribution can be represented by a center of positive charge and a center of negative charge

(a)

(b)

Figure 12.6
(a) Polar water molecules are strongly attracted to positive ions by their negative ends. (b) They are also strongly attracted to negative ions by their positive ends.

12.1 • Characteristics of Chemical Bonds • **405**

12.1.C Bond Polarity and Dipole Moments
Objective To understand bond polarity and how it is related to molecular polarity

LABORATORY
EXPERIMENT 49
Dyes and Dying, Traditional

TEACHING TIPS

• A nonpolar molecule can have bonds with dipole moments. This concept will be covered later, when we discuss molecular structure.

• Confine your examples to simple molecules in this section. We have not yet discussed molecular shape, which plays a role in determining the polarity of more complex molecules.

• Students are often confused about why we use minus and plus signs to show charges on ions but use δ^- and δ^+ to show the charges on polar atoms in a molecule. The difficulty comes from not understanding that there should be a difference between full and partial charges.

• Now is an excellent time to discuss the importance of polarity in molecules by referring to the properties of water. Discuss the ability of water to dissolve polar and ionic substances (Figure 12.6) and the strong attraction that water molecules have for each other, which results in the high boiling point of water.

SECTION 12.1
Review Questions

1. A chemical bond is a force that holds two atoms together so that they act like a unit (as in a molecule or polyatomic ion). Electrons (specifically valence electrons) are the most important subatomic particles in bonds.

2. An ionic bond involves a transfer of electrons from one atom to another; in a covalent bond, two atoms share a pair of electrons.

3. In a polar covalent bond, the electrons spend more time closer to one atom than to the other. In a covalent bond, the electrons are shared equally between the atoms.

4. a. O_2

   b. HF

   c. NaCl

5. The polarity of a bond depends on the difference between the electronegativity values of the atoms forming the bond. If the atoms have similar electronegativities, the electrons are shared almost equally and the bond shows little polarity. If the atoms have very different electronegativity values, a very polar bond is formed.

6. a. H—Cl
   $\longmapsto$

   b. H—H
   none

   c. H—I
   $\longmapsto$

   d. Br—Br
   none

   e. CO
   $\longmapsto$

CHEMISTRY EXPLORERS
Linus Pauling • 1901–1994

Linus Pauling is the only person in history to receive two unshared Nobel Prizes. He received the Nobel Prize in Chemistry in 1954, and the Nobel Peace Prize in 1962. As a professor of chemistry at California Institute for Technology, Pauling developed the electronegativity scale of the elements and was awarded the Nobel Prize in Chemistry for his work on the chemical bond. In 1939 he published *The Nature of the Chemical Bond*, which is often cited as the most influential science book of the twentieth century. Pauling was an opponent of nuclear weapons and was awarded the Nobel Peace Prize for his campaign against open-air nuclear testing.

Linus Pauling was a man whose interests varied from chemical bonds to world peace; from electric cars to human health. The British publication *New Scientist* ranked Linus Pauling as one of the twenty greatest scientists of all time, with Albert Einstein being the only other scientist included from the twentieth century. Very good company indeed!

SECTION 12.1
REVIEW QUESTIONS

❶ What is meant by the term *chemical bond*? What subatomic particles are most important in bonds?

❷ How are ionic bonds and covalent bonds different?

❸ How is a polar covalent bond different from a covalent bond?

❹ Match the compounds HF, NaCl, and O_2 with the following figures.

          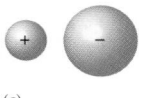

(a)   (b)   (c)

❺ How do electronegativity values help in determining the polarity of a bond?

❻ For each of the binary molecules below, draw an arrow under the molecules showing its dipole moment. If it has none, write "none."

   a. H—Cl

   b. H—H

   c. H—I

   d. Br—Br

   e. CO

RESEARCH LINKS
CLASSZONE.COM

CHEMISTRY EXPLORERS
Linus Pauling

The photograph of Linus Pauling shows him with an orange, and for good reason—he was a strong advocate of massive daily doses of vitamin C. While the recommended daily dosage for an adult is 75–90 mg daily, Pauling was known to take several grams daily. He published *Vitamin C and the Common Cold* in 1970. Many people still take vitamin C to ward off a cold or diminish its strength. Whether or not this works is still under debate.

Characteristics of Ions and Ionic Compounds

Objectives

- *To learn about stable electron configurations*
- *To learn to predict the formulas of ionic compounds*
- *To learn about the structures of ionic compounds*
- *To understand factors governing ionic size*

A. Stable Electron Configurations and Charges on Ions

We have seen many times that when a metal and a nonmetal react to form an ionic compound, the metal atom loses one or more electrons to the nonmetal.

Let's Review

Charges on Ions

- Group 1 metals always form 1+ cations.
- Group 2 metals always form 2+ cations.
- Aluminum in Group 3 always forms a 3+ cation.
- Group 7 nonmetals form 1− anions.
- Group 6 elements always form 2− anions.

This is illustrated in **Table 12.2.**

Notice something very interesting about the ions in Table 12.2: all have the electron configuration of neon, a noble gas. That is, sodium loses its one valence electron (the $3s$) to form Na^+, which has a [Ne] electron configuration. Likewise, Mg loses its two valence electrons to form Mg^{2+}, which also has a [Ne] electron configuration. On the other hand, the nonmetal

---

Table 12.2

The Formation of Ions by Metals and Nonmetals

Group	Ion Formation	Electron Configuration		
		Atom		**Ion**
1	$Na \rightarrow Na^+ + e^-$	$[Ne]3s^1$	$\xrightarrow{\text{e}^- \text{ lost}}$	[Ne]
2	$Mg \rightarrow Mg^{2+} + 2e^-$	$[Ne]3s^2$	$\xrightarrow{\text{2e}^- \text{ lost}}$	[Ne]
3	$Al \rightarrow Al^{3+} + 3e^-$	$[Ne]3s^23p^1$	$\xrightarrow{\text{3e}^- \text{ lost}}$	[Ne]
6	$O + 2e^- \rightarrow O^{2-}$	$[He]2s^22p^4 + 2e^- \rightarrow [He]2s^22p^6 = [Ne]$		
7	$F + e^- \rightarrow F^-$	$[He]2s^22p^5 + e^- \rightarrow [He]2s^22p^6 = [Ne]$		

12.2 • Characteristics of Ions and Ionic Compounds • **407**

SECTION 12.2
INTRODUCE

Student Preparation

Assign students to read Section 12.2 and to answer the Review Questions at the end of the section before coming to class.

 Active Learning
Team Learning Worksheet

After introducing the material in Section 12.2 in class, place students in groups and have them work together on **Section 12.2: Team Learning Worksheet.**

SECTION 12.2
GUIDE THE LEARNING

Homework

You may wish to assign these selected end-of-chapter problems as homework for this section: 19, 20a–c, 21, 22, 23, 24, 26, 28, 29

Additional end-of-chapter problems can be used for extra practice.

12.2.A Stable Electron Configurations and Charges on Ions

Objective To learn about stable electron configurations and to learn to predict the formulas of ionic compounds

 TEACHING TIPS

- Now is an excellent time to review the electron configurations for atoms and write electron configurations for ions. Emphasize that the ion formed from a particular atom arises because of the stability associated with a noble gas electron configuration.

- This section also gives students an opportunity to understand why certain atoms are more likely to form negative ions and others to form positive ions. Use the electron configurations to discuss this point.

TECHNOLOGY

 Table 12.2

- The concept that atoms have a strong tendency to adopt a noble gas configuration is central to understanding the electronic structure of ions and the Lewis structures of molecules. This concept is emphasized in this chapter and should be stressed in class discussions.

- Science focuses on observing patterns (laws) and developing explanations (theories or models). The fact that the atoms in a compound have a tendency to achieve a noble gas electron configuration is an observation, not an explanation. Knowing this tendency helps us to make predictions, but does not answer the "why?" question. With this observation in mind, students should be able to predict, for example, that a sodium atom will lose only one electron when becoming an ion, and that a calcium atom will lose two electrons.

- You may want to begin a discussion of bonding by using a simple example of ionic bonding and another of covalent bonding to illustrate how atoms attain electron configurations of noble gases. One possibility is NaCl, in which Na loses an electron to Cl so that the sodium ion has the same electron configuration as Ne and the chloride ion has the same electron configuration as Ar. In the case of H_2, each hydrogen shares an electron with the other so that both hydrogens have the same electron configuration as He.

Active Reading Question

Atoms achieve noble gas electron configurations in almost all stable chemical compounds.

---

atoms gain just the number of electrons needed for them to achieve the noble gas electron configuration. The O atom gains two electrons and the F atom gains one electron to give O^{2-} and F^-, respectively, both of which have the [Ne] electron configuration. We can summarize these observations as follows:

Atoms in stable compounds almost always have a noble gas electron configuration.

Electron Configurations of Ions

1. Representative (main-group) metals form ions by losing enough electrons to achieve the configuration of the previous noble gas (that is, the noble gas that occurs before the metal in question on the periodic table).

   For example, note from the periodic table inside the back cover of this book that neon is the noble gas before sodium and magnesium. (See Table 12.2) Similarly, helium is the noble gas before lithium and beryllium.

2. Nonmetals form ions by gaining enough electrons to achieve the configuration of the next noble gas (that is, the noble gas that follows the element in question on the periodic table).

   For example, note that neon is the noble gas that follows oxygen and fluorine, and argon is the noble gas that follows sulfur and chlorine. (See Table 12.2)

This brings us to an important general principle. In observing millions of stable compounds, chemists have learned that in almost all stable chemical compounds of the representative elements, all of the atoms have achieved a noble gas electron configuration.

The importance of this observation cannot be overstated. It forms the basis for all of our fundamental ideas about why and how atoms bond to each other.

When representative metals and nonmetals react, they transfer electrons in such a way that both the cation and the anion have noble gas electron configurations.

Active Reading Question

What rule helps us determine the most stable electron configuration and charge of a particular ion?

On the other hand, when nonmetals react with each other, they share electrons in ways that lead to a noble gas electron configuration for each atom in the resulting molecule. For example, oxygen ($[He]2s^22p^4$), which needs two more electrons to achieve an [Ne] configuration, can get these electrons by combining with two H atoms (each of which has one electron),

to form water, H_2O. This fills the valence orbitals of oxygen.

In addition, each H shares two electrons with the oxygen atom,

$$H \overset{\displaystyle O}{} H$$

which fills the H $1s$ orbital, giving it a $1s^2$ or [He] electron configuration. We will have much more to say about covalent bonding later.

Let's Review

Electron Configurations and Bonding

- When a *nonmetal and a Group 1, 2, or 3 metal* react to form a binary ionic compound, the ions form in such a way that the valence-electron configuration of the *nonmetal* is *completed* to achieve the configuration of the *next* noble gas, and the valence orbitals of the *metal* are *emptied* to achieve the configuration of the *previous* noble gas. In this way, both ions achieve noble gas electron configurations.

- When *two nonmetals* react to form a covalent bond, they share electrons in a way that completes the valence-electron configurations of both atoms. That is, both nonmetals attain noble gas electron configurations by sharing electrons.

Predicting Formulas of Ionic Compounds

To show how to predict which ions form when a metal reacts with a non-metal, we will consider the formation of an ionic compound from calcium and oxygen. We can predict the compound that will form by considering the valence electron configurations of the two atoms.

Ca: $[Ar]4s^2$

O: $[He]2s^22p^4$

From Figure 12.4 we see that the electronegativity of oxygen (3.5) is much greater than that of calcium (1.0), giving a difference of 2.5. Because of this large difference, electrons are transferred from calcium to oxygen to form an oxygen anion and a calcium cation. How many electrons are transferred? We can base our prediction on the observation that noble gas configurations are the most stable. Note that oxygen needs two electrons to fill its valence orbitals ($2s$ and $2p$) and achieve the configuration of neon ($1s^22s^22p^6$), which is the next noble gas.

$$O + 2e^- \rightarrow O^{2-}$$

$$[He]2s^22p^4 + 2e^- \rightarrow [He]2s^22p^6, \text{ or } [Ne]$$

By losing two electrons, calcium can achieve the configuration of argon (the previous noble gas).

$$Ca \rightarrow Ca^{2+} + 2e^-$$

$$[Ar]4s^2 \rightarrow [Ar] + 2e^-$$

Two electrons are therefore transferred as follows:

$$Ca + O \rightarrow Ca^{2+} + O^{2-}$$

TEACHING TIPS

- Students should already know how to predict the charge on an ion from the group number on the periodic table. Now is a good time to review this idea and to point out that students can also predict the charge on an ion by looking at the valence electron configuration.

- Now is a good time to review predicting the products in chemical reactions between elements. Students can now predict the correct product by using the valence electron configurations for each atom. Once they have determined the number of electrons that are lost or gained to achieve the core electron configuration of a noble gas, they will be able to determine the charge on the ion and hence the formula for the product in the reaction.

information

Differences in electronegativities greater than 2.0 lead to ionic bonds.

Table 12.3

 Active Learning
Group Activity

Table 12.3 can be used in a team activity. Student teams can be assigned one row of the table. Each team must show how each element in its group gains or loses electrons to attain the electron configuration of the nearest noble gas. Students do not need to know the term *isoelectronic* to see that the electron configuration of each element's ion is the same. This activity also reinforces the concept that negative ions are formed by adding electrons and positive ions are formed by losing electrons.

 Active Reading Question

To achieve noble gas electron configurations, Al must lose three electrons (to have a 3+ charge) and O must gain two electrons (to have a 2– charge). Since compounds are electrically neutral, two aluminum ions are required for every three oxygen ions.

12.2.B Ionic Bonding and Structures of Ionic Compounds
Objective To learn about ionic structures and to understand factors governing ionic size

MATH

$3 \times (2-)$ balances
$2 \times (3+)$.

To predict the formula of the ionic compound, we use the fact that chemical compounds are always electrically neutral—they have the same total quantities of positive and negative charges. In this case, we must have equal numbers of Ca^{2+} and O^{2-} ions, and the empirical formula of the compound is CaO.

> Chemical compounds are always electrically neutral.

The same principles can be applied to many other cases. For example, consider the compound formed from aluminum and oxygen. Aluminum has the electron configuration $[Ne]3s^23p^1$. To achieve the neon configuration, aluminum must lose three electrons, forming the Al^{3+} ion.

$$Al \rightarrow Al^{3+} + 3e^-$$
$$[Ne]3s^23p^1 \rightarrow [Ne] + 3e^-$$

Therefore, the ions will be Al^{3+} and O^{2-}. Because the compound must be electrically neutral, there will be three O^{2-} ions for every two Al^{3+} ions, and the compound has the empirical formula Al_2O_3.

Table 12.3 shows common elements that form ions with noble gas electron configurations in ionic compounds.

Table 12.3

Common Ions with Noble Gas Configurations in Ionic Compounds

Group 1	Group 2	Group 3	Group 6	Group 7	Electron Configuration
Li^+	Be^{2+}				[He]
Na^+	Mg^{2+}	Al^{3+}	O^{2-}	F^-	[Ne]
K^+	Ca^{2+}		S^{2-}	Cl^-	[Ar]
Rb^+	Sr^{2+}		Se^{2-}	Br^-	[Kr]
Cs^+	Ba^{2+}		Te^{2-}	I^-	[Xe]

Notice that our discussion in this section refers to metals in Groups 1, 2, and 3 (the representative metals). The transition metals exhibit more complicated behavior (they form a variety of ions), which we will not consider in this text.

Active Reading Question

How can we predict that solid aluminum oxide has the formula Al_2O_3?

B. Ionic Bonding and Structures of Ionic Compounds

When metals and nonmetals react, the resulting ionic compounds are very stable; large amounts of energy are required to "take them apart." For example, the melting point of sodium chloride is approximately 800 °C. The strong bonding in these ionic compounds results from the attractions between the oppositely charged cations and anions.

Structures of Ionic Compounds We write the formula of an ionic compound such as lithium fluoride simply as LiF, but this is really the empirical, or simplest, formula. The actual solid contains huge and equal numbers of

410 • Chapter 12 • Chemical Bonding

Teaching Support
BACKGROUND INFORMATION

Ionic Compounds

When chemists use the term *ionic compound,* they are usually referring to the solid state of that compound. In the solid state, ions are close together. That is, solid ionic compounds contain a large collection of positive and negative ions packed together in a way that minimizes the −....− and +....+ repulsions and maximizes the +...−

attractions. This situation stands in contrast to the gas phase of an ionic substance, in which the ions are generally quite far apart. In the gas phase, a pair of ions may get close enough to interact, but large collections of ions do not exist. Thus, when we speak of the stability of an ionic compound, we are referring to the solid state, in which the large attractive forces present among oppositely charged ions tend to stabilize the ions. For example, the O^{2-} ion is not as stable as an isolated, gas-phase species but, of course, is

Li^+ and F^- ions packed together in a way that maximizes the attractions of the oppositely charged ions. A representative part of the lithium fluoride structure is shown in **Figure 12.7a.** In this structure, the larger F^- ions are packed together like hard spheres, and the much smaller Li^+ ions are placed regularly among the F^- ions. The structure shown in **Figure 12.7b** represents only a tiny part of the actual structure, which continues in all three dimensions with the same pattern as that shown.

The structures of virtually all binary ionic compounds can be explained by a model that involves packing the ions as though they were hard spheres. The larger spheres (usually the anions) are packed together, and the small ions occupy the interstices (spaces or holes) among them.

To understand the packing of ions, it helps to realize that *a cation is always smaller than the parent atom, and an anion is always larger than the parent atom.* This makes sense because when a metal loses all of its valence electrons to form a cation, it gets much smaller. On the other hand, in forming an anion, a nonmetal gains enough electrons to achieve the next noble gas electron configuration and so becomes much larger. The relative sizes of the Group 1 and Group 7 atoms and their ions are shown in **Figure 12.8.**

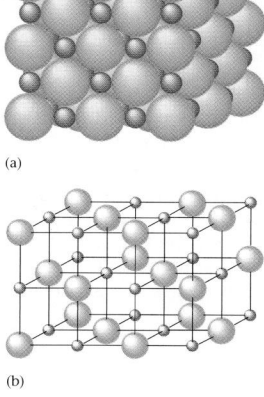

(a)

(b)

Figure 12.7
The structure of lithium fluoride. (a) This structure represents the ions as packed spheres. (b) This structure shows the positions (centers) of the ions. The spherical ions are packed in a way that maximizes the ionic attractions.

Atom	Cation	Atom	Anion
Li 152	Li$^+$ 60	F 72	F$^-$ 136
Na 186	Na$^+$ 95	Cl 99	Cl$^-$ 181
K 227	K$^+$ 133	Br 114	Br$^-$ 195
Rb 248	Rb$^+$ 148	I 133	I$^-$ 216
Cs 265	Cs$^+$ 169		

Figure 12.8
Relative sizes of some ions and their parent atoms. Note that cations are smaller and anions are larger than their parent atoms. The sizes (radii) are given in units of picometers (1 pm = 10^{-12} m).

information

When spheres are packed together, they do not fill up all of the space. The spaces (holes) that are left can be occupied by smaller spheres.

12.2 • Characteristics of Ions and Ionic Compounds • 411

very stable in many solid ionic compounds. That is, MgO(*s*), which contains Mg^{2+} and O^{2-} ions, is very stable, but the isolated, gas-phase ion pair $Mg^{2+}...O^{2-}$ is not energetically favorable in comparison with the separate neutral gaseous atoms. In this section and in most other cases where we are describing the nature of ionic compounds, the discussion refers to the solid state, in which many ions are simultaneously interacting.

When *two nonmetals* react to form a covalent bond, they share electrons in a way that completes the valence electron configurations of both atoms. That is, both nonmetals attain noble gas electron configurations.

When a *nonmetal and a representative-group metal* react to form a binary ionic compound, the ions form such that the valence electron configuration of the nonmetal achieves the electron configuration of the next noble gas atom and the valence orbitals of the metal are emptied. In this way, both ions achieve noble gas electron configurations.

TEACHING TIP

Students have difficulty understanding polyatomic ions. These atoms are bonded together covalently and will not break up into atoms or simple ions. For example, when sodium sulfate dissolves in water, sodium and sulfate ions are formed, but the sulfate ion cannot break into sulfur and oxygen ions.

CRITICAL THINKING ?

The structure of ionic compounds results from the packing of ions as hard spheres. Because the anions are usually larger than the cations, the solids consist of a matrix of anions in which the cations fill the holes among the anions. Not only do these ions achieve close packing, but an attraction of oppositely charged ions, or *lattice energy*, also occurs. Without size differences, packing would not be as close and compounds would not be as stable.

SECTION 12.2
ASSESS

SECTION 12.2
Review Questions

1. A Group 1 or 2 metal loses the number of electrons required for it to reach the electron configuration of the previous noble gas. For example, Na loses one electron and Ca loses two electrons.

2. Once oxygen has gained two electrons, it has the same electron configuration as neon. This configuration is favored and oxygen will not easily gain another electron.

3. First, we write the electron configuration of the atom. We then determine how many electrons to add or remove from the atom to give a noble gas electron configuration. Once we know the charges of the cation and anion, we predict the formula, keeping in mind that chemical compounds are always electrically neutral.

4. a. Mg: [Ne]$3s^2$
   S: [Ne]$3s^23p^4$
   compound: MgS

CRITICAL THINKING ?

Ions have different sizes than their parent atoms.

What if ions stayed the same sizes as their parent atoms? How would that change the structures of ionic compounds?

Ionic Compounds Containing Polyatomic Ions

So far in this chapter we have discussed only binary ionic compounds, which contain ions derived from single atoms. However, many compounds contain polyatomic ions: charged species composed of several atoms. For example, ammonium nitrate contains the NH_4^+ and NO_3^- ions.

 NH_4^+ NO_3^-

These ions with their opposite charges attract each other in the same way as do the simple ions in binary ionic compounds. However, the *individual* polyatomic ions are held together by covalent bonds, with all of the atoms behaving as a unit. For example, in the ammonium ion, NH_4^+, there are four N—H covalent bonds. Likewise, the nitrate ion, NO_3^-, contains three covalent N—O bonds. Thus, although ammonium nitrate is an ionic compound because it contains the NH_4^+ and NO_3^- ions, it also contains covalent bonds in the individual polyatomic ions. When ammonium nitrate is dissolved in water, it behaves as a strong electrolyte like the binary ionic compounds sodium chloride and potassium bromide. As we saw in Chapter 8, this occurs because when an ionic solid dissolves, the ions are freed to move independently and can conduct an electric current.

SECTION 12.2
REVIEW QUESTIONS

❶ How can the periodic table be used to predict how many electrons a certain metal atom loses to form an ion in an ionic compound? Provide two examples.

❷ How can we predict that oxygen will form an O^{2-} ion and not an O^{3-} ion?

❸ How do we use electron configurations to predict formulas of ionic compounds?

❹ Write the electron configurations for the pairs of atoms given below. Use them to predict the formula for an ionic compound formed from these elements.

   a. Mg, S
   b. K, Cl
   c. Cs, F
   d. Ba, Br

❺ Why are cations smaller than their parent atoms? Why are anions larger?

❻ How are polyatomic anions different from simple anions?

❼ Choose the elements from Groups 1, 2, 6 and 7 that form ions having the same electron configuration as argon. Write the symbols, with charges for these ions, and their common electron configuration.

RESEARCH LINKS
CLASSZONE.COM

412 • Chapter 12 • Chemical Bonding

---

b. K: [Ar]$4s^1$
   Cl: [Ne]$3s^23p^5$
   compound: KCl

c. Cs: [Xe]$6s^1$
   F: [He]$2s^22p^5$
   compound: CsF

d. Ba: [Xe]$6s^2$
   Br: [Ar]$4s^24p^5$
   compound: $BaBr_2$

5. Cations are smaller than their parent atoms because the electrons in the valence level are removed and the remaining electrons are pulled closer to the cation's nucleus by the positive charge imbalance. Anions are larger than their parent atoms because electrons are added, increasing the electron–electron repulsions and causing the electron

"cloud" to be larger than that of the parent atom.

6. Polyatomic ions contain covalently bonded atoms within the group of atoms that carry the charge. Simple ions are single atoms with electrons added or taken away.

7. K^+, Ca^{2+}, S^{2-}, Cl^-; $1s^22s^22p^63s^23p^6$

412 • Chapter 12 • Chemical Bonding

Lewis Structures

Objectives

- *To learn to write Lewis structures*
- *To learn to write Lewis structures for molecules with multiple bonds*

Key Terms

- Lewis structure
- Duet rule
- Octet rule
- Bonding pair
- Lone pairs (unshared pairs)
- Single bond
- Double bond
- Triple bond
- Resonance

A. Writing Lewis Structures

Bonding involves only the valence electrons of atoms. Valence electrons are transferred when a metal and a nonmetal react to form an ionic compound. Valence electrons are shared between nonmetals in covalent bonds.

The **Lewis structure** is a representation of a molecule that shows how the valence electrons are arranged among the atoms in the molecule. These representations are named after G. N. Lewis, who conceived the idea while lecturing to a class of general chemistry students in 1902. The rules for writing Lewis structures are based on observations of many molecules from which chemists have learned that the *most important requirement for the formation of a stable compound is that the atoms achieve noble gas electron configurations.*

We have already seen this rule operate in the reaction of metals and nonmetals to form binary ionic compounds. An example is the formation of KBr, where the K^+ ion has the [Ar] electron configuration and the Br^- ion has the [Kr] electron configuration.

In writing Lewis structures, we include only the valence electrons.

Using dots to represent valence electrons, we write the Lewis structure for KBr as follows:

K^+ $[\,:\!\overset{..}{\underset{..}{Br}}\!:\,]^-$

Noble gas   Noble gas
configuration [Ar]   configuration [Kr]

No dots are shown on the K^+ ion because it has lost its only valence electron (the $4s$ electron). The Br^- ion is shown with eight electrons because it has a filled valence shell.

Active Reading Question

Why do we show only valence electrons when drawing Lewis structures?

Next, we will consider Lewis structures for molecules with covalent bonds involving nonmetals in the first and second periods. The principle of achieving a noble gas electron configuration applies to these elements as follows:

⇒ Hydrogen forms stable molecules where it shares two electrons. That is, it follows a **duet rule**. For example, when two hydrogen atoms, each with one electron, combine to form the H_2 molecule, we have

---

Student Preparation

Assign students to read Section 12.3 and to answer the Review Questions at the end of the section before coming to class.

Active Learning
Team Learning Worksheet

After introducing the material in Section 12.3 in class, place students in groups and have them work together on **Section 12.3: Team Learning Worksheet.**

SECTION 12.3
GUIDE THE LEARNING

Homework

You may wish to assign these selected end-of-chapter problems as homework for this section: 30, 31, 32, 33a–b, 34a–b, 35c–d, 36, 37

Additional end-of-chapter problems can be used for extra practice.

12.3.A Writing Lewis Structures

Objective To learn to write Lewis structures

TEACHING TIP

Drawing Lewis structures provides a way for students to use their knowledge about electron configurations to predict bonding in covalent molecules.

Active Reading Question

The valence electrons are the electrons that are involved in bonding. They are the electrons that are either shared in covalent bonds or transferred in ionic bonds.

Lewis structure
A representation of a molecule or polyatomic ion showing how valence electrons are arranged among the atoms in the molecule or ion

nformation

Remember that the electrons in the highest principal energy level of an atom are called the valence electrons.

nformation

Lewis structures show only valence electrons.

TEACHING TIP

You can show why noble gases do not generally form compounds by drawing the Lewis structures for several noble gases.

By sharing electrons, each hydrogen in H_2 has, in effect, two electrons; that is, each hydrogen has a filled valence shell.

[He] configuration

⇨ Helium does not form bonds because its valence orbital is already filled; it is a noble gas. Helium has the electron configuration $1s^2$ and can be represented by the following Lewis structure:

He:

[He] configuration

information

Carbon, nitrogen, oxygen, and fluorine almost always obey the octet rule in stable molecules.

⇨ The second-row nonmetals carbon through fluorine form stable molecules when they are surrounded by enough electrons to fill the valence orbitals—that is, the one $2s$ and the three $2p$ orbitals. Eight electrons are required to fill these orbitals, so these elements typically obey the **octet rule**; they are surrounded by eight electrons. An example is the F_2 molecule, which has the following Lewis structure:

:F· ⟶ :F:F: ⟵ ·F:

F atom with seven F_2 F atom with seven
valence electrons   molecule   valence electrons

Bonding pair
A pair of electrons that are shared between two atoms forming a covalent or polar-covalent bond

Lone pair (unshared pair)
Electron pairs in a Lewis structure that are not involved in bonding

Note that each fluorine atom in F_2 is, in effect, surrounded by eight valence electrons, two of which are shared with the other atom. This is a **bonding pair** of electrons, as we discussed earlier. Each fluorine atom also has three pairs of electrons that are not involved in bonding. These are called **lone pairs** or **unshared pairs**.

⇨ Neon does not form bonds because it already has an octet of valence electrons (it is a noble gas). The Lewis structure is

:Ne:

Note that only the valence electrons $(2s^2 2p^6)$ of the neon atom are represented by the Lewis structure. The $1s^2$ electrons are core electrons and are not shown.

Next we want to develop some general procedures for writing Lewis structures for molecules. Remember that Lewis structures involve only the valence electrons on atoms, so before we proceed, we will review the relationship of an element's position on the periodic table to the number of valence electrons it has.

G. N. Lewis in his lab

414 • Chapter 12 • Chemical Bonding

Teaching Support
BACKGROUND INFORMATION

Lewis Structures: Comments about the Octet Rule

• The second-row elements C, N, O, and F should always be assumed to obey the octet rule.

• The second-row elements B and Be often have fewer than eight electrons around them in their compounds.

These electron-deficient compounds are very reactive.

• The second-row elements never exceed the octet rule, since their valence orbitals ($2s$ and $2p$) can accommodate only eight electrons.

• Third-row and heavier elements often satisfy the octet rule but can exceed the octet rule, presumably by using their empty valence d orbitals.

• When writing the Lewis structure for a molecule, satisfy the octet rule for the atoms first. If electrons remain after the octet rule has been satisfied, then place them on the elements having available d orbitals (elements in Period 3 or beyond).

Recall that the group number gives the total number of valence electrons. For example, all Group 6 elements have six valence electrons (valence configuration ns^2np^4).

Group 6

| O $2s^22p^4$ |
| S $3s^23p^4$ |
| Se $4s^24p^4$ |
| Te $5s^25p^4$ |

Similarly, all Group 7 elements have seven valence electrons (valence configuration ns^2np^5).

Group 7

| F $2s^22p^5$ |
| Cl $3s^23p^5$ |
| Br $4s^24p^5$ |
| I $5s^25p^5$ |

Let's Review

Writing the Lewis structure for a molecule

- We must include all the valence electrons from all atoms. The total number of electrons available is the sum of all the valence electrons from all the atoms in the molecule.

- Atoms that are bonded to each other share one or more pairs of electrons.

- The electrons are arranged so that each atom is surrounded by enough electrons to fill the valence orbitals of that atom. This means two electrons for hydrogen and eight electrons for second-row nonmetals.

12.3 • Lewis Structures • **415**

Meeting Individual Needs
ADVANCED LEARNERS

Have students explain why third-row nonmetals can sometimes form more bonds than the number predicted by the octet rule.

- The rules for writing Lewis structures help students consistently write correct Lewis structures. Students who do not follow these rules will be less successful in drawing correct Lewis structures, especially for more complex molecules.

- Emphasize that to write correct structures for molecules, it is necessary to sum all the valence electrons from all the atoms. Make sure that students do not attach valence electrons to individual atoms and then try to write a Lewis structure. This method can sometimes produce a correct structure, but often does not do so for molecules containing multiple bonds and for complex molecules.

EXAMPLE 12.2

More Examples

Write Lewis structures for each of the following molecules.

1. CCl_4

2. PH_3

```
      ..
     :Cl:              H—P—H
      |                    |
 ..   |   ..               H
:Cl—C—Cl:
 ..   |   ..
     :Cl:
      ..
```

The best way to make sure we arrive at the correct Lewis structure for a molecule is to use a systematic approach. We will use the approach summarized by the following rules.

Steps for Writing Lewis Structures

Step 1 Obtain the sum of the valence electrons from all of the atoms. Do not worry about keeping track of which electrons come from which atoms. It is the *total* number of valence electrons that is important.

Step 2 Use one pair of electrons to form a bond between each pair of bound atoms. For convenience, a line (instead of a pair of dots) is often used to indicate each pair of bonding electrons.

Step 3 Arrange the remaining electrons to satisfy the duet rule for hydrogen and the octet rule for each second-row element.

EXAMPLE 12.2

Writing Lewis Structures: Simple Molecules

Write the Lewis structure of the water molecule.

Solution

We will follow the steps listed above.

ℹ️ information

The number of valence electrons in an atom is the same as the group number on the periodic table for representative elements.

Step 1 Find the sum of the *valence* electrons for H_2O:

$$\begin{array}{ccccccc} 1 & + & 1 & + & 6 & = & 8 \text{ valence electron} \\ \uparrow & & \uparrow & & \uparrow & & \\ H & & H & & O & & \\ \text{(Group 1)} & & \text{(Group 1)} & & \text{(Group 6)} & & \end{array}$$

Step 2 Using a pair of electrons per bond, we draw in the two O—H bonds, using a line to indicate each pair of bonding electrons.

H—O—H

Note that H—O—H represents H : O : H.

Step 3 We arrange the remaining electrons around the atoms to achieve a noble gas electron configuration for each atom. Four electrons have been used in forming the two bonds, so four electrons $(8 - 4)$ remain to be distributed. Each hydrogen is satisfied with two electrons (duet rule), but oxygen needs eight electrons to have a noble gas electron configuration. So the remaining four electrons are added to oxygen as two lone pairs. Dots are used to represent the lone pairs.

```
        ..
 H—O—H    Lone pairs
        ..
```

ℹ️ information

A line is used to represent a shared pair of electrons (bonding electrons) and dots are used to represent unshared pairs.

This is the correct Lewis structure for the water molecule. Each hydrogen shares two electrons, and the oxygen has four electrons and shares four to give a total of eight.

```
 H  O  H
 ↑  ↑  ↑
2e⁻ 8e⁻ 2e⁻
```

Practice Problem • Exercise 12.2

Write the Lewis structure for HCl.

B. Lewis Structures of Molecules with Multiple Bonds

Now let's write the Lewis structure for carbon dioxide. Summing the valence electrons gives

$$4 + 6 + 6 = 16$$
$$\uparrow \qquad \uparrow \qquad \uparrow$$
$$C \qquad O \qquad O$$
(Group 4)   (Group 6)   (Group 6)

After forming a bond between the carbon and each oxygen,

O—C—O

we distribute the remaining electrons to achieve noble gas electron configurations on each atom. In this case, twelve electrons (16 − 4) remain after the bonds are drawn. The distribution of these electrons is determined by a trial-and-error process. We have six pairs of electrons to distribute. Suppose we try three pairs on each oxygen to give

Is this correct? To answer this question we need to check two things:

1. The total number of electrons. There are sixteen valence electrons in this structure, which is the correct number.

2. The octet rule for each atom. Each oxygen has eight electrons around it, but the carbon has only four. This cannot be the correct Lewis structure.

How can we arrange the sixteen available electrons to achieve an octet for each atom? Suppose we place two shared pairs between the carbon and each oxygen:

O⬭C⬭O
↑   ↑   ↑
8   8   8
electrons electrons electrons

Now each atom is surrounded by eight electrons, and the total number of electrons is sixteen, as required. This is the correct Lewis structure for carbon dioxide, which has two *double* bonds. A **single bond** involves two atoms sharing one electron pair. A **double bond** involves two atoms sharing two pairs of electrons.

In considering the Lewis structure for CO_2, you may have come up with

:O≡C—Ö: or   :Ö—C≡O:

Note that both of these structures have the required sixteen electrons and that both have octets of electrons around each atom (verify this for yourself). Both of these structures have a **triple bond** in which three electron pairs are shared. Are these valid Lewis structures for CO_2? Yes. So there really are three Lewis structures for CO_2:

:Ö—C≡O: Ö=C=Ö   :O≡C—Ö:

 information

:Ö—C—Ö:

represents

:Ö:C:Ö:

 information

Ö=C=Ö

represents

Ö::C::Ö

Single bond
A covalent or polar covalent bond in which one pair of electrons is shared by two atoms

Double bond
A covalent or polar covalent bond in which two pairs of electrons are shared by two atoms

Triple bond
A covalent or polar covalent bond in which three pairs of electrons are shared by two atoms

---

12.3 • Lewis Structures • **417**

- Stress that resonance structures must all be correct Lewis structures. Students may think they can draw one correct structure and other resonance structures that are incorrect Lewis structures.

- The concept of resonance offers an opportunity to discuss the limitations of the bonding model we have developed.

- Students often have more trouble writing Lewis structures for ions than writing them for molecules. They are not sure what to do with the charge and how many electrons are available for the Lewis structure.

MISCONCEPTION
Chemistry

Students often look at a species that has a negative charge and think that an electron has been removed.

Resonance
A condition occurring when more than one valid Lewis structure can be written for a particular molecule

 information

:C≡N:

represents

:C⫶⫶N:

This brings us to a new term, **resonance**. A molecule shows resonance when *more than one Lewis structure can be drawn for the molecule*. In such a case, we call the various Lewis structures *resonance structures*.

Of the three resonance structures for CO_2 shown, the one in the center with two double bonds most closely fits our experimental information about the CO_2 molecule. In this text we will not be concerned about how to choose which resonance structure for a molecule gives the "best" description of that molecule's properties.

Lewis Structures for Polyatomic Ions Next, let's consider the Lewis structure of the CN^- (cyanide) ion. Summing the valence electrons, we have

$$CN^-$$
$$4 + 5 + 1 = 10$$

Note that the negative charge means an extra electron must be added. After first drawing a single bond (C—N), we distribute the remaining electrons to achieve a noble gas configuration for each atom. Eight electrons remain to be distributed. We can try various possibilities, such as

C̈—N̈   or   :C̈—N: or   :C—N̈:

These structures are incorrect. To show why none is a valid Lewis structure, count the electrons around the C and N atoms. In the left structure, neither atom satisfies the octet rule. In the center structure, C has eight electrons but N has only four. In the right structure, the opposite is true. Remember that both atoms must simultaneously satisfy the octet rule. Therefore, the correct arrangement is

:C≡N:

CELEBRITY CHEMICAL   Capsaicin

The hot taste of peppers is from capsaicin.

Can you imagine why someone might add pepper to things like paint and fiber-optic cables? It's certainly not to flavor them so we can eat them! In fact, it's just the opposite. The idea is to use pepper as an environmentally safe animal deterrent.

The compound that gives pepper its characteristic "hot" taste is called capsaicin. Burlington Biomedical and Scientific Corporation in Farmingdale, New York, has found a way to manufacture a compound closely related to capsaicin that tastes painfully spicy and intensely bitter. One application for this compound is to add it to paint used for boats to prevent barnacles

from sticking to the surface. Other applications include adding capsaicin to fiber-optic cables to prevent rodents from gnawing on them and using it to coat sutures employed in animal surgery to prevent pets from disturbing a healing wound.

418 • Chapter 12 • Chemical Bonding

CELEBRITY CHEMICAL
Capsaicin

Encourage students to search the Internet to find out more about the sources of capsaicin and its use. One interesting idea is to research the production of Tabasco sauce in the United States.

Consider having students use the molecular structure to practice identifying bonding concepts. Ask

them to fill in any lone pairs of electrons that are not shown in the drawing.

When covering Section 12.4, capsaicin can be used to discuss shape. Students can identify the shape at each carbon or nitrogen in the chain. This activity provides an excellent opportunity to review resonance using the benzene ring as an example. Finally, you can ask students to identify atoms that have

shapes that differ from their electron pair arrangements.

Challenge students to build a model of capsaicin.

(Satisfy yourself that both carbon and nitrogen have eight electrons.) In this case, we have a triple bond between C and N, in which three electron pairs are shared. Because this is an anion, we indicate the charge outside of square brackets around the Lewis structure.

$$[:C{\equiv}N:]^-$$

Active Reading Question

When drawing a Lewis structure for a negatively charged ion, how do you determine the number of valence electrons that are present?

In summary, sometimes we need double or triple bonds to satisfy the octet rule. Writing Lewis structures is a trial-and-error process. Start with single bonds between the bonded atoms, and add multiple bonds as needed.

We will write the Lewis structure for NO_2^- in Example 12.3 to make sure the procedures for writing Lewis structures are clear.

EXAMPLE 12.3

Writing Lewis Structures: Resonance Structures

Write the Lewis structure for the NO_2^- anion.

Solution

Step 1 Find the sum of the valence electrons for NO_2^-.

Valence electrons: $6 + 5 + 6 + 1 = 18$ electrons
O   N   O   −1
                      charge

Step 2 Put in single bonds.

O—N—O

Step 3 Satisfy the octet rule. In placing the electrons, we find that there are two Lewis structures that satisfy the octet rule:

$$[\ddot{O}{=}N{-}\ddot{O}:]^- \quad \text{and} \quad [:\ddot{O}{-}N{=}\ddot{O}]^-$$

Verify that each atom in these structures is surrounded by an octet of electrons. Try some other arrangements to see whether other structures exist in which the eighteen electrons can be used to satisfy the octet rule.

It turns out that these are the only two that work. Note that this is another case in which resonance occurs; there are two valid Lewis structures.

Practice Problem • Exercise 12.3

Ozone is a very important constituent of the atmosphere. At upper levels, it protects us by absorbing high-energy radiation from the sun. Near the earth's surface, it produces harmful air pollution. Write the Lewis structure for ozone, O_3.

Now let's consider a few more cases in Example 12.4.

Active Reading Question

Find the total number of valence electrons in each atom in the ion and then add electrons to account for the negative charge. For example, if the charge of the ion is 1–, add one electron to the total; if the charge is 2–, add two electrons to the total.

TEACHING TIP

While writing Lewis structures is a trial-and-error process, some trials are better than others and can be predicted. For example, in most cases, carbon will have four bonds and no lone pairs, nitrogen will have three bonds and one lone pair, oxygen will have two bonds and two lone pairs, and halogens will have one bond and three lone pairs. These rules are not absolute (take carbon monoxide, for example), but they provide a good start.

EXAMPLE 12.3

More Examples

Write Lewis structures for each of the following molecules.

1. SO_3

2. CO_3^{2-}

Answer to Practice Problem 12.3

Step 1 O_3: $3(6) = 18$ valence electrons

Step 2 O—O—O

Step 3

$$\ddot{O}{=}\ddot{O}{-}\ddot{O}: \quad \text{and} \quad :\ddot{O}{-}\ddot{O}{=}\ddot{O}$$

This molecule shows resonance (it has two valid Lewis structures).

EXAMPLE 12.4

More Examples

Give the Lewis structure for each of the following:

1. NI_3

$$\ddot{\underset{\cdot\cdot}{I}}-N-\ddot{\underset{\cdot\cdot}{I}}$$
$$|$$
$$\ddot{\underset{\cdot\cdot}{I}}$$

2. NO^+

$$[\mathbf{:}N\!\!\equiv\!\!O\mathbf{:}]^+$$

3. $PO_4{}^{3-}$

$$\begin{bmatrix} & \ddot{O}\mathbf{:} & \\ \mathbf{:}\ddot{O}-P-\ddot{O}\mathbf{:} \\ & \ddot{O}\mathbf{:} & \end{bmatrix}^{3-}$$

4. SCN^-

(C is the central atom)

$$\left[\mathbf{:}\ddot{\underset{\cdot\cdot}{S}}-C\!\!\equiv\!\!N\mathbf{:}\right]^-$$

EXAMPLE 12.4
Writing Lewis Structures: Summary

Give the Lewis structure for each of the following:

a. HF   e. CF_4
b. N_2 f. NO^+
c. NH_3 g. $NO_3{}^-$
d. CH_4

Solution

In each case, we apply the three steps for writing Lewis structures. Recall that lines are used to indicate shared electron pairs and that dots are used to indicate nonbonding pairs (lone pairs). The table below summarizes our results.

Molecule or Ion	Total Valence Electrons	Draw Single Bonds	Calculate Number of Electrons Remaining	Use Remaining Electrons to Achieve Noble Gas Configurations	Check	
					Atom	Electrons
HF	$1 + 7 = 8$	H—F	$8 - 2 = 6$	H—F̈:	H / F	2 / 8
N_2	$5 + 5 = 10$	N—N	$10 - 2 = 8$	:N≡N:	N	8
NH_3	$5 + 3(1) = 8$	H—N—H / H	$8 - 6 = 2$	H—N̈—H / H	H / N	2 / 8
CH_4	$4 + 4(1) = 8$	H—C—H (H top/bottom)	$8 - 8 = 0$	H—C—H (H top/bottom)	H / C	2 / 8
CF_4	$4 + 4(7) = 32$	F—C—F (F top/bottom)	$32 - 8 = 24$	:F̈—C—F̈: (F top/bottom)	F / C	8 / 8
NO^+	$5 + 6 - 1 = 10$	N—O	$10 - 2 = 8$	$[\mathbf{:}N\!\!\equiv\!\!O\mathbf{:}]^+$	N / O	8 / 8
$NO_3{}^-$	$5 + 3(6) + 1 = 24$	O—N—O (O top/bottom)	$24 - 6 = 18$	$NO_3{}^-$ shows resonance	N / O	8 / 8

Practice Problem • Exercise 12.4

Write the Lewis structures for the following molecules:

a. NF_3 f. SO_4^{2-}
b. O_2 g. NH_4^+
c. CO   h. ClO_3^-
d. PH_3 i. SO_2
e. H_2S

information

In a molecule of a binary compounds where there is one atom of a given element and several atoms of a second element, the single atom is almost always the central atom.

Answer to Practice Problem 12.4

See page 439a for answer.

TEACHING TIPS

• Students are often surprised to learn that the octet rule has exceptions. Remind them that many elements usually obey the octet rule. If an atom that can exceed the octet rule is bonded to atoms that obey the octet rule, the available electrons should be distributed to form octets on all atoms. Any remaining electrons can then be placed on atoms that can exceed the octet rule.

• We do not discuss exceptions in which the octet rule is exceeded. The Critical Thinking question in Section 12.4 does allude to this possibility, and it is mentioned again in the Something Extra section of the Models of Molecules Laboratory.

Remember that when writing Lewis structures, you don't have to worry about which electrons come from which atoms in a molecule. It is best to think of a molecule as a new entity that uses all of the available valence electrons from the various atoms to achieve the strongest possible bonds. Think of the valence electrons as belonging to the molecule, rather than to the individual atoms. Simply distribute the valence electrons so that noble gas electron configurations are obtained for each atom, without regard to the origin of each particular electron.

Some Exceptions to the Octet Rule

The idea that covalent bonding can be predicted by achieving noble gas electron configurations for all atoms is a simple and very successful idea. The rules we have used for Lewis structures describe correctly the bonding in most molecules. However, with such a simple model, we should expect some exceptions. Boron, for example, tends to form compounds in which the boron atom has fewer than eight electrons around it—that is, it does not have a complete octet. Boron trifluoride, BF_3, a gas at normal temperatures and pressures, reacts very energetically with molecules such as water and ammonia that have unshared electron pairs (lone pairs).

The violent reactivity of BF_3 with electron-rich molecules arises because the boron atom is electron-deficient. The Lewis structure that seems most consistent with the properties of BF_3 (twenty-four valence electrons) is

Note that in this structure the boron atom has only six electrons around it. The octet rule for boron could be satisfied by drawing a structure with a double bond between the boron and one of the fluorines. However, experiments indicate that each B—F bond is a single bond in accordance with the above Lewis structure. This structure is also consistent with the reactivity of BF_3 with electron-rich molecules. For example, BF_3 reacts vigorously with NH_3 to form H_3NBF_3.

12.3 • Lewis Structures • **421**

(continued)

correctly predicts the configurations for most atoms, chromium and copper do not agree with its predictions. Detailed studies show that the configurations of chromium and copper result from complex electron interactions that are not taken into account in the simple model. This disagreement does not mean that we should discard the simple model that is so useful for most atoms. Instead, we must

apply it with caution and not expect it to be correct in every case.

• We often learn much more from a model when it is wrong than when it is right. If a model makes a wrong prediction, it usually means we do not understand some fundamental characteristic of nature. We often learn by making mistakes.

The molecule NO_2 has an odd number of valence electrons $(5 + 6 + 6 = 17)$. Lewis structures are drawn with pairs of electrons.

SECTION 12.3
ASSESS

 SECTION 12.3
Review Questions

1. The octet rule forms the basis for bonding because eight electrons are required to complete the s and p orbitals. The rule is not a sextet rule because the s and p orbitals must both be complete to form a stable atom within a molecule.

2. A bonding pair of electrons is involved in bonding and a lone pair of electrons is not. Otherwise, there is no difference between the two.

3. Only two electrons fit into an orbital. When orbitals overlap, atoms share the electrons in them, which results in shared pairs or multiples of pairs.

4. a. ClF; VE = 14;

b. Br_2; VE = 14;

c. H_2S; VE = 8;

d. O_3; VE = 18;

e. CH_4; VE = 8;

f. C_2H_6; VE = 14;

$$H-N: + B-F: \rightarrow H-N-B-F:$$

Note that in the product H_3NBF_3, which is very stable, boron has an octet of electrons. It is also characteristic of beryllium to form molecules where the beryllium atom is electron-deficient.

Any molecule that contains an odd number of electrons does not conform to our rules for Lewis structures. For example, NO and NO_2 have eleven and seventeen valence electrons, respectively, and conventional Lewis structures cannot be drawn for these cases.

Even though there are exceptions, most molecules can be described by Lewis structures in which all the atoms have noble gas electron configurations, and this is a very useful model for chemists.

Active Reading Question

Why is there no conventional Lewis structure for the molecule NO_2?

SECTION 12.3
REVIEW QUESTIONS

❶ Why is bonding based primarily on an octet rule? Why not a sextet rule?

❷ What is the difference between a bonding pair of electrons and a lone pair of electrons?

❸ Why do pairs of atoms share pairs (or multiples of pairs) of electrons? Why not share odd numbers?

❹ For each molecule below, do the following:
  i. Give the sum of the valence electrons for all atoms.
  ii. Draw the Lewis structure.
  iii. Circle the octet (or duet) for each atom in the structure.
  iv. Include any resonance structures.
   a. ClF
   b. Br_2
   c. H_2S
   d. O_3
   e. CH_4
   f. C_2H_6
   g. HCN
   h. CO

RESEARCH LINKS
CLASSZONE.COM

g. HCN; VE = 10;

h. CO; VE = 10;

Structures of Molecules

Objectives

- *To understand molecular structure and bond angles*
- *To learn to predict molecular geometry from the number of electron pairs*
- *To learn to apply the VSEPR model to molecules with double bonds*

A. Molecular Structure

So far in this chapter we have considered the Lewis structures of molecules. These structures represent the arrangement of the *valence electrons* in a molecule. We use the word *structure* in another way when we talk about the **molecular structure** or **geometric structure** of a molecule. These terms refer to the three-dimensional arrangement of the *atoms* in a molecule. For example, the water molecule is known to have the molecular structure

which is often called "bent" or "V-shaped." To describe the structure more precisely, we often specify the *bond angle*. For the H_2O molecule the bond angle is about 105°.

On the other hand, some molecules exhibit a **linear structure** (all atoms in a line). An example is the CO_2 molecule.

Note that a linear molecule has a 180° bond angle.

A third type of molecular structure is illustrated by BF_3, which is planar or flat (all four atoms in the same plane) with 120° bond angles.

 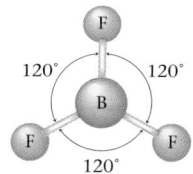

The name usually given to this structure is **trigonal planar**, although triangular might seem to make more sense.

Another type of molecular structure is illustrated by methane, CH_4. This molecule has the molecular structure called a **tetrahedral structure** or a *tetrahedron*.

Key Terms

- Molecular structure (geometric structure)
- Linear structure
- Trigonal planar structure
- Tetrahedral structure
- Valence shell electron pair repulsion (VSEPR) model
- Trigonal pyramid

Molecular structure (geometric structure) The three-dimensional arrangement of atoms in a molecule

---

SECTION 12.4
INTRODUCE

Student Preparation

Assign students to read Section 12.4 and to answer the Review Questions at the end of the section before coming to class.

 Active Learning
Team Learning Worksheet

After introducing the material in Section 12.4 in class, place students in groups and have them work together on **Section 12.4: Team Learning Worksheet.**

SECTION 12.4
GUIDE THE LEARNING

Homework

You may wish to assign these selected end-of-chapter problems as homework for this section: 39, 41, 42, 43, 44, 46, 47, 48, 49, 51, 52

Additional end-of-chapter problems can be used for extra practice.

12.4.A Molecular Structure
Objective To understand molecular structure and bond angles

TEACHING TIPS

- Use models in class to demonstrate each of the shapes in this section. It is difficult for students to visualize the shapes of molecules without models.

- The Hands-On Chemistry, "Geometric Balloons," can be used as a class demonstration for this section.

- Students can make models at home using toothpicks and gumdrops or marshmallows to help them with problems.

CHEMISTRY IN YOUR WORLD

Science, Technology, and Society

Taste—It's the Structure That Counts

Why do certain substances taste sweet, sour, bitter, or salty? Of course, it has to do with the taste buds on our tongues. But how do these taste buds work? For example, why does sugar taste sweet to us? The answer to this question remains elusive, but it does seem clear that sweet taste depends on how certain molecules fit the "sweet receptors" in our taste buds.

One of the mysteries of the sweet taste sensation is the wide variety of molecules that tastes sweet. The chemical structure of common table sugar (called sucrose) is shown on the right.

Sugar cubes are pure sucrose.

Sucrose

Aspartame
(NutraSweet)

One artificial sweetener, aspartame, is used in many products including candy and diet soda. Some people are allergic to aspartame.

Another widely used artificial sweetener is sucralose which is made by modifying sucrose (compare the structure of sucralose to sucrose shown above). Look at the groups with blue circles in each structure. Sucralose is 600 times as sweet as sucrose and is used to sweeten beverages, baked goods, yogurt, and desserts.

Sucralose
(Splenda)

Some brands of yogurt are sweetened with sucralose instead of sugar.

Chemistry in Your World

Taste—It's the Structure That Counts

The three most common artificial sweeteners were all discovered by accident. Saccharin was discovered in 1879 at Johns Hopkins University in the laboratory of noted nineteenth-century chemist Ira Remsen. An associate of Remsen, Mr. Fahlberg, noticed that a substance he had prepared and spilled on his hands tasted unusually sweet. Fahlberg perfected a commercial synthesis process and took out a patent on the substance he named saccharin after *saccharum,* the Latin word for sugar.

In 1937, Michael Sveda, a graduate student at the University of Illinois, was preparing a series of sulfamate compounds because they were thought to have interesting pharmacological properties. Sveda noticed a markedly sweet taste on a cigarette he was smoking and was able to trace the taste to the sodium cyclohexylsulfamate (sodium cyclamate) compound he had prepared.

12

The blue lines shown connecting the H atoms in the center structure above define the four identical triangular faces of the tetrahedron.

In the next section we will discuss these various molecular structures in more detail and learn how to predict the molecular structure of a molecule by looking at the molecule's Lewis structure.

B. The VSEPR Model

The structures of molecules play a very important role in determining their properties. For example, as we can see in the "Chemistry In Your World" feature, taste is directly related to molecular structure. Structure is particularly important for biological molecules; a slight change in the structure of a large biomolecule can completely destroy its usefulness to a cell and may even change the cell from a normal one to a cancerous one.

Many experimental methods now exist for determining the molecular structure of a molecule—that is, the three-dimensional arrangement of the atoms. These methods must be used when accurate information about the structure is required. However, it is often useful to be able to predict the *approximate* molecular structure of a molecule. Now we will consider a simple model that allows us to do this. The **valence shell electron pair repulsion (VSEPR) model** is useful for predicting the molecular structures of molecules formed from nonmetals. The main idea of this model is that

> The structure around a given atom is determined by minimizing repulsions between electron pairs.

This means that the bonding and nonbonding electron pairs (lone pairs) around a given atom are positioned *as far apart as possible*.

Two Pairs of Electrons To see how this model works, we will first consider the molecule $BeCl_2$, which has the following Lewis structure (it is an exception to the octet rule):

$$:\ddot{C}l-Be-\ddot{C}l:$$

Note that there are two pairs of electrons around the beryllium atom. What arrangement of these electron pairs allows them to be as far apart as possible to minimize the repulsions? The best arrangement places the pairs on opposite sides of the beryllium atom at 180° from each other.

$$\underset{180°}{-Be-}$$

This is the maximum possible separation for two electron pairs. Now that we have determined the optimal arrangement of the electron pairs around the central atom, we can specify the molecular structure of $BeCl_2$, that is, the

Valence shell electron pair repulsion (VSEPR) model
A model used to predict molecular geometry. Based on the idea that pairs of electrons surrounding an atom repel each other and that the atoms in a molecule are positioned to minimize this repulsion

12.4 • Structures of Molecules • **425**

12.4.B The VSEPR Model
Objective To learn to predict molecular geometry from the number of electron pairs

 TEACHING TIPS

• When teaching the VSEPR model, stress the difference between the arrangement of the electron pairs and the molecular structure. Students can easily confuse the two.

• Point out the differences between $BeCl_2$ and water. This distinction will help students see the difference between electron pair structure and molecular shape. Many students do not understand why water has a bent shape and $BeCl_2$ is linear.

TECHNOLOGY

 Animation
VSEPR: Two Electron Pair

(continued)

The corresponding calcium salt was also sweet, and both compounds were widely used in artificial sweeteners (often mixed with saccharin) until 1970, when the U.S. FDA banned cyclamates because of their tetrogenic effects in animals. Cyclamates are still used in many other countries as artificial sweeteners.

Aspartame was discovered by accident by chemist James L. Schlatter while working at G. D. Searle in 1965. Schlatter had prepared

aspartame as an intermediate. A methanol solution of the material bumped onto the outside of its flask, and Schlatter accidently got some of it on his hands. When he subsequently licked his finger to pick up a piece of paper, Schlatter noticed an extremely sweet taste. He traced this taste to the dipeptide, which eventually became the basis for a multibillion-dollar business.

We assume that pairs of valence electrons (bonding pairs and lone pairs) will distribute themselves to minimize repulsions. For example, three pairs will distribute themselves on a plane 120° apart from one another. The molecule BF_3 will have a trigonal planar shape.

TECHNOLOGY

Animations
VSEPR: Three Electron Pair
VSEPR: Four Electron Pair

---

positions of the atoms. Because each electron pair on beryllium is shared with a chlorine atom, the molecule has a *linear structure* with a 180° bond angle.

$$:\overset{..}{\underset{..}{Cl}}\text{—}Be\text{—}\overset{..}{\underset{..}{Cl}}:$$
180°

> Whenever two pairs of electrons are present around an atom, they should always be placed at an angle of 180° to each other to give a linear arrangement.

 Active Reading Question

> **What is the main idea of the valence shell electron pair repulsion (VSEPR) model? How does it help us determine the shape of a molecule?**

Three Pairs of Electrons Next let's consider BF_3, which has the following Lewis structure (it is another exception to the octet rule):

$$:\overset{..}{\underset{..}{F}}\text{—}B\text{—}\overset{..}{\underset{..}{F}}:$$

Here the boron atom is surrounded by three pairs of electrons. What arrangement minimizes the repulsions among the three pairs of electrons? Here the greatest distance between the electron pairs is achieved by angles of 120°.

120° B 120°
120°

Because each of the electron pairs is shared with a fluorine atom, the molecular structure is

F 120° B 120° F   or   F---B---F
120°

This is a planar (flat) molecule with a triangular arrangement of F atoms, commonly described as a trigonal planar structure.

> Whenever three pairs of electrons are present around an atom, they should always be placed at the corners of a triangle (in a plane at an angle of 120° to each other).

Four Pairs of Electrons Next let's consider the methane molecule, which has the Lewis structure

H—C—H   or   H:C:H

Hands-On Chemistry
MINI-LAB

Geometric Balloons

Materials Each student/group will need nine uninflated balloons. You can decrease the number of balloons used by not having each group make each geometry.

Purpose Students will see three-dimensional models of simple molecules.

Discussion This activity is especially good for understanding tetrahedral geometry because this geometry is now seen to be "natural." While model kits are helpful, the angles are predetermined. In this exercise, students see that the geometries discussed in the book occur simply because the balloons cannot occupy the same space. This is analogous to saying that electrons repel each other and electron pairs try to get as far apart from one another as possible. Thus the

knot represents the center atom, and each balloon represents an electron pair.

In the case of three balloons, if one is a lone pair, the shape is bent or V-shaped (as with SO_2); if there are two lone pairs, it is linear (as with CO_2). With four balloons, if there is one lone pair, the shape is trigonal pyramidal (as with NH_3); with two lone pairs, the shape is bent or V-shaped (as with H_2O); with three lone pairs, the shape is linear (like HCl).

HANDS-ON CHEMISTRY • MINI-LAB •

Geometric Balloons

Materials
• Nine round balloons

Procedure

1. Obtain nine round balloons.

2. Blow up all of the balloons to approximately the same size and tie each one.

3. Tie two of the balloons together. Then tie three of the remaining balloons together. Tie the final four balloons together

4. Observe the geometry of each of the balloon figures. What are the angles between each balloon for each balloon figure?

Results/Analysis

1. Relate your findings to VSEPR theory. What does the knot in the center of each cluster represent? What does each balloon represent? Why do these geometries occur naturally?

2. Consider the cluster with three balloons. What is the arrangement of atoms (shape) if one balloon represents a lone pair of electrons? What if there were two lone pairs of electrons?

3. Consider the cluster with four balloons. What is the arrangement of atoms (shape) if one balloon represents a lone pair of electrons? What if there were two lone pairs of electrons? What if there were three lone pairs of electrons?

There are four pairs of electrons around the central carbon atom. What arrangement of these electron pairs best minimizes the repulsions? First we try a square planar arrangement:

The carbon atom and the electron pairs are all in a plane represented by the surface of the paper, and the angles between the pairs are all 90°.

Is there another arrangement with angles greater than 90° that would put the electron pairs even farther away from each other? The answer is yes. We can get larger angles than 90° by using the following three-dimensional structure, which has angles of approximately 109.5°.

In this drawing the wedge indicates a position above the surface of the paper and the dashed lines indicate positions behind that surface. The solid line indicates a position on the surface of the page. The figure formed by connecting the lines is called a tetrahedron, so we call this arrangement of electron pairs the *tetrahedral arrangement*.

This is the maximum possible separation of four pairs around a given atom.

> Whenever four pairs of electrons are present around an atom, they should always be placed at the corners of a tetrahedron (the tetrahedral arrangement).

CRITICAL THINKING

You have seen that molecules with four electron pairs, such as CH_4, are tetrahedral.

What if a molecule had six electron pairs like SF_6? Predict the geometry and bond angles of SF_6.

*i*nformation

A tetrahedron has four equal triangular faces.

(continued)

Many students initially believe that a central atom with four other atoms around it will naturally form a square planar geometry. This activity can be used to confront this misconception. Once the tetrahedral geometry is formed naturally, you can show that it requires an input of energy to make a square planar geometry. Thus the square planar geometry is higher in energy and therefore less stable. In addition, if you drop the square planar geometry on the floor, it naturally converts back to the tetrahedral geometry.

If you wish, have students do five balloons (trigonal bipyramid, as with PCl_5) or six balloons (octahedral, as with SF_6). These geometries are not in the text. It is probably best to focus only on molecules that do not exceed the octet rule at this point. The reason for molecules exceeding the octet rule (the *d* orbitals are involved) is considered to be wrong by many chemists and it is not necessary to introduce this issue here.

EXAMPLE 12.5

More Examples

Describe the molecular structure (shape) of the following molecules using the VSEPR model.

1. Cl_2O
   Bent (V-shaped)

2. N_2O (N is a central atom)
   Linear

 Animation
VSEPR

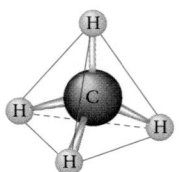

Figure 12.9
The molecular structure of methane. The tetrahedral arrangement of electron pairs produces a tetrahedral arrangement of hydrogen atoms.

Now that we have the arrangement of electron pairs that gives the least repulsion, we can determine the positions of the atoms and thus the molecular structure of CH_4. In methane each of the four electron pairs is shared between the carbon atom and a hydrogen atom. Thus the hydrogen atoms are placed as shown in **Figure 12.9,** and the molecule has a tetrahedral structure with the carbon atom at the center.

Recall that the main idea of the VSEPR model is to find the arrangement of electron pairs around the central atom that minimizes the repulsions. Then we can determine the *molecular structure* by knowing how the electron pairs are shared with the peripheral atoms. A systematic procedure for using the VSEPR model to predict the structure of a molecule is outlined here.

Steps for Predicting Molecular Structure Using the VSEPR Model

Step 1 Draw the Lewis structure for the molecule.

Step 2 Count the electron pairs and arrange them in the way that minimizes repulsions (that is, put the pairs as far apart as possible).

Step 3 Determine the positions of the atoms from the way the electron pairs are shared.

Step 4 Determine the name of the molecular structure from the positions of the *atoms*.

EXAMPLE 12.5

Predicting Molecular Structure Using the VSEPR Model, I

Ammonia, NH_3, is used as a fertilizer (injected into the soil) and as a household cleaner (in aqueous solution). Predict the structure of ammonia using the VSEPR model.

Solution

Step 1 Draw the Lewis structure.

$$H-\overset{\displaystyle\cdot\cdot}{N}-H$$
$$|$$
$$H$$

Step 2 Count the pairs of electrons and arrange them to minimize repulsions. The NH_3 molecule has four pairs of electrons around the N atom: three bonding pairs and one nonbonding pair. From the discussion of the methane molecule, we know that the best arrangement of four electron pairs is the tetrahedral structure shown in Figure 12.10a.

Step 3 Determine the positions of the atoms. The three H atoms share electron pairs as shown in Figure 12.10c.

Step 4 Name the molecular structure. It is very important to recognize that the name of the molecular structure is always based on the *positions of the atoms. The placement of the electron pairs determines the structure, but the name is based on the positions of the atoms.* Thus it is incorrect to say that the NH_3 molecule is tetrahedral. It has a tetrahedral arrangement of electron pairs but *not* a tetrahedral arrangement of atoms. The molecular structure of ammonia is a **trigonal pyramid** (one side is different from the other three) rather than a tetrahedron.

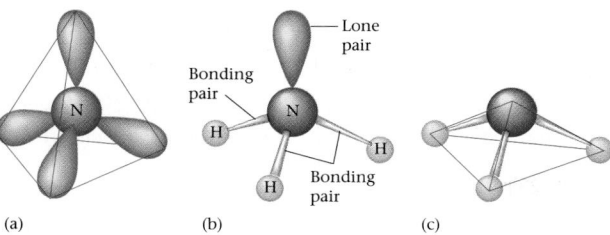
(a)   (b)   (c)

Figure 12.10
(a) The tetrahedral arrangement of electron pairs around the nitrogen atom in the ammonia molecule. (b) Three of the electron pairs around nitrogen are shared with hydrogen atoms as shown, and one is a lone pair. Although the arrangement of *electron pairs* is tetrahedral, as in the methane molecule, the hydrogen atoms in the ammonia molecule occupy only three corners of the tetrahedron. A lone pair occupies the fourth corner (c) The NH_3 molecule has the trigonal pyramid structure (a pyramid with a triangle as a base).

EXAMPLE 12.6

Predicting Molecular Structure Using the VSEPR Model, II

Describe the molecular structure of the water molecule.

Solution

Step 1 The Lewis structure for water is:

H—Ö—H

Step 2 There are four pairs of electrons: two bonding pairs and two nonbonding pairs. To minimize repulsions, these are best arranged in a tetrahedral structure as shown in **Figure 12.11a**.

Step 3 Although H_2O has a tetrahedral arrangement of *electron pairs*, it is *not a tetrahedral molecule*. The *atoms* in the H_2O molecule form a V-shape, as shown in **Figure 12.11b** and **c.**

Step 4 The molecular structure is called V-shaped or bent.

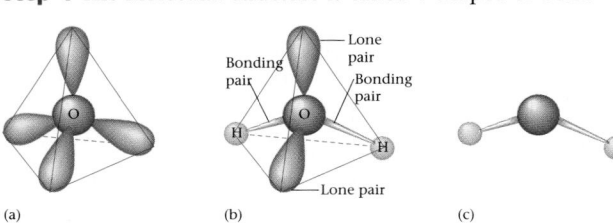
(a)   (b)   (c)

Figure 12.11
(a) The tetrahedral arrangement of the four electron pairs around oxygen in the water molecule. (b) Two of the electron pairs are shared between oxygen and the hydrogen atoms, and two are lone pairs. (c) The V-shaped molecular structure of the water molecule.

✔ **Practice Problem • Exercise 12.6**

Predict the arrangement of electron pairs around the central atom. Then sketch and name the molecular structure for each of the following molecules or ions.

a. NH_4^+ c. NF_3 e. ClO_3^-
b. SO_4^{2-} d. H_2S f. BeF_2

CRITICAL
THINKING

If NH_3 did not have a lone pair of electrons, the molecule would be an exception to the octet rule, as BF_3 is. The bonded pairs would spread so that they are 120° apart, and NH_3 would have a trigonal planar structure.

More Examples

Describe the molecular structure (shape) of the following molecules using the VSEPR model.

1. H_2Se
   Bent (V-shaped)

2. ClO_4^-
   Tetrahedral

✔ **Answer to Practice Problem 12.6**

See page 439b for answer.

CRITICAL
THINKING ❓

What if NH_3 did not have a lone pair? How would that change its molecular structure?

We need to know the total number of electron pairs (bonding pairs and lone pairs) around an atom before we can determine the shape of the molecule.

12.4.C Molecules with Double Bonds

Objective To learn to apply the VSEPR model to molecules with double bonds

⚠️ **LABORATORY**
EXPERIMENT 50:
Models of Molecules

Tools for Predicting Molecular Structure Using the VSEPR Model

- Two pairs of electrons on a central atom in a molecule are always placed 180° apart. This is a linear arrangement of pairs.
- Three pairs of electrons on a central atom in a molecule are always placed 120° apart in the same plane as the central atom. This is a trigonal planar (triangular) arrangement of pairs.
- Four pairs of electrons on a central atom in a molecule are always placed 109.5° apart. This is a tetrahedral arrangement of electron pairs.
- When *every pair* of electrons on the central atom is *shared* with another atom, the molecular structure has the same name as the arrangement of electron pairs.

Number of Pairs	Name of Arrangement
2	linear
3	trigonal planar
4	tetrahedral

- When one or more of the electron pairs around a central atom are unshared (lone pairs), the name for the molecular structure is *different* from that for the arrangement of electron pairs (see cases 4 and 5 in Table 12.4).

🔖 **Active Reading Question**

Why must we draw the Lewis structure for a molecule before trying to determine its shape?

The various cases we have considered are summarized in **Table 12.4** on the following page.

C. Molecules with Double Bonds

Up to this point we have applied the VSEPR model only to molecules (and ions) that contain single bonds. Now we will show that this model applies equally well to species with one or more double bonds. We will develop the procedures for dealing with molecules with double bonds by considering examples whose structures are known.

First we will examine the structure of carbon dioxide, a substance that may be contributing to the warming of Earth. The carbon dioxide molecule has the Lewis structure:

Carbon dioxide is known by experiment to be a linear molecule. That is, it has a 180° bond angle.

430 • Chapter 12 • Chemical Bonding

TECHNOLOGY

📧 Table 12.4

Arrangement of Electron Pairs and the Resulting Molecular Structures for Two, Three, and Four Electron Pairs can be used when having students predict molecular structures in class.

Table 12.4

Arrangements of Electron Pairs and the Resulting Molecular Structures for Two, Three, and Four Electron Pairs

Case	Number of Electron Pairs	Bonds	Electron Pair Arrangement	Partial Lewis Structure	Molecular Structure	Example
1	2	2	180° Linear	A — B — A	A–B–A Linear	F — Be — F BeF_2
2	3	3	120° Trigonal planar (triangular)	A, B, A, A	Trigonal planar (triangular)	F, B, F, F BF_3
3	4	4	109.5°	A — B — A, A, A	Tetrahedral	H, C, H, H, H CH_4
4	4	3	109.5°	A — B — A, A	Trigonal pyramid	H, N, H, H NH_3
5	4	2	109.5° Tetrahedral	A — B — A	Bent or V-shaped	H, O, H

Recall that two electron pairs around a central atom can minimize their mutual repulsions by taking positions on opposite sides of the atom (at 180° from each other). This causes a molecule like $BeCl_2$, which has the Lewis structure

:Cl—Be—Cl:

to have a linear structure. Now recall that CO_2 has two double bonds and is known to be linear, so the double bonds must be at 180° from each other. Therefore, we conclude that each double bond in this molecule acts *effectively* as one repulsive unit. This conclusion makes sense if we think of a bond in terms of an electron density "cloud" between two atoms. For example, we can picture the single bonds in $BeCl_2$ as follows:

Cl   Be   Cl

12.4 • Structures of Molecules • **431**

Meeting Individual Needs

INCLUSION STRATEGIES

To help students better envision bond angles, have them use protractors to draw angle measures, such as 180°, 120°, and 109.5°. You may want to review how to use a protractor. Have students determine the angle measures between various objects in the classroom.

The minimum repulsion between these two electron density clouds occurs when they are on opposite sides of the Be atom (180° angle between them).

Each double bond in CO_2 involves the sharing of four electrons between the carbon atom and an oxygen atom. Thus we might expect the bonding cloud to be "fatter" than for a single bond:

However, the repulsive effects of these two clouds produce the same result as for single bonds; the bonding clouds have minimum repulsions when they are positioned on opposite sides of the carbon. The bond angle is 180°, and so the molecule is linear:

In summary, examination of CO_2 leads us to the conclusion that in using the VSEPR model for molecules with double bonds, each double bond should be treated the same as a single bond. In other words, although a double bond involves four electrons, these electrons are restricted to the space between a given pair of atoms. Therefore, these four electrons do not function as two independent pairs but are "tied together" to form one effective repulsive unit.

We reach this same conclusion by considering the known structures of other molecules that contain double bonds. For example, consider the ozone molecule, which has eighteen valence electrons and exhibits two resonance structures:

$$:\ddot{O}-\ddot{O}=\ddot{O}: \longleftrightarrow :\ddot{O}=\ddot{O}-\ddot{O}:$$

The ozone molecule is known to have a bond angle close to 120°. Recall that 120° angles represent the minimum repulsion for three pairs of electrons.

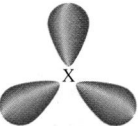

This indicates that the double bond in the ozone molecule is behaving as one effective repulsive unit:

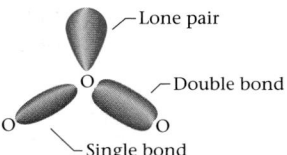

When using the VSEPR model to predict the molecular geometry of a molecule, a double bond is counted the same as a single electron pair.

Thus CO_2 has two "effective pairs" that lead to its linear structure, whereas O_3 has three "effective pairs" that lead to its bent structure with a 120° bond angle. Therefore, to use the VSEPR model for molecules (or ions) that have double bonds, we use the same tools as those given on p. 430, but we count any double bond the same as a single electron pair. Although we have not shown it here, triple bonds also count as one repulsive unit in applying the VSEPR model.

EXAMPLE 12.7

Predicting Molecular Structure Using the VSEPR Model, III

Predict the structure of the nitrate ion.

Solution

Step 1 The Lewis structures for NO_3^- are

Step 2 In each resonance structure there are effectively three pairs of electrons: the two single bonds and the double bond (which counts as one pair). These three "effective pairs" will require a trigonal planar arrangement (120° angles).

Step 3 The atoms are all in a plane, with the nitrogen at the center and the three oxygens at the corners of a triangle (trigonal planar arrangement).

Step 4 The NO_3^- ion has a trigonal planar structure.

SECTION 12.3
REVIEW QUESTIONS

❶ How does drawing a Lewis structure for a molecule help in determining its molecular shape?

❷ When is the molecular structure for a molecule the same as the arrangement of electron pairs?

❸ What causes the name for the molecular structure to be different from the name for the arrangement of electron pairs?

❹ If double bonds contain four electrons instead of two, why should they be treated the same as single bonds when determining molecular structure?

❺ Predict the molecular structure for each of the following molecules or ions.

  a. SO_3^{2-}

  b. HCN

  c. Cl_2O

  d. PCl_3

RESEARCH LINKS
CLASSZONE.COM

12.4 • Structures of Molecules • **433**

EXAMPLE 12.7

More Examples

Describe the molecular structure (shape) of the following molecules using the VSEPR model.

1. C_2H_2
   Linear

2. CO_3^{2-}
   Trigonal planar

SECTION 12.4
ASSESS

SECTION 12.4
Review Questions

1. The Lewis structure shows how many electron pairs surround each atom in the molecule. It enables you to determine the molecular structure by counting the number of bonding pairs and lone pairs for each atom.

2. The molecular structure is the same as the arrangement of electron pairs when there are no lone pairs on the central atom in the structure.

3. The name for the molecular structure differs from that for the electron pair arrangement when there are lone pairs around the central atom.

4. The electrons in a double bond are restricted to the space between the two atoms and so cannot operate as independent pairs.

5. **a.** trigonal pyramid
   b. linear
   c. bent (V-shaped)
   d. trigonal pyramid

Chapter 12 Review

Key Terms

Key Ideas

12.1 Characteristics of Chemical Bonds

- Chemical bonds hold groups of atoms together to form molecules and ionic solids.
- Bonds are classified as:
  - Ionic: Formed when one or more electrons are transferred to form positive and negative ions
  - Covalent: Electrons are shared equally between identical atoms
    - ◆ Polar covalent bond: unequal electron sharing between different atoms
- Electronegativity is the relative ability of an atom to attract the electrons shared with another atom in a bond.
- The difference in electronegativity of the atoms forming a bond determines the polarity of that bond.

12.2 Characteristics of Ions and Ionic Compounds

- In stable compounds, atoms tend to achieve the electron configuration of the nearest noble gas atom.
- In ionic compounds:
  - Nonmetals tend to gain electrons to reach the electron configuration of the next noble gas atom.
  - Metals tend to lose electrons to reach the electron configuration of the previous noble gas atom.
- Ions group together to form compounds which are electrically neutral.

12.3 Lewis Structures

- In covalent compounds, nonmetals share electrons so that both atoms achieve noble gas configurations.
- Lewis structures represent the valence electron arrangements of the atoms in a compound.
- The rules for drawing Lewis structures recognize the importance of noble gas electron configurations.
  - Duet rule for hydrogen
  - Octet rule for most other atoms
- Some molecules have more than one valid Lewis structure, called resonance.
- Some molecules violate the octet rule for the component atoms.
  - Examples are BF_3, NO_2, and NO.

12.4 Structures of Molecules

- Molecular structure describes how the atoms in a molecule are arranged in space.
- Molecular structure can be predicted by using the valence shell electron pair repulsion (VSEPR) model.

434 • Chapter 12 • Chemical Bonding

Meeting Individual Needs	**Assessment Resources**
CHAPTER REVIEW	CHAPTER 12
Chapter 12 Review Worksheet at the appropriate level: **Basic** **Standard** **Challenge**	**Chapter 12 Test**
CHAPTER SUMMARY	**TECHNOLOGY**
A **Chapter Summary** that includes additional Active Reading Questions for Chapter 12 is available.	**Computerized Test Bank for Chapter 12**

Chapter 12 Assessment

All exercises with blue numbers have answers in the back of this book.

12.1 Characteristics of Chemical Bonds

A. Types of Chemical Bonds

1. Define a chemical bond.

2. What types of elements react to form *ionic* compounds? Give an example of the formation of an ionic compound from its elements.

3. What type of bonding requires the complete *transfer* of an electron from one atom to another? What type of bonding involves the sharing (either equally or unequally) of electrons between atoms?

4. Describe the type of chemical bonding that exists between the atoms in the hydrogen molecule, H_2.

5. Describe the type of chemical bonding that exists between the atoms in the hydrogen fluoride molecule, HF.

B. Electronegativity

6. What do chemists mean by the term *electronegativity*? What does its electronegativity tell us about the atom?

7. What does it mean to say that a bond is *polar*? What are the conditions that give rise to a bond's being polar?

8. For each of the following sets of elements, identify the element expected to be most electronegative and that expected to be least electronegative.

   a. K, Sc, Ca   b. Br, F, At   c. C, O, N

9. On the basis of the electronegativity values given in Figure 12.4, indicate whether each of the following bonds would be expected to be ionic, covalent, or polar covalent.

   a. S—S
   b. S—O
   c. S—H
   d. S—K

10. Which of the following molecules contain polar covalent bonds?

   a. phosphorus, P_4
   b. oxygen, O_2
   c. ozone, O_3
   d. hydrogen fluoride, HF

11. On the basis of the electronegativity values given in Figure 12.4, indicate which is the more polar bond in each of the following pairs.

   a. H—O or H—N
   b. H—N or H—F
   c. H—O or H—F
   d. H—O or H—Cl

12. On the basis of the electronegativity values given in Figure 12.4, indicate which bond of the following pairs has a more ionic character.

   a. Na—O or Na—N
   b. K—S or K—P
   c. Na—Cl or K—Cl
   d. Na—Cl or Mg—Cl

C. Bond Polarity and Dipole Moments

13. What is a *dipole moment*? Give four examples of molecules that possess dipole moments, and draw the direction of the dipole as shown in this section.

14. Why is the presence of a dipole moment in the water molecule so important? What are some properties of water that are determined by its polarity?

15. In each of the following diatomic molecules, which end of the molecule is positive relative to the other end?

   a. hydrogen fluoride, HF
   b. chlorine monofluoride, ClF
   c. iodine monochloride, ICl

16. For each of the following bonds, draw a figure indicating the direction of the bond dipole, including which end of the bond is positive and which is negative.

   a. P—F
   b. P—O
   c. P—C
   d. P—H

17. For each of the following bonds, draw a figure indicating the direction of the bond dipole, including which end of the bond is positive and which is negative.

   a. S—P
   b. S—O
   c. S—N
   d. S—Cl

Chapter 12 Assessment

1. A chemical bond represents a force that holds groups of two or more atoms together and makes them function as a unit.

2. An ionic compound results when a metallic element reacts with a nonmetallic element. An example is
$2Na(s) + Cl_2(g) \rightarrow 2Na^{(+)}Cl^{(-)}(s)$.

3. ionic; covalent

4. When two hydrogen atoms are brought close together, each hydrogen atom contributes its electron to the formation of a covalent bond. The pair of electrons is shared equally by the two hydrogen atoms.

5. By bonding with each other, the atoms (H and F) share a pair of valence electrons. Because the atoms have different attractions for the electrons, this sharing is not equal. The bonding in HF is polar covalent.

6. Electronegativity is the ability of an atom to attract a shared pair of electrons toward itself in forming a chemical bond. The larger the electronegativity, the greater the attraction for a shared electron.

7. A bond is polar if the shared electron pair is attracted more strongly by one of the bonded atoms than the other because of differences in electronegativity values. A molecule may have polar bonds but not necessarily be a polar molecule. To determine the polarity of a molecule, its overall shape must be considered.

8. (a) K < Ca < Sc
   (b) At < Br < F
   (c) C < N < O

9. (a) covalent
   (b) polar covalent
   (c) polar covalent
   (d) ionic

10. (a) no polar covalent bonds
   (b) no polar covalent bonds
   (c) no polar covalent bonds
   (d) polar covalent bonds

11. (a) H—O
   (b) H—F
   (c) H—F
   (d) H—O

12. (a) Na—O
   (b) K—S
   (c) K—Cl
   (d) Na—Cl

13. A dipole moment occurs in a molecule that has separate centers of positive and negative charge. Examples include
$^{\delta+}C \rightarrow O^{\delta-}$; $^{\delta+}N \rightarrow O^{\delta-}$; $^{\delta+}Cl \rightarrow F^{\delta-}$; $^{\delta+}Br \rightarrow Cl^{\delta-}$.

14. The presence of strong dipoles and a large overall dipole moment makes water a very polar substance. Properties of water that are dependent on its dipole moment include its freezing point, melting point, vapor pressure, and ability to dissolve many substances.

15. (a) H
   (b) Cl
   (c) I

16. (a) $^{\delta+}P \rightarrow F^{\delta-}$
   (b) $^{\delta+}P \rightarrow O^{\delta-}$
   (c) $^{\delta+}P \rightarrow C^{\delta-}$
   (d) P and H have similar electronegativities.

17. (a) $^{\delta+}P \rightarrow S^{\delta-}$
   (b) $^{\delta+}S \rightarrow O^{\delta-}$
   (c) $^{\delta+}S \rightarrow N^{\delta-}$
   (d) $^{\delta+}S \rightarrow Cl^{\delta-}$

18. gaining

19. See *Solutions Guide*.

20. (a) Li: [He]$2s^1$; Li$^+$: [He]
    (b) Br: [Ar]$4s^23d^{10}4p^5$; Br$^-$: [Kr]
    (c) Cs: [Xe]$6s^1$; Cs$^+$: [Xe]
    (d) S: [Ne]$3s^23p^4$; S^{2-}: [Ar]
    (e) Mg: [Ne]$3s^2$; Mg^{2+}: [Ne]

21. (a) Ca^{2+}
    (b) N^{3-}
    (c) Br$^-$
    (d) Mg^{2+}

22. (a) Na$_2$S
    (b) BaSe
    (c) MgBr$_2$
    (d) Li$_3$N
    (e) KH

23. (a) Al^{3+}, [Ne]; S^{2-}, [Ar]
    (b) Mg^{2+}, [Ne]; N^{3-}, [Ne]
    (c) Rb$^+$, [Kr]; O^{2-}, [Ne]
    (d) Cs$^+$, [Xe]; I$^-$, [Xe]

24. The formula of an ionic compound is the empirical formula (the smallest whole-number ratio of the positive and negative ions present).

25. An ionic solid such as NaCl consists of an array of alternating positively and negatively charged ions. In most ionic solids, the ions are packed as tightly as possible.

26. In forming the cation, the electrons in the valence electron shell are removed from the atom. The valence shell of the cation is the next lowest energy level compared with the parent atom.

27. In forming an anion, an atom gains electrons in its outermost (valence) shell. Having additional electrons in the valence shell increases the repulsive forces between electrons, and the outermost shell becomes larger to accommodate this increase.

28. (a) F$^-$ is larger than Li$^+$. The F$^-$ ion has a filled $n = 2$ shell. A lithium atom has lost the electron from the $n = 2$ shell, leaving $n = 1$ as its outermost shell.
    (b) Cl$^-$ is larger than Na$^+$. The Cl$^-$ ion has a filled $n = 3$ shell. A sodium atom has lost the electron from the $n = 3$ shell, leaving $n = 2$ as its outermost shell.
    (c) Ca is larger than Ca^{2+}. The calcium ion has $n = 3$ as its outer shell, and the calcium atom has $n = 4$ as its outer shell.

12.2 Characteristics of Ions and Ionic Compounds

A. Stable Electron Configurations and Charges on Ions

18. Nonmetals form negative ions by (losing/gaining) enough electrons to achieve the electron configuration of the next noble gas.

19. Explain how the atoms in *covalent* molecules achieve configurations similar to those of the noble gases. How does this differ from the situation in ionic compounds?

20. Write the electron configuration for each of the following atoms and for the simple ion that the element most commonly forms. In each case, indicate which noble gas has the same electron configuration as the ion.
    a. lithium, $Z = 3$ d. sulfur, $Z = 16$
    b. bromine, $Z = 35$ e. magnesium, $Z = 12$
    c. cesium, $Z = 55$

21. What simple ion does each of the following elements most commonly form?
    a. calcium, $Z = 20$
    b. nitrogen, $Z = 7$
    c. bromine, $Z = 35$
    d. magnesium, $Z = 12$

22. On the basis of their electron configurations, predict the formula of the simple binary ionic compound likely to form when the following pairs of elements react with each other.
    a. sodium, Na, and sulfur, S
    b. barium, Ba, and selenium, Se
    c. magnesium, Mg, and bromine, Br
    d. lithium, Li, and nitrogen, N
    e. potassium, K, and hydrogen, H

23. Name the noble gas atom that has the same electron configuration as each of the ions in the following compounds.
    a. aluminum sulfide, Al$_2$S$_3$
    b. magnesium nitride, Mg$_3$N$_2$
    c. rubidium oxide, Rb$_2$O
    d. cesium iodide, CsI

B. Ionic Bonding and Structures of Ionic Compounds

24. Is the formula we write for an ionic compound the *molecular* formula or the *empirical* formula? Why?

25. Describe in general terms the structure of ionic solids such as NaCl. How are the ions packed in the crystal?

26. Why are cations always smaller than the atoms from which they are formed?

27. Why are anions always larger than the atoms from which they are formed?

28. For each of the following pairs, indicate which species is larger. Explain your reasoning in terms of the electron structure of each species.
    a. Li$^+$ or F$^-$ c. Ca^{2+} or Ca
    b. Na$^+$ or Cl$^-$ d. Cs$^+$ or I$^-$

29. For each of the following pairs, indicate which is larger.
    a. Cl$^-$ or I$^-$ c. Cl$^-$ or Cl
    b. Cl$^-$ or Na$^+$ d. Cl$^-$ or S^{2-}

12.3 Lewis Structures

A. Writing Lewis Structures

30. Why are the *valence* electrons of an atom the only electrons likely to be involved in bonding to other atoms?

31. Explain the "duet" and "octet" rules and how they are used to describe the arrangement of electrons in a molecule.

32. How many electrons are involved when two atoms in a molecule are connected by a "double bond"? Write the Lewis structure of a molecule containing a double bond.

33. Give the *total* number of *valence* electrons in each of the following molecules.
    a. CBr$_4$ c. C$_6$H$_6$
    b. NO$_2$ d. H$_2$O$_2$

34. Write a Lewis structure for each of the following simple molecules. Show all bonding valence electron pairs as lines and all nonbonding valence electron pairs as dots.
    a. NH$_3$ c. NCl$_3$
    b. CCl$_4$ d. SiBr$_4$

B. Lewis Structures of Molecules with Multiple Bonds

35. Write a Lewis structure for each of the following simple molecules. Show all bonding valence electron pairs as lines and all nonbonding valence electron pairs as dots.
    a. H$_2$S   c. C$_2$H$_4$
    b. SiF$_4$ d. C$_3$H$_8$

(d) I$^-$ is larger than Cs$^+$. The I$^-$ ion has a filled $n = 5$ shell. A cesium atom has lost the electron from the $n = 6$ shell, leaving $n = 5$ as its outermost shell. However, cesium has a greater nuclear charge than iodine, so the electrons are drawn in closer.

29. (a) I$^-$
    (b) Cl$^-$
    (c) Cl$^-$
    (d) S^{2-}

30. The valence electrons effectively represent the outside edge of the atom. These electrons are most likely influenced by the electrons of another atom.

31. When atoms form covalent bonds, they try to attain a valence electron configuration similar to that of the nearest noble gas element. Thus hydrogen in a bond would have two electrons (like helium; the duet rule) and others would have eight electrons (like neon and argon; the octet rule).

32. 4 electrons; an example is O$_2$.

33. (a) 32
    (b) 17
    (c) 30
    (d) 14

36. Write a Lewis structure for each of the following simple molecules. Show all bonding valence electron pairs as lines and all nonbonding valence electron pairs as dots. For those molecules that exhibit resonance, draw the various possible resonance forms.

    a. Cl_2O

    b. CO_2

    c. SO_3

37. Write a Lewis structure for each of the following polyatomic ions. Show all bonding valence electron pairs as lines and all nonbonding valence electron pairs as dots. For those ions that exhibit resonance, draw the various possible resonance forms.

    a. sulfate ion, SO_4^{2-}

    b. phosphate ion, PO_4^{3-}

    c. sulfite ion, SO_3^{2-}

38. Write a Lewis structure for each of the following polyatomic ions. Show all bonding valence electron pairs as lines and all nonbonding valence electron pairs as dots. For those ions that exhibit resonance, draw the possible resonance forms.

    a. hydrogen phosphate ion, HPO_4^{2-}

    b. dihydrogen phosphate ion, $H_2PO_4^-$

    c. phosphate ion, PO_4^{3-}

12.4 Structures of Molecules

A. Molecular Structure

39. What is the geometric structure of the water molecule? How many pairs of valence electrons are there on the oxygen atom in the water molecule? What is the approximate H—O—H bond angle in water?

40. What is the geometric structure of the ammonia molecule? How many pairs of electrons surround the nitrogen atom in NH_3? What is the approximate H—N—H bond angle in ammonia?

41. What is the geometric structure of the boron trifluoride molecule, BF_3? How many pairs of valence electrons are present on the boron atom in BF_3? What are the approximate F—B—F bond angles in BF_3?

42. What is the geometric structure of the CH_4 molecule? How many pairs of valence electrons are present on the carbon atom of CH_4? Refer to Figure 12.9 and estimate the H—C—H bond angles in CH_4.

B. The VSEPR Model

43. Why is the geometric structure of a molecule important, especially for biological molecules?

44. What general principles determine the molecular structure (shape) of a molecule?

45. Although the valence electron pairs in ammonia have a tetrahedral arrangement, the overall geometric structure of the ammonia molecule is *not* described as being tetrahedral. Explain.

46. Although both the BF_3 and NF_3 molecules contain the same number of atoms, the BF_3 molecule is flat, whereas the NF_3 molecule is trigonal pyramidal. Explain.

47. For the indicated atom in each of the following molecules or ions, give the number and arrangement of the electron pairs around that atom.

    a. P in PH_3

    b. Cl in ClO_4^-

    c. O in H_2O

48. Using the VSEPR theory, predict the molecular structure of each of the following molecules.

    a. CCl_4

    b. H_2S

    c. GeI_4

49. For each of the following molecules or ions, indicate the bond angle expected between the central atom and any two adjacent hydrogen atoms.

    a. H_2O

    b. NH_3

    c. NH_4^+

    d. CH_4

C. Molecules with Double Bonds

50. Using the VSEPR theory, predict the molecular structure of each of the following polyatomic ions.

    a. dihydrogen phosphate ion, $H_2PO_4^-$

    b. perchlorate ion, ClO_4^-

    c. sulfite ion, SO_3^{2-}

51. Predict the geometric structure of the carbonate ion, CO_3^{2-}. What are the bond angles in this molecule?

52. Predict the geometric structure of the acetylene molecule, C_2H_2. What are the bond angles in this molecule?

37. (a) SO_4^{2-} (b) PO_4^{3-}

  (c) SO_3^{2-}

38. (a) HPO_4^{2-}

  (b) $H_2PO_4^-$

  (c) PO_4^{3-}

39. Water is a bent (or V-shaped) molecule. There are four pairs of valence electrons on the oxygen atom (two lone pairs and two bonding pairs). The expected bond angle is approximately 109.5° (for water, the angle is closer to 105° because of the lone pair repulsions).

40. Trigonal pyramidal structure with four electron pairs (three bonding pairs and one lone pair). The bond angle is somewhat less than 109.5° (because of the lone pair).

41. BF_3 is a trigonal planar molecule. Boron is surrounded by three bonding pairs of electrons and no lone pairs. The F—B—F bond angles are 120°.

42. Tetrahedral structure with four bonding electron pairs. The bond angles are 109.5°.

43. For biological molecules, a slight change in the geometric structure can completely destroy the molecule's usefulness to a cell or cause a destructive change in the cell.

44. The general molecular structure is determined by the number of electron pairs around the central atom (bonding and lone pairs).

34. (a) NH_3 (c) NCl_3

  (b) CI_4 (d) $SiBr_4$

35. (a) H_2S (c) C_2H_4

  (b) SiF_4 (d) C_3H_8

36. (a) Cl_2O (b) CO_2

  (c) SO_3

45. One of the four pairs of valence electrons surrounding the nitrogen is a lone pair of electrons. This lone pair does not enter into the description of the molecule's overall shape. While the lone pair does influence the geometry, we name the shape by considering only the atoms in the molecule.

46. In NF_3 the nitrogen is surrounded by four electron pairs (tetrahedral geometry); in BF_3 the boron is surrounded by three electron pairs (trigonal planar).

47. (a) four electron pairs (tetrahedral geometry)
(b) four electron pairs (tetrahedral geometry)
(c) four electron pairs (tetrahedral geometry)

48. (a) tetrahedral
(b) bent (V-shaped)
(c) tetrahedral

49. (a) < 109.5°
(b) < 109.5°
(c) 109.5°
(d) 109.5°

50. (a) tetrahedral
(b) tetrahedral
(c) trigonal pyramidal

51. Trigonal planar, 120° bond angles

52. The acetylene molecule is linear, with bond angles of 180°, because of the presence of the triple bond between carbon atoms.

53. See *Solutions Guide*.

54. (a) S—F
(b) P—O
(c) C—H

55. The energy required to break the bond

56. (a) Be
(b) N
(c) F

57. (a) O
(b) Br
(c) I

58. (a) Na^+
(b) I^-
(c) K^+
(d) Ca^{2+}
(e) S^{2-}
(f) Mg^{2+}
(g) Al^{3+}
(h) N^{3-}

59. (a) bent (or V-shaped)
(b) trigonal planar
(c) trigonal planar
(d) linear

Critical Thinking

53. What is *resonance*? Give three examples of molecules or ions that exhibit resonance, and draw Lewis structures for each of the possible resonance forms.

54. In each case, which of the following pairs of bonded elements forms the more polar bond?
  a. S—F or S—Cl
  b. N—O or P—O
  c. C—H or Si—H

55. What do we mean by the *bond energy* of a chemical bond?

56. For each of the following pairs of elements, identify which element would be expected to be more electronegative. It should not be necessary to look at a table of actual electronegativity values.
  a. Be or Ba
  b. N or P
  c. F or Cl

57. In each of the following molecules, which end of the molecule is negative relative to the other end?
  a. carbon monoxide, CO
  b. iodine monobromide, IBr
  c. hydrogen iodide, HI

58. What simple ion does each of the following elements most commonly form?
  a. sodium
  b. iodine
  c. potassium
  d. calcium
  e. sulfur
  f. magnesium
  g. aluminum
  h. nitrogen

59. Using the VSEPR theory, predict the molecular structure of each of the following molecules or ions containing multiple bonds.
  a. SO_2
  b. SO_3
  c. HCO_3^- (hydrogen is bonded to oxygen)
  d. HCN

60. Explain the difference between a covalent bond formed between two atoms of the same element and a covalent bond formed between atoms of two different elements.

61. Rank the following from smallest to greatest radius:
K^+ Ca^{2+} Cl^- S^{2-} Ar
Explain.

62. Consider the following molecules:
O_3 H_2O SO_2 OCl_2
Which molecules can be described as having a bent shape? Do the bent molecules all have the same geometry? Explain.

63. Consider the molecules CO_2 and OF_2.
  a. Draw a valid Lewis structure for each molecule.
  b. Name the molecular geometry of each molecule.
  c. Name the molecular structure (shape) of each molecule.
  d. Both molecules have the general formula XY_2. Do they have the same shape? Why or why not?

60. In a covalent bond formed between two atoms of the same element, the electron pair is shared equally and the bond is nonpolar; in a bond between atoms of different elements, the electron pair is shared unequally and the bond is polar (unless the different elements happen to have the same electronegativity values).

61. Ca^{2+}, K^+, Ar, Cl^-, S^{2-}

62. All of the molecules can be described as bent. The geometries of the molecules are: O_3 is trigonal planar; H_2O is tetrahedral; SO_2 is trigonal planar; OCl_2 is tetrahedral.

63. (a) $\ddot{O}=C=\ddot{O}$
$:\!\ddot{F}-\ddot{O}-\ddot{F}\!:$

(b) CO_2 has a linear geometry and OF_2 has a tetrahedral geometry.
(c) CO_2 has a linear shape, OF_2 has a bent or V-shape.
(d) They do not have the same shapes. CO_2 has no lone pairs around the carbon atom, while OF_2 has two lone pairs of electrons around the oxygen atom.

1 Which of the following atoms is the most electronegative?

A Na   C Cl

B P   D I

2 Which of the following is **true** concerning trends on the periodic table?

A In general, smaller atoms have larger ionization energies and smaller electronegativity values.

B In general, smaller atoms have smaller ionization energies and smaller electronegativity values.

C In general, smaller atoms have smaller ionization energies and larger electronegativity values.

D In general, smaller atoms have larger ionization energies and larger electronegativity values.

3 Diatomic molecules that are formed from two different types of nonmetal atoms generally form _____.

A ionic bonds

B polar covalent bonds

C nonpolar covalent bonds

D no bonds

4 Consider the carbon monoxide molecule pictured below. Note that the bond may be a single, double, or triple bond. What can best be said about the electrons involved in the bond?

Box A   Box B

A There is an equal chance of a bonding electron's being in the area marked by either box.

B A bonding electron is more likely to exist in the area marked by Box A because carbon needs more electrons to get to a noble gas electron configuration.

C A bonding electron is more likely to exist in the area marked by Box B because the oxygen nucleus has a stronger attraction for electrons than does the carbon nucleus.

D Because we never know where the electron is, we cannot say where a bonding electron is more likely to be.

5 Which of the following does not have a noble gas electron configuration?

A The Na^+ ion

B The Mg^{2+} ion

C The S^{2-} ion

D The Fe^{3+} ion

6 The electron configuration $1s^2 2s^2 2p^6 3s^2 3p^6$ is the correct electron configuration for the most stable form of which ion?

A The calcium ion

B The magnesium ion

C The fluoride ion

D The oxide ion

7 What is the expected ground state electron configuration for the most stable **ion** of bromine?

A $[Ar]\,4s^2 3d^{10} 4p^5$

B $[Ar]\,4s^2 3d^{10} 4p^6$

C $[Ar]\,4s^2 4d^{10} 4p^6$

D $[Ar]\,4s^2 4d^{10} 4p^5$

8 How many resonance structures can be drawn for the carbonate ion?

A 1

B 2

C 3

D 4

9 Write the name of each of the following shapes of molecules

a.

b.

c.

Answer to Practice Problem 12.4

Molecule or Ion	Total Valence Electrons	Draw Single Bonds	Calculate Number of Electrons Remaining	Use Remaining Electrons to Achieve Noble Gas Configurations	Check Atom	Electrons
a. NF_3	$5 + 3(7) = 26$	F—N (F, F)	$26 - 6 = 20$	:F̈—N̈—F̈: :F̈:	N, F	8, 8
b. O_2	$2(6) = 12$	O—O	$12 - 2 = 10$	:Ö=Ö:	O	8
c. CO	$4 + 6 = 10$	C—O	$10 - 2 = 8$	:C≡O:	C, O	8, 8
d. PH_3	$5 + 3(1) = 8$	H, H, P, H	$8 - 6 = 2$	H—P̈—H, H	P, H	8, 8
e. H_2S	$2(1) + 6 = 8$	H—S—H	$8 - 4 = 4$	H—S̈—H	S, H	8, 2
f. SO_4^{2-}	$6 + 4(6) + 2 = 32$	O—S—O (O,O)	$32 - 8 = 24$	[:Ö: :Ö—S—Ö: :Ö:]²⁻	S, O	8, 8
g. NH_4^+	$5 + 4(1) - 1 = 8$	H—N—H (H,H)	$8 - 8 = 0$	[H—N—H, H]⁺	N, H	8, 2
h. ClO_3^-	$7 + 3(6) + 1 = 26$	O Cl (O,O)	$26 - 6 = 20$	[:Ö—Cl̈—Ö: :Ö:]⁻	Cl, O	8, 2
i. SO_2	$6 + 2(6) = 18$	O—S—O	$18 - 4 = 14$	Ö=S̈—Ö: and :Ö—S̈=Ö	S, O	8, 8

Answer to Practice Problem 12.6

a. NH_4^+

The Lewis structure is

$$\begin{bmatrix} & H & \\ H-&N&-H \\ & | & \\ & H & \end{bmatrix}^+$$

The four pairs of electrons around the nitrogen require a tetrahedral arrangement of electron pairs. The NH_4^+ ion has a tetrahedral molecular structure (case 3 in Table 12.4), because all electron pairs are shared.

b. SO_4^{2-}

The Lewis structure is

$$\begin{bmatrix} & :\ddot{O}: & \\ & | & \\ :\ddot{O}-&S&-\ddot{O}: \\ & | & \\ & :\ddot{O}: & \end{bmatrix}^{2-}$$

The four electron pairs around the sulfur require a tetrahedral arrangement. The SO_4^{2-} has a tetrahedral molecular structure (case 3 in Table 12.4).

c. NF_3

The Lewis structure is

$$:\ddot{F} \underset{:\ddot{F}:}{\overset{\ddot{N}}{|}} \ddot{F}:$$

The four pairs of electrons on the nitrogen require a tetrahedral arrangement. Only three of the pairs are shared with the fluorine atoms, leaving one lone pair. The molecular structure is a trigonal pyramid (case 4 in Table 12.4).

d. H_2S

The Lewis structure is

$$H-\ddot{S}-H$$

The four pairs of electrons around the sulfur require a tetrahedral arrangement. Two pairs are shared with hydrogen atoms, leaving two lone pairs. The molecular structure is bent or V-shaped (case 5 in Table 12.4).

e. ClO_3^-

The Lewis structure is

$$\begin{bmatrix} :\ddot{O}-&Cl&-\ddot{O}: \\ & | & \\ & :\ddot{O}: & \end{bmatrix}^-$$

The four pairs of electrons require a tetrahedral arrangement. Three pairs are shared with oxygen atoms, leaving one lone pair. The molecular structure is a trigonal pyramid (case 4 in Table 12.4).

f. BeF_2

The Lewis structure is

$$:\ddot{F}-Be-\ddot{F}:$$

The two electron pairs on beryllium require a linear arrangement. Because both pairs are shared by fluorine atoms, the molecular structure is also linear (case 1 in Table 12.4).

Planning Guide

Section	Segment		Text Features and Components	Labs, Demonstrations, & Activities
13.1 Describing the Properties of Gases 3 Blocks pp. 442–457	A	Pressure		**TE** Mini-Demo *p. 444* **TE** Teaching Support: Demonstration *pp. 444–445* **LM** Experiment 51: Gas Laws and Drinking Straws Lab Manual Report Sheets Teacher's Lab Guide
	B	Pressure and Volume: Boyle's Law		**SE** Hands-On Chemistry: The Cartesian Diver *p. 447* **TE** Mini-Demo *p. 447* **RP** Classroom Activities and Projects *TE p. 447*
	C	Volume and Temperature: Charles's Law		**TE** Teaching Support: Demonstration *pp. 450–451* **LM** Experiment 52: Determining Absolute Zero, Microscale Lab Manual Report Sheets Teacher's Lab Guide
	D	Volume and Moles: Avogadro's Law		**TE** Mini-Demo *p. 455* **SE** Hands-On Chemistry: Candle and the Tumbler *p. 456* **LM** Experiment 53: The *P-n* Relationship of Gases, CBL Lab Manual Report Sheets Teacher's Lab Guide
13.2 Using Gas Laws to Solve Problems 2 Blocks pp. 458–473	A	The Ideal Gas Law	**SE** Chemistry in Your World: Snacks Need Chemistry, Too! *p. 463*	**TE** Teaching Support: Demonstration *pp. 458–459* **TE** Teaching Support: Demonstration *pp. 460–461* **LM** Experiment 54: Molar Volume and the Universal Gas Constant, Microscale Lab Manual Report Sheets Teacher's Lab Guide
		continued on next page		

Key **SE** Student Edition **TE** Teacher Edition **RP** Teacher Resource Package
AR Additional Materials **LM** Lab Materials **🖼** Transparencies
💿 DVD **📀** CD-ROM **ℹ** classzone.com

All Learners	Technology	Review & Assessment	Standards
TE Teaching Tips *pp. 442–444*	**●** Video: Collapsing Can **●** Animation: Visualizing Molecular Motion: Single Molecule **●** Animation: Visualizing Molecular Motion: Many Molecules **●** Transparency: Figure 13.2 **●** Lab Generator CD **●** EasyPlanner	**SE** Active Reading Question *p. 443* **TE** More Examples *p. 445* **SE** Practice Problem *p. 446* **SE** Key Terms *p. 479* **SE** Questions and Problems *p. 480*	**TE** **NSES** UCP1, UCP3, A1, A2, B2, B4, G1, G2, G3
TE Teaching Tips *pp. 446–449* **RP** MINT: Math Concepts *TE p. 448*	**●** Transparency: Figure 13.3 **●** Transparency: Table 13.1 **●** Animation: Boyle's Law: A Molecular Level View **●** Animation: Boyle's Law: A Graphical View **●** EasyPlanner	**SE** Active Reading Question *p. 448* **TE** More Examples *p. 448* **SE** Practice Problem *p. 449* **TE** More Examples *p. 450* **SE** Key Terms *p. 479* **SE** Questions and Problems *p. 480*	
TE Teaching Tips *pp. 451–452* **TE** Meeting Individual Needs *p. 454*	**●** Transparency: Figure 13.5 **●** Video: Liquid Nitrogen and Balloons **●** Animation: Charles's Law: A Molecular Level View **●** Animation: Charles's Law: A Graphical View **●** Lab Generator CD **●** EasyPlanner	**SE** Critical Thinking *p. 451* **SE** Active Reading Questions *p. 452* **TE** More Examples *p. 452* **SE** Practice Problem *p. 453* **TE** More Examples *p. 453* **TE** More Examples *p. 454* **SE** Key Terms *p. 479* **SE** Questions and Problems *pp. 480–481*	
TE Teaching Tip *p. 455* **RP** Team Learning Worksheet (Sec. 13.1)	**●** Transparency: Figure 13.6 **●** Lab Generator CD **●** EasyPlanner	**SE** Active Reading Question *p. 455* **TE** More Examples *p. 456* **SE** Practice Problem *p. 457* **SE** Review Questions (13.1.A–13.1.D) *p. 457* **SE** Key Terms *p. 479* **SE** Questions and Problems *p. 481*	
TE Teaching Tips *pp. 458–459, 462*	**●** Animation: Ideal Gas Law $PV = nRT$ **●** Animation: Changes in Gas Volume, Pressure, and Concentration **●** Lab Generator CD **●** EasyPlanner	**SE** Practice Problem *p. 459* **TE** More Examples *p. 459* **SE** Practice Problem *p. 460* **TE** More Examples *p. 460* **SE** Practice Problem *p. 461* **TE** More Examples *p. 461* **TE** More Examples *p. 462* **SE** Practice Problem *p. 463* **SE** Key Terms *p. 479* **SE** Questions and Problems *p. 481*	**TE** **NSES** UCP1, UCP2, UCP3, A1, A2, B2, B4, E1, E2, F6

Planning Guide

Section	Segment		Text Features and Components	Labs, Demonstrations, & Activities
13.2 (continued)	B	**Dalton's Law of Partial Pressures**	**SE** Top Ten Components of Air *p. 464*	**TE** Teaching Support: Demonstration *pp. 464–465*
	C	**Gas Stoichiometry**	**SE** Chemistry in Your World: The Chemistry of Air Bags *p. 471*	**TE** Teaching Support: Demonstration *p. 470* **TE** Teaching Support: Demonstration *pp. 472–473*
13.3 **Using a Model to Describe Gases** **1 Block** pp. 474–478	A	**Laws and Models: A Review**		**TE** Mini-Demo *p. 474*
	B	**The Kinetic Molecular Theory of Gases**	**SE** Celebrity Chemical: Carbon Monoxide *p. 475* **SE** Chemistry in Your World: Signs of Pollution *p. 476*	
	C	**The Implications of the Kinetic Molecular Theory**		**TE** Mini-Demo *p. 476* **TE** Mini-Demo *p. 477*
	D	**Real Gases**		

Key
SE Student Edition   **TE** Teacher Edition   **RP** Teacher Resource Package
AR Additional Materials   **LM** Lab Materials   🗁 Transparencies
💿 DVD   💾 CD-ROM   ⓘ classzone.com

All Learners	Technology	Review & Assessment	Standards
TE Teaching Tips *p. 464*	**(tr)** Transparency: Figure 13.7 **(tr)** Transparency: Figure 13.8 **(ep)** EasyPlanner	**SE** Active Reading Question *p. 465* **TE** More Examples *p. 466* **SE** Practice Problem *p. 467* **SE** Active Reading Question *p. 467* **TE** More Examples *p. 468* **SE** Practice Problem *p. 469* **SE** Key Terms *p. 479* **SE** Questions and Problems *pp. 481–482*	
TE Teaching Tips *pp. 469, 471* **RP** MINT: Reading Concepts *TE p. 469* **RP** MINT: Math Concepts *TE p. 469* **RP** Team Learning Worksheet (Sec. 13.2)	**(ep)** EasyPlanner	**SE** Practice Problem *p. 470* **TE** More Examples *p. 470* **SE** Practice Problem *p. 471* **TE** More Examples *p. 471* **TE** More Examples *p. 472* **SE** Key Terms *p. 479* **SE** Review Questions (13.2.A–13.2.C) *p. 473* **SE** Questions and Problems *p. 482*	
TE Teaching Tip *p. 474*	**(ep)** EasyPlanner	**SE** Active Reading Question *p. 475* **SE** Questions and Problems *p. 482*	**TE NSES** UCP2, UCP3, A1, A2, B2, B4, E1, E2, F1, F4, F5, F6
TE Teaching Tips *p. 475*	**(tr)** Transparency: Assumptions of the Kinetic Molecular Theory of Gases **(an)** Animation: Kinetic Molecular Theory/Heat Transfer **(ep)** EasyPlanner	**SE** Key Terms *p. 479* **SE** Questions and Problems *p. 482*	
TE Teaching Tips *pp. 476–477* **TE** Meeting Individual Needs *p. 476*	**(an)** Animation: Visualizing Molecular Motion **(ep)** EasyPlanner	**TE** More Examples *p. 477* **SE** Questions and Problems *p. 483*	
TE Teaching Tip *p. 478* **RP** Team Learning Worksheet (Sec. 13.3)	**(ep)** EasyPlanner	**SE** Critical Thinking *p. 478* **SE** Active Reading Question *p. 478* **SE** Review Questions (13.3.A–13.3.D) *p. 478* **SE** Questions and Problems *p. 483*	

Resource Materials for Chapter 13

SE Chapter Review *p. 479*

SE Critical Thinking *pp. 483–484*

SE Standardized Test Practice *p. 485*

AR English/Spanish Summaries

(audio) English Summaries Audio

(audio) Spanish Summaries Audio

RP Meeting Individual Needs Toolkit (MINT)
    Reading Concepts
    Math Concepts
    Chapter Review Worksheets
    Chapter Summaries

RP Solutions Guide

RP Standardized Test Practice

RP Chapter Tests

RP Test Bank

(tg) Test Generator

In this chapter our goals are for students to:

- Learn about atmospheric pressure and how barometers work
- Learn the various units of pressure
- Understand Boyles law
- Learn about Charles's law and absolute zero
- Understand Avogadro's law
- Understand the ideal gas law and use it in calculations
- Understand the relationship between the partial and total pressures of a gas mixture
- Understand the relationship between laws and models
- Understand the basic postulates of the kinetic molecular theory
- Understand the meaning of temperature
- Describe the properties of real gases
- Learn about the molar volume of an ideal gas and the definition of STP

Chapter 13

Gases

Hoop of steam being ejected from the Bocca Nuova crater on Mount Etna in Sicily.

440

IN YOUR LIFE

We are all familiar with gases. In fact, we live immersed in a gaseous "sea"— a mixture of nitrogen [$N_2(g)$], oxygen [$O_2(g)$], water vapor [$H_2O(g)$], and small amounts of other gases. So it is important from a practical point of view for us to understand the properties of gases.

For example, you know that blowing air into a balloon causes it to expand—the volume of the balloon increases as you put more air into it. On the other hand, when you add more air to an inflated basketball, the ball doesn't expand, it gets "harder." In this case the added air increases the pressure inside the ball rather than causing an increase in volume. Although you probably have never tried this, can you guess what happens when an inflated balloon is placed in a freezer? The balloon gets smaller—its volume decreases. (You can easily do this experiment at home.) When we cool a gas, its volume decreases.

The Breitling Orbiter 3, *shown over the Swiss Alps, recently completed a nonstop trip around the world.*

WHAT DO YOU KNOW?

Prereading Questions

1. How does a gas differ from a solid and a liquid?

2. Have you heard of the term *barometric pressure*? What does it mean?

3. How does a law differ from a theory?

4. What does the temperature of a sample measure?

Gases • Chapter 13 • **441**

Prereading Questions

1. The particles in a gas are spread apart much farther than the particles in a solid or a liquid.

2. *Answers will vary.* Barometric pressure is the pressure of the air in the atmosphere.

3. A law is a summary of observations; it explains *what* we see. A theory is an attempt to explain *why* the observed behavior occurs.

4. Temperature is a measure of the average kinetic energy of the particles in a system.

TECHNOLOGY IN THE CLASSROOM

 Transparencies
Figures: 13.2, 13.3, 13.5, 13.6, 13.7, 13.8
Table: 13.1
Assumptions of Kinetic Molecular Theory

 Power Presentation DVD
PowerPoint Slides
Animations
Visualizing Molecular Motion: Single Molecule/Many Molecules
Boyle's Law: A Molecular Level View/A Graphical View
Charles's Law: A Molecular Level View/A Graphical View
Ideal Gas Law $PV = nRT$
Changes in Gas Volume, Pressure, and Concentration
Kinetic Molecular Theory/Heat Transfer
Videos
Collapsing Can
Liquid Nitrogen and Balloons
eEdition
EasyPlanner

 Lab Generator CD
English Summaries CD
Spanish Summaries CD
ML Test Generator

 classzone.com

Assign students to read Section 13.1 and to answer the Review Questions at the end of the section before coming to class.

 Active Learning
Team Learning Worksheet

After introducing the material in Section 13.1 in class, place students in groups and have them work together on **Section 13.1: Team Learning Worksheet**.

Homework

You may wish to assign these selected end-of-chapter problems as homework for this section: 1, 2, 3, 4a–b, 5a–b, 6a–b, 7, 9, 11, 14, 16, 18, 19, 20

Additional end-of-chapter problems can be used for extra practice.

 TEACHING TIPS

- Students have many ideas about gases before they learn about them. Ask students about their conceptions of how a gas behaves. If your students have portfolios, they can write down their ideas and put them away for later review.

- This chapter emphasizes the scientific method in action. Focus on the way that observations lead to natural laws and our attempts to explain these laws with theories or models.

- Students should understand that while laws are based on observations, laws do not explain *why* the observed behavior occurs. Laws can help us make predictions, but they are not explanations. Knowing the law of gravity, for example, allows us to predict that if we drop a pen it will fall to the ground. It does not explain why the pen fell, what gravity is, or how gravity "works."

- Students already have some experience with gases. They know that as you blow into a balloon, it expands. The gas

laws should make sense to students. Have students come up with real-world examples to help them understand the gas laws.

- We have taken an atomic/molecular-level perspective throughout the text, so our model for understanding the behavior of gases is based on looking at a gas as a collection of individual particles.

SECTION 13.1
Describing the Properties of Gases

Key Terms
- Barometer
- Torr (mm Hg)
- Standard atmosphere
- Pascal
- Boyle's law
- Absolute zero
- Charles's law
- Avogadro's law

Objectives
- *To learn about atmospheric pressure and how barometers work*
- *To learn the units of pressure*
- *To understand how the pressure and volume of a gas are related*
- *To do calculations involving Boyle's law*
- *To learn about absolute zero*
- *To understand how the volume and temperature of a gas are related*
- *To do calculations involving Charles's law*
- *To understand how the volume and number of moles of a gas are related*
- *To do calculations involving Avogadro's law*

Gases provide an excellent example of the scientific method (first discussed in Chapter 1). Recall that scientists study matter by making *observations* that are summarized into *laws*. We try to explain the observed behavior by hypothesizing what the atoms and molecules of the substance are doing. This explanation based on the microscopic world is called a *model* or *theory*.

Our experiences show us that when we make a change in a property of a gas, other properties change in a predictable way. In this chapter we will discuss relationships among the characteristics of gases such as pressure, volume, temperature, and amount of gas. These relationships were discovered by making observations as simple as seeing that a balloon expands when you blow into it, or that a sealed balloon will shrink if you put it into the freezer. But we also want to explain these observations. Why do gases behave the way they do? To explain gas behavior we will propose a model called the kinetic molecular theory.

A. Pressure

We know that a gas uniformly fills any container, is easily compressed, and mixes completely with any other gas. One of the most obvious properties of a gas is that it exerts pressure on its surroundings. For example, when you blow up a balloon, the air pushes against the elastic sides of the balloon and keeps it firm.

The gases most familiar to us form the earth's atmosphere. The pressure exerted by the gaseous mixture that we call air can be dramatically demonstrated by the experiment shown in **Figure 13.1**. A small volume of water is placed in a metal can and the water is boiled, which fills the can with steam. The can is then sealed and allowed to cool. Why does the can collapse as it cools? It is the atmospheric pressure that crumples the can. When the can is cooled after being sealed so that no air can flow in, the water vapor (steam) inside the can condenses to a very small volume of liquid water. As a gas, the water vapor filled the can, but when it is condensed to a liquid, the liquid does not come close to filling the can. The H_2O molecules formerly present as a gas are now collected in a much smaller volume of liquid, and there are very few molecules of gas left to exert pressure outward and counteract the air pressure. As a result, the pressure exerted by the gas molecules in the atmosphere smashes the can.

 DID YOU KNOW

As a gas, water occupies 1300 times as much space as it does as a liquid at 25 °C and atmospheric pressure.

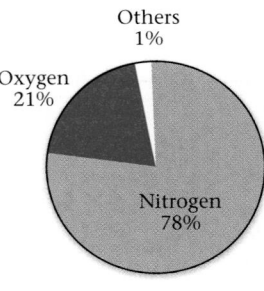

Percent Composition of Dry Air

Others 1%
Oxygen 21%
Nitrogen 78%

13.1.A Pressure

Objective To learn about atmospheric pressure and the various units of pressure and to learn the way barometers work

 TEACHING TIP

Use real-world examples to introduce the concept of pressure. Good examples include automobile tires, basketballs, balloons, and soda bottles.

(a)

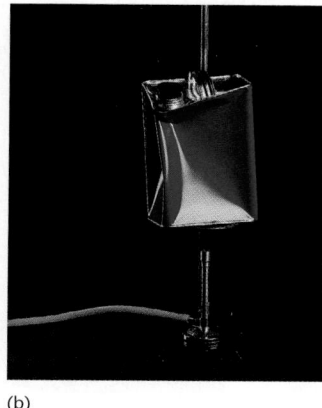
(b)

Figure 13.1
The pressure exerted by the gases in the atmosphere can be demonstrated by boiling water in a can (a), and then turning off the heat and sealing the can. As the can cools, the water vapor condenses, lowering the gas pressure inside the can. This causes the can to crumple (b).

 LABORATORY
EXPERIMENT 51:
Gas Laws and Drinking Straws

TECHNOLOGY

 Video
Collapsing Can

 Animations
Visualizing Molecular Motion:
  Single Molecule
Visualizing Molecular Motion:
  Many Molecules

TEACHING TIPS

- You might want to discuss how barometers work. If you are fortunate enough to have a classroom barometer, discuss it while you show students how it functions.

- You may want to extend the discussion of barometers to include barometers made with substances other than mercury. Many students believe that only mercury will work for a barometer.

Measuring Pressure A device that measures atmospheric pressure, the **barometer**, was invented in 1643 by an Italian scientist named Evangelista Torricelli (1608–1647), who had been a student of the famous astronomer Galileo. Torricelli's barometer is constructed by filling a glass tube with liquid mercury and inverting it in a dish of mercury.

> **Barometer**
> A device that measures atmospheric pressure

Notice that a large quantity of mercury stays in the tube. In fact, at sea level the height of this column of mercury averages 760 mm. Why does this mercury stay in the tube, seemingly in defiance of gravity? The pressure exerted by the atmospheric gases on the surface of the mercury in the dish keeps the mercury in the tube.

Active Reading Question

In the mercury barometer shown above, what keeps all of the mercury from flowing out of the tube? Why does some of the mercury flow out of the tube?

DID YOU KNOW

Soon after Torricelli died, a German physicist named Otto von Guericke invented an air pump. In a famous demonstration for the King of Prussia in 1683, Guericke placed two hemispheres together, pumped the air out of the resulting sphere through a valve, and showed that teams of horses could not pull the hemispheres apart. Then, after secretly opening the air valve, Guericke easily separated the hemispheres by hand. The King of Prussia was so impressed that he awarded Guericke a lifetime pension!

Active Reading Question

Atmospheric pressure is able to hold the mercury in the tube. However, atmospheric pressure is able to hold only a certain amount (for example, a standard atmosphere can hold 760 mm of mercury).

13.1 • Describing the Properties of Gases • **443**

Pressure conversion problems provide a means for students to review unit conversions and begin thinking about gases. These problems prepare students for the conversions they will perform later in the chapter.

MINI-DEMO

Make a water barometer using a large test tube and a dish of water. Fill the test tube with water, cover the end with your fingers, invert the test tube in the dish of water, and remove your hand. The water will stay in the test tube because the weight of the atmosphere pressing down on the water is greater than the weight of the water in the tube.

The *information box* explains that to measure a given pressure, a water barometer would be 13.6 times as high as a mercury barometer. Consider asking students to determine the height of water in a water barometer at 1 atm.

The atmosphere can hold water to a height of about 34 feet. We calculate this height by knowing that the atmosphere can hold up about 760 mm Hg (assuming a pressure of about 1.0 atm) and that mercury is 13.6 times as dense as water. Thus the atmosphere can hold about 760 × 13.6 mm, or about 34 feet. This activity provides an excellent way to explain why mercury barometers are preferable to water barometers.

Atmospheric Pressure

Atmospheric pressure results from the mass of air being pulled toward the center of the earth by gravity—in other words it results from the weight of the air.

Changing weather conditions cause the atmospheric pressure to vary so that the barometric pressure at sea level is not always 760 mm. A "low" pressure system is often found during stormy weather. A "high" pressure often indicates fair weather.

Atmospheric pressure varies with altitude. In Breckenridge, Colorado (elevation 9600 feet), the atmospheric pressure is about 520 mm because there is less air pushing down on the earth's surface than at sea level.

Units of Pressure

ℹ️ information

Mercury is used to measure pressure because of its high density. The column of water required to measure a given pressure would be 13.6 times as high as a mercury column.

Because instruments used for measuring pressure (see **Figure 13.2**) often contain mercury, the most commonly used units for pressure are based on the height of the mercury column (in millimeters) that the gas pressure can support. The unit **mm Hg** (millimeters of mercury) is often called the **torr** in honor of Torricelli. The terms *torr* and *mm Hg* are both used by chemists. A related unit for pressure is the **standard atmosphere** (abbreviated atm).

1 standard atmosphere = 1.000 atm = 760.0 mm Hg = 760.0 torr

The SI unit for pressure is the **pascal** (abbreviated Pa).

1 standard atmosphere = 101,325 Pa

Thus 1 atmosphere is about 100,000 or 10^5 pascals. Because the pascal is so small we will use it sparingly in this book. A unit of pressure that is employed in the engineering sciences and that we use for measuring tire pressure is pounds per square inch, abbreviated psi.

1.000 atm = 14.69 psi

Teaching Support
DEMONSTRATION

Collapsing Can

Materials
- Heating unit (hot plate or ring stand, ring and burner)
- Aluminum fluid can (a washed-out gallon ditto fluid can or paint thinner can works well)
- Rubber stopper to fit the opening in the can
- Hot pad

Preparation Thoroughly wash out the can to remove any remains of flammable solvents. Place about 50 mL of water into the clean can.

Presentation Place the rubber stopper in the opening of the can so that it fits securely but not tightly. Heat the water to boiling. The stopper pops out of the

can. Ask students why the stopper popped out of the can. Remove the can from the heat source, and seal the opening firmly with the stopper or a screw cap. Allow the can to stand on the demonstration table. Within about one minute, the can will crush inward with very visible results!

Teaching Notes Ask students what the pressure was inside the can before it was heated. Ask what the pressure is when the stopper pops and steam escapes

(a)   (b)

Figure 13.2
A device called a manometer is used for measuring the pressure of a gas in a container. The pressure of the gas is equal to h (the difference in mercury levels) in units of torr (equivalent to mm Hg). (a) Gas pressure = atmospheric pressure − h. (b) Gas pressure = atmospheric pressure + h.

More Examples

1. The height of mercury in a mercury barometer is measured to be 732 mm. Represent this pressure in atm, torr, and pascals.
   0.963 atm; 732 torr; 9.76×10^4 Pa

2. The pressure of a gas is measured to be 2.79×10^5 Pa. Represent this pressure in atm, torr, and psi.
   2.75 atm; 2.10×10^3 torr; 40.4 psi

ℹ️ nformation

To convert pressure to the units needed, remember

1.000 atm
760.0 mm Hg
760.0 torr
14.69 psi
101,325 Pa

Sometimes we need to convert from one unit of pressure to another. We do this by using conversion factors. The process is illustrated in Example 13.1.

EXAMPLE 13.1

Pressure Unit Conversions

The pressure of the air in a tire is measured to be 28 psi. Represent this pressure in atmospheres, torr, and pascals.

Solution

Where do we want to go?

$$28 \, \frac{\text{lb}}{\text{in.}^2} \rightarrow ? \text{ atm} \rightarrow ? \text{ torr} \rightarrow ? \text{ pascals}$$

What do we know?

- $28 \, \dfrac{\text{lb}}{\text{in.}^2}$
- $1.000 \text{ atm} = 14.69 \, \dfrac{\text{lb}}{\text{in.}^2}$
- $1.000 \text{ atm} = 760.0 \text{ torr}$
- $1.000 \text{ atm} = 101,325 \text{ Pa}$

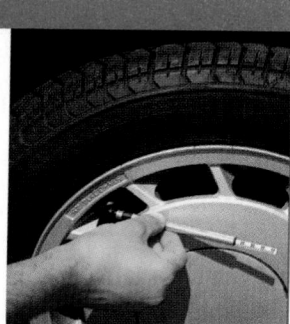

Checking the air pressure in a tire

How do we get there?

To convert from pounds per square inch to atmospheres, we need the equivalence statement

$$1.000 \text{ atm} = 14.69 \text{ psi}$$

which leads to the conversion factor

$$\frac{1.000 \text{ atm}}{14.69 \text{ psi}}$$

$$28 \text{ psi} \times \frac{1.000 \text{ atm}}{14.69 \text{ psi}} = 1.9 \text{ atm}$$

To convert from atmospheres to torr, we use the equivalence statement

$$1.000 \text{ atm} = 760.0 \text{ torr}$$

MATH ➕

$1.9 \times 760.0 = 1444$

1444 [Rounds to] 1400

$1400 = 1.4 \times 10^3$

13.1 • Describing the Properties of Gases • **445**

(continued)

from the unsealed container. Ask what the pressure is when the can is sealed. In all cases, have students compare the pressure to atmospheric pressure. The can crushes inward because as it cools, the steam condenses back to water, leaving a lower pressure inside the can than the atmospheric pressure. The atmosphere crushes the can.

Variation If you cannot find gallon cans for this demonstration, use an aluminum soda can. Place about 10 mL of water in the can, heat the water to boiling, and invert the can into a tub of cold water using tongs. The can will crush immediately with a loud bang.

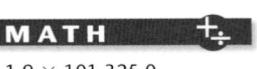

1.9 × 101,325.0
= 192,517.5

192,517.5 Rounds to 190,000

190,000 = 1.9 × 10⁵

which leads to the conversion factor

$$\frac{760.0 \ \text{torr}}{1.000 \ \text{atm}}$$

$$1.9 \ \text{atm} \times \frac{760.0 \ \text{torr}}{1.000 \ \text{atm}} = 1.4 \times 10^3 \ \text{torr}$$

To change from torr to pascals, we need the equivalence statement

$$1.000 \ \text{atm} = 101,325 \ \text{Pa}$$

which leads to the conversion factor

$$\frac{101,325 \ \text{Pa}}{1.000 \ \text{atm}}$$

$$1.9 \ \text{atm} \times \frac{101,325 \ \text{Pa}}{1.000 \ \text{atm}} = 1.9 \times 10^5 \ \text{Pa}$$

Does it make sense?

The best way to check a problem like this is to make sure the units on the answer are the units required.

 Practice Problem • Exercise 13.1

On a summer day in Breckenridge, Colorado, the atmospheric pressure is 525 mm Hg. What is this air pressure in atmospheres?

B. Pressure and Volume: Boyle's Law

The first careful experiments on gases were performed by the Irish scientist Robert Boyle (1627–1691). Using a J-shaped tube closed at one end (see **Figure 13.3**), which he reportedly set up in the multistory entryway of his house, Boyle studied the relationship between the pressure of the trapped gas and its volume. Representative values from Boyle's experiments are given in **Table 13.1**. The units given for the volume (cubic inches) and pressure (inches of mercury) are the ones Boyle used. Keep in mind that the metric system was not in use at this time.

Figure 13.3
A J-tube similar to the one used by Boyle. The pressure on the trapped gas can be changed by adding or withdrawing mercury.

Table 13.1

A Sample of Boyle's Observations (moles of gas and temperature both constant)

Experiment	Pressure (in. Hg)	Volume (in.³)	Pressure × Volume (in. Hg) × (in.³)	
			Actual	Rounded*
1	29.1	48.0	1396.8	1.40×10^3
2	35.3	40.0	1412.0	1.41×10^3
3	44.2	32.0	1414.4	1.41×10^3
4	58.2	24.0	1396.8	1.40×10^3
5	70.7	20.0	1414.0	1.41×10^3
6	87.2	16.0	1395.2	1.40×10^3
7	117.5	12.0	1410.0	1.41×10^3

*Three significant figures are allowed in the product because both of the numbers that are multiplied together have three significant figures.

446 • Chapter 13 • Gases

Hands-On Chemistry
MINI-LAB

The Cartesian Diver

Materials Each student/group will need a diver and plastic soft drink bottle. The diver can be made from a plastic pipet that is cut and fitted with a nut, an inverted test tube, or an eyedropper that just floats in a plastic soft drink bottle filled with water. The divers should contain just enough water to float.

To make a diver with the plastic pipet, cut off most of the tip (leave enough of it to fit a hex nut). Fill the pipet about halfway with water and place it in a beaker of water. If the diver sinks, remove a bit of water until the diver just floats. Place the diver in a plastic soft drink bottle that is filled with water and cap the bottle. The diver should sink easily when the bottle is squeezed. If the diver does not sink easily, remove the diver and add more water to it.

A glass eyedropper can be used as a diver as well (no hex nut is required). See the preceding instructions. In addition, an inverted test tube can function as a diver. Fill a test tube halfway with water, cover the opening with your fingers, invert the tube, and place it in a filled plastic soft drink bottle.

To expand this activity to a closed diver, you can use condiment packets from fast food restaurants.

HANDS-●N CHEMISTRY
•MINI-LAB•

The Cartesian Diver

Materials
- Cartesian diver
- water

Procedure
1. Obtain a Cartesian diver from your teacher.
2. Squeeze the diver. What happens? Make careful observations.

Results/Analysis
1. Explain your observations. Feel free to experiment with the diver. It is a good idea to take the diver apart and experiment with variables (for example, what happens if the bottle is not completely filled with water?). Be sure to reconstruct the diver so that it works again—this effort will help you better understand it.

First let's examine Boyle's observations (Table 13.1) for general trends. Note that as the pressure increases, the volume of the trapped gas decreases. In fact, if you compare the data from experiments 1 and 4, you can see that as the pressure is doubled (from 29.1 to 58.2), the volume of the gas is halved (from 48.0 to 24.0). The same relationship can be seen in experiments 2 and 5 and in experiments 3 and 6 (approximately).

We can see the relationship between the volume of a gas and its pressure more clearly by looking at the product of the values of these two properties ($P \times V$) using Boyle's observations. This product is shown in the last column of Table 13.1. Note that for all the experiments,

$$P \times V = 1.4 \times 10^3 \text{ (in. Hg)} \times \text{in.}^3$$

with only a slight variation due to experimental error. Other similar measurements on gases show the same behavior. This means that the relationship of the pressure and volume of a gas can be expressed as

pressure times volume equals a constant

or in terms of an equation as

$$PK = k$$

which is called **Boyle's law**, where k is a constant at a specific temperature for a given amount of gas. For the data we used from Boyle's experiment, $k = 1.41 \times 10^3$ (in. Hg) × in.^{3}

It is often easier to visualize the relationships between two properties if we make a graph. **Figure 13.4** uses the data given in Table 13.1 to show how pressure is related to volume. This graph shows that V decreases as P increases. When this type of relationship exists, we say that volume and pressure are *inversely proportional*; when one increases, the other decreases. Boyle's law is illustrated by the gas samples below.

Large pressure
Small volume

Small pressure
Large volume

Figure 13.4
A plot of *P* versus *V* from Boyle's data in Table 13.1

Boyle's law
The pressure of a given sample of a gas is inversely related to the volume of the gas at constant temperature. $PV = k$

P = 1 atm
V = 1 L
T = 298 K

P = 2 atm
V = 0.50 L
T = 298 K

P = 4 atm
V = 0.25 L
T = 298 K

13.1 • Describing the Properties of Gases • **447**

(continued)

Purpose Students will investigate Boyle's law and density/buoyancy relationships and develop and test their own ideas.

Discussion When you squeeze the soft drink bottle, water enters the diver. The gas (air) in the diver is compressible, whereas the water is relatively noncompressible. When water enters the diver, the volume of the gas decreases (as a result of the increased pressure caused by squeezing the bottle). The diver now has more mass but the same volume (overall volume of the diver—some students will find this distinction confusing). The density of the diver increases and the diver sinks. When you release the bottle, the pressure on the trapped air decreases. The volume of the air therefore increases, which pushes water out of the diver. The diver then rises.

TEACHING TIPS

- Emphasize to students that in Boyle's law, the temperature and the amount of gas are both constant. This idea is important in working through the initial laws toward the ideal gas equation.

- Many beginning students have trouble with the algebra required to rearrange the law to solve for the variable. Remind students that mathematics and chemistry work together and that this resolution is the same as solving an algebra problem.

 Active Reading Question

Answers will vary. For example, we can decrease the volume of an inflated balloon by increasing the pressure around it.

EXAMPLE 13.2

More Examples

1. A sample of helium gas has a pressure of 3.54 atm in a container with a volume of 23.1 L. This sample is transferred to a new container and the pressure is measured to be 1.87 atm. What is the volume of the new container? Assume constant temperature.

   43.7 L

2. A steel tank of argon gas has a pressure of 34.6 atm. If all of the argon is transferred to a new tank with a volume of 456 L, the pressure is measured to be 2.94 atm. What is the volume of the original container? Assume constant temperature.

   38.7 L

 TEACHING TIP

Encourage students to sketch a picture of the problem in order to be able to solve it. This is a good way for students to summarize important points and for you to notice any misconceptions they may have.

 information

For Boyle's law to hold, the amount of gas (moles) must not be changed. The temperature must also be constant.

A Closer Look

Boyle's law means that if we know the volume of a gas at a given pressure, we can predict the new volume if the pressure is changed, *provided that neither the temperature nor the amount of gas is changed.* For example, if we represent the original pressure and volumes as P_1 and V_1 and the final values as P_2 and V_2, using Boyle's law we can write

$$P_1 V_1 = k$$

and

$$P_2 V_2 = k$$

We can also say

$$P_1 V_1 = k = P_2 V_2$$

$$P_1 V_1 = P_2 V_2 \qquad \text{Boyle's law (constant temperature and amount of gas)}$$

We can solve for the final volume (V_2) by dividing both sides of the equation by P_2.

$$\frac{P_1 V_1}{P_2} = \frac{P_2 V_2}{P_2}$$

Canceling the P_2 terms on the right gives

$$\frac{P_1}{P_2} \times V_1 = V_2$$

or

$$V_2 = V_1 \times \frac{P_1}{P_2}$$

This equation tells us that we can calculate the new gas volume (V_2) by multiplying the original volume (V_1) by the ratio of the original pressure to the final pressure (P_1/P_2).

 Active Reading Question

Provide a real world example of Boyle's law.

EXAMPLE 13.2

Calculating Volume Using Boyle's Law

Freon-12 (the common name for the compound CCl_2F_2) was once widely used in refrigeration systems, but has now been replaced by other compounds that do not lead to the breakdown of the protective ozone in the upper atmosphere. Consider a 1.5-L sample of gaseous CCl_2F_2 at a pressure of 56 torr. If the pressure is changed to 150 torr at a constant temperature,

- Will the volume of the gas increase or decrease?
- What will be the new volume of the gas?

Solution
Where do we want to go?

Will the volume of the gas increase or decrease?

$$V_{final} = ? \text{ L}$$

Meeting Individual Needs
MATH CONCEPTS

For a review on making and interpreting graphs, have students read *Graphing* located in the *Teacher Resources*. A worksheet is available to go along with the handout.

What do we know?

Initial	Final
$P_1 = 56$ torr	$P_2 = 150$ torr
$V_1 = 1.5$ L	$V_2 = ?$ L

- Temperature is constant
- Boyle's law $\quad P_1V_1 = P_2V_2$

How do we get there?

Drawing a picture is often helpful as we solve a problem. Notice that the pressure is increased from 56 torr to 150 torr, so the volume must decrease:

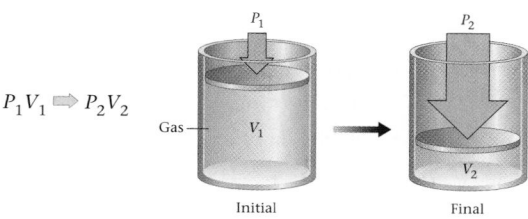

$$P_1V_1 \Rightarrow P_2V_2$$

We can verify this by using Boyle's law in the form

$$V_2 = V_1 \times \frac{P_1}{P_2}$$

Note that V_2 is obtained by "correcting" V_1 using the ratio P_1/P_2. Because P_1 is less than P_2, the ratio P_1/P_2 is a fraction that is less than 1. Thus V_2 must be a fraction of (smaller than) V_1; the volume decreases.

We calculate V_2 as follows:

$$V_2 = V_1 \times \frac{P_1}{P_2} = 1.5 \text{ L} \times \frac{56 \text{ torr}}{150 \text{ torr}} = 0.56 \text{ L}$$

Does it make sense?

Since the pressure increases we would expect the volume to decrease. The volume of the gas decreases from 1.5 L to 0.56 L.

✓ Practice Problem • Exercise 13.2

A sample of neon to be used in a neon sign has a volume of 1.51 L at a pressure of 635 torr. Calculate the volume of the gas after it is pumped into the glass tubes of the sign, where it shows a pressure of 785 torr.

Neon signs in Hong Kong

ⓘ nformation

The fact that the volume decreases in Example 13.2 makes sense because the pressure was increased. *To help catch errors, make it a habit to check whether an answer to a problem makes physical sense.*

 TEACHING TIPS

- Students sometimes confuse the idea of an inverse relationship with that of a line having a negative slope. A linear graph with a negative slope represents a direct relationship between the variables. To make this distinction clear, focus on the idea that *inverse* means the relationship varies with the reciprocal ($\frac{1}{x}$). Have students examine the shape of the graph in Figure 13.4. Ask what will happen to the pressure as the volume becomes extremely large (the pressure approaches zero, but will never reach zero). As the volume gets smaller, the pressure increases (pressure approaches infinity). Thus the graph must not touch the axes—it is a hyperbola, not a straight line.

- Remind students to check their answers to make sure that they make sense. Show students how to predict in advance whether volume and pressure should increase or decrease. This check allows students to see whether the answer makes sense.

- Discuss the answer to Example 13.2. Pressure increased by almost 3 times (56 torr to 150 torr), so the volume should decrease by about a factor of 3. We should expect the volume to be about 0.5 L (1.5/3 = 0.5), which is close to the actual answer of 0.6 L. In these cases, encourage students to estimate the answers before solving the problem.

✓ Answer to Practice Problem 13.2

Initial Conditions	Final Conditions
$P_1 = 635$ torr	$P_2 = 785$ torr
$V_1 = 1.51$ L	$V_2 = ?$

Solving Boyle's law for V_2 gives

$$V_2 = V_1 \times \frac{P_1}{P_2}$$

$$= 1.51 \text{ L} \times \frac{635 \text{ torr}}{785 \text{ torr}}$$

$$= 1.22 \text{ L}$$

Note that the volume decreased, as the increase in pressure led us to expect.

EXAMPLE 13.3

More Examples

1. A sample of neon gas has a pressure of 7.43 atm in a container with a volume of 45.1 L. This sample is transferred to a container with a volume of 18.4 L. What is the new pressure of the neon gas? Assume constant temperature.

   18.2 atm

2. A steel tank of oxygen gas has a volume of 2.00 L. If all of the oxygen is transferred to a new tank with a volume of 5.50 L, the pressure is measured to be 6.75 atm. What was the original pressure of the oxygen gas? Assume constant temperature.

   18.6 atm

13.1.C Volume and Temperature: Charles's Law

Objective To learn about absolute zero and about the laws relating the volume and temperature of a sample of gas at constant moles and pressure, and to do calculations involving that law

 LABORATORY
EXPERIMENT 52:
Determining Absolute Zero, Microscale

TECHNOLOGY

 Figure 13.5

 Video
Liquid Nitrogen and Balloons

Animations
Charles's Law: A Molecular Level View
Charles's Law: A Graphical View

EXAMPLE 13.3

Calculating Pressure Using Boyle's Law

In an automobile engine the gaseous fuel–air mixture enters the cylinder and is compressed by a moving piston before it is ignited. In a certain engine the initial cylinder volume is 0.725 L. After the piston moves up, the volume is 0.075 L. The fuel–air mixture initially has a pressure of 1.00 atm. Calculate the pressure of the compressed fuel–air mixture, assuming that both the temperature and the amount of gas remain constant.

Solution
Where do we want to go?

Pressure of the compressed fuel–air mixture = ? atm

What do we know?

Initial	Final
$P_1 = 1.00$ atm	$P_2 = ?$
$V_1 = 0.725$ L	$V_2 = 0.075$ L

- Temperature is constant
- Amount of gas is constant
- Boyle's law $\qquad P_1V_1 = P_2V_2$

MATH
$$\frac{0.725}{0.075} = 9.666\ldots$$
$$9.666 \;\text{Rounds to}\; 9.7$$

How do we get there?

We solve Boyle's law in the form $P_1V_1 = P_2V_2$ for P_2 by dividing both sides by V_2 to give the equation

$$P_2 = P_1 \times \frac{V_1}{V_2} = 1.00 \text{ atm} \times \frac{0.725\,\cancel{L}}{0.075\,\cancel{L}} = 9.7 \text{ atm}$$

Does it make sense?

Since the volume gets smaller the pressure must increase. Pressure and volume are inversely related.

Figure 13.5
Plots of V (L) versus T (°C) for several gases. Note that each sample of gas contains a different number of moles to spread out the plots.

C. Volume and Temperature: Charles's Law

In the century following Boyle's findings, scientists continued to study the properties of gases. The French physicist Jacques Charles (1746–1823), who was the first person to fill a balloon with hydrogen gas and who made the first solo balloon flight, showed that the volume of a given amount of gas (at constant pressure) increases with the temperature of the gas. That is, the volume increases when the temperature increases. A plot of the volume of a given sample of gas (at constant pressure) versus its temperature (in Celsius degrees) gives a straight line. This type of relationship is called *linear*, and this behavior is shown for several gases in **Figure 13.5**.

The solid lines in Figure 13.5 are based on actual measurements of temperature and volume for the gases listed. As we cool the gases they eventually liquefy, so we cannot determine any experimental points below this temperature. However, when we extend each straight line (which is called

---

Teaching Support
DEMONSTRATION

Helium Hot Air Balloon

Materials
- Commercial Mylar helium balloon (filled)
- Twist tie
- Hot plate
- Small paper cup and string (optional)

Preparation Remove about 5% of the helium from a Mylar balloon. Reseal the balloon with a twist tie. Attach a paper cup to the balloon to form a basket, if desired. Adjust the helium and the weight of the basket until the balloon just hovers in the air.

Presentation Show the balloon and basket to students, discussing the fact that it hovers. Ask for suggestions to make the balloon rise. Place the silver side of the balloon over a hot plate (be careful not to get the balloon too close to the heat). Observe the balloon *extrapolation* and is shown here by a dashed line), something very interesting happens. *All* of the lines extrapolate to zero volume at the same temperature: −273 °C. This suggests that −273 °C is the lowest possible temperature, because a negative volume is physically impossible. In fact, experiments have shown that matter cannot be cooled to temperatures lower than −273 °C. Therefore, this temperature is defined as **absolute zero** on the Kelvin scale.

When the volumes of the gases shown in Figure 13.5 are plotted against temperature on the Kelvin scale rather than the Celsius scale, the graph looks like this.

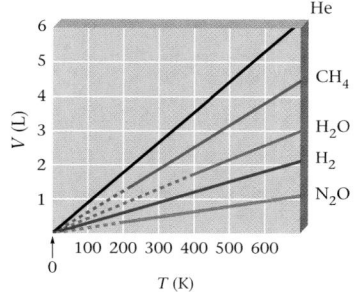

These plots show that the volume of each gas is *directly proportional to the temperature* (in kelvins) and extrapolates to zero when the temperature is 0 K. Let's illustrate this statement with an example. Suppose we have 1 L of gas at 300 K. When we double the temperature of this gas to 600 K (without changing its pressure), the volume also doubles, to 2 L. Verify this type of behavior by looking carefully at the lines for various gases shown in the graph above.

The direct proportionality between volume and temperature (in kelvins) is represented by the equation known as **Charles's law**:

$$V = bT$$

where T is temperature in kelvins and b is the proportionality constant. Charles's law holds for a given sample of gas at constant pressure. It tells us that (for a given amount of gas at a given pressure) the volume of the gas is directly proportional to the temperature on the Kelvin scale:

$$V = bT \quad \text{or} \quad \frac{V}{T} = b = \text{constant}$$

Notice that in the second form, this equation states that the *ratio* of V to T (in kelvins) must be constant. Thus, when we triple the temperature (in kelvins) of a sample of gas, the volume of the gas triples also.

$$\frac{V}{T} = \frac{3 \times V}{3 \times T} = b = \text{constant}$$

We can also write Charles's law in terms of V_1 and T_1 (the initial conditions) and V_2 and T_2 (the final conditions).

$$\frac{V_1}{T_1} = b \quad \text{and} \quad \frac{V_2}{T_2} = b$$

$$\frac{V_1}{T_1} = \frac{V_2}{T_2} \qquad \text{Charles's law (constant } P \text{ and amount of gas)}$$

The air in a balloon expands when it is heated. This means that some of the air escapes from the balloon, lowering the air density inside and thus making the balloon buoyant.

Absolute zero
−273 °C

Charles's law
The volume of a given sample of a gas is directly related to the temperature of the gas at constant pressure. $V = bT$

 TEACHING TIPS

- Explain to students that volume is directly related to temperature only if a graph of V vs. T hits the origin (graph on page 451). In figure 13.5, if temperature doubles, volume does not double. Using the Kelvin scale (graph on page 451), however, we can see that when the temperature doubles, the volume doubles.

- Students often forget that they must convert temperatures to Kelvin to work gas problems correctly. Remind them that this conversion is important because a negative temperature will result in a negative volume, which does not make sense. In Chapter 10, we saw that temperature measures the average kinetic energy of a sample. Does a gas sample at 40 °C have an average kinetic energy twice that of a gas sample at 20 °C? No. Although 40 = 2 × 20, 0 °C is not the lowest possible temperature. To compare relative average kinetic energies by comparing temperatures, we need to use a temperature scale in which zero is the lowest possible temperature (the absolute scale).

CRITICAL ?
THINKING

Students often forget to convert temperatures to units of Kelvin, partly because they do not understand why it is necessary. If the volume of a gas was directly related to its temperature in Celsius, then all gases would have a volume of zero at 0 °C. In addition, gases would exhibit negative volumes at temperatures below 0 °C. On a more subtle note, if a balloon was heated from 20 °C to 40 °C (a cool autumn day to a hot summer day), its volume would double. In reality, the volume would increase by less than 7% (a temperature change from 293 K to 313 K).

(continued)

expanding. When it appears close to capacity, remove it from the heat and release it. The balloon will rise. As it cools, the balloon will descend.

Teaching Notes Make sure the balloon is not fully inflated before you heat it. You may also use a heat gun or hair blow dryer to warm the balloon. Consider repeating this demonstration. The second time that you heat the balloon, ask students what is happening to the mass of the balloon. This

activity can lead into a discussion about the density of the balloon. Extend this discussion to explain how the balloon rises as a result of its change in density (mass is constant, volume increases).

1. *Answers will vary.* For example, if an inflated balloon is taken outside on a very cold day, it will shrink.

2. Temperature is a measure of average kinetic energy. When temperature doubles, the average kinetic energy of a sample doubles. Because of this, we need to use a scale in which the lowest value is zero. In addition, if we use the Celsius scale, we may end up with a negative value for volume, which is impossible.

EXAMPLE 13.4

More Examples

1. A 2.45-L sample of nitrogen gas is collected at 273 K and heated to 325 K. Calculate the volume of the nitrogen gas at 325 K. Assume constant pressure.

   2.92 L

2. A sample of methane gas is collected at 285 K and cooled to 245 K. At 245 K the volume of the gas is 75.0 L. Calculate the volume of the methane gas at 285 K. Assume constant pressure.

   87.2 L

 TEACHING TIP

In Example 13.4, the volume of the gas decreases very slightly (from 2.0 L to 1.9 L). The temperature of the gas changes from 25 °C to 5 °C. While it seems like the temperature decreases by a factor of 5, we can see this is not the case when we convert the temperature to Kelvin.

 Active Reading Questions

1. **Provide a real world example of Charles's law.**

2. **Why must temperature always be in units of Kelvin before using Charles's law?**

EXAMPLE 13.4

Calculating Volume Using Charles's Law, I

A 2.0-L sample of air is collected at 298 K and then cooled to 278 K. The pressure is held constant at 1.0 atm.

- Does the volume increase or decrease?
- Calculate the volume of the air at 278 K.

Solution

Where do we want to go?

Will the volume increase or decrease?

$$V_{final} = ? \text{ L}$$

What do we know?

Initial	Final
$T_1 = 298$ K	$T_2 = 278$ K
$V_1 = 2.0$ L	$V_2 = ?$ L

- Pressure is constant
- Charles's law $\dfrac{V_1}{T_1} = \dfrac{V_2}{T_2}$

How do we get there?

Because the gas is cooled the volume of the gas must decrease (T and V are directly proportional).

To calculate the new volume, V_2, we will use Charles's law in the form

$$\frac{V_1}{T_1} = \frac{V_2}{T_2}$$

for V_2. We can do this by multiplying both sides by T_2 and canceling.

$$T_2 \times \frac{V_1}{T_1} = \frac{V_2}{\cancel{T_2}} \times \cancel{T_2} = V_2$$

Thus

$$V_2 = T_2 \times \frac{V_1}{T_1} = 278\,\cancel{K} \times \frac{2.0\,\text{L}}{298\,\cancel{K}} = 1.9\,\text{L}$$

Does it make sense?

Since the temperature decreases we would expect the volume to decrease. The volume of the gas decreases from 2.0 L to 1.9 L.

information

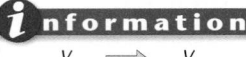

Temperature smaller, volume smaller

EXAMPLE 13.5

Calculating Volume Using Charles's Law, II

A sample of gas at 15 °C (at 1 atm) has a volume of 2.58 L.
The temperature is then raised to 38 °C (at 1 atm).

• Does the volume of the gas increase or decrease?

• Calculate the new volume.

Solution

Where do we want to go?

Will the volume increase or decrease?

V_{final} = ? L

What do we know?

Initial	Final
T_1 = 15 °C	T_2 = 38 °C
V_1 = 2.58 L	V_2 = ? L

• Pressure is constant (1 atm)

• Charles's law $\dfrac{V_1}{T_1} = \dfrac{V_2}{T_2}$

How do we get there?

Because the gas is heated the volume of the gas must increase
(T and V are directly proportional).

The temperatures are given in Celsius. To use Charles's law the temperatures must be in kelvins. To convert from Celsius to Kelvin:

15 °C = 15 + 273 = 299 K

38 °C = 38 + 273 = 311 K

Solving for V_2 gives

$$V_2 = V_1 \times \frac{T_2}{T_1} = 2.58 \text{ L} \left(\frac{311\ K}{288\ K}\right) = 2.79 \text{ L}$$

Does it make sense?

Since the temperature increases we would expect the volume to increase.
The volume of the gas increases from 2.58 L to 2.79 L.

✔ Practice Problem • Exercise 13.5

A child blows a soap bubble that contains air at 28 °C and has a volume
of 23 cm³ at 1 atm. As the bubble rises, it encounters a pocket of cold air
(temperature 18 °C). If there is no change in pressure, will the bubble get
larger or smaller as the air inside cools to 18 °C? Calculate the new volume
of the bubble.

EXAMPLE 13.5

More Examples

1. A sample of oxygen gas has
a volume of 4.55 L at 25 °C.
Calculate the volume of
the oxygen gas when the
temperature is raised to 45 °C.
Assume constant pressure.
4.86 L

2. A sample of hydrogen gas is
collected at 34 °C and heated
to 68 °C. At 68 °C the volume
of hydrogen is 26.0 L.
Calculate the volume of the
hydrogen sample at 34 °C.
23.4 L

✔ Answer to Practice Problem 13.5

Because the temperature of the
gas inside the bubble decreases
(at constant pressure), the
bubble gets smaller. The
conditions are

Initial Conditions

T_1 = 28 °C = 28 + 273 = 301 K

V_1 = 23 cm³

Final Conditions

T_2 = 18 °C = 18 + 273 = 291 K

V_2 = ?

Solving Charles's law,

$$\frac{V_1}{T_1} = \frac{V_2}{T_1}$$

for V_2 gives

$$V_2 = V_1 \times \frac{T_2}{T_1}$$
$$= 23 \text{ cm}^3 \times \frac{291\ K}{301\ K}$$
$$= 22 \text{ cm}^3$$

13.1 • Describing the Properties of Gases • 453

EXAMPLE 13.6

1. Consider a gas with a volume of 5.65 L at 27 °C and 1 atm pressure. At what temperature will this gas have a volume of 6.69 L and 1 atm pressure?

   82 °C (355 K)

2. Consider a gas with a volume of 9.25 L at 47 °C and 1 atm pressure. At what temperature does this gas have a volume of 3.50 L and 1 atm pressure?

   −152 °C (121 K)

EXAMPLE 13.6

Calculating Temperature Using Charles's Law

In former times, gas volume was used as a way to measure temperature by using devices called gas thermometers. Consider a gas that has a volume of 0.675 L at 35 °C and 1 atm pressure. What is the temperature (in units of °C) of a room where this gas has a volume of 0.535 L at 1 atm pressure?

Solution

Where do we want to go?

Temperature of the room = ? °C

What do we know?

Initial	Final
$T_1 = 35$ °C $= 308$ K	$T_2 = ?$ °C
$V_1 = 0.675$ L	$V_2 = 0.535$ L

- Pressure is constant (1 atm)
- Charles's Law $\dfrac{V_1}{T_1} = \dfrac{V_2}{T_2}$

How do we get there?

First we multiply both sides of the Charles's law equation by T_2.

$$T_2 \times \frac{V_1}{T_1} = \frac{V_2}{\cancel{T_2}} \times \cancel{T_2} = V_2$$

Next we multiply both sides by T_1.

$$\cancel{T_1} \times T_2 \times \frac{V_1}{\cancel{T_1}} = T_1 \times V_2$$

This gives

$$T_2 \times V_1 = T_1 \times V_2$$

Now we divide both sides by V_1 (or multiply by $\frac{1}{V_1}$),

$$\frac{1}{\cancel{V_1}} \times T_2 \times \cancel{V_1} = \frac{1}{V_1} \times T_1 \times V_2$$

and obtain

$$T_2 = T_1 \times \frac{V_2}{V_1}$$

We have now isolated T_2 on one side of the equation, and we can do the calculation.

$$T_2 = T_1 \times \frac{V_2}{V_1} = (308 \text{ K}) \times \frac{0.535 \cancel{L}}{0.675 \cancel{L}} = 244 \text{ K}$$

To convert from units of K to units of °C, we subtract 273 from the Kelvin temperature.

$$T_{°C} = T_K - 273 = 244 - 273 = -29 \text{ °C}$$

The room is very cold; the temperature is −29 °C.

Does it make sense?

The units are as required and the room is very cold (−29 °C).

Meeting Individual Needs
ADVANCED LEARNERS

Ask advanced learners to solve a problem similar to Example 13.6, but change the units in the problems so that students will first have to perform dimensional analysis. For instance: Consider a gas that has a volume of 800 mL at 40 °C and 1 atm pressure. What is the temperature (in K) of a room where this gas has a volume of 0.485 L at 1 atm?

D. Volume and Moles: Avogadro's Law

What is the relationship between the volume of a gas and the number of molecules present in the gas sample? Experiments show that when the number of moles of gas is doubled (at constant temperature and pressure), the volume doubles. In other words, the volume of a gas is directly proportional to the number of moles if temperature and pressure remain constant. **Figure 13.6** illustrates this relationship, which can also be represented by the equation

$$V = an \quad \text{or} \quad \frac{V}{n} = a$$

where V is the volume of the gas, n is the number of moles, and a is the proportionality constant. Note that this equation means that the ratio of V to n is constant as long as the temperature and pressure remain constant. Thus, when the number of moles of gas is increased by a factor of 5, the volume also increases by a factor of 5,

$$\frac{V}{n} = \frac{5 \times V}{5 \times n} = a = \text{constant}$$

and so on. In words, this equation means that *for a gas at constant temperature and pressure, the volume is directly proportional to the number of moles of gas*. This relationship is called **Avogadro's law** after the Italian scientist Amadeo Avogadro, who first postulated it in 1811.

For cases where the number of moles of gas is changed from an initial amount to another amount (at constant T and P), we can represent Avogadro's law as

$$\underset{\substack{\text{Initial} \\ \text{amount}}}{\frac{V_1}{n_1}} = a = \underset{\substack{\text{Final} \\ \text{amount}}}{\frac{V_2}{n_2}}$$

$$\frac{V_1}{n_1} = \frac{V_2}{n_2} \quad \text{Avogadro's law (constant } T \text{ and } P)$$

Active Reading Question

Provide a real world example of Avogadro's law.

  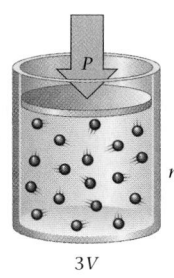

(a) V (b) $2V$ (c) $3V$

$n = 1$ | $n = 2$ | $n = 3$

Figure 13.6
The relationship between volume V and number of moles n. As the number of moles is increased from 1 to 2 (a to b), the volume doubles. When the number of moles is tripled (c), the volume is also tripled. The temperature and pressure remain the same in these cases.

13.1 • Describing the Properties of Gases • **455**

13.1 • Describing the Properties of Gases • **455**

13.1.D Volume and Moles: Avogadro's Law
Objective To understand the law relating the volume and the number of moles of a sample of gas at constant temperature and pressure, and to do calculations involving this law

 LABORATORY
EXPERIMENT 53:
The *P-n* Relationship of Gases, CBL

TEACHING TIP

At this point, all four variables (*P, V, T,* and *n*) have been used in gas law problems. Now is an excellent time to focus on problem-solving skills. Have students write down what they know from the problem, what they are looking for, and what information is needed.

MINI-DEMO

As a qualitative demonstration of Avogadro's law, you can blow up a balloon. Discuss why this scenario is a constant-pressure situation (since the balloon is very flexible, the pressure inside the balloon is essentially always equal to the atmospheric pressure). You can also place a small piece of dry ice in an inflated balloon and tie it. As the dry ice sublimes (and the moles of gas increase), the volume of the balloon will increase.

 Active Reading Question

Answers will vary. An example is blowing into a balloon. As we add more moles of gas, the balloon expands.

TECHNOLOGY

 Figure 13.6

Hands-On Chemistry
MINI-LAB

The Candle and the Tumbler

Materials Each student/group will need a candle, a glass, a test tube that fits over the candle, clay, and matches.

Purpose Students will better understand the gas laws and the kinetic molecular theory.

Discussion This experiment involves a complex system. As the test tube is placed over the flame, air inside the test tube is heated, causing the air to expand and allowing some air to escape the test tube (this release can sometimes be evidenced by air bubbling through the water if the test tube is placed over the candle and into the water with the correct speed). The reaction consumes oxygen (and generates carbon dioxide and water), and eventually the flame goes out. Once the flame is out, the air cools. The amount of gas inside the test tube

(continued on next page)

EXAMPLE 13.7

More Examples

1. If 2.55 mol of helium gas occupies a volume of 59.5 L at a particular temperature and pressure, what volume does 7.83 mol of helium occupy under the same conditions?

183 L

2. If 4.35 g of neon gas occupies a volume of 15.0 L at a particular temperature and pressure, what volume does 2.00 g of neon gas occupy under the same conditions?

6.90 L

HANDS-ON CHEMISTRY • MINI-LAB •

The Candle and the Tumbler

Materials
- candle
- glass
- water
- test tube

Procedure
1. Light a candle and let some wax drip onto the bottom of a glass that is taller than the candle. Blow out the candle and stick the candle to the glass before the wax solidifies.

2. Add water to the glass until the candle is about half-submerged. Do not get the wick of the candle wet.

3. Light the candle. Take a test tube that is wider than the candle and quickly place it over the candle, submerging the opening of the test tube. What happens? Make careful observations.

Results/Analysis
1. Explain your results.

EXAMPLE 13.7

Using Avogadro's Law in Calculations

Suppose we have a 12.2-L sample containing 0.50 mol of oxygen gas, O_2, at a pressure of 1 atm and a temperature of 25 °C. If all of this O_2 is converted to ozone, O_3, at the same temperature and pressure, what will be the volume of the ozone formed?

Solution
Where do we want to go?

Volume of the ozone formed = ? L

What do we know?

Initial (oxygen)	Final (ozone)
$n_1 = 0.50$ mol	$n_2 = ?$ mol
$V_1 = 12.2$ L	$V_2 = ?$ L

- Pressure is constant (1 atm)
- Temperature is constant (25 °C)
- $3\ O_2(g) \rightarrow 2\ O_3(g)$
- Avogadro's law $\quad \dfrac{V_1}{n_1} = \dfrac{V_2}{n_2}$

How do we get there?

To do this problem we need to compare the moles of gas originally present to the moles of gas present after the reaction. We know that 0.50 mol of O_2 is present initially. To find out how many moles of O_3 will be present after the reaction, we need to use the balanced equation for the reaction.

$$3O_2(g) \rightarrow 2O_3(g)$$

We calculate the moles of O_3 produced by using the appropriate mole ratio from the balanced equation.

$$0.50\ \text{mol } O_2 \times \frac{2\ \text{mol } O_3}{3\ \text{mol } O_2} = 0.33\ \text{mol } O_3$$

(continued)

remains constant, but a decrease in temperature gives rise to a lower pressure. Atmospheric pressure pushes water into the test tube until the pressure inside the tube and the weight of the water equal the atmospheric pressure. Of course, oxygen is consumed in the reaction, but carbon dioxide and water are generated. While this reaction gives rise to a net decrease in moles of gas, the decrease is not enough to

account for the amount of water that enters the test tube.

Many students initially claim that the fire uses up oxygen, and therefore the amount of gas inside the tube is less after the reaction than before it takes place. Because of this change, they will say that the pressure decreases and atmospheric pressure will push the water into the tube.

Although this explanation is incorrect, it involves good thinking on the part of

students. First, they know that oxygen is used up in the process of burning. Second, they understand that a decrease in the amount of gas will cause a decrease in pressure. Third, they know that atmospheric pressure will force water into the tube. In fact, this idea is so attractive that many texts (usually at the middle school level) use this activity as a demonstration that air is about 20% oxygen by volume; having the volume change by about 15%–25% is common.

Avogadro's law states that

$$\frac{V_1}{n_1} = \frac{V_2}{n_2}$$

where V_1 is the volume of n_1 moles of O_2 gas and V_2 is the volume of n_2 moles of O_3 gas. In this case we have

Initial Conditions   **Final Conditions**

$n_1 = 0.50$ mol $n_2 = 0.33$ mol

$V_1 = 12.2$ L $V_2 = ?$

Solving Avogadro's law for V_2 gives

$$V_2 = V_1 \times \frac{n_2}{n_1} = 12.2 \text{ L} \left(\frac{0.33 \text{ mol}}{0.50 \text{ mol}}\right) = 8.1 \text{ L}$$

Does it make sense?

Note that the volume decreases, as it should, because fewer molecules are present in the gas after O_2 is converted to O_3.

✔ Practice Problem • Exercise 13.7

Consider two samples of nitrogen gas (composed of N_2 molecules). Sample 1 contains 1.5 mol of N_2 and has a volume of 36.7 L at 25 °C and 1 atm. Sample 2 has a volume of 16.5 L at 25 °C and 1 atm. Calculate the number of moles of N_2 in Sample 2.

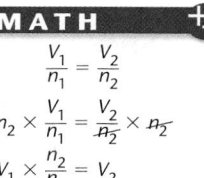

MATH

$$\frac{V_1}{n_1} = \frac{V_2}{n_2}$$

$$n_2 \times \frac{V_1}{n_1} = \frac{V_2}{n_2} \times n_2$$

$$V_1 \times \frac{n_2}{n_1} = V_2$$

SECTION 13.1
REVIEW QUESTIONS

❶ Mercury is a toxic substance. Why is it used instead of water in barometers and manometers?

❷ What is the SI unit for pressure? What is the unit commonly used in chemistry for pressure? Why aren't they the same?

❸ Copy and complete the following table.

torr	atm	pascals	mm Hg
459 torr			
		132,874 Pa	
	3.14 atm		
			842 mm Hg

❹ A 1.04-L sample of gas at 759 mm Hg pressure is expanded until its volume is 2.24 L. What is the pressure in the expanded gas sample (at constant temperature)?

❺ Compare Boyle's law, Charles's law, and Avogadro's law.

   a. What remains constant in each law?

   b. What are the variables in each law?

   c. What do the graphs for these laws look like?

   d. Write each law with V isolated. Using these equations and the graphs from part c, which law(s) show a directly proportional relationship? How can you tell?

❻ If 525 mL of gas at 25.0 °C is heated to 50.0 °C at constant pressure, calculate the new volume of the sample.

❼ A 1.50 mol sample of helium at a certain temperature and pressure has a volume of 31.4 L. A second sample of helium at the same temperature and pressure has a volume of 42.4 L. How many moles of helium are in the second sample?

RESEARCH LINKS
CLASSZONE.COM

(continued)

Ultimately, the idea that the sole cause of the rise in water level is from oxygen being used up fails for several reasons. Most importantly, it disregards that another gas (carbon dioxide) is a product of the reaction. It also neglects any effect resulting from a temperature difference. Careful observation will show students that the water level doesn't start rising significantly until the flame goes out. If oxygen being "used up" was the sole cause, the water level would increase smoothly over the course of the reaction. Because the water level rises dramatically only after the flame is very low or out, heat has a great deal to do with this phenomenon.

✔ Answer to Practice Problem 13.7

Because the temperature and pressure of the two samples are the same, we can use Avogadro's law in the form

$$\frac{V_1}{n_1} = \frac{V_2}{n_2}$$

Sample 1   **Sample 2**

$V_1 = 36.7$ L $V_2 = 16.5$ L

$n_1 = 1.5$ mol $n_2 = ?$

We can now solve Avogadro's law for the value of n_2:

$$n_2 = n_1 \times \frac{V_2}{V_1}$$

$$= 1.55 \text{ mol} \times \frac{16.5 \text{ L}}{36.7 \text{ L}} = 0.67 \text{ mol}$$

Here n_2 is smaller than n_1, which makes sense since V_2 is smaller than V_1.

Note: We isolate n_2 from Avogadro's law by multiplying both sides of the equation by n_2 and then by $\frac{n_1}{V_1}$,

$$\left(n_2 \times \frac{n_1}{V_1}\right)\frac{V_1}{n_1} = \left(n_2 \times \frac{n_1}{V_1}\right)\frac{V_2}{n_2}$$

to give $n_2 = n_1 \times \frac{V_2}{V_1}$.

SECTION 13.1
ASSESS

SECTION 13.1
Review Questions

1. Mercury is used because of its density. The volume (height) needed is inversely proportional to the density of the substance. The column of mercury is much shorter than that of other liquids at the same pressure.

2. The SI unit for pressure is the pascal. The most common unit for pressure is the torr or the atmosphere. The pascal is a very small unit, so the numbers would be very large. Using atm keeps the numbers small.

3. 459 torr, 0.604 atm, 6.12×10^4 pascals, 459 mm Hg; 996.637 torr, 1.31136 atm, 132,874 pascals, 996.637 mm Hg; 2.39×10^3 torr, 3.14 atm, 3.18×10^5 pascals, 2.39×10^3 mm Hg; 842 torr, 1.11 atm, 1.12×105 pascals, 842 mm Hg

4. 352 mm Hg

5.

		Boyle	Charles	Avogadro
a.	constant parameters	T, n	P, n	T, P
b.	variables	P, V	V, T	V, n
c.	graphs	inverse (hyperbola)	direct (line)	direct (line)
d.	laws	$V = \frac{k}{P}$ inverse	$V = kT$ direct	$V = kn$ direct

6. 569 mL

7. 2.03 mol

SECTION 13.2
INTRODUCE

Student Preparation

Assign students to read Section 13.2 and to answer the Review Questions at the end of the section before coming to class.

 Active Learning
Team Learning Worksheet

After introducing the material in Section 13.2 in class, place students in groups and have them work together on **Section 13.2: Team Learning Worksheet**.

SECTION 13.2
GUIDE THE LEARNING

Homework

You may wish to assign these selected end-of-chapter problems as homework for this section: 21, 22, 23, 25, 27, 29, 31, 33, 34, 35, 37, 39, 40, 43, 44

Additional end-of-chapter problems can be used for extra practice.

13.2.A The Ideal Gas Law

Objective To understand the ideal gas law and use it in calculations

 LABORATORY
EXPERIMENT 54:
Molar Volume and the Universal Gas Constant, Microscale

TECHNOLOGY

 Animations
Ideal Gas Law *PV = nRT*
Changes in Gas Volume, Pressure, and Concentration

TEACHING TIP

Emphasize how the ideal gas law can be used to derive all of the other gas laws.

SECTION 13.2
Using Gas Laws to Solve Problems

Key Terms
- Universal gas constant
- Ideal gas law
- Ideal gas
- Combined gas law
- Partial pressure
- Dalton's law of partial pressures
- Molar volume
- Standard temperature and pressure (STP)

Objectives
- *To understand the ideal gas law and use it in calculations*
- *To understand the relationship between the partial and total pressure of a gas mixture*
- *To do calculations involving Dalton's law of partial pressures*
- *To understand the molar volume of an ideal gas*
- *To learn the definition of STP*
- *To do stoichiometry calculations using the ideal gas law*

A. The Ideal Gas Law

We have considered three laws that describe the behavior of gases as revealed by experimental observations.

$$Boyle's\ law:\ PV = k \quad or \quad V = \frac{k}{P}\ (at\ constant\ T\ and\ n)$$

$$Charles's\ law: \qquad\qquad V = bT\ (at\ constant\ P\ and\ n)$$

$$Avogadro's\ law: \qquad\qquad V = an\ (at\ constant\ T\ and\ P)$$

information

Constant *n* means a constant number of moles of gas.

These relationships, which show how the volume of a gas depends on pressure, temperature, and number of moles of gas present, can be combined as follows:

$$V = R\left(\frac{Tn}{P}\right)$$

where *R* is the combined constant and is called the **universal gas constant**. When the pressure is expressed in atmospheres and the volume is in liters, *R* always has the value $0.08206\ \frac{L\ atm}{K\ mol}$. We can rearrange the above equation by multiplying both sides by *P*,

$$P \times V = \cancel{P} \times R\left(\frac{Tn}{\cancel{P}}\right)$$

Ideal gas law
PV = nRT

Ideal gas
A hypothetical gas that exactly obeys the ideal gas law.

to obtain the **ideal gas law**.

$$PV = nRT \quad ideal\ gas\ law \quad R = 0.08206\ \frac{L\ atm}{mol\ K}$$

The ideal gas law involves all the important characteristics of a gas:
- pressure (*P*),
- volume (*V*),
- number of moles (*n*),
- temperature (*T*).

Knowledge of any three of these properties is enough to define completely the condition of the gas, because the fourth property can be determined by using the ideal gas law.

It is important to recognize that the ideal gas law is based on experimental measurements of the properties of gases. A gas that obeys this equation is said to behave *ideally*. That is, this equation defines the behavior of an **ideal gas**. Most gases obey this equation closely at pressures of approximately 1 atm or lower, when the temperature is approximately 0 °C or higher. You should assume ideal gas behavior when working problems involving gases in this text.

Teaching Support
DEMONSTRATION

Marshmallow Man

Materials
- Bag of large marshmallows
- Toothpicks
- Vacuum pump
- Vacuum chamber

Preparation Assemble a marshmallow man from marshmallows and toothpicks. Use a pen to give him a face. Seat him on the platform of the vacuum chamber (you may need to prop him up with a small beaker).

Presentation Place the vacuum chamber over the marshmallow man. Attach the vacuum pump and turn it on. Observe the marshmallow man getting larger as the pressure decreases. When the pressure is released, the marshmallow man deflates, never to inflate the same way again.

EXAMPLE 13.8

Using the Ideal Gas Law in Calculations

A sample of hydrogen gas, H_2, has a volume of 8.56 L at a temperature of 0 °C and a pressure of 1.5 atm. Calculate the number of moles of H_2 present in this gas sample. Assume that the gas behaves ideally.

Solution
Where do we want to go?

Moles of H_2 = ? mol

What do we know?

- P = 1.5 atm
- T = 0 °C = 273 K
- V = 8.56 L
- Ideal gas law $PV = nRT$

How do we get there?

We can calculate the number of moles of gas present by using the ideal gas law, $PV = nRT$. We solve for n by dividing both sides by RT:

$$\frac{PV}{RT} = \frac{n\cancel{RT}}{\cancel{RT}}$$

to give

$$\frac{PV}{RT} = n$$

Thus

$$n = \frac{PV}{RT} = \frac{(1.5\ \cancel{atm})(8.56\ \cancel{L})}{\left(0.08206\ \frac{\cancel{L}\cdot\cancel{atm}}{\cancel{K}\cdot mol}\right)(273\ \cancel{K})} = 0.57\ mol$$

Practice Problem • Exercise 13.8

A weather balloon contains 1.10×10^5 mol of helium and has a volume of 2.70×10^6 L at 1.00 atm pressure. Calculate the temperature of the helium in the balloon in kelvins and in Celsius degrees.

(continued)

Teaching Notes A marshmallow has a large amount of air trapped in the tiny cells in its structure. As the surrounding pressure decreases, the cells swell. If the pump is very strong, the marshmallow man may suddenly deflate (the cells burst).

Variation If you do not have access to a vacuum pump, you can place a single large marshmallow in an Erlenmeyer flask and stopper the flask tightly. Insert the needle of a large plastic syringe through the stopper

and remove the air from the flask with one quick pull of the plunger. (Veterinary supply houses carry large syringes.)

- Remind students that when they solve problems using the ideal gas law, all units for variables must be the same as those in the gas constant R. Show students that the units of R (except those for the variable) from other numbers given in the problem.

- Encourage students to use the ideal gas law to solve most gas law problems, even when some conditions are not changing. All of the other gas laws can be derived from the ideal gas law. If students understand how to perform this derivation, they need not memorize all the other gas laws.

EXAMPLE 13.8

More Examples

1. A 2.50-mol sample of nitrogen gas has a volume of 5.50 L at a temperature of 27 °C. Calculate the pressure of the nitrogen gas.
   11.2 atm

2. A 5.00-mol sample of oxygen gas has a pressure of 1.25 atm at 22 °C. What volume does this gas occupy?
   96.8 L

Answer to Practice Problem 13.8

We are given the following information:

P = 1.00 atm

$V = 2.70 \times 10^6$ L

$n = 1.10 \times 10^5$ mol

We solve for T by dividing both sides of the ideal gas law by nR:

$$\frac{PV}{nR} = \frac{nRT}{nR}$$

to give

$$T = \frac{PV}{nR}$$

$$= \frac{(1.00\ \cancel{atm})(2.70 \times 10^6\ \cancel{L})}{(1.10 \times 10^5\ \cancel{mol})\left(0.08206\ \frac{\cancel{L}\cdot\cancel{atm}}{\cancel{K}\cdot\cancel{mol}}\right)}$$

$$= 299\ K$$

The temperature of the helium is 299 K, or 299 − 273 = 26 °C.

EXAMPLE 13.9

More Examples

1. A sample of neon gas has a volume of 3.45 L at 25 °C and a pressure of 565 torr. Calculate the number of moles of neon present in this gas sample.

   0.105 mol

2. A 0.250-mol sample of argon gas has a volume of 9.00 L at a pressure of 875 mm Hg. What is the temperature (in °C) of the gas?

   232 °C

 Answer to Practice Problem 13.9

We are given the following information about the radon sample:

$n = 1.5$ mol

$V = 21.0$ L

$T = 33$ °C $= 33 + 273 = 306$ K

$P = ?$

We solve the ideal gas law ($PV = nRT$) for P by dividing both sides of the equation by V:

$P = \dfrac{nRT}{V}$

$= \dfrac{(1.5 \text{ mol})\left(0.08206\, \dfrac{\text{L atm}}{\text{K mol}}\right)(306\,\text{K})}{21.0 \text{ L}}$

$= 1.8$ atm

EXAMPLE 13.9

Ideal Gas Law Calculations Involving Conversion of Units

What volume is occupied by 0.250 mol of carbon dioxide gas at 25 °C and 371 torr?

Solution

Where do we want to go?

Volume of CO_2 = ? L

What do we know?

- $P = 371$ torr
- $T = 25$ °C $= 298$ K
- $n = 0.250$ mol CO_2
- Ideal gas law $PV = nRT$

How do we get there?

We can use the ideal gas law to calculate the volume, but we must first convert pressure to atmospheres and temperature to the Kelvin scale.

$$P = 371 \text{ torr} = 371 \text{ torr} \times \frac{1.000 \text{ atm}}{760.0 \text{ torr}} = 0.488 \text{ atm}$$

$$T = 25 \text{ °C} = 25 + 273 = 298 \text{ K}$$

MATH ➕➗

$PV = nRT$

$\dfrac{PV}{P} = \dfrac{nRT}{P}$

$V = \dfrac{nRT}{P}$

We solve for V by dividing both sides of the ideal gas law ($PV = nRT$) by P.

$$V = \frac{nRT}{P} = \frac{(0.250 \text{ mol})\left(0.08206\, \dfrac{\text{L atm}}{\text{K mol}}\right)(298\,\text{K})}{0.488 \text{ atm}} = 12.5 \text{ L}$$

The volume of the sample of CO_2 is 12.5 L.

✔ **Practice Problem • Exercise 13.9**

Radon, a radioactive gas formed naturally in the soil, can cause lung cancer. It can pose a hazard to humans by seeping into houses, and there is concern about this problem in many areas. A 1.5-mol sample of radon gas has a volume of 21.0 L at 33 °C. What is the pressure of the gas?

Note that R has units of $\dfrac{\text{L atm}}{\text{K mol}}$. Accordingly, whenever we use the ideal gas law, we must express the volume in units of liters, the temperature in kelvins, and the pressure in atmospheres. When we are given data in other units, we must first convert to the appropriate units.

The ideal gas law can also be used to calculate the changes that will occur when the conditions of the gas are changed as illustrated in Example 13.10.

EXAMPLE 13.10

Using the Ideal Gas Law Under Changing Conditions

Suppose we have a 0.240-mol sample of ammonia gas at 25 °C with a volume of 3.5 L at a pressure of 1.68 atm. The gas is compressed to a volume of 1.35 L at 25 °C. Use the ideal gas law to calculate the final pressure.

Solution
Where do we want to go?

pressure of NH_3 = ? atm

What do we know?

Initial	Final
V_1 = 3.5 L	V_2 = 1.35 L
P_1 = 1.68 atm	P_2 = ?
T_1 = 25 °C = 298 K	T_2 = 25 °C = 298 K
n_1 = 0.240 mol	n_2 = 0.240 mol

• Ideal gas law $PV = nRT$

How do we get there?

Note that both n and T remain constant—only P and V change. Thus we could simply use Boyle's law ($P_1V_1 = P_2V_2$) to solve for P_2. However, we will use the ideal gas law to solve this problem to introduce the idea that one equation—the ideal gas equation—can be used to solve almost any gas problem.

The key idea here is that in using the ideal gas law to describe a change in conditions for a gas, we always *solve the ideal gas equation in such a way that the variables that change are on one side of the equal sign and the constant terms are on the other side.* That is, we start with the ideal gas equation in the conventional form ($PV = nRT$) and rearrange it so that all the terms that change are moved to one side and all the terms that do not change are moved to the other side. In this case the pressure and volume change and the temperature and number of moles remain constant (as does R, by definition). So we write the ideal gas law as

$$\underset{\text{Change}}{PV} = \underset{\text{Remain constant}}{nRT}$$

Because n, R, and T remain the same in this case, we can write $P_1V_1 = nRT$ and $P_2V_2 = nRT$. Combining these gives

$$P_1V_1 = nRT = P_2V_2 \text{ or } P_1V_1 = P_2V_2$$

and

$$P_2 = P_1 \times \frac{V_1}{V_2} = (1.68 \text{ atm}) \left(\frac{3.5 \cancel{L}}{1.35 \cancel{L}} \right) = 4.4 \text{ atm}$$

✓ Practice Problem • Exercise 13.10

A sample of methane gas that has a volume of 3.8 L at 5 °C is heated to 86 °C at constant pressure. Calculate its new volume.

ⓘ nformation

Does this answer make sense? The volume was decreased (at constant temperature and constant number of moles), which means that the pressure should increase, as the calculation indicates.

(continued)
been punctured and repeat your experiment. Compare the volumes from the experiments.

Teaching Notes The amount of moisture in a kernel of popcorn is the controlling factor in the quality of the pop. The optimum moisture content is 13%–14%. Kernels that are too dry may pop, but their popped volume is less than that obtained with more moist kernels. If the pericarp of the kernel is split or punctured, the pressure cannot build up to a high enough pressure for the kernels

to pop. Now might be a good time to provide popcorn treats for your students. The smell of the popped corn will make everyone hungry!

EXAMPLE 13.10

More Examples

1. Consider a sample of helium gas at 23 °C with a volume of 5.60 L at a pressure of 2.45 atm. The pressure is changed to 8.75 atm and the gas, is cooled to 15 °C. Calculate the new volume of the gas, using the ideal gas law equation.
   1.53 L

2. Consider a sample of helium gas at 28 °C with a volume of 3.80 L at a pressure of 3.15 atm. The gas expands to a volume of 9.50 L and the gas is heated to 43 °C. Calculate the new pressure of the gas, using the ideal gas law equation.
   1.32 atm

✓ Answer to Practice Problem 13.10

To solve this problem, we take the ideal gas law and separate those quantities that change from those that remain constant (on opposite sides of the equation). In this case, volume and temperature change and number of moles and pressure (and, of course, R) remain constant. So $PV = nRT$ becomes $\frac{V}{T} = \frac{nR}{P}$, which leads to

$$\frac{V_1}{T_1} = \frac{nR}{P} \text{ and } \frac{V_2}{T_2} = \frac{nR}{P}$$

Combining these gives

$$\frac{V_1}{T_1} = \frac{nR}{P} = \frac{V_2}{T_2}$$

$$\frac{V_1}{T_1} = \frac{V_2}{T_2} \text{ (Charles's law)}$$

We are given

Initial Conditions
T_1 = 5 °C = 5 + 273 = 278 K

V_1 = 3.8 L

Final Conditions
T_2 = 86 °C = 86 + 273 = 359 K

V_2 = ?

Thus

$$V_2 = \frac{T_2 V_1}{T_1}$$

$$= \frac{(359 \cancel{K})(3.8 \text{ L})}{278 \cancel{K}}$$

$$= 4.9 \text{ L}$$

Check: Is the answer sensible? The temperature was increased (at constant pressure), so the volume should increase. The answer makes sense.

- An almost infinite number of gas law problems exist. Expose students to many different types. Ask them to find mass instead of moles, density, or molar mass for a gas. These types of problems bring together information that students learned earlier in the course and create a more challenging environment.

- By asking different types of questions, you also encourage students to work toward understanding the concepts instead of memorizing formulas and equations.

EXAMPLE 13.11

More Examples

1. Consider a sample of hydrogen gas at 63 °C with a volume of 3.65 L at a pressure of 4.55 atm. The pressure is changed to 2.75 atm and the gas is cooled to –35 °C. Calculate the new volume of the gas.

   4.28 L

2. Consider a sample of oxygen gas at 27 °C with a volume of 9.55 L at a pressure of 2.97 atm. The pressure is changed to 8.25 atm and the gas is heated to 125 °C. Calculate the new volume of the gas using the ideal gas law equation.

   4.56 L

Note that in solving Example 13.10, we actually obtained Boyle's law ($P_1V_1 = P_2V_2$) from the ideal gas equation. You might well ask, "Why go to all this trouble?" The idea is to learn to use the ideal gas equation to solve all types of gas law problems. This way you will never have to ask yourself, "Is this a Boyle's law problem or a Charles's law problem?"

We continue to practice using the ideal gas law in Example 13.11. Remember, the key idea is to rearrange the equation so that the quantities that change are moved to one side of the equation and those that remain constant are moved to the other.

EXAMPLE 13.11

Calculating Volume Changes Using the Ideal Gas Law

A sample of diborane gas, B_2H_6, a substance that bursts into flames when exposed to air, has a pressure of 0.454 atm at a temperature of −15 °C and a volume of 3.48 L. If conditions are changed so that the temperature is 36 °C and the pressure is 0.616 atm, what will be the new volume of the sample?

Solution

Where do we want to go?

$$\text{Volume} = ? \text{ L}$$

(i) nformation

Always convert the temperature to the Kelvin scale and the pressure to atmospheres when applying the ideal gas law.

What do we know?

Initial	Final
$V_1 = 3.48$ L	$V_2 = ?$ L
$P_1 = 0.454$ atm	$P_2 = 0.616$ atm
$T_1 = -15$ °C = 258 K	$T_2 = 36$ °C = 309 K

- n = constant (no gas is added or removed)
- Ideal gas law $PV = nRT$

How do we get there?

We rearrange the ideal gas equation ($PV = nRT$) by dividing both sides by T,

MATH

$$PV = nRT$$
$$\frac{PV}{T} = n\frac{R\cancel{T}}{\cancel{T}}$$
$$\frac{PV}{T} = nR$$

$$\underset{\text{Change}}{\frac{PV}{T}} = \underset{\text{Constant}}{nR}$$

which leads to the equation

$$\frac{P_1V_1}{T_1} = nR = \frac{P_2V_2}{T_2}$$

or

$$\frac{P_1V_1}{T_1} = \frac{P_2V_2}{T_2}$$

We can now solve for V_2 by dividing both sides by P_2 and multiplying both sides by T_2.

$$\frac{1}{P_2} \times \frac{P_1V_1}{T_1} = \frac{\cancel{P_2}V_2}{T_2} \times \frac{1}{\cancel{P_2}} = \frac{V_2}{T_2}$$

$$T_2 \times \frac{P_1V_1}{P_2T_1} = \frac{V_2}{\cancel{T_2}} \times \cancel{T_2} = V_2$$

Chemistry in Your World

Snacks Need Chemistry, Too!

Popcorn is a cereal grain composed mainly of starch and water. Water inside the kernel turns to steam as the kernel is heated. The pressure builds up inside the kernel to approximately 9 atm, and then the pericarp splits open and the popcorn pops. During this process, the starch expands to form the white portion of the popped corn.

To investigate some of the factors affecting the popping of corn, use the Demonstration on popcorn given in this chapter.

Student Activity Assign teams of students to bring in a variety of brands of popcorn. Each team will test-pop 20 kernels of its brand and the data will be pooled to determine the percentage of water in each brand. Have each team determine the mass and volume of 20 kernels of popcorn. Place the kernels into a 250-mL flask and add just

---

That is,

$$\frac{T_2 P_1 V_1}{P_2 T_1} = V_2$$

It is sometimes convenient to think in terms of the ratios of the initial temperature and pressure and the final temperature and pressure. That is,

$$V_2 = \frac{T_2 P_1 V_1}{T_1 P_2} = V_1 \times \frac{T_2}{T_1} \times \frac{P_1}{P_2}$$

Substituting the information given yields

$$V_2 = \frac{309 \ \cancel{K}}{258 \ \cancel{K}} \times \frac{0.454 \ \cancel{atm}}{0.616 \ \cancel{atm}} \times 3.48 \ \text{L} = 3.07 \ \text{L}$$

✅ Practice Problem • Exercise 13.11

A sample of argon gas with a volume of 11.0 L at a temperature of 13 °C and a pressure of 0.747 atm is heated to 56 °C and a pressure of 1.18 atm. Calculate the final volume.

CHEMISTRY IN YOUR WORLD

Consumer Connnection

Snacks Need Chemistry, Too!

Have you ever wondered what makes popcorn pop? The popping is linked with the properties of gases. What happens when a gas is heated? Charles's law tells us that if the pressure is held constant, the volume of the gas must increase as the temperature is increased. But what happens if the gas being heated is trapped at a constant volume? We can see what happens by rearranging the ideal gas law ($PV = nRT$) as follows:

$$P = \left(\frac{nR}{V}\right)T$$

When n, R, and V are held constant, the pressure of a gas is directly proportional to the temperature. Thus, as the temperature of the trapped gas increases, its pressure also increases. This is exactly what happens inside a kernel of popcorn as it is heated. The moisture inside the kernel vaporized by the heat produces increasing pressure. The pressure finally becomes so great that the kernel breaks open, allowing the starch inside to expand to about 40 times its original size.

What's special about popcorn? Why does it pop while "regular" corn doesn't? William da Silva, a biologist at the University of Campinas in Brazil, has traced the "popability" of popcorn to its outer casing, called the pericarp. The molecules in the pericarp of popcorn, which are packed in a much more orderly way than in regular corn, transfer heat unusually quickly, producing a very fast pressure jump that pops the kernel. In addition, because the pericarp of popcorn is much thicker and stronger than that of regular corn, it can withstand more pressure, leading to a more explosive pop when the moment finally comes.

Popcorn popping

(continued)

enough vegetable oil to cover the kernels. Make a cover for the flask from aluminum foil. Find the mass of the system before popping. Heat the flask until all kernels pop. Remove the foil and allow the steam to escape. After the flask cools, recover it and find the mass of the system after popping. Determine the mass of the water lost, and measure the volume of the popped corn. Determine the percentage of moisture for each brand by finding the ratio of the mass

of water lost to the mass of the unpopped corn. Collect the information from all teams, including volume of the unpopped corn, volume of the popped corn, and percentage of moisture. Compare the data for the different brands of popcorn.

We are given the following information:

Initial Conditions

$P_1 = 0.747$ atm

$T_1 = 13$ °C $= 13 + 273 = 286$ K

$V_1 = 11.0$ L

Final Conditions

$P_2 = 1.18$ atm

$T_2 = 56$ °C $= 56 + 273 = 329$ K

$V_2 = ?$

In this case the number of moles remains constant. Thus we can say

$$\frac{P_1 V_1}{T_1} = nR \text{ and } \frac{P_2 V_2}{T_2} = nR$$

or

$$\frac{P_1 V_1}{T_1} = \frac{P_2 V_2}{T_2}$$

Solving for V_2 gives

$$V_2 = V_1 \times \frac{T_2}{T_1} \times \frac{P_1}{P_2}$$

$$= (11.0 \ \text{L})\left(\frac{329 \ \cancel{K}}{286 \ \cancel{K}}\right)\left(\frac{0.747 \ \cancel{atm}}{1.18 \ \cancel{atm}}\right)$$

$$= 8.01 \ \text{L}$$

Objective To understand the relationship between the partial and total pressures of a gas mixture, and to use this relationship in calculations

Have students use the Top Ten to solve a gas problem. For example, in a 200-L drum of air at 1 atm pressure, what would be the partial pressure of each gas in the Top Ten? How many moles of each gas are present in the drum?

 TEACHING TIPS

• When introducing Dalton's law of partial pressures, encourage students to think about the mixtures of gases at the molecular level. The presence of additional gases does not affect the number of times that a particular gas molecule hits the side of the container (since it is mostly empty space anyway). This concept helps students understand why the pressures are additive.

• The observations summarized in Dalton's law of partial pressures are extremely important when developing a theory to explain the gas laws.

Divers use a mixture of oxygen and helium in their breathing tanks when diving to depths greater than 150 feet.

MATH $+ \div$

$$PV = nRT$$
$$\frac{PV}{V} = \frac{nRT}{V}$$
$$P = \frac{nRT}{V}$$

Partial pressure
The independent pressure exerted by a gas in a mixture of gases.

Dalton's law of partial pressures
For a mixture of gases in a container, the total pressure exerted is the sum of the partial pressures of each of the gases.

The equation obtained in Example 13.11,

$$\frac{P_1 V_1}{T_1} = \frac{P_2 V_2}{T_2}$$

is often called the **combined gas law** equation. It holds when the amount of gas (moles) is held constant. While it may be convenient to remember this equation, it is not necessary because you can always use the ideal gas equation.

B. Dalton's Law of Partial Pressures

Many important gases contain a mixture of components. One notable example is air. Scuba divers who are going deeper than 150 feet use another important mixture, helium and oxygen. Normal air is not used because the nitrogen present dissolves in the blood in large quantities as a result of the high pressures experienced by the diver under several hundred feet of water. When the diver returns too quickly to the surface, the nitrogen bubbles out of the blood just as soda fizzes when it's opened, and the diver gets "the bends"—a very painful and potentially fatal condition. Because helium gas is only sparingly soluble in blood, it does not cause this problem.

Studies of gaseous mixtures show that each component behaves independently of the others. In other words, a given amount of oxygen exerts the same pressure in a 1.0-L vessel whether it is alone or in the presence of nitrogen (as in the air) or helium.

Among the first scientists to study mixtures of gases was John Dalton. In 1803 Dalton summarized his observations in this statement:

Top Ten Components of Air (dry air at sea level)	
Component	Volume Percent
N_2	78
O_2	21
Ar	0.93
CO_2	0.01–0.10
Ne	0.0018
He	5.2×10^{-4}
CH_4	2.0×10^{-4}
Kr	1.1×10^{-4}
H_2, N_2O	5.0×10^{-4}

Dalton's law of partial pressures For a mixture of gases in a container, the total pressure exerted is the sum of the partial pressures of the gases present.

The **partial pressure** of a gas is the pressure that the gas would exert if it were alone in the container. **Dalton's law of partial pressures** can be expressed as follows for a mixture containing three gases:

$$P_{total} = P_1 + P_2 + P_3$$

where the subscripts refer to the individual gases (gas 1, gas 2, and gas 3). The pressures P_1, P_2, and P_3 are the partial pressures; that is, each gas is responsible for only part of the total pressure.

2.4 atm

0.50 mol H_2

5.0 L at 20 °C
$P_{H_2} = 2.4$ atm

6.0 atm

1.25 mol He

5.0 L at 20 °C
$P_{He} = 6.0$ atm

8.4 atm

1.25 mol He + 0.50 mol H_2

1.75 mol gas

5.0 L at 20 °C
$P_{total} = P_{H_2} + P_{He}$
= 2.4 atm + 6.0 atm
= 8.4 atm

464 • Chapter 13 • Gases

Teaching Support
DEMONSTRATION

Egg in a Bottle
Materials
• Flask with an opening slightly smaller than the egg you intend to use
• Peeled hard-boiled eggs
• Water
• Hot plate

Preparation Hard-boil the eggs the evening before the demonstration and allow them to cool.

Presentation Peel a hard-boiled egg, and show students that it will not fit through the opening to the bottle. Explain to them that a knowledge of gas laws will help put the egg in the bottle.

Place about $\frac{1}{2}$ inch of water in the flask. Heat the water to boiling using the hot plate. Remove the flask from the hot plate and place the egg over the opening to the bottle. The egg will be pushed into the bottle with considerable force and noise. Now ask students how we can remove the egg from the bottle. After discussing some options, pour the water out of the flask. Tip the bottle upside down and show students that the egg will not fall out. With the egg in the neck of the flask, blow hard into the flask. The egg will pop out into your mouth!

Active Reading Question

The partial pressure of a gas is the pressure of one of the gases in a mixture of gases. It is the pressure the gas would exert if it were alone.

Assuming that each gas behaves ideally, we can calculate the partial pressure of each gas from the ideal gas law:

$$P_1 = \frac{n_1 RT}{V} \qquad P_2 = \frac{n_2 RT}{V} \qquad P_3 = \frac{n_3 RT}{V}$$

The total pressure of the mixture, P_{total}, can be represented as

$$P_{total} = P_1 + P_2 + P_3 = \frac{n_1 RT}{V} + \frac{n_2 RT}{V} + \frac{n_3 RT}{V}$$

$$= n_1\left(\frac{RT}{V}\right) + n_2\left(\frac{RT}{V}\right) + n_3\left(\frac{RT}{V}\right)$$

$$= (n_1 + n_2 + n_3)\left(\frac{RT}{V}\right)$$

$$= n_{total}\left(\frac{RT}{V}\right)$$

where n_{total} is the sum of the numbers of moles of the gases in the mixture. Thus, for a mixture of ideal gases, it is the *total number of moles of particles* that is important, not the *identity* of the individual gas particles. This idea is illustrated in **Figure 13.7.**

Active Reading Question

What is meant by the partial pressure of a gas?

The fact that the pressure exerted by an ideal gas is affected by the *number* of gas particles and is independent of the *nature* of the gas particles tells us two crucial things about ideal gases:

- The volume of the individual gas particle (atom or molecule) must not be very important.
- The forces among the particles must not be very important.

If these factors were important, the pressure of the gas would depend on the nature of the individual particles. For example, an argon atom is much larger than a helium atom. Yet 1.75 mol of argon gas in a 5.0-L container at 20 °C exerts the same pressure as 1.75 mol of helium gas in a 5.0-L container at 20 °C.

<table>
<tr><td>8.4 atm</td><td>8.4 atm</td><td>8.4 atm</td></tr>
</table>

1.75 mol He

5.0 L at 20 °C
P_{total} = 8.4 atm

0.75 mol H_2
0.75 mol He
0.25 mol Ne
1.75 mol

5.0 L at 20 °C
P_{total} = 8.4 atm

1.00 mol N_2
0.50 mol O_2
0.25 mol Ar
1.75 mol

5.0 L at 20 °C
P_{total} = 8.4 atm

Figure 13.7
The total pressure of a mixture of gases depends on the number of moles of gas particles (atoms or molecules) present, not on the identities of the particles. Note that these three samples show the same total pressure because each contains 1.75 mol of gas. The detailed nature of the mixture is unimportant.

TECHNOLOGY

 Figure 13.7

(continued)

Teaching Notes You can use a small coffee stirrer to open the egg valve slightly, which will make removing the egg by blowing slightly easier. You can also use a quart milk bottle or any other quart bottle with an opening of the correct size. Remember that these bottles are not Pyrex and must be heated slowly. Fill the bottle with hot water and empty it. Then fill the bottle with almost boiling water, let it sit 5–10 seconds, and empty it, immediately placing the egg on the opening. Place the small end of the egg on the opening so the egg does not split as it enters the bottle.

EXAMPLE 13.12

More Examples

1. A 5.00-g sample of helium gas is added to a 5.00-g sample of neon in a 2.50-L container at 27 °C. Calculate the partial pressure of each gas and the total pressure.

   12.3 atm He; 2.44 atm Ne; 14.7 atm total

2. Equal masses of oxygen and nitrogen gas are present in a container. Which gas exerts the larger partial pressure? By what factor?

   N_2 exerts a partial pressure that is 1.14 times as great as the partial pressure of O_2.

The same idea applies to the forces among the particles. Although the forces among gas particles depend on the nature of the particles, this seems to have little influence on the behavior of an ideal gas. We will see that these observations strongly influence the model that we will construct to explain ideal gas behavior.

EXAMPLE 13.12

Using Dalton's Law of Partial Pressures, I

Mixtures of helium and oxygen are used in the "air" tanks of underwater divers for deep dives. For a particular dive, 12 L of O_2 at 25 °C and 1.0 atm and 46 L of He at 25 °C and 1.0 atm were pumped into a 5.0-L tank. Calculate the partial pressure of each gas and the total pressure in the tank at 25 °C.

Solution

Where do we want to go?

$$P_{O_2} = ?\ \text{atm} \qquad P_{He} = ?\ \text{atm} \qquad P_{total} = ?\ \text{atm}$$

MATH

$PV = nRT$

$\dfrac{PV}{RT} = \dfrac{nRT}{RT}$

$\dfrac{PV}{RT} = n$

What do we know?

oxygen	helium
$V_{O_2} = 12$ L	$V_{He} = 46$ L
$P_{O_2} = ?$ atm	$P_{He} = ?$ atm
$T_{O_2} = 25$ °C $= 298$ K	$T_{He} = 25$ °C 298 K

- Volume of tank $= 5.0$ L
- Ideal gas law $\qquad PV = nRT$
- $P_{total} = P_{O_2} + P_{He}$

How do we get there?

Because the partial pressure of each gas depends on the moles of that gas present, we must first calculate the number of moles of each gas by using the ideal gas law in the form

$$n = \frac{PV}{RT}$$

$$\text{Moles of } O_2 = n_{O_2} = \frac{(1.0\ \text{atm})(12\ \text{L})}{(0.08206\ \text{L atm/K mol})(298\ \text{K})} = 0.49\ \text{mol}$$

$$\text{Moles of He} = n_{He} = \frac{(1.0\ \text{atm})(46\ \text{L})}{(0.08206\ \text{L atm/K mol})(298\ \text{K})} = 1.9\ \text{mol}$$

The tank containing the mixture has a volume of 5.0 L, and the temperature is 25 °C (298 K). We can use these data and the ideal gas law to calculate the partial pressure of each gas.

$$P = \frac{nRT}{V}$$

$$P_{O_2} = \frac{(0.49\ \text{mol})(0.08206\ \text{L atm/K mol})(298\ \text{K})}{5.0\ \text{L}} = 2.4\ \text{atm}$$

$$P_{He} = \frac{(1.9\ \text{mol})(0.08206\ \text{L atm/K mol} (298\ \text{K})}{5.0\ \text{L}} = 9.3\ \text{atm}$$

The total pressure is the sum of the partial pressures.

$$P_{total} = P_{O_2} + P_{He} = 2.4 \text{ atm} + 9.3 \text{ atm} = 11.7 \text{ atm}$$

✓ Practice Problem • Exercise 13.12

A 2.0-L flask contains a mixture of nitrogen gas and oxygen gas at 25 °C. The total pressure of the gaseous mixture is 0.91 atm, and the mixture is known to contain 0.050 mol N_2. Calculate the partial pressure of oxygen and the moles of oxygen present.

A mixture of gases always occurs when a gas is collected by displacement of water. For example, **Figure 13.8** shows the collection of the oxygen gas that was produced by the decomposition of solid potassium chlorate. The gas is collected by bubbling it into a bottle initially filled with water. Thus the gas in the bottle is really a mixture of water vapor and oxygen. (Water vapor is present because molecules of water escape from the surface of the liquid and collect as a gas in the space above the liquid.) Therefore, the total pressure exerted by this mixture is the sum of the partial pressure of the gas being collected and the partial pressure of the water vapor. The partial pressure of the water vapor is called the vapor pressure of water. Because water molecules are more likely to escape from hot water than from cold water, the *vapor pressure* of water increases with temperature. This is shown by the values of water vapor pressure at various temperatures shown in **Table 13.2.**

Table 13.2

The Vapor Pressure of Water as a Function of Temperature

T (°C)	P (torr)
0.0	4.579
10.0	9.209
20.0	17.535
25.0	23.756
30.0	31.824
40.0	55.324
60.0	149.4
70.0	233.7
90.0	525.8

◗ Active Reading Question

Why must we worry about the partial pressure of water vapor when collecting a gas by the displacement of water?

KClO₃

Oxygen plus water vapor

Figure 13.8
The production of oxygen by thermal decomposition of $KClO_3$

 Answer to Practice Problem 13.12

As usual when dealing with gases, we can use the ideal gas equation $PV = nRT$. First consider the information given:

$P = 0.91 \text{ atm} = P_{total}$

$V = 2.0 \text{ L}$

$T = 25 \text{ °C} = 25 + 273 = 298 \text{ K}$

Given this information, we can calculate the number of moles of gas in the mixture:

$$n_{total} = n_{N_2} + n_{O_2}.$$

Solving for n in the ideal gas equation gives

$$n_{total} = \frac{P_{total}V}{RT}$$

$$= \frac{(0.91 \text{ atm})(2.0 \text{ L})}{\left(0.08206\frac{\text{L atm}}{\text{K mol}}\right)(298 \text{ K})}$$

$$= 0.074 \text{ mol}$$

We also know that 0.050 mol of N_2 is present. Because

$$n_{total} = n_{N_2} + n_{O_2} = 0.074 \text{ mol}$$
$$\uparrow$$
$$(0.050 \text{ mol})$$

we can calculate the moles of O_2 present.

$0.050 \text{ mol} + n_{O_2} = 0.074 \text{ mol}$

$n_{O_2} = 0.074 \text{ mol} - 0.050 \text{ mol} = 0.024 \text{ mol}$

Now that we know the moles of oxygen present, we can calculate the partial pressure of oxygen from the ideal gas equation.

$$P_{O_2} = \frac{n_{O_2}RT}{V}$$

$$= \frac{(0.024 \text{ mol})\left(0.08206\frac{\text{L atm}}{\text{K mol}}\right)(298 \text{ K})}{2.0 \text{ L}}$$

$$= 0.29 \text{ atm}$$

Although it is not requested, note that the partial pressure of the N_2 must be 0.62 atm, because

$$\underbrace{0.62 \text{ atm}}_{P_{N_2}} + \underbrace{0.29 \text{ atm}}_{P_{O_2}} = \underbrace{0.91 \text{ atm}}_{P_{total}}$$

◗ Active Reading Question

Water molecules escape from the surface of liquid water and collect as a gas in the space above the liquid.

TECHNOLOGY

 Figure 13.8

EXAMPLE 13.13

EXAMPLE 13.13

More Examples

1. A sample of oxygen gas is saturated with water vapor at 30.0 °C. The total pressure is 753 torr and the vapor pressure of water at 30.0 °C is 31.824 torr. What is the partial pressure of the oxygen gas in atm?

   0.949 atm

2. A sample of oxygen gas is saturated with water vapor at 27 °C. The total pressure is 785.0 torr and the partial pressure of oxygen is 758.3 torr. What is the vapor pressure of water at 27 °C?

   26.7 torr

Using Dalton's Law of Partial Pressures, II

A sample of solid potassium chlorate, $KClO_3$, was heated in a test tube (see Figure 13.8) and decomposed according to the reaction

$$2KClO_3(s) \rightarrow 2KCl(s) + 3O_2(g)$$

The oxygen produced was collected by displacement of water at 22 °C. The resulting mixture of O_2 and H_2O vapor had a total pressure of 754 torr and a volume of 0.650 L. Calculate the partial pressure of O_2 in the gas collected and the number of moles of O_2 present. The vapor pressure of water at 22 °C is 21 torr.

Solution
Where do we want to go?

$$P_{O_2} = ? \text{ atm}$$
$$n_{O_2} = ? \text{ mol}$$

What do we know?

oxygen	water vapor
$n_{O_2} = ?$ mol	
$P_{O_2} = ?$ atm	$P_{H_2O} = 21$ torr
$T_{O_2} = 22 °C = 295$ K	$T_{H_2O} = 22 °C = 295$ K

- $P_{total} = 754 \text{ torr} = P_{O_2} + P_{H_2O}$
- Ideal Gas Law $PV = nRT$
- $V_{total} = 0.650 \text{ L} = V_{O_2} + V_{H_2O}$

How do we get there?

We can find the partial pressure of O_2 from Dalton's law of partial pressures:

$$P_{total} = P_{O_2} + P_{H_2O} = P_{O_2} + 21 \text{ torr} = 754 \text{ torr}$$

or

$$P_{O_2} + 21 \text{ torr} = 754 \text{ torr}$$

MATH ➕➗

$$PV = nRT$$
$$\frac{PV}{RT} = \frac{nRT}{RT}$$
$$\frac{PV}{RT} = n$$

We can solve for P_{O_2} by subtracting 21 torr from both sides of the equation.

$$P_{O_2} = 754 \text{ torr} - 21 \text{ torr} = 733 \text{ torr}$$

Next we solve the ideal gas law for the number of moles of O_2.

$$n_{O_2} = \frac{P_{O_2}V}{RT}$$

In this case, $P_{O_2} = 733$ torr. We change the pressure to atmospheres as follows:

$$\frac{733 \text{ torr}}{760 \text{ torr/atm}} = 0.964 \text{ atm}$$

Then,

$$V = 0.650 \text{ L}$$

$T = 22\ °C = 22 + 273 = 295\ K$

$R = 0.08206\ L\ atm/K\ mol$

so

$$n_{O_2} = \frac{(0.964\ \cancel{atm})(0.650\ \cancel{L})}{(0.08206\ \cancel{L}\ \cancel{atm}/\cancel{K}\ mol)(295\ \cancel{K})} = 2.59 \times 10^{-2}\ mol$$

 Practice Problem • Exercise 13.13

Consider a sample of hydrogen gas collected over water at 25 °C where the vapor pressure of water is 24 torr. The volume occupied by the gaseous mixture is 0.500 L, and the total pressure is 0.950 atm. Calculate the partial pressure of H_2 and the number of moles of H_2 present.

C. Gas Stoichiometry

We have seen in this chapter just how useful the ideal gas equation is. For example, if we know the pressure, volume, and temperature for a given sample of gas, we can calculate the number of moles present: $n = PV/RT$. This fact makes it possible to do stoichiometric calculations for reactions involving gases.

EXAMPLE 13.14

Gas Stoichiometry: Calculating Volume

Calculate the volume of oxygen gas produced at 1.00 atm and 25 °C by the complete decomposition of 10.5 g of potassium chlorate. The balanced equation for the reaction is

$$2KClO_3(s) \rightarrow 2KCl(s) + 3O_2(g)$$

Solution
Where do we want to go?

Volume of O_2 produced = ? L

What do we know?

- $2KClO_3(s) + 2KCl(s) \rightarrow 3O_2(g)$
- $P = 1.00\ atm$
- $T = 25\ °C = 298\ K$
- $10.5\ g\ KClO_3$
- Ideal gas law $PV = nRT$

How do we get there?
We'll summarize the steps required to do this problem in the following schematic:

Grams of KClO₃	⇒₁	Moles of KClO₃	⇒₂	Moles of O₂	⇒₃	Volume of O₂

 Answer to Practice Problem 13.13

The volume is 0.500 L, the temperature is 25 °C (or 25 + 273 = 298 K), and the total pressure is given as 0.950 atm. Of this total pressure, 24 torr is due to the water vapor. We can calculate the partial pressure of the H_2 because we know that

$$P_{total} = P_{H_2} + P_{H_2O} = 0.950\ atm$$
$$\uparrow$$
$$24\ torr$$

Before we carry out the calculation, however, we must convert the pressures to the same units. Converting P_{H_2O} to atmospheres gives

$$24\ \cancel{torr} \times \frac{1.000\ atm}{760.0\ \cancel{torr}} = 0.032\ atm$$

Thus

$$P_{total} = P_{H_2} + P_{H_2O}$$
$$= 0.950\ atm$$
$$= P_{H_2} + 0.032\ atm$$

and

$$P_{H_2} = 0.950\ atm - 0.032\ atm$$
$$= 0.918\ atm$$

Now that we know the partial pressure of the hydrogen gas, we can use the ideal gas equation to calculate the moles of H_2.

$$n_{H_2} = \frac{P_{H_2}V}{RT}$$
$$= \frac{(0.918\ \cancel{atm})(0.500\ \cancel{L})}{\left(0.08206\ \frac{\cancel{L}\ \cancel{atm}}{\cancel{K}\ mol}\right)(298\ \cancel{K})}$$
$$= 0.0188\ mol$$
$$= 1.88 \times 10^{-2}\ mol$$

The sample of gas contains 1.88×10^{-2} mol of H_2, which exerts a partial pressure of 0.918 atm.

13.2.C Gas Stoichiometry

Objective To understand the molar volume of an ideal gas, learn the definition of STP, and use these concepts and the ideal gas equation

 TEACHING TIP

Review the basics of stoichiometry before beginning to work gas stoichiometry problems. This point is a good place to reteach the mole and mole ratio and to review unit conversions.

Meeting Individual Needs
READING CONCEPTS

It may have been some time since students have dealt with chemical equations. For a review of chemical equations, have students read *Reading Chemical Equations* located in the *Teacher Resources*.

Meeting Individual Needs
MATH CONCEPTS

For students who are still struggling with stoichiometry problems, have them read *Dimensional Analysis* located in the *Teacher Resources*. A worksheet is available to go along with the handout.

EXAMPLE 13.14

More Examples

Consider the reaction represented by the equation $P_4(s) + 6H_2(g) \rightarrow 4PH_3(g)$. At 27 °C and 1.25 atm, what volume of hydrogen gas is required to react with 5.65 g of phosphorus?

5.39 L

 Answer to Practice Problem 13.14

We will solve this problem by taking the following steps:

Step 1 Using the atomic mass of zinc (65.38 g), we calculate the moles of zinc in 26.5 g.

$26.5 \text{ g Zn} \times \dfrac{1 \text{ mol Zn}}{65.38 \text{ g Zn}} =$

0.405 mol Zn

Step 2 Using the balanced equation, we next calculate the moles of H_2 produced.

$0.405 \text{ mol Zn} \times \dfrac{1 \text{ mol } H_2}{1 \text{ mol Zn}} =$

0.405 mol H_2

Step 3 Now that we know the moles of H_2, we can compute the volume of H_2 by using the ideal gas law, where

$P = 1.50$ atm

$V = ?$

$n = 0.405$ mol

$R = 0.08206$ L atm/K mol

$T = 19 °C = 19 + 273 = 292 \text{ K}$

$V = \dfrac{nRT}{P}$

$= \dfrac{(0.405 \text{ mol})\left(08206 \frac{\text{L atm}}{\text{K mol}}\right)(292 \text{ K})}{1.50 \text{ atm}}$

$= 6.47$ L of H_2

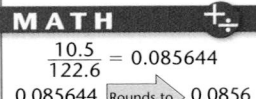

MATH

$\dfrac{10.5}{122.6} = 0.085644$

0.085644 **Rounds to** 0.0856

$0.0856 = 8.56 \times 10^{-2}$

Step 1 To find the moles of $KClO_3$ in 10.5 g, we use the molar mass of $KClO_3$ (122.6 g).

$$10.5 \text{ g KClO}_3 \times \dfrac{1 \text{ mol KClO}_3}{122.6 \text{ g KClO}_3} = 8.56 \times 10^{-2} \text{ mol KClO}_3$$

Step 2 To find the moles of O_2 produced, we use the mole ratio of O_2 to $KClO_3$ derived from the balanced equation.

$$8.56 \times 10^{-2} \text{ mol KClO}_3 \times \dfrac{3 \text{ mol } O_2}{2 \text{ mol KClO}_3} = 1.28 \times 10^{-1} \text{ mol } O_2$$

Step 3 To find the volume of oxygen produced, we use the ideal gas law $PV = nRT$, where

$P = 1.00$ atm

$V = ?$

$n = 1.28 \times 10^{-1}$ mol, the moles of O_2 we calculated

$R = 0.08206$ L atm/K mol

$T = 25 °C = 25 + 273 = 298 \text{ K}$

Solving the ideal gas law for V gives

$$V = \dfrac{nRT}{P} = \dfrac{(1.28 \times 10^{-1} \text{ mol})\left(0.08206 \frac{\text{L atm}}{\text{K mol}}\right)(298 \text{ K})}{1.00 \text{ atm}} = 3.13 \text{ L}$$

Thus 3.13 L of O_2 will be produced.

 Practice Problem • Exercise 13.14

Calculate the volume of hydrogen produced at 1.50 atm and 19 °C by the reaction of 26.5 g of zinc with excess hydrochloric acid according to the balanced equation

$$Zn(s) + 2HCl(aq) \rightarrow ZnCl_2(aq) + H_2(g)$$

Molar Volume

It is useful to define the volume occupied by 1 mol of a gas under certain specified conditions. For 1 mol of an ideal gas at 0 °C (273 K) and 1 atm, the volume of the gas given by the ideal gas law is

$$V = \dfrac{nRT}{P} = \dfrac{(1.00 \text{ mol})(0.08206 \text{ L atm/K mol})(273 \text{ K})}{1.00 \text{ atm}} = 22.4 \text{ L}$$

This volume of 22.4 L is called the **molar volume** of an ideal gas.

The conditions 0 °C and 1 atm are called **standard temperature and pressure** (abbreviated **STP**). Properties of gases are often given under these conditions.

> The molar volume of an ideal gas is 22.4 L at STP.
> 22.4 L contains 1 mol of an ideal gas at STP.

Molar volume
The volume of 1 mole of an ideal gas is equal to 22.4 L at 0 °C and 1 atm.

Standard temperature and pressure (STP)
0 °C and 1 atm

EXAMPLE 13.15

Gas Stoichiometry: Calculations Involving Gases at STP

A sample of nitrogen gas has a volume of 1.75 L at STP. How many moles of N_2 are present?

Solution

Where do we want to go?

Amount of N_2 produced = ? mol

What do we know?

- V = 1.75 L at STP
- 1.00 mol = 22.4 L (STP)

How do we get there?

We could solve this problem by using the ideal gas equation, but we can take a shortcut by using the molar volume of an ideal gas at STP. Because 1 mol of an ideal gas at STP has a volume of 22.4 L, a 1.75-L sample of N_2 at STP contains considerably less than 1 mol. We can find how many moles by using the equivalence statement

1.000 mol = 22.4 L (STP)

which leads to the conversion factor we need:

$$1.75 \text{ L } N_2 \times \frac{1.000 \text{ mol } N_2}{22.4 \text{ L } N_2} = 7.81 \times 10^{-2} \text{ mol } N_2$$

✅ Practice Problem • Exercise 13.15

Ammonia is commonly used as a fertilizer to provide a source of nitrogen for plants. A sample of $NH_3(g)$ occupies 5.00 L at 25 °C and 15.0 atm. What volume will this sample occupy at STP?

CHEMISTRY IN YOUR WORLD

Consumer Connection

The Chemistry of Air Bags

Most experts agree that air bags represent a very important advance in automobile safety. These bags, which are stored in the auto's steering wheel or dash, are designed to inflate rapidly (within about 40 ms) in the event of a crash, cushioning the front seat occupants against impact. The bags then deflate immediately to allow vision and movement after the crash. Air bags are activated when a severe deceleration (an impact) causes a steel ball to compress a spring and electrically ignite a detonator cap, which, in turn, causes sodium azide (NaN_3) to decompose explosively, forming sodium and nitrogen gas:

$$2NaN_3(s) \rightarrow 2Na(s) + 3N_2(g)$$

This system works very well and requires a relatively small amount of sodium azide (100 g yields 56 L $N_2(g)$ at 25 °C and 1.0 atm).

When a vehicle containing air bags reaches the end of its useful life, the sodium azide present in the activators must be given proper disposal. Sodium azide, besides being explosive is toxic.

The air bag is an application of chemistry that has saved thousands of lives.

Inflated air bags

Chemistry in Your World

The Chemistry of Air Bags

This application involving sodium azide (NaN_3) provides a good opportunity to reteach Lewis structures. The azide ion N_3^- has the Lewis structure $\ddot{N}{=}N{=}\ddot{N}$ because it has 16 electrons. Notice that this ion is isoelectronic with CO_2, which also has a linear structure.

HN_3 (hydrazoic acid) can be formed by careful addition of H_2SO_4 to NaN_3.

However, HN_3 is very toxic and highly explosive and has a repulsive, intensely irritating odor. The Lewis structure of HN_3 is $H{-}\overset{\ddot{N}=N=\ddot{N}}{}$ and the H—N—N angle is 112°, a little smaller than the angle of 120° predicted by VSEPR theory.

You can use this feature to review stoichiometry. NaN_3 reacts with water to form hydrozoic acid:
$NaN_3 + H_2O \rightarrow HN_3 + NaOH$
Since most air bags are not used during

a car's lifetime, they could begin piling up in junkyards. If a typical airbag contains 150 g sodium azide, how much hydrazoic acid could be released if water leaked into the sodium azide? This problem of toxic air bags can be solved by igniting the air bag or by using recyclable modules that contain sodium azide pellets in a reusable form.

EXAMPLE 13.15

More Examples

1. A sample of argon gas has a volume of 3.45 L at STP. What is the mass of the argon?

   6.15 g

2. A sample of hydrogen gas occupies a volume of 15.0 L at STP. What volume will this sample occupy at 22 °C and 2.50 atm?

   6.48 L

✅ Answer to Practice Problem 13.15

The most convenient method of solution involves using the molar volume at STP. First we use the ideal gas equation to calculate the moles of NH_3 present:

$$n = \frac{PV}{RT}$$

where P = 15.0 atm, V = 5.00 L, and T = 25 °C + 273 = 298 K.

$$n = \frac{(15.0 \text{ atm})(5.00 \text{ L})}{\left(0.08206 \frac{\text{L atm}}{\text{K mol}}\right)(298 \text{ K})} =$$

3.07 mol

At STP each mole of gas occupies 22.4 L. Therefore, 3.07 mol has the volume

$$3.07 \text{ mol} \times \frac{22.4 \text{ L}}{1 \text{ mol}} = 68.8 \text{ L}$$

🍎 TEACHING TIP

Consider having students verify the claim in the Chemistry in Your World feature that 100 g of NaN_3 yields 56 L of nitrogen gas at 25 °C and 1.00 atm.

EXAMPLE 13.16

More Examples

1. When magnesium reacts with hydrochloric acid, hydrogen gas is produced:
$Mg(s) + 2HCl(aq) \rightarrow$
$MgCl_2(aq) + H_2(g)$.
Calculate the volume of hydrogen gas produced at STP by reacting 5.00 g Mg and an excess of HCl(aq).

4.61 L

2. When subjected to an electric current, water decomposes to hydrogen and oxygen gas:
$2H_2O(l) \rightarrow 2H_2(g) + O_2(g)$.
If 25.0 g of water is decomposed, what volume of oxygen gas is produced at STP?

15.5 L

EXAMPLE 13.16

Gas Stoichiometry: Reactions Involving Gases at STP

Quicklime, CaO, is produced by heating calcium carbonate, $CaCO_3$. Calculate the volume of CO_2 produced at STP from the decomposition of 152 g of $CaCO_3$ according to the reaction

$$CaCO_3(s) \rightarrow CaO(s) + CO_2(g)$$

Solution

Where do we want to go?

Volume of CO_2 produced = ? L

What do we know?

- $CaCO_3(s) + CaO(s) \rightarrow CO_2(g)$
- STP conditions
- 1.00 mol = 22.4 L (STP)
- 152 g $CaCO_3$

How do we get there?

The strategy for solving this problem is summarized by the following schematic:

Step 1 Using the molar mass of $CaCO_3$ (100.1 g), we calculate the number of moles of $CaCO_3$.

$$152 \text{ g } CaCO_3 \times \frac{1 \text{ mol } CaCO_3}{100.1 \text{ g } CaCO_3} = 1.52 \text{ mol } CaCO_3$$

Step 2 Each mole of $CaCO_3$ produces 1 mol of CO_2, so 1.52 mol of CO_2 will be formed.

ⓘ nformation

Remember that the molar volume of an ideal gas is 22.4 L at STP.

Step 3 We can convert the moles of CO_2 to volume by using the molar volume of an ideal gas, because the conditions are STP.

$$1.52 \text{ mol } CO_2 \times \frac{22.4 \text{ L } CO_2}{1 \text{ mol } CO_2} = 34.1 \text{ L } CO_2$$

Thus the decomposition of 152 g of $CaCO_3$ produces 34.1 L of CO_2 at STP.

Note that the final step in Example 13.16 involves calculating the volume of gas from the number of moles. Because the conditions were specified as STP, we were able to use the molar volume of a gas at STP. If the conditions of a problem are different from STP, we must use the ideal gas law to compute the volume.

Teaching Support

DEMONSTRATION

Density of Gases

Materials

- Balloons filled with a variety of gases (helium, methane, carbon dioxide, air)
- Ribbons or string

Preparation Fill the balloons to about equal volume. It is helpful to use a different color balloon for each type of gas. You can generate

CO_2 by using dry ice. If you have lecture bottles of any gases, they may be used to fill the balloons. Tie a ribbon or string to each balloon. Be sure that the string is at least 1 m long. Gather the balloons together, holding them together at the necks so students cannot observe the densities before the demonstration.

Presentation Find a volunteer for each balloon. Give the volunteer the balloon, having him or her hold it by the neck with the end of the string in the volunteer's other

SECTION 13.2
REVIEW QUESTIONS

1 When solving gas problems the ideal gas law can be used even when some of the properties are constant. Explain how to do this.

2 At what temperature will 6.21 g of oxygen gas exert a pressure of 5.00 atm in a 10.0-L container?

3 The pressure of a gas is affected by the number of particles and not affected by the kind of gas in the container. What does this fact tell us about ideal gases?

4 A 1.50 L sample of neon gas at 1.10 atm and 25 °C is heated to 45 °C. The neon gas is then subjected to a pressure of 1.50 atm. Determine the new volume of the neon gas.

5 Calculate the partial pressure (in torr) of each gas in the mixture.

10.0 atm

1.0 mol CO₂
2.0 mol O₂
3.0 mol N₂

6 In Figure 13.8 oxygen gas is being collected over water. Assume this experiment is being done at 25 °C. Write an equation for it, and find the pressure of the oxygen gas (assume the pressure in the bottle is P_T).

7 Magnesium metal reacts with hydrochloric acid to produce hydrogen gas and a solution of magnesium chloride. Write and balance the chemical equation for this reaction, and determine the volume of the hydrogen gas generated (at 1.00 atm, 25 °C) by reacting 10.0 g Mg with an excess of hydrochloric acid.

8 When water is subjected to an electric current, it decomposes to hydrogen and oxygen gas. If 1.00 g of water is decomposed at 1.00 atm and 25 °C, what volume of oxygen gas is collected?

RESEARCH LINKS
CLASSZONE.COM

13.2 • Using Gas Laws to Solve Problems • **473**

SECTION 13.2
ASSESS

SECTION 13.2
Review Questions

1. Collect all parameters that are constant on one side of the equation and those that change on the other side. Find the initial and final values of the variables from the problem. Place the initial values in the equation, and set the final values into the equation on a separate line. Because the constants are the same in both equations, you can set the variable side of the initial equation equal to the variable side of the final equation. Solve for the missing variable.

2. 2868 °C

3. With ideal gases, the volume of the individual particles must not be very important and the forces among the particles must not be very important.

4. 1.17 L

5. P_{N_2} = 5.0 atm, P_{O_2} = 3.3 atm, and P_{CO_2} = 1.67 atm

6. $P_T = P_{oxygen} + P_{water\ vapor}$
   $P_T = P_{oxygen} + 23.756$ torr
   $P_T - 23.756$ torr $= P_{oxygen}$

7. 10.1 L

8. 0.679 L O_2

(continued)

hand. Have all volunteers hold the balloons about 6 feet from the floor. Ask all volunteers to drop the balloons at the same time. Observe the order in which the balloons fall (or rise). You will need to repeat the demonstration to actually have students observe the order— the first time they just see what happens. (It is important to have the strings so that volunteers do not lose the balloons.)

Teaching Notes Write the gases on the board. Have students match the balloon colors with the gases and explain how they arrived at their conclusions. You can also use this activity to review many concepts by asking students to order the balloons from largest to smallest in each catetgory: pressure, volume, temperature, number of particles, mass of gas, density, average kinetic energy, average speed of particles.

Student Preparation

Assign students to read Section 13.3 and to answer the Review Questions at the end of the section before coming to class.

Active Learning
Team Learning Worksheet

After introducing the material in Section 13.3 in class, place students in groups and have them work together on **Section 13.3: Team Learning Worksheet**.

SECTION 13.3
GUIDE THE LEARNING

Homework

You may wish to assign these selected end-of-chapter problems as homework for this section: 46, 48, 49, 50, 52, 53, 54

Additional end-of-chapter problems can be used for extra practice.

13.3.A Laws and Models: A Review

Objective To understand the relationship between laws and models (theories)

TEACHING TIP

Now is a good time to review the difference between laws and models. The gas laws allow students to predict the behavior of gases, and the kinetic molecular theory explains why gases behave in the manner they do.

MINI-DEMO

Before class, make the following apparatus. Use an Erlenmeyer or round-bottom flask with a narrow mouth. Place about 5 mL of water in the flask and heat the water to boiling. Continue heating until only about 1 mL of water remains. Now for the tricky part: Remove the flask from the heat and, while holding it with a towel to avoid burns, cover the opening with a balloon (partially inflated or containing a little soapy solution works best). A partner can be of great assistance in getting the balloon on the flask. As the flask cools, the balloon will be drawn into the flask. The most difficult part

is getting the balloon over the mouth of the warm flask without splitting or puncturing it. Be patient and practice your technique.

In class, show the flask to students and challenge them for explanations.

SECTION 13.3
Using a Model to Describe Gases

Key Term
- Kinetic molecular theory

Objectives
- *To understand the relationship between laws and models (theories)*
- *To understand the postulates of the kinetic molecular theory*
- *To understand temperature*
- *To learn how the kinetic molecular theory explains the gas laws*
- *To describe the properties of real gases*

A. Laws and Models: A Review

In this chapter we have considered several properties of gases and have seen how the relationships among these properties can be expressed by various laws written in the form of mathematical equations. The most useful of these is the ideal gas equation, which relates all the important gas properties. However, under certain conditions gases do not obey the ideal gas equation. For example, at high pressures and/or low temperatures, the properties of gases deviate significantly from the predictions of the ideal gas equation. On the other hand, as the pressure is lowered and/or the temperature is increased, almost all gases show close agreement with the ideal gas equation. This means that an ideal gas is really a hypothetical substance. At low pressures and/or high temperatures, real gases *approach* the behavior expected for an ideal gas.

Building a Model for Gases At this point we want to build a model, a theory, to explain *why* a gas behaves as it does. We want to answer the question, *What are the characteristics of the individual gas particles that cause a gas to behave as it does?*

Let's Review

Scientific Method
- A law is a generalization of observed behavior.
- Laws are useful → We can predict behavior of similar systems.

However, laws do not tell us *why* nature behaves the way it does. Scientists try to answer this question by constructing theories (building models). The models in chemistry are speculations about how individual atoms or molecules (microscopic particles) cause the behavior of macroscopic systems (collections of atoms and molecules in large enough numbers so that we can observe them).

A model is considered successful if it explains known behavior and predicts correctly the results of future experiments.

A model can never be proved absolutely true. By its very nature any model is an approximation and is destined to be modified.

Models range from the simple, to predict approximate behavior, to the extraordinarily complex, to account precisely for observed behavior. In this text, we use relatively simple models that fit most experimental results.

Active Reading Question

 Active Reading Question

Explain the difference between a law and a theory.

B. The Kinetic Molecular Theory of Gases

A relatively simple model that attempts to explain the behavior of an ideal gas is the **kinetic molecular theory**. This model is based on speculations about the behavior of the individual particles (atoms or molecules) in a gas. The assumptions of the kinetic molecular theory (KMT) can be stated as follows:

Assumptions of the Kinetic Molecular Theory of Gases

1. Gases consist of tiny particles (atoms or molecules).

2. These particles are so small, compared with the distances between them, that the volume (size) of the individual particles can be assumed to be negligible (zero).

3. The particles are in constant random motion, colliding with the walls of the container. These collisions with the walls cause the pressure exerted by the gas.

4. The particles are assumed not to attract or to repel each other.

5. The average kinetic energy of the gas particles is directly proportional to the Kelvin temperature of the gas.

The kinetic energy referred to in assumption 5 is the energy associated with the motion of a particle.

Kinetic energy (KE) is given by $KE = \frac{1}{2}mv^2$, where m is the mass of the particle and v is the velocity (speed) of the particle.

The greater the mass or velocity of a particle, the greater its kinetic energy. This means that if a gas is heated to higher temperatures, the average speed of the particles increases; therefore, their kinetic energy increases.

A law explains *what* happened, while a **theory** attempts to explain *why* it happened.

13.3.B The Kinetic Molecular Theory of Gases

Objective To understand the basic postulates of the kinetic molecular theory

 TEACHING TIPS

• The assumptions of the kinetic molecular theory form the basis for understanding the behavior of gases. Encourage students to develop a mental movie of an ideal gas on a molecular level that can form the basis for understanding the theory.

• Point out that we previously encountered four of these assumptions but are now bringing them all together. Assumption 1 comes from Dalton's atomic theory (discussed in Chapter 3). Assumptions 2 and 4 come from Dalton's law of partial pressures. Assumption 5 was discussed in Chapter 10.

TECHNOLOGY

 Assumptions of the Kinetic Molecular Theory of Gases

Animation
Kinetic Molecular Theory/Heat Transfer

CELEBRITY CHEMICAL Carbon Monoxide (CO)

Carbon monoxide is a colorless, odorless gas originally discovered in the United States by Joseph Priestley in 1799. It is formed in the combustion of fossil fuels (carbon-based molecules formed by the decay of ancient life forms) when the oxygen supply is limited.

Carbon monoxide is quite toxic, because it binds to hemoglobin 200 times more strongly than oxygen does. Thus, when carbon monoxide is present in inhaled air, it preferentially binds to the hemoglobin and excludes the oxygen needed

for human survival. This gas is especially dangerous because it has no taste or odor. The most common type of carbon monoxide poisonings occur in homes where the flow of oxygen to the furnace has become restricted, often due to squirrels or birds building nests in intake air flues. Today carbon monoxide detectors are available that automatically sound an alarm when the carbon monoxide levels become unsafe.

13.3 • Using a Model to Describe Gases • **475**

CELEBRITY CHEMICAL

Carbon Monoxide (CO)

Carbon forms several oxides, including CO, CO_2, C_2O_3, C_5O_2, $C_{12}O_9$, and C_2O, most of which are quite unstable. Tricarbon dioxide, C_3O_2, which is often called carbon suboxide, is a foul-smelling gas obtained by dehydrating malonic acid using P_4O_{10}. C_3O_2 is a linear molecule with $\ddot{O}=C=C=C=\ddot{O}$ as its Lewis structure.

It has a melting point of $-112.5\ °C$ and a boiling point of $6.7\ °C$, and it polymerizes at room temperature to a yellow solid.

Carbon monoxide, CO, which has a melting point of $-205\ °C$ and a boiling point of $-192\ °C$, is a colorless, odorless, flammable gas. It is widely used as a fuel in the form of producer gas (25% CO, 4% CO_2, 70% N_2) or water gas (50% H_2, 40% CO, 5% CO_2, and 5% N_2 and CH_4); the latter fuel is made by the reaction of steam and hot coke. Because of its

toxicity, carbon monoxide in the atmosphere creates a real concern. Automobiles are the most common source of carbon monoxide, but the introduction of catalytic converters on cars has greatly diminished the amount of CO in exhaust gases. Although the number of cars in the United States approximately doubled between 1970 and 1990, the average concentration of CO decreased by 40% over the same period.

Objective To understand the term *temperature* and learn how the kinetic molecular theory explains the gas laws

TEACHING TIPS

- Begin this section with a review of temperature and its meaning. Encourage students to think about the model for gases at the molecular level.

- Once students understand the molecular-level action of gases with changing temperature, investigate and develop models at the molecular level to illustrate the *P, T* and *V, T* relationships. Observing gases at the macroscopic level allows us to predict behavior, whereas developing a model at the microscopic level allows us to understand why gases behave as they do.

MINI-DEMO

Add 100 mL of water (and a few drops of food coloring if desired) to a 250-mL beaker, and place a 50-mL beaker upside down in the water. Place this apparatus on a hot plate and heat the water to boiling (the smaller beaker will bounce). Allow the water to boil for a few minutes, and then remove it from the heat. Water will rise in the 50-mL beaker. As the water boils, steam enters the 50-mL beaker and pushes the air out (which is why the beaker bounces). After a few minutes, the small beaker is filled with steam. As this system cools, the steam condenses, lowering the pressure in the 50-mL beaker. Atmospheric pressure pushes the water up into the 50-mL beaker.

CHEMISTRY IN YOUR WORLD

Science, Technology, and Society

Signs of Pollution

About 6% of the cars on the road produce 50% of auto-based air pollution. However, finding these offenders can be difficult. Scientists at the University of Denver in Colorado have developed a system that can measure the pollution produced by individual cars as they pass a roadside detector. This information is then transmitted to a billboard display. When the emissions are within acceptable limits, a smiling car is displayed. When the emissions are too high, a frowning car is displayed with the message that the problem is "costing you money." This "smart sign" operates reliably even with traffic flows exceeding 1,000 vehicles per hour. The system has given

millions of readings at a cost of about 2 cents each, approximately 2% of the passing vehicles see the "frowning car."

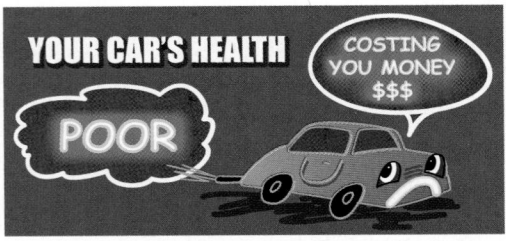

Although real gases do not conform exactly to the five assumptions listed, we will see next that these assumptions do indeed explain *ideal* gas behavior—behavior shown by real gases at high temperatures and/or low pressures.

C. The Implications of the Kinetic Molecular Theory

Now we will show how the kinetic molecular theory explains some of the observed properties of gases.

The Meaning of Temperature

The temperature of a substance reflects the vigor of the motions of the components that make up the substance. Thus the temperature of a gas reflects how rapidly, on average, its individual particles are moving. At high temperatures the particles move very fast and hit the walls of the container frequently, and at low temperatures the particles' motions are slower and they collide with the walls of the container much less often. As assumption 5 of the KMT states, the Kelvin temperature of a gas is directly proportional to the *average kinetic energy* of the gas particles.

The Relationship Between Pressure and Temperature

To see how the meaning of temperature given above helps to explain gas behavior, picture a gas in a rigid container. As the gas is heated to a higher temperature, the particles move faster, hitting the walls more often. And, of course, the impacts become more forceful as the particles move faster. If the pressure is due to collisions with the walls, the gas pressure should increase as temperature is increased.

476 • Chapter 13 • Gases

Chemistry in Your World

Signs of Pollution

Student Project Have students design a road sign to encourage people to reduce pollution. Teams of students can create an ad campaign to focus on reducing pollution in the local community.

Meeting Individual Needs
ADVANCED LEARNERS

Consider discussing a semi-quantitative relationship between pressure and volume with mathematically inclined students. Imagine a sample of gas in a cubic container with sides of 1 ft. If we transfer this sample to a cube with sides of 2 ft, the gas particles will have to travel (on average) twice as far from one wall to the next, and half as many

collisions will occur (decreasing the pressure by a factor of 2). In addition, the area of each wall will be four times as large (4 ft^2 versus 1 ft^2). Because pressure is a measure of force per area, this change will cause the pressure to decrease by a factor of 4. Thus the pressure should be reduced overall by a factor of 8 (2 × 4). This finding is consistent with Boyle's law, as the second container has a volume 8 times larger than the first container's volume.

Is this what we observe when we measure the pressure of a gas as it is heated? Yes. A given sample of gas in a rigid container (if the volume is not changed) shows an increase in pressure as its temperature is increased.

The Relationship Between Volume and Temperature

Now picture the gas in a container with a movable piston. The gas pressure P_{gas} is balanced by an external pressure P_{ext}. What happens when we heat the gas to a higher temperature?

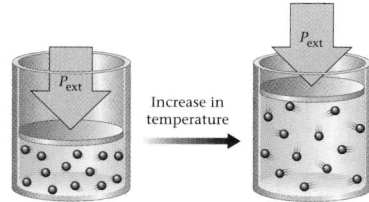

As the temperature increases, the particles move faster, causing the gas pressure to increase. As soon as the gas pressure P_{gas} becomes greater than P_{ext} (the pressure holding the piston), the piston moves up until $P_{gas} = P_{ext}$. Therefore, the KMT predicts that the volume of the gas will increase as we raise its temperature at a constant pressure. This agrees with experimental observations (as summarized by Charles's law).

EXAMPLE 13.17

Using the Kinetic Molecular Theory to Explain Gas Law Observations

Use the KMT to predict what will happen to the pressure of a gas when its volume is decreased (n and T constant). Does this prediction agree with the experimental observations?

Solution
When we decrease the gas's volume (make the container smaller), the particles hit the walls more often because they do not have to travel so far between the walls. This would suggest an increase in pressure. This prediction on the basis of the model is in agreement with experimental observations of gas behavior (as summarized by Boyle's law).

temperature increases, volume increases as a result of an instantaneous increase in pressure (the volume increase then brings the pressure back to its original value).

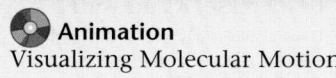

Place about 50 small balls (or beads) in a one-quart closed jar to simulate a sample of gas. Shake the jar and ask students to tell you how pressure,

volume, moles, and temperature are represented (pressure can be "heard" from collisions with the container; volume is the volume of the jar; moles are a function of the number of particles; temperature is related to how fast the jar is shaken). Ask students how to increase the pressure of the gas sample. Demonstrate their suggestions (shake the jar faster, add more

balls, transfer all of the balls to a smaller container).

Use this opportunity to demonstrate which factors must be held constant. If students tell you to increase temperature, remove most of the balls and shake a little faster. They will "hear" that the pressure has been decreased. Spend time discussing several possibilities.

EXAMPLE 13.17

More Examples

1. Use the kinetic molecular theory to predict what will happen to the pressure of a gas when the number of moles is increased at constant volume and temperature.

   When we increase the number of moles of gas at constant V and T, the gas particles continue to move at the same average speed. More gas particles will create more collisions with the walls of the container. As pressure is a result of collisions with the walls, gas pressure should increase as the number of moles of gas increases.

2. Use the kinetic molecular theory to predict what will happen to the volume of a gas when the number of moles is increased at constant pressure and temperature.

   Picture the gas in a container with a movable piston. When we increase the number of moles of gas at constant P and T, the gas particles continue to move at the same average speed. More gas particles will create more collisions with the walls of the container. Since pressure is due to collisions with the walls, gas pressure should increase as the number of moles of gas increases. When the pressure of the gas inside the container exceeds the external pressure, the piston moves up until the internal and external pressures are equal. We predict, therefore, that the volume of the gas increases with an increasing number of moles of gas (which is verified by Avogadro's law).

13.3.D Real Gases
Objective To describe the
properties of real gases

 TEACHING TIP

Students should understand
that although our model for
gases assumes ideal behavior
and gases are not ideal, we can
nevertheless use the model to
predict behavior and understand
gases. The difficulties with real
gases surface when we have
small volumes and large
pressures. The ideal gas law still
allows us to predict the behavior
of gases under most everyday
conditions.

CRITICAL
THINKING ?

If gases always behaved ideally,
they would never liquefy (there
would be no attraction between
gas particles). Thus, once a
substance became a gas, it
would always be a gas. A tragic
consequence of this scenario
would be that once water from
the oceans evaporated, it could
not be replenished. Since water
evaporates constantly, eventually
all water would be gaseous.

 Active Reading Question

We assume that gas particles are
so small that individual particles
have a negligible (zero) volume.
We also assume that gas particles
do not attract or repel each other.

SECTION 13.3
ASSESS

 SECTION 13.3
Review Questions

1. A law is a summary of
observations, while a theory
is an explanation of those
observations.

2. Real gases behave as ideal
gases under normal, everyday
conditions and under many
other conditions as long as
the volume is not very small
or the pressure very large.

3. Gases consist of atoms or
molecules that are in constant
random motion and collide
with the walls of their
container, causing pressure.
Compared to the volume the
gas takes up, the size of the

478 • Chapter 13 • Gases

 CRITICAL
THINKING ?

You have learned that no
gas behaves ideally.

What if all gases behaved
ideally under all
conditions? How would
the world be different?

D. Real Gases

So far in our discussion of gases, we have assumed that we are dealing
with an ideal gas—one that exactly obeys the equation $PV = nRT$. Of
course, there is no such thing as an ideal gas. An ideal gas is a hypothetical
substance consisting of particles with zero volumes and no attractions for
one another. All is not lost, however, because real gases behave very much
like ideal gases under many conditions. For example, in a sample of helium
gas at 25 °C and 1 atm pressure, the He atoms are so far apart that the tiny
volume of each atom has no importance. Also, because the He atoms are
moving so rapidly and have very little attraction for one another, the ideal
gas assumption that there are no attractions is virtually true. Thus a sample
of helium at 25 °C and 1 atm pressure very closely obeys the ideal gas law.

As real gases are compressed into smaller and smaller volumes (see **Figure
13.9**), the particles of the gas begin to occupy a significant fraction of the
available volume. That is, in a very small container the space taken up by the
particles becomes important. Also, as the volume of the container gets
smaller, the particles move much closer together and are more likely to
attract one another. Thus, in a highly compressed state (small V, high P), the
facts that real gas molecules take up space and have attractions for one
another become important. Under
these conditions a real gas does
not obey the equation $PV = nRT$
very well. In other words, under
conditions of high pressure (small
volume), real gases act differently
from the ideal gas behavior.

Because we typically deal
with gases that have pressures
near 1 atm, however, we can
safely assume ideal gas behavior
in our calculations.

(a)   (b)
Figure 13.9
A gas sample is compressed
(the volume is decreased).

 Active Reading Question

**What are the two main assumptions of the kinetic molecular theory that
are true about ideal gases but not true about real gases?**

SECTION 13.3
REVIEW QUESTIONS

① Explain the difference between a *law* and
a *theory*.

② When do real gases behave as ideal gases?

③ What are the main ideas of the kinetic
molecular theory of gases?

④ Use the kinetic molecular theory to draw
a molecular-level picture of a gas. Briefly
describe the motion of the gas particles.

⑤ Use the kinetic molecular theory to explain
Avogadro's law.

 RESEARCH LINKS
CLASSZONE.COM

particles is negligible (zero).
The particles are assumed to
neither attract nor repel one
another. The temperature
of a gas is a measure of the
average kinetic energy of
the particles.

4. Drawings may look like
Figure 13.9. The particles are
in constant random motion,
colliding with the walls of
the container. The vigor of
the particles' motion is

directly proportional to the
temperature of the gas.

5. Avogadro's law states that
the volume of a gas at
constant pressure and
temperature is directly
related to the number of
moles. Consider a gas in
a container fitted with a
piston. As we add more
moles of gas, initially there
will be more collisions with
the walls of the container,

causing the gas pressure
to increase. As pressure
increases, the piston will
respond by making the
volume of the container
larger until internal and
external pressures are again
equal. Thus, adding more
moles of gas results in an
increase in volume of the
container as long as
pressure and temperature
are held constant.

Chapter 13 Review

Key Terms

13.1 Barometer

Torr (mm Hg)

Standard atmosphere

Pascal

Boyle's law

Absolute zero

Charles's law

Avogadro's law

13.2 Universal gas constant

Ideal gas law

Ideal gas

Combined gas law

Partial pressure

Dalton's law of partial
    pressures

Molar volume

Standard temperature and
    pressure (STP)

13.3 Kinetic molecular theory

RESEARCH LINKS
CLASSZONE.COM

Key Ideas

13.1 Describing the Properties of Gases

- The common units for pressure are mm Hg (torr), atmosphere (atm), and pascal (Pa). The SI unit is the pascal.

- Boyle's law states that the volume of a given amount of gas at constant temperature varies inversely to its pressure. $PV = k$

- Charles's law states that the volume of a given amount of an ideal gas at constant pressure varies directly with its temperature (in kelvins). $V = bT$

  - At absolute zero (0 K; −273 °C) the volume of an ideal gas extrapolates to zero.

- Avogadro's law states for an ideal gas at constant temperature and pressure, the volume varies directly with the number of moles of gas (n). $V = an$

13.2 Using Gas Laws to Solve Problems

- The ideal gas law describes the relationship among P, V, n, and T for an ideal gas. $PV = nRT$

$$R = \left(0.08206 \, \frac{\text{L atm}}{\text{mol K}}\right)$$

A gas that obeys this law exactly is called an ideal gas.

- From the ideal gas law we can obtain the combined gas law which applies when n is constant.

$$\frac{P_1 V_1}{T_1} = \frac{P_2 V_2}{T_2}$$

- Dalton's law of partial pressures states the total pressure of a mixture of gases is equal to the sum of the individual (partial) pressures of the gases. $P_{\text{total}} = P_1 + P_2 + P_3 + \ldots$

- Standard temperature and pressure (STP) is defined as $P = 1$ atm and $T = 273$ K (0 °C).

- The volume of one mole of an ideal gas (the molar volume) is 22.4 L at STP.

13.3 Using a Model to Describe Gases

- The kinetic molecular theory (KMT) is a model based on the properties of individual gas components that explains the relationship of P, V, T, and n for an ideal gas.

- A law is a summary of experimental observation.

- A model (theory) is an attempt to explain observed behavior.

- The temperature of an ideal gas reflects the average kinetic energy of the gas particles.

- The pressure of a gas increases as its temperature increases because the gas particles speed up.

- The volume of a gas must increase because the gas particles speed up as a gas is heated to a higher temperature.

Chapter 13 • Review • **479**

Meeting Individual Needs

CHAPTER REVIEW

Chapter 13 Review Worksheet at the appropriate level:
    Basic
    Standard
    Challenge

CHAPTER SUMMARY

A **Chapter Summary** that includes additional Active Reading Questions for Chapter 13 is available.

Assessment Resources

CHAPTER 13

Chapter 13 Test

TECHNOLOGY

 Computerized Test Bank for Chapter 13

Chapter 13 Assessment

1. Solids are rigid and incompressible and have definite shapes and volumes. Liquids are less rigid than solids; although they have definite volumes, liquids take the shape of their containers. Gases have no fixed volume or shape; they take the volume and shape of their container, and are affected more by changes in their pressure and temperature than are liquids and solids.

2. The pressure of the atmosphere represents the weight of the several-mile-thick layer of gases pressing down on the earth. Pressure represents a force exerted over an area.

3. A tube filled with mercury is inverted in a pool of mercury that is open to the atmosphere. The mercury in the tube falls to a level at which the pressure of the atmosphere is sufficient to support the column of mercury.

4. (a) 1.038 atm
   (b) 0.989 atm
   (c) 0.989 atm
   (d) 1.01 atm

5. (a) 758.1 mm Hg
   (b) 1691 mm Hg
   (c) 748 mm Hg
   (d) 819.3 mm Hg

6. (a) 1.03×10^5 Pa
   (b) 9.78×10^4 Pa
   (c) 1.125×10^5 Pa
   (d) 1.07×10^5 Pa

7. (a) 59.7 mL
   (b) 1.88 atm
   (c) 3.40 L

8. (a) 146 mL
   (b) 0.354 L
   (c) 687 mm Hg

9. The volume will increase by a factor of 1.80.

10. 20.0 atm

11. Absolute zero is the temperature at which the volume of an ideal gas sample is predicted to become zero; it is the lowest possible temperature believed to exist.

12. Measure the volume of a gas at several different temperatures (keep pressure and moles of gas constant). Plot these data and extrapolate the line (continue past the points you have measured). The temperature at which the gas has zero volume is absolute zero.

All exercises with blue numbers have answers in the back of this book.

13.1 Describing the Properties of Gases
A. Pressure

1. How are the three states of matter similar, and how do they differ?

2. What is meant by "the pressure of the atmosphere"? What causes this pressure?

3. Describe a simple mercury barometer. How is such a barometer used to measure the pressure of the atmosphere?

4. Convert the following pressures into *atmospheres*.
   a. 105.2 kPa
   b. 75.2 cm Hg
   c. 752 mm Hg
   d. 767 torr

5. Convert the following pressures into units of *mm Hg*.
   a. 0.9975 atm
   b. 225,400 Pa
   c. 99.7 kPa
   d. 1.078 atm

6. Convert the following pressures into pascals.
   a. 774 torr
   b. 0.965 atm
   c. 112.5 kPa
   d. 801 mm Hg

B. Pressure and Volume: Boyle's Law

7. For each of the following sets of pressure and volume data, calculate the missing quantity. Assume that the temperature and the amount of gas remain constant.
   a. V = 53.2 mL at 785 mm Hg;
      V = ? at 700. mm Hg
   b. V = 2.25 L at 1.67 atm;
      V = 2.00 L at ? atm
   c. V = 5.62 L at 695 mm Hg;
      V = ? at 1.51 atm

8. For each of the following sets of pressure and volume data, calculate the missing quantity. Assume that the temperature and the amount of gas remain the same.
   a. V = 291 mL at 1.07 atm;
      V = ? at 2.14 atm
   b. V = 1.25 L at 755 mm Hg;
      V = ? at 3.51 atm
   c. V = 2.71 L at 101.4 kPa;
      V = 3.00 L at ? mm Hg

9. If the pressure exerted on the gas in a weather balloon decreases from 1.01 atm to 0.562 atm as it rises, by what factor will the volume of the gas in the balloon increase as it rises?

10. What pressure (in atmospheres) is required to compress 1.00 L of gas at 760. mm Hg pressure to a volume of 50.0 mL?

C. Volume and Temperature: Charles's Law

11. What is meant by the *absolute zero* of temperature?

12. How can Charles's law be used to determine absolute zero?

13. If a 45.0-mL sample of gas at 26.5 °C is heated to 55.2 °C, what is the new volume of the gas sample (at constant pressure)?

14. For each of the following sets of volume and temperature data, calculate the missing quantity. Assume that the pressure and the mass of gas remain constant.
    a. V = 25.0 L at 0 °C; V = 50.0 L at ? °C
    b. V = 247 mL at 25 °C;
       V = 255 mL at ? °C
    c. V = 1.00 mL at 2272 °C; V = ? at 25 °C

15. For each of the following sets of volume and temperature data, calculate the missing quantity. Assume that the pressure and the mass of gas remain constant.
    a. V = 2.01×10^2 L at 1150 °C;
       V = 5.00 L at ? °C
    b. V = 44.2 mL at 298 K; V = ? at 0 K
    c. V = 44.2 mL at 298 K; V = ? at 0 °C

16. If 5.00 L of an ideal gas is cooled from 24 °C to −272 °C, what will the volume of the gas become?

13. 49.2 mL

14. (a) 273 °C
    (b) 35 °C
    (c) 298 mL

15. (a) −238 °C
    (b) 0 mL
    (c) 40.5 mL

16. 0.02 L (20 mL)

17. A sample of neon gas occupies 266 mL at 25.2 °C. At what temperature would the volume of this sample of neon be reduced to half its initial size (at constant pressure)? At what temperature would the volume of this sample of neon be doubled (at constant pressure)?

18. The label on an aerosol spray can contains a warning that the can should not be heated to over 130 °F because of the danger of explosion due to the pressure increase as it is heated. Calculate the potential volume of the gas contained in a 500.-mL aerosol can when it is heated from 25 °C to 54 °C (approximately 130 °F), assuming a constant pressure.

D. Volume and Moles: Avogadro's Law

19. If 0.214 mol of argon gas occupies a volume of 652 mL at a particular temperature and pressure, what volume would 0.375 mol of argon occupy under the same conditions?

20. If 46.2 g of oxygen gas occupies a volume of 100. L at a particular temperature and pressure, what volume will 5.00 g of oxygen gas occupy under the same conditions?

13.2 Using Gas Laws to Solve Problems

A. The Ideal Gas Law

21. Under what conditions do *real* gases behave most ideally?

22. Show how Boyle's law can be derived from the ideal gas law.

23. Given each of the following sets of values for an ideal gas, calculate the unknown quantity.

    a. $P = 782$ mm Hg; $V = ?$; $n = 0.210$ mol; $T = 27$ °C

    b. $P = ?$ mm Hg; $V = 644$ mL; $n = 0.0921$ mol; $T = 303$ K

    c. $P = 745$ mm Hg; $V = 11.2$ L; $n = 0.401$ mol; $T = ?$ K

24. Given each of the following sets of values for an ideal gas, calculate the unknown quantity.

    a. $P = 1.01$ atm; $V = ?$; $n = 0.00831$ mol; $T = 25$ °C

    b. $P = ?$ atm; $V = 602$ mL; $n = 8.01 \times 10^{-3}$ mol; $T = 310.$ K

    c. $P = 0.998$ atm; $V = 629$ mL; $n = ?$ mol; $T = 35$ °C

25. What volume does 4.24 g of nitrogen gas occupy at 58.2 °C and 2.04 atm?

26. Suppose two 200.0-L tanks are to be filled separately with the gases helium and hydrogen. What mass of each gas is needed to produce a pressure of 135 atm in its respective tank at 24 °C?

27. At what temperature does 16.3 g of nitrogen gas have a pressure of 1.25 atm in a 25.0-L tank?

28. Determine the pressure in a 125-L tank containing 56.2 kg of oxygen gas at 21 °C.

29. What will be the new volume if 125 mL of He gas at 100. °C and 0.981 atm is cooled to 25 °C and the pressure is increased to 1.15 atm?

30. What will the volume of the sample become if 459 mL of an ideal gas at 27 °C and 1.05 atm is cooled to 15 °C and 0.997 atm?

B. Dalton's Law of Partial Pressures

31. Explain why the measured properties of a mixture of gases depend only on the total number of moles of particles, not on the identities of the individual gas particles. How is this observation summarized as a law?

32. We often collect small samples of gases in the laboratory by bubbling the gas into a bottle or flask containing water. Explain why the gas becomes saturated with water vapor and how we must take the presence of water vapor into account when calculating the properties of the gas sample.

33. If 4.0 g of $O_2(g)$ and 4.0 g of $He(g)$ are placed in a 5.0-L vessel at 65 °C, what will be the partial pressure of each gas and the total pressure in the vessel?

34. A tank contains a mixture of 3.0 mol N_2, 2.0 mol O_2, and 1.0 mol CO_2 at 25 °C and a total pressure of 10.0 atm. Calculate the partial pressure (in torr) of each gas in the mixture.

35. A sample of oxygen gas is saturated with water vapor at 27 °C. The total pressure of the mixture is 772 torr, and the vapor pressure of water is 26.7 torr at 27 °C. What is the partial pressure of the oxygen gas?

17. The volume of the neon gas would become half the initial value at 149 K. The volume would double at 596 K.

18. 548 mL

19. 1.14 L

20. 10.8 L

21. Real gases behave most ideally at relatively high temperatures and low pressures.

22. $PV = nRT$; If n, R, and T are all constant, then $PV =$ constant, or $P_1V_1 = P_2V_2$.

23. (a) 5.02 L
    (b) 3.56 atm
    (c) 334 K

24. (a) 0.201 L
    (b) 0.338 atm
    (c) 2.48×10^{-2} mol

25. 2.01 L

26. 4440 g He; 2240 g H_2

27. 655 K

28. 340 atm

29. 85.2 mL

30. 464 mL

31. This is Dalton's law of partial pressures:
$P_{total} = P_1 + P_2 + \ldots P_n$. We assume that the gas particles themselves take up no space and do not interact with one another. Under these conditions, there is no difference in the bulk behavior of different gases.

32. The pressure of the water vapor must be subtracted from the total pressure.

33. $P_{oxygen} = 0.693$ atm;
$P_{helium} = 5.54$ atm;
$P_{total} = 6.233$ atm (6.2 atm considering significant figures)

34. 5.0 atm N_2; 3.3 atm O_2; 1.7 atm CO_2

35. 745 torr

36. 1.98×10^{-2} mol O_2, 732 torr

37. 3.41 L CO_2

38. 14.7 L O_2

39. 9.31 g of NH_4Cl is produced. NH_3 is the limiting reactant, so HCl is in excess.

40. 5.03 L (dry volume)

41. 359 L

42. 184 mL

43. 15.6 L; P_{oxygen} = 0.225 atm; $P_{nitrogen}$ = 0.256 atm; $P_{carbon\ dioxide}$ = 0.163 atm; P_{neon} = 0.356 atm

44. 2.34 L Cl_2

45. 0.709 L Cl_2

46. A law is a statement that precisely expresses generally observed behavior. A theory consists of a set of assumptions/ hypotheses that is put forth to explain the law.

47. A theory is successful if it explains known experimental observations; no; no.

48. We assume that the volume of the particles themselves in a gas sample is negligible compared to the volume of their container. This idea helps us explain observations such as the compressibility of gases.

49. Pressure is due to the atoms or molecules of a gas colliding with the walls of the container.

50. kinetic energy

---

36. A 500.-mL sample of O_2 gas at 24 °C was prepared by decomposing a 3.0% aqueous solution of hydrogen peroxide, H_2O_2, in the presence of a small amount of manganese catalyst by the reaction

$$2H_2O_2(aq) \rightarrow 2H_2O(g) + O_2(g)$$

The oxygen thus prepared was collected by displacement of water. The total pressure of gas collected was 755 mm Hg. What is the partial pressure of O_2 in the mixture? How many moles of O_2 are in the mixture? (The vapor pressure of water at 24 °C is 23 mm Hg.)

C. Gas Stoichiometry

37. When calcium carbonate is heated strongly, carbon dioxide gas is released

$$CaCO_3(s) \rightarrow CaO(s) + CO_2(g)$$

What volume of $CO_2(g)$, measured at STP, is produced if 15.2 g of $CaCO_3(s)$ is heated?

38. Consider the following *unbalanced* chemical equation for the combustion of propane.

$$C_3H_8(g) + O_2(g) \rightarrow CO_2(g) + H_2O(g)$$

What volume of oxygen gas at 25 °C and 1.04 atm is needed for the complete combustion of 5.53 g of propane?

39. Ammonia and gaseous hydrogen chloride combine to form ammonium chloride.

$$NH_3(g) + HCl(g) \rightarrow NH_4Cl(s)$$

If 4.21 L of $NH_3(g)$ at 27 °C and 1.02 atm is combined with 5.35 L of HCl(g) at 26 °C and 0.998 atm, what mass of $NH_4Cl(s)$ will be produced? Which gas is the limiting reactant? Which gas is present in excess?

40. If water is added to magnesium nitride, ammonia gas is produced when the mixture is heated.

$$Mg_3N_2(s) + 3H_2O(l) \rightarrow 3MgO(s) + 2NH_3(g)$$

If 10.3 g of magnesium nitride is treated with water, what volume of ammonia gas would be collected at 24 °C and 752 mm Hg?

41. What volume does a mixture of 14.2 g of He and 21.6 g of H_2 occupy at 28 °C and 0.985 atm?

42. A sample of hydrogen gas has a volume of 145 mL when measured at 44 °C and 1.47 atm. What volume would the hydrogen sample occupy at STP?

43. A mixture contains 5.00 g *each* of O_2, N_2, CO_2, and Ne gas. Calculate the volume of this mixture at STP. Calculate the partial pressure of each gas in the mixture at STP.

44. Given the following *unbalanced* chemical equation for the combination reaction of sodium metal and chlorine gas

$$Na(s) + Cl_2(g) \rightarrow NaCl(s)$$

what volume of chlorine gas, measured at STP, is necessary for the complete reaction of 4.81 g of sodium metal?

45. Potassium permanganate, $KMnO_4$, is produced commercially by oxidizing aqueous potassium manganate, K_2MnO_4, with chlorine gas. The *unbalanced* chemical equation is

$$K_2MnO_4(aq) + Cl_2(g) \rightarrow KMnO_4(s) + KCl(aq)$$

What volume of $Cl_2(g)$, measured at STP, is needed to produce 10.0 g of $KMnO_4$?

13.3 Using a Model to Describe Gases

A. Laws and Models: A Review

46. What is a scientific *law*? What is a *theory*? How do these concepts differ? Does a law explain a theory, or does a theory attempt to explain a law?

47. When is a scientific theory considered to be successful? Are all theories successful? Will a theory that has been successful in the past necessarily be successful in the future?

B. The Kinetic Molecular Theory of Gases

48. What do we assume about the volume of the actual molecules themselves in a sample of gas, compared to the bulk volume of the gas overall? Why?

49. How do chemists explain on a molecular basis the fact that gases in containers exert pressure on the walls of the container?

50. Temperature is a measure of the average _____ of the molecules in a sample of gas.

C. The Implications of the Kinetic Molecular Theory

51. How is the phenomenon of temperature explained on the basis of the kinetic molecular theory? What microscopic property of gas molecules is reflected in the temperature measured?

52. Explain, in terms of the kinetic molecular theory, how an increase in the temperature of a gas confined to a rigid container causes an increase in the pressure of the gas.

D. Real Gases

53. What does it mean for a gas to behave nonideally? How do we know that real gases behave nonideally?

54. Why does decreasing the volume of a gas cause nonideal behavior?

Critical Thinking

55. A helium tank contains 25.2 L of helium at 8.40 atm pressure. Determine how many 1.50-L balloons at 755 mm Hg can be inflated with the gas in the tank, assuming that the tank will also have to contain He at 755 mm Hg after the balloons are filled (that is, it is not possible to empty the tank completely). The temperature is 25 °C in all cases.

56. As weather balloons rise from the earth's surface, the pressure of the atmosphere becomes less, tending to cause the volume of the balloons to expand. However, the temperature is much lower in the upper atmosphere than at sea level. Would this temperature effect tend to make such a balloon expand or contract? Weather balloons do, in fact, expand as they rise. What does this tell you?

57. Sulfur trioxide, SO_3, is produced in enormous quantities each year for use in the synthesis of sulfuric acid.

$$S(s) + O_2(g) \rightarrow SO_2(g)$$

$$2SO_2(g) + O_2(g) \rightarrow 2SO_3(g)$$

What volume of $O_2(g)$ at 350. °C and a pressure of 5.25 atm is needed to completely convert 5.00 g of sulfur to sulfur trioxide?

58. A particular balloon is designed by its manufacturer to be inflated to a volume of no more than 2.5 L. If the balloon is filled with 2.0 L of helium at sea level, is released, and rises to an altitude at which the atmospheric pressure is only 500. mm Hg, will the balloon burst?

59. An expandable vessel contains 729 mL of gas at 22 °C. What volume will the gas sample in the vessel have if it is placed in a boiling water bath (100. °C)?

60. A weather balloon is filled with 1.0 L of helium at 23 °C and 1.0 atm. What volume does the balloon have when it has risen to a point in the atmosphere where the pressure is 220 torr and the temperature is −31 °C?

61. Consider the following *unbalanced* chemical equation:

$$Cu_2S(s) + O_2(g) \rightarrow Cu_2O(s) + SO_2(g)$$

What volume of oxygen gas, measured at 27.5 °C and 0.998 atm, is required to react with 25 g of copper(I) sulfide? What volume of sulfur dioxide gas is produced under the same conditions?

62. A mixture contains 5.0 g of He, 1.0 g of Ar, and 3.5 g of Ne. Calculate the volume of this mixture at STP. Calculate the partial pressure of each gas in the mixture at STP.

63. In an experiment 350.0 mL of hydrogen gas was collected over water at 27 °C and 72 cm Hg. Then the absolute temperature doubled, the total pressure changed to 1.00 atm, and one-third of the gas leaked out of the container. What would the final volume be?

64. A balloon will burst at a volume of 2.00 L. If it is partially filled at a temperature of 20 °C and a pressure of 775 mm Hg to a volume of 0.750 L, what is the temperature at which it will burst?

65. One method for estimating the temperature at the center of the sun is based on the ideal gas law. If the center of the sun is assumed to be a mass of gases with average molar mass of 2.00 g and if the density and pressure are 1.4 g/cm³ and 1.3×10^9 atm, respectively, calculate the temperature.

---

51. Temperature is a measure of the average kinetic energy of a sample. The speed of the particles depends on the temperature of the sample and the mass of the particles. So, for a given gas, the temperature reflects how rapidly the particles are moving.

52. As the temperature of a gas increases, the average kinetic energy of the gas particles increases; the particles will therefore move faster. By moving at a higher speed, the particles will collide with the wall more often (and with more force) and the pressure will increase.

53. Any gas that does not follow the ideal gas law is not behaving ideally. In addition, if there are reasons to believe that the assumptions of the kinetic molecular theory are poor assumptions, the gas sample is not behaving ideally. The fact that gases condense into liquids, for example, shows nonideal behavior.

54. When the volume of a gas is decreased, the gas particles take up a greater percentage of the volume of the container. The assumption of the kinetic molecular theory that gas particles take up a negligible volume is less correct.

55. 125 balloons

56. A decrease in temperature would tend to make the volume of the weather balloon decrease. Since the overall volume of the weather balloon increases when it rises to a higher altitude, the decrease in pressure must be more important than the decrease in temperature.

57. 2.28 L O_2

58. The volume would be 3.0 L, so the balloon will burst.

59. 922 mL

60. 2.8 L

61. 5.8 L O_2; 3.9 L SO_2

62. 32 L;
$P_{He} = 0.86$ atm;
$P_{Ar} = 0.017$ atm;
$P_{Ne} = 0.12$ atm

63. 442 mL

64. 508 °C

65. 2.26×10^7 K

66. Boron

67. 0.0228 mol; 2.75×10^{21} molecules

68. $C_3H_6O_2$; Students should draw two possible Lewis structures.

69. The balloon will not pop since it can expand to 3.00 L, and the hydrogen gas expands to a volume of 2.45 L at 1.00 atm and 25 °C.

70. (a) $PV = nRT$

$$\frac{V}{n} = \frac{RT}{P} = constant$$

$$\frac{V_1}{n_1} = \frac{RT}{P} = \frac{V_2}{n_2}$$

$$\frac{V_1}{n_1} = \frac{V_2}{n_2}$$

(b) An increase in number of moles of gas increases the number of collisions with the container (if volume stays constant), which would increase the pressure (since pressure is due to collisions of gas particles with the walls of the container). In order for the pressure to remain constant, the volume must increase so that the distance the particles must travel increases and thus the collision rate overall stays the same (thus the pressure stays the same). Since temperature is a measure of the average kinetic energy of the particles and changing the temperature would change the speed of the particles, the temperature must remain constant for this argument to hold.

(c) 10.0 g He = 2.50 mol He

20.0 g Ar = 0.501 mol Ar

$$\frac{V_{He}}{2.50 \text{ mol}} = \frac{V_{Ar}}{0.501 \text{ mol}}$$

$$\frac{V_{He}}{V_{Ar}} = \frac{2.50}{0.501} = 4.99$$

The container with He is 4.99 times as large as the container with Ar.

66. A 0.0712-g sample of X_4H_{10} has a volume of 30.0 cm^3 at 801 mm Hg and 20.0 °C. What is the element X?

67. A certain German sports car engine has a cylinder volume of 618 cm^3. The cylinder is full of air at 75 °C and 802 mm Hg. How many moles of gas are in the cylinder? If air is 20.0% oxygen by volume, how many molecules of oxygen are present?

68. A certain compound contains 48.6% carbon, 8.18% hydrogen, and 43.2% oxygen by mass. The gas at 150.0 °C and 1.00 atm has a density of 2.13 g/L. Suggest two possible Lewis structures for the compound.

69. You buy a deflated balloon that can expand to a maximum volume of 3.00 L. You decide to fill the balloon with hydrogen gas generated by the following reaction:

$$Zn(s) + 2HCl(aq) \rightarrow ZnCl_2(aq) + H_2(g)$$

If you react an excess of zinc with 100.0 mL of 2.00 M HCl and fill the balloon with all of the hydrogen generated (at 1.00 atm and 25 °C), will the balloon pop? Fully support your answer.

70. Sometimes a law can be written as a statement and a mathematical equation. For example, Boyle's law can be stated as follows: the pressure of a gas is inversely proportional to its volume at constant temperature and number of moles of gas. Boyle's law can also be stated mathematically as $P_1V_1 = P_2V_2$.

Avogadro's law states that the volume of a gas is directly related to the number of moles of gas at constant temperature and pressure.

    a. Starting with $PV = nRT$, derive Avogadro's law. Hint: See Example 13.10 on page 461 for a derivation of Boyle's law. Use the same ideas to derive Avogadro's law.

    b. Explain Avogadro's law using the ideas of the kinetic molecular theory. Use complete sentences.

    c. Use Avogadro's law (as derived in part a) to solve the following problem. Consider two containers, one with 10.0 g of He gas and one with 20.0 g of Ar gas, both at the same pressure and temperature. Which container has the greater volume, and by what factor? Show all work.

1 You are holding two helium balloons, a large balloon and a small balloon. How do the pressures of helium compare?

A The pressure in the large balloon is greater than the pressure in the small balloon. This is best explained by the fact that there are more moles of gas in the large balloon, thus greater pressure.

B The pressure in the small balloon is greater than the pressure in the large balloon. This is best explained by the fact that as the volume of a container decreases, the pressure of the gas increases.

C The pressure in the large balloon is greater than the pressure in the small balloon. The fact that there is greater pressure in the balloon is why the volume is larger; as the particles push more on the inside, the volume increases.

D The pressures are essentially the same and about equal to atmospheric pressure.

2 Determine the pressure exerted by 1.80 mol of gas in a 2.92-L container at 32.0 °C.

A 1.62 atm

B 8.57 atm

C 15.4 atm

D 22.4 atm

3 Consider a gas at 1.00 atm in a 5.00-L container at 20.0 °C. What pressure does the gas exert when transferred to a volume of 2.00 L at 43 °C?

A 0.812 atm

B 2.70 atm

C 3.14 atm

D 5.38 atm

4 Consider a mixture of equal masses of helium and hydrogen gases in a steel container. Which gas exerts the greater partial pressure, and by what factor?

A The helium gas exerts about twice as much pressure as the hydrogen gas.

B The helium gas exerts about four times as much pressure as the hydrogen gas.

C The hydrogen gas exerts about twice as much pressure as the helium gas.

D The helium gas exerts about the same pressure as the hydrogen gas.

5 You are holding three balloons each containing 10.0 g of a different gas. The balloon containing which gas is the largest balloon?

A H_2

B He

C O_2

D Each of the balloons is the same size.

6 A 4.37 gram sample of a certain diatomic gas occupies a volume of 3.00 L at 1.00 atm and a temperature of 45 °C. Identify this gas.

A F_2 C H_2

B N_2 D O_2

7 The choices below are all assumptions of the kinetic molecular theory. All of these assumptions are accepted for ideal gases. Which of these does **not** apply for **real gases**?

A Gases consist of particles in constant motion.

B Gas particles have no attraction for one another.

C Temperature is a measure of average kinetic energy.

D Pressure is due to collisions of gas particles with the walls of the container.

Use the graphs below to answer questions 8–10.

8 Which of the above graphs best represents the relationship between the pressure and temperature (measured in kelvins) of one mole of an ideal gas?

9 Which of the above graphs best represents the relationship between the pressure and volume of one mole of an ideal gas?

10 Which of the above graphs best represents the relationship between the volume and temperature (measured in kelvins) of one mole of an ideal gas?

Assessment Resources
CHAPTER 13

For additional practice with standardized testing, see *Standardized Test Practice* located in the *Teacher Resources*.

Chapter 13
Standardized Test Practice

1. D
2. C
3. B
4. C
5. A
6. A
7. B
8. A
9. D
10. A

Test-Taking Strategy

Encourage students to interpret their answer when they finish solving the problem. The final step in problem solving is to check that the answer makes sense. Encourage students to read the problem statement again and determine if their answer seems logical.

Planning Guide

Section	Segment		Text Features and Components	Labs, Demonstrations, & Activities
14.1 Intermolecular Forces and Phase Changes **3 Blocks** pp. 488–497	A	**Intermolecular Forces**		(LM) Experiment 55: Magic Sand, Traditional Lab Manual Report Sheets Teacher's Lab Guide
	B	**Water and Its Phase Changes**		(TE) Teaching Support: Demonstration *pp. 492–493* (LM) Experiment 56: Freezing Point—A Physical Property, Traditional Lab Manual Report Sheets Teacher's Lab Guide (LM) Experiment 57: Heating and Cooling Behavior of a Pure Substance, Traditional Lab Manual Report Sheets Teacher's Lab Guide
	C	**Energy Requirements for the Changes of State**	(SE) Chemistry in Your World: Whales Need Changes of State *p. 494* (SE) Top Ten Lowest Melting Points *p. 496*	(LM) Experiment 58: Heat of Fusion of Ice Lab Manual Report Sheets Teacher's Lab Guide (LM) Experiment 59: Energy and Changes of State, CBL Lab Manual Report Sheets Teacher's Lab Guide
		continued on next page		

Key			
(SE) Student Edition	(TE) Teacher Edition	(RP) Teacher Resource Package	
(AR) Additional Materials	(LM) Lab Materials	(transparencies icon) Transparencies	
(DVD icon) DVD	(CD-ROM icon) CD-ROM	(classzone icon) classzone.com	

All Learners	Technology	Review & Assessment	Standards
TE Teaching Tips *pp. 489–491* **TE** Meeting Individual Needs *p. 489* **TE** Misconception *p. 490* **TE** Meeting Individual Needs *p. 491*	⊙ Animation: Intermolecular Forces: Dipole–Dipole Forces ⊙ Animation: Intermolecular Forces: Hydrogen Bonding Forces ⊙ Animation: Intermolecular Forces: London Dispersion Forces ▣ Lab Generator CD ⊙ EasyPlanner	**SE** Active Reading Question *p. 489* **SE** Critical Thinking *p. 490* **SE** Active Reading Question *p. 490* **SE** Active Reading Question *p. 491* **SE** Key Terms *p. 512* **SE** Questions and Problems *p. 514*	**TE** **NSES** UCP1, UCP3, UCP5, A1, A2, B2, B4, B5, C5, C6
TE Teaching Tips *p. 492*	▤ Transparency: Figure 14.2 ⊙ Animation: Changes of State ▣ Lab Generator CD ⊙ EasyPlanner	**SE** Key Terms *p. 512* **SE** Questions and Problems *p. 514*	
TE Teaching Tips *pp. 493, 496* **RP** Team Learning Worksheet (Sec. 14.1)	▣ Lab Generator CD ⊙ EasyPlanner	**SE** Active Reading Question *p. 495* **TE** More Examples *p. 495* **TE** More Examples *p. 496* **SE** Practice Problem *p. 497* **SE** Review Questions (14.1.A–14.1.C) *p. 497* **SE** Key Terms *p. 512* **SE** Questions and Problems *pp. 514–515*	

Planning Guide

Section	Segment		Text Features and Components	Labs, Demonstrations, & Activities

14.2 Vapor Pressure and Boiling Point
 1.5 Blocks
 pp. 498–503
	A	**Evaporation and Vapor Pressure**	(SE) Chemistry Explorers: Dorothy Hodgkin *p. 499*	(TE) Mini-Demo *p. 499*
				 (TE) Teaching Support: Demonstration *pp. 500–501*
				 (LM) Experiment 60: Vapor Pressure of Water, CBL
				     Lab Manual
				     Report Sheets
				     Teacher's Lab Guide

	B	**Boiling Point and Vapor Pressure**		(TE) Mini-Demo *p. 501* (SE) Hands-On Chemistry: Hot Molecules *p. 503*
14.3 Properties of Solids **0.5 Block** pp. 504–511	A	**The Solid State: Types of Solids**		
	B	**Bonding in Solids**	(SE) Celebrity Chemical: Titanium *p. 508* (SE) Chemistry in Your World: Metal with a Memory *p. 510*	

Key	(SE) Student Edition	(TE) Teacher Edition	(RP) Teacher Resource Package
	(AR) Additional Materials	(LM) Lab Materials	(⊟) Transparencies
	(◉) DVD	(▮) CD-ROM	(ⓘ) classzone.com

All Learners	Technology	Review & Assessment	Standards
TE Teaching Tips *pp. 498–499*	**Lab Generator CD** **EasyPlanner**	**SE** Active Reading Question *p. 498* **SE** Active Reading Question *p. 500* **TE** More Examples *p. 501* **SE** Key Terms *p. 512* **SE** Questions and Problems *p. 515*	**TE** **NSES** UCP3, UCP4, UCP5, A1, A2, B2, B4, B5
TE Misconception *p. 501* **RP** Team Learning Worksheet (Sec. 14.2)	**Video: Boiling Water with Ice Water** **Transparency: Figure 14.6** **EasyPlanner**	**SE** Critical Thinking *p. 502* **SE** Active Reading Question *p. 502* **SE** Review Questions (14.2.A–14.2.B) *p. 503* **SE** Questions and Problems *p. 515*	
TE Teaching Tip *p. 504* **TE** Meeting Individual Needs *p. 505* **RP** MINT: Reading Concepts *TE p. 504*	**EasyPlanner**	**SE** Key Terms *p. 513* **SE** Questions and Problems *p. 515*	**TE** **NSES** UCP2, UCP5, A1, A2, B2, B5, E1, E2, F1, F6, G2
TE Teaching Tips *pp. 506, 509* **TE** Meeting Individual Needs *p. 507* **TE** Meeting Individual Needs *p. 509* **RP** Team Learning Worksheet (Sec. 14.3)	**Animation: Structure of an Ionic Solid (NaCl)** **Animation: Molecular Solids** **Animation: Electron Sea Model** **EasyPlanner**	**SE** Active Reading Question *p. 506* **SE** Active Reading Question *p. 508* **SE** Practice Problem *p. 511* **TE** More Examples *p. 511* **SE** Review Questions (14.3.A–14.3.B) *p. 511* **SE** Key Terms *p. 513* **SE** Questions and Problems *p. 515*	

Resource Materials for Chapter 14

SE Chapter Review *pp. 512–513*

SE Critical Thinking *p. 516*

SE Standardized Test Practice *p. 517*

AR English/Spanish Summaries

English Summaries Audio

Spanish Summaries Audio

RP Meeting Individual Needs Toolkit (MINT)
 Reading Concepts
 Chapter Review Worksheets
 Chapter Summaries

RP Solutions Guide

RP Standardized Test Practice

RP Chapter Tests

RP Test Bank

Test Generator

Chapter 14
Overview

In this chapter our goals are for students to:

- Learn about dipole–dipole attraction, hydrogen bonding, and London dispersion forces

- Understand the effect of intermolecular forces on the properties of liquids

- Explore some important properties of water

- Understand and use heat of fusion and heat of vaporization

- Understand the relationship among vaporization, condensation, and vapor pressure

- Relate the boiling point of water to its vapor pressure

- Learn about the various types of crystalline solids

- Learn about bonding in crystalline solids

Liquids and Solids

LOOKING AHEAD

Ice, the solid form of water, provides recreation for this ice climber.

486

IN YOUR LIFE

You have only to think about water to appreciate how different the three states of matter are. Flying, swimming, and ice skating are all done in contact with water in its various states. We swim in liquid water and skate on water in its solid form (ice). Airplanes fly in an atmosphere containing water in the gaseous state (water vapor). To allow these various activities, the arrangements of the water molecules must be significantly different in their gas, liquid, and solid forms.

A swimmer in water, one of the earth's most important substances

WHAT DO YOU KNOW?

Prereading Questions

1. At a molecular level, how do gases, liquids, and solids compare?

2. What is meant by the boiling point of a liquid?

3. What does it mean for a liquid to evaporate?

Liquids and Solids • Chapter 14 • **487**

Student Preparation

Assign students to read Section 14.1 and to answer the Review Questions at the end of the section before coming to class.

 Active Learning
Team Learning Worksheet

After introducing the material in Section 14.1 in class, place students in groups and have them work together on **Section 14.1: Team Learning Worksheet.**

Homework

You may wish to assign these selected end-of-chapter problems as homework for this section:
1, 3, 5, 6, 7, 8, 10, 13, 14, 15, 16, 17, 19, 21, 23

Additional end-of-chapter problems can be used for extra practice.

SECTION 14.1
Intermolecular Forces and Phase Changes

Key Terms

- Intermolecular forces
- Intramolecular forces
- Dipole–dipole attraction
- Hydrogen bonding
- London dispersion forces
- Normal boiling point
- Heating/cooling curve
- Normal freezing point
- Molar heat of fusion
- Molar heat of vaporization

Objectives

- *To learn about dipole–dipole, hydrogen bonding, and London dispersion forces*
- *To understand the effect of intermolecular forces on the properties of liquids*
- *To learn some of the important features of water*
- *To learn about interactions among water molecules*
- *To understand and use heat of fusion and heat of vaporization*

In Chapter 13 we saw that the particles of a gas are far apart, are in rapid random motion, and have little effect on each other. Solids are obviously very different from gases.

Gases	Solids
• Low density	• High density
• Highly compressible	• Slightly compressible
• Fill container	• Rigid (keeps its shape)

These properties indicate that the components of a solid are close together and exert large attractive forces on each other.

The properties of liquids lie somewhere between those of solids and of gases—but not midway between, as can be seen from some of the properties of the three states of water. For example, it takes about seven times more energy to change liquid water to steam (a gas) at 100 °C than to melt ice to form liquid water at 0 °C.

$$H_2O(s) \rightarrow H_2O(l) \qquad \text{energy required} \approx 6 \text{ kJ/mol}$$
$$H_2O(l) \rightarrow H_2O(g) \qquad \text{energy required} \approx 41 \text{ kJ/mol}$$

These values indicate that going from the liquid to the gaseous state involves a much greater change than going from the solid to the liquid. Therefore, we can conclude that the solid and liquid states are more similar than the liquid and gaseous states. This is also demonstrated by the densities of the three states of water (see **Table 14.1**). Note that water in its gaseous state is about 2000 times less dense than in the solid and liquid states and that the latter two states have very similar densities.

We find in general that the liquid and solid states show many similarities and are strikingly different from the gaseous state.

Table 14.1

Densities of the Three States of Water

State	Density (g/cm³)
solid (0 °C, 1 atm)	0.9168
liquid (25 °C, 1 atm)	0.9971
gas (100 °C, 1 atm)	5.88×10^{-4}

Gas   Liquid   Solid

The best way to picture the solid state is in terms of closely packed, highly ordered particles in contrast to the widely spaced, randomly arranged particles of a gas. The liquid state lies in between, but its properties indicate that it much more closely resembles the solid than the gaseous state. It is useful to picture a liquid in terms of particles that are generally quite close together, but with a more disordered arrangement than in the solid state and with some empty spaces. For most substances, the solid state has a higher density than the liquid. However, water is an exception to this rule. Ice has an unusual amount of empty space and so is less dense than liquid water, as indicated in Table 14.1.

In this chapter we will explore the important properties of liquids and solids. We will illustrate many of these properties by considering one of the earth's most important substances: water.

A. Intermolecular Forces

Most substances consisting of small molecules are gases at normal temperatures and pressures. Examples are oxygen gas (contains O_2), nitrogen gas (contains N_2), methane gas (contains CH_4), and carbon dioxide gas (contains CO_2). A notable exception to this rule is water. Given the small size of its molecules we might expect water to be a gas at normal temperatures and pressures. Think about how different the world would be if water were a gas at 25 °C and 1 atm pressure. The oceans would be empty chasms, the Mississippi River would be a wide, dry ditch, and it would never rain! Life on earth as we know it would be impossible if water were a gas under normal conditions.

So why is water a liquid rather than a gas at normal temperatures and pressures? The answer has to do with something called **intermolecular forces**—forces that occur between the molecules.

Notice that molecules are held together by bonds, sometimes called **intramolecular forces**, that occur inside the molecules. Intermolecular forces exist *between* molecules. We have seen that covalent bonding forces within molecules arise from the sharing of electrons, but how do intermolecular forces arise? Actually several types of intermolecular forces exist. To illustrate one type, we will consider the forces that exist among water molecules.

Active Reading Question

What type of force is represented by the lines in a Lewis structure? What type of force is responsible for holding molecules together in a solid or a liquid?

As we saw in Chapter 12, water is a polar molecule—it has a dipole moment. When molecules with dipole moments are put together, they orient themselves to take advantage of their charge distributions. Molecules with dipole moments can attract each other by lining up so that the positive and negative ends are close to each other, as shown here.

Intermolecular forces
Attractive forces that occur between molecules

Intramolecular forces
Attractive forces that occur between atoms in a molecule; chemical bonds

---

Objective To learn about dipole–dipole attraction, hydrogen bonding, and London dispersion forces and to understand the effect of these forces on the properties of liquids

LABORATORY
EXPERIMENT 55:
Magic Sand, Traditional

TECHNOLOGY

Animations
Intermolecular Forces:
   Dipole–Dipole Forces
Intermolecular Forces:
   Hydrogen Bonding Forces

TEACHING TIPS

• Help students draw a clear distinction between intramolecular forces (covalent and ionic bonds) and intermolecular forces.

• This section offers an excellent opportunity to review the main concepts about bonding and prepare students to look at the forces that exist between molecules. It is especially helpful to review the concept of a dipole and what it means before moving into intermolecular forces. Now is the time to show how electronegativity and the arrangement of atoms are tied to the polarity of molecules.

Active Reading Question

The lines in a Lewis structure represent chemical bonds, or intramolecular forces. The force that holds molecules together in a liquid or solid is termed an intermolecular force.

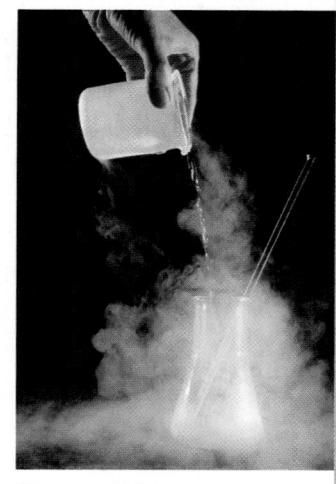

Nitrogen, which forms a liquid at 77 K, is being poured causing moisture in the air to freeze to produce a fog.

Meeting Individual Needs
READING STRATEGIES

Explain that the prefix *inter-* means between or among things, and the prefix *intra-* means within, in, or interior. List the following words on the board and discuss the meaning of each: interact, intercept, interference, international, intramural, intrastate, intranet.

- Some students think that dipole–dipole interactions and hydrogen bonds are completely unrelated. Stress that all of these interactions result from polarity.

- Students sometimes have trouble deciding when molecules should have hydrogen bonds between them. Use examples such as NH_3, CH_3OH, and HF to show that in each case the H is bonded directly to the N, O, or F. Molecules such as $(CH_3)_3N$ do not form hydrogen bonds, even though they contain both N and H, because no H is bonded to the N to produce the dipole needed for a hydrogen bond.

MISCONCEPTION Chemistry

Students are often confused by the term *hydrogen bond*. They sometimes do not realize that hydrogen bonds are dipole–dipole interactions and may believe that a hydrogen bond is the covalent chemical bond that exists between atoms in a molecule (such as the N—H bond in ammonia). They also often have the misconception that the hydrogen bond is the O—H, N—H, or F—H bond and not the attractive force between the dipoles. We use dashed lines to represent hydrogen bonds to help students see this idea more clearly. Stress that a hydrogen bond is an attractive force between molecules.

CRITICAL THINKING ?

Consider water molecules. We can tell that the intramolecular bonds are stronger than the intermolecular forces because if we add energy to a sample of liquid water, it will turn into steam long before it is transformed into hydrogen and oxygen gases. If bonds were weaker than intermolecular forces, reactions would be more likely to occur than phase changes.

Dipole–dipole attraction
The attractive force between the positively charged end of one polar molecule with the negatively charged end of another polar molecule

Hydrogen bonding
Special name for unusually strong dipole–dipole attractions that occur among molecules in which hydrogen is bonded to a highly electronegative atom (such as nitrogen, oxygen, or fluorine)

CRITICAL THINKING ?

You have learned the difference between intermolecular forces and intramolecular forces.

What if intermolecular forces were stronger than intramolecular forces? What differences could you observe in the world?

Figure 14.1
The boiling points of the covalent hydrides of elements in Group 6

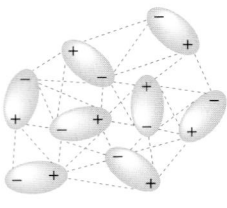

This is called a **dipole–dipole attraction**. In the liquid, the dipoles find the best compromise between attraction and repulsion, as shown here.

Dipole–dipole forces are typically only about 1% as strong as covalent or ionic bonds, and they become weaker as the distance between the dipoles increases. In the gas phase, where the molecules are usually very far apart, these forces are relatively unimportant.

Hydrogen Bonding

Particularly strong dipole–dipole forces occur between molecules in which hydrogen is bound to a highly electronegative atom, such as nitrogen, oxygen, or fluorine. Two factors account for the strengths of these interactions: the great polarity of the bond and the close approach of the dipoles, which is made possible by the very small size of the hydrogen atom. Because dipole–dipole attractions of this type are so unusually strong, they are given a special name—**hydrogen bonding**.

Hydrogen bonding has a very important effect on various physical properties. For example, the boiling points for the covalent compounds of hydrogen with the elements in Group 6 are given in **Figure 14.1**. Note that the boiling point of water is much higher than would be expected from the trend shown by the other members of the series. Why? Because the especially large electronegativity value of the oxygen atom compared with that of other group members causes the O—H bonds to be much more polar than the S—H, Se—H, or Te—H bonds. This leads to very strong hydrogen-bonding forces among the water molecules. An unusually large quantity of energy is required to overcome these interactions and separate the molecules to produce the gaseous state. That is, water molecules tend to remain together in the liquid state even at relatively high temperatures, hence the very high boiling point of water.

 Active Reading Question

What observation shows us that hydrogen bonding is quite strong?

 Active Reading Question

Water exhibits hydrogen bonding, and the boiling point for water is much higher than the boiling points of other covalent hydrides in Group 6 (see Figure 14.1).

London Dispersion Forces

Even molecules without dipole moments must exert forces on each other. We know this because all substances—even the noble gases—exist in the liquid and solid states at very low temperatures. There must be forces to hold the atoms or molecules as close together as they are in these condensed states. The forces that exist among noble gas atoms and non-polar molecules are called **London dispersion forces**. To understand the origin of these forces, consider a pair of noble gas atoms. Although we usually assume that the electrons of an atom are uniformly distributed about the nucleus,

No polarity

this is apparently not true at every instant. Atoms can develop a temporary dipolar arrangement of charge as the electrons move around the nucleus. This *instantaneous dipole* can then *induce* a similar dipole in a neighboring atom.

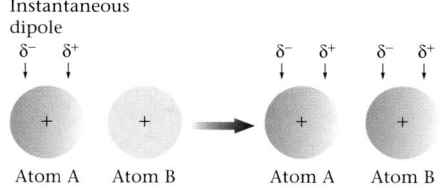

The interatomic attraction thus formed is both weak and short-lived, but it can be very significant for large atoms and large molecules, as we will see.

The motions of the atoms must be greatly slowed down before the weak London dispersion forces can lock the atoms into place to produce a solid. This explains, for instance, why the noble gas elements have such low freezing points (see **Table 14.2**).

Nonpolar molecules such as H_2, N_2, and I_2, none of which has a permanent dipole moment, also attract each other by London dispersion forces.

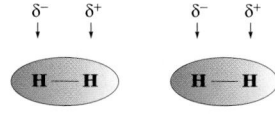

Molecule A   Molecule B
Instantaneous dipole on A
induces a dipole on B.

London forces become more significant as the sizes of atoms or molecules increase. Larger size means there are more electrons available to form the dipoles.

Active Reading Question

Rank intermolecular forces from weakest to strongest (given molecules of equal size).

London dispersion forces
Relatively weak intermolecular forces resulting from a temporarily uneven distribution of electrons that induces a dipole in a neighbor

Table 14.2

The Freezing Points of the Group 8 Elements

Element	Freezing Point (°C)
helium*	−272.0 (25 atm)
neon	−248.6
argon	−189.4
krypton	−157.3
xenon	−111.9

*Helium will not freeze unless the pressure is increased above 1 atm.

Objective To learn some of the important features of water

 LABORATORY

EXPERIMENT 56:
Freezing Point—A Physical Property, Traditional

LABORATORY

EXPERIMENT 57:
Heating and Cooling Behavior of a Pure Substance, Traditional

TEACHING TIPS

• This section provides an opportunity to review calorimetry and the specific heat capacity for water.

• Because water is such a common substance, many interesting phenomena related to it can be discussed in class. For example, you might discuss why ice floats, why pipes burst when they freeze (and why human tissue does not behave in the same way after freezing), why potholes form in road surfaces in the winter, and how water can crack large rocks and cause them to fall. If students are familiar with pressure cookers, this section offers an excellent opportunity to explain why foods cook faster in them.

TECHNOLOGY

 Figure 14.2

 Animation
Changes of State

Drinking water is important when exercising.

DID YOU KNOW

The water we drink often has a taste because of the substances dissolved in it.

Normal boiling point
The boiling temperature of a liquid under one atmosphere of pressure. The temperature at which the vapor pressure of a liquid is exactly one atmosphere.

Figure 14.2
The heating/cooling curve for water heated or cooled at a constant rate. The plateau at the boiling point is longer than the plateau at the melting point, because it takes almost seven times as much energy (and thus seven times the heating time) to vaporize liquid water as to melt ice.

B. Water and Its Phase Changes

In the world around us we see many solids (soil, rocks, trees, concrete, and so on), and we are immersed in the gases of the atmosphere. But the liquid we most commonly see is water; it is virtually everywhere, covering about 70% of the earth's surface. Approximately 97% of the earth's water is found in the oceans, which are actually mixtures of water and huge quantities of dissolved salts.

Water is one of the most important substances on earth. It is crucial for sustaining the reactions within our bodies that keep us alive, but it also affects our lives in many indirect ways. The oceans help moderate the earth's temperature. Water cools automobile engines and nuclear power plants. Water provides a means of transportation on the earth's surface and acts as a medium for the growth of many of the creatures we use as food, and much more.

Pure water is a colorless, tasteless substance that at 1 atm pressure freezes to form a solid at 0 °C and vaporizes completely to form a gas at 100 °C. This means that (at 1 atm pressure) the liquid range of water occurs between the temperatures 0 °C and 100 °C.

Heating Water What happens when we heat liquid water? First the temperature of the water rises. Just as with gas molecules, the motions of the water molecules increase as it is heated. Eventually the temperature of the water reaches 100 °C; now bubbles develop in the interior of the liquid, float to the surface, and burst—the boiling point has been reached. An interesting thing happens at the boiling point: even though heating continues, the temperature stays at 100 °C until all the water has changed to vapor. Only when all of the water has changed to the gaseous state does the temperature begin to rise again. (We are now heating the vapor.) At 1 atm pressure, liquid water always changes to gaseous water at 100 °C, the **normal boiling point** for water.

The experiment just described is represented in **Figure 14.2**, which is called the **heating/cooling curve** for water. Going from left to right on this graph means energy is being added (heating). Going from right to left on the graph means that energy is being removed (cooling).

Teaching Support

DEMONSTRATION

Boiling Water at Reduced Temperatures

Materials
• 1-L round-bottom flask (do not use a flat-bottom flask—it may implode as a result of the low pressure)
• Ice (in a small resealable bag)
• Thermometer
• One-hole stopper to fit the flask

• Ring stand
• Clamp for round-bottom flask
• Oven mitt
• Burner

Preparation Carefully insert the thermometer through the one-hole stopper. (Use glycerin to lubricate the stopper. Protect your hand during the process.) Fill the flask half full with tap water.

Presentation Clamp the flask to the ring stand. Heat the water until it boils and the

Cooling Water When liquid water is cooled, the temperature decreases until it reaches 0 °C, where the liquid begins to freeze (see Figure 14.2). The temperature remains at 0 °C until all the liquid water has changed to ice and then begins to drop again as cooling continues. At 1 atm pressure, water freezes (or, in the opposite process, ice melts) at 0 °C. This is called the **normal freezing point** of water. Liquid and solid water can coexist indefinitely if the temperature is held at 0 °C. However, at temperatures below 0 °C liquid water freezes, while at temperatures above 0 °C ice melts.

Interestingly, water expands when it freezes. That is, one gram of ice at 0 °C has a greater volume than one gram of liquid water at 0 °C. This has very important practical implications. For instance, water in a confined space can break its container when it freezes and expands. This accounts for the bursting of water pipes and engine blocks that are left unprotected in freezing weather.

The expansion of water when it freezes also explains why ice cubes float. Recall that density is defined as mass/volume. When one gram of liquid water freezes, its volume becomes greater (it expands). Therefore, the *density* of one gram of ice is less than the density of one gram of water, because in the case of ice we divide by a slightly larger volume. For example, at 0 °C the density of liquid water is

$$\frac{1.00 \text{ g}}{1.00 \text{ mL}} = 1.00 \text{ g/mL}$$

and the density of ice is

$$\frac{1.00 \text{ g}}{1.09 \text{ mL}} = 0.917 \text{ g/mL}$$

The lower density of ice also means that ice floats on the surface of lakes as they freeze, providing a layer of insulation that helps prevent lakes and rivers from freezing solid in the winter. This means that aquatic life continues to have liquid water available through the winter.

C. Energy Requirements for the Changes of State

It is important to recognize that changes of state from solid to liquid and from liquid to gas are *physical* changes. No *chemical* bonds are broken in these processes. Ice, water, and steam all contain H_2O molecules. When water is boiled to form steam, water molecules are separated from each other (see **Figure 14.3**) but the individual molecules remain intact.

It takes energy to melt ice and to vaporize water, because intermolecular forces between water molecules must be overcome. In ice the molecules are virtually locked in place, although they can vibrate about their positions. When energy is added, the vibrational motions increase, and the molecules eventually achieve the greater movement and disorder characteristic of liquid water. The ice has melted. As still more energy is added, the gaseous state is eventually reached, in which the individual molecules are far apart

Normal freezing point
The freezing temperature of a liquid under one atmosphere of pressure

information

Remember that temperature is a measure of the random motions (average kinetic energy) of the particles in a substance.

—H_2O

Figure 14.3
Both liquid water and gaseous water contain H_2O molecules. In liquid water the H_2O molecules are close together, whereas in the gaseous state the molecules are widely separated. The bubbles contain gaseous water.

14.1 • Intermolecular Forces and Phase Changes • **493**

14.1.C Energy Requirements for the Changes of State

Objective To learn about interactions among water molecules and understand and use heat of fusion and heat of vaporization

LABORATORY
EXPERIMENT 58:
Heat of Fusion of Ice

LABORATORY
EXPERIMENT 59:
Energy and Changes of State, CBL

TEACHING TIPS

- Remind students that during a phase change, no temperature change occurs, and that no change of phase occurs when the temperature is changing.

- Remind students that energy is required for a phase change, even though the temperature is not changing during that time. The energy applied to the system is used to overcome the intermolecular forces.

(continued)

vapor fills the flask. (*Note:* Time required could be as long as 10 minutes.) Remove the heat source and firmly insert the stopper assembly into the flask. Invert the flask assembly, taking care not to break the thermometer. Place the resealable bag of ice on top of the inverted flask. The ice will cool the gas within the flask. Have a student volunteer read the temperature on the thermometer every minute or so as the flask continues to cool and the water continues to boil.

Teaching Notes Condensing water vapor reduces the pressure inside the flask. Boiling occurs whenever the vapor pressure of the water equals the atmospheric pressure, so boiling will occur below the "normal" boiling point. Do not let the temperature go below 20 °C. The flask may implode at such a low pressure.

This demonstration is also applicable in Section 14.2.

and interact relatively little. However, the gas still consists of water molecules. It would take *much* more energy to overcome the covalent bonds and decompose the water molecules into their component atoms.

Molar heat of fusion
The energy required to melt one mole of a solid

Molar heat of vaporization
The energy required to vaporize one mole of a liquid

The energy required to melt 1 mol of a substance is called the **molar heat of fusion**. For ice, the molar heat of fusion is 6.02 kJ/mol. The energy required to change 1 mol of liquid to its vapor is called the **molar heat of vaporization**. For water, the molar heat of vaporization is 40.6 kJ/mol at 100 °C. Notice in Figure 14.2 that the plateau that corresponds to the vaporization of water is much longer than that for the melting of ice. This occurs because it takes much more energy (almost seven times as much) to vaporize a mole of water than to melt a mole of ice. This is consistent with our models of solids, liquids, and gases.

Gas

Liquid

Solid

CHEMISTRY IN YOUR WORLD

Connection to Biology

Whales Need Changes of State

Sperm whales are prodigious divers. They commonly dive a mile or more into the ocean, hovering at that depth in search of schools of squid or fish. To remain motionless at a given depth, the whale must have the same density as the surrounding water. Because the density of seawater increases with depth, the sperm whale has a system that automatically increases its density as it dives. This system involves the spermaceti organ found in the whale's head. Spermaceti is a waxy substance with the formula

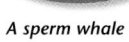

which is a liquid above 30 °C. At the ocean surface the spermaceti in the whale's head is a liquid, warmed by the flow of blood through the spermaceti organ. When the whale dives, this blood flow decreases and the colder water causes the spermaceti to begin freezing. Because solid

spermaceti is more dense than the liquid state, the sperm whale's density increases as it dives, matching the increase in the water's density.* When the whale wants to resurface, blood flow through the spermaceti organ increases, remelting the spermaceti and making the whale more buoyant. So the sperm whale's sophisticated density-regulating mechanism is based on a simple change of state.

―――――――――
*For most substances, the solid state is more dense than the liquid state. Water is an important exception.

A sperm whale

Chemistry in Your World
Whales Need Changes of State

This Chemistry in Your World offers an opportunity to discuss why the density of most solids exceeds that of the liquid. Have students think about what happens as a liquid solidifies at the atomic/molecular level. Are the particles more tightly packed? What does this structure do to the volume of the solid compared to that of the liquid? How does it change the density of a sample?

Have students draw molecular-level pictures to support their arguments.

Next, discuss the solidification of water. Why does water expand when it freezes? What happens to the density of water when it freezes? Once again, have students discuss this issue at the molecular level. Review hydrogen bonding and its effect on the structure of ice. Finally, discuss the biological implications of the expansion of water when it freezes. Discuss the effect on

cells and cell structure. What would happen if ice did not float (if ice were more dense than water)? Have students research the environmental effects of the spring overturn of water in lakes and streams. Since the density of water is at its maximum at 4 °C, the water in lakes turns over as it cools or warms in the spring and fall. What effect does this change have on life in these habitats? If ice were more dense than water, what would happen?

In liquids, the particles (molecules) are relatively close together, so most of the intermolecular forces are still present. However, when the molecules go from the liquid to the gaseous state, they must be moved far apart. To separate the molecules enough to form a gas, virtually all of the intermolecular forces must be overcome, and this requires large quantities of energy.

 Active Reading Question

> **Which is greater, the molar heat of fusion of water or the molar heat of vaporization of water? Why?**

EXAMPLE 14.1

Calculating Energy Changes: Solid to Liquid

Calculate the energy required to melt 8.5 g of ice at 0 °C. The molar heat of fusion for ice is 6.02 kJ/mol.

Solution

Where do we want to go?

Energy to melt 8.5 g ice at 0 °C = ? kJ

What do we know?

- 8.5 g ice at 0 °C
- molar heat of fusion for ice = 6.02 kJ/mol
- molar mass H_2O = 18.02 g/mol

How do we get there?

- Convert the mass of water to moles since the heat of fusion for water is per mole of water.

$$8.5 \ \cancel{g \ H_2O} \times \frac{1 \ mol \ H_2O}{18 \ \cancel{g \ H_2O}} = 0.47 \ mol \ H_2O$$

- The molar heat of fusion represents the equivalence statement

6.02 kJ required for 1 mol H_2O

This leads to the conversion factor used below to calculate the energy required to melt 8.5 g ice:

$$0.47 \ \cancel{mol \ H_2O} \times \frac{6.02 \ kJ}{\cancel{mol \ H_2O}} = 2.8 \ kJ$$

Does it make sense?

Since our sample is about $\frac{1}{2}$ mol the amount of energy should be about half the molar heat of fusion (6.02 kJ). Our answer is 2.8 kJ which is about half the molar heat of fusion.

The molar heat of vaporization of water is larger than the molar heat of fusion of water. The molar heat of fusion is a measure of the energy required to melt one mole of water, changing it from solid to liquid. To vaporize the water, not only must intermolecular forces be overcome, but the molecules also must be separated. This requires more energy.

EXAMPLE 14.1

More Examples

1. Calculate the energy released when 15.5 g of ice freezes at 0 °C. The molar heat of fusion of ice is 6.02 kJ/mol.

   5.18 kJ

2. Calculate the energy required to melt 12.5 g of ice at 0 °C and change it to water at 25 °C. The specific heat capacity of liquid water is 4.18 J/g °C and the molar heat of fusion of ice is 6.02 kJ/mol.

   5.48 kJ

14.1 • Intermolecular Forces and Phase Changes • **495**

EXAMPLE 14.2

More Examples

1. Calculate the energy required to vaporize 35.0 g of water at 100 °C. The molar heat of vaporization of water is 40.6 kJ/mol.

   78.9 kJ

2. Calculate the energy required to heat 22.5 g of liquid water at 0 °C and change it to steam at 100 °C. The specific heat capacity of liquid water is 4.18 J/g °C, and the molar heat of vaporization of water is 40.6 kJ/mol.

   60.1 kJ

Top Ten Lowest Melting Points

Element	Melting Point (° C)
Helium	−270.
Hydrogen	−259
Neon	−249
Fluorine	−220.
Oxygen	−218
Nitrogen	−210.
Argon	−189
Krypton	−157
Xenon	−112
Chlorine	−101

EXAMPLE 14.2

Calculating Energy Changes: Liquid to Gas

Calculate the energy (in kJ) required to heat 25 g of liquid water from 25 °C to 100. °C and change it to steam at 100. °C. The specific heat capacity of liquid water is 4.18 J/g °C, and the molar heat of vaporization of water is 40.6 kJ/mol.

Solution
Where do we want to go?

Energy required = ? kJ

What do we know?

- 25 g water to 25 g steam
- $T_{initial}$ = 25 °C
- T_{final} = 100. °C
- Specific heat capacity for water (solid) = 4.184 J/g °C
- molar heat of vaporization for water = 40.6 kJ/mol
- molar mass H_2O = 18.02 g/mol
- Energy to heat a liquid = $Q = s \times m \times \Delta T$

How do we get there?

We need to split the problem into two parts:

- heating the water to its boiling point
- converting the water to steam at the boiling point

Part 1 Heating to Boiling

We begin by heating the water from 25 °C to 100. °C.

$$\Delta T = 100. °C - 25 °C = 75 °C$$

To determine the energy to heat the water we use the equation

Energy required (Q)	=	Specific heat capacity (s)	×	Mass of water (m)	×	Temperature change (ΔT)

which we can represent by the equation

$$Q = s \times m \times \Delta T$$

Thus

$$Q = 4.184 \ \frac{J}{g \, °C} \times 25 \ g \times 75 \ °C = 7.8 \times 10^3 \ J$$

Energy required to heat 25 g of water from 25 °C to 100. °C   Specific heat capacity   Mass of water   Temperature change

$$= 7.8 \times 10^3 \ J \times \frac{1 \ kJ}{1000 \ J} = 7.8 \ kJ$$

Part 2 Vaporization

Now we must use the molar heat of vaporization to calculate the energy required to vaporize the 25 g of water at 100. °C. The heat of vaporization is given per mole rather than per gram, so we must first convert the 25 g of water to moles.

$$25 \text{ g H}_2\text{O} \times \frac{1 \text{ mol H}_2\text{O}}{18.02 \text{ g H}_2\text{O}} = 1.4 \text{ mol H}_2\text{O}$$

We can now calculate the energy required to vaporize the water.

$$\underbrace{\frac{40.6 \text{ kJ}}{\text{mol H}_2\text{O}}}_{\substack{\text{Molar heat of} \\ \text{vaporization}}} \times \underbrace{1.4 \text{ mol H}_2\text{O}}_{\text{Moles of water}} = 57 \text{ kJ}$$

The total energy is the sum of the two parts.

$$\underbrace{7.8 \text{ kJ}}_{\substack{\text{Heat from} \\ 25 \text{ °C to} \\ 100. \text{ °C}}} + \underbrace{57 \text{ kJ}}_{\substack{\text{Change to} \\ \text{vapor}}} = 65 \text{ kJ}$$

✔ Practice Problem • Exercise 14.2

Calculate the total energy required to melt 15 g of ice at 0 °C, heat the water to 100. °C, and vaporize it to steam at 100. °C.
Hint: Break the process into three parts and then find the sum.

SECTION 14.1
REVIEW QUESTIONS

❶ What is the difference between intermolecular forces and intramolecular forces?

❷ Is a hydrogen bond a true chemical bond? Explain.

❸ How can molecules without dipoles condense to form liquids or solids?

❹ Draw a cooling curve for a sample of steam (120 °C) which condenses to liquid water and cools to eventually form ice (0 °C).

❺ Why are changes of state considered to be physical changes and not chemical changes?

❻ Why doesn't the temperature of a substance (such as ice) change during melting? What is happening to the energy being added to the system?

❼ Calculate the energy required to change 1.00 mol of ice at −10. °C to water at 15 °C. The heat capacity of ice is 2.03 J/g °C, the heat capacity of water is 4.184 J/g °C, and the molar heat of fusion for ice is 6.02 kJ/mol.

RESEARCH LINKS
CLASSZONE.COM

Answer to Practice Problem 14.2

Energy to melt the ice:

$$15 \text{ g H}_2\text{O} \times \frac{1 \text{ mol H}_2\text{O}}{18 \text{ g H}_2\text{O}} =$$
0.83 mol H₂O

$$0.83 \text{ mol H}_2\text{O} \times \frac{6.02 \text{ kJ}}{\text{mol H}_2\text{O}} =$$
5.0 kJ

Energy to heat the water from 0 °C to 100 °C:

$$4.18 \frac{\text{J}}{\text{g °C}} \times 15 \text{ g} \times 100 \text{ °C} =$$
6300 J

$$6300 \text{ J} \times \frac{1 \text{ kJ}}{1000 \text{ J}} = 6.3 \text{ kJ}$$

Energy to vaporize the water at 100 °C:

$$0.83 \text{ mol H}_2\text{O} \times \frac{40.6 \text{ kJ}}{\text{mol H}_2\text{O}} =$$
34 kJ

Total energy required:

5.0 kJ + 6.3 kJ + 34 kJ = 45 kJ

SECTION 14.1
ASSESS

SECTION 14.1
Review Questions

1. Intermolecular forces occur between molecules; intramolecular forces occur within molecules.

2. A hydrogen bond is an attractive force that occurs between molecules. It is not a true chemical bond, which we consider to be formed within a molecule.

3. Molecules without dipoles can condense to form liquids as a result of London dispersion forces. These forces provide enough attraction to cause the molecules to condense into the next state.

4. See Figure 14.2 drawn from steam downward.

5. A change of state does not change the molecules of the substance in any way. Their motion simply increases or decreases. A chemical change requires that the molecule be changed to a different chemical.

6. The temperature of a substance doesn't change during melting because the energy being added to the system is used to overcome the attractive forces holding the molecules together in the solid state.

7. 7.52 kJ

SECTION 14.2
INTRODUCE

Student Preparation

Assign students to read Section 14.2 and to answer the Review Questions at the end of the section before coming to class.

 Active Learning
Team Learning Worksheet

After introducing the material in Section 14.2 in class, place students in groups and have them work together on **Section 14.2: Team Learning Worksheet.**

SECTION 14.2
GUIDE THE LEARNING

Homework

You may wish to assign these selected end-of-chapter problems as homework for this section: 24, 25, 26, 28, 29, 30, 31, 32

Additional end-of-chapter problems can be used for extra practice.

14.2.A Evaporation and Vapor Pressure

Objective To understand the relationship among vaporization, condensation, and vapor pressure

 LABORATORY
EXPERIMENT 60:
Vapor Pressure of Water, CBL

TEACHING TIPS

- The idea that evaporation is an endothermic process is difficult for many students to grasp. Take time to explain that the temperature of the liquid drops because the molecules with higher kinetic energy are going into the gas phase. Energy flows in if the container is not insulated; the temperature of the liquid will then remain constant.

- The familiar scents of fingernail polish remover and rubbing alcohol tell us that these liquids evaporate relatively easily.

SECTION 14.2
Vapor Pressure and Boiling Point

Key Terms
- Vaporization (evaporation)
- Condensation
- Vapor pressure

Objectives
- *To understand the relationship among vaporization, condensation, and vapor pressure*
- *To relate the boiling point of water to its vapor pressure*

A. Evaporation and Vapor Pressure

We all know that a liquid can evaporate from an open container. This is clear evidence that the molecules of a liquid can escape the liquid's surface and form a gas. This process, which is called **vaporization** or **evaporation**, requires energy to overcome the relatively strong intermolecular forces in the liquid.

To help you understand the energy changes that accompany evaporation, consider the microscopic view of a liquid shown in **Figure 14.4.**

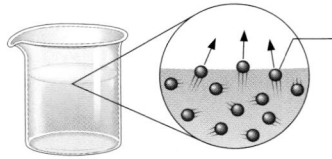

The high energy molecules escape the surface.

Figure 14.4
The microscopic view of a liquid near its surface

Vaporization (evaporation)
The process in which a liquid is converted to a gas

Remember that the temperature of a substance reflects the *average* kinetic energy of the components of that substance. Not all components have this average value of the kinetic energy, however. In fact, some components have a relatively small kinetic energy (are moving relatively slowly), whereas other components may have a kinetic energy much higher than the average (are moving much faster than the "average component"). To escape into the vapor phase a given component must have sufficient speed to overcome the intermolecular forces of the liquid. Thus only the fastest-moving components can escape the surface of the liquid.

Now consider what will happen if the evaporation process is taking place from an insulated container (no energy can flow in or out as heat). What will happen to the temperature of the liquid as evaporation occurs? Because the higher-energy components escape as evaporation occurs, the *average* energy of the remaining components will decrease. As the average kinetic energy of the components of the liquid drops, the temperature decreases. Thus evaporation is a cooling process—it is endothermic.

Active Reading Question

Why is evaporation a cooling process?

On the other hand, if a liquid evaporates from a container that is not insulated, energy will flow in (heat) as evaporation occurs to keep the temperature constant. Again, this process shows that evaporation is endothermic.

The fact that vaporization requires energy has great practical significance; in fact, one of the most important roles that water plays in our world is to act as a coolant. Because of the strong hydrogen bonding among its molecules in the liquid state, water has an unusually large heat of vaporization

498 • Chapter 14 • Liquids and Solids

Active Reading Question

When a liquid evaporates, the highest energy (fastest moving) molecules escape the liquid. The slower molecules are left in the substance. Temperature is a measure of average kinetic energy, and the average kinetic energy decreases as the faster moving particles escape. Therefore, the liquid cools.

(41 kJ/mol). A significant portion of the sun's energy is spent evaporating water from the oceans, lakes, and rivers rather than warming the earth. The vaporization of water is also crucial to our body's temperature-control system, which relies on the evaporation of perspiration.

Vapor Pressure

When we place a given amount of liquid in a container and then close it, we observe that the amount of liquid at first decreases slightly but eventually becomes constant. The decrease occurs because there is a transfer of molecules from the liquid to the vapor phase.

Sweat cools the body by evaporation

However, as the number of vapor molecules increases, it becomes more and more likely that some of them will return to the liquid. The process by which vapor molecules form a liquid is called **condensation**. Eventually, the same number of molecules are leaving the liquid as are returning to it: the rate of condensation equals the rate of evaporation. *At this point no further change occurs in the amounts of liquid or vapor, because the two opposite processes exactly balance each other;* the system is at *equilibrium*. Note that this system is highly *dynamic* on the molecular level—molecules are constantly escaping from and entering the liquid. However, there is no *net* change because the two opposite processes *balance* each other.

As a real life example, consider two island cities connected by a bridge. Suppose the traffic flow on the bridge is the same in both directions. There is motion—we can see the cars traveling across the bridge—but the number

Condensation
The process in which a vapor is converted to a liquid

information

A system at equilibrium is dynamic on the molecular level, but shows no visible changes.

CHEMISTRY EXPLORERS
Dorothy Hodgkin • 1910–1994

Dorothy Hodgkin was born in Cairo, Egypt. She became interested in chemistry and crystals at about the age of 10, and on her sixteenth birthday received a book by the Nobel Prize-winning physicist William Bragg. The book discussed how to use X rays to analyze crystals, and from that point on, her career path was set.

Dr. Hodgkin used X-ray analysis to determine the structures of proteins. She is most famous, however, for three very important discoveries. In 1945 she determined the structure of penicillin, and this knowledge helped manufacturers create penicillin. In 1954 she determined the structure of

vitamin B$_{12}$, which led to her winning the Nobel Prize in Chemistry in 1964. While both of these are important and useful discoveries, Dr. Hodgkin considered her greatest scientific achievement to be the discovery of insulin in 1969. Insulin is now used in the treatment of diabetes.

Dr. Hodgkin's great achievements helped change the way we think about molecules that are necessary for life. She was one of the first people to use molecular structure to explain biological function.

14.2 • Vapor Pressure and Boiling Point • **499**

Vapor pressure is dependent upon the type of intermolecular forces present and the size of the molecules. For a given size molecule, the stronger the intermolecular forces, the lower the vapor pressure. Since different substances exhibit different intermolecular forces and have different sizes, they are expected to have different vapor pressures.

Vapor pressure
The pressure exerted by a vapor in equilibrium with its liquid phase at a certain temperature

information

Vapor, not *gas*, is the term we customarily use for the gaseous state of a substance that exists naturally as a solid or liquid at 25 °C and 1 atm.

of cars in each city is not changing because an equal number enter and leave each one. The result is no *net* change in the number of autos in each city: an equilibrium exists.

The pressure of the vapor present at equilibrium with its liquid is called the *equilibrium vapor pressure* or, more commonly, the **vapor pressure** of the liquid. A simple barometer can be used to measure the vapor pressure of a liquid, as shown in **Figure 14.5**. Because mercury is so dense, any common liquid injected at the bottom of the column of mercury floats to the top, where it produces a vapor, and the pressure of this vapor pushes some mercury out of the tube. When the system reaches equilibrium, the vapor pressure can be determined from the change in the height of the mercury column.

In effect, we are using the space above the mercury in the tube as a closed container for each liquid. However, in this case as the liquid vaporizes, the vapor formed creates a pressure that pushes some mercury out of the tube and lowers the mercury level. The mercury level stops changing when the excess liquid floating on the mercury comes to equilibrium with the vapor. The change in the mercury level (in millimeters) from its initial position (before the liquid was injected) to its final position is equal to the vapor pressure of the liquid.

The vapor pressures of liquids vary widely (see Figure 14.5). Liquids with high vapor pressures are said to be *volatile*—they evaporate rapidly.

The vapor pressure of a liquid at a given temperature is determined by the *intermolecular forces* that act among the molecules. Liquids in which the intermolecular forces are large have relatively low vapor pressures, because such molecules need high energies to escape to the vapor phase. For example, although water is a much smaller molecule than diethyl ether, C_2H_5—O—C_2H_5, the strong hydrogen-bonding forces in water cause its vapor pressure to be much lower than that of ether (see Figure 14.5).

Why do substances have different vapor pressures?

Figure 14.5
(a) It is easy to measure the vapor pressure of a liquid by using a simple barometer of the type shown here.
(b) The water vapor pushed the mercury level down 24 mm (760–736), so the vapor pressure of water is 24 mm Hg at this temperature.
(c) Diethyl ether is much more volatile than water and thus shows a higher vapor pressure. In this case, the mercury level has been pushed down 545 mm (760–215), so the vapor pressure of diethyl ether is 545 mm Hg at this temperature.

500 • Chapter 14 • Liquids and Solids

Teaching Support
DEMONSTRATION

Cooling by Evaporation

Materials
- 4 thermometers
- 4 circles of filter paper
- Fine copper wire or small rubber bands
- Small containers of water, methanol, ethanol, and acetone

Preparation Wrap the bulb of each thermometer with a half-circle of filter paper and secure it with fine copper wire or a small rubber band.

Presentation Note the temperature of the room on the board. You will need four student volunteers to assist in this demonstration. Ask each volunteer to take one of the containers of liquid and a thermometer. Have them dip the thermometers into the liquids, wetting the filter paper. Remove the

thermometers from the liquids and observe what happens to the temperatures. Continue making observations for each thermometer until the lowest temperature is reached. Note that the volunteers should hold the thermometers still and not wave them in the air to speed up the process. Record the lowest temperature for each liquid on a table on the board. While students are waiting to find the lowest temperature for each substance, use

EXAMPLE 14.3

Using Knowledge of Intermolecular Forces to Predict Vapor Pressure

Predict which substance in each of the following pairs will show the largest vapor pressure at a given temperature.

a. $H_2O(l)$, $CH_3OH(l)$

b. $CH_3OH(l)$, $CH_3CH_2CH_2CH_2OH(l)$

Solution

a. Water contains two polar O—H bonds; methanol (CH_3OH) has only one. Therefore, the hydrogen bonding among H_2O molecules is expected to be much stronger than that among CH_3OH molecules. This gives water a lower vapor pressure than methanol.

b. Each of these molecules has one polar O—H bond. However, because $CH_3CH_2CH_2CH_2OH$ is a much larger molecule than CH_3OH, it has much greater London forces and thus is less likely to escape from its liquid. Thus $CH_3CH_2CH_2CH_2OH(l)$ has a lower vapor pressure than $CH_3OH(l)$.

B. Boiling Point and Vapor Pressure

Look at the photo of water boiling. When water boils, bubbles form in the interior of the liquid, and then rise to the surface where they "pop." What causes these bubbles to form at the boiling point and not at a lower temperature? An air bubble acts as a "birth place" for a bubble growing in the interior of water as high-energy H_2O ( ) molecules enter. represent N_2 molecules; represent O_2 molecules.

 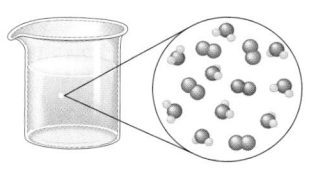

Bubble expands as H_2O molecules enter

Assume we start with a tiny air bubble in the water. This bubble expands when high-energy water molecules enter the bubble and produce enough internal pressure to push back the water surrounding the bubble. The formation of a bubble can happen only when the average kinetic energy of the water molecules is great enough to produce a pressure inside the bubble that can oppose the atmospheric pressure pushing down on the surface of the water (see **Figure 14.6**). That is, the vapor pressure of the water must be equal to atmospheric pressure before boiling can occur. This explains why the boiling of water occurs at 100 °C at an atmospheric pressure of 1 atm and not at a lower temperature. Only when the water temperature reaches 100 °C are bubbles able to form in the interior of the liquid because the water molecules are energetic enough to sustain a pressure of 1 atm inside the bubbles. At temperatures below 100 °C

i n f o r m a t i o n

As you heat water, notice that tiny bubbles form well below the boiling point. These bubbles result from dissolved air being expelled from the water.

14.2 • Vapor Pressure and Boiling Point • **501**

(continued)

reference materials to have other students find the boiling point of each substance. Record this information on the board.

Teaching Notes Ask students to explain why the temperatures drop when the thermometers covered with wet filter paper are exposed to the air. On the basis of the observations of the behavior of the four liquids, what is the relationship between the normal boiling point and the effectiveness of the liquids in cooling by evaporation? You

can relate this issue to the technique of giving a person with a high fever a sponge bath or a rubdown with alcohol to reduce the fever.

EXAMPLE 14.3

More Examples

Predict which substance in each of the following pairs will show the largest vapor pressure at a given temperature.

1. $H_2O(l)$, $HF(l)$
   HF. Hydrogen bonding occurs in both samples, but H_2O has two O—H bonds that are capable of hydrogen bonding with other water molecules.

2. $CH_3OCH_3(l)$, $CH_3CH_2OH(l)$
   CH_3OCH_3. No hydrogen bonding can exist in CH_3OCH_3 because the hydrogen atoms are attached to carbon atoms, not the oxygen atom. Hydrogen bonding does occur in CH_3CH_2OH.

14.2.B Boiling Point and Vapor Pressure

Objective To relate the boiling point of water to its vapor pressure

TECHNOLOGY

Video
Boiling Water with Ice Water

MISCONCEPTION
Chemistry

Ask students what they think is inside the bubbles formed when water boils. Students often have interesting misconceptions about the phenomenon of boiling. For example, they may think that air or hydrogen and oxygen is in the bubbles. Clearly, it is difficult for students to understand that boiling is a physical, not a chemical, process.

MINI-DEMO

When discussing boiling, keep a boiling beaker of water in front of the class so you can refer to it. If possible, get some liquid nitrogen (check with hospital supply stores). Showing both a hot liquid and a cold liquid boiling can dispel misconceptions that all boiling occurs at high temperatures.

Figure 14.6

CRITICAL THINKING

If the water molecule was linear, it would not be polar. Both O—H bonds are polar, and with a linear shape, the individual bond dipoles would cancel. Methane has a molar mass similar to that of water; it is nonpolar and has a boiling point around −170 °C. Even polar H_2S has a boiling point around −70 °C because it does not exhibit hydrogen bonding. Thus it would be safe to say that a nonpolar water molecule would be a gas at room conditions. Life would be impossible in such a case. Even assuming nonpolar water was a liquid, it would not dissolve ionic compounds.

 Active Reading Question

Boiling temperature is dependent upon atmospheric pressure. As atmospheric pressure decreases, the temperature at which water boils decreases. The atmospheric pressure in Leadville, Colorado, is less than the atmospheric pressure in Madison, Wisconsin; therefore, the temperature of boiling water in Leadville is lower than that in Madison. It takes longer for a potato to cook in cooler water.

Figure 14.6
The formation of the bubble in the interior of water is opposed by atmospheric pressure.

Atmospheric pressure

1 atm

Tiny air bubble cannot expand

Temperature of water less than 100 °C

Atmospheric pressure

1 atm

Internal pressure in bubble equals 1 atm

Temperature of water equals 100 °C

 CRITICAL THINKING

You have seen that the water molecule has a bent shape and is therefore a polar molecule. This characteristic accounts for many of water's interesting properties.

What if the water molecule were linear? How would it affect the properties of water? How would life be different?

the external pressure (1 atm) pushing on the surface of the water prevents bubble formation. So water boils at 100 °C (1 atm atmospheric pressure) because its vapor pressure is 1 atm at 100 °C.

Given this information, why do you suppose that water boils at 90 °C in Leadville, Colorado (elevation 10,000 ft)? Because Leadville is located at a high elevation where the atmospheric pressure is much less than 1 atm, the pressure pushing on the surface of water there is much less than at sea level. Thus you do not have to heat water to as high a temperature in Leadville to enable bubbles to form in the interior of the water. As a consequence, water can boil at a lower temperature in Leadville than in Los Angeles.

We have seen that the boiling point of water changes with atmospheric pressure. **Table 14.3** shows the boiling point of water at various locations around the world.

Active Reading Question

It takes longer to boil a potato in Leadville, Colorado, than in Madison, Wisconsin. Why is this?

Table 14.3

Boiling Point of Water at Various Locations

Location	Feet Above Sea Level	P_{atm} (atm)	Boiling Point (°C)
Top of Mt. Everest, Tibet	29,028	0.32	70
Top of Mt. McKinley, Alaska	20,320	0.45	79
Top of Mt. Whitney, California	14,494	0.57	85
Top of Mt. Washington, New Hampshire	6,293	0.78	93
Boulder, Colorado	5430	0.80	94
Madison, Wisconsin	900	0.96	99
New York City, New York	10	1.00	100
Death Valley, California	−282	1.01	100.3

502 • Chapter 14 • Liquids and Solids

Hands-On Chemistry
MINI-LAB

Hot Molecules

Materials Each student/group will need a model kit (alternatively, they can use toothpicks and clay).

Purpose Students will explore the relationships between the shape of a molecule and the physical property of boiling point. In addition, they will review Lewis structures and the VSEPR theory.

Discussion The stronger the intermolecular attractions, the higher the boiling point. For small molecules, dipole–dipole interactions (of which hydrogen bonding is a special case) are stronger than London forces. When comparing two molecules with only London forces, the larger molecule (with more electrons) has a greater probability of a momentary dipole and, therefore, has stronger attractions (and a higher boiling point).

a. H_2O has a higher boiling point than CH_4 (100 °C versus −164 °C). Water is polar and methane is not (water also exhibits hydrogen bonding).

b. C_6H_{14} (have students make the straight chain) has a higher boiling point than C_2H_6 (69 °C versus −88.6 °C). Hexane and ethane are both nonpolar, but hexane is a larger molecule.

HANDS-ON CHEMISTRY • MINI-LAB •

Hot Molecules

Materials
- molecular model kit

Procedure
1. Obtain a molecular model kit from your teacher.
2. Build models for each pair of molecules.
   a. H_2O, CH_4
   b. C_2H_6, C_6H_{14}
   c. C_8H_{18}, C_8H_{18} (make one molecule with all the carbons connected in a line and one other molecule)
   d. C_2H_6O, C_2H_6O (make two different molecules)

Results/Analysis
1. Use your models to decide which of the molecules in each pair has the highest boiling point. Explain your reasoning.
2. Use your models to decide which of the molecuules in each pair has the highest vapor pressure. Explain your reasoning.

SECTION 14.2
REVIEW QUESTIONS

❶ Use your knowledge of evaporation to explain why perspiration cools you on a warm, dry day.

❷ Would you expect your hand to feel cooler if you dipped it into water and removed it to the air, or if you dipped your hand into methyl alcohol and removed it to the air? Explain. Note: Do not dip your hand in methyl alcohol.

❸ Explain how a barometer can be used to measure the vapor pressure of a liquid.

❹ Water and methane (CH_4) have very similar molar masses. However, water is a liquid under normal conditions, and methane is a gas. Use intermolecular forces to explain this.

❺ Why does water boil at 100 °C at sea level?

❻ What is the difference between boiling and evaporation?

RESEARCH LINKS
CLASSZONE.COM

SECTION 14.2 Review Questions

1. Perspiration cools you on a warm day because the perspiration on your skin evaporates. The evaporation process is endothermic, which causes your skin to feel cool.

2. Your hand would feel cooler if you dipped it into methyl alcohol and removed it to the air. At the same temperature, the vapor pressure of methyl alcohol is higher than that of water. More molecules of methyl alcohol would leave the surface of your skin, making your skin feel cool.

3. See Figure 14.5. Add the liquid to a column of mercury in a mercury barometer. Because mercury is so dense, the liquid will go to the surface of the mercury. The liquid will produce a vapor and the pressure increase will push the mercury level down. The distance it is pushed is the vapor pressure of the liquid.

4. Methane is a nonpolar molecule that exhibits London dispersion forces. Water is a polar molecule that exhibits strong hydrogen bonding. Since hydrogen bonding is much stronger than London forces, water molecules are held together with greater force.

5. At sea level, the atmospheric pressure is 1 atm. The vapor pressure of water at 100 °C is 1 atm. Boiling occurs when the vapor pressure of a liquid equals the atmospheric pressure.

6. Evaporation occurs at temperatures below the boiling point. The phase change occurs at the surface of the liquid. At the boiling point, the vapor pressure of the liquid equals atmospheric pressure, so the change of state can take place anywhere within the liquid. Boiling is a much faster process than evaporation for this reason.

(continued)

c. The straight chain (*n*-octane) has a higher boiling point. For example, the boiling point of iso-octane (used in gasoline; also called 2,2,4-trimethylpentane) is 99.2 °C and the boiling point of *n*-octane is 125.7 °C. The *n*-octane molecules have more regions of attraction.

d. Ethanol (CH_3CH_2OH, 78.5 °C) has a higher boiling point than dimethyl ether (CH_3OCH_3, −25 °C). Both molecules are polar, but ethanol exhibits hydrogen bonding.

SECTION 14.3
INTRODUCE

Student Preparation

Assign students to read Section 14.3 and to answer the Review Questions at the end of the section before coming to class.

 Active Learning
Team Learning Worksheet

After introducing the material in Section 14.3 in class, place students in groups and have them work together on **Section 14.3: Team Learning Worksheet**.

SECTION 14.3
GUIDE THE LEARNING

Homework

You may wish to assign these selected end-of-chapter problems as homework for this section: 34, 35, 38, 39, 40, 41

Additional end-of-chapter problems can be used for extra practice.

14.3.A The Solid State: Types of Solids

Objective To learn about the various types of crystalline solids

 TEACHING TIP

Now is an excellent time to connect with the earth science teacher and bring some samples of crystalline solids to class. Quartz and calcite are favorite choices, and a graphite rod (from a battery) or copper wire is a good example of an atomic solid.

SECTION 14.3
Properties of Solids

Key Terms

- Crystalline solids
- Ionic solids
- Molecular solids
- Atomic solids
- Electron sea model
- Alloy
- Substitutional alloy
- Interstitial alloy

Objectives

- *To learn about the types of crystalline solids*
- *To understand the interparticle forces in crystalline solids*
- *To learn how the bonding in metals determines metallic properties*

A. The Solid State: Types of Solids

Solids play a very important role in our lives. The concrete we drive on, the trees that shade us, the windows we look through, the paper that holds this print, the diamond in an engagement ring, and the plastic lenses in eyeglasses are all important solids. Most solids, such as wood, paper, and glass, contain mixtures of various components. However, some natural solids, such as diamonds and table salt, are nearly pure substances.

Many substances form **crystalline solids**—those with a regular arrangement of their components. This is illustrated by the partial structure of sodium chloride shown in **Figure 14.7**. The highly ordered arrangement of the components in a crystalline solid produces beautiful, regularly shaped crystals such as those shown in **Figure 14.8**.

There are many different types of crystalline solids. For example, both sugar and salt have beautiful crystals that we can easily see. However, although both dissolve readily in water, the properties of the resulting solutions are quite different. The salt solution readily conducts an electric current; the sugar solution does not. This behavior arises from the different natures of the components in these two solids. Common salt, NaCl, is an ionic solid that contains Na^+ and Cl^- ions. When solid sodium chloride dissolves in water, sodium ions and chloride ions are distributed throughout the resulting solution. These ions are free to move through the solution to conduct an electric current. Table sugar (sucrose), on the other hand, is composed of neutral molecules that are dispersed throughout the water when the solid dissolves. No ions are present, and the resulting solution does not conduct electricity. These examples illustrate two important types of crystalline solids: **ionic solids**, represented by sodium chloride; and **molecular solids**, represented by sucrose.

Crystalline solid
A solid characterized by the regular arrangement of its components

Ionic solid
A solid that contains cations and anions

Molecular solid
A solid composed of molecules

 = Cl^-

 = Na^+

Figure 14.7
The regular arrangement of sodium and chloride ions in sodium chloride, a crystalline solid

---

Figure 14.8
Several crystalline solids

Quartz, SiO_2

Rock salt, NaCl

Red beryl, $Be_3Al_2Si_6O_{18}$

Meeting Individual Needs
READING CONCEPTS

One way to understand the relationships among the many types of solids is to make a concept map. For students who are unfamiliar with concept maps, have them read *Making and Using Graphic Organizers* located in the *Teacher Resources*.

A third type of crystalline solid is represented by elements such as graphite and diamond (both pure carbon), boron, silicon, and all metals. These substances, which contain atoms covalently bonded to each other, are called **atomic solids**.

We have seen that crystalline solids can be grouped conveniently into three classes.

Atomic solid
A solid that contains atoms at the lattice points

Notice that the names of the three classes come from the components of the solid. An ionic solid contains ions, a molecular solid contains molecules, and an atomic solid contains atoms. Examples of the three types of solids are shown below.

ℹ nformation

The internal forces in a solid determine many of the properties of the solid.

Diamond   Sodium chloride   Ice

The properties of a solid are determined primarily by the nature of the forces that hold the solid together. For example, although argon, copper, and diamond are all atomic solids (their components are atoms), they have strikingly different properties. Argon has a very low melting point (−189 °C), whereas diamond and copper melt at high temperatures (about 3500 °C and 1083 °C, respectively). Copper is an excellent conductor of electricity (it is widely used for electrical wires), whereas both argon and diamond are insulators. The shape of copper can easily be changed; it is both malleable (will form thin sheets) and ductile (can be pulled into a wire). Diamond, on the other hand, is the hardest natural substance known. The marked differences in properties among these three atomic solids are due to differences in bonding. We will explore the bonding in solids next.

Copper can be formed into many different kinds of objects.

14.3 • Properties of Solids • **505**

14.3.B Bonding in Solids

Objective To understand the interparticle forces in crystalline solids and learn about how the bonding in metals determines metallic properties

 TEACHING TIPS

- Models of different crystal structures can be used very effectively to discuss the different types of solids.

- Remind students that the formulas for ionic solids are actually empirical formulas, not molecular formulas.

 Active Reading Question

Answers will vary. Sodium chloride is an example of an ionic solid, ice is an example of a molecular solid, and graphite is an example of an atomic solid.

TECHNOLOGY

 Animations
Structure of an Ionic Solid (NaCl)
Molecular Solids

B. Bonding in Solids

We have seen that crystalline solids can be divided into three classes, depending on the fundamental particle or unit of the solid. Ionic solids consist of oppositely charged ions packed together, molecular solids contain molecules, and atomic solids have atoms as their fundamental particles. Examples of the various types of solids are given in **Table 14.4**.

 Active Reading Question

Give an example of an ionic solid, a molecular solid, and an atomic solid.

Ionic Solids

Ionic solids are stable substances with high melting points that are held together by the strong forces that exist between oppositely charged ions. The structures of ionic solids can be visualized best by thinking of the ions as spheres packed together as efficiently as possible. For example, in NaCl the larger Cl^- ions are packed together much like one would pack balls in a box. The smaller Na^+ ions occupy the small spaces ("holes") left among the spherical Cl^- ions.

● $= Cl^-$ ○ $= Na^+$

Molecular Solids

In a molecular solid the fundamental particle is a molecule. Examples of molecular solids include ice (contains H_2O molecules), dry ice (contains CO_2 molecules), sulfur (contains S_8 molecules), and white phosphorus (contains tetrahedral P_4 molecules).

Table 14.4		
Examples of the Various Types of Solids		
Type of Solid	**Examples**	**Fundamental Unit(s)**
ionic	sodium chloride, NaCl(*s*)	Na^+, Cl^- ions
ionic	ammonium nitrate, NH_4NO_3(*s*)	NH_4^+, NO_3^- ions
molecular	dry ice, CO_2(*s*)	CO_2 molecules
molecular	ice, H_2O(*s*)	H_2O molecules
atomic	diamond, C(*s*)	C atoms
atomic	iron, Fe(*s*)	Fe atoms
atomic	argon, Ar(*s*)	Ar atoms

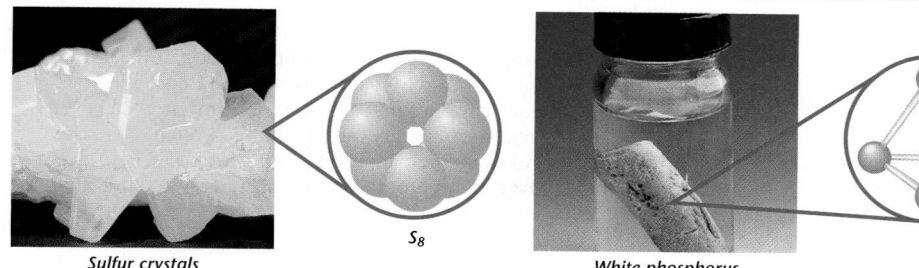

Sulfur crystals S_8

White phosphorus P_4

Molecular solids tend to melt at relatively low temperatures because the intermolecular forces that exist among the molecules are relatively weak. If the molecule has a dipole moment, dipole–dipole forces hold the solid together. In solids with nonpolar molecules, London dispersion forces hold the solid together.

Atomic Solids

The properties of atomic solids vary greatly because of the different ways in which the fundamental particles, the atoms, can interact with each other. For example, the solids of the Group 8 elements have very low melting (freezing) points (see Table 14.2), because these atoms, having filled valence orbitals, cannot form covalent bonds with each other. So the forces in these solids are the relatively weak London dispersion forces.

On the other hand, diamond, a form of solid carbon, is one of the hardest substances known and has an extremely high melting point (about 3500 °C). The incredible hardness of diamond arises from the very strong covalent carbon–carbon bonds in the crystal, which lead to a giant molecule. In fact, the entire crystal can be viewed as one huge molecule. A small part of the diamond structure is represented below.

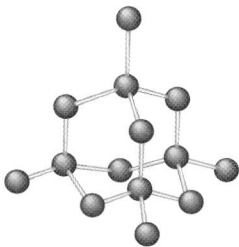

In diamond each carbon atom is bound covalently to four other carbon atoms to produce a very stable solid. Several other elements also form solids whereby the atoms join together covalently to form giant molecules. Silicon and boron are examples.

At this point you might be asking yourself, "Why aren't solids such as a crystal of diamond, which is a 'giant molecule,' classified as molecular solids?" The answer is that, by convention, a solid is classified as a molecular solid only if (like ice, dry ice, sulfur, and phosphorus) it contains small molecules. Substances like diamond that contain giant molecules are called network solids.

Diamonds are prized for use as jewelry because they reflect light and take millions of years to form in nature.

14.3 • Properties of Solids • **507**

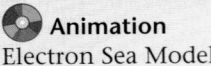
The electron sea model explains why metals are able to conduct heat and electricity, why metals can be hammered into sheets (they are malleable), and why metals can be pulled into wire (they are ductile).

TECHNOLOGY

Animation
Electron Sea Model

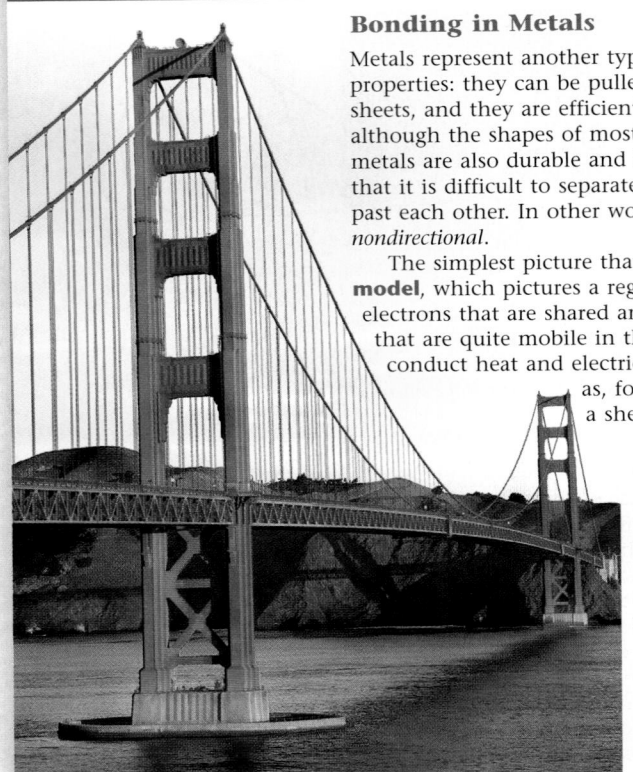

Bonding in Metals

Metals represent another type of atomic solid. Metals have familiar physical properties: they can be pulled into wires, they can be hammered into sheets, and they are efficient conductors of heat and electricity. However, although the shapes of most pure metals can be changed relatively easily, metals are also durable and have high melting points. These facts indicate that it is difficult to separate metal atoms but relatively easy to slide them past each other. In other words, the bonding in most metals is *strong* but *nondirectional*.

The simplest picture that explains these observations is the **electron sea model**, which pictures a regular array of metal atoms in a "sea" of valence electrons that are shared among the atoms in a nondirectional way and that are quite mobile in the metal crystal. The mobile electrons can conduct heat and electricity, and the atoms can be moved rather easily, as, for example, when the metal is hammered into a sheet or pulled into a wire.

Active Reading Question

What properties of a metal does the electron sea model explain?

Metals can be drawn into wires which can be used to construct cables like these on the Golden Gate bridge.

CELEBRITY CHEMICAL   Titanium (Ti)

Titanium is a wonderful structural material. It is 43% less dense than steel but has 30% greater yield strength than steel when alloyed with metals such as aluminum and tin. Titanium also has excellent resistance to fatigue and corrosion. Titanium is especially well suited for making bicycle frames. After their first ride on a bicycle with a titanium frame, most experienced cyclists find themselves searching for the right words to describe the "magic" of titanium. In fact, the magic of titanium results from its combination of toughness, stretchability, and resilience. It resists deforming under pedaling loads but does not transmit road shocks to the rider nearly as much as steel.

Titanium, a lustrous metal with a melting point of 1667 °C, is quite abundant in the earth's crust,

ranking ninth among the elements. Unfortunately, it is difficult to obtain from its ores in pure form. Titanium becomes very brittle when trace impurities such as C, N, and O are present, and it must be processed with great care. Its stretchability also makes it difficult to machine on a lathe to make specific parts. The resulting bicycle makes all these troubles worthwhile, however.

Titanium is also used to make artificial hip joints.

508 • Chapter 14 • Liquids and Solids

CELEBRITY CHEMICAL

Titanium (Ti)

Ask students to research other uses for titanium.

Because of the nature of the metallic crystal, other elements can be introduced relatively easily to produce substances called alloys. An **alloy** is best defined as *a substance that contains a mixture of elements and has metallic properties*. There are two common types of alloys.

In a **substitutional alloy** some of the host metal atoms are *replaced* by other metal atoms of similar sizes. For example, in brass approximately one-third of the atoms in the host copper metal have been replaced by zinc atoms.

Alloy
A substance that contains a mixture of elements and has metallic properties

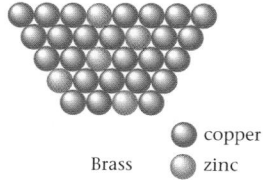

copper
Brass zinc

Sterling silver (93% silver and 7% copper) and pewter (85% tin, 7% copper, 6% bismuth, and 2% antimony) are other examples of substitutional alloys.

An **interstitial alloy** is formed when some of the interstices (holes) among the closely packed metal atoms are occupied by atoms much smaller than the host atoms.

iron
Steel carbon

Steel, the best-known interstitial alloy, contains carbon atoms in the "holes" of an iron crystal. The presence of interstitial atoms changes the properties of the host metal. Pure iron is relatively soft, ductile, and malleable because of the absence of strong directional bonding. The spherical metal atoms can be moved rather easily with respect to each other. However, when carbon, which forms strong directional bonds, is introduced into an iron crystal, the presence of the directional carbon–iron bonds makes the resulting alloy harder, stronger, and less ductile than pure iron. The amount of carbon directly affects the properties of steel. *Mild steels* (containing less than 0.2% carbon) are still ductile and malleable and are used for nails, cables, and chains. *Medium steels* (containing 0.2–0.6% carbon) are harder than mild steels and are used in rails and structural steel beams. *High-carbon steels* (containing 0.6–1.5% carbon) are tough and hard and are used for springs, tools, and cutlery.

Many types of steel also contain elements in addition to iron and carbon. Such steels are often called *alloy steels* and can be viewed as being mixed interstitial (carbon) and substitutional (other metals) alloys. An example is stainless steel, which has chromium and nickel atoms substituted for some of the iron atoms. The addition of these metals greatly increases the steel's resistance to corrosion.

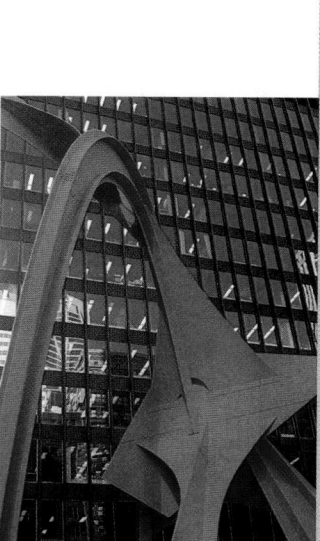

A steel sculpture in Chicago

TEACHING TIP

Alloys were introduced very early in the course in Chapter 2. Now is an excellent time to review them by bringing in samples of alloys such as sterling silver, brass, and steel and discussing the molecular-level structure of each alloy.

Meeting Individual Needs
ADVANCED LEARNERS

Ask students to research the cost of 304-stainless steel and 316-stainless steel. Then have them write a paragraph explaining why there is a cost difference between the two types of metal. Students should include in their explanations the uses for each type of steel.

CHEMISTRY IN YOUR WORLD

Science, Technology, and Society

Metal with a Memory

An upset mother walks into the optical shop carrying her mangled pair of $400 glasses. Her child had gotten into her purse, found her glasses, and twisted them into a pretzel. She hands them to the optometrist with little hope that they can be fixed. The optometrist says not to worry and drops the glasses into a dish of warm water where the glasses spring back into their original shape. The optometrist hands the restored glasses to the woman and says there is no charge for repairing them.

How can the frames "remember" their original shape when placed in warm water? The answer is a nickel-titanium alloy called Nitinol that was developed in the late 1950s and early 1960s at the Naval Ordnance Laboratory in White Oak, Maryland, by William J. Buehler. (The name Nitinol comes from *Ni*ckel *Ti*tanium *N*aval *O*rdnance *L*aboratory.) Nitinol has an amazing ability to remember a shape originally impressed in it.

  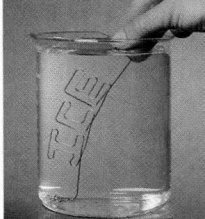

Nitinol has many medical applications, including hooks used by orthopedic surgeons to attach ligaments and tendons to bones and stents that are inserted in partially blocked arteries to keep them open.

Before insertion, the stents are crushed down so they can be fed into the artery through a thin tube. As the crushed stent heats up in the blood it returns to its original shape.

Nitinol is also used for the wires in braces to straighten teeth. The wires are formed into the correct shape and then inserted into the patient's mouth. As they warm up the wire tries to return to its original shape putting constant pressure on the teeth out of position. This constant pressure speeds up the moving and straightening process!

510 • Chapter 14 • Liquids and Solids

Chemistry in Your World

Metal with a Memory

You can perform the demonstration illustrated in this Chemistry in Your World by ordering memory metal from a supplier. The Institute for Chemical Education at the University of Wisconsin has Memory Metal kits that include the *ICE* sample, an explanation of how it works, and transparency masters for class. Both Flinn Scientific and Educational Innovations (see *Teacher Resources*) carry memory metal as well.

Students can also find more information on memory metal in *ChemMatters* magazine and on the Internet. Ask students to research other uses for this amazing substance.

EXAMPLE 14.4

Identifying Types of Crystalline Solids

Name the type of crystalline solid formed by each of the following substances:

   a. ammonia

   b. iron

   c. cesium fluoride

   d. argon

   e. sulfur

Solution

   a. Solid ammonia contains NH_3 molecules, so it is a molecular solid.

   b. Solid iron contains iron atoms as the fundamental particles. It is an atomic solid.

   c. Solid cesium fluoride contains the Cs^+ and F^- ions. It is an ionic solid.

   d. Solid argon contains argon atoms, which cannot form covalent bonds to each other. It is an atomic solid.

   e. Sulfur contains S_8 molecules, so it is a molecular solid.

 Practice Problem • Exercise 14.4

Name the type of crystalline solid formed by each of the following substances:

   a. sulfur trioxide

   b. barium oxide

   c. gold

SECTION 14.3
REVIEW QUESTIONS

1 Salt and sugar are both crystalline solids. How are they different?

2 What are the forces holding each type of crystalline solid together? Predict which type would have the lowest boiling point. Explain your choice.

3 What is the difference between a substitutional alloy and an interstitial alloy?

4 How are metals different from other atomic solids such as diamond?

5 Name the type of crystalline solid formed by each of the following substances.

   a. ice

   b. copper

   c. calcium chloride

14.3 • Properties of Solids • **511**

EXAMPLE 14.4

More Examples

Name the type of crystalline solid formed by each of the following substances:

1. water
   molecular solid

2. calcium oxide
   ionic solid

3. krypton
   atomic solid

 Answer to Practice Problem 14.4

a. contains SO_3 molecules—a molecular solid

b. contains Ba^{2+} and O^{2-} ions—an ionic solid

c. contains Au atoms—an atomic solid

SECTION 14.3
ASSESS

 SECTION 14.3 Review Questions

1. Salt is an ionic solid and sugar is a molecular solid.

2. molecular: dipole–dipole forces and London dispersion forces; ionic: electrostatic; atomic: covalent. The lowest boiling point would be molecular because the intermolecular forces are weakest in these crystals.

3. In a substitutional alloy, the host metal's atoms are replaced by other metal atoms of similar sizes. In an interstitial alloy, some of the holes among the closely packed metal atoms are occupied by atoms that are much smaller than the host metal's atoms.

4. Diamond has directed covalent bonds. In metals, the bonding is nondirectional.

5. a. molecular solid

   b. atomic solid (metal)

   c. ionic solid

Chapter 14 Review

Key Terms

14.1
Intermolecular forces
Intramolecular forces
Dipole–dipole attraction
Hydrogen bonding
London dispersion forces
Normal boiling point
Heating/cooling curve
Normal freezing point
Molar heat of fusion
Molar heat of vaporization

Key Ideas

14.1 Intermolecular Forces and Phase Changes

■ Intermolecular forces are the forces that occur among the molecules in a substance.

■ The classes of intermolecular forces are

• Dipole–dipole: due to the attractions among molecules that have dipole moments

• Hydrogen bonding: particularly strong dipole–dipole forces that occur when hydrogen is bound to a highly electronegative atom (such as O, N, F)

• London dispersion forces: forces that occur among nonpolar molecules (or atoms) when accidental dipoles develop in the electron "cloud"

■ Phase changes can occur when energy enters or leaves a compound.

• As energy enters a system a substance can change from a solid to a liquid to a gas.

• The molar heat of fusion is the energy required to melt 1 mol of a solid substance.

• The normal melting point is the temperature at which a solid melts at a pressure of 1 atm.

• The normal boiling point is the temperature at which a liquid boils at a pressure of 1 atm.

• A substance with relatively large intermolecular forces requires relatively large amounts of energy to produce phase changes.

◆ Water is an example of a substance with large intermolecular forces (hydrogen bonding).

14.2
Vaporization (evaporation)
Condensation
Vapor pressure

14.2 Vapor Pressure and Boiling Point

■ The equilibrium pressure of vapor over a liquid in a closed container is called the vapor pressure.

■ The vapor pressure of a liquid is a balance between condensation and evaporation.

■ Vapor pressure is relatively low for a substance (such as water) with large intermolecular forces.

■ The boiling point of a liquid occurs at a temperature at which the vapor pressure of the liquid equals the atmospheric pressure.

RESEARCH LINKS
CLASSZONE.COM

Meeting Individual Needs

CHAPTER REVIEW

Chapter 14 Review Worksheet at the appropriate level:
Basic
Standard
Challenge

CHAPTER SUMMARY

A **Chapter Summary** that includes additional Active Reading Questions for Chapter 14 is available.

Assessment Resources

CHAPTER 14

Chapter 14 Test

TECHNOLOGY

 Computerized Test Bank for Chapter 14

14.3 Properties of Solids

- Types of solids
  - Ionic solid—the components are ions.
  - Molecular solid—the components are molecules.
  - Atomic solids—the components are atoms.

- Bonding in solids
  - Ionic solids are bound together by the attractions among the oppositely charged ions.
  - Molecular solids are bound together by the intermolecular forces among the molecules.
  - Atomic solids
    - The solids produced from noble gases have weak London dispersion forces.
    - Many atomic solids form "giant molecules" that are held together by covalent bonds
- Metals are held together by nondirectional covalent bonds (called the electron sea model) among the closely packed atoms.
  - Metals form alloys of two types.
    - Substitutional: different atoms are substituted for the host metal atoms.
    - Interstitial: small atoms are introduced into the "holes" in the metallic structure.

RESEARCH LINKS
CLASSZONE.COM

Chapter 14 Assessment

Chapter 14 Assessment (left column — answers)

1. Dipole–dipole interactions occur when molecules possessing dipole moments orient themselves so that the positive and negative ends of the adjacent molecules attract each other. Any three polar liquids will possess dipole–dipole forces among their molecules [e.g., $CHCl_3(l)$, $SO_2(l)$, $NO_2(l)$].

2. Dipole–dipole forces are stronger at shorter distances; they are relatively short range forces.

3. Hydrogen bonding is a special case of dipole–dipole forces that can come into play in molecules in which hydrogen atoms are directly bonded to highly electronegative atoms (such as nitrogen, oxygen, or fluorine). Three examples of substances exhibiting hydrogen bonding are water, ammonia, and ethyl alcohol (CH_3CH_2OH).

4. Hydrogen bonding can exist when H is bonded to O, N, or F. This additional intermolecular force requires more energy to separate the molecules for boiling.

5. The magnitude of the dipole–dipole interactions is strongly dependent on the distance between the dipoles. In the vapor phase the molecules are too far apart for these interactions to be very strong.

6. All atoms and molecules exhibit London dispersion forces among each other.

7. (a) London dispersion forces
   (b) London dispersion forces
   (c) dipole–dipole forces and London dispersion forces
   (d) hydrogen bonding and London dispersion forces

8. The boiling points increase with an increase in the molar mass of the noble gas. The valence electrons of a larger atom will be farther from the nucleus.

Chapter 14 Assessment (middle columns — exercises)

All exercises with blue numbers have answers in the back of this book.

14.1 Intermolecular Forces and Phase Changes

A. Intermolecular Forces

1. What is a dipole–dipole attraction? Give three examples of liquid substances in which you would expect dipole–dipole attractions to be large.

2. How is the strength of dipole–dipole interactions related to the *distance* between polar molecules? Are dipole–dipole forces short-range or long-range forces?

3. What is meant by *hydrogen bonding*? Give three examples of substances that would be expected to exhibit hydrogen bonding in the liquid state.

4. The normal boiling point of water is unusually high, compared to the boiling points of H_2S, H_2Se, and H_2Te. Explain this observation in terms of the *hydrogen bonding* that exists in water, but that does not exist in the other compounds.

5. Why are the dipole–dipole interactions between polar molecules *not* important in the vapor phase?

6. Although the noble gas elements are monatomic and could not give rise to dipole–dipole forces or hydrogen bonding, these elements still can be liquefied and solidified. Explain.

7. Discuss the types of intermolecular forces acting in the liquid state of each of the following substances.

   a. Kr   c. NF_3
   b. S_8 d. H_2O

8. The boiling points of the noble gas elements are listed below. Comment on the trend in the boiling points. Why do the boiling points vary in this manner?

He	−272 °C	Kr	−152.3 °C
Ne	−245.9 °C	Xe	−107.1 °C
Ar	−185.7 °C	Rn	−61.8 °C

9. When 50 mL of liquid water at 25 °C is added to 50 mL of ethanol (ethyl alcohol), also at 25 °C, the combined volume of the mixture is considerably *less* than 100 mL. Give a possible explanation.

B. Water and Its Phase Changes

10. What are some important physical properties of water? How do these properties of water help moderate the earth's environment?

Chapter 14 Assessment (right column — exercises)

11. Describe some uses, both in nature and in industry, of water as a *cooling* agent.

12. We all have observed that ice *floats* on liquid water. Why? What is unusual about this?

13. Discuss some implications of the fact that, unlike most substances, water *expands* in volume when it freezes.

14. Describe, on both a microscopic and a macroscopic basis, what happens to a sample of water as it is heated from room temperature to 50 °C above its normal boiling point.

15. Figure 14.2 presents the *cooling curve* for water. Discuss the meaning of the different portions of this curve (for example, explain what each flat section and each sloping section represents).

C. Energy Requirements for the Changes of State

16. Describe in detail the microscopic processes that take place when a solid melts.

17. Describe in detail the microscopic processes that take place when a liquid boils.

18. Explain the difference between *intra*molecular and *inter*molecular forces.

19. Which type of forces (*intra*molecular or *inter*molecular) must be overcome to melt a solid or vaporize a liquid?

20. Discuss the similarities and differences between the arrangements of molecules and the forces between molecules in liquid water versus steam, and in liquid water versus ice.

21. The following data have been collected for substance X. Construct a heating curve for substance X. (The drawing does not need to be absolutely to scale, but it should clearly show relative differences.)

normal melting point	−15 °C
molar heat of fusion	2.5 kJ/mol
normal boiling point	134 °C
molar heat of vaporization	55.3 kJ/mol

22. The molar heats of fusion and vaporization for water are 6.02 kJ/mol and 40.6 kJ/mol, respectively, and the specific heat capacity of liquid water is 4.18 J/g °C. What quantity of heat energy is required to melt 25.0 g of ice at 0 °C? What quantity of heat is required to vaporize 37.5 g of liquid water at 100. °C? What quantity of heat is required to warm 55.2 g of liquid water from 0 °C to 100. °C?

Bottom section (continuation of answers)

At a greater distance from the nucleus, the electron clouds are easier to distort so as to give a momentary dipole moment. Thus, as the size of the noble gas atoms increases, so does the magnitude of the London dispersion forces.

9. Strong hydrogen bonding occurs in both ethanol and water. Thus the molecules have great attraction for one another and are able to approach one another very closely; in fact, they must approach one another more closely in the mixture than either can approach a like molecule in the separate liquids.

10. Pure water is a colorless, tasteless substance that has a normal freezing point of 0 °C and a normal boiling point of 100 °C. It has a relatively large specific heat capacity and is able to absorb massive amounts of energy from the sun, preventing rapid or unusually large changes in temperature in the environment.

23. Given that the specific heat capacities of ice and steam are 2.06 J/g °C and 2.03 J/g °C, respectively, and considering the information about water given in exercise 22, calculate the total quantity of heat evolved when 10.0 g of steam at 200. °C is condensed, cooled, and frozen to ice at −50. °C.

14.2 Vapor Pressure and Boiling Point

A. Evaporation and Vapor Pressure

24. Describe, on a microscopic basis, the processes of *evaporation* and *condensation*. Which process requires the input of energy?

25. What is *vapor pressure*? On a microscopic basis, how does a vapor pressure develop in a closed flask containing a small amount of liquid? What processes are going on in the flask?

26. What do we mean by a *dynamic equilibrium*? Describe how the development of a vapor pressure above a liquid represents such an equilibrium.

27. Describe an experimental method that could be used to determine the vapor pressure of a volatile liquid.

28. Which substance in each pair would be expected to be more volatile at a particular temperature? Explain your reasoning.

   a. $H_2O(l)$ or $H_2S(l)$
   b. $H_2O(l)$ or $CH_3OH(l)$
   c. $CH_3OH(l)$ or $CH_3CH_2OH(l)$

29. Although water and ammonia differ in molar mass by only one unit, the boiling point of water is over 100 °C higher than that of ammonia. What forces in liquid water that do *not* exist in liquid ammonia could account for this observation?

30. Two molecules that contain the same number of each kind of atom but that have different molecular structures are said to be *isomers* of each other. For example, both ethyl alcohol and dimethyl ether (shown below) have the formula C_2H_6O and are isomers. Based on considerations of intermolecular forces, which substance would you expect to be more volatile? Which would you expect to have the higher boiling point? Explain.

   dimethyl ether   ethyl alcohol

   $CH_3—O—CH_3$ $CH_3—CH_2—OH$

B. Boiling Point and Vapor Pressure

31. Potatoes and other vegetables often require longer cooking times at higher elevations. Explain why it takes longer to cook something at higher elevations.

32. Why is the boiling temperature of water less than 100 °C at high altitudes?

14.3 Properties of Solids

A. The Solid State: Types of Solids

33. What are crystalline solids? What kind of microscopic structure do such solids have? How is this microscopic structure reflected in the macroscopic appearance of such solids?

34. On the basis of the smaller units that make up the crystals, cite three types of crystalline solids. For each type of crystalline solid, give an example of a substance that forms that type of solid.

B. Bonding in Solids

35. How do *ionic* solids differ in structure from *molecular* solids? What are the fundamental particles in each? Give two examples of each type of solid and indicate the individual particles that make up the solids in each of your examples.

36. How do the physical properties of ionic solids, in general, differ from the properties of molecular solids? Give an example of each to illustrate your discussion.

37. Ionic solids are generally considerably harder than most molecular solids. Explain.

38. Ionic solids typically have melting points hundreds of degrees higher than the melting points of molecular solids. Explain.

39. What types of forces exist between the individual particles in an ionic solid? Are these forces relatively strong or relatively weak?

40. Compare the intermolecular forces that exist in a sample of solid krypton, Kr, with those that exist in diamond, C.

41. What is an *alloy*? Explain the differences in structure between substitutional and interstitial alloys. Give an example of each type.

42. Explain how the properties of a metal may be modified by alloying the metal with some other substance. Discuss, in particular, how the properties of iron are modified in producing the various types of steel.

15. The sloped portions represent changes in temperature. The flat portions represent phase changes.

16. As heat energy is added to a solid, the vibrational motions of the particles increase. Eventually the particles are vibrating so strongly that they come apart and begin to move in the more random manner of particles of a liquid.

17. As a liquid reaches its boiling point, bubbles of vapor begin to form in the liquid. These rise to the surface and burst. As the liquid remains at its boiling point, the energy added is used to overcome attractive forces among particles.

18. Intramolecular forces are forces within a molecule (for example, a covalent bond is an intramolecular force). Intermolecular forces are forces between or among different molecules.

19. intermolecular

20. In ice, water molecules are in more or less regular fixed positions in the ice crystal. In liquid water, the molecules are in less fixed positions and move freely. In both solid and liquid water, strong hydrogen bonds exist between water molecules. In steam, the water molecules are far apart and move randomly. The water molecules in the vapor phase exert minimal force on one another and act relatively independently.

21. Refer to the *Solutions Guide*.

22. 8.35 kJ; 84.4 kJ; 23.1 kJ

23. 33.1 kJ

24. Evaporation represents molecules of a liquid entering the vapor phase; condensation is the reverse process. Evaporation requires an input of energy so that the molecules have enough energy to escape the bulk liquid.

11. Water, as perspiration, helps cool the human body. Nuclear power plants use water to cool the reactor core.

12. Ice floats because it is less dense than liquid water. Generally a solid is more dense than a liquid, but water is an exception to this rule.

13. Water pipes can be broken during cold weather. Also, ice can float on water, which is crucial for aquatic life (and ultimately for humans).

14. From room temperature to 100 °C, adding energy as heat to water raises the temperature of the water (and the molecules of water move more quickly). At 100 °C, water molecules possess enough kinetic energy to escape readily from the liquid's surface (the temperature remains constant during this process). If heated above 100 °C, steam molecules absorb additional kinetic energy and the temperature of the steam increases.

25. Vapor pressure is the pressure of vapor at equilibrium above a liquid in a sealed container at a given temperature. Molecules in the liquid evaporate, but as the number of molecules in the vapor state increases, some of these molecules rejoin (condense). Between evaporation and condensation, dynamic equilibrium eventually is reached.

26. A dynamic equilibrium is a situation in which two opposite processes are occurring at the same speed; there is no net change in the system. As a liquid evaporates into the empty space above it, molecules accumulate in the vapor state. Condensation eventually will occur at the same rate as evaporation. At this point, a fixed pressure of vapor has developed, and there will be no further net change in the amount of liquid present.

27. See Section 14.2.A about the behavior of a liquid in a closed container.

28. (a) H_2S. H_2O exhibits hydrogen bonding, and H_2S does not. (b) CH_3OH. H_2O exhibits stronger hydrogen bonding than CH_3OH because there are two locations where hydrogen bonding is possible on water. (c) CH_3OH. Both are capable of hydrogen bonding, but generally lighter molecules are more volatile than heavier molecules.

29. The polarity of the O—H bond in water is greater than the polarity of the N—H bond in ammonia (oxygen is more electronegative than nitrogen).

30. Hydrogen bonding can exist in ethyl alcohol but not dimethyl ether. Therefore, ethyl alcohol would be less volatile (higher boiling point).

Critical Thinking

For exercises 43–52 choose one of the following terms to match the definition or description given.

   a. alloy
   b. specific heat
   c. crystalline solid
   d. dipole–dipole attraction
   e. equilibrium vapor pressure
   f. intermolecular
   g. intramolecular
   h. ionic solids
   i. London dispersion forces
   j. molar heat of fusion
   k. molar heat of vaporization
   l. molecular solids
   m. normal boiling point
   n. semiconductor

43. boiling point at pressure of 1 atm

44. energy required to melt 1 mol of a substance

45. forces between atoms in a molecule

46. forces between molecules in a solid

47. instantaneous dipole forces for nonpolar molecules

48. lining up of opposite charges on adjacent polar molecules

49. maximum pressure of vapor that builds up in a closed container

50. mixture of elements having metallic properties overall

51. repeating arrangement of component species in a solid

52. solids that melt at relatively low temperatures

53. In carbon compounds a given group of atoms can often be arranged in more than one way. This means that more than one structure may be possible for the same atoms. For example, both the molecules diethyl ether and 1-butanol have the same number of each type of atom, but they have different structures and are said to be *isomers* of one another.

   diethyl ether $CH_3—CH_2—O—CH_2—CH_3$
   1-butanol $CH_3—CH_2—CH_2—CH_2—OH$

Which substance would you expect to have the larger vapor pressure? Why?

54. Which of the substances in each of the following sets would be expected to have the highest boiling point? Explain why.

   a. Ga, KBr, O_2
   b. Hg, NaCl, He
   c. H_2, O_2, H_2O

55. When a person has a severe fever, one therapy to reduce the fever is an "alcohol rub." Explain how the evaporation of alcohol from the person's skin removes heat energy from the body.

56. What is steel? How do the properties of steel differ from the properties of its constituents?

57. Which is stronger, a dipole–dipole attraction between two molecules or a covalent bond between two atoms within the same molecule? Explain.

58. What are London dispersion forces and how do they arise in a nonpolar molecule? Are London forces typically stronger or weaker than dipole–dipole attractions between polar molecules? Are London forces stronger or weaker than covalent bonds? Explain.

59. Discuss the types of intermolecular forces acting in the liquid state of each of the following substances.

   a. N_2
   b. NH_3
   c. He
   d. CO_2 (linear, nonpolar)

60. What do we mean when we say a liquid is *volatile*? Do volatile liquids have large or small vapor pressures? What types of intermolecular forces occur in highly volatile liquids?

61. Although methane, CH_4, and ammonia, NH_3, differ in molar mass by only one unit, the boiling point of ammonia is over 100 °C higher than that of methane (a nonpolar molecule). Explain.

31. At higher altitudes the boiling temperatures of liquids are lower because less atmospheric pressure exists above the liquid. The temperature at which food cooks is determined by the temperature to which water in the food can be heated before it escapes as steam. By boiling at a lower temperature, the food must cook longer.

32. The boiling point is the point at which the vapor pressure of the liquid is equal to the atmospheric pressure. At higher altitudes, the atmospheric pressure is lower, so the boiling temperature is lower.

33. A crystalline solid is a solid with a regular, repeating microscopic arrangement of its components (atoms, molecules, or ions). This highly ordered microscopic arrangement is frequently reflected macroscopically in beautiful, regularly shaped crystals.

(continued on page 517a)

1 Which of the following correctly pairs the molecule with the strongest intermolecular attraction present for that case?

A Li_2O: dipole–dipole; F_2: London dispersion; SO_2: dipole–dipole

B Li_2O: dipole–dipole; F_2: dipole–dipole; SO_2: dipole–dipole

C Li_2O: ion-ion; F_2: London dispersion; SO_2: dipole–dipole

D Li_2O: ion–ion; F_2: dipole–dipole; SO_2: London dispersion

2 The difference in the strengths of the intermolecular forces among methane (CH_4) molecules and ammonia (NH_3) molecules is mainly due to

A the fact that ammonia is polar and methane is nonpolar.

B the fact that methane is polar and ammonia is nonpolar.

C the fact that methane (with four hydrogens) has a greater chance to exhibit hydrogen bonding than ammonia (with three hydrogens).

D the different molar masses.

3 In the diagram below, which lines represent the hydrogen bonds?

A The dotted lines between the hydrogen atoms of one water molecule and the oxygen atoms of a different water molecule.

B The solid lines between a hydrogen atom and oxygen atom in the same water molecule.

C Both the solid lines and dotted lines represent the hydrogen bonds.

D There are no hydrogen bonds represented in the diagram.

4 Which of the following decreases as the strength of intermolecular forces increases?

A boiling point   C vapor pressure

B melting point   D surface tension

5 The vapor pressure of water at 100.0 °C is

A 0.53 atm   C 1.0 atm

B 0.95 atm   D 1.2 atm

6 Which of the following is not an example of an atomic solid?

A iron   C argon

B water   D graphite

7 Table sugar is an example of

A an atomic solid.

B an ionic solid.

C a network solid.

D a molecular solid.

For questions 8–11, identify the strongest intermolecular force exhibited by each of the following molecules.

8 CH_4

9 O_2

10 CO

11 K_2O

12 Use the heating-cooling curve below to answer the following questions

a. What is the freezing point of the liquid?

b. What is the boiling point of the liquid?

c. Which is greater, the heat of fusion or heat of vaporization? Explain.

Chapter 14

Standardized Test Practice

1. C

2. A

3. A

4. C

5. C

6. B

7. D

8. London dispersion forces

9. London dispersion forces

10. Dipole–dipole interactions

11. Ion–ion forces

12. a. The freezing point of the liquid is 40 °C.

b. The boiling point of the liquid is 120 °C.

c. The heat of fusion is the energy required to melt the solid to form the liquid (or the energy released when the liquid freezes). The heat of vaporization is the energy required to vaporize the liquid (or the energy released when the gas condenses). The heat of vaporization is larger because it requires more energy to turn a liquid into a gas than to turn a solid into a liquid. We can see this on the heating-cooling curve because the line for melting is longer than the line for vaporizing.

Test-Taking Strategy

Encourage students to quickly skim questions and mark the ones that they can answer quickly. Students should answer those questions first before moving on to the more difficult or time-consuming questions.

(continued from page 516)

34. ionic solids (NaCl); molecular solids (ice); atomic solids (copper)

35. The fundamental particles in ionic solids are positive and negative ions. For example, the ionic solid sodium chloride consists of an alternating regular array of Na^+ and Cl^- ions. An ionic solid such as calcium bromide consists of a regular array of Ca^{2+} and Br^- ions. In ionic crystals, each ion is surrounded by and attracted to a group of oppositely charged ions. The fundamental units of molecular solids are molecules (two examples are the sugars glucose, $C_6H_{12}O_6$, and sucrose, $C_{12}H_{22}O_{11}$). These molecules are held together by relatively weaker forces, leading to lower melting points for molecular solids as compared to ionic solids.

36. Ionic solids tend to be harder and have higher melting and boiling points. Compare table salt (NaCl) to table sugar (sucrose), for example.

37. The strong electrostatic forces make it very difficult to move or displace ions from one another; the solid is therefore perceived as hard. Molecular solids are held together by dipole–dipole forces, which are weaker than electrostatic forces. Thus the molecular solid is more easily deformed.

38. Ionic solids have strong electrostatic forces (due to the attraction of positively and negatively charged ions). These forces require a great deal of energy to be overcome.

39. Strong electrostatic forces exist between oppositely charged ions in ionic solids.

40. In solid Kr, the only forces that exist are the very weak London dispersion forces. In diamond, however, each carbon atom is held to its four nearest neighbors by strong covalent bonds.

41. An alloy represents a mixture of elements that, as a whole, shows metallic properties. In a substitutional alloy, some of the host metal atoms are replaced by (substituted with) other atoms (brass, for example). In an interstitial alloy, other small atoms occupy the spaces between the larger host metal atoms (carbon steel, for example).

42. The presence of a second metal's atoms in a metal's lattice changes the properties (usually making the alloy stronger because irregularities keep the crystal from being easily deformed). Steels with relatively high carbon content are exceptionally strong. Steels produced by alloying iron with nickel, chromium, and cobalt are more resistant to corrosion (rusting) than iron itself is.

43. m

44. j

45. g

46. f

47. i

48. d

49. e

50. a

51. c

52. l

53. Diethyl ether should have a higher vapor pressure because it does not exhibit hydrogen bonding, whereas 1-butanol does.

54. (a) KBr (ionic bonding)
(b) NaCl (ionic bonding)
(c) H_2O (hydrogen bonding)

55. Energy is required for a substance to evaporate (this energy is called the heat of vaporization). Applying rubbing alcohol to skin causes internal heat from the body to be absorbed as the heat of vaporization of the alcohol.

56. "Steel" is a general term applied to alloys consisting mostly of iron. Steel is much stronger and harder than iron, which is relatively soft, malleable, and ductile.

57. Dipole–dipole interactions are typically 1% as strong as a covalent bond.

58. London dispersion forces arise from instantaneous dipoles; they are weaker than dipole–dipole forces or covalent bonds.

59. (a) London dispersion forces
(b) hydrogen bonding and London dispersion forces
(c) London dispersion forces
(d) London dispersion forces

60. A volatile liquid is one that evaporates relatively easily. Such liquids generally have high vapor pressures because they have relatively weak intermolecular forces (London dispersion forces or weak dipole–dipole interactions).

61. In NH_3, strong hydrogen bonding can exist. Because CH_4 molecules are nonpolar, only the relatively weak London dispersion forces exist.

15 Solutions

Planning Guide

Section	Segment	Text Features and Components	Labs, Demonstrations, & Activities
15.1 Forming Solutions 2.5 Blocks pp. 520–527	**A** Solubility		**SE** Hands-On Chemistry: Colors in Motion *p. 524* **TE** Teaching Support: Demonstration *pp. 520–521* **TE** Teaching Support: Demonstration *pp. 522–523* **TE** Mini-Demo *p. 523* **TE** Mini-Demo *p. 524* **LM** Experiment 61: Solution Properties, Traditional Lab Manual Report Sheets Teacher's Lab Guide **LM** Experiment 62: Polar and Nonpolar Solvents, Microscale Lab Manual Report Sheets Teacher's Lab Guide
	B Solution Composition: An Introduction		**TE** Mini-Demo *p. 525* **TE** Mini-Demo *p. 525* **LM** Experiment 63: Temperature and Solubility, Microscale Lab Manual Report Sheets Teacher's Lab Guide
	C Factors Affecting the Rate of Dissolving	**SE** Chemistry Explorers: Ellen Swallow Richards *p. 527*	**TE** Mini-Demo *p. 526*
15.2 Describing Solution Composition 1 Block pp. 528–540	**A** Solution Composition: Mass Percent		**SE** Hands-On Chemistry: Rainbow in a Straw *p. 528*
	B Solution Composition: Molarity		**TE** Mini-Demo *p. 531* **TE** Mini-Demo *p. 534* **LM** Experiment 64: Chloride in Water Lab Manual Report Sheets Teacher's Lab Guide

continued on next page

Key
SE Student Edition   **TE** Teacher Edition   **RP** Teacher Resource Package
AR Additional Materials   **LM** Lab Materials   Transparencies
DVD   CD-ROM   classzone.com

All Learners	Technology	Review & Assessment	Standards
TE Teaching Tips *pp. 520–521, 524* **TE** Misconception *p. 523*	**Transparency:** Figure 15.1 **Animation:** Dissolution of a Solid in a Liquid (Ionic) **Video:** Ammonia Fountain **Lab Generator CD** **EasyPlanner**	**SE** Active Reading Questions *p. 522* **SE** Active Reading Question *p. 524* **SE** Key Terms *p. 554* **SE** Questions and Problems *p. 555*	**TE** **NSES** UCP1, A1, A2, B2, F1, F3, F4, F5, F6
	Video: Supersaturated Sodium Acetate **Lab Generator CD** **EasyPlanner**	**SE** Active Reading Question *p. 526* **SE** Critical Thinking *p. 526* **SE** Key Terms *p. 554* **SE** Questions and Problems *p. 555*	
TE Teaching Tip *p. 526* **RP** MINT: Challenge Projects *TE p. 526* **RP** Team Learning Worksheet (Sec. 15.1)	**EasyPlanner**	**SE** Review Questions (15.1.A–15.1.C) *p. 527* **SE** Questions and Problems *p. 555*	
TE Teaching Tips *p. 528* **RP** MINT: Math Concepts *TE p. 529*	**EasyPlanner**	**SE** Practice Problem *p. 529* **TE** More Examples *p. 529* **TE** More Examples *p. 529* **SE** Practice Problem *p. 530* **SE** Key Terms *p. 554* **SE** Questions and Problems *p. 555*	**TE** **NSES** UCP1, UCP3, A1, A2, B2
TE Teaching Tips *pp. 530–533* **TE** Misconception *p. 531*	**Lab Generator CD** **EasyPlanner**	**SE** Active Reading Question *p. 530* **TE** More Examples *p. 531* **SE** Practice Problem *p. 532* **TE** More Examples *p. 532* **SE** Practice Problem *p. 533* **TE** More Examples *p. 533* **SE** Practice Problem *p. 534* **TE** More Examples *p. 534* **SE** Practice Problem *p. 535* **TE** More Examples *p. 535* **SE** Key Terms *p. 554* **SE** Questions and Problems *pp. 555–556*	

Planning Guide

Section	Segment		Text Features and Components	Labs, Demonstrations, & Activities
15.2 **(continued)**	**C**	**Dilution**	**SE** Top Ten Elements in Seawater *p. 537*	**TE** Mini-Demo *p. 536* **SE** Hands-On Chemistry: Can We Add Concentrations? *p. 537* **SE** Hands-On Chemistry: Good to the Last Drop! *p. 540*

15.3
Properties
of
Solutions
 	
2 Blocks
pp. 541–553
	A	**Stoichiometry of Solution Reactions**		**TE** Mini-Demo *p. 542*
				LM Experiment 65: Hard Water Analysis, Microscale
				    Lab Manual
				    Report Sheets
				    Teacher's Lab Guide

	B	**Neutralization Reactions**		
	C	**Normality**	**SE** Celebrity Chemical: Mercury *p. 550*	
	D	**Boiling Point and Freezing Point**		**TE** Teaching Support: Demonstration *pp. 552–553*

Key	**SE** Student Edition	**TE** Teacher Edition	**RP** Teacher Resource Package
	AR Additional Materials	**LM** Lab Materials	**🔌** Transparencies
	💿 DVD	**💾** CD-ROM	**ⓘ** classzone.com

All Learners	Technology	Review & Assessment	Standards
TE Misconception *p. 535* **TE** Teaching Tips *pp. 537–538* **RP** Team Learning Worksheet (Sec. 15.2)	**⊙** Video: Dilution **⊙** EasyPlanner	**SE** Active Reading Question *p. 538* **SE** Practice Problem *p. 539* **TE** More Examples *p. 539* **SE** Review Questions (15.2.A–15.2.C) *p. 540* **SE** Key Terms *p. 554* **SE** Questions and Problems *p. 556*	
TE Teaching Tips *pp. 541, 543* **RP** MINT: Reading Concepts *TE p. 542*	**▮** Lab Generator CD **⊙** EasyPlanner	**SE** Critical Thinking *p. 541* **SE** Active Reading Question *p. 541* **TE** More Examples *p. 542* **TE** More Examples *p. 543* **SE** Practice Problem *p. 544* **SE** Questions and Problems *p. 557*	**TE** **NSES** UCP1, UCP3, A1, A2, B2, B3, F5, G3
TE Teaching Tips *pp. 544–545* **TE** Meeting Individual Needs *p. 545*	**⊙** Video: Acid–Base Titration **⊙** EasyPlanner	**SE** Active Reading Question *p. 545* **TE** More Examples *p. 545* **SE** Practice Problem *p. 546* **SE** Key Terms *p. 554* **SE** Questions and Problems *p. 557*	
TE Teaching Tips *pp. 546–548*	**⊙** EasyPlanner	**TE** More Examples *p. 548* **SE** Active Reading Question *p. 549* **SE** Practice Problem *p. 549* **TE** More Examples *p. 549* **SE** Practice Problem *p. 551* **TE** More Examples *p. 551* **SE** Key Terms *p. 554* **SE** Questions and Problems *p. 557*	
TE Teaching Tips *p. 552* **RP** Team Learning Worksheet (Sec. 15.3)	**⊙** EasyPlanner	**SE** Active Reading Question *p. 553* **SE** Review Questions (15.3.A–15.3.D) *p. 553* **SE** Key Terms *p. 554* **SE** Questions and Problems *p. 557*	

Resource Materials for Chapter 15

SE Chapter Review *p. 554*

SE Critical Thinking *p. 558*

SE Standardized Test Practice *p. 559*

AR English/Spanish Summaries

▮ English Summaries Audio

▮ Spanish Summaries Audio

RP Meeting Individual Needs Toolkit (MINT)
Reading Concepts
Math Concepts
Challenge Projects
Chapter Review Worksheets
Chapter Summaries

RP Solutions Guide

RP Standardized Test Practice

RP Chapter Tests

RP Test Bank

⊕ Test Generator

In this chapter our goals are for students to:

- Understand the process of dissolving and why certain substances dissolve in water
- Understand qualitative descriptions of the concentration of a solution
- Understand the factors that affect the rate at which a solid dissolves
- Understand and use the concentration terms: mass percent and molarity
- Learn to calculate the concentration of a solution made by dilution
- Understand the strategy for solving problems in solution reactions
- Learn to do calculations for acid–base reactions
- Learn about normality and equivalent weight
- Understand the effect of a solute on solution properties

Chapter 15
Solutions

Bubbles on the surface of a soap solution

518

IN YOUR LIFE

Solutions are very important to all of us. In fact we can walk, talk, laugh, and work only because millions of chemical reactions are occurring every second in the solutions in our bodies. We also encounter many solutions as we go through a typical day—the liquid soap we use in our morning shower, the cranberry juice we drink for breakfast, the sports drinks we have for lunch, the gasoline we put in our cars and the "energy drink" we may have in the middle of the afternoon. Even the "pure water" from the water fountain or a water bottle is a solution—it contains dissolved minerals from the earth, chlorine compounds to disinfect it, and traces of many other substances. A solution that we often take for granted is the one we live in—the air is a solution of nitrogen (N_2), oxygen (O_2), water vapor, carbon dioxide, and traces of many other gases. Solutions are clearly essential to our existence.

Brass, a solid solution of copper and zinc, is used to make musical instruments and many other objects.

WHAT DO YOU KNOW?

Prereading Questions

1. What is meant by the term *solution* (as in, a solution of salt and water)?

2. What happens when you mix water and oil?

3. What can you do to get sugar to dissolve more quickly in water?

4. A certain cookie is made by mixing 150.0 g of dough with 25.0 g of chocolate chips. What is the mass percent of chocolate chips in the cookie?

5. What is meant by a precipitation reaction?

6. What is the net ionic equation for all reactions of a strong acid and a strong base?

7. Why is salt scattered on roads during the winter in cold weather climates?

Solutions • Chapter 15 • **519**

Prereading Questions

1. A solution is a homogeneous mixture. While solutions can have different phases, in this text we deal almost exclusively with aqueous solutions.

2. You can add oil to water, cap the container, and shake it vigorously to get the two to mix. Upon sitting, however, the oil and water will separate again.

3. *Answers will vary.* You can stir the sugar, grind the sugar, and heat the water.

4. 14.3% (25/175 × 100%)

5. In a precipitation reaction, an ionic solid forms from two ionic solutions.

6. $H^+(aq) + OH^-(aq) \rightarrow H_2O(l)$

7. Salt lowers the freezing point of water.

TECHNOLOGY IN THE CLASSROOM

 Transparencies
Figure: 15.1

 Power Presentation DVD
PowerPoint Slides
Animation
Dissolution of a Solid in a Liquid (Ionic)
Videos
Supersaturated Sodium Acetate
Dilution
Acid–Base Titration
Ammonia Fountain
eEdition
EasyPlanner

 Lab Generator CD
English Summaries CD
Spanish Summaries CD
ML Test Generator

 classzone.com

Student Preparation

Assign students to read Section 15.1 and to answer the Review Questions at the end of the section before coming to class.

 Active Learning
Team Learning Worksheet

After introducing the material in Section 15.1 in class, place students in groups and have them work together on **Section 15.1: Team Learning Worksheet.**

Homework

You may wish to assign these selected end-of-chapter problems as homework for this section: 1, 2, 3, 4, 6, 8, 10, 11

Additional end-of-chapter problems can be used for extra practice.

15.1.A Solubility

Objective To understand the process of dissolving and learn why certain substances dissolve in water

 LABORATORY
EXPERIMENT 61:
Solution Properties, Traditional

🔬 **LABORATORY**
EXPERIMENT 62:
Polar and Nonpolar Solvents, Microscale

🍎 **TEACHING TIPS**

- Introduce the topic of solubility by using examples from daily life, and then move to the molecular level to help students understand how a substance dissolves.

- This section offers an excellent opportunity to repeat the conductivity demonstration used in earlier chapters. It will remind students that we can tell whether a solution contains ions by its conductivity.

SECTION 15.1
Forming Solutions

Key Terms
- Solution
- Solvent
- Solute
- Aqueous solution
- Saturated
- Unsaturated
- Supersaturated
- Concentrated
- Dilute

Objectives
- *To understand the process of dissolving*
- *To learn why certain substances dissolve in water*
- *To learn qualitative terms describing the concentration of a solution*
- *To understand the factors that affect the rate at which a solid dissolves*

A **solution** is a homogeneous mixture, a mixture in which the components are uniformly intermingled. This means that a sample from one part is the same as a sample from any other part. For example, the first sip of coffee is the same as the last sip.

The atmosphere that surrounds us is a gaseous solution containing $O_2(g)$, $N_2(g)$, and other gases randomly dispersed. Solutions can also be solids. For example, brass is a homogeneous mixture—a solution—of copper and zinc.

These examples illustrate that a solution can be a gas, a liquid, or a solid (see **Table 15.1**). The substance present in the largest amount is called the **solvent**, and the other substance or substances are called **solutes**. For example, when we dissolve a teaspoon of sugar in a glass of water, the sugar is the solute and the water is the solvent.

Aqueous solutions are solutions with water as the solvent. Because they are so important, in this chapter we will concentrate on the properties of aqueous solutions.

Solution
A homogeneous mixture

Solvent
The dissolving medium in a solution

Solute
The substance dissolved in the solvent to make a solution

Aqueous solution
A solution with water as a solvent

Table 15.1
Various Types of Solutions

Example	State of Solution	Original State of Solute	State of Solvent
air, natural gas	gas	gas	gas
antifreeze in water	liquid	liquid	liquid
brass	solid	solid	solid
carbonated water (soda)	liquid	gas	liquid
seawater, sugar solution	liquid	solid	liquid

A. Solubility

What happens when you put a teaspoon of sugar in your iced tea and stir it, or when you add salt to water for cooking vegetables? Why do the sugar and salt "disappear" into the water? What does it mean when something dissolves—that is, when a solution forms?

Teaching Support	• 75 mL of alcohol (isopropanol or ethanol, 70%–100%)
DEMONSTRATION	

Sum of the Parts
Materials
- Beaker
- Food coloring
- $\frac{1}{4}$ cup sand
- $\frac{1}{2}$ cup sugar
- Marbles (to fill the beaker)
- 2-cup measuring cup
- Two 100-mL graduated cylinders

Preparation Mark the 100-mL line on the graduated cylinder with a grease pencil.

Presentation Begin with beaker full of marbles. Ask students whether the beaker is full. Ask for predictions about what will happen if sand is poured into the beaker of marbles and then do so. Discuss whether the beaker is now full. (If you don't mind wet sand, pour water into the sand/marble mixture until it is about to overflow.)

Solubility of Ionic Substances

We saw in Chapter 8 that when sodium chloride dissolves in water, the resulting solution conducts an electric current. This convinces us that the solution contains *ions* that can move (this is how the electric current is conducted). The dissolving of solid sodium chloride in water is shown below.

NaCl + H$_2$O = Na$^+$ ● = Cl$^-$

In the solid state the ions are packed closely together. However, when the solid dissolves, the ions are separated and dispersed throughout the solution. The strong ionic forces that hold the sodium chloride crystal together are overcome by the strong attractions between the ions and the polar water molecules. This process is represented in **Figure 15.1.** Notice that each polar water molecule orients itself in a way to maximize its attraction with a Cl$^-$ or Na$^+$ ion. The negative end of a water molecule is attracted to a Na$^+$ ion, while the positive end is attracted to a Cl$^-$ ion. The strong forces holding the positive and negative ions in the solid are replaced by strong water–ion interactions, and the solid dissolves (the ions disperse).

It is important to remember that when an ionic substance (such as a salt) dissolves in water, it breaks up into *individual* cations and anions, which are dispersed in the water. For instance, when ammonium nitrate, NH$_4$NO$_3$, dissolves in water, the resulting solution contains NH$_4^+$ and NO$_3^-$ ions, which move around independently. This process can be represented as

$$NH_4NO_3(s) \xrightarrow{\text{H}_2\text{O}(l)} NH_4^+(aq) + NO_3^-(aq)$$

where (*aq*) indicates that the ions are surrounded by water molecules.

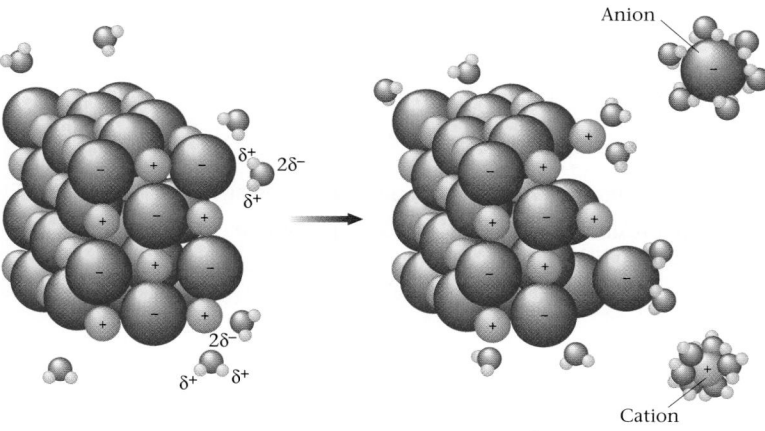

Anion

Cation

δ$^+$ 2δ$^-$
δ$^+$
2δ$^-$
δ$^+$ δ$^+$

Figure 15.1
Polar water molecules interact with the positive and negative ions of a salt. These interactions replace the strong ionic forces holding the ions together in the undissolved solid, thus assisting in the dissolving process.

i n f o r m a t i o n

Cations are positive ions.
Anions are negative ions.

15.1 • Forming Solutions • **521**

🍎 **TEACHING TIP**

Entropy is also a driving force for dissolving. If you have already discussed entropy (Chapter 10), you may wish to remind students of entropy now.

TECHNOLOGY

📖 **Figure 15.1**

💿 **Animation**
Dissolution of a Solid in a Liquid (Ionic)

(continued)

Next, turn to a new system. Place 1 cup of water into the 2-cup measuring cup. Ask the class what the final volume will be when $\frac{1}{2}$ cup sugar is added to the measuring cup. Add the sugar and stir to dissolve all of it. Note the final volume. Discuss why the volume is not 1.5 cups but still more than 1 cup.

Finally, ask what happens when liquids are mixed. Begin by measuring 50 mL

of water into one 100-mL graduated cylinder. In a second graduated cylinder, measure 50 mL of water. Color one water sample with blue food coloring and the other with yellow. Ask students to predict the final volume when the two water samples are mixed. Mix the two samples in one graduated cylinder. Record the volume. Discuss the color change. (Did a reaction occur? If not, why did the colors change? Did the volumes add?) Repeat the experiment,

this time using 50 mL of water and 50 mL of alcohol. Mix the two samples and note the volume. Discuss why the volume is less than the sum of the individual volumes.

Teaching Notes Addition of sugar or alcohol interferes with the attractions between the water molecules. The molecules assume a more compact arrangement, which reduces the volume.

Video

Ammonia Fountain
This video shows an example
of a gas (ammonia) dissolved
in a liquid (water).

Active Reading Questions

1. Water is a polar substance, so it
   generally dissolves other polar
   substances (like dissolves like).

2. Table salt is an ionic
   compound, and table sugar
   is a polar substance. In both
   cases, there are regions of
   positive and negative charge
   in the structure. Because
   water is a polar substance,
   it can dissolve other polar
   substances.

Solubility of Polar Substances

Water also dissolves many nonionic substances. Sugar is one example of a
nonionic solute that is very soluble in water. Another example is ethanol,
C_2H_5OH. Why is ethanol so soluble in water? The answer lies in the structure of the ethanol molecule.

Polar bond

The molecule contains a polar O—H bond like those in water, which makes
it very compatible with water. Just as hydrogen bonds form among water
molecules in pure water (see p. 490), ethanol molecules can form hydrogen
bonds with water molecules in a solution of the two.

The sugar molecule is shown below. Common table sugar has the
chemical name sucrose.

Notice that this molecule has many polar —OH groups, each of which can
hydrogen-bond to a water molecule. Because of the attractions between
sucrose and water molecules, solid sucrose is quite soluble in water.

Active Reading Questions

1. Does water generally dissolve polar or nonpolar substances? Explain.

2. What is similar about table salt and table sugar that allows them both
   to be soluble in water?

522 • Chapter 15 • Solutions

Teaching Support
DEMONSTRATION

Supersaturation

Materials
- Heating unit
- 500-mL Erlenmeyer flask
- 100-mL beaker
- Sodium acetate trihydrate
- Glass baking dish (8″ × 8″ or smaller)

Preparation Measure out 175 g of sodium
acetate trihydrate. Place it in a 500-mL flask
containing 50 mL of water. Heat the flask
slowly on a heating unit (a water bath
makes it easier to heat), swirling the flask
occasionally until a clear, homogeneous
solution is obtained. Remove the flask from
the heat and invert a 100-mL beaker over
the mouth of the flask. Allow the solution
to cool undisturbed until it reaches room
temperature (1–3 hours). (*Note:* Be careful not
to disturb the solution or it will crystallize.)

Substances Insoluble in Water

Many substances do not dissolve in water. For example, when petroleum leaks from a damaged tanker, it does not disperse uniformly in the water (does not dissolve) but rather floats on the surface because its density is less than that of water. Petroleum is a mixture of molecules like this one.

Since carbon and hydrogen have very similar electronegativities, the bonding electrons are shared almost equally and the bonds are essentially nonpolar. The resulting molecule with its nonpolar bonds is not compatible with the polar water molecules, which prevents it from being soluble in water. This situation is represented in **Figure 15.2.**

Figure 15.2
An oil layer floating on water. For a substance to dissolve, the water–water hydrogen bonds must be broken to make a "hole" for each solute particle. However, the water–water interactions will break only if they are replaced by similar strong interactions with the solute.

The oil from this tanker spreads out on the water as fire boats spray water to put out the fire.

 MINI-DEMO

You can show the immiscibility of oil and water by dissolving a small amount of food coloring in 50 mL of water in a 250-mL flask and adding 50 mL of vegetable oil to the water. Stopper the flask and shake it. Allow the flask to stand, and two layers will form.

MISCONCEPTION Chemistry

Many students have heard the phrase "oil and water don't mix" and take it to mean that oil and water repel each other. However, oil and water do not repel each other. In fact, oil and water attract one another. However, in order for water and oil to mix, the oil must have an attraction to water at least equal to the attraction that the water molecules have to themselves. Although there are attractive London dispersion forces between oil and water, water exhibits hydrogen bonding. Therefore, it is more correct to say that water is more attractive to water than it is to oil.

(continued)

After the solution reaches room temperature, cover it with parafilm until it is needed. Place one or two crystals of sodium acetate trihydrate in the baking dish.

Presentation Slowly pour the solution of supersaturated sodium acetate trihydrate on the crystals in the baking dish. Crystallization occurs immediately, forming a tower of solid sodium acetate.

Teaching Notes After the demonstration you can cut up the solid with a spatula and return it to the flask. The supersaturated solution is restored by heating as in the preparation. The mixture can be used repeatedly if it is not contaminated. You may need to add small amounts of water to compensate for evaporation.

Packing materials, or peanuts, are now made from both polystyrene and starch. Polystyrene peanuts do not dissolve in water. You can, however, dissolve them in acetone. Fill a large beaker full of peanuts and add a little acetone to it. The peanuts will shrink down to a small gooey mass in the acetone. These peanuts are not particularly friendly to the environment, as most are discarded if they are not reused. Bring in a sample of biodegradable peanuts as well. These peanuts are made of starch and will dissolve in water. Put some of them into a resealable bag, add water, and then seal the bag. Shake the bag and watch the peanuts disappear into solution. Discuss the usefulness of this property of packing peanuts.

 TEACHING TIPS

- Students can remember *like dissolves like* but often have trouble figuring out which substances are alike and which are not. Use the structures of similar molecules such as CH_3OH and water to show their similarities.

- Explaining why two nonpolar substances mix is difficult without bringing in the concept of entropy.

 Active Reading Question

The table salt solution would consist of 2 moles of particles: 1 mole of sodium ions and 1 mole of chloride ions. The table sugar solution would consist of 1 mole of sugar molecules.

How Substances Dissolve

Notice in Figure 15.2 that the water molecules in liquid water are associated with each other by hydrogen-bonding interactions. For a solute to dissolve in water, a "hole" must be made in the water structure for each solute particle. This will occur only if the lost water–water interactions are replaced by similar water–solute interactions.

In the case of sodium chloride, strong interactions occur between the polar water molecules and the Na^+ and Cl^- ions. This allows the sodium chloride to dissolve.

In the case of ethanol or sucrose, hydrogen-bonding interactions can occur between the O—H groups on these molecules and water molecules, making these substances soluble as well.

But oil molecules are not soluble in water, because the many water–water interactions that would have to be broken to make "holes" for these large molecules are not replaced by favorable water–solute interactions.

 Active Reading Question

Consider two one liter samples of solutions each containing 1.0 mol solute. One is a solution of table salt and one is a solution of table sugar. If you could see highly magnified views (molecular level), how would the solutions compare?

These considerations account for the observed behavior that *"like dissolves like."* In other words, we observe that a given solvent usually dissolves solutes that have polarities similar to its own. For example, water dissolves most polar solutes, because the solute–solvent interactions formed in the solution are similar to the water–water interactions present in the pure solvent. Likewise, nonpolar solvents dissolve nonpolar solutes. For example, dry-cleaning solvents used for removing grease stains from clothes are nonpolar liquids. "Grease" is composed of nonpolar molecules, so a nonpolar solvent is needed to remove a grease stain.

HANDS-ON CHEMISTRY • MINI-LAB •

Colors in Motion

Materials
- large clear container
- water
- water soluble markers
- filter paper

Procedure
1. Add water to a large clear container so that it covers the bottom of the container to a depth of about $\frac{1}{4}$ inch. Cover the container.
2. Obtain a piece of filter paper and use water soluble markers to place 4 dots at least $\frac{1}{2}$ inch apart and $\frac{1}{2}$ inch from the bottom of the paper.
3. Place the filter paper in the container so that the bottom of the paper is under water. The dots should not be submerged.
4. Make observations for the next several minutes.

Results/Analysis
1. Why do some colors separate while others do not?
2. Why do some colors move farther than others up the paper?
3. How do the separation of the colors and their rate of movement relate to solubility and intermolecular forces?

Hands-On Chemistry
MINI-LAB

Colors in Motion

Materials Each student/group will need a large, clear container (a beaker or a 2-L soft drink bottle cut in half works well), filter paper, water-soluble markers (at least one primary color and one nonprimary color), and water.

Purpose Students will apply the concept of solubility to paper chromatography.

Discussion Paper chromatography separates a mixture into its individual components. The components that are not soluble in the solvent (water, in this case) are left on the original dot. The components that are completely soluble move with the water as it travels up the filter paper. Components that are partially soluble are brought to different levels up the filter paper. The distance traveled reflects the solubility (this property can be quantified by the retention factor, or Rf, which is a ratio of the distance

B. Solution Composition: An Introduction

Even for very soluble substances, there is a limit to how much solute can be dissolved in a given amount of solvent. For example, when you add sugar to a glass of water, the sugar rapidly disappears at first. However, as you continue to add more sugar, at some point the solid no longer dissolves but collects at the bottom of the glass. When a solution contains as much solute as will dissolve at that temperature, we say it is **saturated**. If a solid solute is added to a solution already saturated with that solute, the added solid does not dissolve. A solution that has *not* reached the limit of solute that will dissolve in it is said to be **unsaturated**. When more solute is added to an unsaturated solution, it dissolves.

Sometimes when a solid is dissolved to the saturation limit at an elevated temperature and then allowed to cool, all of the solid may remain dissolved. This type of solution is called a **supersaturated** solution—it contains more dissolved solid than a saturated solution will hold at that temperature. A supersaturated solution is very unstable. Adding a crystal of the solid will cause immediate precipitation of solid until the solution reaches the saturation point.

Although a chemical compound always has the same composition, a solution is a mixture and the amounts of the substances present can vary in different solutions. For example, coffee can be strong or weak. Strong coffee has more coffee dissolved in a given amount of water than weak coffee. To describe a solution completely, we must specify the amounts of solvent and solute. We sometimes use the qualitative terms *concentrated* and *dilute* to describe a solution. A relatively large amount of solute is dissolved in a **concentrated** solution (strong coffee is concentrated). A relatively small amount of solute is dissolved in a **dilute** solution (weak coffee is diluted).

As we will see in Section 15.2, the concentration of a solution is a measure of the amount of solute dissolved in a given volume of solution. We can use this idea to better understand the terms *concentrated* and *dilute*.

For example, compare the two solutions below in which each dot represents a solute molecule. Which solution is more concentrated?

Solution A
Volume = 1.0 L

Solution B
Volume = 1.0 L

The volume of each of the solutions is the same. However, the amount of solute in solution A is less than the amount of solute in solution B. Because of this, solution B is more concentrated than solution A.

When comparing the concentrations of two solutions you have to consider both the amount of solute and the volume of solution.

Saturated
Describes a solution that contains as much solute as will dissolve at that temperature

Unsaturated
Describes a solution in which more solute can dissolve than is dissolved already at that temperature

Supersaturated
Describes a solution that contains more solute than a saturated solution will hold at that temperature

Concentrated
Describes a solution in which a relatively large amount of solute is dissolved in a solution

Dilute
Describes a solution in which a relatively small amount of solute is dissolved in a solution

Sodium acetate crystallizing from a saturated solution

TECHNOLOGY

 Video
Supersaturated Sodium Acetate

MINI-DEMO

Illustrate the terms *unsaturated, saturated,* and *supersaturated.* Make a supersaturated solution of $Na_2S_2O_3$ before class. To do so, place 300 mL of water in a 600-mL beaker and add $Na_2S_2O_3$ until crystals remain after stirring. Heat the solution to boiling and allow it to cool slowly, undisturbed. In class, begin by adding about 1 g $Na_2S_2O_3$ to 300 mL of water in a 600-mL beaker. Tell students that this solution is an unsaturated solution. Next, place 300 mL of water in another 600-mL beaker and add $Na_2S_2O_3$ until no more will dissolve. Tell students that it is a saturated solution. They can identify it easily because crystals are found on the bottom. Finally, bring out your previously prepared beaker of supersaturated $Na_2S_2O_3$. Explain how you made the solution and then add a single crystal of $Na_2S_2O_3$ to the supersaturated solution. Observe the crystallization and discuss with the class. Ask students whether the solution is now saturated.

MINI-DEMO

Prepare a relatively concentrated solution of a colorful substance such as $CuSO_4$ or $Ni(NO_3)_2$. You can even use food coloring in water. In class, make several dilutions of the solution in different beakers. Discuss the concentrations of the solutions relative to one another.
Show that qualitative terms for concentration are useful, but that we need to have a way of determining the exact amount of solute in a solution.

(continued)

traveled by a particular component to the distance traveled by the solvent; it is not necessary to calculate this value here).

Some colors will separate if they are made of two or more fundamental colors (for example, green is made of blue and yellow). The colors that move the farthest with the water consist of components that are the most soluble in water. Since water is polar, the colors that move the greatest distance consist of the most polar components.

Tea dissolves much faster in the hot water on the left than in the cold water on the right.

For example, the following two solutions have the same concentration.

Solution X
Volume = 1.0 L

Solution Y
Volume = 2.0 L

Although the volume of solution Y is twice the volume of solution X the amount of solute in solution Y is also twice as much as that in Solution X.

Active Reading Question

Draw pictures of two solutions such that the solution with more solute is less concentrated than the solution with less solute.

Although these qualitative terms serve a useful purpose, we often need to know the exact amount of solute present in a given amount of solution. Now, we will consider various ways to describe the composition of a solution.

C. Factors Affecting the Rate of Dissolving

When a solid is being dissolved in a liquid to form a solution, the dissolving process may occur rapidly or slowly. Three factors affect the speed of the dissolving process: *surface area, stirring,* and *temperature.*

Because the dissolving process occurs at the surface of the solid being dissolved, the greater the amount of surface area exposed to the solvent, the faster the dissolving will occur. For example, if we want to dissolve a cube of sugar in water, how can we speed up the process? The answer is to grind up the cube into tiny crystals. Because the crystals from the ground-up cube expose much more surface area to the water than the original cube did, the sugar dissolves much more quickly.

The dissolving process is also increased by stirring the solution. Stirring removes newly dissolved particles from the solid surface and continuously exposes the surface to fresh solvent.

Finally, dissolving occurs more rapidly at higher temperatures. (Sugar dissolves much more rapidly in hot tea than iced tea.) Higher temperatures cause the solvent molecules to move more rapidly, thus increasing the rate of the dissolving process.

In addition to dissolving faster at higher temperatures, most solids are more soluble at higher temperatures. That is, in most cases more solid will dissolve in water at 90 °C than in water at 25 °C. The opposite is true for gases dissolved in water. The solubility of a gas in water typically decreases as the temperature increases.

Let's Review

Factors Affecting Dissolving

- Surface area
- Stirring
- Temperature

CHEMISTRY EXPLORERS

Ellen Swallow Richards • 1842–1911

Ellen Swallow Richards was born in Massachusetts in 1842. She was the first woman in America to be accepted to a scientific school, the first woman to attend the Massachusetts Institute of Technology (MIT), and the first woman professional chemist in the nation. She spent her professional career in research and teaching at MIT, where she founded the field of home economics.

In the 1880s, Richards worked as water analyst for the Massachusetts State Board of Health while teaching at MIT. She conducted a two-year survey analyzing over 100,000 samples of drinking water in Massachusetts. From this study, she produced the first state water quality standards in the United States, which in turn led to the first modern sewage treatment plants. Her later studies in food quality led to state food and drug standards.

The next time you drink a glass of water, make a toast to Ellen Swallow Richards. It is her pioneering work that led to safe drinking water.

SECTION 15.1
REVIEW QUESTIONS

❶ Draw a molecular (microscopic) level picture to show how salt and sugar look when dissolved in water.

❷ Determine the number of moles of each type of ion in solution when 1 mole of each of the following dissolves in water:

   a. sodium sulfate

   b. ammonium acetate

   c. calcium chloride

   d. copper(II) sulfate

❸ Chemists often say "like dissolves like." What does this mean?

❹ Why does water by itself not dissolve a grease stain?

❺ Can a dilute solution also be saturated? Explain.

❻ Increasing the number of collisions between solid and solvent particles increases the rate at which a solid dissolves. Explain how stirring, increasing surface area, and heating increase the number of collisions.

RESEARCH LINKS
CLASSZONE.COM

15.1 • Forming Solutions • **527**

CHEMISTRY EXPLORERS
Ellen Swallow Richards

The Chemical Heritage Foundation calls Ellen Swallow Richards the most prominent female American chemist of the 19th century. She was the first president of the American Home Economics Association, which was formed in 1908. In 1876, Richards established a laboratory at MIT for the instruction of women in chemistry. She is generally recognized as creating the fields of ecology and home economics.

SECTION 15.1
ASSESS

SECTION 15.1
Review Questions

1. The student drawings should look like the figure at the beginning of Section 15.1.A.

2. a. 3 mol

   b. 2 mol

   c. 3 mol

   d. 2 mol

3. "Like dissolves like" means that polar substances tend to dissolve polar substances and nonpolar substances tend to dissolve other nonpolar substances. A polar substance will not usually dissolve in a nonpolar substance.

4. Water is a polar substance, and grease is a mixture of nonpolar substances. Water cannot dissolve the grease.

5. A dilute solution can also be saturated. *Dilute* means that not very much solute is dissolved in the solution; *saturated* means that the solution cannot hold any more solute at that temperature. A substance that is fairly insoluble would not dissolve very much and so could be both dilute and saturated.

6. Stirring increases the rate of dissolving by physically mixing the particles and increasing their rate of collision. The availability of an increased surface area increases the rate of dissolving because more particles on the surface come in contact with the solvent. This factor results in increased collisions with the solvent. At a higher temperature the particles are moving faster, increasing the number of collisions that occur within the container and so increasing the rate of dissolving.

Student Preparation

Assign students to read Section 15.2 and to answer the Review Questions at the end of the section before coming to class.

 Active Learning
Team Learning Worksheet

After introducing the material in Section 15.2 in class, place students in groups and have them work together on **Section 15.2: Team Learning Worksheet**.

Homework

You may wish to assign these selected end-of-chapter problems as homework for this section: 12a–b, 13a–b, 14, 16, 19, 20, 21a–b, 22a–b, 24, 26, 27a–b, 29a–b, 31a–b, 32, 34

Additional end-of-chapter problems can be used for extra practice.

15.2.A Solution Composition: Mass Percent

Objective To understand the concentration term *mass percent* and learn how to calculate it

 TEACHING TIPS

- Now is a good time to review percents. Students often forget to calculate the mass of the entire solution, and instead use the mass of the solvent and leave out the mass of the solute. Make sure students understand that a percentage is the amount as a portion of the total.

- Review the rules for determining significant figures.

- A common example of a solution with a concentration expressed in mass percent is vinegar. You may want to bring a bottle to class that has a label giving the mass percent.

SECTION 15.2
Describing Solution Composition

Key Terms
- Mass percent
- Molarity (*M*)
- Standard solution
- Dilution

Objectives
- *To understand mass percent and how to calculate it*
- *To understand and use molarity*
- *To learn to calculate the concentration of a solution made by diluting a stock solution*

A. Solution Composition: Mass Percent

One way of describing a solution's composition is **mass percent**, which expresses the mass of solute present in a given mass of solution. The definition of mass percent follows:

$$\text{Mass percent} = \frac{\text{mass of solute}}{\text{mass of solution}} \times 100\%$$

$$= \frac{\text{grams of solute}}{\text{grams of solute} + \text{grams of solvent}} \times 100\%$$

For example, suppose a solution is prepared by dissolving 1.0 g of sodium chloride in 48 g of water. The solution has a mass of 49 g (48 g of H_2O plus 1.0 g of NaCl), and there is 1.0 g of solute (NaCl) present. The mass percent of solute, then, is

$$\frac{1.0 \text{ g solute}}{49 \text{ g solution}} \times 100\% = 0.020 \times 100\% = 2.0\% \text{ NaCl}$$

information

The mass of the solution is the sum of the masses of the solute and the solvent.

HANDS-ON CHEMISTRY • MINI-LAB •

Rainbow in a Straw

Materials
- five paper cups containing five different colored solutions of NaCl
- clear, colorless plastic straw

Procedure
1. Obtain five paper cups containing five different colored solutions. You will also need a clear, colorless plastic straw.

2. Each of your five solutions has a different concentration of NaCl. Your task is to order the solutions from least concentrated to most concentrated. You may only use the five solutions and the straw. You may need to experiment a little and you may make some mistakes along the way.

Results/Analysis
1. How does concentration of the solution relate to density of the solution?

2. List the order of solutions from least concentrated to most concentrated.

Hands-On Chemistry
MINI-LAB

Rainbow in a Straw

Materials Each group will need five cups, a clear colorless plastic straw, and five colored salt solutions. The salt solutions should vary from 0% (just water) to 20% (20 g salt in 100 g total solution) by 5% increments, and each should be a different color.

Purpose Students will better understand what is meant by *concentration* and should see how the density of a solution is related to its concentration.

Discussion The higher the salt concentration, the more dense the solution. Students should first place one end of the straw in a solution and then place a finger over the top opening. Next, students should remove the straw from the solution and, keeping the finger over the opening, put the straw into another solution. Releasing the finger allows the next solution to enter the straw. The finger is placed over the opening

EXAMPLE 15.1

Solution Composition: Calculating Mass Percent

A solution is prepared by mixing 1.00 g of ethanol, C_2H_5OH, with 100.0 g of water. Calculate the mass percent of ethanol in this solution.

Solution

Where do we want to go?

Mass percent of ethanol = ? %

What do we know?

- 1.00 g ethanol (C_2H_5OH)
- 100.0 g H_2O
- mass percent = $\dfrac{\text{mass of solute}}{\text{mass of solution}} \times 100\%$

How do we get there?

$$\text{Mass percent } C_2H_5OH = \left(\frac{\text{grams of } C_2H_5OH}{\text{grams of solution}}\right) \times 100\%$$

$$= \left(\frac{1.00 \text{ g } C_2H_5OH}{100.0 \text{ g } H_2O + 1.00 \text{ g } C_2H_5OH}\right) \times 100\%$$

$$= \frac{1.00 \text{ g}}{101.0 \text{ g}} \times 100\%$$

$$= 0.990\% \ C_2H_5OH$$

 Practice Problem • Exercise 15.1

A 135-g sample of seawater is evaporated to dryness, leaving 4.73 g of solid residue (the salts formerly dissolved in the seawater). Calculate the mass percent of solute present in the original seawater.

EXAMPLE 15.2

Solution Composition: Determining Mass of Solute

Although milk is not a true solution (it is really a suspension of tiny globules of fat, protein, and other substrates in water), it does contain a dissolved sugar called lactose. Cow's milk typically contains 4.5% by mass of lactose, $C_{12}H_{22}O_{11}$. Calculate the mass of lactose present in 175 g of milk.

Solution

Where do we want to go?

Mass lactose in 175 g milk = ? g

What do we know?

- 4.5% lactose ($C_{12}H_{22}O_{11}$) {solute}
- 175 g milk {solution}
- mass percent = $\dfrac{\text{mass of solute}}{\text{mass of solution}} \times 100\%$

15.2 • Describing Solution Composition • **529**

Using the definition of mass percent, we have

$$\frac{\text{Mass of solute}}{\text{Mass of solution}} =$$

$$\frac{\text{grams of solute}}{\text{grams of solute + grams of solvent}} \times$$

$$100\% = 40.0\%$$

There are 425 g of solute (formaldehyde). Substituting, we have

$$\frac{425 \text{ g}}{425 \text{ g + grams of solvent}} \times 100\% = 40.0\%$$

We must now solve for grams of solvent (water). This will take some patience, but we can do it if we proceed step by step. First we divide both sides by 100%.

$$\frac{425 \text{ g}}{425 \text{ g + grams of solvent}} \times$$

$$\frac{100\%}{100\%} = \frac{40.0\%}{100\%} = 0.400$$

Now we have

$$\frac{425 \text{ g}}{425 \text{ g + grams of solvent}} = 0.400$$

Next we multiply both sides by (425 g + grams of solvent).

$$(425 \text{ g + grams of solvent}) \times$$

$$\frac{425}{425 \text{ g + grams of solvent}} =$$

$$0.400 \times (425 \text{ g + grams of solvent})$$

This gives

$$425 \text{ g} = 0.400 \times (425 \text{ g + grams of solvent})$$

Carrying out the multiplication gives

$$425 \text{ g} = 170. \text{ g} + 0.400 \text{ (grams of solvent)}$$

Now we subtract 170. g from both sides,

$$425 \text{ g} - 170. \text{ g} = 170. \text{ g} - 170. \text{ g} +$$

$$0.400 \text{ (grams of solvent)}$$

$$255 \text{ g} = 0.400 \text{ (grams of solvent)}$$

and divide both sides by 0.400.

$$\frac{255 \text{ g}}{0.400} = \frac{0.400}{0.400} \text{ (grams of solvent)}$$

We finally have the answer:

$$\frac{255 \text{ g}}{0.400} = 638 \text{ g} = \text{grams of solvent}$$

$$= \text{mass of water needed}$$

15.2.B Solution Composition: Molarity

Objective To understand molarity and learn to use molarity to calculate the number of moles of solute present

 LABORATORY
EXPERIMENT 64:
Chloride in Water

How do we get there?

$$\text{Mass percent} = \frac{\text{grams of solute}}{\text{grams of solution}} \times 100\%$$

We now substitute the quantities we know:

$$\text{Mass percent} = \frac{\overset{\text{Mass of lactose}}{\text{grams of solute}}}{\underset{\text{Mass of milk}}{175 \text{ g}}} \times 100\% = 4.5\% \quad \overset{\text{Mass percent}}{}$$

We now solve for grams of solute by multiplying both sides by 175 g,

$$175 \text{ g} \times \frac{\text{grams of solute}}{175 \text{ g}} \times 100\% = 4.5\% \times 175 \text{ g}$$

and then dividing both sides by 100%,

$$\text{Grams of solute} \times \frac{100\%}{100\%} = \frac{4.5\%}{100\%} \times 175 \text{ g}$$

to give

$$\text{Grams of solute} = 0.045 \times 175 \text{ g} = 7.9 \text{ g lactose}$$

 Practice Problem • Exercise 15.2

What mass of water must be added to 425 g of formaldehyde to prepare a 40.0% (by mass) solution of formaldehyde? This solution, called formalin, is used to preserve biological specimens.
Hint: Substitute the known quantities into the definition for mass percent, and then solve for the unknown quantity (mass of solvent).

B. Solution Composition: Molarity

When a solution is described in terms of mass percent, the amount of solution is given in terms of its mass. However, it is often more convenient to measure the volume of a solution than to measure its mass. Because of this, chemists often describe a solution in terms of concentration. We define the *concentration* of a solution as the amount of solute in a *given volume* of solution. The most commonly used expression of concentration is **molarity (M)**. Molarity describes the amount of solute in moles and the volume of the solution in liters.

Molarity is the number of moles of solute per volume of solution in liters.

$$M = \text{molarity} = \frac{\text{moles of solute}}{\text{liters of solution}} = \frac{\text{mol}}{\text{L}}$$

A solution that is 1.0 molar (written as 1.0 *M*) contains 1.0 mol of solute per liter of solution.

Active Reading Question

Adding 1.0 mole of solute to 1.0 L of water does not make a 1.0 *M* solution. Why not?

TEACHING TIPS

• Students need to understand the importance of calculations involving molarity. This concept will be used in solution stoichiometry, titration, and acid–base calculations.

• Emphasize that *molarity* is an important term because we are often interested in moles of reactants or products. When performing stoichiometric calculations with solutions, we need to work in units of moles. Stress that molarity involves two amounts: the number of moles of solute and the volume of solution.

Active Reading Question

A 1.0 *M* solution is defined as 1.0 mol of solute per 1.0 L of *solution*, not 1.0 L of water. When the solute is added to 1.0 L water, the total volume of the solution will be slightly larger than 1.0 L.

We need to consider both the amount of solute and the volume when determining the concentration of a solution. For example, consider the following two solutions where each dot represents 1.0 mol of solute.

Concentration
$= \dfrac{2.0 \text{ mol solute}}{1.0 \text{ L solution}} = 2.0 \; M$

Solution A
Volume = 1.0 L

Concentration
$= \dfrac{2.0 \text{ mol solute}}{2.0 \text{ L solution}} = 1.0 \; M$

Solution B
Volume = 2.0 L

EXAMPLE 15.3

Solution Composition: Calculating Molarity, I

Calculate the molarity of a solution prepared by dissolving 11.5 g of solid NaOH in enough water to make 1.50 L of solution.

Solution

Where do we want to go?

molarity NaOH = ? M

What do we know?

- 11.5 g NaOH
- $V = 1.50$ L
- $M = \dfrac{\text{moles of solute}}{\text{liters of solution}}$
- molar mass NaOH = 40.0 g/mol

How do we get there?

We have the mass (in grams) of solute, so we need to convert the mass of solute to moles (using the molar mass of NaOH). Then we can divide the number of moles by the volume in liters.

 Mass of solute $\Rightarrow$ Moles of solute $\Rightarrow$ Molarity

Use molar mass   Moles Liters

We compute the number of moles of solute, using the molar mass of NaOH (40.0 g).

$$11.5 \; \cancel{\text{g NaOH}} \times \dfrac{1 \text{ mol NaOH}}{40.0 \; \cancel{\text{g NaOH}}} = 0.288 \text{ mol NaOH}$$

Then we divide by the volume of the solution in liters.

$$\text{Molarity} = \dfrac{\text{moles of solute}}{\text{liters of solution}} = \dfrac{0.288 \text{ mol NaOH}}{1.50 \text{ L solution}} = 0.192 \; M \text{ NaOH}$$

EXAMPLE 15.3

More Examples

1. Calculate the molarity of a solution prepared by dissolving 15.6 g of solid KBr in enough water to make 1.25 L of solution.
   0.105 M

2. Calculate the molarity of a solution prepared by dissolving 250.0 g of solid $Ca(NO_3)_2$ in enough water to make 2.50 L of solution.
   0.609 M

Students may need to be
reminded to change mL to L
when completing molarity
calculations.

EXAMPLE 15.4

More Examples

1. Calculate the molarity of
a solution prepared by
dissolving 2.80 g of solid
NaCl in enough water to
make 135 mL of solution.
0.355 *M*

2. Calculate the molarity of
a solution prepared by
dissolving 8.55 g of $MgCl_2$
in enough water to make
65.0 L of solution.
1.38 *M*

✔ Answer to Practice Problem 15.4

The moles of ethanol can be
obtained from its molar mass
(46.1).

$$1.00 \text{ g } C_2H_5OH \times \frac{1 \text{ mol } C_2H_5OH}{46.1 \text{ g } C_2H_5OH} =$$
$$2.17 \times 10^{-2} \text{ mol } C_2H_5OH$$

Volume in liters =

$$101 \text{ mL} \times \frac{1 \text{ L}}{100 \text{ mL}} = 0.101 \text{ L}$$

$$\text{Molarity of } C_2H_5OH = \frac{\text{moles of } C_2H_5OH}{\text{liters of solution}}$$

$$= \frac{2.17 \times 10^{-2} \text{ mol}}{0.101 \text{ L}} = 0.215 \text{ M}$$

EXAMPLE 15.4

Solution Composition: Calculating Molarity, II

Calculate the molarity of a solution prepared by dissolving 1.56 g of gaseous HCl into enough water to make 26.8 mL of solution.

Solution

Where do we want to go?

$$\text{molarity HCl} = ? \ M$$

What do we know?

- 1.56 g HCl (*g*)
- $V = 26.8$ mL
- $M = \dfrac{\text{moles of solute}}{\text{liters of solution}}$
- molar mass HCl = 36.5 g/mol

How do we get there?

First we calculate the number of moles of HCl (molar mass = 36.5 g).

$$1.56 \text{ g HCl} \times \frac{1 \text{ mol HCl}}{36.5 \text{ g HCl}} = 0.0427 \text{ mol HCl}$$
$$= 4.27 \times 10^{-2} \text{ mol HCl}$$

Next we change the volume of the solution from milliliters to liters, using the equivalence statement 1 L = 1000 mL, which gives the appropriate conversion factor.

$$26.8 \text{ mL} \times \frac{1 \text{ L}}{1000 \text{ mL}} = 0.0268 \text{ L}$$
$$= 2.68 \times 10^{-2} \text{ L}$$

Finally, we divide the moles of solute by the liters of solution.

$$\text{Molarity} = \frac{4.27 \times 10^{-2} \text{ mol HCl}}{2.68 \times 10^{-2} \text{ L solution}} = 1.59 \ M \text{ HCl}$$

✔ Practice Problem • Exercise 15.4

Calculate the molarity of a solution prepared by dissolving 1.00 g of ethanol, C_2H_5OH, in enough water to give a final volume of 101 mL.

It is important to realize that the description of a solution's composition may not accurately reflect the true chemical nature of the solute as it is present in the dissolved state. Solute concentration is always written in terms of the form of the solute *before* it dissolves. For example, describing a solution as 1.0 *M* NaCl means that the solution was prepared by dissolving 1.0 mol of solid NaCl in enough water to make 1.0 L of solution; it does not mean that the solution contains 1.0 mol of NaCl units. Actually the solution contains 1.0 mole of Na^+ ions and 1.0 mole of Cl^- ions. That is, it contains 1.0 *M* Na^+ and 1.0 *M* Cl^-.

EXAMPLE 15.5

Solution Composition: Calculating Ion Concentration from Molarity

Give the concentrations of all the ions in each of the following solutions:

a. $0.50\ M\ Co(NO_3)_2$

b. $1\ M\ FeCl_3$

Solution

a. When solid $Co(NO_3)_2$ dissolves, it produces ions as follows:

$$Co(NO_3)_2(s) \xrightarrow{H_2O(l)} Co^{2+}(aq) + 2NO_3^-(aq)$$

which we can represent as

$$1\ mol\ Co(NO_3)_2(s) \xrightarrow{H_2O(l)} 1\ mol\ Co^{2+}(aq) + 2\ mol\ NO_3^-(aq)$$

$Co(NO_3)_2$

Co^{21}

$NO_3^2 \quad NO_3^2$

A solution of cobalt(II) nitrate

Therefore, a solution that is $0.50\ M\ Co(NO_3)_2$ contains $0.50\ M\ Co^{2+}$ and $(2 \times 0.50)\ M\ NO_3^-$, or $1.0\ M\ NO_3^-$.

b. When solid $FeCl_3$ dissolves, it produces ions as follows:

$$FeCl_3(s) \xrightarrow{H_2O(l)} Fe^{3+}(aq) + 3Cl^-(aq)$$

or

$$1\ mol\ FeCl_3(s) \xrightarrow{H_2O(l)} 1\ mol\ Fe^{3+}(aq) + 3\ mol\ Cl^-(aq)$$

A solution that is $1\ M\ FeCl_3$ contains $1\ M\ Fe^{3+}$ ions and $3\ M\ Cl^-$ ions.

$FeCl_3$

Fe^{3+}

$Cl^- \quad Cl^- \quad Cl^-$

✓ Practice Problem • Exercise 15.5

Give the concentrations of the ions in each of the following solutions:

a. $0.10\ M\ Na_2CO_3$

b. $0.010\ M\ Al_2(SO_4)_3$

Often we need to determine the number of moles of solute present in a given volume of a solution of known molarity. To do this, we use the definition of molarity. When we multiply the molarity of a solution by the volume (in liters), we get the moles of solute present in that sample:

$$\text{Liters of solution} \times \text{molarity} = \cancel{\text{liters of solution}} \times \frac{\text{moles of solute}}{\cancel{\text{liters of solution}}}$$
$$= \text{moles of solute}$$

🍎 TEACHING TIPS

- Beginning students may struggle when asked to determine the concentration of ions in a solution. Emphasize that students should write an equation for the dissociation of the ions in solution and use the mole ratios in the balanced equation to determine the concentrations of the ions. For example, a $1\ M$ solution of $CaCl_2$ contains Ca^{2+} ions in a concentration of $1\ M$ and Cl^- ions in a concentration of $2\ M$. This means that $2\ mol$ of chloride ions are found in the solution for every $1\ mol$ of calcium ions.

- When students are calculating ion concentrations from molarity, have them draw microscopic pictures of the solutions to emphasize the relative numbers of each ion.

- Some students may have difficulty in rearranging the definition of molarity (M = mol solute/volume solution) to solve for the appropriate variable. You may want to provide examples.

EXAMPLE 15.5

More Examples

Give the concentrations of all ions in each of the following solutions.

1. $1.20\ M\ Na_2SO_4$
   $2.40\ M\ Na^+$, $1.20\ M\ SO_4^{2-}$

2. $0.750\ M\ K_2CrO_4$
   $1.50\ M\ K^+$, $0.750\ M\ CrO_4^{2-}$

✓ Answer to Practice Problem 15.5

When Na_2CO_3 and $Al_2(SO_4)_3$ dissolve in water, they produce ions as follows:

$$Na_2CO_3(s) \xrightarrow{H_2O(l)} 2Na^+(aq) + CO_3^{-2}(aq)$$

$$Al_2(SO_4)_3(s) \xrightarrow{H_2O(l)} 2Al^{3+}(aq) + 3SO_4^{2-}(aq)$$

Therefore, in a $0.10\ M\ Na_2CO_3$ solution, the concentration of Na^+ ions is $2 \times 0.10\ M = 0.20\ M$ and the concentration of CO_3^{2-} ions is $0.10\ M$. In a $0.010\ M\ Al_2(SO_4)_3$ solution, the concentration of Al^{3+} ions is $2 \times 0.010\ M = 0.020\ M$ and the concentration of SO_4^{2-} ions is $3 \times 0.010\ M = 0.030\ M$.

EXAMPLE 15.6

EXAMPLE 15.6

Solution Composition: Calculating Number of Moles from Molarity

More Examples

1. How many moles of Na^+ ions are present in 42.0 mL of 0.350 M NaCl solution?

   1.47×10^{-2} mol Na^+

2. How many moles of Na^+ ions are present in 42.0 mL of 0.350 M Na_3PO_4 solution?

   4.41×10^{-2} mol Na^+

 Answer to Practice Problem 15.6

When solid $AlCl_3$ dissolves, it produces ions as follows:

$$AlCl_3(s) \xrightarrow{H_2O(l)} Al^{3+}(aq) + 3Cl^-(aq)$$

Thus a 1.0×10^{-3} M $AlCl_3$ solution contains 1.0×10^{-3} M Al^{3+} ions and 3.0×10^{-3} M Cl^- ions.

To calculate the moles of Cl^- ions in 1.75 L of the 1.0×10^{-3} M $AlCl_3$ solution, we must multiply the volume by the molarity.

1.75 L solution $\times 3.0 \times 10^{-3}$ M Cl^-

$= 1.75$ L̶ ̶s̶o̶l̶u̶t̶i̶o̶n̶ $\times$

$\dfrac{3.0 \times 10^{-3} \text{ mol } Cl^-}{\text{L̶ ̶s̶o̶l̶u̶t̶i̶o̶n̶}}$

$= 5.25 \times 10^{-3}$ mol Cl^-

$= 5.3 \times 10^{-3}$ mol Cl^-

MINI-DEMO

Prepare a standard solution of a colorful compound in class to illustrate the proper method for making solutions. Good examples are potassium permanganate, copper sulfate, and copper nitrate. Use a volumetric flask, balance, and distilled water. This standard solution can then be used to illustrate creating diluted solutions in Section 15.2.C.

How many moles of Ag^+ ions are present in 25 mL of a 0.75 M $AgNO_3$ solution?

Solution

Where do we want to go?

Moles Ag^+ in sample solution = ? mol

What do we know?

- Molarity of solution = 0.75 M
- $V = 25$ mL
- Moles = $M \times V$

MATH

$M = \dfrac{\text{moles of solute}}{\text{liters of solution}}$

Liters $\times M \Rightarrow$ Moles of solute

How do we get there?

A 0.75 M $AgNO_3$ solution contains 0.75 M Ag^+ ions and 0.75 M NO_3^- ions. Next we must convert the volume given from mL to L.

$$25 \text{ m̶L̶} \times \frac{1 \text{ L}}{1000 \text{ m̶L̶}} = 0.025 \text{ L} = 2.5 \times 10^{-2} \text{ L}$$

Now we multiply the volume times the molarity.

$$2.5 \times 10^{-2} \text{ L̶ ̶s̶o̶l̶u̶t̶i̶o̶n̶} \times \frac{0.75 \text{ mol } Ag^+}{\text{L̶ ̶s̶o̶l̶u̶t̶i̶o̶n̶}} = 1.9 \times 10^{-2} \text{ mol } Ag^+$$

 Practice Problem • Exercise 15.6

Calculate the number of moles of Cl^- ions in 1.75 L of 1.0×10^{-3} M $AlCl_3$.

Standard solution
A solution in which the concentration is accurately known

A **standard solution** is a solution whose *concentration is accurately known*. When the appropriate solute is available in pure form, a standard solution can be prepared by weighing out a sample of solute, transferring it completely to a *volumetric flask* (a flask of accurately known volume), and adding enough solvent to bring the volume up to the mark on the neck of the flask. This procedure is illustrated in **Figure 15.3.**

Figure 15.3
Steps involved in the preparation of a standard aqueous solution. (a) Put a weighed amount of a substance (the solute) into the volumetric flask, and add a small quantity of water. (b) Dissolve the solid in the water by gently swirling the flask *(with the stopper in place)*. (c) Add more water (with gentle swirling) until the level of the solution just reaches the mark etched on the neck of the flask. Then mix the solution thoroughly by inverting the flask several times.

Wash bottle

Volume marker (calibration mark)

Weighed amount of solute

(a) (b) (c)

534 • Chapter 15 • Solutions

EXAMPLE 15.7

To analyze the alcohol content of a certain substance, a chemist needs 1.00 L of an aqueous 0.200 M $K_2Cr_2O_7$ (potassium dichromate) solution. How much solid $K_2Cr_2O_7$ (molar mass = 294.2 g/mol) must be weighed out to make this solution?

Solution

Where do we want to go?

Mass of $K_2Cr_2O_7$ needed to make solution = ? g

What do we know?

- Molarity of solution = 0.200 M
- V = 1.00 L
- Molar mass $K_2Cr_2O_7$ = 294.2 g/mol
- Moles = $M \times V$

How do we get there?

We need to calculate the number of grams of solute ($K_2Cr_2O_7$) present (and thus the mass needed to make the solution). First we determine the number of moles of $K_2Cr_2O_7$ present by multiplying the volume (in liters) by the molarity.

$$1.00 \text{ L solution} \times \frac{0.200 \text{ mol } K_2Cr_2O_7}{\text{L solution}} = 0.200 \text{ mol } K_2Cr_2O_7$$

MATH

Liters × M ⟹ Moles of solute

Then we convert the moles of $K_2Cr_2O_7$ to grams, using the molar mass of $K_2Cr_2O_7$ (294.2 g).

$$0.200 \text{ mol } K_2Cr_2O_7 \times \frac{294.2 \text{ g } K_2Cr_2O_7}{\text{mol } K_2Cr_2O_7} = 58.8 \text{ g } K_2Cr_2O_7$$

Therefore, to make 1.00 L of 0.200 M $K_2Cr_2O_7$, the chemist must weigh out 58.8 g of $K_2Cr_2O_7$ and dissolve it in enough water to make 1.00 L of solution. This is most easily done by using a 1.00-L volumetric flask.

✔ Practice Problem • Exercise 15.7

Formalin is an aqueous solution of formaldehyde, HCHO, used as a preservative for biological specimens. How many grams of formaldehyde must be used to prepare 2.5 L of 12.3 M formalin?

C. Dilution

To save time and space in the laboratory, solutions that are routinely used are often purchased or prepared in concentrated form (called *stock solutions*). Water (or another solvent) is then added to achieve the molarity desired for a particular solution. The process of adding more solvent to a solution is called **dilution**. For example, the common laboratory acids are purchased as concentrated solutions and diluted with water as they are needed. A typical dilution calculation involves determining how much water must be added to an amount of stock solution to achieve a solution of the desired concentration. The key to doing these calculations is to remember that *only water is added in the dilution*. The amount of solute in the final, more dilute, solution is the *same* as the amount of solute in the original concentrated stock solution.

> **Dilution**
> The process of adding solvent to a solution to lower the concentration of solute

---

EXAMPLE 15.7

More Examples

1. What mass of $NaNO_3$ is required to make 2.50 L of a 0.150 M solution of $NaNO_3$?
   31.9 g

2. What mass of $(NH_4)_2SO_4$ is required to make 1.25 L of a 0.250 M solution of $(NH_4)_2SO_4$?
   41.3 g

✔ Answer to Practice Problem 15.7

We must first determine the number of moles of formaldehyde in 2.5 L of 12.3 M formalin. Remember that volume of solution (in liters) times molarity gives moles of solute. In this case, the volume of solution is 2.5 L and the molarity is 12.3 mol of HCHO per liter of solution.

$$2.5 \text{ L solution} \times \frac{12.3 \text{ mol HCHO}}{\text{L solution}} = 31 \text{ mol HCHO}$$

Next, using the molar mass of HCHO (30.0 g), we convert 31 mol of HCHO to grams.

$$31 \text{ mol HCHO} \times \frac{30.0 \text{ g HCHO}}{1 \text{ mol HCHO}} = 9.3 \times 10^2 \text{ g HCHO}$$

Therefore, 2.5 L of 12.3 M formalin contains 9.3×10^2 g of formaldehyde. We must weigh out 930 g of formaldehyde and dissolve it in enough water to make 2.5 L of solution.

15.2.C Dilution

Objective To learn to calculate the concentration of a solution made by diluting a stock solution

🔍 MISCONCEPTION Chemistry

The key concept here is the idea that the concentrated solution has the same number of moles as the dilute solution. Students may be confused about this concept because they think of a *dilute* solution as containing less solute than a *concentrated* solution. In this case, the solution has increased in volume and the number of moles of solute has remained the same. Stress that *concentration* is the amount of solute per volume available.

⊙ Video
Dilution

If you did the Mini-Demo in Section 15.2.B, use the standard solution you prepared. If you did not, then make a colored solution before class using food coloring in water. Arbitrarily choose a concentration for the food coloring solution. Begin with the concentration of your standard or food coloring solution. Use a pipet to transfer 1 mL of the standard solution to a small container. Add 9 mL water to the solution and have students calculate the concentration of the new solution. Repeat the process, using the new solution to create a more dilute solution for successive dilutions. (*Note:* You can do this demonstration on the overhead projector by using a well tray and drops of solution measured with a Beral pipet.) Even when the color is no longer evident, the solution still contains solute in a concentration that can be calculated.

For example, consider the following solutions in which each dot represents 1.0 mol of solute particles.

$$\text{Concentration} = \frac{8.0 \text{ mol solute}}{1.0 \text{ L solution}} = 8.0 \ M$$

Solution 1
Volume = 1.0 L

i nformation

Dilution with water doesn't alter the number of moles of solute present.

If we double the volume of the solution by adding water, we do not change the moles of solute, but the concentration becomes half of its original value.

$$\text{Concentration} = \frac{8.0 \text{ mol solute}}{2.0 \text{ L solution}} = 4.0 \ M$$

Solution 2
Volume = 2.0 L

If the volume is doubled again, the concentration is again cut by 2, becoming one-fourth of the original concentration.

$$\text{Concentration} = \frac{8.0 \text{ mol solute}}{4.0 \text{ L solution}} = 2.0 \ M$$

Solution 3
Volume = 4.0 L

i nformation

The molarities of stock solutions of the common concentrated acids are:

Sulfuric (H_2SO_4)　　18 M
Nitric (HNO_3)　　　16 M
Hydrochloric (HCl)　12 M

Notice in all three solutions,

Moles of solute after dilution = moles of solute before dilution

The number of moles of solute stays the same but more water is added, increasing the volume, so the molarity decreases.

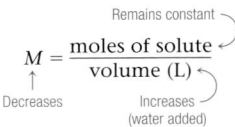

Remains constant

$$M = \frac{\text{moles of solute}}{\text{volume (L)}}$$

Decreases　　　　Increases
　　　　　　　(water added)

For example, suppose we want to prepare 500. mL of 1.00 M acetic acid, $HC_2H_3O_2$, from a 17.5 M stock solution of acetic acid. What volume of the stock solution is required?

Where do we want to go?
　Volume of stock solution needed = ? L

Can We Add Concentrations?

Materials Each group will need water, food coloring, and three clear, colorless cups of equal diameter.

Purpose Students will achieve a better understanding of the concept of concentration (including the realization that we cannot add concentrations of solutions). In addition, they will practice doing

calculations by adding different volumes of solutions with different concentrations.

Discussion The concentration of solution A is 1.0 D, the concentration of solution B is 0.5 D, and the concentration of solution C is 0.75 D.

There will be 5 drops of food coloring from half (5.0 mL) of solution A and 2.5 drops of food coloring from solution B (this statement assumes homogeneous solutions). Therefore, there are 7.5 drops of food coloring in 10 mL of solution, giving a concentration of 0.75 D.

What do we know?
- Molarity of stock solution = 17.5 M
- Solution required

  V_{dilute} = 500.0 mL

  M_{dilute} = 1.00 M
- Moles = $M \times V$

How do we get there?

Find the moles of acetic acid needed in the dilute solution.

- Convert the volume of the dilute solution to L.

$$500. \text{ mL solution} \times \frac{1 \text{ L solution}}{1000 \text{ mL solution}} = 0.500 \text{ L solution}$$

$\underbrace{}_{\substack{V_{dilute\ solution} \\ (in\ mL)}}$ $\underbrace{}_{Convert\ mL\ to\ L}$

- Moles acetic acid needed = $M \times V$

$$0.500 \text{ L solution} \times \frac{1.00 \text{ mol HC}_2\text{H}_3\text{O}_2}{\text{L solution}} = 0.500 \text{ mol HC}_2\text{H}_3\text{O}_2$$

$\underbrace{}_{M_{dilute\ solution}}$

Find the volume of the stock (concentrated) solution that contains 0.500 mol acetic acid.

Because volume × molarity = moles, we have

$$V \text{ (in liters)} \times \frac{17.5 \text{ mol HC}_2\text{H}_3\text{O}_2}{\text{L solution}} = 0.500 \text{ mol HC}_2\text{H}_3\text{O}_2$$

Solving for V $\left(\text{by dividing both sides by } \frac{17.5 \text{ mol}}{\text{L solution}}\right)$ gives

$$V = \frac{0.500 \text{ mol HC}_2\text{H}_3\text{O}_2}{\frac{17.5 \text{ mol HC}_2\text{H}_3\text{O}_2}{\text{L solution}}} = 0.0286 \text{ L, or } 28.6 \text{ mL, of solution}$$

Top Ten Elements in Seawater	
Element	Amount (kg/mi³)
Oxygen	3.9×10^{12}
Hydrogen	5.0×10^{11}
Chlorine	9.2×10^{10}
Sodium	5.3×10^{10}
Magnesium	6.1×10^{9}
Sulfur	4.3×10^{9}
Calcium	1.9×10^{9}
Potassium	1.9×10^{9}
Bromine	3.1×10^{8}
Carbon	1.3×10^{8}

MATH

Liters × M ➪ Moles of solute

HANDS-ON CHEMISTRY • MINI-LAB •

Can We Add Concentrations?

Materials
- water
- food coloring
- graduated cylinder

Procedure
1. Place 10.0 mL of water and add 10 drops of food coloring. Label the concentration of this solution 1.0 D (where D has units of drops/mL). This is solution A.

2. Add 10.0 mL of water to another cup and add 5 drops of food coloring to the water. This is solution B.

3. Add half of solution A and half of solution B to a third cup to make solution C.

Results/Analysis
1. What is the concentration of solution B in units of D?

2. How does this solution C look compared to solution A and solution B?

3. What is the concentration of solution C in units of D?

4. Can you add the concentrations of solution A and solution B to get the concentration of solution C? Why or why not? How does your answer to question 2 help you answer this question?

TOP TEN

Have students calculate the molarity of each element in the Top Ten. They may need to think carefully about the assumptions that must be used to determine the molarity for seawater.

 TEACHING TIP

Understanding the process of dilution is important for most students intending to work in quantitative fields. Using the formula $M \times V$ = mol can help students only if they understand what is happening. Make sure that students focus on the idea that the number of moles of solute remains constant.

(continued)

The coloring of the solution should lie between the colors of solutions A and B, indicating that this calculation makes sense. If we could add concentrations, solution C would be the darkest of the three.

In comparing the colors, students should compare equal volumes of each solution (which requires that they remove half of solution C). They should place all three cups on a sheet of white paper and look into the cups from above.

A misconception may come to light when students pour half of solution A into the third cup. The concentration of the solution is still 1.0 D. This fact may not be obvious to some students, who may claim that the concentration is 0.5 D because only half of the solution is present.

Consider having students carry out a more complicated calculation. For example, what if they added 3.0 mL of solution A to 7.0 mL of solution B? In this case, the final solution contains 6.5 drops of food coloring (3.0 drops from solution A and 3.5 drops from solution B) in 10.0 mL of solution. The concentration is 0.65 D. In doing such a calculation, students see that by mixing two solutions, the new concentration is not always an average of the two initial concentrations.

- The formula $M_1V_1 = M_2V_2$ works well but some students memorize it without understanding *why* it works. Emphasize what each variable means and explain that the formula works only because the moles of solute are the same before and after dilution. Consider asking students to solve for the volume of water that must be added to achieve a dilution. In this way, students learn to think about what they are solving for, instead of just plugging numbers into an equation.

- Make sure that students answer the question being asked. Students often give the volume of concentrated solution when the question asks for the volume of water needed to make the dilution.

 Active Reading Question

The number of moles of acetic acid is the same in each solution. Since water was added to create the diluted solution, its volume is greater, so its concentration is lower. The concentration of the diluted solution is 0.050 M.

Therefore, to make 500. mL of a 1.00 M acetic acid solution, we take 28.6 mL of 17.5 M acetic acid and dilute it to a total volume of 500. mL. This process is illustrated in **Figure 15.4.** Because *the moles of solute remain the same* before and after dilution, we can write

Initial conditions				Final conditions	
M_1	$\times$	V_1	$=$ moles of solute $=$	M_2	$\times$	V_2
Molarity before dilution		Volume before dilution		Molarity after dilution	Volume after dilution

Does it make sense?

We can check our calculations on acetic acid by showing that $M_1 \times V_1 = M_2 \times V_2$. In the above example, $M_1 = 17.5\ M$, $V_1 = 0.0286\ L$, $V_2 = 0.500\ L$, and $M_2 = 1.00\ M$, so

$$M_1 \times V_1 = 17.5\ \frac{mol}{L} \times 0.0286\ L = 0.500\ mol$$

$$M_2 \times V_2 = 1.00\ \frac{mol}{L} \times 0.500\ L = 0.500\ mol$$

and therefore

$$M_1 \times V_1 = M_2 \times V_2$$

This shows that the volume (V_2) we calculated is correct.

 Active Reading Question

You add 95.0 mL of water to 5.0 mL of 5.0 M acetic acid. Compare the concentration and number of moles of acetic acid in the concentrated acid to the concentration and number of moles of acetic acid in the dilute solution.

Figure 15.4
(a) 28.6 mL of 17.5 M acetic acid solution is transferred to a volumetric flask that already contains some water.
(b) Water is added to the flask (with swirling) to bring the volume to the calibration mark, and the solution is mixed by inverting the flask several times.
(c) The resulting solution is 1.00 M acetic acid.

(a)   (b)   (c)

500 mL

538 • Chapter 15 • Solutions

EXAMPLE 15.8

Calculating Concentrations of Diluted Solutions

What volume of 16 M sulfuric acid must be used to prepare 1.5 L of a 0.10 M H_2SO_4 solution?

Solution

Where do we want to go?

Volume of H_2SO_4 needed to make solution = ? mL

What do we know?

• Moles solute = $M_1 \times V_1 = M_2 \times V_2$

Initial Conditions (concentrated)	Final Conditions (dilute)
$M_1 = 16\ M$	$M_2 = 0.10\ M$
$V_1 = ?$	$V_2 = 1.5\ L$

How do we get there?

We can solve the equation

$$M_1 \times V_1 = M_2 \times V_2$$

for V_1 by dividing both sides by M_1

$$\frac{\cancel{M_1} \times V_1}{\cancel{M_1}} = \frac{M_2 \times V_2}{M_1}$$

to give

$$V_1 = \frac{M_2 \times V_2}{M_1}$$

Now we substitute the known values of M_2, V_2, and M_1.

$$V_1 = \frac{\left(0.10\ \frac{mol}{L}\right)(1.5\ L)}{16\ \frac{mol}{L}} = 9.4 \times 10^{-3}\ L$$

$$9.4 \times 10^{-3}\ L \times \frac{1000\ mL}{1\ L} = 9.4\ mL$$

Therefore, $V_1 = 9.4 \times 10^{-3}$ L, or 9.4 mL. To make 1.5 L of 0.10 M H_2SO_4 using 16 M H_2SO_4, we must take 9.4 mL of the concentrated acid and dilute it with water to a final volume of 1.5 L. The correct way to do this is to add the 9.4 mL of acid to about 1 L of water and then dilute to 1.5 L by adding more water.

✔ Practice Problem • Exercise 15.8

What volume of 12 M HCl must be taken to prepare 0.75 L of 0.25 M HCl?

Approximate dilutions can be carried out using a calibrated beaker. Here concentrated sulfuric acid is being added to water to make a dilute solution.

DID YOU KNOW

It is always best to add concentrated acid to water, not water to the acid. That way, if any splashing occurs accidentally, it is dilute acid that splashes.

EXAMPLE 15.8

More Examples

1. What volume of 19 M NaOH must be used to prepare 1.0 L of a 0.15 M NaOH solution?
   7.9 mL

2. What volume of water is needed to prepare 500.0 mL of a 0.250 M $Ca(NO_3)_2$ solution from a 5.00 M $Ca(NO_3)_2$ solution?
   475 mL

✔ Answer to Practice Problem 15.8

We are given the following information:

$M_1 = 12\ \frac{mol}{L}$ $\quad M_2 = 0.25\ \frac{mol}{L}$

$V_1 = ?$ (what we need to find) $\quad V_2 = 0.75\ L$

Using the fact that the moles of solute do not change upon dilution, we know that

$$M_1 \times V_1 = M_2 \times V_2$$

Solving for V_1 by dividing both sides by M_1 gives

$$V_1 = \frac{M_2 \times V_2}{M_1}$$

$$= \frac{0.25\ \frac{mol}{L} \times 0.75\ L}{12\ \frac{mol}{L}}$$

and

$$V_1 = 0.016\ L = 16\ mL$$

SECTION 15.2
Review Questions

1. 5.0%

2. 0.83 M

3. Mg^{2+} concentration = 0.450 M; NO_3^- concentration = 0.900 M

4. mol KOH = 0.075 mol

5. 0.170 M

6. The key idea in working with dilution is to remember that the moles of solute remain the same.

7. 1.17 M NaCl

HANDS-ON CHEMISTRY   • MINI-LAB •

Good to the Last Drop!

Materials

- water
- food coloring
- graduated cylinder

Procedure

1. Place 10.0 mL, of water and add 20 drops of food coloring. Label the concentration of this solution 2.0 D (where D has units of drops/mL). This is solution A.

2. Take 1.0 mL of solution A and place it in an empty cup. Add 9.0 mL of water. This is solution B.

3. Take 1.0 mL of solution B and place it in an empty cup. Add 9.0 mL of water. This is solution C.

4. Continue this successive dilution until you can no longer see any color.

Results/Analysis

1. What is the concentration of solution B in units of D?

2. What is the concentration of solution C in units of D?

3. What is the concentration of the solution in step 4 in units of D?

SECTION 15.2
REVIEW QUESTIONS

① Vinegar is made by adding 33 g of acetic acid to 625 g of water. What is the percent by mass of acetic acid in this solution of vinegar?

② Assuming the density of vinegar is 1.0 g/mL, what is the molarity of vinegar? (Use the percent by mass of acetic acid in vinegar from question 1.) The molar mass of acetic acid is 60.05 g/mol.

③ A solution is labeled "0.450 M magnesium nitrate." Calculate the concentration of each ion present in solution.

④ Calculate the number of moles of KOH in 150.0 mL of a 0.500 M KOH solution.

⑤ If 4.25 g of $CaBr_2$ is dissolved in enough water to make 125 mL of solution, what is the molarity of the solution?

⑥ What is the key idea to remember when working with the dilution of a solution?

⑦ Calculate the new concentration when 50.0 mL of water is added to 725.0 mL of 1.25 M NaCl.

RESEARCH LINKS
CLASSZONE.COM

Hands-On Chemistry
MINI-LAB

Good to the Last Drop!

Materials Each group will need water, food coloring, and 7–8 cups.

Purpose Students will better understand the concepts of concentration and dilution. This activity also allows for practice with calculations.

Discussion Solution A has a concentration of 2 D; solution B has a concentration of 0.2 D; solution C has a concentration of 0.02 D. Successive dilutions are used when we need a very small concentration of a solution in the lab. For example, suppose we have a 1.0 M solution and need a 1.0×10^{-4} M solution. Taking 1.0 L of the 1.0 M solution and diluting it with 9999 L of water would make the desired solution, but would not be terribly efficient (nor would taking 1.0 mL of the 1.0 M solution and adding 9999 mL of water). If we followed the procedure used in this activity, we would have our needed solution in five dilutions and use only 45 mL of water (to make 10 mL of the solution).

It will take 4–5 dilutions for the solution to appear colorless (that is, 2–3 more than it takes to make solution C). Ask students whether the colorless solution contains any food coloring, and have them explain their answers.

Properties of Solutions

Objectives

- *To learn to solve stoichiometric problems involving solution reactions*
- *To do calculations involving acid–base reactions*
- *To learn about normality and equivalent weight*
- *To use normality in stoichiometric calculations*
- *To understand the effect of a solute on solution properties*

Key Terms

- Neutralization reaction
- Equivalent of an acid
- Equivalent of a base
- Equivalent weight
- Colligative property

A. Stoichiometry of Solution Reactions

Because so many important reactions occur in solution, it is important to be able to do stoichiometric calculations for solution reactions. The principles needed to perform these calculations are similar to those developed in Chapter 9. It is helpful to think in terms of the following steps:

Steps for Solving Stoichiometric Problems Involving Solutions

Step 1 Write the balanced equation for the reaction. For reactions involving ions, it is best to write the net ionic equation.

Step 2 Calculate the moles of reactants.

Step 3 Determine which reactant is limiting.

Step 4 Calculate the moles of other reactants or products, as required.

Step 5 Convert to grams or other units, if required.

CRITICAL THINKING

What if all ionic solids were soluble in water? How would it affect reactions in aqueous solution?

Active Reading Question

When solving stoichiometry problems for solution reactions, what type of chemical equation is most convenient to use?

EXAMPLE 15.9

Solution Stoichiometry: Calculating Mass of Reactants and Products

Calculate the mass of solid NaCl that must be added to 1.50 L of a 0.100 *M* AgNO₃ solution to precipitate all of the Ag⁺ ions in the form of AgCl. Calculate the mass of AgCl formed.

Solution

Where do we want to go?

Mass of AgCl formed = ? g

What do we know?

- $V = 1.50$ L
- $M = 0.100\ M\ AgNO_3$
- $NaCl(s) + AgNO_3(aq) \rightarrow AgCl(s) + NaNO_3(aq)$

15.3 • Properties of Solutions • **541**

SECTION 15.3
INTRODUCE

Student Preparation

Assign students to read Section 15.3 and to answer the Review Questions at the end of the section before coming to class.

Active Learning
Team Learning Worksheet

After introducing the material in Section 15.3 in class, place students in groups and have them work together on **Section 15.3: Team Learning Worksheet.**

SECTION 15.3
GUIDE THE LEARNING

Homework

You may wish to assign these selected end-of-chapter problems as homework for this section: 35, 36, 38, 39, 40, 41a–b, 42, 45, 48, 50, 51

Additional end-of-chapter problems can be used for extra practice.

15.3.A Stoichiometry of Solution Reactions

Objective To understand the strategy for solving stoichiometric problems for solution reactions

LABORATORY
EXPERIMENT 65:
Hard Water Analysis, Microscale

CRITICAL THINKING

This question is the reverse of the Critical Thinking from Chapter 8 (What if no ionic solids were soluble in water?). The answer is basically the same—we would get no reactions in aqueous solutions—but the reason is different. We can write the equation KCl(*aq*) + NaNO₃(*aq*) → KNO₃(*aq*) + NaCl(*aq*), but it isn't a chemical reaction because all of the ions are spectator ions; there is no net ionic equation. This case demonstrates the importance of having students think about what a reaction "looks like" at a molecular level.

TEACHING TIPS

- Begin this section with a review of basic stoichiometry. The steps outlined in the text form the basis for a review of the principles for solving stoichiometry problems.

- Remind students to balance all chemical equations before beginning a problem.

- Now is a good time to review writing net ionic equations. Using a net ionic equation simplifies the work done in solving solution problems. It also focuses students' attention on the species reacting and, therefore, on the question being asked.

Active Reading Question

The net ionic equation is generally the most convenient to use.

EXAMPLE 15.9

More Examples

1. Calculate the mass of solid sodium sulfate that must be added to 250.0 mL of a 0.200 M solution of barium nitrate to precipitate all of the barium ions in the form of barium sulfate. Also calculate the mass of barium sulfate formed.

   7.10 g Na_2SO_4 required; 11.7 g $BaSO_4$ produced

2. Calculate the mass of NaI that must be added to 425.0 mL of a 0.100 M $Pb(NO_3)_2$ solution to precipitate all of the Pb^{2+} ions as PbI_2. Also calculate the mass of PbI_2 formed.

   12.7 g NaI required; 19.6 g PbI_2 produced

MINI-DEMO

When working problems in solution stoichiometry, it is more interesting to students if you can show them the reaction. Before class, make dilute solutions of the reactants for the examples you plan to present. Then for each example, write the reactants on the board, and then stop and mix the chemicals together. Have students name the products and complete the equation. Balance the equation and proceed with the solution stoichiometry problem. This approach allows students to be actively involved in a review of earlier topics while solving a new problem.

MATH

Liters × M ⟹ Moles of solute

When aqueous sodium chloride is added to a solution of silver nitrate, a white silver chloride precipitate forms.

How do we get there?

Step 1 *Write the balanced equation for the reaction.*

When added to the $AgNO_3$ solution (which contains Ag^+ and NO_3^- ions), the solid NaCl dissolves to yield Na^+ and Cl^- ions. Solid AgCl forms according to the following balanced net ionic reaction:

$$Ag^+(aq) + Cl^-(aq) \rightarrow AgCl(s)$$

Step 2 *Calculate the moles of reactants.*

In this case we must add just enough Cl^- ions to react with all the Ag^+ ions present, so we must calculate the moles of Ag^+ ions present in 1.50 L of a 0.100 M $AgNO_3$ solution. (Remember that a 0.100 M $AgNO_3$ solution contains 0.100 M Ag^+ ions and 0.100 M NO_3^- ions.)

$$1.50 \, \cancel{L} \times \frac{0.100 \text{ mol } Ag^+}{\cancel{L}} = 0.150 \text{ mol } Ag^+$$

Moles of Ag^+ present in 1.5 L of 0.100 M $AgNO_3$

Step 3 *Determine which reactant is limiting.*

In this situation we want to add just enough Cl^- to react with the Ag^+ present. That is, we want to precipitate *all* the Ag^+ in the solution. Thus the Ag^+ present determines the amount of Cl^- needed.

Step 4 Calculate the moles of Cl^- required.

We have 0.150 mol of Ag^+ ions and, because one Ag^+ ion reacts with one Cl^- ion, we need 0.150 mol of Cl^-,

$$0.150 \, \cancel{\text{mol } Ag^+} \times \frac{1 \text{ mol } Cl^-}{1 \, \cancel{\text{mol } Ag^+}} = 0.150 \text{ mol } Cl^-$$

so 0.150 mol of AgCl will be formed.

$$0.150 \text{ mol } Ag^+ + 0.150 \text{ mol } Cl^- \rightarrow 0.150 \text{ mol AgCl}$$

Step 5 *Convert to grams of NaCl required.*

To produce 0.150 mol Cl^-, we need 0.150 mol NaCl. We calculate the mass of NaCl required as follows:

$$0.150 \, \cancel{\text{mol NaCl}} \times \frac{58.4 \text{ g NaCl}}{\cancel{\text{mol NaCl}}} = 8.76 \text{ g NaCl}$$

Moles	⟹	Mass

Times molar mass

The mass of AgCl formed is

$$0.150 \, \cancel{\text{mol AgCl}} \times \frac{143.3 \text{ g AgCl}}{\cancel{\text{mol AgCl}}} = 21.5 \text{ g AgCl}$$

EXAMPLE 15.10

Solution Stoichiometry: Determining Limiting Reactants and Calculating Mass of Products

When $Ba(NO_3)_2$ and K_2CrO_4 react in aqueous solution, the yellow solid $BaCrO_4$ is formed. Calculate the mass of $BaCrO_4$ that forms when 3.50×10^{-3} mol of solid $Ba(NO_3)_2$ is dissolved in 265 mL of 0.0100 M K_2CrO_4 solution.

Barium chromate precipitating

Solution

Where do we want to go?

Mass of $BaCrO_4$ formed in the reaction = ? g

What do we know?

- Amount $Ba(NO_3)_2(s) = 3.50 \times 10^{-3}$ mol
- K_2CrO_4
  - 0.100 M
  - $V = 265$ mL
- $Ba(NO_3)_2(s) + K_2CrO_4(aq) \rightarrow BaCrO_4(s) + 2KNO_3(aq)$

How do we get there?

Step 1 The original K_2CrO_4 solution contains the ions K^+ and CrO_4^{2-}. When the $Ba(NO_3)_2$ is dissolved in this solution, Ba^{2+} and NO_3^- ions are added. The Ba^{2+} and CrO_4^{2-} ions react to form solid $BaCrO_4$. The balanced net ionic equation is

$$Ba^{2+}(aq) + CrO_4^{2-}(aq) \rightarrow BaCrO_4(s)$$

Step 2 Next we determine the moles of reactants. We are told that 3.50×10^{-3} mol of $Ba(NO_3)_2$ is added to the K_2CrO_4 solution. Each formula unit of $Ba(NO_3)_2$ contains one Ba^{2+} ion, so 3.50×10^{-3} mol of $Ba(NO_3)_2$ gives 3.50×10^{-3} mol of Ba^{2+} ions in solution.

3.50×10^{-3} mol $Ba(NO_3)_2$ — dissolves to give → 3.50×10^{-3} mol Ba^{2+}

Because $V \times M$ = moles of solute, we can compute the moles of K_2CrO_4 in the solution from the volume and molarity of the original solution. First we must convert the volume of the solution (265 mL) to liters.

$$265 \text{ mL} \times \frac{1 \text{ L}}{1000 \text{ mL}} = 0.265 \text{ L}$$

Next we determine the number of moles of K_2CrO_4, using the molarity of the K_2CrO_4 solution (0.0100 M).

$$0.265 \text{ L} \times \frac{0.0100 \text{ mol } K_2CrO_4}{\text{L}} = 2.65 \times 10^{-3} \text{ mol } K_2CrO_4$$

We know that

2.65×10^{-3} mol K_2CrO_4 — dissolves to give → 2.65×10^{-3} mol CrO_4^{2-}

so the solution contains 2.65×10^{-3} mol of CrO_4^{2-} ions.

15.3 • Properties of Solutions • **543**

EXAMPLE 15.10

More Examples

1. Calculate the mass of the white solid $CaCO_3$ that forms when 25.0 mL of a 0.100 M $Ca(NO_3)_2$ solution is mixed with 20.0 mL of a 0.150 M Na_2CO_3 solution.

   0.250 g $CaCO_3$

2. Calculate the mass of the blood-red solid Ag_2CrO_4 that forms when 50.0 mL of a 0.250 M $AgNO_3$ solution is mixed with 30.0 mL of a 0.250 M K_2CrO_4 solution.

   2.07 g Ag_2CrO_4

🍎 TEACHING TIP

Include some examples in class in which a salt dissolves to produce multiple moles of an ion per mole of compound. Such an example illustrates the need for writing net ionic equations when solving solution stoichiometry problems.

Step 1 When the aqueous solutions of Na_2SO_4 (containing Na^+ and SO_4^{2-} ions) and $Pb(NO_3)_2$ (containing Pb^{2+} and NO_3^- ions) are mixed, solid $PbSO_4$ is formed.

$$Pb^{2+}(aq) + SO_4^{2-}(aq) \rightarrow PbSO_4(s)$$

Step 2 We must first determine whether Pb^{2+} or SO_4^{2-} is the limiting reactant by calculating the moles of Pb^{2+} and SO_4^{2-} ions present. Because 0.0500 M $Pb(NO_3)_2$ contains 0.0500 M Pb^{2+} ions, we can calculate the moles of Pb^{2+} ions in 1.25 L of this solution as follows:

$$1.25 \, \cancel{L} \times \frac{0.0500 \text{ mol } Pb^{2+}}{\cancel{L}} =$$
$$0.0625 \text{ mol } Pb^{2+}$$

The 0.0250 M Na_2SO_4 solution contains 0.0250 M SO_4^{2-} ions, and the number of moles of SO_4^{2-} ions in 2.00 L of this solution is

$$2.00 \, \cancel{L} \times \frac{0.0250 \text{ mol } SO_4^{2-}}{\cancel{L}} =$$
$$0.0500 \text{ mol } PbSO_4^{2-}$$

Step 3 Pb^{2+} and SO_4^{2-} react in a 1:1 ratio, so the amount of SO_4^{2-} ions is limiting because a smaller number of SO_4^{2-} moles is present.

Step 4 The Pb^{2+} ions are present in excess, and only 0.0500 mol of solid $PbSO_4$ will be formed.

Step 5 We calculate the mass of $PbSO_4$ by using the molar mass of $PbSO_4$ (303.3 g).

$$0.500 \, \cancel{\text{mol } PbSO_4} \times \frac{303.3 \text{ g } PbSO_4}{1 \, \cancel{\text{mol } PbSO_4}} =$$
$$15.2 \text{ g } PbSO_4$$

15.3.B Neutralization Reactions

Objective To learn how to do calculations involved in acid–base reactions

 TEACHING TIP

This section presents an opportunity to help students learn to approach solving problems by thinking through them. These problems are applications of material that students have seen previously. Focus students' attention on the basic requirements for solving problems in chemistry: writing what is known, writing

a balanced equation, determining what is being asked for, deciding what needs to be found to get what is asked for, and then solving the problem.

Step 3 The balanced equation tells us that one Ba^{2+} ion reacts with one CrO_4^{2-}. Because the number of moles of CrO_4^{2-} ions (2.65×10^{-3}) is smaller than the number of moles of Ba^{2+} ions (3.50×10^{-3}), the CrO_4^{2-} will run out first.

$$Ba^{2+}(aq) \quad + \quad CrO_4^{2-}(aq) \quad \rightarrow \quad BaCrO_4(s)$$

3.50×10^{-3} mol	2.65×10^{-3} mol

Smaller
(runs out first)

Therefore, the CrO_4^{2-} is limiting.

Moles of CrO_4^{2-}	$\Rightarrow$ limits	Moles of $BaCrO_4$

Step 4 The 2.65×10^{-3} mol of CrO_4^{2-} ions will react with 2.65×10^{-3} mol of Ba^{2+} ions to form 2.65×10^{-3} mol of $BaCrO_4$.

2.65×10^{-3} mol Ba^{2+}	$+$	2.65×10^{-3} mol CrO_4^{2-}	$\Rightarrow$	2.65×10^{-3} mol $BaCrO_4(s)$

Step 5 The mass of $BaCrO_4$ formed is obtained from its molar mass (253.3 g) as follows:

$$2.65 \times 10^{-3} \, \cancel{\text{mol } BaCrO_4} \times \frac{253.3 \text{ g } BaCrO_4}{\cancel{\text{mol } BaCrO_4}} = 0.671 \text{ g } BaCrO_4$$

Practice Problem • Exercise 15.10

When aqueous solutions of Na_2SO_4 and $Pb(NO_3)_2$ are mixed, $PbSO_4$ precipitates. Calculate the mass of $PbSO_4$ formed when 1.25 L of 0.0500 M $Pb(NO_3)_2$ and 2.00 L of 0.0250 M Na_2SO_4 are mixed.

Hint: Calculate the moles of Pb^{2+} and SO_4^{2-} in the mixed solution, decide which ion is limiting, and calculate the moles of $PbSO_4$ formed.

B. Neutralization Reactions

So far we have considered the stoichiometry of reactions in solution that result in the formation of a precipitate. Another common type of solution reaction occurs between an acid and a base. We introduced these reactions in Chapter 8. Recall from that discussion that an acid is a substance that furnishes H+ ions. A strong acid, such as hydrochloric acid, HCl, dissociates (ionizes) completely in water.

$$HCl(aq) \rightarrow H+(aq) + Cl^-(aq)$$

Strong bases are water-soluble metal hydroxides, which are completely dissociated in water. An example is NaOH, which dissolves in water to give Na^+ and OH^- ions.

$$NaOH(s) \xrightarrow{H_2O(l)} Na^+(aq) + OH^-(aq)$$

15

When a strong acid and strong base react, the net ionic reaction is

$$H^+(aq) + OH^-(aq) \rightarrow H_2O(l)$$

An acid–base reaction is often called a **neutralization reaction**. When just enough strong base is added to react exactly with the strong acid in a solution, we say the acid has been *neutralized*. One product of this reaction is always water. The steps in dealing with the stoichiometry of any neutralization reaction are the same as those we followed previously.

> **Neutralization reaction**
> An acid–base reaction

 Active Reading Question

What does it mean to say an acid has been neutralized?

EXAMPLE 15.11

Solution Stoichiometry: Calculating Volume in Neutralization Reactions

What volume of a 0.100 *M* HCl solution is needed to neutralize 25.0 mL of a 0.350 *M* NaOH solution?

Solution

Where do we want to go?

Volume of HCl required for neutralization = ? L

What do we know?

- HCl molarity = 0.100 *M*
- NaOH sample
  - 0.350 *M*
  - *V* = 25.0 mL
- $HCl(aq) + NaOH(aq) \rightarrow H_2O(l) + NaCl(aq)$

How do we get there?

Step 1 *Write the balanced equation for the reaction.*

Hydrochloric acid is a strong acid, so all the HCl molecules dissociate to produce H^+ and Cl^- ions. Also, when the strong base NaOH dissolves, the solution contains Na^+ and OH^- ions. When these two solutions are mixed, the H^+ ions from the hydrochloric acid react with the OH^- ions from the sodium hydroxide solution to form water. The balanced net ionic equation for the reaction is

$$H^+(aq) + OH^-(aq) \rightarrow H_2O(l)$$

Step 2 *Calculate the moles of reactants.*

In this problem we are given a volume (25.0 mL) of 0.350 *M* NaOH, and we want to add just enough 0.100 *M* HCl to provide just enough H^+ ions to react with all the OH^-. Therefore, we must calculate the number of moles of OH^- ions in the 25.0-mL sample of 0.350 *M* NaOH. To do this, we first change the volume to liters and multiply by the molarity.

$$25.0 \text{ mL NaOH} \times \frac{1 \text{ L}}{1000 \text{ mL}} \times \frac{0.350 \text{ mol OH}^-}{\text{L NaOH}} = 8.75 \times 10^{-3} \text{ mol OH}^-$$

Moles of OH^- present in 25.0 mL of 0.350 *M* NaOH

15.3 • Properties of Solutions • **545**

 TEACHING TIP

Neutralization reaction problems often ask for volume, which is a new variable for students. In stoichiometry, we tend to ask for moles or mass.

Active Reading Question

An acid has been neutralized when enough strong base has been added to react completely with a strong acid.

EXAMPLE 15.11

More Examples

1. What volume of 0.150 *M* HNO_3 solution is needed to neutralize 45.0 mL of a 0.550 *M* KOH solution?

   165 mL

2. What volume of 1.00×10^{-2} *M* HCl solution is needed to neutralize 35.0 mL of a 5.00×10^{-3} *M* $Ba(OH)_2$ solution?

   35.0 mL

TECHNOLOGY

 Video

Acid–Base Titration

Meeting Individual Needs
ENGLISH LANGUAGE LEARNERS

If students struggle with the meaning of *neutralization reactions,* discuss the meaning of the word *neutral.* Explain how a sports referee is a neutral participant in a game. Although the referee is involved in the event, he or she is not on either side. Relate this to the neutral product in a neutralization reaction. It is neither acidic nor basic.

15.3 • Properties of Solutions • **545**

Answer to Practice Problem 15.11

Step 1 Because nitric acid is a strong acid, the nitric acid solution contains H^+ and NO_3^- ions. The KOH solution contains K^+ and OH^- ions. When these solutions are mixed, the H^+ and OH^- react to form water.

$$H^+(aq) + OH^-(aq) \rightarrow H_2O(l)$$

Step 2 The number of moles of OH^- present in 125 mL of 0.050 *M* KOH is

$$125 \text{ mL} \times \frac{1 \text{ L}}{1000 \text{ mL}} \times \frac{0.050 \text{ mol OH}^-}{\text{L}}$$

$$= 6.3 \times 10^{-3} \text{ mol OH}^-$$

Step 3 H^+ and OH^- react in a 1:1 ratio, so we need 6.3×10^{-3} mol of H^+ from the 0.100 *M* HNO_3.

Step 4 6.3×10^{-3} mol of OH^- requires 6.3×10^{-3} mol of H^+ to form 6.3×10^{-3} mol of H_2O.

Therefore,

$$V \times \frac{0.100 \text{ mol H}^+}{\text{L}} =$$
$$6.3 \times 10^{-3} \text{ mol H}^+$$

where *V* represents the volume in liters of 0.100 *M* HNO_3 required. Solving for *V*, we have

$$V = \frac{6.3 \times 10^{-3} \text{ mol H}^+}{\dfrac{0.100 \text{ mol H}^+}{\text{L}}}$$

$$= 6.3 \times 10^{-2} \text{ L}$$

$$= 6.3 \times 10^{-2} \text{ L} \times \frac{1000 \text{ mL}}{\text{L}}$$

$$= 63 \text{ mL}$$

15.3.C Normality

Objective To learn about normality and equivalent weight and use these concepts in stoichiometric calculations

 TEACHING TIP

It may help to introduce the idea of equivalents from the standpoint of equivalence statements. Since the chapter on measurement, students have been using equivalence statements to convert from one system to another. In this section, an equivalence exists between moles of hydrogen (or hydroxide) ions and an equivalent. If students can view this process as a conversion, it will simplify their thinking about normality.

Step 3 *Determine which reactant is limiting.*

This problem requires the addition of just enough H^+ ions to react exactly with the OH^- ions present, so the number of moles of OH^- ions present determines the number of moles of H^+ that must be added. The OH^- ions are limiting.

Step 4 *Calculate the moles of H^1 required.*

The balanced equation tells us that the H^+ and OH^- ions react in a 1:1 ratio, so 8.75×10^{-3} mol of H^+ ions is required to neutralize (exactly react with) the 8.75×10^{-3} mol of OH^- ions present.

Step 5 *Calculate the volume of 0.100 M HCl required.*

Next we must find the volume (*V*) of 0.100 *M* HCl required to furnish this amount of H^+ ions. Because the volume (in liters) times the molarity gives the number of moles, we have

$$V \times \underbrace{\frac{0.100 \text{ mol H}^+}{\text{L}}}_{\substack{\text{Unknown} \\ \text{volume} \\ \text{(in liters)}}} = \underbrace{8.75 \times 10^{-3} \text{ mol H}^+}_{\substack{\text{Moles of} \\ \text{H}^+ \text{ needed}}}$$

Now we must solve for *V* by dividing both sides of the equation by $\dfrac{0.100 \text{ mole H}^+}{\text{L}}$.

$$V \times \frac{\dfrac{0.100 \text{ mol H}^+}{\text{L}}}{\dfrac{0.100 \text{ mol H}^+}{\text{L}}} = \frac{8.75 \times 10^{-3} \text{ mol H}^+}{\dfrac{0.100 \text{ mol H}^+}{\text{L}}}$$

$$V = 8.75 \times 10^{-2} \text{ L}$$

Changing liters to milliliters, we have

$$V = 8.75 \times 10^{-2} \text{ L} \times \frac{1000 \text{ mL}}{\text{L}} = 87.5 \text{ mL}$$

Therefore, 87.5 mL of 0.100 *M* HCl is required to neutralize 25.0 mL of 0.350 *M* NaOH.

Practice Problem • Exercise 15.11

Calculate the volume of 0.10 *M* HNO_3 needed to neutralize 125 mL of 0.050 *M* KOH.

Equivalent of an acid
The amount of acid that can furnish one mole of hydrogen ions (H^+)

Equivalent of a base
The amount of base that can furnish one mole of hydroxide ions (OH^-)

Equivalent weight
The mass (in grams) of one equivalent of an acid or a base

C. Normality

Normality is another unit of concentration that is sometimes used, especially when dealing with acids and bases. The use of normality focuses mainly on the H^+ and OH^- available in an acid–base reaction. Before we discuss normality, however, we need to define some terms. One **equivalent of an acid** is the *amount of that acid that can furnish 1 mol of H^+ ions*. Similarly, one **equivalent of a base** is defined as the *amount of that base that can furnish 1 mol of OH^- ions*. The **equivalent weight** of an acid or a base is the mass in grams of 1 equivalent (equiv) of that acid or base.

The common strong acids are HCl, HNO$_3$, and H$_2$SO$_4$. For HCl and HNO$_3$ each molecule of acid furnishes one H$^+$ ion, so 1 mol of HCl can furnish 1 mol of H$^+$ ions. This means that

Furnishes 1 mol of H$^+$
↓
1 mol HCl = 1 equiv HCl

Molar mass (HCl) = equivalent weight (HCl)

Likewise, for HNO$_3$,

1 mol HNO$_3$ = 1 equiv HNO$_3$

Molar mass (HNO$_3$) = equivalent weight (HNO$_3$)

However, H$_2$SO$_4$ can furnish *two* H$^+$ ions per molecule, so 1 mol of H$_2$SO$_4$ can furnish *two* mol of H$^+$. This means that

Because each mole of H$_2$SO$_4$ can furnish 2 mol of H$^+$, we need to take only $\frac{1}{2}$ mol of H$_2$SO$_4$ to get 1 equiv of H$_2$SO$_4$. Therefore,

$$\frac{1}{2} \text{ mol H}_2\text{SO}_4 = 1 \text{ equiv H}_2\text{SO}_4$$

and

$$\text{Equivalent weight (H}_2\text{SO}_4) = \frac{1}{2} \text{ molar mass (H}_2\text{SO}_4)$$
$$= \frac{1}{2} (98 \text{ g}) = 49 \text{ g}$$

The equivalent weight of H$_2$SO$_4$ is 49 g.

The common strong bases are NaOH and KOH. For NaOH and KOH, each formula unit furnishes one OH$^-$ ion, so we can say

1 mol NaOH = 1 equiv NaOH

Molar mass (NaOH) = equivalent weight (NaOH)

1 mol KOH = 1 equiv KOH

Molar mass (KOH) = equivalent weight (KOH)

These ideas are summarized in **Table 15.2.**

Table 15.2

The Molar Masses and Equivalent Weights of the Common Strong Acids and Bases

	Molar Mass (g)	Equivalent Weight (g)
Acid		
HCl	36.5	36.5
HNO$_3$	63.0	63.0
H$_2$SO$_4$	98.0	$49.0 = \frac{98.0}{2}$
Base		
NaOH	40.0	40.0
KOH	56.1	56.1

15.3 • Properties of Solutions • **547**

EXAMPLE 15.12

More Examples

1. Arsenic acid, H_3AsO_4, can furnish three H^+ ions per molecule. Calculate the equivalent weight of H_3AsO_4.
   47.31 g

2. Calculate the equivalent weight of HBr.
   80.91 g

 TEACHING TIP

The key idea in understanding normality is determining equivalents. This step is analogous to determining moles in other solution problems.

EXAMPLE 15.12

Solution Stoichiometry: Calculating Equivalent Weight

Phosphoric acid, H_3PO_4, can furnish three H^+ ions per molecule. Calculate the equivalent weight of H_3PO_4.

Solution
Where do we want to go?

Equivalent weight for H_3PO_4 = ? g/equivalent

What do we know?
• Molar mass = 98.0 g/mol

How do we get there?
The key point here involves how many protons (H^+ ions) each molecule of H_3PO_4 can furnish.

| H_3PO_4 | $\Rightarrow$ furnishes | $? H^+$ |

Because each H_3PO_4 can furnish three H^+ ions, 1 mol of H_3PO_4 can furnish 3 mol of H^+ ions:

| 1 mol H_3PO_4 | $\Rightarrow$ furnishes | 3 mol H^+ |

So 1 equiv of H_3PO_4 (the amount that can furnish 1 mol of H^+) is one-third of a mole.

| $\frac{1}{3}$ mol H_3PO_4 | $\Rightarrow$ furnishes | 1 mol H^+ |

This means the equivalent weight of H_3PO_4 is one-third its molar mass.

| Equivalent weight | = | $\dfrac{\text{Molar mass}}{3}$ |

$$\text{Equivalent weight } (H_3PO_4) = \frac{\text{molar mass } (H_3PO_4)}{3} = \frac{98.0 \text{ g}}{3} = 32.7 \text{ g}$$

Normality (N) is defined as the number of equivalents of solute per liter of solution.

$$\text{Normality} = N = \frac{\text{number of equivalents}}{\text{liter of solution}} = \frac{\text{equivalents}}{\text{liter}} = \frac{\text{equiv}}{L}$$

This means that a 1 N solution contains 1 equivalent of solute per liter of solution. Notice that when we multiply the volume of a solution in liters by the normality, we get the number of equivalents.

$$N \times V = \frac{\text{equiv}}{\cancel{L}} \times \cancel{L} = \text{equiv}$$

Active Reading Question

What is the normality of a 4.0 *M* H$_2$SO$_4$ solution?

EXAMPLE 15.13

Solution Stoichiometry: Calculating Normality

A solution of sulfuric acid contains 86 g of H$_2$SO$_4$ per liter of solution. Calculate the normality of this solution.

Solution

Where do we want to go?

Normality = ? equivalent/L

What do we know?

- Molar mass = 98.0 g/mol
- H$_2$SO$_4$
  - 1.00 L
  - 86 g
- $N = \dfrac{\text{equivalents}}{\text{L}}$

How do we get there?

To find the number of equivalents present, we must calculate the number of equivalents represented by 86 g of H$_2$SO$_4$. To do this calculation, we focus on the definition of the equivalent: it is the amount of acid that furnishes 1 mol of H$^+$. Because H$_2$SO$_4$ can furnish two H$^+$ ions per molecule, 1 equiv of H$_2$SO$_4$ is $\frac{1}{2}$ mol of H$_2$SO$_4$, so

$$\text{Equivalent weight (H}_2\text{SO}_4) = \frac{\text{molar mass (H}_2\text{SO}_4)}{2} = \frac{98.0 \text{ g}}{2} = 49.0 \text{ g}$$

We have 86 g of H$_2$SO$_4$

$$86 \text{ g H}_2\text{SO}_4 \times \frac{1 \text{ equiv H}_2\text{SO}_4}{49.0 \text{ g H}_2\text{SO}_4} = 1.8 \text{ equiv H}_2\text{SO}_4$$

$$N = \frac{\text{equiv}}{\text{L}} = \frac{1.8 \text{ equiv H}_2\text{SO}_4}{1.0 \text{ L}} = 1.8 \text{ } N \text{ H}_2\text{SO}_4$$

Does it make sense?

We know that 86 g is more than 1 equivalent of H$_2$SO$_4$ (49 g) so this answer makes sense.

 information

To calculate the concentration of a solution, first write the appropriate definition. Then decide how to calculate the quantities shown in the definition.

✍ **Practice Problem • Exercise 15.13**

Calculate the normality of a solution containing 23.6 g of KOH in 755 mL of solution.

 Active Reading Question

8.0 *N* H$_2$SO$_4$

EXAMPLE 15.13

More Examples

1. A solution of phosphoric acid contains 50.0 g of H$_3$PO$_4$ per liter of solution. Calculate the normality of this solution.

   1.53 *N*

2. A solution of hydrochloric acid contains 25.0 g of HCl per liter of solution. Calculate the normality of this solution.

   0.686 *N*

Answer to Practice Problem 15.13

From the definition of normality, *N* = equiv/L, we need to calculate (1) the equivalents of KOH and (2) the volume of the solution in liters. To find the number of equivalents, we use the equivalent weight of KOH, which is 56.1 g (see Table 15.2).

$$23.6 \text{ g KOH} \times \frac{1 \text{ equiv KOH}}{56.1 \text{ g KOH}} =$$

0.421 equiv KOH

Next we convert the volume to liters.

$$755 \text{ mL} \times \frac{1 \text{ L}}{1000 \text{ mL}} = 0.755 \text{ L}$$

Finally, we substitute these values into the equation that defines normality.

$$\text{Normality} = \frac{\text{equiv}}{\text{L}}$$

$$= \frac{0.421 \text{ equiv}}{0.755 \text{ L}}$$

$$= 0.558 \text{ } N$$

The main advantage of using equivalents is that 1 equiv of acid contains the same number of available H^+ ions as the number of OH^- ions present in 1 equiv of base. That is,

0.75 equiv (base) will react exactly with 0.75 equiv (acid).

0.23 equiv (base) will react exactly with 0.23 equiv (acid).

And so on.

In each of these cases, the *number of* H^+ ions furnished by the sample of acid is the same as the *number of* OH^- ions furnished by the sample of base.

n equivalents of any acid will exactly neutralize *n* equivalents of any base.

$$\boxed{n \text{ equiv acid}} \quad \leftarrow \text{ reacts exactly with } \rightarrow \quad \boxed{n \text{ equiv base}}$$

Because we know that equal equivalents of acid and base are required for neutralization, we can say that

equiv (acid) = equiv (base)

That is,

$$N_{acid} \times V_{acid} = \text{equiv (acid)} = \text{equiv (base)} = N_{base} \times V_{base}$$

For any neutralization reaction,
$$N_{acid} \times V_{acid} = N_{base} \times V_{base}$$

CELEBRITY CHEMICAL   Mercury (Hg)

Mercury was isolated from its principal ore, cinnabar (HgS), as early as 500 B.C. Cinnabar was widely used in the ancient world as a red pigment (vermilion). Mercury, whose mobility inspired its naming after the messenger of the gods in Roman mythology, was of special interest to alchemists. Alchemists hoped to find a way to change cheap metals into gold, and it was generally thought that mercury, which easily forms alloys with many metals, was the key to this process. Mercury has a common name of quicksilver.

Mercury is a very dense (13.6 times denser than water), shiny liquid that has a surprisingly high vapor pressure for a heavy metal. Because mercury vapor is quite toxic, it must be stored in stoppered containers and handled in well-ventilated areas. Many instances of suspected mercury poisoning occurred in the days before its hazards were understood.

For example, it is very possible that Sir Isaac Newton, the renowned physicist, suffered from mercury poisoning at one time in his career and

had to "retire" to the country away from his laboratory to regain his strength. Some have speculated that Mozart, the famous composer, may have died of mercury poisoning due to the mercury salts that were used to treat an illness. Also, the "mad hatters" of *Alice in Wonderland* fame have a historical connection to mercury. Apparently, the mercury salts used by workers in London to treat felt used in hats caused the hatters to become "mad" over the years. It turns out that a change in personality is a characteristic of heavy metal poisoning.

The Mad Hatter's Tea Party, an illustration by Sir John Tenniel, from Alice's Adventures in Wonderland

---

CELEBRITY CHEMICAL

Mercury (Hg)

Paracelsus introduced the use of mercury as a treatment for syphilis. In 1799, Edward Howard used mercury fulminate as a detonator for explosives. Mercury has many uses in daily life, such as in mercury-vapor lamps, electrical switches, thermometers, and barometers.

With the notable exception of iron, almost all metals can form alloys with

mercury. These alloys are called amalgams. Sodium amalgams form in electrolytic cells used to produce chlorine. Dental amalgam is also prepared with mercury. The key to creating dental amalgam is for it to form a smooth paste within 90 seconds. It must then set within 3–5 minutes and within 2 hours it must be hard enough to withstand biting and chewing stresses. Standard dental alloy is generally composed of silver (67%–74%),

tin (25%–27%), copper (0–6%), and zinc (0–2%). This alloy is mixed with mercury (1:1 mass ratio) just before use.

EXAMPLE 15.14

Solution Stoichiometry: Using Normality in Calculations

What volume of a 0.075 N KOH solution is required to react exactly with 0.135 L of 0.45 N H_3PO_4?

Solution

Where do we want to go?

Volume KOH required to react = ? L

What do we know?

- 0.075 N KOH
- H_3PO_4
  - 0.135 L
  - 0.45 N
- In neutralization → equivalents$_{acid}$ = equivalents$_{base}$
- $N_{acid} \times V_{acid} = N_{base} \times V_{base}$

How do we get there?

We know that for neutralization, equiv (acid) = equiv (base), or

$$N_{acid} \times V_{acid} = N_{base} \times V_{base}$$

We want to calculate for the volume of base, V_{base}, so we solve for V_{base} by dividing both sides by N_{base}.

$$\frac{N_{acid} \times V_{acid}}{N_{base}} = \frac{N_{base} \times V_{base}}{N_{base}} = V_{base}$$

Now we can substitute the given values N_{acid} = 0.45 N, V_{acid} = 0.135 L, and N_{base} = 0.075 N into the equation.

$$V_{base} = \frac{N_{acid} \times V_{acid}}{N_{base}} = \frac{\left(0.45 \frac{equiv}{L}\right)(0.135 \text{ L})}{0.075 \frac{equiv}{L}} = 0.81 \text{ L}$$

This gives V_{base} = 0.81 L, so 0.81 L of 0.075 N KOH is required to react exactly with 0.135 L of 0.45 N H_3PO_4.

✔ Practice Problem • Exercise 15.14

What volume of 0.50 N H_2SO_4 is required to react exactly with 0.250 L of 0.80 N KOH?

EXAMPLE 15.14

More Examples

1. What volume of 0.500 N NaOH is required to react exactly with 125 mL of 0.500 N H_2SO_4?

   125 mL

2. What volume of 1.00 N H_3PO_4 is required to react exactly with 25.0 mL of 0.500 N NaOH?

   12.5 mL

✔ Answer to Practice Problem 15.14

To solve this problem, we use the relationship

$$N_{acid} \times V_{acid} = N_{base} \times V_{base}$$

where

$$N_{acid} = 0.50 \frac{equiv}{L}$$
$$V_{acid} = ?$$
$$N_{base} = 0.80 \frac{equiv}{L}$$
$$V_{base} = 0.250 \text{ L}$$

We solve the equation

$$N_{acid} \times V_{acid} = N_{base} \times V_{base}$$

for V_{acid} by dividing both sides by N_{acid}.

$$\frac{N_{acid} \times V_{acid}}{N_{acid}} = \frac{N_{base} \times V_{base}}{N_{acid}}$$

$$V_{acid} = \frac{N_{base} \times V_{base}}{N_{acid}}$$

$$= \frac{0.80 \frac{equiv}{L} \times (0.250 \text{ L})}{\left(0.50 \frac{equiv}{L}\right)}$$

$$V_{acid} = 0.40 \text{ L}$$

Therefore, 0.40 L of 0.50 N H_2SO_4 is required to neutralize 0.250 L of 0.80 N KOH.

Objective To understand the effect of a solute on solution properties

 TEACHING TIPS

- This section ties the properties of solutions to the properties of liquids learned in the preceding chapter. Students can now think about how a solution behaves as compared with a pure liquid.

- Now is an excellent time to bring real-world examples, such as high-altitude cooking and methods of melting ice on winter roads, into the classroom.

- The goal in this section is to have students understand why the boiling point is elevated and the freezing point is lowered in solutions. Do not expect beginning students to calculate the quantitative effects of these occurrences. The point that colligative properties depend on the number of particles in solution is key to this section.

D. Boiling Point and Freezing Point

We saw in Chapter 14 that at an atmospheric pressure of 1 atm water freezes at 0 °C and boils at 100 °C. If we dissolve a solute such as NaCl in water, does the presence of the solute affect the freezing point of the water? Yes. A 1.0 M NaCl solution freezes at about −1 °C and boils at about 104 °C. The presence of solute "particles" in the water extends the liquid range of water—that is, water containing a solute exists as a liquid over a wider temperature range than does pure water.

Why does this happen? For example, what effect do the particles have that causes the boiling point of water to increase? To answer this question we need to reconsider the boiling process. Recall that for water to boil, bubbles must be able to form in the interior of the liquid. That is, energetic water molecules in the bubble must be able to exert an internal pressure large enough to push back the atmospheric pressure.

Now consider the situation in a solution that contains a solute.

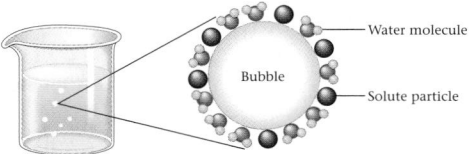

The forming bubble is now surrounded by solute particles as well as water molecules. As a result, solute particles may block the pathway of some of the water molecules trying to enter the bubble. Because fewer H_2O molecules can enter the bubble, the molecules that do get inside it must have relatively high energies to produce the internal pressure necessary to maintain the bubble.

Compare the situation with and without a solute shown below.

Pure water Solution (contains solute)

To produce the same pressure, the smaller number of molecules found in the bubble in the solution must have higher energies (speeds) than those in the bubble in pure water.

Thus, to cause the water in the solution to boil, we must heat the water to a temperature higher than 100 °C to produce the higher-energy water molecules needed. In other words, the boiling point of the solution occurs at a higher temperature than does the boiling point of pure water. The presence of the solute increases the boiling point of water. The more solute present, the higher the boiling point, because the smaller number of H_2O molecules able to enter the bubble must have increasing energies.

Teaching Support	
DEMONSTRATION	

Making Ice Cream Freeze

Materials Each group will need: 1-quart resealable plastic bag, 1-gallon resealable plastic bag, 1–2 L crushed ice, $\frac{1}{2}$ cup rock salt, 1 cup milk mixture (any combination of whole or low-fat milk, half and half, or cream), $\frac{1}{4}$ cup sugar,

1 teaspoon vanilla extract, small paper cups, and plastic spoons.

Preparation Make the ice cream mixture the night before in quantities large enough for the entire class. Alternatively, you can bring all ingredients to school along with the appropriate measuring spoons.

Presentation Place about 1 cup of the mixture into the small plastic bag. (If you haven't already mixed in the sugar and vanilla, do so at this time.) Seal the plastic bag securely and make sure all of the

Note that the raising of the boiling point depends on the number and not the specific identity of the solute particles. It's the number that matters—the more particles present, the more those particles block water molecules from entering the bubble. A solution property that depends on the *number* of solute particles present is called a **colligative property**. Raising of the boiling point by a solute is one of the colligative properties of solutions.

Another colligative property of solutions is the lowering of the freezing point. (As mentioned before, a 1 M NaCl solution freezes at approximately -1 °C.) This property is particularly important in cold areas of the world where salt is applied to icy roads. When the applied salt dissolves in the thin layer of water on the surface of ice, forming a very concentrated solution, it causes the ice to melt (it lowers the freezing point of water). The same property is also used to protect automobile engines. The coolant used

in engines is a solution containing ethylene glycol $\begin{pmatrix} & H & H \\ & | & | \\ H-&C-&C-H \\ & | & | \\ & OH & OH \end{pmatrix}$ dissolved

in water. The solute (ethylene glycol) raises the boiling point and lowers the freezing point of the water, thereby protecting the engine from overheating and freezing.

> **Colligative property**
> A property that is dependent only on the number of solute particles present in solution

 Active Reading Question

When salt is added to water, what is true about the freezing point of the solution compared to the freezing point of pure water? What is true about the boiling point of the solution compared to the boiling point of water?

SECTION 15.3
REVIEW QUESTIONS

❶ The key to solving stoichiometry problems is the mole. How do we find the number of moles when solutions are mixed to produce a reaction?

❷ How many milliliters of 0.10 M Pb(NO₃)₂ solution are required to precipitate all the lead, as PbI₂, from 125.0 mL of 0.10 M NaI solution?

❸ Determine the mass of Ag₂CrO₄ produced when 100.0 mL of 0.500 M silver nitrate is added to 100.0 mL of 0.500 M potassium chromate.

❹ Once you have determined moles of H⁺ or OH⁻ in a neutralization reaction how can you find the volume of the substance? What is the critical information you need to determine volume?

❺ What volume of 0.25 M NaOH is required to neutralize 125.0 mL of 0.15 M HCl?

❻ How is normality different from molarity?

❼ Is a 1 M H₂SO₄ solution the same as a 1 N H₂SO₄ solution? Explain.

❽ Other than for taste, why is salt added to water when cooking pasta?

 RESEARCH LINKS
CLASSZONE.COM

15.3 • Properties of Solutions • **553**

1. When solutions are mixed, the number of moles must be determined before proceeding with the problem. A net ionic equation also must be written for the reaction to determine the concentrations of the ions present.

2. 62.5 mL

3. 8.30 g Ag₂CrO₄

4. The volume can be determined by dividing the number of moles by the molarity of the solution. The critical information needed to find the volume is the molarity of the solution.

5. 75 mL NaOH

6. Molarity is based on the number of moles of solute per liter of solution; normality is based on the number of equivalents of solute per liter of solution.

7. These solutions are not the same. A 1 M solution contains 2 mol hydrogen ions per liter of solution, whereas a 1 N solution contains 1 equivalent of hydrogen ions per liter of solution. Since an equivalent of hydrogen ions is the same as 1 mol of hydrogen ions, the 1 M solution contains twice as many hydrogen ions as the 1 N solution.

8. The salt added to water when cooking pasta raises the boiling point of the water, which increases the speed of cooking by a small amount. The main reason for adding salt is flavoring.

(continued)

substances are well mixed (the sugar should be dissolved completely). Place the small plastic bag and its contents into the larger plastic bag. Add crushed ice and rock salt. Seal the larger bag. Shake or roll it until the ice cream hardens. Remove the small bag from the larger one. Carefully wipe off the outside of the small bag. Scoop out the ice cream into paper cups and enjoy the results of freezing-point depression!

Teaching Notes Make sure you complete this experiment away from all chemicals. Students should do this experiment in the classroom instead of the lab. Do not use any chemistry glassware for this demonstration.

Chapter 15 Review

Key Terms

Key Ideas

15.1 Forming Solutions

- A solution is a homogeneous mixture of a solute dissolved in a solvent.
- Substances with similar polarities tend to dissolve with each other to form a solution.
- Water is a very polar substance and tends to dissolve ionic solids or other polar substances.
- Various terms are used to describe solutions:
  - Saturated—contains the maximum possible dissolved solid
  - Unsaturated—not saturated
  - Supersaturated—contains more dissolved solid than should dissolve at a given temperature
  - Concentrated—contains a relatively large amount of solute
  - Dilute—contains a relatively small amount of solute
- The rate of dissolution is affected by
  - Surface area of solute
  - Stirring
  - Temperature

15.2 Describing Solution Composition

- Descriptions of solution composition:
  - Mass percent of solute $= \dfrac{\text{mass of solute}}{\text{mass of solution}} \times 100\%$

  - Molarity $= \dfrac{\text{moles of solute}}{\text{liters of solution}}$

  - Normality $= \dfrac{\text{equivalents of solute}}{\text{liters of solution}}$

- Dilution of a solution occurs when additional solvent is added to lower the concentration of a solution.
  - No solute is added so

    mol solute (before dilution) = mol solute (after dilution)

- A standard solution can be diluted to produce solutions with appropriate concentrations for various laboratory procedures.

15.3 Properties of Solutions

- Moles of a dissolved reactant or product can be calculated from the known concentration and volume of the substance

  Mol = (concentration)(volume)

- The properties of a solvent are affected by dissolving a solute.
- The boiling point of a solvent increases as the amount of dissolved solute increases.
- The melting point of a solvent decreases as the amount of dissolved solute increases.

RESEARCH LINKS
CLASSZONE.COM

All exercises with blue numbers have answers in the back of this book.

15.1 Forming Solutions

A. Solubility

1. Explain why a solution is a *homogeneous* mixture. Give two examples of homogeneous mixtures.

2. In a solution, the substance present in the largest amount is called the _____, whereas the other substances present are called the _____.

3. Discuss how an *ionic* solute dissolves in water. How are the strong interionic forces in the solid overcome to permit the solid to dissolve? How are the dissolved positive and negative ions shielded from one another, preventing them from recombining to form the solid?

4. Why are some molecular solids (such as sugar or ethyl alcohol) soluble in water, while other molecular solids (such as petroleum) are insoluble in water? What structural features(s) of *some* molecular solids may tend to make them soluble in water?

B. Solution Composition: An Introduction

5. A solution that contains as much solute as will dissolve at a given temperature is said to be _____.

6. A solution that has not reached its limit of dissolved solute is said to be _____.

7. A solution is a homogeneous mixture and, unlike a compound, has _____ composition.

8. The label "concentrated H_2SO_4" on a bottle means that there is a relatively _____ amount of H_2SO_4 present in the solution.

C. Factors Affecting the Rate of Dissolving

9. What does it mean to increase the surface area of a solid? Explain why this change causes an increase in the rate of dissolving.

10. Use a molecular explanation to explain why increasing the temperature speeds up the rate of dissolving a solid in a liquid.

11. Explain why the solubility of a gas generally decreases with an increase in temperature.

15.2 Describing Solution Composition

A. Solution Composition: Mass Percent

12. Calculate the mass percent of calcium chloride in each of the following solutions.

    a. 5.00 g of calcium chloride in 95.0 g of water

    b. 1.00 g of calcium chloride in 19.0 g of water

    c. 15.0 g of calcium chloride in 285 g of water

    d. 2.00 mg of calcium chloride in 0.0380 g of water

13. Calculate the mass, in grams, of NaCl present in each of the following solutions.

    a. 11.5 g of 6.25% NaCl solution

    b. 6.25 g of 11.5% NaCl solution

    c. 54.3 g of 0.91% NaCl solution

    d. 452 g of 12.3% NaCl solution

14. A laboratory assistant prepared a potassium chloride solution for her class by dissolving 5.34 g of KCl in 152 g of water. What is the mass percent of the solution she prepared?

15. If 67.1 g of $CaCl_2$ is added to 275 g of water, calculate the mass percent of $CaCl_2$ in the solution.

16. What mass of each solute is present in 285 g of a solution that contains 5.00% by mass NaCl and 7.50% by mass Na_2CO_3?

17. A hexane solution contains as impurities 5.2% (by mass) heptane and 2.9% (by mass) pentane. Calculate the mass of each component present in 93 g of the solution.

B. Solution Composition: Molarity

18. A solution that is labeled "0.105 *M* NaOH" would contain _____ mol of NaOH per liter of solution.

19. How many moles of each ion are present, per liter, in a solution that is labeled "0.221 *M* $CaCl_2$"?

20. If you were to prepare exactly 1.00 L of a 5 *M* NaCl solution, you would *not* need exactly 1.00 L of water. Explain.

6. unsaturated

7. variable

8. large

9. Increasing the surface area of a solid increases the amount of solid that comes into contact with the solvent.

10. An increase in temperature means an increase in the average kinetic energy. Thus, in a warmer solution, the particles of the liquid solvent are moving more rapidly. As a result, there is an increased rate of solute–solvent interactions, which increases the rate of dissolving.

11. An increase in temperature means an increase in the average kinetic energy. In a warmer solution, the solvent and solute particles are moving more rapidly. If the solute particles are gaseous, faster-moving particles are more likely to have enough energy to escape from the liquid.

12. (a) 5.00% $CaCl_2$
    (b) 5.00% $CaCl_2$
    (c) 5.00% $CaCl_2$
    (d) 5.00% $CaCl_2$

13. (a) 0.719 g NaCl
    (b) 0.719 g NaCl
    (c) 0.49 g NaCl
    (d) 55.6 g NaCl

14. 3.39% KCl

15. 19.6% $CaCl_2$

16. 14.3 g NaCl

17. 4.8 g heptane; 2.7 g pentane; 86 g hexane

18. 0.105

19. 0.221 mol Ca^{2+}; 0.442 mol Cl^-

20. A 5.00 M solution means there are 5.00 moles of solute per 1.00 L of solution (not water). To make such a solution, we would add enough water to 5.00 moles of solute so that the total volume of the solution is 1.00 L.

Chapter 15 Assessment

1. A homogeneous mixture is a combination of two (or more) pure substances that is uniform in composition and appearance throughout. Examples of homogeneous mixtures include rubbing alcohol (70% isopropyl alcohol and 30% water) and gasoline (a mixture of hydrocarbons).

2. solvent; solute

3. When an ionic solute dissolves in water, a given ion is pulled into solution by the attractive ion–dipole forces exerted by several water molecules. Although the ionic forces in the crystal are stronger than the ion–dipole forces, entropy is also a driving force for an ionic solid to dissolve, because the solution is more disordered than the pure water and solid ionic crystal. After entering the solution, the dissolved ion is surrounded completely by water molecules, which tends to prevent the ion from reentering the crystal.

4. The intermolecular forces must be similar in the two substances for them to mix. Polar and ionic solids may dissolve in water.

5. saturated

21. (a) 2.0 M
  (b) 1.0 M
  (c) 0.67 M
  (d) 0.50 M

22. (a) 0.253 M
  (b) 0.106 M
  (c) 0.434 M
  (d) 1.7×10^{-3} M

23. 1.99 M

24. 0.0902 M

25. 0.623 M Fe^{3+}; 1.87 M Cl^-

26. 0.619 M

27. (a) 0.0133 mol; 0.838 g
  (b) 2.34 mol; 39.9 g
  (c) 0.00505 mol; 0.490 g
  (d) 0.0299 mol; 1.09 g

28. 6.04 g NH_4Cl

29. (a) 4.60×10^{-3} mol Al^{3+};
  1.38×10^{-2} mol Cl^-
  (b) 1.70 mol Na^+;
  0.568 mol PO_4^{3-}
  (c) 2.19×10^{-3} mol Cu;
  4.38×10^{-3} mol Cl^-
  (d) 3.96×10^{-5} mol Ca^{2+};
  7.91×10^{-5} mol OH^-

30. 4.25 g

31. (a) 0.0837 M
  (b) 0.320 M
  (c) 0.0964 M
  (d) 0.622 M

32. 56 mL HCl; 42 mL HNO_3;
  38 mL H_2SO_4; 39 mL $HC_2H_3O_2$;
  45 mL H_3PO_4

33. Transfer 6.21 mL of the
  3.02 M solution to a 125-mL
  volumetric flask and add water
  to the calibration mark.

34. 167 mL

21. For each of the following solutions, the number of moles of solute is given, followed by the total volume of solution prepared. Calculate the molarity.

  a. 0.50 mol KBr; 250 mL

  b. 0.50 mol KBr; 500. mL

  c. 0.50 mol KBr; 750 mL

  d. 0.50 mol KBr; 1.0 L

22. For each of the following solutions, the mass of the solute is given, followed by the total volume of the solution prepared. Calculate the molarity.

  a. 4.25 g $CuCl_2$; 125 mL

  b. 0.101 g $NaHCO_3$; 11.3 mL

  c. 52.9 g Na_2CO_3; 1.15 L

  d. 0.14 mg KOH; 1.5 mL

23. If a 45.3-g sample of potassium nitrate is dissolved in enough water to make 225 mL of solution, what will be the molarity?

24. An alcoholic iodine solution ("tincture" of iodine) is prepared by dissolving 5.15 g of iodine crystals in enough alcohol to make a volume of 225 mL. Calculate the molarity of iodine in the solution.

25. Suppose 1.01 g of $FeCl_3$ is placed in a 10.0-mL volumetric flask, water is added, the mixture is shaken to dissolve the solid, and then water is added to the calibration mark of the flask. Calculate the molarity of each ion present in the solution.

26. If 495 g of NaOH is dissolved to a final total volume of 20.0 L, what is the molarity of the solution?

27. Calculate the number of *moles* and the number of *grams* of the indicated solutes present in each of the following solution samples.

	mol	g
a. 127 mL of 0.105 M HNO_3		
b. 155 mL of 15.1 M NH_3		
c. 2.51 L of 2.01×10^{-3} M KSCN		
d. 12.2 mL of 2.45 M HCl		

28. What mass (in grams) of NH_4Cl is needed to prepare 450. mL of 0.251 M NH_4Cl solution?

29. Calculate the number of moles of *each* ion present in each of the following solutions.

  a. 10.2 mL of 0.451 M $AlCl_3$ solution

  b. 5.51 L of 0.103 M Na_3PO_4 solution

  c. 1.75 mL of 1.25 M $CuCl_2$ solution

  d. 25.2 mL of 0.00157 M $Ca(OH)_2$ solution

30. Standard silver nitrate solutions are used in the analysis of samples containing chloride ion. How many grams of silver nitrate are needed to prepare 250. mL of a 0.100 M $AgNO_3$ solution?

C. Dilution

31. Calculate the new molarity that results when 250. mL of water is added to each of the following solutions.

  a. 125 mL of 0.251 M HCl

  b. 445 mL of 0.499 M H_2SO_4

  c. 5.25 L of 0.101 M HNO_3

  d. 11.2 mL of 14.5 M $HC_2H_3O_2$

32. Many laboratories keep bottles of 3.0 M solutions of the common acids on hand. Given the following molarities of the concentrated acids, determine how many milliliters of each concentrated acid would be required to prepare 225 mL of a 3.0 M solution of the acid.

Acid	Molarity of Concentrated Reagent
HCl	12.1 M
HNO_3	15.9 M
H_2SO_4	18.0 M
$HC_2H_3O_2$	17.5 M
H_3PO_4	14.9 M

33. A chemistry student needs 125 mL of 0.150 M NaOH solution for an experiment, but the only solution available in the laboratory is 3.02 M. Describe how the student could prepare the solution he needs.

34. How much *water* must be added to 500. mL of 0.200 M HCl to produce a 0.150 M solution? (Assume that the volumes are additive.)

15.3 Properties of Solutions

A. Stoichiometry of Solution Reactions

35. One way to determine the amount of chloride ion in a water sample is to react the sample with standard $AgNO_3$ solution to produce solid $AgCl$.

$$Ag^+(aq) + Cl^-(aq) \rightarrow AgCl(s)$$

If a 25.0-mL water sample requires 27.2 mL of 0.104 M $AgNO_3$ in such a reaction, what is the concentration of Cl^- in the sample?

36. What volume (in mL) of 0.25 M Na_2SO_4 solution is needed to precipitate all the barium, as $BaSO_4(s)$, from 12.5 mL of 0.15 M $Ba(NO_3)_2$ solution?

$$Ba(NO_3)_2(aq) + Na_2SO_4(aq) \rightarrow$$
$$BaSO_4(s) + 2NaNO_3(aq)$$

37. If 36.2 mL of 0.158 M $CaCl_2$ solution is added to 37.5 mL of 0.149 M Na_2CO_3, what mass of calcium carbonate, $CaCO_3$, will be precipitated? The reaction is

$$CaCl_2(aq) + Na_2CO_3(aq) \rightarrow$$
$$CaCO_3(s) + 2NaCl(aq)$$

38. When aqueous solutions of lead(II) ion are treated with potassium chromate solution, a bright yellow precipitate of lead(II) chromate, $PbCrO_4$, forms. How many grams of lead chromate form when a 1.00-g sample of $Pb(NO_3)_2$ is added to 25.0 mL of 1.00 M K_2CrO_4 solution?

B. Neutralization Reactions

39. What volume of 0.200 M HCl solution is needed to neutralize 25.0 mL of 0.150 M $NaOH$ solution?

40. The concentration of a sodium hydroxide solution is to be determined. A 50.0-mL sample of 0.104 M HCl solution requires 48.7 mL of the sodium hydroxide solution to reach the point of neutralization. Calculate the molarity of the $NaOH$ solution.

41. What volume of 1.00 M $NaOH$ is required to neutralize each of the following solutions?

    a. 25.0 mL of 0.154 M acetic acid, $HC_2H_3O_2$

    b. 35.0 mL of 0.102 M hydrofluoric acid, HF

    c. 10.0 mL of 0.143 M phosphoric acid, H_3PO_4

    d. 35.0 mL of 0.220 M sulfuric acid, H_2SO_4

C. Normality

42. Explain why the equivalent weight of H_2SO_4 is half the molar mass of this substance. How many hydrogen ions does each H_2SO_4 molecule produce when reacting with an excess of OH^- ions?

43. How many equivalents of hydroxide ion are needed to react with 1.53 equivalents of hydrogen ion? How can you tell when no balanced chemical equation is given for the reaction?

44. For each of the following solutions, the mass of solute taken is indicated, along with the total volume of solution prepared. Calculate the normality of each solution.

    a. 0.113 g $NaOH$;   10.2 mL

    b. 12.5 mg $Ca(OH)_2$;   100. mL

    c. 12.4 g H_2SO_4;   155 mL

45. Calculate the normality of each of the following solutions.

    a. 0.134 M $NaOH$

    b. 0.00521 M $Ca(OH)_2$

    c. 4.42 M H_3PO_4

46. A solution of phosphoric acid, H_3PO_4, is found to contain 35.2 g of H_3PO_4 per liter of solution. Calculate the molarity and normality of the solution.

47. What volume of 0.172 N H_2SO_4 is required to neutralize 56.2 mL of 0.145 M $NaOH$?

48. What volume of 0.151 N $NaOH$ is required to neutralize 24.2 mL of 0.125 N H_2SO_4? What volume of 0.151 N $NaOH$ is required to neutralize 24.1 mL of 0.125 M H_2SO_4?

D. Boiling Point and Freezing Point

49. What is meant by the term "colligative property"?

50. Explain on a molecular level why the increase in boiling point is a colligative property.

51. Antifreeze that you use in your car could also be called "antiboil." Explain why.

35. 0.113 M

36. 7.5 mL

37. 0.560 g $CaCO_3$

38. 0.976 g $PbCrO_4$

39. 18.8 mL

40. 0.107 M $NaOH$

41. (a) 3.85 mL $NaOH$
    (b) 3.57 mL $NaOH$
    (c) 4.29 mL $NaOH$
    (d) 15.4 mL $NaOH$

42. Each mole of H_2SO_4 provides two moles of H^+ ions. Thus it is necessary to take only half a mole of H_2SO_4 to provide 1 mole of H^+ ions. The equivalent weight is therefore half the molar mass.

43. 1.53 equivalents OH^- ion. By definition, one equivalent of OH^- ion exactly neutralizes one equivalent of H^+ ion.

44. (a) 0.277 N
    (b) 3.37×10^{-3} N
    (c) 1.63 N

45. (a) 0.134 N
    (b) 0.0104 N
    (c) 13.3 N

46. 0.359 M; 1.08 N

47. 47.4 mL

48. 20.0 mL; 39.9 mL

49. Colligative properties are properties of a solution that depend only on the number— not the identity—of the solute particles.

50. For a solution to boil, bubbles must form in the solution. Solute particles block water from entering these bubbles. It is not the nature of these particles that matters, but the number of the particles. Thus the increase in boiling point is a colligative property.

51. Antifreeze solution is a concentrated aqueous solution that has a lower freezing point than water. It also has a higher boiling point than water (a solute in water both lowers the freezing point and raises the boiling point).

52. 0.167 M Co^{3+};
    0.117 M Ni^{2+};
    0.567 M Cl$^-$

53. 0.072 g AgCl; 1.2 M Ag$^+$

54. 1.93 g

55. 56 mol water

56. 2.56 M

57. (a) 0.0909 M
    (b) 0.127 M
    (c) 0.192 M
    (d) 1.6 M

58. (a) 0.50 N HC$_2$H$_3$O$_2$
    (b) 5.00 × 10^{-3} N H$_2$SO$_4$
    (c) 0.10 N KOH

59. 9.6 × 10^{-2} N

60. [A] > [D] > [C] > [B]

Critical Thinking

52. Suppose 50.0 mL of 0.250 M CoCl$_2$ solution is added to 25.0 mL of 0.350 M NiCl$_2$ solution. Calculate the concentration, in moles per liter, of each of the ions present after mixing. Assume that the volumes are additive.

53. Calculate the mass of AgCl formed, and the concentration of silver ion remaining in solution, when 10.0 g of solid AgNO$_3$ is added to 50. mL of 1.0 × 10^{-2} M NaCl solution. Assume there is no volume change upon addition of the solid.

54. What mass of BaSO$_4$ will be precipitated from a large container of concentrated Ba(NO$_3$)$_2$ solution if 37.5 mL of 0.221 M H$_2$SO$_4$ is added?

55. Strictly speaking, the solvent is the component of a solution that is present in the largest amount on a *mole* basis. For solutions involving water, water is almost always the solvent because there tend to be many more water molecules present than molecules of any conceivable solute. To see why this is so, calculate the number of moles of water present in 1.0 L of water. Recall that the density of water is very nearly 1.0 g/mL under most conditions.

56. A 14.2-g sample of CaCl$_2$ is added to a 50.0-mL volumetric flask. After dissolving the salt, water is added to the calibration mark of the flask. Calculate the molarity of the solution.

57. Calculate the new molarity when 150. mL of water is added to each of the following solutions.
    a. 125 mL of 0.200 M HBr
    b. 155 mL of 0.250 M Ca(C$_2$H$_3$O$_2$)$_2$
    c. 0.500 L of 0.250 M H$_3$PO$_4$
    d. 15 mL of 18.0 M H$_2$SO$_4$

58. Calculate the normality of each of the following solutions.
    a. 0.50 M acetic acid, HC$_2$H$_3$O$_2$
    b. 0.00250 M sulfuric acid, H$_2$SO$_4$
    c. 0.10 M potassium hydroxide, KOH

59. If 27.5 mL of 3.5 × 10^{-2} N Ca(OH)$_2$ solution is needed to neutralize 10.0 mL of nitric acid solution of unknown concentration, what is the normality of the nitric acid?

60. The figures below are molecular-level representations of four aqueous solutions of the same solute. Arrange the solutions from most to least concentrated.

Solution A
Volume = 1.0 L

Solution B
Volume = 4.0 L

Solution C
Volume = 2.0 L

Solution D
Volume = 2.0 L

1 Which of the following aqueous solutions has the greatest number of ions in solution?

A   2.0-L of 1.50 M sodium phosphate

B   3.0-L of 1.50 M sodium chloride

C   2.0-L of 2.00 M potassium fluoride

D   1.0-L of 3.00 M sodium sulfate

2 When a solvent contains as much of the solute as it can hold, the solution is said to be

A   unsaturated

B   supersaturated

C   saturated

D   dilute

3 Which of the following actions does not generally increase the rate of a solute dissolving in a solvent?

A   Increasing the surface area of the solute

B   Stirring the solution

C   Raising the temperature of the solution

D   Adding more solute

4 Determine the concentration of a solution made by dissolving 10.0 g of sodium chloride in 750.0 mL of solution.

A   0.133 M

B   0.171 M

C   0.228 M

D   0.476 M

5 You have two solutions of sodium chloride. One is a 2.00 M solution and the other is a 4.00 M solution. You have much more of the 4.00 M solution and you add the solutions together. Which of the following could be the concentration of the final solution?

A   3.00 M

B   3.80 M

C   6.00 M

D   8.00 M

6 What is the minimum volume of a 2.00 M NaOH (aq) solution needed to make 150.0 mL of a 0.800 M NaOH (aq) solution?

A   60.0 mL

B   90.0 mL

C   120. mL

D   150. mL

7 You have equal masses of different solutes dissolved in equal volumes of solution. Which of the solutes would make the solution with the highest concentration measured in molarity?

A   NaOH

B   KCl

C   KOH

D   LiOH

8 You react 250.0 mL of 0.10 M barium nitrate with 200.0 mL of 0.10 M potassium phosphate. What ions are left in solution after the reaction is complete?

A   potassium ion, nitrate ion, barium ion

B   potassium ion, nitrate ion, phosphate ion

C   potassium ion, nitrate ion

D   barium ion, nitrate ion, phosphate ion

9 What volume of 0.500 M NaOH is needed to neutralize 45.0 mL of 0.400 M HCl?

A   36.0 mL

B   45.0 mL

C   56.3 mL

D   71.3 mL

10 Which of the following has the largest equivalent weight?

A   HCl

B H_2SO_4

C H_3PO_4

D HNO_3

11 When a solute is dissolved in a solvent, the boiling point of the solution is higher than the boiling point of the pure solvent. Answer the following questions about this phenomenon.

a.   Explain why adding a solute to a solvent raises the boiling point.

b.   Explain why adding 1 mole of table salt to water raises the boiling point more than adding 1 mole of table sugar to the same amount of water.

Chapter 15 • Standardized Test Practice • **559**

1. A

2. C

3. D

4. C

5. B

6. A

7. D

8. B

9. A

10. D

11. a. In order to boil, bubbles must be able to form in the interior of the liquid. A solute added to water will block the pathway of water molecules entering the bubble, so fewer water molecules can enter the bubble. To exert the same pressure, the fewer molecules must have higher energy, so the temperature must be higher.

b. Boiling point is a colligative property, which means that it depends on the number of solute particles in solution. Since table salt (NaCl) forms ions (Na^+ and Cl^-) in solution, there are more particles in the solution for table salt than table sugar.

Test-Taking Strategy

When answering a multi-step question, encourage students to organize their thought process by writing down where they want to go, what they know, and how they can get there. An organized approach will help prevent overlooking an intermediate step.

Planning Guide

Section	Segment		Text Features and Components	Labs, Demonstrations, & Activities
16.1 Properties of Acids and Bases **1 Block** pp. 562–572	A	Acids and Bases	**SE** Chemistry in Your World: Gum That Foams *p. 564*	
	B	Acid Strength		**TE** Mini-Demo *p. 566* **LM** Experiment 66: Acids and Bases, Microscale Lab Manual Report Sheets Teacher's Lab Guide
	C	Water as an Acid and a Base		**TE** Mini-Demo *p. 569*
16.2 Determining the Acidity of a Solution **2 Blocks** pp. 573–581	A	The pH Scale	**SE** Hands-On Chemistry: Cabbage Juice Indicator *p. 578*	**TE** Group Activity *p. 575* **TE** Mini-Demo *p. 576* **TE** Teaching Support: Demonstration *pp. 576–577* **LM** Experiment 67: Acid Rain Lab Manual Report Sheets Teacher's Lab Guide
	B	Measuring pH		**LM** Experiment 68: Indicators, Traditional Lab Manual Report Sheets Teacher's Lab Guide
	continued on next page			

Key
SE Student Edition   **TE** Teacher Edition   **RP** Teacher Resource Package
AR Additional Materials   **LM** Lab Materials   **⬛** Transparencies
◉ DVD   **▭** CD-ROM   **ⓘ** classzone.com

All Learners	Technology	Review & Assessment	Standards
TE Teaching Tips *pp. 562–563*	**Animation:** Proton Transfer **Animation:** Brønsted–Lowry Reaction **EasyPlanner**	**SE** Active Reading Question *p. 563* **TE** More Examples *p. 564* **SE** Practice Problem *p. 565* **TE** More Examples *p. 565* **SE** Key Terms *p. 587* **SE** Questions and Problems *p. 589*	**TE** **NSES** UCP1, UCP2, UCP5, A1, A2, B2, B3, C4, C6, E1
TE Teaching Tips *pp. 566–567* **TE** Meeting Individual Needs *p. 565* **TE** Meeting Individual Needs *p. 568*	**Transparency:** Figure 16.1 **Lab Generator CD** **EasyPlanner**	**SE** Critical Thinking *p. 566* **SE** Active Reading Question *p. 566* **SE** Active Reading Question *p. 567* **SE** Key Terms *p. 587* **SE** Questions and Problems *p. 589*	
TE Teaching Tips *pp. 569–570* **TE** Meeting Individual Needs *p. 570* **RP** MINT: Math Concepts *TE p. 570* **RP** Team Learning Worksheet (Sec. 16.1)	**Animation:** Self-Ionization of Water **EasyPlanner**	**SE** Critical Thinking *p. 569* **TE** More Examples *p. 570* **SE** Practice Problem *p. 571* **TE** More Examples *p. 572* **SE** Review Questions (16.1.A–16.1.C) *p. 572* **SE** Key Terms *p. 587* **SE** Questions and Problems *pp. 589–590*	
TE Teaching Tips *pp. 573–574, 577*	**Transparency:** Figure 16.3 **Video:** The pH Scale **Lab Generator CD** **EasyPlanner**	**SE** Critical Thinking *p. 573* **SE** Practice Problem *p. 574* **TE** More Examples *p. 574* **SE** Active Reading Question *p. 574* **SE** Active Reading Question *p. 574* **TE** More Examples *p. 575* **SE** Practice Problem *p. 576* **TE** More Examples *p. 576* **SE** Practice Problem *p. 577* **TE** More Examples *p. 577* **SE** Practice Problem *p. 578* **TE** More Examples *p. 578* **SE** Key Terms *p. 588* **SE** Questions and Problems *pp. 590–591*	**TE** **NSES** UCP1, UCP2, UCP3, A1, A2, B2, E1, E2, F6, G1, G2, G3
TE Teaching Tips *p. 579*	**Lab Generator CD** **EasyPlanner**	**SE** Key Terms *p. 588* **SE** Questions and Problems *p. 591*	

Planning Guide

Section	Segment		Text Features and Components	Labs, Demonstrations, & Activities
16.2 (continued)	C	**Calculating the pH of Strong Acid Solutions**	(SE) Chemistry Explorers: Arnold Beckman *p. 581*	
16.3 Titrations and Buffers **3 Blocks** pp. 582–586	A	**Acid–Base Titrations**		(LM) Experiment 69: Analysis of Vinegar, Microscale (LM) Experiment 70: Quantitative Titration, Traditional (LM) Experiment 71: Conductivity Titration, CBL Lab Manual Report Sheets Teacher's Lab Guide
	B	**Buffered Solutions**		(TE) Mini-Demo *p. 585* (LM) Experiment 72: Acids, Bases, and Buffers, CBL Lab Manual Report Sheets Teacher's Lab Guide

Key	(SE) Student Edition	(TE) Teacher Edition	(RP) Teacher Resource Package
	(AR) Additional Materials	(LM) Lab Materials	Transparencies
	DVD	CD-ROM	classzone.com

All Learners	Technology	Review & Assessment	Standards
TE Teaching Tip *p. 580* **TE** Meeting Individual Needs *p. 580* **RP** Team Learning Worksheet (Sec. 16.2)	**EasyPlanner**	**SE** Practice Problem *p. 580* **TE** More Examples *p. 580* **SE** Review Questions (16.2.A–16.2.C) *p. 581* **SE** Questions and Problems *p. 591*	
TE Teaching Tips *pp. 582, 584*	Transparency: Figure 16.8 Video: Acid–Base Titration Lab Generator CD EasyPlanner	**SE** Active Reading Question *p. 582* **TE** More Examples *p. 583* **SE** Practice Problem *p. 584* **SE** Key Terms *p. 588* **SE** Questions and Problems *p. 591*	**TE** **NSES** UCP2, UCP3, UCP5, A1, A2, B2, B3, F1, F4, F5, F6
TE Teaching Tips *pp. 585–586* **RP** Team Learning Worksheet (Sec. 16.3)	Animation: Buffers Lab Generator CD EasyPlanner	**SE** Active Reading Question *p. 586* **SE** Review Questions (16.3.A–16.3.B) *p. 586* **SE** Key Terms *p. 588* **SE** Questions and Problems *p. 591*	

Resource Materials for Chapter 16

SE Chapter Review *pp. 587–588*

SE Critical Thinking *p. 592*

SE Standardized Test Practice *p. 593*

AR English/Spanish Summaries

English Summaries Audio

Spanish Summaries Audio

RP Meeting Individual Needs Toolkit (MINT)
    Math Concepts
    Chapter Review Worksheets
    Chapter Summaries

RP Solutions Guide

RP Standardized Test Practice

RP Chapter Tests

RP Test Bank

Test Generator

Chapter 16

Overview

In this chapter our goals are for students to:

- Understand the Arrhenius and Brønsted–Lowry models for acids and bases

- Understand acid strength

- Understand the relationship between acid strength and strength of the conjugate base

- Learn about the ionization of water

- Understand and use the terms pH and pOH

- Learn methods for measuring the pH of a solution

- Learn to calculate the pH of solutions of strong acids

- Learn about acid–base titrations

- Understand the general characteristics of buffered solutions

Chapter 16

Acids and Bases

LOOKING AHEAD

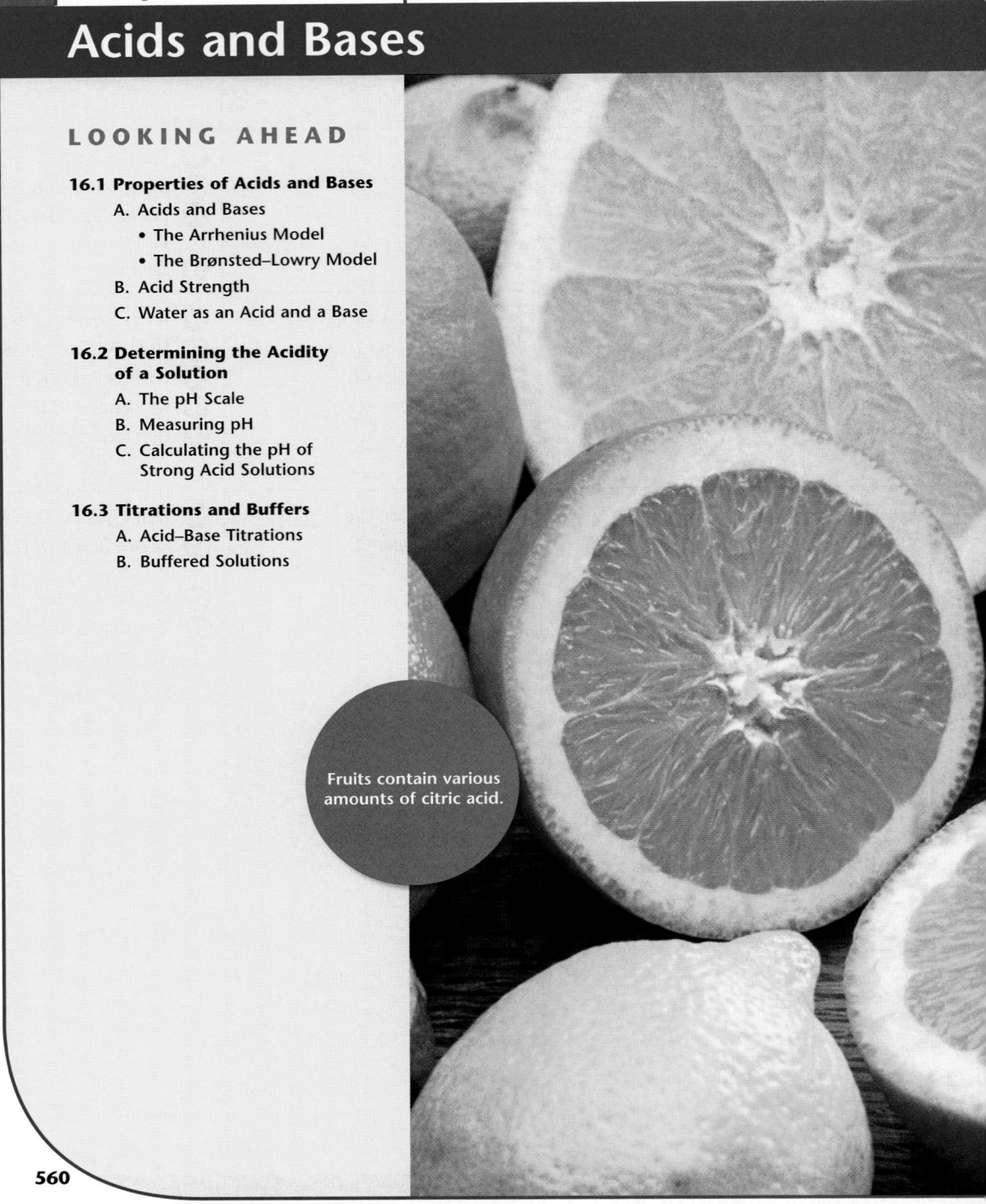

Fruits contain various amounts of citric acid.

560

16

IN YOUR LIFE

Acids are very important substances. They cause lemons to be sour, digest food in the stomach (and sometimes cause heartburn), dissolve rock to make fertilizer, dissolve your tooth enamel to form cavities. Acids are essential industrial chemicals. In fact, the chemical in first place in terms of the amount manufactured in the United States is sulfuric acid, H_2SO_4. Eighty *billion* pounds of this material are used every year in the manufacture of fertilizers, detergents, plastics, pharmaceuticals, storage batteries, and metals. The acid–base properties of substances also can be used to make interesting novelties such as the foaming chewing gum described in Chemistry in Your World.

Red cabbage juice can be used as an indicator of acidity.

WHAT DO YOU KNOW?

Prereading Questions

1. What is meant by the term *acid*? Name two products you think are acidic.

2. What is the meant by the term *base*?

3. What do you know about the pH scale?

4. What is the net ionic equation for the reaction between a strong acid and a strong base?

Acids and Bases • Chapter 16 • **561**

Prereading Questions

1. An acid is a species that donates H^+ in solution, or is an electron acceptor. Acidic products include fruit juices, soft drinks, vinegar, and milk.

2. A base is a species that donates (OH^-) in solution, or is an electron donor.

3. *Answers will vary.* The pH scale gives us a measure of the acidity of a solution. At 25 °C, a pH of 7.00 means the solution is neutral, below 7.00 means the solution is acidic, and above 7.00 means the solution is basic. pH is defined as $-\log[H^+]$, so the pH scale is logarithmic.

4. $H^+(aq) + OH^-(aq) \rightarrow H_2O(l)$

TECHNOLOGY IN THE CLASSROOM

 Transparencies
Figures: 16.1, 16.3, 16.8

 Power Presentation DVD
PowerPoint Slides
Animations
Proton Transfer
Brønsted–Lowry
   Reaction
Self-Ionization of Water
Videos
The pH Scale
Acid–Base Titration
Buffers
eEdition
EasyPlanner

 Lab Generator CD
English Summaries CD
Spanish Summaries CD
ML Test Generator

classzone.com

Assign students to read Section 16.1 and to answer the Review Questions at the end of the section before coming to class.

 Active Learning
Team Learning Worksheet

After introducing the material in Section 16.1 in class, place students in groups and have them work together on **Section 16.1: Team Learning Worksheet.**

Homework

You may wish to assign these selected end-of-chapter problems as homework for this section: 1, 2, 4, 5, 7, 8, 9a–b, 10a–b, 11a–b, 12a–b, 14, 15, 17a–b, 18a–b, 19, 21, 22a–b, 23a–b, 24, 25

Additional end-of-chapter problems can be used for extra practice.

16.1.A Acids and Bases

Objective To learn about two models of acids and bases and the relationship of conjugate acid–base pairs

 TEACHING TIPS

- Spend time developing the model for acid–base pairs in this section. Students need to be able to look at a chemical equation and identify these pairs.

- The Brønsted–Lowry definition of acids and bases is preferable because it emphasizes that for one reactant to act like an acid, the other reactant must act like a base.

TECHNOLOGY

Animations
Proton Transfer
Brønsted–Lowry Reaction

Key Terms

- Acids
- Bases
- Arrhenius concept of acids and bases
- Brønsted–Lowry model
- Conjugate acid
- Conjugate base
- Conjugate acid–base pair
- Hydronium ion
- Completely ionized (completely dissociated)
- Strong acid
- Weak acid
- Diprotic acid
- Oxyacids
- Organic acids
- Carboxyl group
- Amphoteric substance
- Ionization of water
- Ion-product constant

Objectives

- *To learn about two models of acids and bases*
- *To understand the relationship of conjugate acid–base pairs*
- *To understand the concept of acid strength*
- *To understand the relationship between acid strength and the strength of the conjugate base*
- *To learn about the ionization of water*

A. Acids and Bases

Acids were first recognized as substances that taste sour. Vinegar tastes sour because it is a dilute solution of acetic acid; citric acid is responsible for the sour taste of a lemon. Bases, sometimes called *alkalis*, are characterized by their bitter taste and slippery feel. Most hand soaps and commercial preparations for unclogging drains are highly basic.

The Arrhenius Model

The first person to recognize the essential nature of acids and bases was Svante Arrhenius. On the basis of his experiments with electrolytes, Arrhenius postulated that **acids** *produce hydrogen ions in aqueous solution,* whereas **bases** *produce hydroxide ions.*

For example, when hydrogen chloride gas is dissolved in water each molecule produces ions as follows:

$$HCl(g) \xrightarrow{H_2O} H^+(aq) + Cl^-(aq)$$

This solution is the strong acid known as hydrochloric acid. On the other hand, when solid sodium hydroxide is dissolved in water, its ions separate producing a solution containing Na^+ and OH^- ions.

$$NaOH(s) \xrightarrow{H_2O} Na^+(aq) + OH^-(aq)$$

This solution is called a strong base.

The label on a bottle of concentrated hydrochloric acid

The Brønsted–Lowry Model

Although the **Arrhenius concept of acids and bases** was a major step forward in understanding acid–base chemistry, this concept is limited because it allows for only one kind of base—the hydroxide ion. A more general definition of acids and bases was suggested by the Danish chemist Johannes Brønsted and the English chemist Thomas Lowry.

> In the **Brønsted–Lowry model,** an acid is a proton (H^+) donor, and a base is a proton acceptor.

Acid
A substance that produces hydrogen ions (H^+) in solution; a proton donor

Base
A substance that produces hydroxide ions (OH^-) in solution; a substance that accepts a proton

Arrhenius concept of acids and bases
Acids produce hydrogen ions (H^+) in solution; bases produce hydroxide ions (OH^-) in solution.

According to the Brønsted–Lowry model, the general reaction that occurs when an acid is dissolved in water can best be represented as an acid (HA) donating a proton to a water molecule to form a new acid (the **conjugate acid**) and a new base (the **conjugate base**).

$$HA(aq) + H_2O(l) \rightarrow H_3O^+(aq) + A^-(aq)$$

Acid   Base   Conjugate   Conjugate
                        acid   base

This model emphasizes the significant role of the polar water molecule in pulling the proton from the acid. Note that the conjugate base is everything that remains of the acid molecule after a proton is lost. The conjugate acid is formed when the proton is transferred to the base. A **conjugate acid–base pair** consists of two substances related to each other by the donating and accepting of a *single proton*. In the above equation there are two conjugate acid–base pairs: HA (acid) and A$^-$ (base), and H$_2$O (base) and H$_3$O$^+$ (acid). For example, when hydrogen chloride is dissolved in water it behaves as an acid.

Acid–conjugate base pair

$$HCl(aq) + H_2O(l) \rightarrow H_3O^+(aq) + Cl^-(aq)$$

Base–conjugate acid pair

In this case HCl is the acid that loses an H$^+$ ion to form Cl$^-$, its conjugate base. On the other hand, H$_2$O (behaving as a base) gains an H$^+$ ion to form H$_3$O$^+$ (the conjugate acid).

How can water act as a base? Remember that the oxygen of the water molecule has two unshared electron pairs, either of which can form a covalent bond with an H$^+$ ion. When gaseous HCl dissolves in water, the following reaction occurs.

$$H-\overset{..}{\underset{|}{O}}: + H-Cl \rightarrow \left[H-\overset{..}{\underset{|}{O}}-H \right]^+ + Cl^-$$
     H δ^+ δ^- H

Note that an H$^+$ ion is transferred from the HCl molecule to the water molecule to form H$_3$O$^+$, which is called the **hydronium ion**.

Active Reading Question

How are the substances in a conjugate acid–base pair related to each other?

information

Recall that (*aq*) means the substance is hydrated—it has water molecules clustered around it.

Conjugate acid
The substance formed when a proton is added to a base

Conjugate base
The remaining substance when a proton is lost from an acid

Conjugate acid–base pair
Two substances related to each other by the donating and accepting of a single proton

Hydronium ion
H$_3$O$^+$

TEACHING TIPS

• It is important to show students that acidic and basic substances work together. A proton donor must have a substance to accept the proton. The idea that water can act as both an acid and a base can be developed here.

• This occasion marks the first time that students have seen the hydronium ion. Make sure that they understand how it forms from the donation of a proton to water.

Active Reading Question

The substances differ only by one proton. For example, the conjugate base of the acid HF is the F$^-$ ion.

EXAMPLE 16.1

More Examples

Which of the following represent conjugate acid–base pairs?

a. $HClO_4$, ClO_4^-

b. HCl, ClO^-

c. $H_2PO_4^-$, HPO_4^{2-}

d. HNO_3, NO_3^-

a, c, and d

EXAMPLE 16.1

Identifying Conjugate Acid–Base Pairs

Which of the following represent conjugate acid–base pairs?

    a. HF, F^-

    b. NH_4^+, NH_3

    c. HCl, H_2O

Solution

a. and **b.** HF, F^- and NH_4^+, NH_3 are conjugate acid–base pairs because the two species differ by one H^+.

$$HF \rightarrow H^+ + F^-$$

$$NH_4^+ \rightarrow H^+ + NH_3$$

c. HCl and H_2O are not a conjugate acid–base pair because they are not related by the removal or addition of one H^+. The conjugate base of HCl is Cl^-. The conjugate acid of H_2O is H_3O^+.

CHEMISTRY IN YOUR WORLD

Science, Technology, and Society

Gum That Foams

Mad Dawg chewing gum is a practical joker's dream come true. It is noticeably sour when someone first starts to chew it, but the big surprise comes about ten chews later when brightly colored foam oozes from the person's mouth. Although the effect is dramatic, the cause is simple acid–base chemistry.

The foam consists of sugar and saliva churned into a bubbling mess by carbon dioxide released from the gum. The carbon dioxide is formed when sodium bicarbonate ($NaHCO_3$) present in the gum is mixed with citric acid and malic acid (also present in the gum) in the moist environment of the mouth. As $NaHCO_3$ dissolves in the water of the saliva, it separates into its ions:

$$NaHCO_3(s) \xrightarrow{H_2O} Na^+(aq) + HCO_3^-(aq)$$

The bicarbonate ion, when exposed to H^+ ions from acids, decomposes to carbon dioxide and water.

$$H^+(aq) + HCO_3^-(aq) \rightarrow H_2O(l) + CO_2(g)$$

The acids present in the gum also cause it to be sour, stimulating extra salivation and thus extra foam.

Although the chemistry behind Mad Dawg is well understood, the development of the gum into a safe, but fun, product was not so easy. In fact, early versions of the gum exploded because the acids and the sodium bicarbonate mixed prematurely. As solids, citric and malic acids and sodium bicarbonate do not react with each other. However, the presence of water frees the ions to move and react. In the manufacture of the gum, colorings and flavorings are applied as aqueous solutions. The water caused the gum to explode in early attempts to manufacture it. The makers of Mad Dawg obviously solved the problem.

Chewing Mad Dawg gum

Chemistry in Your World

Gum That Foams

Have students investigate other candies or treats that produce unexpected reactions. Are these materials other examples of acid–base chemistry at work? Pop Rocks and other candies that fizz are excellent possibilities. Also have students investigate how jelly beans or jawbreakers are made. In both cases, a number of layers are applied to produce the finished candy.

You can have students make CO_2 rockets. Use 2-L soft drink bottles (empty) fitted with corks in place of the screw caps. Place 50.0 mL of vinegar in the bottle. Place 2 teaspoons of baking soda in a paper tissue. Roll the tissue into a tube shape and stuff it into the bottle. Cork the bottle immediately, point it away from other people, and shake the bottle. As the pressure builds, the cork will be launched from the bottle.

EXAMPLE 16.2

Writing Conjugate Bases

Write the conjugate base for each of the following:

    a. $HClO_4$

    b. H_3PO_4

    c. $CH_3NH_3^+$

Solution

To get the conjugate base for an acid, we must remove an H^+ ion.

    a. $\underset{\text{Acid}}{HClO_4} \rightarrow H^+ + \underset{\text{Conjugate base}}{ClO_4^-}$

    b. $\underset{\text{Acid}}{H_3PO_4} \rightarrow H^+ + \underset{\text{Conjugate base}}{H_2PO_4^-}$

    c. $\underset{\text{Acid}}{CH_3NH_3^+} \rightarrow H^+ + \underset{\text{Conjugate base}}{CH_3NH_2}$

 Practice Problem • Exercise 16.2

Which of the following represent conjugate acid–base pairs?

    a. H_2O, H_3O^+

    b. OH^-, HNO_3

    c. H_2SO_4, SO_4^{2-}

    d. $HC_2H_3O_2$, $C_2H_3O_2^-$

B. Acid Strength

We have seen that when an acid dissolves in water, a proton is transferred from the acid to water:

$$HA(aq) + H_2O(l) \rightarrow H_3O^+(aq) + A^-(aq)$$

In this reaction a new acid, H_3O^+ (called the conjugate acid), and a new base, A^- (the conjugate base), are formed. The conjugate acid and base can react with one another,

$$H_3O^+(aq) + A^-(aq) \rightarrow HA(aq) + H_2O(l)$$

to re-form the parent acid and a water molecule. Therefore, this reaction can occur "in both directions." The forward reaction is

$$HA(aq) + H_2O(l) \rightarrow H_3O^+(aq) + A^-(aq)$$

and the reverse reaction is

$$H_3O^+(aq) + A^-(aq) \rightarrow HA(aq) + H_2O(l)$$

Note that the products in the forward reaction are the reactants in the reverse reaction. We usually represent the situation in which the reaction can occur in both directions by double arrows:

$$HA(aq) + H_2O(l) \rightleftharpoons H_3O^+(aq) + A^-(aq)$$

16.1 • Properties of Acids and Bases • **565**

CRITICAL THINKING

Whether an acid is harmful to human tissue reflects the concentration of H^+ ions in solution. A weak acid, such as vinegar, has a much lower concentration of H^+ ions than a strong acid such as HCl. For example, a 1.0 *M* solution of HCl has more than 200 times as many H^+ ions as an equal volume of a 1.0 *M* solution of acetic acid (vinegar is only about 5% acetic acid). If acetic acid were a strong acid, it would not be safe as a salad dressing because the high concentration of H^+ ions would damage human tissues.

Active Reading Question

A strong acid is an acid that dissociates completely. A weak acid dissociates to a small degree. If we dilute a strong acid solution, the acid still dissociates completely, and the acid is still strong.

MINI-DEMO

Use a conductivity apparatus with various solutions of strong and weak acids. The brightness of the light is evident for strong acids, whereas the bulb is weakly lit for weak acids. You can use these variations to discuss the difference in the number of ions produced in strong and weak acids.

Strong acid
An acid that completely dissociates to produce H^+ ions in solution

Weak acid
An acid that dissociates to a slight extent in aqueous solution

CRITICAL THINKING

Vinegar contains acetic acid and is used in salad dressings.

What if acetic acid was a strong acid instead of a weak acid? Would it be safe to use vinegar as a salad dressing?

---

information

A strong acid is completely dissociated in water. No HA molecules remain. Only H_3O^+, H_2O, and A^- are present.

A hydrochloric acid solution readily conducts electric current, as shown by the brightness of the bulb.

This situation represents a competition for the H^+ ion between H_2O (in the forward reaction) and A^- (in the reverse reaction). If H_2O "wins" this competition—that is, if H_2O has a very high attraction for H^+ compared to A^-, then the solution will contain mostly H_3O^+ and A^-. We describe this situation by saying that the H_2O molecule is a much stronger base (more attraction for H^+) than A^-. In this case the forward reaction predominates:

$$HA(aq) + H_2O(l) \Rightarrow H_3O^+(aq) + A^-(aq)$$

We say that the acid HA is **completely ionized** or **completely dissociated**. This situation represents a **strong acid**.

The opposite situation can also occur. Sometimes A^- "wins" the competition for the H^+ ion. In this case A^- is a much stronger base than H_2O and the reverse reaction predominates:

$$HA(aq) + H_2O(l) \Leftarrow H_3O^+(aq) + A^-(aq)$$

Here A^- has a much larger attraction for H^+ than does H_2O, and most of the HA molecules remain intact. This situation represents a **weak acid**.

Active Reading Question

Why is it not correct to say that a weak acid is a diluted strong acid?

Strong Acids We can determine what is actually going on in a solution by measuring its ability to conduct an electric current. Recall from Chapter 8 that a solution can conduct a current in proportion to the number of ions that are present. When 1 mole of solid sodium chloride is dissolved in 1 L of water, the resulting solution is an excellent conductor of an electric current because the Na^+ and Cl^- ions separate completely. We call NaCl a strong electrolyte.

Similarly, when 1 mole of hydrogen chloride is dissolved in 1 L of water, the resulting solution is an excellent conductor. Therefore, hydrogen chloride is also a strong electrolyte, which means that each HCl molecule must produce H^+ and Cl^- ions. This tells us that the forward reaction predominates:

$$HCl(aq) + H_2O(l) \rightleftharpoons H_3O^+(aq) + Cl^-(aq)$$

(Accordingly, the arrow pointing right is longer than the arrow pointing left.) In solution there are virtually no HCl molecules, only H^+ and Cl^- ions. This shows that Cl^- is a very poor base compared to the H_2O molecule; it has virtually no ability to attract H^+ ions in water. This aqueous solution of hydrogen chloride (called *hydrochloric acid*) is a strong acid.

In general, the strength of an acid is defined by the position of its ionization (dissociation) reaction:

$$HA(aq) + H_2O(l) \rightleftharpoons H_3O^+(aq) + A^-(aq)$$

A strong acid is one for which *the forward reaction predominates*. This means that almost all the original HA is dissociated (ionized) (see **Figure 16.1**). There is an important connection between the strength of an acid and that of its conjugate base.

A strong acid contains a relatively weak conjugate base—one that has a low attraction for protons.

Figure 16.1
Graphical representation of the behavior of acids of different strengths in aqueous solution. A strong acid is completely dissociated. In contrast, only a small fraction of the molecules of a weak acid are dissociated.

Active Reading Question

The conjugate base of a weak acid is a stronger base than the conjugate base of a strong acid.

A strong acid can be described as an acid whose conjugate base is a much weaker base than water (see **Figure 16.2**). In this case the water molecules win the competition for the H^+ ions.

Active Reading Question

Which is a stronger base, a conjugate base from a strong acid or a conjugate base from a weak acid?

Weak Acids In contrast to hydrochloric acid, when acetic acid, $HC_2H_3O_2$, is dissolved in water, the resulting solution conducts an electric current only weakly. That is, acetic acid is a weak electrolyte, which means that only a few ions are present. In other words, for the following reaction, the reverse reaction predominates (thus the arrow pointing left is longer).

$$HC_2H_3O_2(aq) + H_2O(l) \rightleftharpoons H_3O^+(aq) + C_2H_3O_2^-(aq)$$

In fact, measurements show that only about one in one hundred (1%) of the $HC_2H_3O_2$ molecules is dissociated (ionized) in a 0.1 M solution of acetic acid. Thus acetic acid is a weak acid. When acetic acid molecules are placed in water, almost all of the molecules remain undissociated. This tells us that the acetate ion, $C_2H_3O_2^-$, is an effective base—it very successfully attracts H^+ ions in water. This means that acetic acid remains largely in the form of $HC_2H_3O_2$ molecules in solution. A weak acid is one for which the *reverse reaction predominates*.

$$HA(aq) + H_2O(l) \Longleftarrow H_3O^+(aq) + A^-(aq)$$

Most of the acid originally placed in the solution is still present as HA at equilibrium. That is, a weak acid dissociates (ionizes) only to a very small extent in aqueous solution (Figure 16.1). In contrast to a strong acid, a weak acid has a conjugate base that is a much stronger base than water. In this case a water molecule is not very successful in pulling an H^+ ion away from the conjugate base. *A weak acid contains a relatively strong conjugate base* (Figure 16.2).

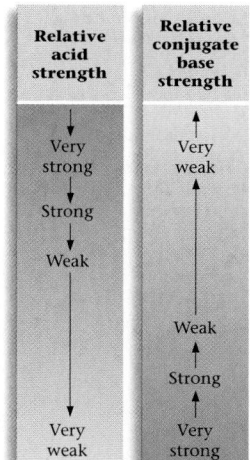

Figure 16.2
The relationship of acid strength and conjugate base strength for the dissociation reaction

information

A weak acid is mostly undissociated in water.

TEACHING TIPS

- This occasion marks the first time that students have been introduced to chemical equilibrium. It will be discussed in more detail in Chapter 17. For now, emphasize how the competition for a proton between a conjugate base and water determines which reaction (forward or reverse) dominates.

- After discussing forward and reverse reactions, students should understand that $C_2H_3O_2^-$ is a stronger base than H_2O, and H_2O is a stronger base than Cl^-.

- When discussing the statement "A weak acid contains a relatively strong conjugate base," emphasize the term *relatively*. The conjugate base of a weak acid is not a strong base in the way that NaOH is a strong base. For the reaction of the conjugate base in water, the reverse reaction dominates. However, if we compare two unequally weak acids, the conjugate base of the weaker of the two acids is the stronger base, although both bases are weak (compared to OH^-).

16.1 • Properties of Acids and Bases • **567**

An acetic acid solution conducts only a small amount of current as shown by the dimly lit bulb.

The various ways of describing the strength of an acid are summarized in **Table 16.1**.

Strong Acids The common strong acids are:

- sulfuric acid, $H_2SO_4(aq)$
- hydrochloric acid, $HCl(aq)$
- nitric acid, $HNO_3(aq)$
- perchloric acid, $HClO_4(aq)$

Sulfuric acid is actually a **diprotic acid**, an acid that can furnish two protons. The acid H_2SO_4 is a strong acid that is virtually 100% dissociated in water:

$$H_2SO_4(aq) \rightarrow H^+(aq) + HSO_4^-(aq)$$

The HSO_4^- ion is also an acid but it is a weak acid:

$$HSO_4^-(aq) \rightleftharpoons H+(aq) + SO_4^{2-}(aq)$$

Most of the HSO_4^- ions remain undissociated.

Oxyacids Most acids are **oxyacids**, in which the acidic hydrogen is attached to an oxygen atom. The strong acids we have mentioned, except hydrochloric acid, are typical examples. **Organic acids**, those with a carbon-atom backbone, commonly contain the **carboxyl group**:

$$-C\begin{matrix} \nearrow O \\ \searrow O-H \end{matrix}$$

Acids of this type are usually weak. An example is acetic acid, CH_3COOH, which is often written as $HC_2H_3O_2$.

$$CH_3-C\begin{matrix} \nearrow O \\ \searrow O-H \end{matrix}$$

Other Acids There are some important acids in which the acidic proton is attached to an atom other than oxygen. The most significant of these are the hydrohalic acids HX, where X represents a halogen atom. Examples are $HCl(aq)$, a strong acid, and $HF(aq)$, a weak acid.

Diprotic acid
An acid that can furnish two protons

Oxyacid
An acid in which the acidic proton is attached to an oxygen atom

Organic acid
An acid with a carbon-atom backbone and a carboxyl group

Table 16.1		
Ways to Describe Acid Strength		
Property	**Strong Acid**	**Weak Acid**
the acid ionization (dissociation) reaction	forward reaction predominates	reverse reaction predominates
strength of the conjugate base compared with that of water	A^- is a much weaker base than H_2O	A^- is a much stronger base than H_2O

Meeting Individual Needs
ENGLISH LANGUAGE LEARNERS

Explain that the word *predominate* is used to describe something that is larger in number, quantity, or importance. Ask students to use the term *predominate* in a sentence, not chemistry related, to determine whether they have a solid understanding of its meaning. For instance, "General education courses predominate students' schedules in the first year of college."

C. Water as an Acid and a Base

A substance is said to be *amphoteric* if it can behave either as an acid or as a base. Water is the most common **amphoteric substance**. We can see this clearly in the **ionization of water**, which involves the transfer of a proton from one water molecule to another to produce a hydroxide ion and a hydronium ion.

$$H_2O(l) + H_2O(l) \rightleftharpoons H_3O^+(aq) + OH^-(aq)$$

In this reaction one water molecule acts as an acid by furnishing a proton, and the other acts as a base by accepting the proton. The forward reaction for this process does not occur to a very great extent. That is, in pure water only a tiny amount of H_3O^+ and OH^- exist. At 25 °C the actual concentrations are

$$[H_3O^+] = [OH^-] = 1.0 \times 10^{-7} \, M$$

Notice that in pure water the concentrations of $[H_3O^+]$ and $[OH^-]$ are equal because they are produced in equal numbers in the ionization reaction.

One of the most interesting and important things about water is that the mathematical *product* of the H_3O^+ and OH^- concentrations is always constant. We can find this constant by multiplying the concentrations of H_3O^+ and OH^- at 25 °C:

$$[H_3O^+][OH^-] = (1.0 \times 10^{-7})(1.0 \times 10^{-7}) = 1.0 \times 10^{-14}$$

We call this constant K_w. Thus at 25 °C:

$$[H_3O^+][OH^-] = 1.0 \times 10^{-14} = K_w$$

To simplify the notation we often write H_3O^+ as just H^+. Thus we would write the K_w expression as follows:

$$[H^+][OH^-] = 1.0 \times 10^{-14} = K_w \text{ at 25 °C}$$

K_w is called the **ion-product constant** for water. The units are customarily omitted when the value of the constant is given and used.

It is important to recognize the meaning of K_w. In any aqueous solution at 25 °C, *no matter what it contains*, the product of $[H^+]$ and $[OH^-]$ must always equal 1.0×10^{-14}. This means that if the $[H^+]$ goes up, the $[OH^-]$ must go down so that the product of the two is still 1.0×10^{-14}. For example, if HCl gas is dissolved in water, increasing the $[H^+]$, the $[OH^-]$ must decrease.

There are three possible situations we might encounter in an aqueous solution.

- If we add an acid to water (an H^+ donor), we get an *acidic solution*. In this case, because we have added a source of H^+, the $[H^+]$ will be greater than the $[OH^-]$.

- On the other hand, if we add a base (a source of OH^-) to water, the $[OH^-]$ will be greater than the $[H^+]$. This is a *basic solution*.

- Finally, we might have a situation in which $[H^+] = [OH^-]$. This is called a *neutral solution*. Pure water is automatically neutral but we can also obtain a neutral solution by adding equal amounts of H^+ and OH^-.

Amphoteric substance
A substance that can behave either as an acid or as a base

nformation

Square brackets ([ ]) are used to indicate the concentration of a substance in moles per liter (*M*).

MATH

$K_w = [H^+][OH^-]$
$= 1.0 \times 10^{-14}$

CRITICAL THINKING

What if the *K* for the auto-ionization of water were 1×10^{14} instead of 1×10^{-14}?

MINI-DEMO

A conductivity tester can be used to demonstrate that pure water does not conduct a current. Thus, in the auto-ionization of water, the reverse reaction must dominate—very few ions are present.

TEACHING TIP

Emphasize the definitions of acidic, basic, and neutral solutions. Note that the emphasis should be on the relationship of the concentrations of the ions, not on the pH of the solution.

EXAMPLE 16.3

More Examples

Calculate [H^+] or [OH^-] as required for each of the following at 25 °C and state whether the solution is neutral, acidic, or basic.

a. [H^+] = 3.4×10^{-4} M
[OH^-] = 2.9×10^{-11} M;
acidic

b. [H^+] = 2.6×10^{-8} M
[OH^-] = 3.9×10^{-7} M; basic

c. [OH^-] = 6.2×10^{-9} M
[H^+] = 1.6×10^{-6} M; acidic

d. [OH^-] = 8.1×10^{-3} M
[H^+] = 1.2×10^{-12} M; basic

---

information

Remember that H^+ represents H_3O^+.

Let's Review

1. An *acidic solution*, where [H^+] > [OH^-]
2. A *basic solution*, where [OH^-] > [H^+]
3. A *neutral solution*, where [H^+] = [OH^-]

In each case, however, K_w = [H^+][OH^-] = 1.0×10^{-14}.

EXAMPLE 16.3

Calculating Ion Concentrations in Water

Calculate [H^+] or [OH^-] as required for each of the following solutions at 25 °C, and state whether the solution is neutral, acidic, or basic.

    a. 1.0×10^{-5} M OH^-
    b. 1.0×10^{-7} M OH^-
    c. 10.0 M H^+

Solution

a. 1.0×10^{-5} M OH^-

Where do we want to go?

    [H^+] = ? M

What do we know?

- K_w = [H^+] [OH^-] = 1.0×10^{-14}
- [OH^-] = 1.0×10^{-5} M

How do we get there?

    K_w = [H^+] [OH^-] = 1.0×10^{-14}

MATH

The more negative the exponent, the smaller the number.

Dividing both sides of the equation by [OH^-] we get

$$[H^+] = \frac{1.0 \times 10^{-14}}{[OH^-]} = \frac{1.0 \times 10^{-14}}{1.0 \times 10^{-5}} = 1.0 \times 10^{-9}\ M$$

Since [OH^-] = 1.0×10^{-5} M is greater than [H^+] = 1.0×10^{-9} M the solution is basic.

b. 1.0×10^{-7} M OH^-

Where do we want to go?

    [H^+] = ? M

What do we know?

- K_w = [H^+] [OH^-] = 1.0×10^{-14}
- [OH^-] = 1.0×10^{-7} M

Meeting Individual Needs

INCLUSION STRATEGIES

If students struggle with multiplying and dividing powers, review the exponent rules. Point out in Example 16.3 that you subtract the exponent in the denominator from the exponent in the numerator to obtain the exponent of the quotient.

Meeting Individual Needs

MATH CONCEPTS

For students who need additional help with exponents, have them read *Exponents and Square Roots* located in the *Teacher Resources*. A worksheet is available to go along with the handout.

How do we get there?

$$K_w = [H^+] [OH^-] = 1.0 \times 10^{-14}$$

Dividing both sides of the equation by $[OH^-]$ we get

$$[H^+] = \frac{1.0 \times 10^{-14}}{[OH^-]} = \frac{1.0 \times 10^{-14}}{1.0 \times 10^{-7}} = 1.0 \times 10^{-7} \ M$$

Since $[OH^-] = [H^+] = 1.0 \times 10^{-7} \ M$ the solution is neutral

c. $10.0 \ M \ H^+$

Where do we want to go?

$$[OH^-] = ? \ M$$

What do we know?

- $K_w = [H^+] [OH^-] = 1.0 \times 10^{-14}$

- $[H^+] = 10.0 \ M$

How do we get there?

$$K_w = [H^+] [OH^-] = 1.0 \times 10^{-14}$$

Dividing both sides of the equation by $[H^+]$ we get

$$[OH^-] = \frac{1.0 \times 10^{-14}}{[H^+]} = \frac{1.0 \times 10^{-14}}{10.0} = 1.0 \times 10^{-15} \ M$$

Since $[H^+] = 10.0 \ M$ is greater than $[OH^-] = 1.0 \times 10^{-15} \ M$ the solution is acidic.

✔ Practice Problem • Exercise 16.3

Calculate $[H^+]$ in a solution in which $[OH^-] = 2.0 \times 10^{-2} \ M$. Is this solution acidic, neutral, or basic?

✔ Answer to Practice Problem 16.3

Because $[H^+][OH^-] = 1.0 \times 10^{-14}$, we can solve for $[H^+]$.

$$[H^+] = \frac{1.0 \times 10^{-14}}{[OH^-]}$$

$$= \frac{1.0 \times 10^{-14}}{2.0 \times 10^{-2}}$$

$$= 5.0 \times 10^{-13} \ M$$

This solution is basic: $[OH^-] = 2.0 \times 10^{-2} \ M$ is greater than $[H^+] = 5.0 \times 10^{-13} \ M$.

EXAMPLE 16.4

More Examples

1. Which is greater, $[OH^-]$ or $[H^+]$, if $[H^+] = 2.8 \times 10^{-5}\ M$ in an aqueous solution at 25 °C?

   $[H^+]$ is greater than $[OH^-]$.

2. How many times greater is $[OH^-]$ than $[H^+]$ if $[H^+] = 1.0 \times 10^{-9}\ M$ in an aqueous solution at 25 °C?

   1.0×10^5 times greater

SECTION 16.1
ASSESS

SECTION 16.1
Review Questions

1. The Arrhenius definition of an acid states that acids produce H^+ in solution and bases produce OH^-. This definition allows for only one kind of base. In the Brønsted–Lowry model, the emphasis is on the role of water in producing an acid or a base. This definition allows substances such as ammonia to be classified as bases.

2. Both a and b are conjugate acid–base pairs. For c, the correct pairs would be $H_2PO_4^-$, HPO_4^{2-} and PO_4^{3-}, HPO_4^{2-}. For d, the correct pairs are HNO_3, NO_3^- and NO_2^-, HNO_2.

3. See Figure 16.1 (strong acid).

4. See Figure 16.1 (weak acid).

5. $H_2O(l) + H_2O(l) \rightarrow H_3O^+(aq) + OH^-(aq)$
   $\quad$ Acid $\quad\quad$ Base $\quad\quad$ Acid $\quad\quad$ Base

6. A solution is acidic if $[H^+] > [OH^-]$. A solution is basic if $[H^+] < [OH^-]$. A solution is neutral if $[H^+] = [OH^-]$.

EXAMPLE 16.4

Using the Ion-Product Constant in Calculations

Is it possible for an aqueous solution at 25 °C to have $[H^+] = 0.010\ M$ and $[OH^-] = 0.010\ M$?

Solution
The concentration 0.010 M can also be expressed as $1.0 \times 10^{-2}\ M$. Thus, if $[H^+] = [OH^-] = 1.0 \times 10^{-2}\ M$, the product $[H^+][OH^-] = (1.0 \times 10^{-2})(1.0 \times 10^{-2}) = 1.0 \times 10^{-4}$.

This is not possible. The product of $[H^+]$ and $[OH^-]$ must always be 1.0×10^{-14} in water at 25 °C, so a solution could not have $[H^+] = [OH^-] = 0.010\ M$.

If H^+ and OH^- are added to water in these amounts, they will react with each other to form H_2O,

$$H^+ + OH^- \rightarrow H_2O$$

until the product $[H^+][OH^-] = 1.0 \times 10^{-14}$.

This is a general result. When H^+ and OH^- are added to water in amounts such that the product of their concentrations is greater than 1.0×10^{-14}, they will react to form water until enough H^+ and OH^- are consumed (until $[H^+][OH^-] = 1.0 \times 10^{-14}$).

SECTION 16.1
REVIEW QUESTIONS

❶ How is the Arrhenius concept of an acid different from the Brønsted–Lowry model of an acid?

❷ Which of the following represent conjugate acid–base pairs? For those pairs that are not conjugates, write the correct conjugate acid or base for each species in the pair.
   a. HSO_4^-, SO_4^{2-}
   b. HBr, BrO^-
   c. $H_2PO_4^-$, PO_4^{3-}
   d. HNO_3, NO_2^-

❸ Draw a molecular-level view of an aqueous solution of the strong acid HCl.

❹ Draw a molecular-level view of an aqueous solution of the weak acid HF.

❺ Use the Brønsted–Lowry model to label the acid–base pairs in the following equation for the ionization of water:

$$H_2O(l) + H_2O(l) \rightleftharpoons H_3O^+(aq) + OH^-(aq)$$

❻ What does it mean to say a solution is acidic? Basic? Neutral?

RESEARCH LINKS
CLASSZONE.COM

Determining the Acidity of a Solution

Objectives

- *To understand pH and pOH*
- *To learn to find pH and pOH for various solutions*
- *To use a calculator to find pH*
- *To learn methods for measuring pH of a solution*
- *To learn to calculate the pH of strong acids*

Key Terms

- pH scale
- Indicators
- Indicator paper
- pH meter

A. The pH Scale

To express small numbers conveniently, chemists often use the "p scale," which is based on common logarithms (base 10 logs). In this system, if N represents some number, then

$$pN = -\log N = (-1) \times \log N$$

That is, the p means to take the log of the number that follows and multiply the result by -1. For example, to express the number 1.0×10^{-7} on the p scale.

1. Enter $(-)$.
2. Press the $\boxed{\log}$ key.
3. Enter 1.0×10^{-7}.

$$p(1.0 \times 10^{-7}) = -\log(1.0 \times 10^{-7}) = 7.00$$

Because the $[H^+]$ in an aqueous solution is typically quite small, using the p scale in the form of the **pH scale** provides a convenient way to represent solution acidity. The pH is defined as

$$pH = -\log[H^+]$$

To obtain the pH value of a solution, we must compute the negative log of the $[H^+]$. On a typical calculator, this involves the following steps:

Steps for Calculating pH on a Calculator

Step 1 Enter $(-)$.
Step 2 Press the $\boxed{\log}$ key.
Step 3 Enter the $[H^+]$.

In the case where $[H^+] = 1.0 \times 10^{-5}\ M$, following the above steps gives a pH value of 5.00.

To represent pH to the appropriate number of significant figures, you need to know the following rule for logarithms:

> The number of decimal places for a log must be equal to the number of significant figures in the original number.

2 significant figures

$[H^+] = 1.0 \times 10^{-5}\,M$ and $pH = 5.00$

2 decimal places

information

The pH scale provides a compact way to represent solution acidity.

CRITICAL THINKING

What if an elected official decided to ban all products with a pH outside of the 6–8 range? Would the ban affect products you buy? Give some examples of products that would no longer be available.

EXAMPLE 16.5

More Examples

Calculate the pH value for each of the following aqueous solutions at 25 °C.

a. a solution in which $[H^+] = 2.1 \times 10^{-5}\ M$

pH = 4.68

b. a solution in which $[OH^-] = 5.9 \times 10^{-8}\ M$

pH = 6.77

 Answer to Practice Problem 16.5

a. Because $[H^+] = 1.0 \times 10^{-3}\ M$, we get pH = 3.00 by using the regular steps.

b. Because $[OH^-] = 5.0 \times 10^{-5}\ M$, we can find $[H^+]$ from the K_w expression.

$$[H^+] = \frac{K_w}{[OH^-]}$$
$$= \frac{1.0 \times 10^{-14}}{5.0 \times 10^{-5}}$$
$$= 2.0 \times 10^{-10}\ M$$

Then we follow the regular steps to get pH from $[H^+]$.

pH = 9.70

 Active Reading Question

Acid and base concentrations are often small (less than 1.00 M in solution). It is more cumbersome to say "The concentration of a solution of strong acid is $3.1 \times 10^{-5}\ M$" than to say "The pH of the solution is 4.51."

🍎 **TEACHING TIP**

Point out to students that a change of 1 in pH represents a change of 10 in hydrogen ion concentration.

Active Reading Question

Solution A is 10 times more acidic than solution B.

EXAMPLE 16.5
Calculating pH

Calculate the pH value for each of the following solutions at 25 °C.

    a. A solution in which $[H^+] = 1.0 \times 10^{-9}\ M$

    b. A solution in which $[OH^-] = 1.0 \times 10^{-6}\ M$

Solution (a)
For this solution $[H^+] = 1.0 \times 10^{-9}$.

    $-\log 1.0 \times 10^{-9} = 9.00$

    pH = 9.00

Solution (b)
In this case we are given the $[OH^-]$. Thus we must first calculate $[H^+]$ from the K_w expression. We solve

$$K_w = [H^+][OH^-] = 1.0 \times 10^{-14}$$

for $[H^+]$ by dividing both sides by $[OH^-]$.

$$[H^+] = \frac{1.0 \times 10^{-14}}{[OH^-]} = \frac{1.0 \times 10^{-14}}{1.0 \times 10^{-16}} = 1.0 \times 10^{-8}$$

Now that we know the $[H^+]$, we can calculate the pH by following the example above. Doing so yields pH = 8.00.

✅ **Practice Problem • Exercise 16.5**

Calculate the pH value for each of the following solutions at 25 °C.

    a. A solution in which $[H^+] = 1.0 \times 10^{-3}\ M$

    b. A solution in which $[OH^-] = 5.0 \times 10^{-5}\ M$

📖 **Active Reading Question**

Why do we use the "p scale" in acid–base chemistry?

Because the pH scale is a log scale based on 10, the pH changes by 1 for every power-of-10 change in the $[H^+]$.

🛈 **information**

The pH decreases as $[H^+]$ increases, and vice versa.

For example, a solution of pH 3 has an H^+ concentration of $10^{-3}\ M$, which is 10 times that of a solution of pH 4 ($[H^+] = 10^{-4}\ M$) and 100 times that of a solution of pH 5. This is illustrated in **Table 16.2**. Also note from Table 16.2 that *the pH decreases as the $[H^+]$ increases*. That is, a lower pH means a more acidic solution. The pH scale and the pH values for several common substances are shown in **Figure 16.3**.

📖 **Active Reading Question**

Solution A has a pH of 4.00. Solution B has a pH of 5.00. Which solution, A or B, is more acidic? How many times more acidic is it?

Table 16.2

The Relationship of the H^+ Concentration of a Solution to Its pH

$[H^+]$	pH
1.0×10^{-1}	1.00
1.0×10^{-2}	2.00
1.0×10^{-3}	3.00
1.0×10^{-4}	4.00
1.0×10^{-5}	5.00
1.0×10^{-6}	6.00
1.0×10^{-7}	7.00

Log scales similar to the pH scale are used for representing other quantities. For example,

$$pOH = -\log[OH^-]$$

Therefore, in a solution in which

$$[OH^-] = 1.0 \times 10^{-12}\ M$$

the pOH is

$$-\log[OH^-] = -\log(1.0 \times 10^{-12}) = 12.00$$

Figure 16.3
The pH scale and pH values of some common substances

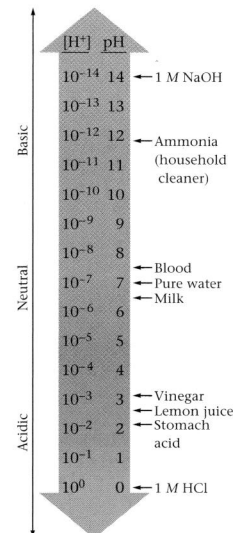

EXAMPLE 16.6

Calculating pH and pOH

Calculate the pH and pOH for each of the following solutions at 25 °C.

a. $1.0 \times 10^{-3}\ M\ OH^-$ **b.** $1.0\ M\ H^+$

Solution

a. We are given the $[OH^-]$, so we can calculate the pOH value by taking $-\log[OH^-]$.

$$pOH = -\log[OH^-] = -\log(1.0 \times 10^{-3}) = 3.00$$

To calculate the pH, we must first solve the K_w expression for $[H^+]$.

$$[H^+] = \frac{K_w}{[OH^-]} = \frac{1.0 \times 10^{-14}}{1.0 \times 10^{-3}} = 1.0 \times 10^{-11}\ M$$

Now we compute the pH.

$$pH = -\log[H^+] = -\log(1.0 \times 10^{-11}) = 11.00$$

b. In this case we are given the $[H^+]$ and we can compute the pH.

$$pH = -\log[H^+] = -\log(1.0) = 0$$

We next solve the K_w expression for $[OH^-]$

$$[OH^-] = \frac{K_w}{[H^+]} = \frac{1.0 \times 10^{-14}}{1.0} = 1.0 \times 10^{-14}\ M$$

Now we compute the pOH.

$$pOH = -\log[OH^-] = -\log(1.0 \times 10^{-14}) = 14.00$$

16.2 • Determining the Acidity of a Solution • **575**

EXAMPLE 16.6

More Examples

Calculate the pH and pOH values for each of the following aqueous solutions at 25 °C.

a. a solution in which
$[H^+] = 3.6 \times 10^{-9}\ M$
pH = 8.44; pOH = 5.56

b. a solution in which
$[OH^-] = 9.2 \times 10^{-2}\ M$
pOH = 1.04; pH = 12.96

Active Learning
Group Activity

To emphasize that each pH unit corresponds to a ten-fold change in $[H^+]$, consider the following class project.

1. Obtain a 4-foot-long piece of butcher paper.

2. Hang the paper on the wall so that the 4-foot length lies in a horizontal direction.

3. Near the left edge of the paper, use a black marker to draw a vertical line. This line will be the beginning reference for the remainder of the activity. Begin all marks from this reference line. Using a colored marker, make a 1-mm horizontal mark near the bottom of the butcher paper beginning at the vertical reference line. Label this mark "pH = 7.00."

4. Discuss ways to represent other pH values on this paper. If a 1-mm mark corresponds to a pH of 7.00 or $[H^+] = 1.0 \times 10^{-7}\ M$, a 10-mm mark is required for pH = 6.00, a 100-mm mark for pH = 5.00, and so on. Since 1000 mm is just under 3.5 feet, a pH of 4.00 is the lowest pH that can be represented on the butcher paper.

5. Calculate how large the paper would have to be to represent additional pH values. For example, to show a pH of 0.00 ($[H^+] = 1\ M$), you would need a line almost 33,000 feet long.

6. Refer to this chart as you discuss pH values to remind students that the pH scale is a log scale.

Expressing integer pH values greater than 7.00 on this scale would require lines that start at 10 times smaller than the beginning 1-mm line. These lines would not be useful for class visualization. You can discuss this effect and explain why you are not representing these values.

Use pH paper or a pH meter to show the pH of various solutions. Some possible solutions are vinegar, HCl, NaOH, liquid drain cleaner, salt water, lemon juice, other fruit juices, and soap solutions. You may want to bring in samples of household items for pH testing. As you show students each item and find its pH, have students classify the item as acidic, basic, or neutral.

EXAMPLE 16.7

More Examples

1. The pH of a solution is 5.67. What is the pOH of the solution?
   pOH = 8.33

2. The pH of a solution is 9.23. What is the pOH of the solution?
   pOH = 4.77

✓ Answer to Practice Problem 16.7

pOH + pH = 14.00

pOH = 14.00 − pH

= 14.00 − 3.5

pOH = 10.5

We can obtain a convenient relationship between pH and pOH by starting with the K_w expression

$$[H^+][OH^-] = 1.0 \times 10^{-14}$$

and taking the negative log of both sides.

$$-\log([H^+][OH^-]) = -\log(1.0 \times 10^{-14})$$

Because the log of a product equals the sum of the logs of the terms, that is, $\log(A \times B) = \log A + \log B$, we have

$$\underbrace{-\log[H^+]}_{pH} + \underbrace{(-\log[OH^-])}_{pOH} = -\log(1.0 \times 10^{-14}) = 14.00$$

nformation

The symbol *p* means −log.

which gives the equation

$$pH + pOH = 14.00$$

This means that once we know either the pH or the pOH for a solution, we can calculate the other. For example, if a solution has a pH of 6.00, the pOH is calculated as follows:

$$pH + pOH = 14.00$$
$$pOH = 14.00 - pH$$
$$pOH = 14.00 - 6.00 = 8.00$$

EXAMPLE 16.7

Calculating pOH from pH

Red blood cells can exist only over a narrow range of pH.

The pH of blood is about 7.4. What is the pOH of blood?

Solution

$$pH + pOH = 14.00$$
$$pOH = 14.00 - pH$$
$$= 14.00 - 7.4$$
$$= 6.6$$

The pOH of blood is 6.6.

✓ Practice Problem • Exercise 16.7

A sample of rain in an area with severe air pollution has a pH of 3.5. What is the pOH of this rainwater?

It is also possible to find the $[H^+]$ or $[OH^-]$ from the pH or pOH. To find the $[H^+]$ from the pH, we must go back to the definition of pH:

$$pH = -\log[H^+]$$

or

$$-pH = \log[H^+]$$

To arrive at $[H^+]$ on the right-hand side of this equation we must "undo" the log operation. This is called taking the *antilog* or the *inverse* log.

576 • Chapter 16 • Acids and Bases

Teaching Support

DEMONSTRATION

Colorful Indicators

Materials

- 12 1-L water bottles (empty)
- Dry ice (CO_2)
- 0.1 *M* sodium hydroxide
- Phenolphthalein
- Methylene blue
- Bromothymol blue
- Thymolphthalein
- Phenol red
- Methyl red
- Yamada's universal indicator

Preparation Make 100 mL of each indicator solution. Use distilled water for all dilutions. Thymolphthalein: 0.04 g in 50 mL ethanol and diluted to 100 mL; phenolphthalein: 0.05 g in 50 mL ethanol diluted to 100 mL; phenol red: 0.04 g in 11 mL 0.1 *M* NaOH diluted to 100 mL;

bromothymol blue: 0.04 g in 6.4 mL 0.01 *M* NaOH diluted to 100 mL; methyl red: 0.02 g in 60 mL ethanol diluted to 100 mL; methylene blue: 0.01 g in 100 mL water; Yamada's universal indicator: 0.005 g thymol blue, 0.012 g methyl red, 0.06 g bromothymol blue, 0.1 g phenolphthalein in 100 mL ethanol; add enough 0.01 *M* NaOH to turn the solution green and dilute to 200 mL with water.

Cut the tops off the water bottles to form tall cylinders. Fill each three-

Inverse log (−pH) = [H⁺]

There are different methods for carrying out the inverse log operation on various calculators. One common method is the two-key (2nd) (log) sequence. (Consult your calculator's manual to find out how to do the antilog or inverse log operation.) The steps in going from pH to [H⁺] are as follows:

Steps for Calculating [H⁺] from pH

Step 1 Take the inverse log (antilog) by using the (2nd) (log) keys in that order. (Your calculator may require different keys for this operation.)

Step 2 Enter (−).

Step 3 Enter the pH.

For practice, we will convert pH = 7.0 to [H⁺].

pH = 7.0

−pH = −7.0

The inverse log of −7.0 gives 1×10^{-7}

[H⁺] = 1×10^{-7} M

This process is illustrated further in Example 16.8.

EXAMPLE 16.8

Calculating [H⁺] from pH

The pH of a human blood sample was measured to be 7.41. What is the [H⁺] in this blood?

Solution

pH = 7.41

−pH = −7.41

[H⁺] = inverse log (−7.41) = 3.9×10^{-8}

so,

[H⁺] = 3.9×10^{-8} M.

Notice that because the pH has two decimal places, we need two significant figures for [H⁺].

Practice Problem • Exercise 16.8

The pH of rainwater in a polluted area was found to be 3.50. What is the [H⁺] for this rainwater?

Measuring the pH of the water in a river

MATH

This operation may involve a 10^x key on some calculators.

TEACHING TIPS

- Some calculators have an inverse log key; others use 10^x for the inverse log function. This discrepancy can cause difficulties for students. Make sure they understand how to use their calculators to find inverse logs.

- This discussion represents another opportunity for a review of significant figures. Remind students that the correct number of significant figures will be the same as the number of digits to the right of the decimal in the log number.

EXAMPLE 16.8

More Examples

1. The pH of a solution is 3.14. What is the [H⁺] of the solution?
   [H⁺] = 7.2×10^{-4} M

2. The pH of a solution is 8.53. What is the [H⁺] of the solution?
   [H⁺] = 3.0×10^{-9} M

Answer to Practice Problem 16.8

Step 1 pH = 3.50

Step 2 −pH = −3.50

Step 3 (inv) (log) −3.50 =
3.2×10^{-4}

[H⁺] = 3.2×10^{-4} M

(continued)

fourths full with distilled water and pair cylinders. Add indicators (1–2 mL) to the pairs in the following sequence: pair 1: thymolphthalein; pair 2: phenolphthalein; pair 3: phenol red; pair 4: bromothymol blue; pair 5: methyl red and methylene blue; pair 6: Yamada's universal indicator. Pour 0.1 M NaOH into a graduated cylinder. Add just enough to the first pair to produce a blue color. Note the amount added to each cylinder and add the same

amount to each of the other cylinders.

Presentation Explain that you have made a solution of pH 11 in each cylinder and that each pair of cylinders contains a different indicator. One cylinder in each pair will act as a control; nothing will be added to it. Place dry ice in one cylinder of each pair and note color changes.

Teaching Notes Discuss how dry ice can change the pH of a solution. It dissolves to form carbonic acid (H_2CO_3), which then reacts with water. Write the

reaction equations on the board. Use Figure 16.4 to find the pH ranges for the indicators. Neutralize and dispose of the solutions. You may wish to save the Yamada's pair of cylinders to use after you have discussed the rest of the indicators. When you place the dry ice in the Yamada's pair, the colors will change one after another through the pH range. If you add a little 0.1 M HCl at the end of the color changes, you may be able to produce one last color at the lowest pH.

EXAMPLE 16.9

More Examples

1. The pOH of a solution is 5.67. What is the $[OH^-]$ of the solution?

$[OH^-] = 2.1 \times 10^{-6}\ M$

2. The pOH of a solution is 11.28. What is the $[OH^-]$ of the solution?

$[OH^-] = 5.2 \times 10^{-12}\ M$

Answer to Practice Problem 16.9

Step 1 pOH = 10.50

Step 2 −pOH = −10.50

Step 3 [inv][log] −10.50 = 3.2×10^{-11}

$[OH^-] = 3.2 \times 10^{-11}\ M$

A similar procedure is used to change from pOH to $[OH^-]$, as shown in Example 16.9.

EXAMPLE 16.9

Calculating $[OH^-]$ from pOH

The pOH of the water in a fish tank is found to be 6.59. What is the $[OH^-]$ for this water?

Solution

We use the same steps as for converting pH to $[H^+]$, except that we use the pOH to find $[OH^-]$.

pOH = 6.59

−pOH = −6.59

The inverse log (−6.59) = 2.6×10^{-7}

$[OH^-] = 2.6 \times 10^{-7}\ M$

Note that two significant figures are required.

Practice Problem • Exercise 16.9

The pOH of a liquid drain cleaner was found to be 10.50. What is the $[OH^-]$ for this cleaner?

HANDS-ON CHEMISTRY • MINI-LAB •

Cabbage Juice Indicator

Materials
- samples to test
- cabbage juice indicator
- water
- reference solutions
- droppers

Procedure

1. Bring some samples from home to test for pH levels. If they are liquids, the samples should be clear, white, or light-colored. If they are solids, they should be at least a little soluble in water.

2. Obtain cabbage juice indicator from your teacher. The pH indicator is made by boiling red cabbage leaves in water.

3. Take a small amount of your sample (about 5 mL of the liquid or a small amount of solid dissolved in 5 mL of water) and add a few of drops of cabbage juice indicator to the sample.

4. Use the reference solutions provided by your teacher to determine the approximate pH of each of your samples.

5. Compare your results with those of your classmates.

Results/Analysis

1. Do you see any patterns in pH values? For example, are most cleaning supplies acidic, basic, or neutral? What about most foods?

2. Do any of the pH values surprise you? Why?

Hands-On Chemistry
MINI-LAB

Cabbage Juice Indicator

Materials Each student/group will need cabbage juice indicator and at least one solution from home (film canisters can be given to students to hold their samples). Students may also need some water and reference solutions. To make these reference solutions, add a few drops of cabbage juice indicator to solutions of HCl and NaOH ranging in concentration from 0.10 M to $1.0 \times 10^{-6}\ M$ and to pure water (which will give you solutions with pH values ranging from 1.00 to 14.00). Make sure you boil the water when making these solutions to remove dissolved CO_2. If not removed by boiling; the dissolved carbon dioxide in the water will change the pH of the water and cause inconsistent results, especially with pHs in the 5–9 range. To make the indicator, place red cabbage leaves in a small amount of water and boil the water

B. Measuring pH

The traditional way of determining the pH of a solution is by using **indicators**—substances that exhibit different colors in acidic and basic solutions. We can represent a generic indicator as a weak acid HIn. Let's assume that for a particular indicator HIn is red and the anion In^- is blue.

$$HIn \rightleftharpoons In^- + H^+$$

Thus, in a solution containing lots of H^+, the indicator will be red (the HIn form).

$$HIn \underset{\substack{\text{acidic} \\ \text{solution}}}{\rightleftharpoons} In^- + H^+$$

In a basic solution, the H^+ will be removed from HIn to form the blue $In-$ ion and the solution will be blue.

$$HIn \underset{\substack{\text{basic} \\ \text{solution}}}{\rightleftharpoons} In^- + H^+$$

In intermediate pH regions, significant amounts of both HIn and In^- will be present and the solution will be some shade of purple (red plus blue).

Many substances exist that turn different colors when H^+ is present (HIn) than when H^+ is absent (In^-). Some of these indicators are shown in **Figure 16.4** along with the colors of their HIn and In^- forms. Note that different indicators change at different pH values depending on the acid strength of HIn for a particular indicator.

A convenient way to measure the approximate pH of a solution is by using **indicator paper**—a strip of paper coated with a combination of indicators. Indicator paper turns a specific color for each pH value (see **Figure 16.5**).

The pH value of a solution can be measured electronically using a **pH meter** (see **Figure 16.6**). A pH meter contains a probe that is very sensitive to the $[H^+]$ in a solution. When the probe is inserted into a solution, the $[H^+]$ in the solution produces a voltage that appears as a pH reading on the meter. Because a pH meter can determine the pH value of a solution so quickly and accurately, these devices are now used almost universally.

C. Calculating the pH of Strong Acid Solutions

We will now learn to calculate the pH for a solution containing a strong acid of known concentration. For example, if we know a solution contains 1.0 *M* HCl, how can we find the pH of the solution? To answer this question we must know that when HCl dissolves in water, each molecule dissociates (ionizes) into H^+ and Cl^- ions. That is, we must know that HCl is a strong acid. Thus, although the label on the bottle says 1.0 *M* HCl, the solution contains virtually no HCl molecules. A 1.0 *M* HCl solution contains H^+ and Cl^- ions rather than HCl molecules. Typically, container labels indicate the substance(s) used to make up the solution but do not necessarily describe the solution components after dissolution. In this case,

$$1.0 \text{ } M \text{ HCl} \rightarrow 1.0 \text{ } M \text{ } H^+ \text{ and } 1.0 \text{ } M \text{ } Cl^-$$

Therefore, the $[H^+]$ in the solution is 1.0 *M*. The pH is then

$$pH = -\log[H^+] = -\log(1.0) = 0$$

Figure 16.5
Indicator paper being used to measure the pH of a solution. The pH is determined by comparing the color that the solution turns the paper to the color chart.

Figure 16.6
A pH meter

Indicator (acid–base)
A chemical that changes color depending on the pH of a solution

Indicator paper
A strip of paper coated with a combination of acid–base indicators

pH meter
A device used to measure the pH of a solution

16.2 • Determining the Acidity of a Solution • **579**

(continued)
for several minutes. Let the indicator cool before using it.

Purpose Students can identify some of the acids and bases in everyday life.

Discussion Many cleaning supplies are basic. Fruits, fruit juices, and soft drinks are acidic. Unless the student brings boiled distilled water, it is doubtful that any sample will be neutral. This activity can be used as a starting point for emphasizing that acids and bases are not "bad" chemicals.

TEACHING TIP

Focus students' attention on the molecular view of a strong acid. Once they understand that the acid ionizes completely in solution, they are ready to find the hydrogen ion concentration and the pH.

EXAMPLE 16.10

More Examples

1. Calculate the pH of 0.025 M $HClO_4$.
   pH = 1.60

2. Calculate the pH of 1.2×10^{-5} M HBr.
   pH = 4.92

 Answer to Practice Problem 16.10

Because HCl is a strong acid, it is completely dissociated:

5.0×10^{-3} M HCl →
  5.0×10^{-3} M H^+ and
  5.0×10^{-3} M Cl^-

so $[H^+] = 5.0 \times 10^{-3}$ M.

pH = $-\log(5.0 \times 10^{-3})$ = 2.30

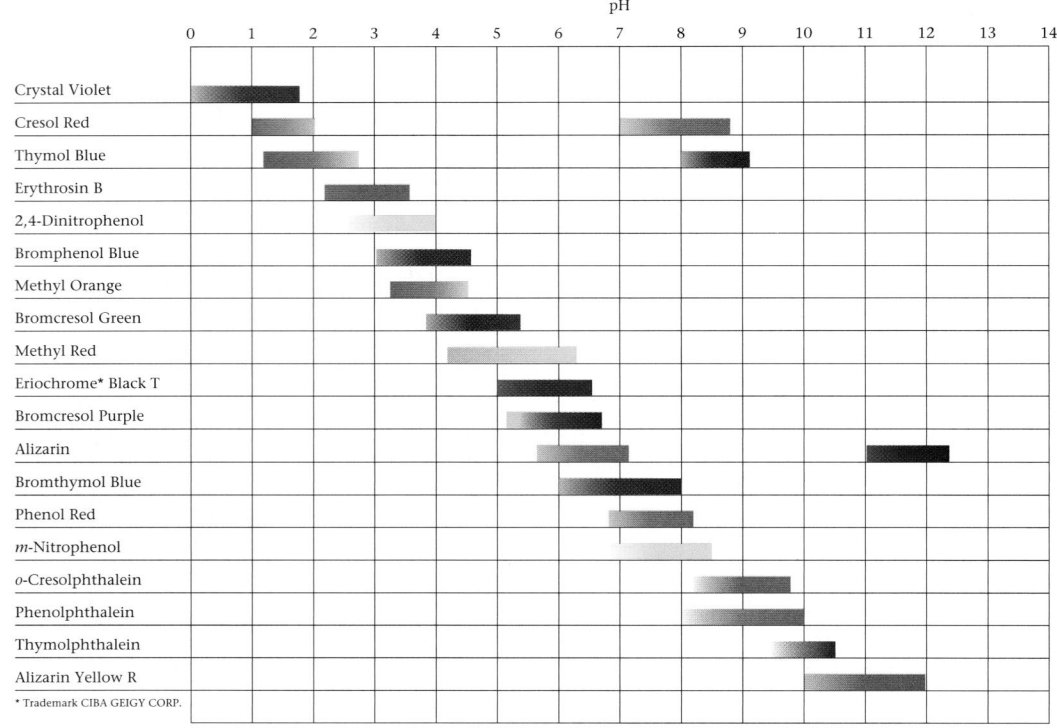

The pH ranges shown are approximate. Specific transition ranges depend on the indicator solvent chosen.

Figure 16.4
The useful pH ranges for several common indicators. Note that most indicators have a useful range of about two pH units.

EXAMPLE 16.10

Calculating the pH of Strong Acid Solutions

Calculate the pH of 0.10 M HNO_3.

Solution
HNO_3 is a strong acid, so the ions in solution are H^+ and NO_3^-. In this case,

0.10 M HNO_3 → 0.10 M H^+ and 0.10 M NO_3^-

Thus

$[H^+] = 0.10$ M and pH = $-\log(0.10)$ = 1.00

Practice Problem • Exercise 16.10
Calculate the pH of a solution of 5.0×10^{-3} M HCl.

580 • Chapter 16 • Acids and Bases

Meeting Individual Needs
ADVANCED LEARNERS

If you have excellent mathematics students looking for additional challenges, ask them to calculate the pH of 1.0 L of water after 1.0×10^{-7} mol of HCl is added.

The answer 7.00 is not correct because H^+ is coming from both the water and HCl; thus the pH is lower than 7.00. Students might decide to add the H^+ from the HCl (1.0×10^{-7} M) to that in pure water

$(1.0 \times 10^{-7}$ $M)$ to give 2.0×10^{-7} M, which leads to a pH of 6.70 $[-\log(2.0 \times 10^{-7})]$. However, the added H^+ from the HCl shifts the water equilibrium to the left, using up some H^+. Thus the pH must be higher than 6.70 but lower than 7.00.

CHEMISTRY EXPLORERS

Arnold Beckman • 1900–2004

Arnold Beckman was born in 1900 in Cullom, Illinois, a town of 500 people that had no electricity or telephones. Beckman says, "In Cullom we were forced to improvise. I think it was a good thing."

The son of a blacksmith, Beckman became so fascinated with chemistry that his father built him a small "chemistry shed" in the backyard for his tenth birthday.

Beckman's interest in chemistry was fostered by his high school teachers, and he eventually attended the University of Illinois, Urbana-Champaign where he earned a bachelor's degree in chemical engineering and a master's degree in physical chemistry. He then went to the California Institute of Technology where he earned a Ph.D. and became a faculty member.

In 1935 Beckman invented something that would cause a revolution in scientific instrumentation. A college friend who worked in a laboratory in the California citrus industry needed an accurate, convenient way to measure the acidity of lemon juice. In response, Beckman invented the pH meter. This compact, sturdy device was an immediate hit. In fact, business was so good that Beckman left Caltech to head his own company.

Over the years Beckman invented many other devices, including an instrument for measuring the light absorbed by molecules. At age 65, after he retired as president of Beckman Instruments, Beckman began a new career—heading a foundation which shared his wealth for the support of scientific research and education. In 1984 he and Mabel, his wife of 58 years, donated $40 million to his alma mater—the University of Illinois—to fund the Beckman Institute. The Beckmans' foundation has also funded many other research institutes, including one at Caltech, and currently gives $20 million each year to various scientific endeavors.

Arnold Beckman was a man known for his incredible creativity but even more he was recognized as a man of absolute integrity. Dr. Beckman has important words for us: "Whatever you do, be enthusiastic about it." Dr. Beckman passed away on May 18, 2004, at the age of 104.

SECTION 16.2
REVIEW QUESTIONS

1 What is the importance of pH?

2 Calculate the pH of an aqueous solution that has a concentration of H^+ equal to
a. $2.30 \times 10^{-4} \, M$
b. $4.37 \times 10^{-11} \, M$

3 Calculate the concentration of H^+ in an aqueous solution with a pH of
a. 3.40
b. 9.20

4 Determine the pOH of a solution that has a concentration of H^+ equal to
a. $1.85 \times 10^{-10} \, M$
b. $9.23 \times 10^{-5} \, M$

5 Determine the pH of a solution that has a concentration of OH^- equal to
a. $2.15 \times 10^{-3} \, M$
b. $7.24 \times 10^{-9} \, M$

6 If you placed phenol red in an acid solution what color would the solution turn?

7 Calculate the pH of 100.0 mL of a 0.150 M aqueous solution of HNO_3.

RESEARCH LINKS
CLASSZONE.COM

16.2 • Determining the Acidity of a Solution • **581**

SECTION 16.2
ASSESS

SECTION 16.2
Review Questions

1. The pH scale represents a convenient way to express a solution's acidity. It allows us to represent small numbers without using exponents.

2. **a.** 3.638
   b. 10.363

3. **a.** 4.0×10^{-4}
   b. 6.3×10^{-10}

4. **a.** 4.27
   b. 9.97

5. **a.** 11.33
   b. 5.86

6. yellow

7. 0.824

CHEMISTRY EXPLORERS
Arnold Beckman

Beckman's invention of the pH meter earned him a place in the National Inventors Hall of Fame in 1987. His pH meter was designated as a National Historic Chemical Landmark by the American Chemical Society. In total, Beckman registered 14 patents. Other early products included an ultraviolet spectrophotometer (1940) and an infrared and visible spectrophotometer (1942). By 2004, the Arnold O. and Mabel M. Beckman Foundation had donated approximately $400 million for the advancement of research and education.

Student Preparation

Assign students to read Section 16.3 and to answer the Review Questions at the end of the section before coming to class.

 Active Learning
Team Learning Worksheet

After introducing the material in Section 16.3 in class, place students in groups and have them work together on **Section 16.3: Team Learning Worksheet.**

SECTION 16.3
GUIDE THE LEARNING

Homework

You may wish to assign these selected end-of-chapter problems as homework for this section: 43, 45, 46, 47, 49, 50

Additional end-of-chapter problems can be used for extra practice.

16.3.A Acid–Base Titrations

Objective To learn about acid–base titrations

LABORATORY
EXPERIMENT 69:
Analysis of Vinegar, Microscale

LABORATORY
EXPERIMENT 70:
Quantitative Titration, Traditional

LABORATORY
EXPERIMENT 71:
Conductivity Titration, CBL

TEACHING TIPS

- It is helpful to demonstrate a titration as you discuss it in class. You can carry out a titration of HCl with NaOH. Stop along the way during the titration and calculate the volume of base needed to titrate the acid. Point out that this exercise is just a stoichiometry problem like many that students have encountered previously.

- Have students draw molecular-level pictures of the solution before the titration, at the equivalence point, and beyond the equivalence point. Many students know that equal numbers of ions are present

at the equivalence point but the ions do not form water molecules. Also, many students forget the spectator ions in solution.

- Some students may realize that for phenolphthalein to turn pink, an excess of NaOH must be added to the acid. Thus the endpoint of the titration is not exactly at the stoichiometric point of the reaction. Discuss the

SECTION 16.3
Titrations and Buffers

Key Terms
- Neutralization reaction
- Titration
- Standard solution
- Buret
- Stoichiometric point (equivalence point)
- Titration curve (pH curve)
- Buffered solution

Objectives
- *To learn about acid–base titrations*
- *To understand the general characteristics of buffered solutions*

A. Acid–Base Titrations

By this time you know that a strong acid solution contains H^+ ions and a solution of strong base contains OH^- ions. As we saw earlier, when a strong acid and a strong base are mixed, the H^+ and OH^- react to form H_2O:

$$H^+(aq) + OH^-(aq) \rightarrow H_2O(l)$$

This reaction is called a **neutralization reaction** because if equal amounts of H^+ and OH^- are available for reaction, a neutral solution (pH = 7) will result.

To analyze the acid or base content of a solution, chemists often perform a titration. A **titration** involves the delivery of a measured volume of a solution of known concentration (the *titrant*) into the solution being analyzed (the *analyte*). The titrant contains a substance that reacts in a known way with the analyte. For example, if the analyte contains a base, the titrant would be a **standard solution** (a solution of known concentration) of a strong acid. To run the titration the standard solution of titrant is loaded into a buret. A **buret** is a cylindrical device with a stopcock at the bottom that allows accurate measurement of the delivery of a given volume of liquid (see **Figure 16.7**). The titrant is added slowly to the analyte until exactly enough has been added to just react with all of the analyte. This point is called the **stoichiometric point** or **equivalence point** for the titration. For an acid–base titration the equivalence point can be determined by using a pH meter or indicator. In the titration of a strong acid and a strong base, the equivalence point occurs when an equal amount of H^+ and OH^- have reacted so that the solution is neutral (pH = 7). Thus the titration would stop when the pH meter shows pH = 7. Alternatively, an indicator could be used that changes color near pH = 7.

Active Reading Question

Why can a strong acid–strong base titration be called a neutralization reaction? What is meant by a neutral solution?

Figure 16.7 shows three steps in the titration of a solution of strong acid (the analyte) with a solution of sodium hydroxide (the titrant). The titration is stopped (equivalence point reached) after the drop of NaOH(aq) that first changes the indicator permanently from colorless to red.

Neutralization reaction
An acid–base reaction

Titration
A technique in which a solution of known concentration is used to determine the concentration of another solution

Standard solution
A solution in which the concentration is accurately known

Buret
A device used for the accurate measurement of the delivery of a given volume of a liquid or solution

Equivalence point (stoichiometric point)
The point in a titration when enough titrant has been added to react exactly with the substance in solution that is being titrated

titration curve (Figure 16.9) and show students that a very small excess of NaOH is required to change the color of the indicator. If we use about 20 mL of NaOH to reach the equivalence point, we have added approximately 400 drops. An excess of one or two drops is less than 0.5% error.

Active Reading Question

The base neutralizes the acid because in a neutral solution, $[H^+] = [OH^-]$.

Figure 16.7
The titration of an acid with a base.
(a) The titrant (the base) is in the buret, and the flask contains the acid solution along with a small amount of indicator.
(b) As base is added drop by drop to the acid solution in the flask during the titration, the indicator changes color, but the color disappears on mixing.
(c) The stoichiometric (equivalence) point is marked by a permanent indicator color change. The volume of base added is the difference between the final and initial buret readings.

(a)   (b)   (c)

EXAMPLE 16.11

The Titration of a Strong Acid with a Strong Base

Determine the volume of 0.100 M NaOH needed to titrate 50.0 mL of 0.200 M HNO_3.

Solution
Where do we want to go?

Volume of 0.100 M NaOH = ? mL

What do we know?

- 50.0 mL 0.200 M HNO_3
- 0.100 M NaOH
- $H^+(aq) + OH^-(aq) \rightarrow H_2O(l)$
- HNO_3 is a strong acid containing H^+ and NO_3^- ions.
- NaOH is a strong base containing Na^+ and OH^- ions.

How do we get there?
The titration is shown in **Figure 16.8.** To reach the equivalence point we must add enough OH^- to just react with the H^+ ions originally present in the $HNO_3(aq)$ solution. The neutralization reaction is:

$H^+(aq) + OH^-(aq) \rightarrow H_2O(l)$

That is, at the equivalence point:

moles OH^- added = moles H^+ originally present
From 0.100 M NaOH   From 50.0 mL 0.200 M HNO_3

We can determine the moles of H^+ originally present in the 50.0-mL sample of 0.200 M HNO_3 by multiplying the volume (in L) times the molarity:

$$50.0 \, \cancel{mL} \times \frac{1 \, L}{1000 \, \cancel{mL}} \times \frac{200 \, mol \, H^+}{L}$$

$$= 0.0500 \, \cancel{L} \times 0.200 \, \frac{mol \, H^+}{\cancel{L}} = 1.00 \times 10^{-2} \, mol$$

Figure 16.8
A molecular-level representation of the solutions in the titration of 0.200 M HNO_3 with 0.100 M NaOH. Note that the solutions contain ions because HNO_3 is a strong acid and NaOH is a strong base.

16.3 • Titrations and Buffers • **583**

EXAMPLE 16.11

More Examples

1. Determine the volume of 0.250 M KOH required to titrate 25.0 mL of 0.150 M HCl.
   15.0 mL of 0.250 M KOH

2. Determine the volume of 0.200 M NaOH required to titrate 75.0 mL of 0.250 M HNO_3.
   93.8 mL of 0.200 M NaOH

TECHNOLOGY

Figure 16.8

Video
Acid–Base Titration

Answer to Practice Problem 16.11

The reaction is

$$H^+ + OH^- \rightarrow H_2O$$

75.00 mL of 0.1500 M KOH contains

$$\text{moles } OH^- = 75.00 \text{ mL} \times$$
$$\frac{1.000 \text{ L}}{1.000 \times 10^3 \text{ mL}} \times 0.1500 \frac{\text{mol } OH^-}{\text{L}} =$$

$$1.125 \times 10^{-2} \text{ mol } OH^-$$

To neutralize the KOH solution, we need an equal number of moles of H^+ from the 0.3000 M HCl solution.

$$1.125 \times 10^{-2} \text{ mol } H^+ =$$
$$V \times 0.3000 \frac{\text{mol } H^+}{\text{L}}$$

$$V = \frac{1.125 \times 10^{-2} \text{ mol } H^+}{0.3000 \frac{\text{mol } H^+}{\text{L}}} =$$

$$3.750 \times 10^{-2} \text{ L}$$

$$3.750 \times 10^{-2} \text{ L} \times \frac{1.000 \times 10^3 \text{ mL}}{1.000 \text{ L}} =$$

$$37.50 \text{ mL}$$

The volume of 0.3000 M HCl required is 37.50 mL.

 TEACHING TIPS

- Discuss the results of Example 16.11. Students should notice that since the acid (HNO_3) is twice as concentrated as the base (NaOH), twice as much base (by volume) should be required for the titration. When numbers work well like this, students should get into the habit of estimating answers to justify calculations.

- If you have the capability to run a titration by using a pH meter and projecting it on the board, students will find it very helpful to see the development of a titration curve. Alternatively, you can read the pH at points throughout a titration and develop the curve on the board.

Thus, to complete the titration (give a neutral solution), we must add 1.00×10^{-2} mol OH^-. What volume of 0.100 M NaOH contains 1.00×10^{-2} mol OH^-?

$$\text{? vol} \times 0.100 \frac{\text{mol } OH^-}{L} = 1.00 \times 10^{-2} \text{ mol } OH^-$$

Rearranging the preceding equation gives

$$\text{? vol} = \frac{1.00 \times 10^{-2}}{0.100} \text{ L} = 1.00 \times 10^{-1} \text{ L}$$

Thus

$$\text{? vol} = 0.100 \text{ L} = 100. \text{ mL}$$

Thus it takes 100. mL of 0.100 M NaOH to neutralize 50.0 mL of 0.200 M HNO_3.

 Practice Problem • Exercise 16.11

Calculate the volume of 0.3000 M HCl needed to titrate 75.00 mL of 0.1500 M KOH(*aq*).

In a modern acid–base titration, typically the probe of a pH meter is inserted in the solution being analyzed and the pH is monitored during the entire titration. A plot of the resulting data (pH versus volume of titrant added) is called the **titration curve** (or **pH curve**). The pH curve for the titration of 0.200 M HNO_3 with 0.100 M NaOH (see Example 16.11) is shown in **Figure 16.9**. Notice from this pH curve that the pH changes very rapidly when the titration nears the equivalence point.

So far we have discussed the titration of a strong acid with a strong base such as NaOH(*aq*). Weak acids can also be titrated with NaOH(*aq*). For example, acetic acid ($HC_2H_3O_2$), the weak acid found in vinegar, can be titrated according to the following reaction:

$$OH^-(aq) + HC_2H_3O_2(aq) \rightarrow H_2O(l) + C_2H_3O_2^-(aq)$$

Here the formula for the entire acid is written in the neutralization reaction instead of just H^+, as is the case for strong acids. This is done because acetic acid is a weak acid and retains its H^+ in water. In contrast, OH^- is such a strong base that it can easily extract the H^+ from $HC_2H_3O_2$.

Titration curve (pH curve)
A plot of pH of solution versus volume of titrant added to a given solution

Figure 16.9
The pH curve for the titration of 50.0 mL of 0.200 M HNO_3 with 0.100 M NaOH. Note that the equivalence point occurs at 100.0 mL of NaOH added, the point where exactly enough OH^- has been added to react with all the H^+ originally present. The pH of 7 at the equivalence point is characteristic of a strong acid–strong base titration.

B. Buffered Solutions

A **buffered solution** is one that resists a change in its pH even when a strong acid or base is added to it. For example, when 0.01 mol of HCl is added to 1 L of pure water, the pH changes from its initial value of 7 to a final value of 2, a change of 5 pH units. However, when 0.010 mol of HCl is added to 1.0 L of a solution containing both 0.10 M acetic acid ($HC_2H_3O_2$) and 0.10 M sodium acetate ($NaC_2H_3O_2$), the pH changes from an initial value of 4.74 to a final value of 4.66, a change of only 0.08 pH units. The latter solution is buffered—it undergoes only a very slight change in pH when a strong acid or base is added to it.

Buffered solutions are vitally important to living organisms whose cells can survive only in a very narrow pH range. Many goldfish have died because their owners did not realize the importance of buffering the aquarium water at an appropriate pH. For humans to survive, the pH of the blood must be maintained between 7.35 and 7.45. This narrow range is maintained by several different buffering systems.

A solution is **buffered** by the *presence of a weak acid and its conjugate base.* An example of a buffered solution is an aqueous solution that contains acetic acid and sodium acetate. The sodium acetate is a salt that furnishes acetate ions (the conjugate base of acetic acid) when it dissolves. To see how this system acts as a buffer, we must recognize that the species present in this solution are

$$HC_2H_3O_2, \quad Na^+, \quad C_2H_3O_2^-$$

When $NaC_2H_3O_2$ is dissolved, it produces the separated ions

What happens in this solution when a strong acid such as HCl is added? In pure water, the H^+ ions from the HCl accumulate, thus lowering the pH.

$$HCl \xrightarrow{100\%} H^+(aq) + Cl^-(aq)$$

However, this buffered solution contains $C_2H_3O_2^-$ ions, which are basic. That is, $C_2H_3O_2^-$ has a strong affinity for H^+, as evidenced by the fact that $HC_2H_3O_2$ is a weak acid. This means that the $C_2H_3O_2^-$ and H^+ ions do not exist together in large numbers. Because the $C_2H_3O_2^-$ ion has a high affinity for H^+, these two combine to form $HC_2H_3O_2$ molecules. Thus the H^+ from the added HCl does not accumulate in solution but reacts with the $C_2H_3O_2^-$ as follows:

$$H^+(aq) + C_2H_3O_2^-(aq) \rightarrow HC_2H_3O_2(aq)$$

Next consider what happens when a strong base such as sodium hydroxide is added to the buffered solution. If this base were added to pure water, the OH^- ions from the solid would accumulate and greatly change (raise) the pH.

$$NaOH \xrightarrow{100\%} Na^+(aq) + OH^-(aq)$$

However, in the buffered solution the OH^- ion, which has a *very strong* affinity for H^+, reacts with $HC_2H_3O_2$ molecules as follows:

$$HC_2H_3O_2(aq) + OH^-(aq) \rightarrow H_2O(l) + C_2H_3O_2^-(aq)$$

information

Water: pH = 7

0.01 M HCl: pH = 2

Buffered solution
A solution that resists a change in pH when either an acid or a base are added

For goldfish to survive, the pH of the water must be carefully controlled.

 LABORATORY
EXPERIMENT 72:
Acids, Bases, and Buffers, CBL

TEACHING TIP

The concept of a buffer is one of the more complex ideas covered up to this point. It is important to go slowly through the explanation of how a buffer works. Students need to see each of the possibilities and understand what happens at each step.

MINI-DEMO

Show the effects of a buffer by making an acetic acid/sodium acetate buffer solution (0.1 M for each) in one flask. Place the same amount of distilled water in another flask. Measure the pH of each. Then add a drop of a solution containing H^+ or OH^- to each flask and check the pH. Repeat the process several times.

TECHNOLOGY

 Animation
Buffers
This animation shows the effects of adding a strong acid to a buffered solution.

16.3 • Titrations and Buffers • 585

Active Reading Question

A buffered solution must contain a weak conjugate acid–base pair.

 TEACHING TIP

Discuss the chemical properties that are necessary to produce a buffer, and why it is important to use a weak acid and its salt.

SECTION 16.3
ASSESS

 SECTION 16.3
Review Questions

1. The amounts of H^+ and OH^- are equal at the stoichiometric point in a titration (they react to form water).

2. $(2.5\ M)(x\ \text{mL}) = B(y\ \text{mL})$ where B is the molarity of the base.

3. The equivalence point can be identified by using a pH meter or by using an indicator that changes color at the appropriate pH.

4. 75.0 mL

5. Buffers keep the acidity of a solution relatively constant in the face of additions of either acid or base.

6. When an acid is added to a buffer, the salt anion in the buffer reacts with the acid to produce a weak acid, thus removing the hydrogen ions from the solution.

Active Reading Question

What species must be present in a buffered solution?

This happens because, although $C_2H_3O_2^-$ has a strong affinity for H^+, OH^- has a much stronger affinity for H^+ and thus can remove H^+ ions from acetic acid molecules.

Note that the buffering materials dissolved in the solution prevent added H^+ or OH^- from building up in the solution. Any added H^+ is trapped by $C_2H_3O_2^-$ to form $HC_2H_3O_2$. Any added OH^- reacts with $HC_2H_3O_2$ to form H_2O and $C_2H_3O_2^-$.

The general properties of a buffered solution are summarized in **Table 16.3.**

Table 16.3

The Characteristics of a Buffer

1. The solution contains a weak acid HA and its conjugate base A^-.

2. The buffer resists changes in pH by reacting with any added H^+ or OH^- so that these ions do not accumulate.

3. Any added H^+ reacts with the base A^-.

$$H^+(aq) + A^-(aq) \rightarrow HA(aq)$$

4. Any added OH^- reacts with the weak acid HA.

$$OH^-(aq) + HA(aq) \rightarrow H_2O(l) + A^-(aq)$$

SECTION 16.3
REVIEW QUESTIONS

① What is true about the amounts of H^+ and OH^- at the stoichiometric point in a titration of a strong acid with a strong base?

② At the equivalence point in a titration you know the volume (x mL) of a standard solution of acid (2.5 M) which has been added to a known volume of base (y mL). Show how you can determine the concentration for the base.

③ List two ways to identify the equivalence point in a titration.

④ Determine the volume of 0.250 M NaOH needed to titrate 125.0 mL of 0.150 M HCl.

⑤ What is the importance of a buffered solution?

⑥ How does a buffer keep the pH from changing greatly when an acid is added to the solution?

 RESEARCH LINKS
CLASSZONE.COM

Chapter 16 Review

Key Terms

Key Ideas

16.1 Properties of Acids and Bases

- The Arrhenius model
  - Acids produce H^+ in aqueous solution.
  - Bases produce OH^- in aqueous solution.
- Brønsted–Lowry model
  - Acid → proton donor
  - Base → proton acceptor
  - $HA(aq) + H_2O(l) \rightleftharpoons H_3O^+(aq) + A^-(aq)$
- Acid strength
  - A strong acid is completely dissociated (ionized).
    - ◆ $HA(aq) + H_2O(l) \rightarrow H_3O^+(aq) + A^-(aq)$
    - ◆ Has a weak conjugate base
  - A weak acid is dissociated (ionized only to a very slight extent).
    - ◆ Has a strong conjugate base
- Water is an acid and a base (amphoteric).
  - $H_2O(l) + H_2O(l) \rightleftharpoons H_3O^+(aq) + OH^-(aq)$
  - $K_w = [H_3O^+][OH^-] = 1.0 \times 10^{-14}$ at 25 °C

Relative acid strength	Relative conjugate base strength
Very strong	Very weak
↓ Strong	↑ Weak
Weak	Strong
Very weak	Very strong

Meeting Individual Needs

CHAPTER REVIEW

Chapter 16 Review Worksheet at the appropriate level:
- **Basic**
- **Standard**
- **Challenge**

CHAPTER SUMMARY

A **Chapter Summary** that includes additional Active Reading Questions for Chapter 16 is available.

Assessment Resources

CHAPTER 16

Chapter 16 Test

TECHNOLOGY

 Computerized Test Bank for Chapter 16

pH scale

Indicators

Indicator paper

pH meter

16.2 Determining the Acidity of a Solution

■ The acidity of a solution is expressed in terms of $[H^+]$.

■ $pH = -\log [H^+]$

   • Lower pH means greater acidity ($[H^+]$).

■ $pOH = -\log [OH^-]$

■ For a neutral solution $[H^+] = [OH^-]$.

■ For an acidic solution $[H^+] > [OH^-]$.

■ For a basic solution $[H^+] < [OH^-]$.

■ The pH of a solution can be measured by

   • Indicators

   • pH meter

■ For a strong acid the concentration of H^+ in the solution equals the initial acid concentration.

 Neutralization reaction

Titration

Standard solution

Buret

Stoichiometric point (equivalence point)

Titration curve (pH curve)

Buffered solution

16.3 Titrations and Buffers

■ An acid–base titration is called a neutralization reaction.

■ In a titration a measured volume of a standard solution (titrant) is added to the solution being analyzed (analyte).

■ The titration is stopped as close to the stoichiometric point (equivalence point) as possible as marked by an indicator or pH meter.

■ A buffered solution is a solution that resists a change in its pH when an acid or base is added.

■ Buffered solutions contain a weak acid and its conjugate base.

The Characteristics of a Buffer

1. The solution contains a weak acid HA and its conjugate base A^-.

2. The buffer resists changes in pH by reacting with any added H^+ or OH^- so that these ions do not accumulate.

3. Any added H^+ reacts with the base A^-.

   $$H^+(aq) + A^-(aq) \rightarrow HA(aq)$$

4. Any added OH^- reacts with the weak acid HA.

   $$OH^-(aq) + HA(aq) \rightarrow H_2O(l) + A^-(aq)$$

All exercises with blue numbers have answers in the back of this book.

16.1 Properties of Acids and Bases

A. Acids and Bases

1. What are some physical properties that historically led chemists to classify various substances as acids and bases?

2. In the Arrhenius definition, what characterizes an acid? What characterizes a base? Why are the Arrhenius definitions too restrictive?

3. What is an acid in the Brønsted–Lowry model? What is a base?

4. How do the components of a conjugate acid–base pair differ from one another? Give an example of a conjugate acid–base pair to illustrate your answer.

5. How does a Brønsted–Lowry acid form its conjugate base when dissolved in water? How is the water involved in this process?

6. When an acid is dissolved in water, what ion does the water form? What is the relationship of this ion to water itself?

7. Which of the following represent conjugate acid–base pairs? For those pairs that are not conjugates, write the correct conjugate acid or base for each species in the pair.

a. H_2SO_4, SO_4^{2-} c. $HClO_4$, Cl^-
b. $H_2PO_4^-$, HPO_4^{2-} d. NH_4^+, NH_2^-

8. In each of the following chemical equations, identify the conjugate acid–base pairs.

a. $NH_3 + H_2O \rightleftharpoons NH_4^+ + OH^-$
b. $PO_4^{3-} + H_2O \rightleftharpoons HPO_4^{2-} + OH^-$
c. $C_2H_3O_2^- + H_2O \rightleftharpoons HC_2H_3O_2 + OH^-$

9. Write the conjugate *acid* for each of the following:

a. HSO_4^- c. ClO_4^-
b. SO_3^{2-} d. $H_2PO_4^-$

10. Write the conjugate *base* for each the following:

a. HCO_3^- c. HCl
b. $H_2PO_4^-$ d. HSO_4^-

11. Write a chemical equation showing how each of the following species behaves as a *base* when dissolved in water.

a. NH_3 c. O_2^-
b. NH_2^- d. F^-

12. Write a chemical equation showing how each of the following species behaves as an *acid* when dissolved in water.

a. $HClO_4$ c. HSO_3^-
b. $HC_2H_3O_2$ d. HBr

B. Acid Strength

13. What does it mean to say that an acid is strong in aqueous solution? What does this reveal about the ability of the acid's anion to attract protons?

14. What does it mean to say that an acid is weak in aqueous solution? What does this reveal about the ability of the acid's anion to attract protons?

15. A strong acid has a weak conjugate base, whereas a weak acid has a relatively strong conjugate base. Explain.

16. Name four strong acids. For each acid, write the equation showing the acid dissociating in water.

17. Which of the following acids have relatively strong conjugate bases?

a. CH_3COOH ($HC_2H_3O_2$)
b. HF
c. H_2S
d. HCl

18. Which of the following bases have relatively strong conjugate acids?

a. SO_4^{2-}
b. Br^-
c. CN^-
d. CH_3COO^- ($C_2H_3O_2^-$)

C. Water as an Acid and a Base

19. Anions containing hydrogen (for example, HCO_3^- and $H_2PO_4^{2-}$) show amphoteric behaviour when reacting with other acids or bases. Write equations illustrating the amphoterism of these anions.

20. Write an equation showing the auto-ionization of water. Write the expression for the ion-product constant, K_w, for water.

21. What happens to the hydroxide ion concentration in aqueous solutions when we increase the hydrogen ion concentration by adding an acid? What happens to the hydrogen ion concentration in aqueous solutions when we increase the hydroxide ion concentration by adding a base? Explain.

5. The portion of the original acid molecule or ion that remains after the proton leaves is the conjugate base. In this model, water behaves as the base since it receives the proton from the acid.

6. When an acid is dissolved in water, the hydronium ion (H_3O^+) is formed. The hydronium ion is the conjugate acid of water.

7. (a) The conjugate base of H_2SO_4 is the HSO_4^- ion. The conjugate acid of SO_4^{2-} is also the HSO_4^- ion.
(b) These constitute a conjugate acid–base pair.
(c) The conjugate base of $HClO_4$ is the ClO_4^- ion. The conjugate acid of Cl^- is HCl.
(d) The conjugate base of NH_4^+ is NH_3. The conjugate acid of NH_2^- is also NH_3.

8. (a) NH_3 (base), NH_4^+ (acid); H_2O (acid), OH^- (base)
(b) PO_4^{3-} (base), H_2O (acid); HPO_4^{2-} (acid), OH^- (base)
(c) $C_2H_3O_2^-$ (base), H_2O (acid); $HC_2H_3O_2$ (acid), OH^- (base)

9. (a) H_2SO_4
(b) HSO_3^-
(c) $HClO_4$
(d) H_3PO_4

10. (a) CO_3^{2-}
(b) HPO_4^{2-}
(c) Cl^-
(d) SO_4^{2-}

11. (a) $NH_3 + H_2O$ $NH_4^+ + OH^-$
(b) $NH_2^- + H_2O$ $NH_3 + OH^-$
(c) $O_2^- + H_2O$ $OH^- + OH^-$
(d) $F^- + H_2O$ $HF + OH^-$

12. (a) $HClO_4 + H_2O \rightarrow ClO_4^- + H_3O^+$
(b) $HC_2H_3O_2 + H_2O$ $C_2H_3O_2^- + H_3O^+$
(c) $HSO_3^- + H_2O$ $SO_3^{2-} + H_3O^+$
(d) $HBr + H_2O \rightarrow Br^- + H_3O^+$

13. A strong acid is one for which the equilibrium in water lies far to the right. A strong acid is completely converted to its conjugate base when dissolved in water. The conjugate base must therefore be poor at attracting or holding onto protons.

14. If an acid is weak in aqueous solution, it does not easily transfer protons to water (and does not fully ionize). Thus the anion of the acid must attract protons rather strongly.

Chapter 16 Assessment

1. Acids were recognized primarily from their sour taste. Bases were recognized from their bitter taste and slippery feel on the skin.

2. In the Arrhenius definition, an acid is a substance that produces hydrogen ions (H^+) when dissolved in water.

An Arrhenius base produces hydroxide ions (OH^-) when dissolved in water. These definitions are not complete because they limit bases to compounds with a hydroxide ion, and the only allowable solvent is water.

3. A Brønsted–Lowry acid is a molecule or ion capable of providing a proton to some other species; acids are proton donors. A Brønsted–Lowry base is a molecule or ion capable of receiving a proton from some other species; bases are proton acceptors.

4. A conjugate acid–base pair differs by one hydrogen ion, H^+. For example, $HC_2H_3O_2$ (acetic acid) differs from its conjugate base, $C_2H_3O_2^-$ (acetate ion), by a single hydrogen ion.

15. A strong acid loses its protons easily and fully ionizes in water. Thus the acid's conjugate base is poor at attracting protons (that is, a very weak base). A weak acid does not ionize fully, so its conjugate base must have a rather strong attraction for a proton (that is, it must be a relatively strong base).

16. sulfuric: $H_2SO_4 + H_2O \rightarrow HSO_4^- + H_3O^+$; hydrochloric: $HCl + H_2O \rightarrow Cl^- + H_3O^+$; nitric: $HNO_3 + H_2O \rightarrow NO_3^- + H_3O^+$; hydrobromic: $HBr + H_2O \rightarrow Br^- + H_3O^+$

17. (a) CH_3COO^- is a relatively strong base
    (b) F^- is a relatively strong base
    (c) HS^- is a relatively strong base
    (d) Cl^- is a very weak base

18. (a) HSO_4^- is a moderately strong acid
    (b) HBr is a strong acid
    (c) HCN is a weak acid
    (d) CH_3COOH is a weak acid

19. $HCO_3^-(aq) + OH^-(aq) \rightarrow CO_3^{2-}(aq) + H_2O(l)$; $HCO_3^-(aq) + H^+(aq) \rightarrow H_2CO_3(aq)$; $H_2PO_4^-(aq) + OH^-(aq) \rightarrow HPO_4^{2-}(aq) + H_2O(l)$; $H_2PO_4^-(aq) + H^+(aq) \rightarrow H_3PO_4(aq)$

20. $H_2O + H_2O \rightleftharpoons H_3O^+ + OH^-$; $K_w = [H_3O^+][OH^-]$

21. The hydrogen ion concentration and hydroxide ion concentration are inversely related in aqueous solutions. That is, as the hydrogen ion concentration increases, the hydroxide ion concentration decreases, and vice versa. This is because $K_w = [H^+][OH^-] = 1.0 \times 10^{-14}$ at 25 °C. This value is a constant, so if H^+ or OH^- is added to the solution, the other ion must decrease.

22. (a) $[H^+] = 2.5 \times 10^{-10}$ M; basic
    (b) $[H^+] = 3.4 \times 10^{-6}$ M; acidic
    (c) $[H^+] = 1.4 \times 10^{-13}$ M; basic
    (d) $[H^+] = 1.1 \times 10^{-8}$ M; basic

23. (a) $[OH^-] = 1.00 \times 10^{-7}$ M; neutral
    (b) $[OH^-] = 1.4 \times 10^{-8}$ M; acidic
    (c) $[OH^-] = 1.4 \times 10^{-14}$ M; acidic
    (d) $[OH^-] = 1.7 \times 10^{-9}$ M; acidic

22. Calculate the $[H^+]$ in each of the following solutions, and indicate whether the solution is acidic, basic, or neutral.
    a. $[OH^-] = 3.99 \times 10^{-5}$ M
    b. $[OH^-] = 2.91 \times 10^{-9}$ M
    c. $[OH^-] = 7.23 \times 10^{-2}$ M
    d. $[OH^-] = 9.11 \times 10^{-7}$ M

23. Calculate the $[OH^-]$ in each of the following solutions, and indicate whether the solution is acidic, basic, or neutral.
    a. $[H^+] = 1.00 \times 10^{-7}$ M
    b. $[H^+] = 7.00 \times 10^{-7}$ M
    c. $[H^+] = 7.00 \times 10^{-1}$ M
    d. $[H^+] = 5.99 \times 10^{-6}$ M

24. For each pair of concentrations, tell which represents the more acidic solution.
    a. $[H^+] = 1.2 \times 10^{-3}$ M or $[H^+] = 4.5 \times 10^{-4}$ M
    b. $[H^+] = 2.6 \times 10^{-6}$ M or $[H^+] = 4.3 \times 10^{-8}$ M
    c. $[H^+] = 0.000010$ M or $[H^+] = 0.0000010$ M

25. For each pair of concentrations, tell which represents the more basic solution.
    a. $[H^+] = 1.59 \times 10^{-7}$ M or $[H^+] = 1.04 \times 10^{-8}$ M
    b. $[H^+] = 5.69 \times 10^{-8}$ M or $[OH^-] = 4.49 \times 10^{-6}$ M
    c. $[H^+] = 5.99 \times 10^{-8}$ M or $[OH^-] = 6.01 \times 10^{-7}$ M

16.2 Determining the Acidity of a Solution

A. The pH Scale

26. Why do scientists tend to express the acidity of a solution in terms of its pH, rather than in terms of the molarity of hydrogen ion present? How is pH defined mathematically?

27. Using Figure 16.3, list the approximate pH of five "everyday" solutions. How do the familiar properties (such as sour taste for acids) of these solutions correspond to their pH?

28. For a hydrogen ion concentration of 2.33×10^{-6} M, how many *decimal places* should we give when expressing the pH of the solution?

29. As the hydrogen ion concentration of a solution *increases*, does the pH of the solution increase or decrease? Explain.

30. Calculate the pH corresponding to each of the hydrogen ion concentrations given below. Tell whether each solution is acidic, basic, or neutral.
    a. $[H^+] = 0.00100$ M
    b. $[H^+] = 2.19 \times 10^{-4}$ M
    c. $[H^+] = 9.18 \times 10^{-11}$ M
    d. $[H^+] = 4.71 \times 10^{-7}$ M

31. Calculate the pH corresponding to each of the hydroxide ion concentrations given below. Tell whether each solution is acidic, basic, or neutral.
    a. $[OH^-] = 1.00 \times 10^{-7}$ M
    b. $[OH^-] = 4.59 \times 10^{-13}$ M
    c. $[OH^-] = 1.04 \times 10^{-4}$ M
    d. $[OH^-] = 7.00 \times 10^{-1}$ M

32. Calculate the pH corresponding to each of the pOH values listed, and indicate whether each solution is acidic, basic, or neutral.
    a. pOH = 4.32
    b. pOH = 8.90
    c. pOH = 1.81
    d. pOH = 13.1

33. For each hydrogen or hydroxide ion concentration listed, calculate the concentration of the complementary ion and the pH and pOH of the solution.
    a. $[H^+] = 1.00 \times 10^{-7}$ M
    b. $[OH^-] = 4.39 \times 10^{-5}$ M
    c. $[H^+] = 4.29 \times 10^{-11}$ M
    d. $[OH^-] = 7.36 \times 10^{-2}$ M

34. Calculate the hydrogen ion concentration, in moles per liter, for solutions with each of the following pH values.
    a. pH = 1.04
    b. pH = 13.1
    c. pH = 5.99
    d. pH = 8.62

24. (a) $[H^+] = 1.2 \times 10^{-3}$ M is more acidic
    (b) $[H^+] = 2.6 \times 10^{-6}$ M is more acidic
    (c) $[H^+] = 0.000010$ M is more acidic

25. (a) $[H^+] = 1.04 \times 10^{-8}$ M is more basic
    (b) $[OH^-] = 4.49 \times 10^{-6}$ M is more basic
    (c) $[OH^-] = 6.01 \times 10^{-7}$ M is more basic

26. The concentrations of hydrogen ion present are generally quite small and are best expressed in scientific notation. The pH scale converts these numbers to numbers that are easier to compare. The pH of a solution is defined as the negative of the base 10 logarithm of the hydrogen ion concentration; that is, $pH = -\log[H^+]$.

27. household ammonia (pH 12); blood (pH 7–8); milk (pH 6–7); vinegar (pH 3); lemon juice (pH 2–3); stomach acid (pH 2)

28. The number 2.33×10^{-6} has three significant figures, so the pH must have three significant figures. However, the number in front of the decimal place is not significant (it comes from the exponent). Thus the pH should be

35. Calculate the hydrogen ion concentration, in moles per liter, for solutions with each of the following pOH values.

    a. pOH = 3.91

    b. pOH = 12.56

    c. pOH = 1.15

    d. pOH = 8.77

36. Calculate the hydrogen ion and hydroxide ion concentrations, in moles per liter, for solutions with each of the following pH or pOH values.

    a. pH = 5.12

    b. pOH = 5.12

    c. pH = 7.00

    d. pOH = 13.00

B. Measuring pH

37. Name three ways we can measure the pH of a solution. Which is the most accurate? Explain.

38. Describe how an indicator works. Use a chemical equation in your explanation.

C. Calculating the pH of Strong Acid Solutions

39. When 1 mol of gaseous hydrogen chloride is dissolved in enough water to make 1 L of solution, approximately how many HCl molecules remain in the solution? Explain.

40. A bottle of acid solution is labeled "3 M HNO_3." What are the substances that are actually present in the solution? Are any HNO_3 molecules present? Why or why not?

41. Calculate the hydrogen ion concentration and the pH of each of the following solutions of strong acids.

    a. 1.04×10^{-4} M HCl

    b. 0.00301 M HNO_3

    c. 5.41×10^{-4} M $HClO_4$

    d. 6.42×10^{-2} M HNO_3

42. Calculate the hydrogen ion concentration and the pH of each of the following solutions of strong acids.

    a. 0.00010 M HCl

    b. 0.0050 M HNO_3

    c. 4.21×10^{-5} M $HClO_4$

    d. 6.33×10^{-3} M HNO_3

16.3 Titrations and Buffers

A. Acid–Base Titrations

43. A 100.0-mL sample of 0.50 M HCl(aq) is titrated with 0.10 M NaOH(aq). What volume of the NaOH solution is required to reach the endpoint of the titration?

44. If 26.5 mL of a 0.20 M aqueous solution of NaOH is required to titrate 50.0 mL of an aqueous solution of HNO_3, what is the concentration of the HNO_3 solution?

B. Buffered Solutions

45. What characteristic properties do buffered solutions possess?

46. What two components make up a buffered solution? Give an example of a combination that would serve as a buffered solution.

47. Which component of a buffered solution is capable of combining with an added strong acid? Using your example from exercise 46, show how this component would react with added HCl.

48. Which component of a buffered solution consumes added strong base? Using your example from exercise 46, show how this component would react with added NaOH.

49. Which of the following combinations would act as buffered solutions?

    a. HCl and NaCl

    b. CH_3COOH and CH_3COOK

    c. H_2S and NaHS

    d. H_2S and Na_2S

50. For those combinations in exercise 49 that behave as buffered solutions, write equations showing how the components of the buffer consume added strong acid (HCl) or strong base (NaOH).

36. (a) $[H^+] = 7.6 \times 10^{-6}$ M; $[OH^-] = 1.3 \times 10^{-9}$ M
(b) $[H^+] = 1.3 \times 10^{-9}$ M; $[OH^-] = 7.6 \times 10^{-6}$ M
(c) $[H^+] = [OH^-] = 1.0 \times 10^{-7}$ M
(d) $[H^+] = 1.0 \times 10^{-1}$ M; $[OH^-] = 1.0 \times 10^{-13}$ M

37. We can measure the pH of a solution with a pH meter, pH paper, and indicators. The pH meter is the most accurate.

38. Indicators are substances that turn a different color when H^+ is present than when H^+ is absent. Consider the equation HIn $\rightleftharpoons$ H^+ + In^-. The substance HIn is a different color from the substance In^-.

39. Essentially no molecules of HCl are present because HCl is a strong acid for which the equilibrium with water lies far to the right.

40. The solution contains water molecules, H_3O^+ ions (protons), and NO_3^- ions. No HNO_3 molecules are present because HNO_3 is a strong acid.

41. (a) $[H^+] = 1.04 \times 10^{-4}$ M; pH = 3.983
(b) $[H^+] = 0.00301$ M; pH = 2.521
(c) $[H^+] = 5.41 \times 10^{-4}$ M; pH = 3.267
(d) $[H^+] = 6.42 \times 10^{-2}$ M; pH = 1.192

42. (a) $[H^+] = 0.00010$ M; pH = 4.00
(b) $[H^+] = 0.0050$ M; pH = 2.30
(c) $[H^+] = 4.21 \times 10^{-5}$ M; pH = 4.376
(d) $[H^+] = 6.33 \times 10^{-3}$ M; pH = 2.199

43. 5.0×10^2 mL

44. 0.11 M

45. A buffered solution is one that resists a change in its pH even when a strong acid or base is added to it. A solution is buffered by the presence of the combination of a weak acid and its conjugate base.

46. A buffered solution consists of a mixture of a weak acid and its conjugate base; one example of a buffered solution is a mixture of acetic acid ($HC_2H_3O_2$) and sodium acetate ($NaC_2H_3O_2$).

reported to the third decimal place (5.633).

29. The pH of a solution is defined as the negative logarithm of the hydrogen ion concentration; that is, pH = $-\log[H^+]$. Mathematically, as $[H^+]$ increases, pH must decrease.

30. (a) 3.000 (acidic)
(b) 3.660 (acidic)
(c) 10.037 (basic)
(d) 6.327 (acidic)

31. (a) 7.00 (neutral)
(b) 1.662 (acidic)
(c) 10.017 (basic)
(d) 13.845 (basic)

32. (a) 9.68 (basic)
(b) 5.10 (acidic)
(c) 12.19 (basic)
(d) 0.9 (acidic)

33. (a) $[OH^-] = 1.00 \times 10^{-7}$ M; pH = 7.00; pOH = 7.00
(b) $[H^+] = 2.3 \times 10^{-10}$ M; pH = 9.64; pOH = 4.36
(c) $[OH^-] = 2.33 \times 10^{-4}$ M;
pH = 10.37; pOH = 3.63
(d) $[H^+] = 1.4 \times 10^{-13}$ M; pH = 12.87; pOH = 1.13

34. (a) 0.0912 M
(b) 8×10^{-14} M
(c) 1.0×10^{-6} M
(d) 2.4×10^{-9} M

35. (a) $[H^+] = 8.1 \times 10^{-11}$ M
(b) $[H^+] = 3.6 \times 10^{-2}$ M
(c) $[H^+] = 1.4 \times 10^{-13}$ M
(d) $[H^+] = 5.9 \times 10^{-6}$ M

47. The conjugate base component of the buffered solution is capable of combining with any strong acid that might be added to the buffered solution. For the example from Question 46, we would have $H^+ + C_2H_3O_2^- \rightarrow HC_2H_3O_2$.

48. The weak acid component of the buffered solution reacts with the strong base. For example, hydroxide reacts with the acetic acid as follows: $OH^- + HC_2H_3O_2 \rightarrow H_2O + C_2H_3O_2^-$.

49. (a) not a buffer
(b) a buffer
(c) a buffer
(d) not a buffer

50. added OH^-:
$OH^- + HC_2H_3O_2 \rightarrow H_2O + C_2H_3O_2^-$;
added H^+:
$H^+ + C_2H_3O_2^- \rightarrow HC_2H_3O_2$;
added OH^-:
$OH^- + H_2S \rightarrow H_2O + HS^-$;
added H^+:
$H^+ + HS^- \rightarrow H_2S$

51. (a) $HCl + NH_3 \rightarrow Cl^- + NH_4^+$
(b) $OH^- + NH_3 \rightarrow H_2O + NH_2^-$

52. (a) acidic
(b) basic
(c) acidic
(d) acidic

53. (a) basic
(b) basic
(c) acidic
(d) basic

54. (a) strong acid
(b) weak acid
(c) strong acid
(d) weak acid
(e) strong acid

55. (a) a conjugate acid–base pair
(b) not a conjugate acid–base pair
(c) a conjugate acid–base pair
(d) a conjugate acid–base pair

56. (a) CH_3NH_2 (base), $CH_3NH_3^+$ (acid); H_2O (acid), OH^- (base)
(b) CH_3COOH (acid), CH_3COO^- (base); NH_3 (base), NH_4^+ (acid)
(c) HF (acid), F^- (base); NH_3 (base), NH_4^+ (acid)

57. (a) HF is a weak acid
(b) HCl is a strong acid
(c) H_2SO_4 is a strong acid
(d) HNO_3 is a strong acid

58. (a) $[OH^-] = 0.000320\ M$
(b) $[OH^-] = 1.54 \times 10^{-8}\ M$
(c) $[OH^-] = 4.02 \times 10^{-7}\ M$

Critical Thinking

51. The concepts of acid–base equilibria were developed in this chapter for aqueous solutions (in aqueous solutions, water is the solvent and is intimately involved in the equilibria). However, the Brønsted–Lowry acid–base theory can be extended easily to other solvents. One such solvent that has been investigated in depth is liquid ammonia, NH_3.

   a. Write a chemical equation indicating how HCl behaves as an acid in liquid ammonia.

   b. Write a chemical equation indicating how OH^- behaves as a base in liquid ammonia.

52. Which of the following conditions indicate an acidic solution?

   a. pH < 7.0   c. $[H^+] > [OH^-]$
   b. pOH < 7.0   d. $[H^+] > 1.0 \times 10^{-7}\ M$

53. Which of the following conditions indicate a basic solution?

   a. pOH < 7.0   c. $[OH^-] < [H^+]$
   b. pH > 7.0   d. $[H^+] < 1.0 \times 10^{-7}\ M$

54. Which of the following acids are classified as strong acids?

   a. HNO_3
   b. CH_3COOH ($HC_2H_3O_2$)
   c. HCl
   d. HF
   e. $HClO_4$

55. Which of the following represent conjugate acid–base pairs? For those pairs that are not conjugates, write the correct conjugate acid or base for each species in the pair.

   a. H_2O, OH^- c. H_3PO_4, $H_2PO_4^-$
   b. H_2SO_4, SO_4^{2-} d. $HC_2H_3O_2$, $C_2H_3O_2^-$

56. In each of the following chemical equations, identify the conjugate acid–base pairs.

   a. $CH_3NH_2 + H_2O \rightleftharpoons CH_3NH_3^+ + OH^-$
   b. $CH_3COOH + NH_3 \rightleftharpoons CH_3COO^- + NH_4^+$
   c. $HF + NH_3 \rightleftharpoons F^- + NH_4^+$

57. Which of the following bases have relatively strong conjugate acids?

   a. F^- c. HSO_4^-
   b. Cl^- d. NO_3^-

58. For each pair of concentrations, tell which represents the more basic solution.

   a. $[H^+] = 0.000013\ M$ or $[OH^-] = 0.0000032\ M$
   b. $[H^+] = 1.03 \times 10^{-6}\ M$ or $[OH^-] = 1.54 \times 10^{-8}\ M$
   c. $[OH^-] = 4.02 \times 10^{-7}\ M$ or $[OH^-] = 0.0000001\ M$

59. A poor, misguided chemistry student is working on a laboratory experiment. He has 90.0 mL of a strong base, 0.400 M NaOH. To this he adds 30.0 mL of a 1.75 M solution of HNO_3. He then adds 240.0 mL of water. Will the resulting solution be neutral? What will the $[H^+]$ and pH be? What is the pOH? Would the solution turn litmus pink?

60. An eyedropper is calibrated by counting the number of drops required to deliver exactly 1.00 mL. Twenty drops are required. What is the volume of one drop? Suppose one such drop of 0.200 M HCl is added to 1.00 mL of water. What is the $[H^+]$? By what factor did the $[H^+]$ change when the one drop was added?

61. Determine the pH of 100.0 mL of a 1.00 M HCl solution. Suppose you double the volume of the solution by adding water. What is the new pH? You double the volume once more with water. What is the new pH? If you continue to add more water, what is the maximum pH that can be reached? Explain your answer.

62. You dissolve 0.500 g of a solid acid (HA) in 100. mL of water. You titrate this solution with 0.150 M NaOH. You find that 29.7 mL of the NaOH solution is required to reach the endpoint of the titration. What is the molar mass of the acid? The equation for the reaction between the acid and base is

$HA(aq) + NaOH(aq) \rightarrow NaA(aq) + H_2O(l)$

---

59. The solution will be acidic, with $[H^+] = 0.0458\ M$ and a pH of 1.339; $[OH^-] = 2.18 \times 10^{-13}\ M$

60. $[H^+] = 9.52 \times 10^{-3}\ M$; changed by a factor of 95,200

61. pH = 0.000; pH = 0.301; pH = 0.602; maximum pH = 7.000, since water contributes $1.00 \times 10^{-7}\ M\ H^+$

62. 112 g/mol

1 Which of the following is not a conjugate acid–base pair?

A H_2O, H_3O^+

B H_2CO_3, CO_3^{2-}

C HCl, Cl^-

D $HC_2H_3O_2$, $C_2H_3O_2^-$

2 Which of the following statements about a strong acid is incorrect?

A   A strong acid is considered to be completely ionized in water.

B   In a reaction between a strong acid and water, the forward reaction predominates.

C   A strong acid has a relatively strong conjugate base.

D   A strong acid is also a strong electrolyte.

3 Which of the following is true about a solution in which $[OH^-] = 4.8 \times 10^{-4}\ M$?

A $[H^+] = 2.1 \times 10^{-11}\ M$ and the solution is basic

B $[H^+] = 2.1 \times 10^{-11}\ M$ and the solution is acidic

C $[H^+] = 4.8 \times 10^{-4}\ M$ and the solution is acidic

D $[H^+] = 4.8 \times 10^{-4}\ M$ and the solution is basic

4 Calculate the pH of a solution in which $[OH^-] = 2.3 \times 10^{-3}\ M$.

A   2.64

B   3.58

C   10.42

D   11.36

5 Solution A has a pH of 2.00. Solution B has a pH of 4.00. Which of the following statements is true?

A   Solution B is two times as acidic as solution A.

B   Solution A is one hundred times as acidic as solution B.

C   Solution A is two times as acidic as solution B.

D   Solution B is one hundred times as acidic as solution A.

6 Calculate the pH of a 0.045 M solution of nitric acid.

A   0.045   C   1.35

B   1.00   D   1.65

7 Which of the following is another term for a solution of known concentration?

A   A standard solution

B   A buffered solution

C   An analyte

D   An indicator solution

8 According to the pH curve, what volume of base is required to reach the endpoint in the titration?

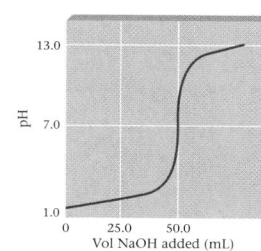

A   0 mL   C   50.0 mL

B   25.0 mL   D   100.0 mL

The following figures are molecular-level representations of acid solutions. Label each as a strong acid or a weak acid.

9

○ H^+
● B^-

10

○ H^+
● A^-

11 Answer the following questions concerning buffered solutions.

a.   Explain what a buffered solution does.

b.   Describe the substances that make up a buffered solution.

b.   Explain how a buffered solution works.

Planning Guide

Section	Segment		Text Features and Components	Labs, Demonstrations, & Activities
17.1 Reaction Rates and Equilibrium **1 Block** pp. 596–604	A	**How Chemical Reactions Occur**		
	B	**Conditions That Affect Reaction Rates**	(SE) Chemistry in Your World: Protecting the Ozone *p. 598*	(TE) Teaching Support: Demonstration *pp. 596–597* (TE) Group Activity *p. 598* (LM) Experiment 73: Iodine Clock Reaction, Traditional Lab Manual Report Sheets Teacher's Lab Guide
	C	**Heterogeneous Reactions**	(SE) Top Ten Antimicrobial Spices *p. 600* (SE) Chemistry in Your World: Some Like It Hot: The Top Ten Spices *p. 600*	(TE) Mini-Demo *p. 599* (TE) Teaching Support: Demonstration *p. 599* (TE) Mini-Demo *p. 600*
	D	**The Equilibrium Condition**		
	E	**Chemical Equilibrium: A Dynamic Condition**		(SE) Hands-On Chemistry: Reaching Equilibrium: Are We There Yet? *p. 604* (LM) Experiment 74: Equilibrium Beads Lab Manual Report Sheets Teacher's Lab Guide
17.2 Characteristics of Equilibrium **0.5 Block** pp. 605–611	A	**The Equilibrium Constant: An Introduction**		
		continued on next page		

Key			
(SE) Student Edition	(TE) Teacher Edition	(RP) Teacher Resource Package	
(AR) Additional Materials	(LM) Lab Materials	(📁) Transparencies	
(💿) DVD	(📀) CD-ROM	(ℹ️) classzone.com	

All Learners	Technology	Review & Assessment	Standards
TE Teaching Tip *p. 596*	**T** Transparency: Figure 17.1 **◉** EasyPlanner	**SE** Key Terms *p. 626* **SE** Questions and Problems *p. 628*	**TE** **NSES** UCP1, UCP2, UCP3, UCP4, A1, A2, B3, B6, E1, E2, F4, F6, G3
TE Teaching Tips *pp. 596–598*	**T** Transparency: Figure 17.2 **T** Transparency: Figure 17.3 **◉** Animation: Gas Phase Reaction of NO and Cl_2 **◉** Animation: Transition States and Activation Energy **◉** Video: Ostwald Process **▤** Lab Generator CD **◉** EasyPlanner	**SE** Critical Thinking *p. 597* **SE** Active Reading Question *p. 597* **SE** Critical Thinking *p. 597* **SE** Key Terms *p. 626* **SE** Questions and Problems *p. 628*	
	◉ Animation: Heterogeneous Catalysis **◉** Animation: Homogeneous Catalysis **◉** Video: Reaction Rate and Concentration **◉** EasyPlanner	**SE** Key Terms *p. 626* **SE** Questions and Problems *p. 628*	
TE Teaching Tips *p. 601* **TE** Misconception *p. 601* **TE** Meeting Individual Needs *p. 602*	**◉** Animation: Equilibrium Decomposition of N_2O_4 **◉** EasyPlanner	**SE** Active Reading Question *p. 602* **SE** Key Terms *p. 626* **SE** Questions and Problems *p. 628*	
TE Teaching Tip *p. 602* **TE** Meeting Individual Needs *p. 603* **RP** Team Learning Worksheet (Sec. 17.1)	**▤** Lab Generator CD **◉** EasyPlanner	**SE** Review Questions (17.1.A–17.1.E) *p. 604* **SE** Questions and Problems *p. 628*	
TE Teaching Tips *pp. 605, 607* **TE** Misconception *p. 606* **TE** Meeting Individual Needs *p. 606* **TE** Meeting Individual Needs *p. 608* **RP** MINT: Math Concepts *TE p. 606*	**◉** EasyPlanner	**SE** Active Reading Question *p. 606* **SE** Practice Problem *p. 606* **TE** More Examples *p. 606* **SE** Active Reading Question *p. 607* **TE** More Examples *p. 608* **SE** Key Terms *p. 627* **SE** Questions and Problems *pp. 628–629*	**TE** **NSES** UCP1, UCP2, UCP3, UCP4, A1, A2, A3

Planning Guide

Section	Segment		Text Features and Components	Labs, Demonstrations, & Activities
17.2 (continued)	**B**	**Heterogeneous Equilibria**	(SE) Celebrity Chemical: Carbon Dioxide *p. 611*	

17.3 Application of Equilibria **2 Blocks** pp. 612–625	**A**	**Le Châtelier's Principle**		(TE) Teaching Support: Demonstration *pp. 612–613*
				 (TE) Mini-Demo *p. 613*
				 (TE) Mini-Demo *p. 616*
				 (TE) Mini-Demo *p. 618*
				 (LM) Experiment 75: Le Châtelier's Principle, Microscale
				     Lab Manual
				     Report Sheets
				     Teacher's Lab Guide

	B	**Applications Involving the Equilibrium Constant**		(LM) Experiment 76: Chemical Equilibrium, Traditional
				     Lab Manual
				     Report Sheets
				     Teacher's Lab Guide
				 (LM) Experiment 77: MOM and Your CBL
				     Lab Manual
				     Report Sheets
				     Teacher's Lab Guide

	C	**Solubility Equilibria**		

Key

(SE) Student Edition	(TE) Teacher Edition	(RP) Teacher Resource Package	
(AR) Additional Materials	(LM) Lab Materials	(🖱) Transparencies	
(◎) DVD	(▶) CD-ROM	(ⓘ) classzone.com	

All Learners	Technology	Review & Assessment	Standards
TE Teaching Tips *p. 609* **RP** Team Learning Worksheet (Sec. 17.2)	**⊙** EasyPlanner	**SE** Active Reading Question *p. 609* **SE** Practice Problem *p. 610* **TE** More Examples *p. 610* **SE** Review Questions (17.2.A–17.2.B) *p. 611* **SE** Key Terms *p. 627* **SE** Questions and Problems *p. 629*	
TE Teaching Tips *pp. 612, 616* **TE** Meeting Individual Needs *p. 615* **TE** Meeting Individual Needs *p. 616* **TE** Meeting Individual Needs *p. 617*	**⊙** Animation: Le Châtelier's Principle **▮** Lab Generator CD **⊙** EasyPlanner	**SE** Active Reading Question *p. 614* **SE** Practice Problem *p. 615* **TE** More Examples *p. 615* **SE** Active Reading Question *p. 617* **TE** More Examples *p. 617* **SE** Practice Problem *p. 618* **SE** Active Reading Question *p. 619* **SE** Practice Problem *p. 619* **TE** More Examples *p. 619* **SE** Key Terms *p. 627* **SE** Questions and Problems *pp. 629–630*	**TE** **NSES** UCP1, UCP3, UCP4, A1, A2, B3, C4, C5, E1, E2, F1, F4, F5
TE Teaching Tip *p. 620* **TE** Meeting Individual Needs *p. 620*	**▮** Lab Generator CD **⊙** EasyPlanner	**SE** Active Reading Question *p. 621* **TE** More Examples *p. 621* **SE** Questions and Problems *p. 630*	
TE Teaching Tip *p. 622* **TE** Meeting Individual Needs *p. 623* **TE** Meeting Individual Needs *p. 624* **RP** Team Learning Worksheet (Sec. 17.3)	**⊙** Animation: Solution Equilibrium **⊙** EasyPlanner	**SE** Active Reading Question *p. 622* **SE** Practice Problem *p. 623* **TE** More Examples *p. 623* **TE** More Examples *p. 623* **SE** Practice Problem *p. 624* **TE** More Examples *p. 624* **SE** Practice Problem *p. 625* **SE** Review Questions (17.3.A–17.3.C) *p. 625* **SE** Key Terms *p. 627* **SE** Questions and Problems *p. 631*	

Resource Materials for Chapter 17

SE Chapter Review *pp. 626–627*

SE Critical Thinking *pp. 631–632*

SE Standardized Test Practice *p. 633*

AR English/Spanish Summaries

▮ English Summaries Audio

▮ Spanish Summaries Audio

RP Meeting Individual Needs Toolkit (MINT)
    Math Concepts
    Chapter Review Worksheets
    Chapter Summaries

RP Solutions Guide

RP Standardized Test Practice

RP Chapter Tests

RP Test Bank

⊙ Test Generator

In this chapter our goals are for students to:

- Understand the collision model of how chemical reactions occur

- Understand activation energy and how a catalyst speeds up a reaction

- Consider reactions with reactants and products in different phases

- Learn how equilibrium is established

- Learn about the characteristics of chemical equilibrium

- Understand the law of chemical equilibrium and how to calculate values for equilibrium constants

- Understand the role that liquids and solids play in constructing the equilibrium expression

- Learn to predict the changes that occur when a system at equilibrium is disturbed

- Learn to calculate equilibrium concentrations from equilibrium constants

- Learn to calculate the solubility product of a salt given its solubility, and vice versa

Chapter 17
Equilibrium

LOOKING AHEAD

Equilibrium can be analogous to traffic flowing both ways on the George Washington bridge between New Jersey and New York.

594

Prereading Questions

1. Heat the reaction, increase the concentrations of the reactants, or add a catalyst.

2. *Answers will vary.* Equilibrium implies a balance. Chemical equilibrium occurs when the rate of the forward reaction equals the rate of the reverse reaction.

3. cations and anions

4. A solution is saturated when as much solute as possible is dissolved at a given temperature.

IN YOUR LIFE

Chemistry is mostly about reactions—processes in which groups of atoms are reorganized. So far we have learned to describe chemical reactions by using balanced equations and to calculate amounts of reactants and products. However, there are many important characteristics of reactions that we have not yet considered.

For example, why does refrigeration prevent food from spoiling? That is, why do the chemical reactions that cause food to decompose occur more slowly at lower temperatures? On the other hand, how can a chemical manufacturer speed up a chemical reaction that runs too slowly to be economical?

It turns out that chemical reactions are also reversible. That is, the reaction can run from "right to left" as written. This has real-life consequences. For example, if we exert ourselves (by running or bike riding, for example) while we are at high elevations, we feel lightheaded. It is also true that athletes who train at high elevations are better able to compete at low elevations, but this effect does not last for long. Why is this?

Refrigeration prevents food spoilage.

WHAT DO YOU KNOW?

Prereading Questions

1. What could you do to speed up a chemical reaction?

2. What do you think of when you hear the word *equilibrium*?

3. When an ionic solid dissolves, what is present in the solution?

4. What does it mean for a solution to be saturated?

Equilibrium • Chapter 17 • **595**

TECHNOLOGY IN THE CLASSROOM

 Transparencies
Figures: 17.1, 17.2, 17.3

 Power Presentation DVD
  PowerPoint Slides
  Animations
    Gas Phase Reaction of NO and Cl_2
    Transition States and Activation Energy
    Heterogeneous Catalysis
    Homogeneous Catalysis
    Equilibrium
    Decomposition of N_2O_4
    Le Châtelier's Principle
    Solution Equilibrium
  Videos
    Ostwald Process
    Reaction Rate and Concentration
  eEdition
  EasyPlanner

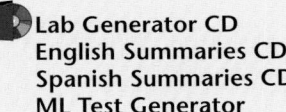 **Lab Generator CD**
  English Summaries CD
  Spanish Summaries CD
  ML Test Generator

 classzone.com

Student Preparation

Assign students to read Section 17.1 and to answer the Review Questions at the end of the section before coming to class.

 Active Learning
Team Learning Worksheet

After introducing the material in Section 17.1 in class, place students in groups and have them work together on **Section 17.1: Team Learning Worksheet**.

Homework

You may wish to assign these selected end-of-chapter problems as homework for this section:
1, 3, 4, 5, 7, 8, 11, 13, 15

Additional end-of-chapter problems can be used for extra practice.

17.1.A How Chemical Reactions Occur

Objective To understand the collision model of how chemical reactions occur

 TEACHING TIP

Use the molecular-level view and Figure 17.1 to show students what happens during a molecular collision.

TECHNOLOGY

 Figure 17.1

17.1.B Conditions That Affect Reaction Rates

Objective To understand activation energy and how a catalyst speeds up a reaction

 TEACHING TIP

Use Figure 17.2 to illustrate the energy changes that occur when the two BrNO molecules from Figure 17.1 interact.

Reaction Rates and Equilibrium

Key Terms

- Collision model
- Activation energy (E_a)
- Catalyst
- Enzymes
- Homogeneous reactions
- Heterogeneous reactions
- Equilibrium
- Chemical equilibrium

Objectives

- *To understand the collision model of chemical reactions*
- *To understand activation energy*
- *To understand how a catalyst speeds up a chemical reaction*
- *To explore reactions with reactants or products in different phases*
- *To learn how equilibrium is established*
- *To learn about the characteristics of chemical equilibrium*

A. How Chemical Reactions Occur

In writing the equation for a chemical reaction, we put the reactants on the left and the products on the right with an arrow between them. But how do the atoms in the reactants reorganize to form the products?

Chemists believe that molecules react by colliding with each other. Some collisions are violent enough to break bonds, allowing the reactants to rearrange to form the products. For example, consider the reaction

$$2BrNO(g) \rightleftharpoons 2NO(g) + Br_2(g)$$

which we think occurs as shown in **Figure 17.1**. Notice that the Br—N bonds in the two BrNO molecules must be broken and a new Br—Br bond must be formed during a collision for the reactants to become products.

The idea that reactions occur during molecular collisions, which is called the **collision model**, explains many characteristics of chemical reactions. For example, it explains why a reaction proceeds faster if the concentrations of the reacting molecules are increased (higher concentrations lead to more collisions and therefore to more reaction events). The collision model also explains why reactions go faster at higher temperatures.

Collision model
Molecules must collide in order to react; used to account for the fact that reaction rate depends on concentrations of reactants and temperature

(a)   (b)   (c)   (d)

Figure 17.1
Visualizing the reaction $2BrNO(g) \rightarrow 2NO(g) + Br_2(g)$. (a) Two BrNO molecules approach each other at high speeds. (b) The collision occurs. (c) The energy of the collision causes the Br—N bonds to break and allows the Br—Br bond to form. (d) The products: one Br_2 and two NO molecules.

B. Conditions That Affect Reaction Rates

It is easy to see why reactions speed up when the *concentrations* of reacting molecules are increased: higher concentrations (more molecules per unit volume) lead to more collisions and so to more reaction events. But reactions also speed up when the *temperature* is increased. Why? The answer lies in the fact that not all collisions possess enough energy to break bonds. A minimum energy called the **activation energy (E_a)** is needed for a

Activation energy (E_a)
The minimum energy required in order to cause a chemical reaction

---

Teaching Support	
DEMONSTRATION	

Temperature and Reaction Rate

Materials

- 12 test tubes
- 0.005 M KMnO$_4$
- 0.75 M H$_2$C$_2$O$_4$ (saturated)
- 2 thermometers
- Water bath (at least a 600-mL beaker, one-third full of water)
- Hot plate

Preparation Place 20 mL KMnO$_4$ in each of six test tubes. Place 20 mL H$_2$C$_2$O$_4$ in each of six additional test tubes. Set up the water bath. Place all test tubes in an empty large beaker.

Procedure Ask a student to determine room temperature. Record this temperature. Place 10 test tubes (5 of each solution) in the water bath and begin heating the water. Assign one student to keep track of the temperature of the water bath. The student should tell you when the temperature of the water reaches reaction to occur (see **Figure 17.2**). If a given collision possesses an energy greater than E_a, that collision can result in a reaction. If a collision has an energy less than E_a, the molecules will bounce apart unchanged.

The reason that a reaction occurs faster as the temperature is increased is that the speeds of the molecules increase with temperature. So at higher temperatures, the average collision is more energetic. This makes it more likely that a given collision will possess enough energy to break bonds and to produce the molecular rearrangements needed for a reaction to occur.

| Higher temperatures | Higher speeds | More high-energy collisions | More collisions that break bonds | Faster reaction |

Active Reading Question

Why does increasing the temperature speed up a chemical reaction?

Figure 17.2
When molecules collide, a certain minimum energy called the activation energy (E_a) is needed for a reaction to occur. If the energy contained in a collision of two BrNO molecules is greater than E_a, the reaction can go "over the hump" to form products. If the collision energy is less than E_a, the colliding molecules bounce apart unchanged.

Is it possible to speed up a reaction without changing the temperature or the reactant concentrations? Yes, by using something called a **catalyst**, *a substance that speeds up a reaction without being consumed.* This may sound too good to be true, but it is a very common occurrence. In fact, you would not be alive now if your body did not contain thousands of catalysts called **enzymes**. Enzymes allow our bodies to speed up complicated reactions that would be too slow to sustain life at normal body temperatures. For example, the enzyme carbonic anhydrase speeds up the reaction between carbon dioxide and water

$$CO_2(g) + H_2O(l) \rightleftharpoons H^+(aq) + HCO_3^-(aq)$$

to help prevent an excess accumulation of carbon dioxide in our blood.

Although we cannot consider the details here, a catalyst works because it provides a new pathway for the reaction—a pathway that has a lower activation energy than the original pathway, as illustrated in **Figure 17.3**. Because of the lower activation energy, more collisions will have enough energy to allow a reaction. This in turn leads to a faster reaction.

Figure 17.3
Comparison of the activation energies for an uncatalyzed reaction (E_a) and for the same reaction with a catalyst present (E'_a). Note that a catalyst works by lowering the activation energy for a reaction.

Catalyst
A substance that speeds up a reaction without being consumed

Enzyme
A large molecule, usually a protein, which catalyzes biological reactions

---

CRITICAL THINKING

Many conditions need to be met to produce a chemical reaction between molecules.

What if all collisions between molecules resulted in a chemical reaction? How would life be different?

CRITICAL THINKING ?

Most modern refrigerators have an internal temperature of 45 °F. What if refrigerators were set at 55 °F in the factory? How would this change affect our lives?

CRITICAL THINKING ?

Most collisions do not result in a chemical reaction because of the energy requirements and positioning of molecules. If all collisions resulted in a chemical reaction, life would be extremely unstable. Virtually everything would happen at a much higher speed (including our aging).

Active Reading Question

As temperature increases, average kinetic energy increases. More collisions occur between reactant molecules, causing more energy to exceed the activation energy.

CRITICAL THINKING

At 55 °F, reactions will occur at a much faster rate than they do at 45 °F. The spoiling of food is a chemical reaction, so food would spoil more quickly. This problem would require us to buy perishable food in smaller quantities and more often.

TEACHING TIP

Compare the reaction curves from Figures 17.2 and 17.3. Point out that Figure 17.2 represents an exothermic reaction and Figure 17.3 represents an endothermic reaction.

TECHNOLOGY

 Figure 17.2

 Figure 17.3

(continued)
10 degrees above room temperature. While waiting for the water bath to heat, run the reaction at room temperature. Using the remaining test tube of $KMnO_4$ and the remaining test tube of $H_2C_2O_4$, explain that you will mix the solutions and students should time the reaction until the color has changed to pale yellow with no remaining purple. The timer should begin as soon as the solutions make contact. Pour the oxalic acid into the potassium permanganate solution. Pour the solutions back and forth twice. Be consistent in all trials. Record the time of the reaction. Place the reacted test tube back in the empty large beaker. Repeat with a second pair of test tubes when the temperature of the water bath is 10 degrees higher than room temperature. Record both the temperature and the time. Increase the water bath temperature by another 10 degrees and repeat the procedure with another pair of test tubes. Continue to repeat the procedure at 10-degree intervals until all test tubes have reacted.

Teaching Notes You can graph time versus temperature as you do the demonstration. Ask students to determine what is happening to the rate of the reaction as the temperature increases. Times for the reaction will vary from about 4 minutes at room temperature to about 5 seconds at the highest temperature.

Animations
Gas Phase Reaction of
NO and Cl_2
Transition States and
Activation Energy

 Video
Ostwald Process
This video provides a real-world
application of catalysis.

 TEACHING TIPS

- Remind students that the
kinetic energy of a collection
of molecules is directly
proportional to the
temperature (K).

- Now is an excellent time to
discuss the use of catalysts.
Catalytic converters in
automobiles use metals such
as palladium and platinum
repeatedly to convert
uncombusted hydrocarbons
into carbon dioxide and
water. In the human body,
enzymes act as catalysts,
thereby speeding up reactions
that would take hours in the
laboratory to fractions of a
second in the body.

Active Learning
Group Activity

Kinetics of Lightsticks
Each team will need three
lightsticks. Students should
prepare a warm water bath (not
to exceed 60 °C) and an ice
bath. When the baths are ready,
each team should activate one
lightstick (the control). The
team should then activate the
other lightsticks, placing one
in the warm water and one in
the ice bath. Have students
compare the lightsticks. Which
is glowing the brightest? What
does this brighter light mean?
Which is dimmest? Why?
Which should stop glowing
first? Why?

Figure 17.4
Data from the Total Ozone
Mapping Spectrometer
(TOMS) Earth Probe for
the month of September,
2003. Areas of depleted
ozone over the Antarctic
are shown in dark blue.

Ozone Destruction A very important example of a reaction involving a catalyst occurs in our atmosphere; it is the breakdown of ozone, O_3, which is catalyzed by chlorine atoms. Ozone is one constituent of the earth's upper atmosphere that is especially crucial, because it absorbs harmful high-energy radiation from the sun. There are natural processes that result in both the formation and the destruction of ozone in the upper atmosphere. The natural balance of all these opposing processes has resulted in an amount of ozone that has been relatively constant over the years. However, the ozone level now seems to be decreasing, especially over Antarctica (see **Figure 17.4**), apparently because chlorine atoms act as catalysts for the decomposition of ozone to oxygen by the following pair of reactions:

$$Cl + O_3 \rightarrow ClO + O_2$$
$$O + ClO \rightarrow Cl + O_2$$
$$\text{Sum: } Cl + O_3 + O + ClO \rightarrow ClO + O_2 + Cl + O_2$$

When species that appear on both sides of the equation are canceled, the end result is the reaction

$$O + O_3 \rightarrow 2O_2$$

CHEMISTRY IN YOUR WORLD

Science, Technology, and Society

Protecting the Ozone

Chlorofluorocarbons (CFCs) are ideal compounds for refrigerators and air conditioners because they are nontoxic and noncorrosive. However, the chemical inertness of these substances, once thought to be their major virtue, turns out to be their fatal flaw. When these compounds leak into the atmosphere, as they inevitably do, they are so unreactive they persist there for decades. Eventually these CFCs reach altitudes where ultraviolet light causes them to decompose, producing chlorine atoms that promote the destruction of the ozone in the stratosphere (see discussion above). Because of this problem, the world's industrialized nations have signed an agreement (called the Montreal Protocol) that banned CFCs in 1996 (with a 10-year grace period for developing nations). So we must find substitutes for the CFCs—and fast.

In fact, the search for substitutes is now well under way. Worldwide production of CFCs has already decreased to half of the 1986 level of 1.13 million metric tons. One strategy for replacing the CFCs has been to switch to similar compounds that contain carbon and hydrogen atoms substituted for chlorine

atoms. For example, the United States appliance industry has switched from Freon-12 (CF_2Cl_2) to the compound CH_2FCH_3 (called HFC-134a) for home refrigerators, and most of the new cars and trucks sold in the United States have air conditioners that employ HFC-134a. Converting the 140 million autos currently on the road in the United States that use CF_2Cl_2 will pose a major headache, but experience suggests that replacement of Freon-12 with HFC-134a is less expensive than was originally feared.

The chemical industry has responded amazingly fast to the ozone depletion emergency. It is encouraging that we can act rapidly when an environmental crisis occurs. Now we need to get better at keeping the environment at a higher priority as we plan for the future.

A modern refrigerator, one of many appliances that now use HFC-134a. This compound is replacing CFCs, which lead to the decomposition of the atmospheric ozone.

Chemistry in Your World
Protecting the Ozone

Use this Chemistry in Your World as an opportunity to interact with the earth science department. Have students research the hole in the ozone layer to determine its effects on plant and animal life. Is the hole in the ozone continuing to grow? Have students find out what products in our society still contain chlorofluorocarbons. Ask them to explain why using these

products in the United States causes problems in Antarctica. This discussion provides an opportunity to integrate the gases chapter (Chapter 13) with this chapter.

Notice that a chlorine atom is used up in the first reaction but a chlorine atom is formed again by the second reaction. Therefore, the amount of chlorine does not change as the overall process occurs. This means that the chlorine atom is a true catalyst: it participates in the process but is not consumed. Estimates show that *one chlorine atom can catalyze the destruction of about one million ozone molecules per second.*

The chlorine atoms that promote this damage to the ozone layer are present because of pollution. Specifically, they come from the decomposition of compounds called Freons, such as CF_2Cl_2, which have been widely used in refrigerators and air conditioners. The Freons have leaked into the atmosphere, where they are decomposed by light to produce chlorine atoms and other substances. As a result, the manufacture of Freons was banned by agreement among the nations of the world as of the end of 1996. Substitute compounds are now being used in most countries in newly manufactured refrigerators and air conditioners.

C. Heterogeneous Reactions

Most of the reactions we have considered in this text occur in one phase. That is, the reactants and products are all gases or the reaction occurs with all reactants and products dissolved in a solution. Reactions involving only one phase are called **homogeneous reactions**.

Many other important reactions involve reactants in two phases. These reactions are **heterogeneous reactions**. An example of a heterogeneous reaction is zinc metal reacting with hydrochloric acid to produce hydrogen gas and aqueous zinc chloride:

$$Zn(s) + 2HCl(aq) \rightarrow H_2(g) + ZnCl_2(aq)$$

This reaction is shown in **Figure 17.5**. The speed of this reaction depends on the surface area of the Zn available to react with H^+ ions from the solution. Large pieces of zinc are associated with a relatively slow reaction; if the zinc is ground up, however, the reaction is greatly accelerated by the increased surface area of the zinc.

(a)

(b)

Figure 17.5
(a) The reaction between Zn and HCl(*aq*).
(b) Molecular-level picture of the reaction

DID YOU KNOW

Although O atoms are too reactive to exist near the earth's surface, they do exist in the upper atmosphere.

Homogeneous reaction
Reaction involving reactants and products in the same state

Heterogeneous reaction
Reaction involving reactants and products in different states

17.1.C Heterogeneous Reactions
Objective To consider reactions with reactants or products in different phases

MINI-DEMO

You can illustrate how the speed of a reaction depends on surface area by using several different 2.0-g samples of zinc (use coarse grades through powdered zinc). Place the Zn samples in separate balloons. Place 30 mL of 1.0 *M* HCl in several 125-mL Erlenmeyer flasks. Attach the balloons so as to cover the mouth of each flask, being careful not to spill any of the zinc into the flask or to tear the balloon. Have students carefully raise all balloons to empty the zinc into the flasks at the same time. Observe the reaction as the assemblies stand on the table. The reaction rates should be apparent from the speed at which the balloons fill with gas.

TECHNOLOGY

Animations
Heterogeneous Catalysis
Homogeneous Catalysis

Teaching Support
DEMONSTRATION

Visualizing a Reaction

Materials
- $KNaC_4H_4O_6$ crystals
- $CoCl_2$ crystals
- 400-mL beaker
- 6% hydrogen peroxide
- Hot plate
- Teaspoon

Preparation Place 6 g of $KNaC_4H_4O_6$ crystals in the beaker. Add 100 mL distilled water and dissolve the crystals.

Procedure Warm the solution of $KNaC_4H_4O_6$ to about 60 °C. Add 40 mL of hydrogen peroxide. Add a few crystals ($\frac{1}{2}$ teaspoon) of $CoCl_2$ to the solution. A vigorous reaction occurs and the solution turns green with lots of bubbling. Eventually the solution will return to its original pink color.

Teaching Notes This reaction involves the oxidation of tartrate by the peroxide to form $CO_2(g)$, $O_2(g)$, and oxalic acid. The green color occurs because of the activated complex for the reaction. The cobalt(II) ion is the catalyst for the reaction. The pink color at the beginning and end of the reaction indicates the presence of the catalyst $[Co^{2+}(aq)]$.

TECHNOLOGY

Video
Reaction Rate and
  Concentration
This video shows the effect of
concentration on the rate of
a reaction.

MINI-DEMO

Sprinkling flour, lycopodium
powder, or granular iron in
a burner flame shows the
dependence of combustion
rate on particle size. Now is
an excellent time to discuss
explosions such as grain dust
explosions in storage silos or
coal dust explosions in mines.

TOP TEN

Students can choose a spice
and write about its origin, its
chemical structure, recipes that
includes the spice, its uses in
alternative medicine, and other
relevant information.

If you are ready for a classroom
adventure, students can bring
in samples of different foods
containing the spices for taste
comparisons.

Figure 17.6
A grain elevator near
Haysville, Kansas, was
severely damaged by a
grain dust explosion.

Another example of the effect of surface area on the rate of a heterogeneous reaction is the explosive combustion of grain dust. Although grains of wheat will burn, the combustion reaction is relatively slow and controlled. In a storage silo, however, the tiny bits of dry plant materials ("grain dust") that become airborne as grain is poured into the silo can combust explosively if a spark occurs. The force of these explosions is quite devastating (see **Figure 17.6**). The reaction of grain dust occurs explosively because the tiny sizes of the dust particles expose a tremendous amount of surface area to the oxygen in the air.

Let's Review

Factors That Affect Reaction Rates

Nature of Reactants: Substances vary greatly in their tendency to react depending on their bond strengths and structures.

Concentration (Pressure): The rate of a homogeneous reaction depends on the number of collisions that occur between reactants. Reaction rates typically increase as concentration (solution reactions) or pressure (gaseous reactions) increases.

Temperature: Because increased temperature accelerates reactant speeds, and thus increases the number of high-energy collisions, reaction rates increase with an increase in temperature.

Surface Area: For heterogeneous reactions, reaction rates increase with increased surface area.

CHEMISTRY IN YOUR WORLD

Consumer Connection

Some Like It Hot: The Top Ten Spices

Have you ever noticed that a direct relationship exists between the temperature of a place and the spiciness of its food? That is, the closer a country is to the equator, the spicier its food tends to be. Think about the difference between Scandinavian food, which uses relatively few spices, and Thai food, which often is extremely "hot." An extensive study headed by biologist Paul Sherman of Cornell University has confirmed this relationship. Sherman and his students reviewed 4600 recipes from more than 90 cookbooks of traditional food from 36 countries and found that the amount of spicing is directly proportional to the warmth of the country's climate.

What's responsible for this interesting correlation? Kinetics. Food spoils by chemical reactions, and

Top Ten Antimicrobial Spices
Garlic
Onion
Allspice
Oregano
Thyme
Cinnamon
Tarragon
Cumin
Cloves
Lemon grass

chemical reactions occur much more rapidly at higher temperatures. That's why we have refrigerators. Keeping food cold makes it last much longer because the bacteria that cause food to spoil grow much more slowly at low temperatures. In ancient times before refrigeration existed, people had to find other ways to preserve their food. Obviously, this issue would be a much greater problem near the equator than near the Arctic Circle. People discovered that certain spices are very effective at killing bacteria. The Top Ten table lists the top ten spices in order of their antimicrobial (bacteria-killing) ability. It seems clear that "hot" spices protect food against hot temperatures.

Garlic is the most popular spice.

600 • Chapter 17 • Equilibrium

Chemistry in Your World

Some Like It Hot: The Top Ten Spices

Have students research methods for preserving food without refrigeration. This project can be done in connection with a social science study.

Students can also undertake a project to determine the effectiveness of refrigeration in controlling the growth of microbes. This project can be used as a connection to biology. Have students obtain two samples

of fresh food. One should be covered and refrigerated, the other covered but not refrigerated. Test each sample for microbes daily by using biological techniques for culturing microbes.

D. The Equilibrium Condition

Equilibrium is a word that implies balance or steadiness. When we say that someone is maintaining his or her equilibrium, we are describing a state of balance among various opposing forces. The term is used in a similar but more specific way in chemistry. Chemists define **equilibrium** as the *exact balancing of two processes, one of which is the opposite of the other.*

> **Equilibrium**
> The exact balance of two processes, one of which is opposite of the other

Evaporation   Condensation

We first encountered the concept of equilibrium in Chapter 14, when we described the way vapor pressure develops over a liquid in a closed container. This equilibrium process is summarized in **Figure 17.7.** The *equilibrium state* occurs when the rate of evaporation exactly equals the rate of condensation.

 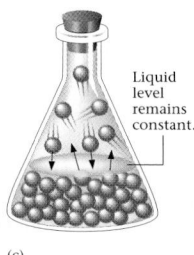

Liquid level is decreasing.

Liquid level remains constant.

(a)   (b)   (c)

Figure 17.7
The establishment of the equilibrium vapor pressure over a liquid in a closed container.
(a) At first there is a net transfer of molecules from the liquid state to the vapor state.
(b) After a while, the amount of the substance in the vapor state becomes constant—both the pressure of the vapor and the level of the liquid stay the same. This is the equilibrium state.
(c) The equilibrium state is very dynamic. The vapor pressure and liquid level remain constant because exactly the same number of molecules escape the liquid as return to it.

So far in this textbook we have usually assumed that reactions proceed to completion—that is, until one of the reactants "runs out." Indeed, many reactions *do* proceed essentially to completion. For such reactions we can assume that the reactants are converted to products until the limiting reactant is completely consumed. On the other hand, there are many chemical reactions that "stop" far short of completion when they are allowed to take place in a closed container. An example is the reaction of nitrogen dioxide to form dinitrogen tetroxide.

$$NO_2(g) + NO_2(g) \rightarrow N_2O_4(g)$$
Reddish-brown   Colorless

The reactant NO_2 is a reddish-brown gas, and the product N_2O_4 is a colorless gas. Imagine an experiment where pure NO_2 is placed in an empty, sealed glass vessel at 25 °C. The initial dark brown color will decrease in intensity as the NO_2 is converted to colorless N_2O_4. However, even over a long period of time, the contents of the reaction vessel do not become colorless. Instead, the intensity of the brown color eventually becomes

17.1 • Reaction Rates and Equilibrium • **601**

 TEACHING TIPS

• Point out that equilibrium can be reached only in closed systems. Such systems include gases in closed containers and ions in solution (since the ions cannot escape). In industry, processes rarely reach equilibrium. Instead, they are designed to maximize the amount of product formed (and avoid the limitation of equilibrium) by removing the product as it is formed.

• Emphasize that equilibrium is *not* a condition in which the reactants and products are present in equal amounts. The balance is between the rates of the forward and reverse reactions.

 MISCONCEPTION Chemistry

Students often think that equilibrium is a static condition. Emphasize that although at the macroscopic level things appear to be constant at equilibrium, at the molecular level chemical reactions continue to occur. The rates of the forward and reverse reactions are equal.

TECHNOLOGY

 Animation
Equilibrium Decomposition of N_2O_4

17.1.E Chemical Equilibrium: A Dynamic Condition

Objective To learn about the characteristics of chemical equilibrium

 LABORATORY
EXPERIMENT 74:
Equilibrium Beads

TEACHING TIP

The concept of equilibrium is one of the most difficult for students to understand. Proceed slowly and use many examples in this chapter.

Chemical equilibrium
A dynamic state where the concentrations of the reactants and the products remain constant over time, as long as the conditions are not changed

nformation

A double arrow ($\rightleftharpoons$) is used to show that a reaction is occurring in both directions.

nformation

Equilibrium is a dynamic situation.

constant, which means that the concentration of NO_2 is no longer changing. This simple observation is a clear indication that the reaction has "stopped" short of completion. In fact, the reaction has not stopped. Rather, the system has reached **chemical equilibrium**, *a dynamic state where the concentrations of all reactants and products remain constant.*

This situation is similar to the one where a liquid in a closed container develops a constant vapor pressure, except that in this case two opposite chemical reactions are involved. When pure NO_2 is first placed in the closed flask, there is no N_2O_4 present. As collisions between NO_2 molecules occur, N_2O_4 is formed and the concentration of N_2O_4 in the container increases. However, the reverse reaction can also occur. A given N_2O_4 molecule can decompose into two NO_2 molecules.

$$N_2O_4(g) \rightarrow NO_2(g) + NO_2(g)$$

That is, chemical reactions are *reversible;* they can occur in either direction. We usually indicate this fact by using double arrows.

$$2NO_2(g) \underset{\text{Reverse}}{\overset{\text{Forward}}{\rightleftharpoons}} N_2O_4(g)$$

In this case the double arrows mean that either two NO_2 molecules can combine to form an N_2O_4 molecule (the *forward* reaction) or an N_2O_4 molecule can decompose to give two NO_2 molecules (the *reverse* reaction).

Equilibrium is reached whether pure NO_2, pure N_2O_4, or a mixture of NO_2 and N_2O_4 is initially placed in a closed container. In any of these cases, conditions will eventually be reached in the container such that N_2O_4 is being formed and is decomposing at exactly the same rate. This leads to chemical equilibrium, a dynamic situation where the concentrations of reactants and products remain the same indefinitely, as long as the conditions are not changed.

 Active Reading Question

What do the double arrows in a chemical equation indicate?

E. Chemical Equilibrium: A Dynamic Condition

Because no changes occur in the concentrations of reactants or products in a reaction system at equilibrium, it may appear that everything has stopped. However, this is not the case. On the molecular level there is frantic activity. Equilibrium is not static but is a highly *dynamic* situation. Consider again the analogy between chemical equilibrium and two island cities connected by a single bridge. Suppose the traffic flow on the bridge is the same in both directions. It is obvious that there is motion (we can see the cars traveling across the bridge), but the number of cars in each city does not change because there is an equal flow of cars entering and leaving. The result is no *net* change in the number of cars in each of the two cities.

To see how this concept applies to chemical reactions, let's consider the reaction between steam and carbon monoxide in a closed vessel at a high temperature where the reaction takes place rapidly.

$$H_2O(g) + CO(g) \rightleftharpoons H_2(g) + CO_2(g)$$

Assume that the same number of moles of gaseous CO and gaseous H_2O are placed in a closed vessel and allowed to react (see **Figure 17.8a**).

Meeting Individual Needs
INCLUSION STRATEGIES

When explaining reversible reactions, write the reversible reaction using the double arrows. Then write the forward reaction and the reverse reaction separately so students can better comprehend the meaning of the double arrow.

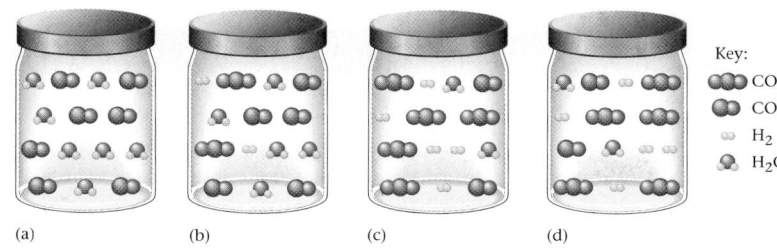

(a) (b) (c) (d)

Key:
- CO_2
- CO
- H_2
- H_2O

Figure 17.8
The reaction of H_2O and CO to form CO_2 and H_2 as time passes.
(a) Equal numbers of moles of H_2O and CO are mixed in a closed container.
(b) The reaction begins to occur, and some products (H_2 and CO_2) are formed.
(c) The reaction continues as time passes and more reactants are changed to products.
(d) Although time continues to pass, the numbers of reactant and product molecules are the same as in (c). No further changes are seen as time continues to pass. The system has reached equilibrium.

When CO and H_2O, the reactants, are mixed, they immediately begin to react to form the products, H_2 and CO_2. This leads to a decrease in the concentrations of the reactants, but the concentrations of the products, which were initially at zero, are increasing (see **Figure 17.8b**). After a certain period of time, the concentrations of reactants and products no longer change at all—equilibrium has been reached (see **Figure 17.8c and d**). Unless the system is somehow disturbed, no further changes in the concentrations will occur.

Why does equilibrium occur? We saw earlier in this chapter that molecules react by colliding with one another, and that the more collisions, the faster the reaction. This is why the speed of a reaction depends on concentrations. In this case the concentrations of H_2O and CO are lowered as the forward reaction occurs—that is, as products are formed.

$$H_2O + CO \rightarrow H_2 + CO_2$$

As the concentrations of the reactants decrease, the forward reaction slows down (see **Figure 17.9**). But, there is also movement in the reverse direction.

$$H_2 + CO_2 \rightarrow H_2O + CO$$

Initially in this experiment, no H_2 and CO_2 are present, so this reverse reaction cannot occur. However, as the forward reaction proceeds, the concentrations of H_2 and CO_2 build up and the speed (or rate) of the reverse reaction increases (Figure 17.9) as the forward reaction slows down. Eventually the concentrations reach levels at which *the rate of the forward reaction equals the rate of the reverse reaction*. The system has reached equilibrium.

Reaction rates

Rate of forward reaction ($H_2O + CO \rightarrow$)
Rate of reverse reaction ($H_2 + CO_2 \rightarrow$)
Equilibrium
Forward rate = Reverse rate

Time

Figure 17.9
The changes with time in the rates of the forward and reverse reactions for $H_2O(g) + CO(g) \rightleftharpoons H_2(g) + CO_2(g)$ when equal numbers of moles of $H_2O(g)$ and $CO(g)$ are mixed. At first, the rate of the forward reaction decreases and the rate of the reverse reaction increases. Equilibrium is reached when the forward rate and the reverse rate become the same.

Meeting Individual Needs
ENGLISH LANGUAGE LEARNERS

Point out that the word *equilibrium* is synonymous with *equal* or in balance. Discuss as a class how the term equilibrium can be applied to various real-world contexts. Explain that in a chemical system, equilibrium is when the rate of the forward reaction is in balance with the rate of the reverse reaction.

SECTION 17.1
Review Questions

1. Molecules must collide for a chemical reaction to occur.

2. A catalyst provides a new pathway with a lower activation energy. Thus, at a given temperature, more molecules have enough energy to react and speed up the chemical reaction.

3. At lower temperatures, molecules have a lower average kinetic energy. Thus, fewer molecules will have the necessary activation energy for the chemical reaction. Since only molecules having this energy actually react, the chemical reaction will proceed at a slower rate.

4. Grinding increases its surface area, which increases the number of collisions that this substance has with other molecules. More collisions increase the chemical reaction rate.

5. *Answers will vary.* An example of a heterogeneous reaction is a precipitation reaction, such as $AgNO_3(aq) + NaCl(aq) \rightarrow AgCl(s) + NaNO_3(aq)$. An example of a homogeneous reaction is $N_2(g) + 3H_2(g) \rightarrow 2NH_3(g)$.

6. The rates of the forward and the reverse reactions are equal at equilibrium.

7. At the molecular level, chemical reactions continue to occur at equilibrium. The rates of the forward and reverse reactions are equal but both are still occurring.

HANDS-ON CHEMISTRY • MINI-LAB •

Reaching Equilibrium: Are We There Yet?

Materials
- two large containers
- water
- large cup, small cup
- permanent marker

Procedure

1. Fill two large containers with different amounts of water. (Plastic milk jugs cut in half horizontally work well.) You will also need a large cup, a small cup, a marker, and a partner.

2. Mark the level of water on the outside of each container.

3. Each person should do the following using his or her container:
   a. Fill the cup as much as possible by dipping it into the container.
   b. Pour the cup of water into your partner's container.

4. Repeat step 3 until the water level in each container is no longer changing. It is important that the same number of transfers occur in each direction.

5. Make five additional transfers as in step 3. Observe what happens to the water levels.

Results/Analysis

1. How many transfers were required until the water levels stopped changing?

2. Why does the level of water in each container stop changing? How is this situation similar to chemical equilibrium?

3. Even after the volume of water in each container stopped changing, water was still being transferred from one container to another. How is this situation similar to chemical equilibrium?

SECTION 17.1
REVIEW QUESTIONS

❶ What is the main idea of the collision model?

❷ How does a catalyst speed up a chemical reaction?

❸ Use collision theory to explain why reactions should occur more slowly at lower temperatures.

❹ Explain how grinding a solid in a heterogeneous reaction can speed up the reaction. Use collision theory in your answer.

❺ Provide an example of a heterogeneous reaction and an example of a homogeneous reaction. Support your answer.

❻ What is equal at equilibrium?

❼ At the macroscopic level a system at equilibrium appears to be unchanging. Is it also unchanging at the molecular level? Explain.

RESEARCH LINKS
CLASSZONE.COM

Hands-On Chemistry
MINI-LAB

Reaching Equilibrium: Are We There Yet?

Materials Each group will need two large containers (plastic milk jugs cut in half work well), a large cup (15 oz), a small cup (5 oz), water, and a marker.

Purpose Students will better understand that chemical equilibrium is a dynamic process even when it appears to be static (it is microscopically dynamic and macroscopically static).

Discussion Students sometimes have difficulty grasping the idea that chemical equilibrium is a dynamic condition. This confusion makes sense because we usually think of equilibrium as a balance, and something that is balanced is not moving. This discussion reveals the benefits of taking a microscopic approach to studying chemistry; that is, a system at equilibrium may appear to the human eye to be unmoving, but at a molecular level it is dynamic. The balance is between the rates of the forward and reverse reactions.

The number of transfers will vary, although equilibrium should be achieved within several minutes.

Characteristics of Equilibrium

Objectives

- *To understand the law of chemical equilibrium*
- *To learn to calculate values for the equilibrium constant*
- *To understand how the presence of solids or liquids affects the equilibrium expression*

Key Terms

- Law of chemical equilibrium
- Equilibrium expression
- Equilibrium constant
- Equilibrium position
- Homogeneous equilibria
- Heterogeneous equilibria

A. The Equilibrium Constant: An Introduction

Science is based on the results of experiments. The development of the equilibrium concept is typical. On the basis of their observations of many chemical reactions, two Norwegian chemists, Cato Maximilian Guldberg and Peter Waage, proposed in 1864 the **law of chemical equilibrium** (originally called the *law of mass action*) as a general description of the equilibrium condition. Guldberg and Waage postulated that for a reaction of the type

$$a\text{A} + b\text{B} \rightleftharpoons c\text{C} + d\text{D}$$

where A, B, C, and D represent chemical species and *a, b, c,* and *d* are their coefficients in the balanced equation, the law of chemical equilibrium is represented by the following **equilibrium expression**:

$$K = \frac{[\text{C}]^c[\text{D}]^d}{[\text{A}]^a[\text{B}]^b}$$

The square brackets indicate the concentrations of the chemical species *at equilibrium* (in units of mol/L), and *K* is a constant called the **equilibrium constant**. Note that the equilibrium expression is a special ratio of the concentrations of the products to the concentrations of the reactants. Each concentration is raised to a power corresponding to its coefficient in the balanced equation.

The law of chemical equilibrium as proposed by Guldberg and Waage is based on experimental observations. Experiments on many reactions showed that the equilibrium condition could always be described by this special ratio, called the equilibrium expression.

To see how to construct an equilibrium expression, consider the reaction where ozone changes to oxygen:

$$\underset{\underset{\text{Reactant}}{\uparrow}}{\overset{\overset{\text{Coefficient}}{\downarrow}}{2\text{O}_3(g)}} \quad \rightleftharpoons \quad \underset{\underset{\text{Product}}{\uparrow}}{\overset{\overset{\text{Coefficient}}{\downarrow}}{3\text{O}_2(g)}}$$

To obtain the equilibrium expression, we place the concentration of the product in the numerator and the concentration of the reactant in the denominator.

$$\frac{[\text{O}_2]}{[\text{O}_3]} \begin{array}{l} \leftarrow \text{Product} \\ \leftarrow \text{Reactant} \end{array}$$

Then we use the coefficients as powers.

$$K = \frac{[\text{O}_2]^3}{[\text{O}_3]^2} \quad \text{Coefficients become powers}$$

MATH

Square brackets, [ ], indicate concentration units of mol/L.

Student Preparation

Assign students to read Section 17.2 and to answer the Review Questions at the end of the section before coming to class.

Active Learning
Team Learning Worksheet

After introducing the material in Section 17.2 in class, place students in groups and have them work together on **Section 17.2: Team Learning Worksheet.**

Homework

You may wish to assign these selected end-of-chapter problems as homework for this section: 16, 17, 19, 20, 21, 23, 25

Additional end-of-chapter problems can be used for extra practice.

17.2.A The Equilibrium Constant: An Introduction

Objective To understand the law of chemical equilibrium and to learn how to calculate values for the equilibrium constant

TEACHING TIPS

- Make sure you use balanced chemical equations, including states for each chemical species, in this section. We discuss heterogeneous equilibria in the next section, and students will need to distinguish among the states of the chemicals.

- Once students understand how to set up the equilibrium expression for a reaction, you can begin to talk about calculations involving the expression. It is important to distinguish between initial conditions and equilibrium conditions when students begin calculations.

In the equilibrium expression, the concentrations of the reactants and products are taken to the power of their coefficients in the balanced equation.

EXAMPLE 17.1

More Examples

Write the equilibrium expression for the following reactions.

1. $CH_3OH(g) \rightleftharpoons CH_2O(g) + H_2(g)$

$$K = \frac{[CH_2O(g)][H_2(g)]}{[CH_3OH(g)]}$$

2. $4NH_3(g) + 5O_2(g) \rightleftharpoons 4NO(g) + 6H_2O(g)$

$$K = \frac{[NO(g)]^4[H_2O(g)]^6}{[NH_3(g)]^4[O_2(g)]^5}$$

 Answer to Practice Problem 17.1

Applying the law of chemical equilibrium gives

 MISCONCEPTION Math

When using calculators to determine equilibrium constants from equilibrium concentrations, students sometimes neglect the order of operations. For example, many students will get an incorrect answer of 4.5 when calculating $\frac{6}{4 \times 3}$, instead of the correct answer, 0.5. This occurs when a student enters

6 ÷ 4 × 3 into the calculator instead of

6 ÷ 4 ÷ 3 or

6 ÷ ((4 × 3)).

Why must you first balance a chemical equation before you can write the equilibrium expression?

EXAMPLE 17.1

Writing Equilibrium Expressions

Write the equilibrium expression for the following reactions.

  a. $H_2(g) + F_2(g) \rightleftharpoons 2HF(g)$ **b.** $N_2(g) + 3H_2(g) \rightleftharpoons 2NH_3(g)$

Solution

Applying the law of chemical equilibrium, we place products over reactants (using square brackets to denote concentrations in units of moles per liter) and raise each concentration to the power that corresponds to the coefficient in the balanced chemical equation.

MATH ✛

A number raised to a power of 1 shows no exponent:

$x^1 = x$

  a. $K = \dfrac{[HF]^2}{[H_2][F_2]}$ ← Product (coefficient of 2 becomes power of 2)

  ← Reactants (coefficients of 1 become powers of 1)

  Note that when a coefficient (power) of 1 occurs, it is not written but is understood.

  b. $K = \dfrac{[NH_3]^2}{[N_2][H_2]^3}$

✔ **Practice Problem • Exercise 17.1**

Write the equilibrium expression for the following reaction.

$$4NH_3(g) + 7O_2(g) \rightleftharpoons 4NO_2(g) + 6H_2O(g)$$

What does the equilibrium expression mean? It means that, for a given reaction at a given temperature, the special ratio of the concentrations of the products to reactants defined by the equilibrium expression will always be equal to the same number—namely, the equilibrium constant K. For example, consider a series of experiments on the ammonia synthesis reaction

$$N_2(g) + 3H_2(g) \rightleftharpoons 2NH_3(g)$$

carried out at 500 °C to measure the concentrations of N_2, H_2, and NH_3 present at equilibrium. The results of these experiments are shown in **Table 17.1.** In this table, subscript zeros next to square brackets are used to *indicate initial concentrations:* the concentrations of reactants and products originally mixed together before any reaction has occurred.

  Consider the results of experiment I. One mole each of N_2 and H_2 were sealed into a 1-L vessel at 500 °C and allowed to reach chemical equilibrium. At equilibrium the concentrations in the flask were found to be $[N_2] = 0.921\ M$, $[H_2] = 0.763\ M$, and $[NH_3] = 0.157\ M$. The equilibrium expression for the reaction

$$N_2(g) + 3H_2(g) \rightleftharpoons 2NH_3(g)$$

is

$$K = \frac{[NH_3]^2}{[N_2][H_2]^3} = \frac{(0.157)^2}{(0.921)(0.763)^3} = 0.0602 = 6.02 \times 10^{-2} \qquad .$$

Meeting Individual Needs
READING STRATEGIES

Read aloud the equilibrium expressions in the solution to Example 17.1, and throughout this section, so students can better interpret the mathematical meaning.

Meeting Individual Needs
MATH CONCEPTS

For students who need extra help with concentrations, have them read *Exponents and Square Roots* located in the *Teacher Resources.* A worksheet is available to go along with the handout.

Table 17.1

Results of Three Experiments for the Reaction $N_2(g) + 3H_2(g) \rightleftharpoons 2NH_3(g)$ at 500 °C

Experiment	Initial Concentrations			Equilibrium Concentrations			$\dfrac{[NH_3]^2}{[N_2][H_2]^3} = K^*$
	$[N_2]_0$	$[H_2]_0$	$[NH_3]_0$	$[N_2]$	$[H_2]$	$[NH_3]$	
I	1.00 M	1.000 M	0	0.921 M	0.763 M	0.157 M	$\dfrac{(0.157)^2}{(0.921)(0.763)^3} = 0.0602$
II	0	0	1.000 M	0.399 M	1.197 M	0.203 M	$\dfrac{(0.203)^2}{(0.399)(1.197)^3} = 0.0602$
III	2.00 M	1.00 M	3.00 M	2.59 M	2.77 M	1.82 M	$\dfrac{(1.82)^2}{(2.59)(2.77)^3} = 0.0602$

*The units for K are customarily omitted.

Similarly, as shown in Table 17.1, we can calculate for experiments II and III that K, the equilibrium constant, has the value 6.02×10^{-2}. In fact, whenever N_2, H_2, and NH_3 are mixed together at this temperature, the system *always* comes to an equilibrium position such that

$$K = 6.02 \times 10^{-2}$$

regardless of the amounts of the reactants and products that are mixed together initially.

It is important to see from Table 17.1 that the *equilibrium concentrations are not always the same*. However, even though the individual sets of equilibrium concentrations are quite different for the different situations, the *equilibrium constant, which depends on the ratio of the concentrations, remains the same*.

Each set of *equilibrium concentrations* is called an **equilibrium position**. It is essential to distinguish between the equilibrium constant and the equilibrium positions for a given reaction system. There is only *one* equilibrium constant for a particular system at a particular temperature, but there is an *infinite* number of equilibrium positions. The specific equilibrium position adopted by a system depends on the initial concentrations; the equilibrium constant does not.

Note that in the preceding discussion, the equilibrium constant was given without units. In certain cases the units are included when the values of equilibrium constants are given, and in other cases they are omitted. We will not discuss the reasons for this. We will omit the units in this text.

> **Equilibrium position**
> A particular set of equilibrium concentrations of all reactants and products in a chemical system

nformation

For a reaction at a given temperature, there are many equilibrium positions but only one value for K.

Active Reading Question

What is the difference between an "equilibrium constant" and an "equilibrium position"?

EXAMPLE 17.2

More Examples

1. For the reaction

   $$2NBr_3(g) \rightleftharpoons N_2(g) + 3Br_2(g)$$

   the system at equilibrium at a particular temperature is analyzed and the following concentrations are found:

   $[NBr_3] = 2.07 \times 10^{-3} \ M$;
   $[N_2] = 4.11 \times 10^{-2} \ M$;
   $[Br_2] = 1.06 \times 10^{-3} \ M$.

   Calculate the value of K for the reaction at this temperature.
   1.14×10^{-5}

2. At high temperatures, elemental bromine, Br_2, dissociates into individual bromine atoms:

   $$Br_2(g) \rightleftharpoons 2Br(g)$$

   This system at equilibrium at a particular temperature is analyzed and the following concentrations are found:

   $[Br_2] = 0.97 \ M$;
   $[Br] = 3.4 \times 10^{-2} \ M$.

   Calculate the value of K for the reaction at this temperature.
   1.2×10^{-3}

EXAMPLE 17.2

Calculating Equilibrium Constants

The reaction of sulfur dioxide with oxygen in the atmosphere to form sulfur trioxide has important environmental implications because SO_3 combines with moisture to form sulfuric acid droplets, an important component of acid rain. The following results were collected for two experiments involving the reaction at 600 °C between gaseous sulfur dioxide and oxygen to form gaseous sulfur trioxide:

$$2SO_2(g) + O_2(g) \rightleftharpoons 2SO_3(g)$$

The law of chemical equilibrium predicts that the value of K should be the same for both experiments. Verify this by calculating the equilibrium constant observed for each experiment.

	Initial	Equilibrium
Experiment I	$[SO_2]_0 = 2.00 \ M$	$[SO_2] = 1.50 \ M$
	$[O_2]_0 = 1.50 \ M$	$[O_2] = 1.25 \ M$
	$[SO_3]_0 = 3.00 \ M$	$[SO_3] = 3.50 \ M$
Experiment II	$[SO_2]_0 = 0.500 \ M$	$[SO_2] = 0.590 \ M$
	$[O_2]_0 = 0$	$[O_2] = 0.045 \ M$
	$[SO_3]_0 = 0.350 \ M$	$[SO_3] = 0.260 \ M$

Solution

The balanced equation for the reaction is

$$2SO_2(g) + O_2(g) \rightleftharpoons 2SO_3(g)$$

From the law of chemical equilibrium, we can write the equilibrium expression:

$$K = \frac{[SO_3]^2}{[SO_2]^2[O_2]}$$

For Experiment I we calculate the value of K by substituting the observed *equilibrium* concentrations,

$$[SO_3] = 3.50 \ M; \ [SO_2] = 1.50 \ M; \ [O_2] = 1.25 \ M$$

into the equilibrium expression:

$$K_I = \frac{(3.50)^2}{(1.50)^2(1.25)} = 4.36$$

For Experiment II at equilibrium:

$$[SO_3] = 0.260 \ M; \ [SO_2] = 0.590 \ M; \ [O_2] = 0.045 \ M$$

and

$$K_{II} = \frac{(0.260)^2}{(0.590)^2(0.045)} = 4.32$$

Notice that the values calculated for K_I and K_{II} are nearly the same, as we expected. That is, the value of K is constant, within differences due to rounding off and due to experimental error. These experiments show *two different equilibrium positions* for this system, but K, the equilibrium constant, is, indeed, constant.

608 • Chapter 17 • Equilibrium

Meeting Individual Needs

ADVANCED LEARNERS

To help students become more environmentally aware, have them write a report on the cause, the components, and the effects of acid rain. Students should include their opinion of their findings, ideas to create awareness of this environmental issue, and ideas for prevention. Alternatively, students can create a simulation of acid rain

and give a detailed explanation relating their model to the effects of acid rain on our society.

B. Heterogeneous Equilibria

So far we have discussed equilibria only for systems in the gaseous state, where all reactants and products are gases. These are examples of **homogeneous equilibria**, in which all substances are in the same state. However, many equilibria involve more than one state and are called **heterogeneous equilibria**. For example, the thermal decomposition of calcium carbonate in the commercial preparation of lime occurs by a reaction involving solids and gases.

$$CaCO_3(s) \rightleftharpoons CaO(s) + CO_2(g)$$
$$\text{Lime}$$

Straightforward application of the law of equilibrium leads to the equilibrium expression

$$K = \frac{[CO_2][CaO]}{[CaCO_3]}$$

> The position of a heterogeneous equilibrium does not depend on the amounts of pure solids or liquids present.

The fundamental reason for this behavior is that the concentrations of pure solids and liquids cannot change. In other words, we might say that the concentrations of pure solids and liquids are constants. Therefore, we can write the equilibrium expression for the decomposition of solid calcium carbonate as

$$K' = \frac{[CO_2]C_1}{C_2}$$

where C_1 and C_2 are constants representing the concentrations of the solids CaO and $CaCO_3$, respectively. This expression can be rearranged to give

$$\frac{C_2K'}{C_1} = K = [CO_2]$$

where the constants C_2, K', and C_1 are combined into a single constant K. This leads us to the following general statement:

> The concentrations of pure solids or pure liquids involved in a chemical reaction are not included in the equilibrium expression for the reaction.

This applies *only* to pure solids or liquids. It does not apply to solutions or gases, because their concentrations can vary.

Active Reading Question

Which species are not included in the equilibrium expression?

For example, consider the decomposition of liquid water to gaseous hydrogen and oxygen:

$$2H_2O(l) \rightleftharpoons 2H_2(g) + O_2(g)$$

where

$$K = [H_2]^2[O_2]$$

Homogeneous equilibrium
An equilibrium system in which all reactants and products are in the same state

Heterogeneous equilibrium
An equilibrium system in which all reactants and products are in different states

17.2.B Heterogeneous Equilibria

Objective To understand the role that liquids and solids play in constructing the equilibrium expression

 TEACHING TIPS

• Students often forget the states of chemical species when writing equilibrium expressions, sometimes including pure liquids and solids in the equilibrium expression. Remind students frequently of this issue as they begin to write expressions for heterogeneous equilibria.

• This section is an excellent place to stress that the amounts represented in an equilibrium expression are concentrations. Solids and liquids have constant concentrations and so are not included in the expression.

Active Reading Question

Solids and liquids are not included in the equilibrium expression.

EXAMPLE 17.3

More Examples

Write the expression for K for the following processes.

1. $CO_2(g) + H_2O(l) \rightleftharpoons H_2CO_3(l)$
   $K = 1/[CO_2(g)]$

2. $ZrI_4(s) \rightleftharpoons Zr(s) + 2I_2(g)$
   $K = [I_2(g)]^2$

Answer to Practice Problem 17.3

a. $K = [O_2]^3$

The solids are not included.

b. $K = [N_2O][H_2O]^2$

The solid is not included. Water is gaseous in this reaction, so it is included.

c. $K = \dfrac{1}{[CO_2]}$

The solids are not included.

d. $K = \dfrac{1}{[SO_3]}$

Water and H_2SO_4 are pure liquids and so are not included.

Water is not included in the equilibrium expression because it is a pure liquid. However, when the reaction is carried out under conditions where the water is a gas rather than a liquid,

$$2H_2O(g) \rightleftharpoons 2H_2(g) + O_2(g)$$

we have

$$K = \frac{[H_2]^2[O_2]}{[H_2O]^2}$$

because the concentration of water vapor can change.

EXAMPLE 17.3

Writing Equilibrium Expressions for Heterogeneous Equilibria

Write the expressions for K for the following processes.

a. Solid phosphorus pentachloride is decomposed to liquid phosphorus trichloride and chlorine gas.

b. Deep-blue solid copper(II) sulfate pentahydrate is heated to drive off water vapor to form white solid copper(II) sulfate.

Solution

a. The reaction is

$$PCl_5(s) \rightleftharpoons PCl_3(l) + Cl_2(g)$$

In this case, neither the pure solid PCl_5 nor the pure liquid PCl_3 is included in the equilibrium expression. The equilibrium expression is

$$K = [Cl_2]$$

b. The reaction is

$$CuSO_4 \cdot 5H_2O(s) \rightleftharpoons CuSO_4(s) + 5H_2O(g)$$

The two solids are not included. The equilibrium expression is

$$K = [H_2O]^5$$

As solid copper(II) sulfate pentahydrate, $CuSO_4 \cdot 5H_2O$, is heated, it loses H_2O, eventually forming white $CuSO_4$.

Practice Problem • Exercise 17.3

Write the equilibrium expression for each of the following reactions.

a. $2KClO_3(s) \rightleftharpoons 2KCl(s) + 3O_2(g)$

b. $NH_4NO_3(s) \rightleftharpoons N_2O(g) + 2H_2O(g)$

c. $CO_2(g) + MgO(s) \rightleftharpoons MgCO_3(s)$

d. $SO_3(g) + H_2O(l) \rightleftharpoons H_2SO_4(l)$

CELEBRITY CHEMICAL

Carbon Dioxide (CO₂)

You can investigate the chemical composition of a variety of minerals and rocks by testing for the formation of carbon dioxide when samples are treated with HCl. Use the overhead projector and small beakers for sample testing. Obtain samples of several rocks and minerals. Good samples include calcite, marble, limestone, quartz, chalk, coral, and clam shells. You will need 3 M HCl

to test the materials. Place enough HCl in each of the small beakers to cover the bottom of the beaker. Place the beakers on an overhead projector on top of a transparency. Place a rock or mineral sample in each beaker, labeling the transparency as you proceed. Use small pieces of rock or mineral, but not powder. Look for bubbles of CO_2, which indicate the presence of carbonate in the sample.

You can integrate this activity with the earth science curriculum by discussing the origins

CELEBRITY CHEMICAL Carbon Dioxide (CO_2)

Carbon dioxide is a very familiar molecule that is the product of human respiration and of the combustion of fossil fuels. This gas also puts the "fizz" in soda pop. It turns out that the simple, familiar CO_2 molecule has profound implications for our continued existence on this planet.

The concentration of carbon dioxide in the earth's atmosphere has risen steadily since the beginning of the Industrial Revolution and is expected to double from today's levels in the next 50 years. This change will have important effects on our environment. Consider the case of global warming. Many scientists feel that the increased CO_2 levels will trap more of the sun's energy near the earth, significantly increasing the earth's average temperature. Some evidence suggests that this is already occurring, although scientists disagree about the contribution of CO_2 to the changes. One thing that everyone does agree on is that the increased CO_2 levels will make plants grow faster.

On the surface the increase in plant growth due to increased CO_2 might seem like a good thing. Surprisingly, this situation could spell disaster for plant eaters, from caterpillars to antelopes, and for the animals that eat these herbivores. Faster plant growth often leads to lower nutritional value. As the plants increase their rate of photosynthesis and use the carbon in CO_2 to build more fiber and starch, the amount of nitrogen—which indicates the amount of proteins present—declines. Studies show that new leaves on plants grown in an atmosphere rich in CO_2 are starchy, but protein-poor. This is bad news for caterpillars, which need to bulk up before they pupate. Studies have indicated that caterpillars eat 40% more of the starchy, protein-poor leaves but grow 10% slower and produce smaller than normal adult butterflies.

Studies on larger herbivores, such as cows and sheep, have been more difficult to carry out. Nevertheless, indications are that plants grown in a CO_2-enriched environment provide less protein and produce slower growth in these species as well.

Research is continuing to try to assess the effects of the increasing CO_2 levels on the food chain.

A Monarch butterfly caterpillar eating a leaf

SECTION 17.2
REVIEW QUESTIONS

① Write the equilibrium expression for
$2NO(g) + O_2(g) \rightleftharpoons 2NO_2(g)$.

② Suppose that for the reaction

$N_2(g) + 3Cl_2(g) \rightleftharpoons 2NCl_3(g)$

it is determined that, at a particular temperature, the equilibrium concentrations are $[N_2] = 0.000104\ M$, $[Cl_2] = 0.000201\ M$, and $[NCl_3] = 0.141\ M$. Calculate the value of K for the reaction at this temperature.

③ How can there be an infinite number of equilibrium *positions* for a particular system at a particular temperature, but only one equilibrium *constant* for this system at this temperature?

④ Why are solids and liquids not included in the equilibrium expression?

⑤ Write the equilibrium expression for the following chemical equations.

  a. $NH_3(g) + HCl(g) \rightleftharpoons NH_4Cl(s)$

  b. $2H_2(g) + O_2(g) \rightleftharpoons 2H_2O(g)$

  c. $2H_2(g) + O_2(g) \rightleftharpoons 2H_2O(l)$

RESEARCH LINKS
CLASSZONE.COM

17.2 • Characteristics of Equilibrium • **611**

SECTION 17.2
Review Questions

1. $K = \dfrac{[NO_2]^2}{[NO]^2[O_2]}$

2. 2.35×10^{13}

3. An equilibrium position is a set of equilibrium concentrations. The equilibrium constant is a specific ratio of these concentrations. For example, $0.5 = \frac{1}{2}, \frac{2}{4}, \frac{3}{6}$, and so on. The fractions $\frac{1}{2}, \frac{2}{4}$, and $\frac{3}{6}$ represent the ratio of different equilibrium conditions. In each case, however, the ratio is equal to 0.5 (which represents the equilibrium constant).

4. The concentrations of pure liquids and pure solids cannot change. For this reason they are not included in the equilibrium expression.

5. **a.** $K = 1/[NH_3][HCl]$

  b. $K = \dfrac{[H_2O]^2}{[H_2]^2[O_2]}$

  c. $K = \dfrac{1}{[H_2]^2[O_2]}$

(continued)

of these samples. For example, limestone is sedimentary rock and marble is metamorphic rock. Both have the same chemical composition, although their appearances are quite different because of the manner in which they were formed.

You can also use this activity as an opportunity to demonstrate some of the features of dry ice. You can purchase dry ice at your local ice company or possibly at a local hospital or an ice cream store. Be careful to protect your hands whenever handling dry ice. Place a piece of dry ice in a beaker of water to observe the formation of fog and the bubbling of CO_2. Dry ice slides very easily on the lab demonstration bench. You can pulverize a sample of dry ice and place it in a balloon (use a funnel). Tie the balloon and wait. As the dry ice sublimes, the balloon will expand. If you add too much, it will pop!

SECTION 17.3
INTRODUCE

Student Preparation

Assign students to read Section 17.3 and to answer the Review Questions at the end of the section before coming to class.

 Active Learning
Team Learning Worksheet

After introducing the material in Section 17.3 in class, place students in groups and have them work together on **Section 17.3: Team Learning Worksheet**.

SECTION 17.3
GUIDE THE LEARNING

Homework

You may wish to assign these selected end-of-chapter problems as homework for this section: 27, 29, 30, 31, 33, 35, 36, 38, 39, 42, 43, 46, 48, 50

Additional end-of-chapter problems can be used for extra practice.

17.3.A Le Châtelier's Principle

Objective To learn to predict the changes that occur when a system at equilibrium is disturbed

 LABORATORY
EXPERIMENT 75:
Le Châtelier's Principle, Microscale

 TEACHING TIP

Proceed slowly through this section, giving lots of examples. Students often have a difficult time with Le Châtelier's principle. Think through each example with students and make sure that they understand how concentrations change each time.

TECHNOLOGY

🔵 **Animation**
Le Châtelier's Principle

SECTION 17.3
Application of Equilibria

Key Terms
- Le Châtelier's principle
- Solubility product constant (K_{sp})

Objectives
- *To learn to predict the changes that occur when a system at equilibrium is disturbed*
- *To learn to calculate equilibrium concentrations*
- *To learn to calculate the solubility product of a salt*
- *To learn to calculate solubility from the solubility product*

A. Le Châtelier's Principle

It is important to understand the factors that control the *position* of a chemical equilibrium. For example, when a chemical is manufactured, the chemists and chemical engineers in charge of production want to choose conditions that favor the desired product as much as possible. That is, they want the equilibrium to lie far to the right (toward products). When the process for the synthesis of ammonia was being developed, extensive studies were carried out to determine how the equilibrium concentration of ammonia depended on the conditions of temperature and pressure.

In this section we will explore how various changes in conditions affect the equilibrium position of a reaction system. We can predict the effects of changes in concentration, pressure, and temperature on a system at equilibrium by using **Le Châtelier's principle**:

> When a change is imposed on a system at equilibrium, the position of the equilibrium shifts in a direction that tends to reduce the effect of that change.

Le Châtelier's principle
If a change is imposed on a system at equilibrium, the equilibrium position will shift to reduce the effect of that change.

The Effect of a Change in Concentration

Let us consider the ammonia synthesis reaction. Suppose there is an equilibrium position described by these concentrations:

$$[N_2] = 0.399 \ M \qquad [H_2] = 1.197 \ M \qquad [NH_3] = 0.203 \ M$$

Increasing $[N_2]$ What will happen if 1.000 mol/L of N_2 is suddenly injected into the system? We can begin to answer this question by remembering that for the system at equilibrium, the rates of the forward and reverse reactions exactly balance,

$$N_2(g) + 3H_2(g) \rightleftharpoons 2NH_3(g)$$

as indicated here by arrows of the same length. When the N_2 is added, there are suddenly more collisions between N_2 and H_2 molecules. This increases the rate of the forward reaction (shown here by the greater length of the arrow pointing in that direction),

$$N_2(g) + 3H_2(g) \xrightarrow{\quad\quad} 2NH_3(g)$$

and the reaction produces more NH_3. As the concentration of NH_3 increases, the reverse reaction also speeds up (as more collisions between NH_3 molecules occur) and the system again comes to equilibrium. However, the new equilibrium position has more NH_3 than was present in the

---

Teaching Support
DEMONSTRATION

FeSCN^{2+} and Le Châtelier's Principle

Materials
- 0.20 M Fe(NO$_3$)$_2$
- Na$_2$HPO$_4$ crystals
- 0.2 M HCl
- 0.002 M KSCN
- Solid KSCN
- 0.20 M AgNO$_3$
- 3 Petri dishes
- Eyedroppers
- Overhead projector

Procedure Cover the bottom of a Petri dish with the KSCN solution and place it on the overhead projector. Add several drops of Fe(NO$_3$)$_3$ to the Petri dish and swirl gently to mix well. The reaction is

$$\text{Fe}^{3+} + \text{SCN}^- \rightleftharpoons \text{FeSCN}^{2+}$$
Yellow   Colorless   Red

Now divide the solution equally among three Petri dishes. Place all three on the overhead projector. The third Petri dish will act as a standard for comparison. Add a small amount of solid KSCN to the first Petri dish.

original position. We say that the equilibrium has shifted to the *right*—toward the products. The original and new equilibrium positions are shown below.

Equilibrium Position I			*Equilibrium Position II*		
$[N_2]$	=	0.399 *M*	$[N_2]$	=	1.348 *M*
$[H_2]$	=	1.197 *M*	$[H_2]$	=	1.044 *M*
$[NH_3]$	=	0.203 *M*	$[NH_3]$	=	0.304 *M*

1.000 mol/L of N_2 added

Note that the equilibrium does in fact shift to the right; the concentration of H_2 decreases (from 1.197 *M* to 1.044 *M*), the concentration of NH_3 increases (from 0.203 *M* to 0.304 *M*), and, of course, because nitrogen was added, the concentration of N_2 shows an increase relative to the original amount present.

It is important to note at this point that, although the equilibrium shifted to a new position, the *value of K did not change*. We can demonstrate this by inserting the equilibrium concentrations from positions I and II into the equilibrium expression.

- Position I: $K = \dfrac{[NH_3]^2}{[N_2][H_2]^3} = \dfrac{(0.203)^2}{(0.399)(1.197)^3} = 0.0602$

- Position II: $K = \dfrac{[NH_3]^2}{[N_2][H_2]^3} = \dfrac{(0.304)^2}{(1.348)(1.044)^3} = 0.0602$

These values of *K* are the same. Therefore, although the *equilibrium position* shifted when we added more N_2, the *equilibrium constant K* remained the same.

Using Le Châtelier's Principle Could we have predicted this shift by using Le Châtelier's principle? Because the change in this case was to add nitrogen, Le Châtelier's principle predicts that the system will shift in a direction that *consumes* nitrogen. This tends to offset the original change— the addition of N_2. Therefore, Le Châtelier's principle correctly predicts that adding nitrogen will cause the equilibrium to shift to the right (see **Figure 17.10**) as some of the added nitrogen is consumed.

(a)   (b)   (c)

Key:
N_2
H_2
NH_3

Figure 17.10
(a) The initial equilibrium mixture of N_2, H_2, and NH_3.
(b) Addition of N_2.
(c) The new equilibrium position for the system containing more N_2 (because of the addition of N_2), less H_2, and more NH_3 than in (a).

To illustrate the effect of a change in concentration on equilibrium, place about 20 mL of 0.2 *M* $CoCl_2$ in a 250-mL flask. Observe the pink color of the solution. Add about 50 mL of concentrated HCl and show students the color change from pink to blue. This change results from the formation of a cobalt complex:

$Co^{2+}(aq) + 4Cl^-(aq) \rightleftharpoons CoCl_4^{2-}$
   Pink   Blue

Divide the solution into two equal parts in two 250-mL flasks. Add water to one of the flasks until the solution turns pink. This activity illustrates Le Châtelier's principle because the water dilutes the chloride concentration and pulls the equilibrium to the left.

(continued)

Notice that the solution becomes more colored, which indicates that more $FeSCN^{2+}$ is forming. Add several drops of $Fe(NO_3)_3$ solution to the second Petri dish. Once again, the solution color intensifies, which indicates further formation of $FeSCN^{2+}$.

To shift the equilibrium again, add a few crystals of Na_2HPO_4 to the first Petri dish. The HPO_4^{2+} reacts with the iron ions to form $FeHPO_4^-$. The red color disappears

because the equilibrium of the initial reaction shifts to the left as iron ions are removed from the solution. Add a few drops of $AgNO_3$ solution to the second Petri dish. Once again, the red color disappears. In this case, the silver ions react with the SCN^- ions to form AgSCN. Finally, add a few drops of HCl to the second Petri dish. The chloride ions react with the silver ions to form the white precipitate AgCl, but the red color returns because the SCN^- ions are released from

the AgSCN and interact with the iron ions in solution once again to re-form $FeSCN^{2+}$.

Teaching Notes During this demonstration, discuss each addition by using the initial reaction to illustrate how the equilibrium is changing. Students need to be able to think about these changes as they occur.

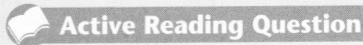
If a reactant is removed, the concentration of the products decreases.

information

A system at equilibrium shifts in the direction that compensates for any imposed change.

Increasing [NH₃] If ammonia had been added instead of nitrogen, the system would have shifted to the left, consuming ammonia. Another way of stating Le Châtelier's principle is as follows:

> When a reactant or product is added to a system at equilibrium, the system shifts away from the added component. On the other hand, if a reactant or product is removed, the system shifts toward the removed component.

For example, if we had removed nitrogen, the system would have shifted to the left and the amount of ammonia present would have been reduced.

In Real Life An example that shows the importance of Le Châtelier's principle is the effect of high elevations on the oxygen supply to the body. If you have ever traveled to the mountains on vacation, you may have noticed that you felt lightheaded and especially tired during the first few days of your visit. These feelings resulted from a decreased supply of oxygen to your body because of the lower air pressure that exists at higher elevations. For example, the oxygen supply in Leadville, Colorado (elevation ~ 10,000 ft), is only about two-thirds that found at sea level. We can understand the effects of diminished oxygen supply in terms of the following equilibrium:

$$Hb(aq) + 4O_2(g) \rightleftharpoons Hb(O_2)_4(aq)$$

where Hb represents hemoglobin, the iron-containing protein that transports O_2 from your lungs to your tissues, where it is used to support metabolism. The coefficient 4 in the equation signifies that each hemoglobin molecule picks up four O_2 molecules in the lungs. Note by Le Châtelier's principle that a lower oxygen pressure will cause this equilibrium to shift to the left, away from oxygenated hemoglobin. This leads to an inadequate oxygen supply at the tissues, which in turn results in fatigue and a "woozy" feeling.

This problem can be solved in extreme cases, such as when climbing Mount Everest or flying in a plane at high altitudes, by supplying extra oxygen from a tank. This extra oxygen pushes the equilibrium to its normal position. However, lugging around an oxygen tank would not be very practical for people who live in the mountains. In fact, nature solves this problem in a very interesting way. The body adapts to living at high elevations by producing additional hemoglobin—the other way to shift this equilibrium to the right. Thus people who live at high elevations have significantly higher hemoglobin levels than those living at sea level. For example, the Sherpas who live in Nepal can function in the rarefied air at the top of Mt. Everest without an auxiliary oxygen supply.

Sherpas in Nepal climb easily at high elevations.

Active Reading Question

If a reactant is removed from a chemical system at equilibrium, what happens to the concentration of the products?

EXAMPLE 17.4

Using Le Châtelier's Principle: Changes in Concentration

Arsenic, As_4, is obtained from nature by first reacting its ore with oxygen (called *roasting*) to form solid As_4O_6. (As_4O_6, a toxic compound fatal in doses of 0.1 g or more, is the "arsenic" made famous in detective stories.) The As_4O_6 is then reduced using carbon:

$$As_4O_6(s) + 6C(s) \rightleftharpoons As_4(g) + 6CO(g)$$

Predict the direction of the shift in the equilibrium position for this reaction that occurs in response to each of the following changes in conditions.

An ore sample containing arsenic

a. Addition of carbon monoxide

b. Addition or removal of C(s) or $As_4O_6(s)$

c. Removal of $As_4(g)$

Solution

a. Le Châtelier's principle predicts a shift away from the substance whose concentration is increased. The equilibrium position will shift to the left when carbon monoxide is added.

b. Because the amount of a pure solid has no effect on the equilibrium position, changing the amount of carbon or tetraarsenic hexoxide will have no effect.

c. When gaseous arsenic is removed, the equilibrium position will shift to the right to form more products. In industrial processes, the desired product is often continuously removed from the reaction system to increase the yield.

Practice Problem • Exercise 17.4

Novelty devices for predicting rain contain cobalt(II) chloride and are based on the following equilibrium:

$$CoCl_2(s) + 6H_2O(g) \rightleftharpoons CoCl_2 \cdot 6H_2O(s)$$
Blue   Pink

What color will this indicator be when rain is likely due to increased water vapor in the air?

When blue anhydrous $CoCl_2$ reacts with water, pink $CoCl_2 \cdot 6H_2O$ is formed.

EXAMPLE 17.4

More Examples

Suppose the reaction system

$$2SO_2(g) + O_2(g) \rightleftharpoons 2SO_3(g)$$

has reached equilibrium. Predict the effect of each of the following changes on the position of the equilibrium.

1. $SO_2(g)$ is added to the system.
shifts to the right

2. The $SO_3(g)$ present is liquefied and removed from the system.
shifts to the right

3. Some of the $O_2(g)$ is removed from the system.
shifts to the left

 Answer to Practice Problem 17.4

When rain is imminent, the concentration of water vapor in the air increases. This shifts the equilibrium to the right, forming $CoCl_2 \cdot 6H_2O(s)$, which is pink.

Meeting Individual Needs
VISUAL LEARNERS

Use the following activity to create interest in Le Châtelier's principle. Pass out pictures of gymnasts posed on various equipment, such as a balance beam, the rings, or the horizontal bars. Explain how the gymnast has to be at equilibrium in order to achieve success. Discuss how a gymnast uses various muscles, positioning, strength, and so on to achieve the balance shown in the picture. Talk about possible situations that could affect these images of equilibrium.

TEACHING TIPS

- Students may have trouble understanding how a change in volume affects the system. The idea that decreasing the volume increases the partial pressures and, therefore, changes the concentrations, is difficult for many students to grasp.

- When working with gases, students should remember to use a balanced equation to make their predictions.

MINI-DEMO

Two everyday examples of Le Châtelier's principle are the novelty barometers often found in gift shops and commercial desiccants (containing Drierite as the moisture indicator). In both cases, $CoCl_2$ is used to indicate the level of moisture. A color change from blue to pink indicates a rise in the moisture content.

The Effect of a Change in Volume

When the volume of a gas is decreased (when a gas is compressed), the pressure increases. This occurs because the molecules present are now contained in a smaller space and they hit the walls of their container more often, giving a greater pressure. Therefore, when the volume of a gaseous reaction system at equilibrium is suddenly reduced, leading to a sudden increase in pressure, by Le Châtelier's principle the system will shift in the direction that reduces the pressure.

For example, consider the reaction

$$CaCO_3(s) \rightleftharpoons CaO(s) + CO_2(g)$$

in a container with a movable piston (see **Figure 17.11**).

Figure 17.11
The reaction system
$CaCO_3(s) \rightleftharpoons$
$CaO(s) + CO_2(g)$.
(a) The system is initially at equilibrium.
(b) The piston is pushed in, decreasing the volume and increasing the pressure. The system shifts in the direction that consumes CO_2 molecules, lowering the pressure again.

(a)　　　　(b)

Decreasing the Volume If the volume is suddenly decreased by pushing in the piston, the pressure of the CO_2 gas initially increases. How can the system offset this pressure increase? By shifting to the left—the direction that reduces the amount of gas present. That is, a shift to the left will use up CO_2 molecules, thereby lowering the pressure. (There will be fewer molecules present to hit the walls, because more of the CO_2 molecules have combined with CaO and thus become part of the solid $CaCO_3$.)

Therefore, when the volume of a gaseous reaction system at equilibrium is decreased (thus increasing the pressure), *the system shifts in the direction that gives the smaller number of gas molecules*. So a decrease in the system volume leads to a shift that decreases the total number of gaseous molecules in the system.

Suppose we are running the reaction

$$N_2(g) + 3H_2(g) \rightleftharpoons 2NH_3(g)$$

information

Shifts in equilibrium brought about by volume changes also produce changes in pressure.

and we have a mixture of the gases nitrogen, hydrogen, and ammonia at equilibrium (see **Figure 17.12a**). If we suddenly reduce the volume, what will happen to the equilibrium position? Because the decrease in volume initially increases the pressure, the system moves in the direction that lowers its pressure. The reaction system can reduce its pressure by reducing the number of gas molecules present. This means that the reaction

$$N_2(g) + 3H_2(g) \rightleftharpoons 2NH_3(g)$$
4 gaseous molecules　　　2 gaseous molecules

shifts to the right, because in this direction four molecules (one of nitrogen and three of hydrogen) react to produce two molecules (of ammonia), thus *reducing the total number of gaseous molecules present*. The equilibrium position shifts to the right—toward the side of the reaction that involves the smaller number of gaseous molecules in the balanced equation.

Meeting Individual Needs
ADVANCED LEARNERS

For students who would like a mathematical verification of the effect of a change in volume, discuss how the partial pressures of the gases change. Suppose that at some temperature the equilibrium concentrations of N_2, H_2, and NH_3 are all 1.0 M (thus at this temperature $K = 1.0$). If we suddenly double the volume, the concentration of each species initially decreases to 0.50 M. If we

put these numbers into the equilibrium expression, we get a value of 4.0. This number is higher than K, so the system must shift to the left to satisfy the equilibrium condition ($K = 1.0$)—that is, in the direction predicted by Le Châtelier's principle.

Increasing the Volume When the container volume is increased (which lowers the pressure of the system), the system shifts so as to increase its pressure. An increase in volume in the ammonia synthesis system produces a shift to the left to increase the total number of gaseous molecules present (to increase the pressure).

Active Reading Question

How does the system shift when the volume of a gaseous reaction system at equilibrium is increased?

(a)   (b)   (c)

Key:
- N_2
- H_2
- NH_3

Figure 17.12
(a) A mixture of $NH_3(g)$, $N_2(g)$, and $H_2(g)$ at equilibrium.
(b) The volume is suddenly decreased.
(c) The new equilibrium position for the system containing more NH_3 and less N_2 and H_2. The reaction $N_2(g) + 3H_2(g) \rightleftharpoons 2NH_3(g)$ shifts to the right (toward the side with fewer molecules) when the container volume is decreased.

EXAMPLE 17.5

Using Le Châtelier's Principle: Changes in Volume

Predict the shift in equilibrium position that will occur for each of the following processes when the volume is reduced.

  a. The preparation of liquid phosphorus trichloride by the reaction

$$P_4(s) + 6Cl_2(g) \rightleftharpoons 4PCl_3(l)$$
6 gaseous molecules   0 gaseous molecules

  b. The preparation of gaseous phosphorus pentachloride according to the equation

$$PCl_3(g) + Cl_2(g) \rightleftharpoons PCl_5(g)$$
2 gaseous molecules   1 gaseous molecule

  c. The reaction of phosphorus trichloride with ammonia

$$PCl_3(g) + 3NH_3(g) \rightleftharpoons P(NH_2)_3(g) + 3HCl(g)$$
4 gaseous molecules   4 gaseous molecules

Solution

  a. P_4 and PCl_3 are a pure solid and a pure liquid, respectively, so we need to consider only the effect on Cl_2. If the volume is decreased, the Cl_2 pressure will initially increase, so the position of the equilibrium will shift to the right, consuming gaseous Cl_2 and lowering the pressure (to counteract the original change).

  b. Decreasing the volume (increasing the pressure) will shift this equilibrium to the right, because the product side contains only one gaseous molecule while the reactant side has two. That is, the system will respond to the decreased volume (increased pressure) by lowering the number of molecules present.

17.3 • Application of Equilibria • **617**

Answer to Practice Problem 17.5

a. No change. Both sides of the equation contain the same number of gaseous components. The system cannot change its pressure by shifting its equilibrium position.

b. Shifts to the left. The system can increase the number of gaseous components present, and so increase the pressure, by shifting to the left.

c. Shifts to the right to increase the number of gaseous components and thus its pressure.

To illustrate the effect of a change in temperature on equilibrium, place about 50 mL of 0.2 M $CoCl_2$ in a small beaker. Observe the pink color of the solution. Add concentrated HCl until the color of the solution changes from pink to blue. This change results from the formation of a cobalt complex:

Heat + $Co^{2+}(aq)$ + $4Cl^-(aq)$ ⇌
  Pink

$CoCl_4^{2-}(aq)$
  Blue

To observe the effect of temperature on the reaction, place the solution in a large test tube and immerse the test tube about halfway into a beaker containing crushed ice and salt. The solution in the bottom part of the test tube will turn pink after several minutes because lowering the temperature pulls the endothermic reaction to the left.

c. Both sides of the balanced reaction equation have four gaseous molecules. A change in volume will have no effect on the equilibrium position. There is no shift in this case, because the system cannot change the number of molecules present by shifting in either direction.

✓ Practice Problem • Exercise 17.5

For each of the following reactions, predict the direction in which the equilibrium will shift when the volume of the container is increased.

a. $H_2(g) + F_2(g) \rightleftharpoons 2HF(g)$

b. $CO(g) + 2H_2(g) \rightleftharpoons CH_3OH(g)$

c. $2SO_3(g) \rightleftharpoons 2SO_2(g) + O_2(g)$

The Effect of a Change in Temperature

It is important to remember that although the changes we have just discussed may alter the equilibrium *position*, they do not alter the equilibrium *constant*. For example, the addition of a reactant shifts the equilibrium position to the right but has no effect on the value of the equilibrium constant; the new equilibrium concentrations satisfy the original equilibrium constant. This was demonstrated earlier in this section for the addition of N_2 to the ammonia synthesis reaction.

The effect of temperature on equilibrium is different, however, because *the value of K changes with temperature*. We can use Le Châtelier's principle to predict the direction of the change in K.

To do this we need to classify reactions according to whether they produce heat or absorb heat. A reaction that produces heat (heat is a "product") is said to be *exothermic*. A reaction that absorbs heat is called *endothermic*. Because heat is needed for an endothermic reaction, energy (heat) can be regarded as a "reactant" in this case.

Exothermic Reaction In an exothermic reaction, heat is treated as a product. For example, the synthesis of ammonia from nitrogen and hydrogen is exothermic (produces heat). We can represent this by treating energy as a product:

$$N_2(g) + 3H_2(g) \rightleftharpoons 2NH_3(g) + 92 \text{ kJ}$$
  Energy
  released

Le Châtelier's principle predicts that when we add energy to this system at equilibrium by heating it, the shift will be in the direction that consumes energy—that is, to the left.

Endothermic Reaction On the other hand, for an endothermic reaction (one that absorbs energy), such as the decomposition of calcium carbonate,

$$CaCO_3(s) + 556 \text{ kJ} \rightleftharpoons CaO(s) + CO_2(g)$$
  Energy
  needed

energy is treated as a reactant. In this case an increase in temperature causes the equilibrium to shift to the right.

Let's Review

Using Le Châtelier's Principle for Changes in Temperature
- Treat energy as a reactant in endothermic processes.
- Treat energy as a product in exothermic processes.
- Predict the direction of the shift in equilibrium position the same way as if a product or reactant were added or removed.

Active Reading Question

What property of a reaction allows you to predict the effect of a temperature change on the equilibrium?

EXAMPLE 17.6

Using Le Châtelier's Principle: Changes in Temperature

For each of the following reactions, predict how the equilibrium will shift as the temperature is increased.

a. $N_2(g) + O_2(g) \rightleftharpoons 2NO(g)$ (endothermic)

b. $2SO_2(g) + O_2(g) \rightleftharpoons 2SO_3(g)$ (exothermic)

Solution

a. This is an endothermic reaction, so energy can be viewed as a reactant.

$$N_2(g) + O_2(g) + \text{energy} \rightleftharpoons 2NO(g)$$

Thus the equilibrium will shift to the right as the temperature is increased (energy added).

b. This is an exothermic reaction, so energy can be regarded as a product.

$$2SO_2(g) + O_2(g) \rightleftharpoons 2SO_3(g) + \text{energy}$$

As the temperature is increased, the equilibrium will shift to the left.

Practice Problem • Exercise 17.6

For the exothermic reaction

$$2SO_2(g) + O_2(g) \rightleftharpoons 2SO_3(g)$$

predict the equilibrium shift caused by each of the following changes.

a. SO_2 is added.   c. The volume is decreased.

b. SO_3 is removed.   d. The temperature is decreased.

We have seen how Le Châtelier's principle can be used to predict the effects of several types of changes on a system at equilibrium. To summarize these ideas, **Table 17.2** shows how various changes affect the equilibrium position of the endothermic reaction $N_2O_4(g) \rightleftharpoons 2NO_2(g)$. The effect of a temperature change on this system is shown in **Figure 17.13**.

17.3 • Application of Equilibria • **619**

Active Reading Question

We need to know whether the reaction is exothermic or endothermic as written. If it is endothermic, an increase in temperature will shift the equilibrium position to the right. If it is exothermic, an increase in temperature will shift the equilibrium position to the left.

EXAMPLE 17.6

More Examples

1. The reaction

$$C_2H_2(g) + 2Br_2(g) \rightleftharpoons C_2H_2Br_4(g)$$

is exothermic as written. Will an increase in temperature shift the position of equilibrium toward the reactants or the products?

reactants

2. The reaction

$$ZrI_4(s) \rightleftharpoons Zr(s) + 2I_2(g)$$

is endothermic as written. Will an increase in temperature shift the position of equilibrium toward the reactants or the products?

products

Answer to Practice Problem 17.6

a. shifts to the right away from added SO_2

b. shifts to the right to replace removed SO_3

c. shifts to the right to decrease its pressure

d. shifts to the right; Energy is a product in this case, so a decrease in temperature favors the forward reaction (which produces energy).

Objective To learn to calculate equilibrium concentrations from equilibrium constants

 LABORATORY
EXPERIMENT 76:
Chemical Equilibrium, Traditional

LABORATORY
EXPERIMENT 77:
MOM and Your CBL

🍎 **TEACHING TIP**

Now is an excellent time to explain the relationship between the value of K and the extent of the reaction. Discuss the meaning of a K value of 1, <1, and >1.

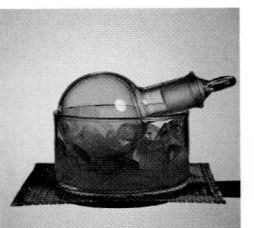

Figure 17.13
Shifting the $N_2O_4(g) \rightleftharpoons 2NO_2(g)$ equilibrium by changing the temperature.
(a) At 100 °C the flask is definitely reddish-brown due to a large amount of NO_2 present.
(b) At 0 °C the equilibrium is shifted toward colorless $N_2O_4(g)$.

Table 17.2

Shifts in the Equilibrium Position for the Reaction:
Energy + $N_2O_4(g) \rightleftharpoons 2NO_2(g)$

Change	Shift
addition of $N_2O_4(g)$	right
addition of $NO_2(g)$	left
removal of $N_2O_4(g)$	left
removal of $NO_2(g)$	right
decrease in container volume	left
increase in container volume	right
increase in temperature	right
decrease in temperature	left

B. Applications Involving the Equilibrium Constant

Knowing the value of the equilibrium constant for a reaction allows us to do many things. For example, the size of K tells us the inherent tendency of the reaction to occur. A value of K much larger than 1 means that at equilibrium, the reaction system will consist of mostly products—the equilibrium lies to the right. For example, consider a general reaction of the type

$$A(g) \rightarrow B(g)$$

where

$$K = \frac{[B]}{[A]}$$

If K for this reaction is 10,000 (10^4), then at equilibrium,

$$\frac{[B]}{[A]} = 10,000 \text{ or } = \frac{[B]}{[A]} = \frac{10,000}{1}$$

That is, at equilibrium [B] is 10,000 times greater than [A]. This means that the reaction strongly favors the product B. Another way of saying this is that the reaction goes essentially to completion. That is, virtually all of A becomes B.

On the other hand, a small value of K means that the system at equilibrium consists largely of reactants—the equilibrium position is far to the left. The given reaction does not occur to any significant extent.

 Let's Review

The Meaning of K
- $K > 1 \rightarrow$ the equilibrium position is far to the right
- $K < 1 \rightarrow$ the equilibrium position is far to the left

Meeting Individual Needs
ENGLISH LANGUAGE LEARNERS

It may confuse ELL students when you describe an equilibrium position as far to the right or far to the left. Until these students comprehend the content, use the phrasing "the reaction system will consist mostly of reactants/products" simultaneously with the phrasing "far to the left/right."

Another way we use the equilibrium constant is to calculate the equilibrium concentrations of reactants and products. For example, if we know the value of K and the concentrations of all the reactants and products except one, we can calculate the missing concentration. This is illustrated in Example 17.7 below.

Active Reading Question

What does the value of the equilibrium constant, K, tell us?

EXAMPLE 17.7

Calculating Equilibrium Concentration Using Equilibrium Expressions

Gaseous phosphorus pentachloride decomposes to chlorine gas and gaseous phosphorus trichloride. In a certain experiment, at a temperature where $K = 8.96 \times 10^{-2}$, the equilibrium concentrations of PCl_5 and PCl_3 were found to be 6.70×10^{-3} M and 0.300 M, respectively. Calculate the concentration of Cl_2 present at equilibrium.

Solution

Where do we want to go?

$$[Cl_2] = ? \, M$$

What do we know?

- $PCl_5(g) \rightleftharpoons PCl_3(g) + Cl_2(g)$ • $[PCl_5] = 6.70 \times 10^{-3}$ M at equilibrium

- $K = \dfrac{[PCl_3][Cl_2]}{[PCl_5]} = 8.96 \times 10^{-2}$ • $[PCl_3] = 0.300$ M at equilibrium

How do we get there?

We want to calculate $[Cl_2]$. We will rearrange the equilibrium expression to solve for the concentration of Cl_2. First we divide both sides of the expression

$$K = \frac{[PCl_3][Cl_2]}{[PCl_5]}$$

by $[PCl_3]$ to give

$$\frac{K}{[PCl_3]} = \frac{\cancel{[PCl_3]}[Cl_2]}{\cancel{[PCl_3]}[PCl_5]} = \frac{[Cl_2]}{[PCl_5]}$$

Next we multiply both sides by $[PCl_5]$.

$$\frac{K[PCl_5]}{[PCl_3]} = \frac{[Cl_2]\cancel{[PCl_5]}}{\cancel{[PCl_5]}} = [Cl_2]$$

Then we can calculate $[Cl_2]$ by substituting the known information.

$$[Cl_2] = K \times \frac{[PCl_5]}{[PCl_3]} = (8.96 \times 10^{-2})\frac{(6.70 \times 10^{-3})}{(0.300)}$$

$$[Cl_2] = 2.00 \times 10^{-3} \, M$$

The equilibrium concentration of Cl_2 is 2.00×10^{-3} M.

Active Reading Question

The value for K gives us a measure of the extent of the reaction. The larger the value for K, the more the products are favored over the reactants.

EXAMPLE 17.7

More Examples

1. Assume the equilibrium constant for the reaction $H_2(g) + F_2(g) \rightleftharpoons 2HF(g)$ has the value 2.1×10^3 at a particular temperature. When the system is analyzed at equilibrium at this temperature, the concentrations of both $H_2(g)$ and $F_2(g)$ are 0.0021 M. What is the concentration of $HF(g)$ in the equilibrium system under these conditions?
   $[HF(g)] = 9.6 \times 10^{-2} \, M$

2. Assume the equilibrium constant for the reaction $2H_2O(g) \rightleftharpoons 2H_2(g) + O_2(g)$ has the value 2.4×10^{-3} at a particular temperature. When the system is analyzed at equilibrium at this temperature, it is found that $[H_2O(g)] = 1.1 \times 10^{-1}$ M and $[H_2(g)] = 1.9 \times 10^{-2}$ M. What is the concentration of $O_2(g)$ in the equilibrium system under these conditions?
   $[O_2(g)] = 8.0 \times 10^{-2} \, M$

Objective To learn to calculate the solubility product of a salt given its solubility, and vice versa

TEACHING TIP

Now is an excellent time to review polyatomic ions and the procedure for writing and balancing chemical equations. Students must be able to break compounds into their component ions and write equations for the dissociation to work with solubility equilibria.

Active Reading Question

In general, the more soluble the salt, the higher the K_{sp} value

TECHNOLOGY

Animation
Solution Equilibrium

This X ray of the large intestine has been enhanced by the patient's consumption of barium sulfate.

information

Pure liquids and pure solids are never included in an equilibrium expression.

Solubility product constant (solubility constant; K_{sp})
The constant for the equilibrium expression representing the dissolving of an ionic solid in water

C. Solubility Equilibria

Solubility is a very important phenomenon. Consider the following examples.

* Because sugar and table salt dissolve readily in water, we can flavor foods easily.

* Because calcium sulfate is less soluble in hot water than in cold water, it coats tubes in boilers, reducing thermal efficiency.

* When food lodges between teeth, acids form that dissolve tooth enamel, which contains the mineral hydroxyapatite, $Ca_5(PO_4)_3OH$. Tooth decay can be reduced by adding fluoride to toothpaste. Fluoride replaces the hydroxide in hydroxyapatite to produce the corresponding fluorapatite, $Ca_5(PO_4)_3F$, and calcium fluoride, CaF_2, both of which are less soluble in acids than the original enamel.

* The use of a suspension of barium sulfate improves the clarity of X rays of the digestive tract. Barium sulfate contains the toxic ion Ba^{2+}, but its very low solubility makes ingestion of solid $BaSO_4$ safe.

We will consider the equilibria associated with dissolving solids in water to form aqueous solutions. When a typical ionic solid dissolves in water, it dissociates completely into separate cations and anions. For example, calcium fluoride dissolves in water as follows:

$$CaF_2(s) \xrightarrow{H_2O(l)} Ca^{2+}(aq) + 2F^-(aq)$$

When the solid salt is first added to the water, no Ca^{2+} and F^- ions are present. However, as dissolving occurs, the concentrations of Ca^{2+} and F^- increase, and it becomes more and more likely that these ions will collide and re-form the solid. Thus two opposite (competing) processes are occurring—the dissolving reaction shown above and the reverse reaction to re-form the solid:

$$Ca^{2+}(aq) + 2F^-(aq) \rightarrow CaF_2(s)$$

Ultimately, equilibrium is reached. No more solid dissolves and the solution is said to be saturated.

We can write an equilibrium expression for this process according to the law of chemical equilibrium:

$$K_{sp} = [Ca^{2+}][F^-]^2$$

where $[Ca^{2+}]$ and $[F^-]$ are expressed in mol/L. The constant K_{sp} is called the **solubility product constant**, or simply the **solubility product**. Because CaF_2 is a pure solid, it is not included in the equilibrium expression.

Active Reading Question

Do very soluble salts have large or small K_{sp} values?

EXAMPLE 17.8

Writing Solubility Product Expressions

Write the balanced equation describing the reaction for dissolving each of the following solids in water. Also write the K_{sp} expression for each solid.

   a. $PbCl_2(s)$ **b.** $Ag_2CrO_4(s)$ **c.** $Bi_2S_3(s)$

Solution

  a. $PbCl_2(s) \rightleftharpoons Pb^{2+}(aq) + 2Cl^-(aq)$; $K_{sp} = [Pb^{2+}][Cl^-]^2$

  b. $Ag_2CrO_4(s) \rightleftharpoons 2Ag^+(aq) + CrO_4^{2-}(aq)$; $K_{sp} = [Ag^+]^2[CrO_4^{2-}]$

  c. $Bi_2S_3(s) \rightleftharpoons 2Bi^{3+}(aq) + 3S^{2-}(aq)$; $K_{sp} = [Bi^{3+}]^2[S^{2-}]^3$

 Practice Problem • Exercise 17.8

Write the balanced equation for the reaction describing the dissolving of each of the following solids in water. Also write the K_{sp} expression for each solid.

  a. $BaSO_4(s)$

  b. $Fe(OH)_3(s)$

  c. $Ag_3PO_4(s)$

EXAMPLE 17.9

Calculating Solubility Products

Copper(I) bromide, CuBr, has a measured solubility of 2.0×10^{-4} mol/L at 25 °C. That is, when excess CuBr(s) is placed in 1.0 L of water, we can determine that 2.0×10^{-4} mol of the solid dissolves to produce a saturated solution. Calculate the solid's K_{sp} value.

Solution
Where do we want to go?

   $K_{sp} = ?$

What do we know?
- Solubility CuBr = 2.0×10^{-4} M
- $CuBr(s) \rightleftharpoons Cu^+(aq) + Br^-(aq)$
- $K_{sp} = [Cu^+][Br^-]$

How do we get there?

We can calculate the value of K_{sp} if we know $[Cu^+]$ and $[Br^-]$, the equilibrium concentrations of the ions. We know that the measured solubility of CuBr is 2.0×10^{-4} mol/L. This means that 2.0×10^{-4} mol of solid CuBr dissolves per 1.0 L of solution to come to equilibrium. The reaction is

   $CuBr(s) \rightarrow Cu^+(aq) + Br^-(aq)$

so

   2.0×10^{-4} mol/L CuBr(s) $\rightarrow$

      2.0×10^{-4} mol/L $Cu^+(aq) + 2.0 \times 10^{-4}$ mol/L $Br^-(aq)$

information

Solubilities must be expressed in mol/L in K_{sp} calculations.

EXAMPLE 17.8

More Examples

Write the balanced equation for dissolving each of the following solids in water. Also write the K_{sp} expression for each solid.

1. $Cr(OH)_3(s)$

  $Cr(OH)_3(s) \rightleftharpoons$
    $Cr^{3+}(aq) + 3OH^-(aq)$;

  $K_{sp} = [Cr^{3+}(aq)][OH^-(aq)]^3$

2. $Ca_3(PO_4)_2(s)$

  $Ca_3(PO_4)_2(s) \rightleftharpoons$
    $3Ca^{2+}(aq) + 2PO_4^{3-}(aq)$;

  $K_{sp} = [Ca^{2+}(aq)]^3[PO_4^{3-}(aq)]^2$

Answer to Practice Problem 17.8

a. $BaSO_4(s) \rightleftharpoons Ba^{2+}(aq) + SO_4^{2-}(aq)$;
  $K_{sp} = [Ba^{2+}][SO_4^{2-}]$

b. $Fe(OH)_3(s) \rightleftharpoons Fe^{3+}(aq) + 3OH^-(aq)$;
  $K_{sp} = [Fe^{3+}][OH^-]^3$

c. $Ag_3PO_4(s) \rightleftharpoons 3Ag^+(aq) + PO_4^{3-}(aq)$;
  $K_{sp} = [Ag^+]^3[PO_4^{3-}]$

EXAMPLE 17.9

More Examples

1. Zinc carbonate, $ZnCO_3(s)$, dissolves in water to give a solution that is 1.7×10^{-5} M at 22 °C. Calculate K_{sp} for $ZnCO_3(s)$ at this temperature (ignoring the fact that CO_3^{2-} reacts with water).

  $K_{sp} = 2.9 \times 10^{-10}$

2. Copper(II) chromate, $CuCrO_4(s)$, dissolves in water to give a solution that contains 1.1×10^{-5} g $CuCrO_4$ per liter at 23 °C. Calculate K_{sp} for $CuCrO_4(s)$ at this temperature.

  $K_{sp} = 3.8 \times 10^{-15}$

READING STRATEGIES

Ask students to compare and contrast the meanings of the terms *solubility* and *solubility product*.

EXAMPLE 17.10

We can now write the equilibrium concentrations

$$[Cu^+] = 2.0 \times 10^{-4}\ mol/L$$

and

$$[Br^-] = 2.0 \times 10^{-4}\ mol/L$$

These equilibrium concentrations allow us to calculate the value of K_{sp} for CuBr.

$$K_{sp} = [Cu^+][Br^-] = (2.0 \times 10^{-4})(2.0 \times 10^{-4})$$

$$= 4.0 \times 10^{-8}$$

The units for K_{sp} values are omitted.

✔ Practice Problem • Exercise 17.9

Calculate the K_{sp} value for barium sulfate, $BaSO_4$, which has a solubility of 3.9×10^{-5} mol/L at 25 °C.

We have seen that the known solubility of an ionic solid can be used to calculate its K_{sp} value. The reverse is also possible: the solubility of an ionic solid can be calculated if its K_{sp} value is known.

EXAMPLE 17.10

Calculating Solubility from K_{sp} Values

The K_{sp} value for solid AgI(s) is 1.5×10^{-16} at 25 °C. Calculate the solubility of AgI(s) in water at 25 °C.

Solution
Where do we want to go?

Solubility for AgI(s) = ? M

What do we know?

- $K_{sp} = 1.5 \times 10^{-16}$
- AgI(s) $\rightleftharpoons$ Ag$^+$(aq) + I$^-$(aq)
- $K_{sp} = [Ag^+][I^-]$

How do we get there?

Because we do not know the solubility of this solid, we will assume that x moles per liter dissolves to reach equilibrium. Therefore,

$$x\ \frac{mol}{L}\ AgI(s) \rightarrow x\ \frac{mol}{L}\ Ag^+(aq) + x\ \frac{mol}{L}\ I^-(aq)$$

and at equilibrium,

$$[Ag^+] = x\ \frac{mol}{L}$$

$$[I^-] = x\ \frac{mol}{L}$$

Substituting these concentrations into the equilibrium expression gives

$$K_{sp} = 1.5 \times 10^{-16} = [Ag^+][I^-] = (x)(x) = x^2$$

624 • Chapter 17 • Equilibrium

Thus

$$x^2 = 1.5 \times 10^{-16}$$

$$x = \sqrt{1.5 \times 10^{-16}} = 1.2 \times 10^{-8} \text{ mol/L}$$

The solubility of AgI(s) is 1.2×10^{-8} mol/L.

 Practice Problem • Exercise 17.10

The K_{sp} value for lead chromate, $PbCrO_4$, is 2.0×10^{-16} at 25 °C. Calculate its solubility at 25 °C.

SECTION 17.3
REVIEW QUESTIONS

❶ When additional reactant is added to a system at equilibrium, what happens to the equilibrium position? What happens to the equilibrium constant?

❷ Suppose the reaction system
$UO_2(s) + 4HF(g) \rightleftharpoons UF_4(g) + 2H_2O(g)$
has already reached equilibrium. Predict the effect of each of the following changes on the position of the equilibrium. Tell whether the equilibrium will shift to the right, shift to the left, or will not be affected.

   a. Additional $UO_2(s)$ is added to the system.

   b. 5.0 mol of $Xe(g)$ is added to the system at constant volume.

   c. The reaction is performed in a glass reaction vessel; $HF(g)$ attacks and reacts with glass.

   d. Water vapor is removed.

   e. The size of the reaction vessel is increased.

❸ Why does changing the volume of a system at equilibrium that contains gas shift the equilibrium position? How can you predict this shift?

❹ When an exothermic reaction is at equilibrium what effect does increasing the temperature have on the equilibrium position? What effect does increasing the temperature have on the equilibrium constant?

❺ A reaction has a small value for K. At equilibrium what does this tell you about each of the following:

   a. amount of reactants

   b. amount of products

   c. extent of reaction

❻ Write the equilibrium expression for $AgCl(s) \rightleftharpoons Ag^+(aq) + Cl^-(aq)$.

❼ The solubility of $PbCrO_4$ is 1.7×10^{-4} g/L. Calculate the K_{sp} value for $PbCrO_4$.

 RESEARCH LINKS
CLASSZONE.COM

17.3 • Application of Equilibria • **625**

Answer to Practice Problem 17.10

$PbCrO_4(s) \rightleftharpoons$
$\quad Pb^{2+}(aq) + CrO_4{}^{2-}(aq)$
$K_{sp} = [Pb^{2+}][CrO_4{}^{2-}]$
$\quad = 2.0 \times 10^{-16}$
Solubility $= x$ mol/L
$\quad = [Pb^{2+}]$
$\quad = [CrO_4{}^{2-}]$
$K_{sp} = (x)(x) = x^2$
$\quad = 2.0 \times 10^{-16}$
$\quad x = 1.4 \times 10^{-8}$ mol/L

SECTION 17.3
ASSESS

SECTION 17.3
Review Questions

1. When additional reactant is added, the equilibrium position shifts to the right (the product side). The equilibrium constant does not change.

2. a. not affected
   b. not affected
   c. left
   d. right
   e. left

3. If the volume is increased, the equilibrium position shifts in the direction that gives the larger number of gas particles. If the volume is decreased, it shifts in the direction that gives the smaller number of gas particles. Use the balanced equation to decide which direction equilibrium shifts.

4. For an exothermic reaction, increasing the temperature will shift the equilibrium position to the left (toward the reactants side) and the value of the equilibrium constant will decrease.

5. a. A small K means that the equilibrium position lies to the left. The reactants will predominate in the vessel.
   b. The amount of products will be small since the equilibrium lies to the left.
   c. The reaction does not proceed very far at all.

6. $K_{sp} = [Ag^+][Cl^-]$

7. 2.9×10^{-8}

Key Terms

Key Ideas

17.1 Reaction Rates and Equilibrium

- Collision model for chemical reactions
  - Reactants must collide to react.
  - A certain threshold energy (the activation energy, E_a) must be supplied by the collision for a reaction to occur.
- A catalyst
  - Speeds up a reaction without being consumed
  - Provides a new pathway for the reaction that has a smaller E_a
  - Enzymes are biological catalysts.

- Chemical equilibrium is established when a chemical reaction is carried out in a closed vessel.
  - The concentrations of both reactants and products remain constant over time.
  - Equilibrium is a highly dynamic state on the microscopic level.
    - ◆ Forward rate = reverse rate
  - In homogeneous reactions all reactants and products are in the same phase.
  - In heterogeneous reactions one or more reactants or products are in different phases.

RESEARCH LINKS
CLASSZONE.COM

Meeting Individual Needs
CHAPTER REVIEW

Chapter 17 Review Worksheet at the appropriate level:
  Basic
  Standard
  Challenge

CHAPTER SUMMARY

A **Chapter Summary** that includes additional Active Reading Questions for Chapter 17 is available.

Assessment Resources
CHAPTER 17

Chapter 17 Test

TECHNOLOGY

 Computerized Test Bank for Chapter 17

17.2	Law of chemical equilibrium
	Equilibrium expression
	Equilibrium constant
	Equilibrium position
	Homogeneous equilibria
	Heterogeneous equilibria

17.2 Characteristics of Equilibrium

- The equilibrium expression is based on the law of chemical equilibrium.
  - For the reaction
    $$aA + bB \rightleftharpoons cC + dD$$
    $$K = \frac{[C]^c[D]^d}{[A]^a[B]^b}$$
  - The equilibrium constant (K) is constant for a given chemical system at a given temperature.
  - The equilibrium position is a set of equilibrium concentrations that satisfy K.
  - There are an infinite number of equilibrium positions.
- Heterogeneous equilibria contain reactants or products in different phases.
  - A pure liquid or solid never appears in the equilibrium expression.

17.3	Le Châtelier's Principle
	Solubility Product Constant (K_{sp})

17.3 Application of Equilibria

- Le Châtelier's principle states that when a change is imposed on a system at equilibrium the position of the equilibrium shifts in the direction which reduces the effect of that change.
- Applications of equilibria
  - The value of K for a system can be calculated from a known set of equilibrium concentrations.
  - Unknown equilibrium concentrations can be calculated if the value of K and the remaining equilibrium concentrations are known.
  - The equilibrium conditions also apply to a saturated solution containing excess solid, MX(s).
    - $K_{sp} = [M^+][X^-]$ = solubility product constant
    - The value of the K_{sp} can be calculated from the measured solubility of MX(s).

RESEARCH LINKS
CLASSZONE.COM

Chapter 17 Assessment

All exercises with blue numbers have answers in the back of this book.

17.1 Reaction Rates and Equilibrium

A. How Chemical Reactions Occur

1. For the reaction $H_2(g) + Br_2(g) \rightarrow 2HBr(g)$, list the types of bonds that must be broken and the type of bond that must form for the chemical reaction to take place.

2. For the reaction $N_2(g) + 3H_2(g) \rightarrow 2NH_3(g)$, list the types of bonds that must be broken and the type of bond that must form for the chemical reaction to take place.

B. Conditions That Affect Reaction Rates

3. How do chemists envision reactions taking place in terms of the *collision model* for reactions? Give an example of a simple reaction and how you might envision the reaction taking place by means of a collision between the molecules.

4. What does the *activation energy* for a reaction represent? How is the activation energy related to whether a collision between molecules is successful?

5. What is a *catalyst*? How does a catalyst speed up a reaction?

6. What are the catalysts found in living cells called? Why are these biological catalysts necessary?

C. Heterogeneous Reactions

7. Explain the difference between a heterogeneous reaction and a homogeneous reaction.

8. Why does increasing the temperature speed up the rate of a chemical reaction?

9. Why is pouring grain into a silo a potentially explosive process? Use the collision theory in your explanation.

D. The Equilibrium Condition

10. How does *equilibrium* represent the balancing of opposing processes? Give an example of an "equilibrium" encountered in everyday life, showing how the processes involved oppose each other.

11. What do chemists mean by a state of *equilibrium*? Give an example of a *physical* equilibrium and of a *chemical* equilibrium.

12. What does it mean to say that chemical reactions are *reversible*? Are all chemical reactions, in principle, reversible? Are some reactions more likely to occur in one direction than in the other?

13. How do chemists recognize a system that has reached a state of chemical equilibrium? When writing chemical equations, how do we indicate reactions that come to a state of chemical equilibrium?

E. Chemical Equilibrium: A Dynamic Condition

14. When a reaction system has reached chemical equilibrium, the concentrations of the reactants and products no longer change with time. Why does the amount of product no longer increase, even though large concentrations of the reactants may still be present?

15. What does it mean to say that the condition of chemical equilibrium is a *dynamic* situation? Although the reaction overall may appear to have stopped, what is still going on in the system?

17.2 Characteristics of Equilibrium

A. The Equilibrium Constant: An Introduction

16. In general terms, what does the equilibrium constant for a reaction represent? What is the algebraic form of the equilibrium constant for a typical reaction? What do square brackets indicate when we write an equilibrium constant?

17. There is only one value of the equilibrium constant for a particular system at a particular temperature, but there is an infinite number of equilibrium positions. Explain.

18. Write the equilibrium expression for each of the following reactions.

    a. $N_2(g) + 3Cl_2(g) \rightleftharpoons 2NCl_3(g)$
    b. $H_2(g) + I_2(g) \rightleftharpoons 2HI(g)$
    c. $N_2(g) + 2H_2(g) \rightleftharpoons N_2H_4(g)$

19. Write the equilibrium expression for each of the following reactions.

    a. $CO(g) + 2H_2(g) \rightleftharpoons CH_3OH(g)$
    b. $2NO_2(g) \rightleftharpoons 2NO(g) + O_2(g)$
    c. $P_4(g) + 6Br_2(g) \rightleftharpoons 4PBr_3(g)$

9. Grain dust becomes airborne when grain is poured into a silo. This dust consists of tiny particles, which exposes a large amount of surface area to the oxygen in the air.

10. In an equilibrium system, two opposing processes are taking place at the same time and at the same speed. There is no net change in a system at equilibrium with time. Every time one process occurs, the opposite process occurs at the same time elsewhere in the system.

11. A state of equilibrium is reached when two opposing processes are exactly balanced. The development of a vapor pressure above a liquid in a closed container is an example of a physical equilibrium. Any chemical reaction that appears to "stop" before completion is an example of chemical equilibrium.

12. Chemical reactions are reversible if they can occur in either direction (as written from left to right, or vice versa). In principle, all chemical reactions are microscopically reversible. In practice, many (but by no means all) reactions are favored in one direction over the other. This is especially true for open systems.

1. The hydrogen–hydrogen bond of H_2 and the bromine–bromine bond of Br_2 must break. Two hydrogen–bromine bonds (one in each of the HBr molecules) must form.

2. A nitrogen–nitrogen triple bond and three hydrogen–hydrogen bonds must be broken. Six nitrogen–hydrogen bonds must form.

3. The collision model pictures chemical reactions as taking place only when the reactant molecules physically collide with one another with enough energy to break the bonds in the reactant molecules. A minimum energy (the activation energy) is needed for a collision to result in reaction. If molecules do not possess this minimum energy when they collide, they just bounce off one another without reacting.

4. The activation energy is the minimum energy required by two molecules for their collision to result in a reaction. If this energy requirement is not met, a collision will not result in a reaction.

5. A catalyst is a substance that speeds up a reaction without being consumed in the reaction. Catalysts work by providing an alternate pathway by which a reaction can take place; this alternate pathway has a lower activation energy.

6. The catalysts found in living cells are called enzymes. They are necessary for life because most of the cells' chemical processes would be too slow at room temperature without a catalyst.

7. In a heterogeneous reaction, reactants are in two phases. Reactions involving only one phase are homogeneous reactions.

8. For a chemical reaction to occur, the reactants must collide with one another. As the temperature increases, the average kinetic energy increases. The particles are moving faster and the collisions will occur more frequently.

1 Which of the following is true about chemical equilibrium?

  A It is microscopically and macroscopically static.

  B It is microscopically and macroscopically dynamic.

  C It is microscopically static and macroscopically dynamic.

  D It is microscopically dynamic and macroscopically static.

2 Which of the following is true about a system at equilibrium?

  A The concentration(s) of the reactant(s) is equal to the concentration(s) of the product(s).

  B No new product molecules are formed.

  C The concentration of reactant(s) is constant over time.

  D The rate of the reverse reaction is equal to the rate of the forward reaction and both rates are equal to zero.

3 Choose the correct equilibrium expression for the equation

$$2H_2(g) + O_2(g) \rightleftharpoons 2H_2O(g).$$

  A $\dfrac{[H_2O]^2}{[H_2]^2[O_2]}$

  B $\dfrac{[H_2O]^2}{[H_2][O_2]}$

  C $\dfrac{[2H_2O]^2}{[2H_2]^2[O_2]}$

  D $\dfrac{1}{[H_2]^2[O_2]}$

4 Consider the reaction represented by the equation

$$N_2(g) + O_2(g) \rightleftharpoons 2NO(g).$$

For the system at chemical equilibrium, which of the following explains what happens after the addition of oxygen gas (assume constant temperature)?

  A The amount of $NO(g)$ increases and the value for K increases.

  B The amount of $NO(g)$ decreases and the value for K increases.

  C The amount of $NO(g)$ decreases and the value for K stays the same.

  D The amount of $NO(g)$ increases and the value for K stays the same.

5 Write a K_{sp} expression for the process of $PbI_2(s)$ dissolving in water.

  A $[Pb^{2+}][I^-]$

  B $[Pb^{2+}][I^-]^2$

  C $\dfrac{[Pb^{2+}][I^-]^2}{[PbI_2]}$

  D $\dfrac{[Pb^{2+}][I^-]}{[PbI_2]}$

6 At a given temperature, the solubility of CaF_2 is 2.15×10^{-4} M. Calculate the K_{sp} value for CaF_2 at this temperature.

  A 4.64×10^{-8}

  B 3.98×10^{-11}

  C 9.94×10^{-12}

  D 2.15×10^{-4}

7 At a certain temperature the equilibrium constant (K) for the following reaction is 9.00×10^2.

$$2H_2(g) + S_2(g) \rightleftharpoons 2H_2S(g)$$

It is found that $[H_2] = 0.010$ M and $[H_2S] = 0.15$ M. Calculate $[S_2]$.

Chapter 17
Standardized Test Practice

1. D

2. C

3. A

4. D

5. B

6. B

7. $[S_2] = 0.25$ M

Test–Taking Strategy

Explain how to work backward from the answer choices to the question when students are unsure of how to solve a problem or when they are running out of time.

Assessment Resources
CHAPTER 17

For additional practice with standardized testing, see *Standardized Test Practice* located in the *Teacher Resources*.

Planning Guide

Section	Segment		Text Features and Components	Labs, Demonstrations, & Activities

18.1 Electron Transfer Reactions
2 Blocks
pp. 636–641
	A	**Oxidation–Reduction Reactions**	TE Teaching Support: Historical Note *p. 637*	LM Experiment 78: Oxidation and Reduction, Microscale
				    Lab Manual
				    Report Sheets
				    Teacher's Lab Guide
				LM Experiment 79: Activity Series
				    Lab Manual
				    Report Sheets
				    Teacher's Lab Guide

	B	**Oxidation States**	SE Celebrity Chemical: Hydrazine *p. 641*	

18.2 Balancing Oxidation–Reduction Reactions
2 Blocks
pp. 642–651
	A	**Oxidation–Reduction Reactions Between Nonmetals**	SE Chemistry in Your World: U.S. Coins *p. 643*
			SE Chemistry in Your World: Real Gold *p. 645*
				TE Teaching Support: Demonstration *p. 642*
				LM Experiment 80: Halogen Activity Series, CBL
				    Lab Manual
				    Report Sheets
				    Teacher's Lab Guide

	B	**Balancing Oxidation–Reduction Reactions by the Half-Reaction Method**		TE Teaching Support: Demonstration *pp. 646–647*
				LM Experiment 81: Analysis of Hydrogen Peroxide, Microscale
				    Lab Manual
				    Report Sheets
				    Teacher's Lab Guide

		continued on next page		

continued on next page

Key			
SE Student Edition	TE Teacher Edition	RP Teacher Resource Package	
AR Additional Materials	LM Lab Materials	Transparencies	
DVD	CD-ROM	classzone.com	

20. Suppose that for the reaction

$$CH_3OH(g) \rightleftharpoons CH_2O(g) + H_2(g)$$

it is determined that, at a particular temperature, the equilibrium concentrations are
$[CH_3OH] = 0.00215\ M$,
$[CH_2O] = 0.441\ M$, and
$[H_2] = 0.0331\ M$.
Calculate the value of K for the reaction at this temperature.

21. Ammonia, a very important industrial chemical, is produced by the direct combination of the following elements under carefully controlled conditions:

$$N_2(g) + 3H_2(g) \rightleftharpoons 2NH_3(g)$$

Suppose, in an experiment, that the reaction mixture is analyzed after equilibrium is reached and it is found, at the particular temperature, that $[NH_3] = 0.34\ M$,
$[H_2] = 2.1 \times 10^{-3}\ M$, and
$[N_2] = 4.9 \times 10^{-4}\ M$.
Calculate the value of K at this temperature.

22. At high temperatures, elemental nitrogen and oxygen react with each other to form nitrogen monoxide.

$$N_2(g) + O_2(g) \rightleftharpoons 2NO(g)$$

Suppose the system is analyzed at a particular temperature, and the equilibrium concentrations are found to be $[N_2] = 0.041\ M$,
$[O_2] = 0.0078\ M$, and
$[NO] = 4.7 \times 10^{-4}\ M$.
Calculate the value of K for the reaction.

B. Heterogeneous Equilibria

23. What is a *homogeneous* equilibrium system? Give an example of a homogeneous equilibrium reaction. What is a *heterogeneous* equilibrium system? Write two chemical equations that represent heterogeneous equilibria.

24. Explain why the position of a heterogeneous equilibrium does not depend on the amounts of pure solid or pure liquid reactants or products present.

25. Write the equilibrium expression for each of the following heterogeneous equilibria.

    a. $2LiHCO_3(s) \rightleftharpoons$
        $Li_2CO_3(s) + H_2O(g) + CO_2(g)$
    b. $PbCO_3(s) \rightleftharpoons PbO(s) + CO_2(g)$
    c. $4Al(s) + 3O_2(g) \rightleftharpoons 2Al_2O_3(s)$

26. Write the equilibrium expression for each of the following heterogeneous equilibria.

    a. $2NBr_3(s) \rightleftharpoons N_2(g) + 3Br_2(g)$
    b. $CuO(s) + H_2(g) \rightleftharpoons Cu(l) + H_2O(g)$
    c. $PbCO_3(s) \rightleftharpoons PbO(s) + CO_2(g)$

17.3 Applications of Equilibria

A. Le Châtelier's Principle

27. In your own words, describe what Le Châtelier's principle tells us about how we can change the position of a reaction system at equilibrium.

28. Discuss in general terms the effect on the net amount of product when an additional amount of one of the reactants is added to an equilibrium system. Does the value of the equilibrium constant change in this situation?

29. For an equilibrium involving gaseous substances, what effect, in general terms, is realized when the volume of the system is decreased?

30. What is the effect on the equilibrium position if an endothermic reaction is performed at a higher temperature? Does the net amount of product increase or decrease? Does the value of the equilibrium constant change if the temperature is increased?

31. For the reaction system

$$4NH_3(g) + 5O_2(g) \rightleftharpoons 4NO(g) + 6H_2O(g)$$

which has already reached a state of equilibrium, predict the effect that each of the following changes will have on the position of the equilibrium. Tell whether the equilibrium will shift to the right, will shift to the left, or will not be affected.

    a. The pressure of oxygen is increased by injecting one additional mole of oxygen into the reaction vessel.

    b. A desiccant (a material that absorbs water) is added to the system.

    c. The system is compressed and the ammonia liquefies.

However, this lack of change does not mean the reaction has "stopped." The concentrations remain the same because the forward and reverse reactions are occurring at the same rate.

16. The equilibrium constant represents a ratio of the equilibrium concentration(s) of the product(s) present to the equilibrium concentration(s) of the reactant(s) present (with the concentration of each species raised to the power of its coefficient in the balanced equation). For a general reaction $aA + bB \rightleftharpoons cC + dD$, the equilibrium constant, K, has the form $[C]^c[D]^d/[A]^a[B]^b$. The square brackets indicate the concentrations of the substances (in units of molarity, M).

17. Depending on the amounts of reactants that were present originally, differing amounts of products and reactants will be present at equilibrium. However, the ratio of the products to the reactants (which is represented by the equilibrium constant) will always be the same. For example, 4/2 and 6/3 involve different numbers, but each of these ratios is equal to 2.

18. (a) $K = [NCl_3(g)]^2/[N_2(g)][Cl_2(g)]^3$
    (b) $K = [HI(g)]^2/[H_2(g)][I_2(g)]$
    (c) $K = [N_2H_4(g)]/[N_2(g)][H_2(g)]^2$

19. (a) $K = [CH_3OH(g)]/[CO(g)][H_2(g)]^2$
    (b) $K = [NO(g)]^2[O_2(g)]/[NO_2(g)]$
    (c) $K = [PBr_3(g)]^4/[P_4(g)][Br_2(g)]^6$

20. $K = 6.79$

21. $K = 2.5 \times 10^{10}$

22. $K = 6.9 \times 10^{-4}$

23. A homogeneous equilibrium system is a system in which all substances present are in the same physical state. An example is $N_2(g) + O_2(g) \rightleftharpoons 2NO(g)$. Heterogeneous equilibrium systems are those involving substances in more than one physical state—for example, $BaCO_3(s) \rightleftharpoons BaO(s) + CO_2(g)$.

24. Equilibrium constants represent ratios of the concentrations of the products and reactants present at equilibrium. The concentration of a pure liquid or solid is constant and is determined by the density of the liquid or solid.

13. A system has reached equilibrium when the product concentrations no longer increase, even though significant amounts of all reactants are present. At that point, the reverse process is occurring at the same rate as the forward process. In other words, every time a product molecule is formed, another product molecule reacts to give back the reactants. Reactions that come to

equilibrium are indicated by a double arrow.

14. Although we recognize a state of chemical equilibrium by the fact that the concentrations of reactants and products no longer change with time, the lack of change results from the fact that two opposing processes are going on at the same time at the same rate (not because the reaction has truly

"stopped"). Further reaction in the forward direction is canceled out by an equal extent of reaction in the reverse direction. The reaction is still proceeding, but the opposite reaction is also proceeding at the same rate.

15. We recognize a state of chemical equilibrium by the fact that the concentrations of reactants and products no longer change with time.

25. (a) $K = [H_2O(g)][CO_2(g)]$
(b) $K = [CO_2(g)]$
(c) $K = 1/[O_2(g)]^3$

26. (a) $K = [N_2(g)][Br_2(g)]^3$
(b) $K = [H_2O(g)]/[H_2(g)]$
(c) $K = [CO_2(g)]$

27. Le Châtelier's principle states that when a change is imposed on a system at equilibrium, the position of the equilibrium shifts in a direction that tends to reduce the effect of the change.

28. When more of one reactant is added to an equilibrium system, the system shifts to the right and adjusts to use up some of the added reactant. A net increase in the amount of product results, as compared with the equilibrium position before the additional reactant was added. The numerical value of the equilibrium constant does not change when a reactant is added. The concentrations of all reactants and products adjust until the ratios satisfy K.

29. When the volume decreases suddenly, the pressure in the container increases. The equilibrium shifts in the direction that gives the smaller number of gas molecules in order to reduce this increase in pressure.

30. If heat is applied (the temperature is raised) to an endothermic reaction, the equilibrium shifts to the right. More product (and less reactant) will be present at equilibrium than if the temperature had not been increased. The value of K increases.

31. (a) shifts right
(b) shifts right
(c) shifts left

32. (a) no effect
(b) shifts left
(c) shifts right
(d) shifts right

33. For an endothermic reaction, a decrease in temperature will shift the position of equilibrium to the left (toward the reactants).

34. For an endothermic reaction, an increase in temperature will shift the position of equilibrium to the right (toward the products).

32. Suppose the reaction system

$$CH_4(g) + 2O_2(g) \rightleftharpoons CO_2(g) + 2H_2O(l)$$

has already reached equilibrium. Predict the effect of each of the following changes on the position of the equilibrium. Tell whether the equilibrium will shift to the right, will shift to the left, or will not be affected.

   a. Any liquid water present is removed from the system.

   b. CO_2 is added to the system by dropping a chunk of dry ice into the reaction vessel.

   c. The reaction is performed in a metal cylinder fitted with a piston, and the piston is compressed to decrease the total volume of the system.

   d. Additional $O_2(g)$ is added to the system from a cylinder of pure O_2.

33. Old-fashioned "smelling salts" consist of ammonium carbonate, $(NH_4)_2CO_3$. The reaction for the decomposition of ammonium carbonate

$$(NH_4)_2CO_3(s) \rightleftharpoons 2NH_3(g) + CO_2(g) + H_2O(g)$$

is endothermic. What would be the effect on the position of this equilibrium if the reaction were performed at a lower temperature?

34. The reaction

$$4NO(g) + 6H_2O(g) \rightleftharpoons 4NH_3(g) + 5O_2(g)$$

is strongly endothermic. Will an increase in temperature shift the equilibrium position toward the products or toward the reactants?

35. Plants synthesize the sugar dextrose according to the following reaction by absorbing radiant energy from the sun (photosynthesis).

$$6CO_2(g) + 6H_2O(g) \rightleftharpoons C_6H_{12}O_6(s) + 6O_2(g)$$

Will an increase in temperature tend to favor or discourage the production of $C_6H_{12}O_6(s)$?

B. Applications Involving the Equilibrium Constant

36. Suppose a reaction has the equilibrium constant $K = 1.3 \times 10^8$. What does the magnitude of this constant tell you about the relative concentrations of products and reactants that will be present once equilibrium is reached? Is this reaction likely to be a good source of the products?

37. Suppose a reaction has the equilibrium constant $K = 4.5 \times 10^{-6}$ at a particular temperature. If an experiment is set up with this reaction, will there be large relative concentrations of products present at equilibrium? Is this reaction useful as a means of producing the products? How might the reaction be made more useful?

38. For the reaction

$$N_2(g) + 3Cl_2(g) \rightleftharpoons 2NCl_3(g)$$

an analysis of an equilibrium mixture is performed. It is found that
$[NCl_3] = 1.9 \times 10^{-1}\ M$,
$[N_2] = 1.4 \times 10^{-3}\ M$,
and $[Cl_2] = 4.3 \times 10^{-4}\ M$.
Calculate K for the reaction.

39. For the reaction

$$3O_2(g) \rightleftharpoons 2O_3(g)$$

$K = 1.8 \times 10^{-7}$ at a particular temperature. If the equilibrium system is analyzed and it is found that $[O_2] = 0.0012\ M$, what is the concentration of O_3 in the system?

40. For the reaction

$$CaCO_3(s) \rightleftharpoons CaO(s) + CO_2(g)$$

it is found that at equilibrium $[CO_2] = 2.1 \times 10^{-3}\ M$ at a particular temperature. Calculate K for the reaction at this temperature.

41. For the reaction

$$N_2(g) + O_2(g) \rightleftharpoons 2NO(g)$$

the equilibrium constant K has the value 1.71×10^{-3} at a particular temperature. If the concentrations of both $N_2(g)$ and $O_2(g)$ are $0.0342\ M$ in an equilibrium mixture at this temperature, what is the concentration of $NO(g)$ under these conditions?

42. For the reaction

$$N_2O_4(g) \rightleftharpoons 2NO_2(g)$$

the equilibrium constant K has the value 8.1×10^{-3} at a particular temperature. If the concentration of $NO_2(g)$ is found to be $0.0021\ M$ in the equilibrium system, what is the concentration of $N_2O_4(g)$ under these conditions?

35. The production of dextrose will be favored.

36. A large equilibrium constant means that at equilibrium the concentration of the products is large compared with the concentration of the reactants. The position of the equilibrium lies far to the right. A reaction with a large equilibrium constant is therefore useful as a means of producing the products.

37. A small equilibrium constant means that at equilibrium the concentration of the products is small compared with the concentration of the reactants. The position of the equilibrium lies far to the left. A reaction with a small equilibrium constant is therefore not useful as a means of producing the products. To become useful, the equilibrium position would have to be shifted to the right.

38. $K = 3.2 \times 10^{11}$

39. $[O_3] = 1.8 \times 10^{-8}\ M$

40. $K = 2.1 \times 10^{-3}$

41. $[NO] = 1.41 \times 10^{-3}\ M$

42. $[N_2O_4] = 5.4 \times 10^{-4}\ M$

43. When an ionic solid is placed in water, the crystal dissolves to produce ions. As the concentrations of the ions in the solutions increase, however, the likelihood of the oppositely charged ions

C. Solubility Equilibria

43. Explain how the dissolving of an ionic solute in water represents an equilibrium process.

44. Why does the amount of excess solid solute present in a solution not affect the amount of solute that ultimately dissolves in a given amount of solvent?

45. Why does neither stirring nor grinding a solute affect the amount of solute that ultimately dissolves in a given amount of solvent?

46. Write the balanced chemical equations describing the dissolving of the following solids in water. Write the expression for K_{sp} for each process.

    a. $NiS(s)$ c. $BaCrO_4(s)$

    b. $CuCO_3(s)$ d. $Ag_3PO_4(s)$

47. Write the balanced chemical equations describing the dissolving of the following solids in water. Write the expression for K_{sp} for each process.

    a. $PbBr_2(s)$ c. $PbCO_3(s)$

    b. $Ag_2S(s)$ d. $Sr_3(PO_4)_2(s)$

48. Zinc carbonate dissolves in water to the extent of 1.12×10^{-4} g/L at 25 °C. Calculate the solubility product K_{sp} for $ZnCO_3$ at 25 °C.

49. A saturated solution of nickel(II) sulfide contains approximately 3.6×10^{-4} g of dissolved NiS per liter at 20 °C. Calculate the solubility product K_{sp} for NiS at 20 °C.

50. The solubility product constant, K_{sp}, for calcium carbonate at room temperature is approximately 3.0×10^{-9}. Calculate the solubility of $CaCO_3$ in grams per liter under these conditions.

51. Chromate ion is used as a qualitative test for lead(II) ion, forming a bright yellow precipitate of lead chromate, $PbCrO_4(s)$. The K_{sp} for $PbCrO_4(s)$ is 2.8×10^{-13} at 25 °C. Calculate the solubility of $PbCrO_4$ in grams per liter at 25 °C.

52. Lead(II) chloride, $PbCl_2(s)$, dissolves in water to the extent of approximately 3.6×10^{-2} M at 20 °C. Calculate the K_{sp} for $PbCl_2(s)$, and calculate its solubility in grams per liter.

53. Mercury(I) chloride, Hg_2Cl_2, was formerly administered orally to induce vomiting. Although we usually think of mercury compounds as highly toxic, the K_{sp} of mercury(I) chloride is small enough (1.3×10^{-18}) that the amount of mercury that dissolves and enters the bloodstream is tiny. Calculate the concentration of mercury(I) ion present in a saturated solution of Hg_2Cl_2.

Critical Thinking

54. Before two molecules can react, chemists envision that the molecules must first *collide* with each other. Is collision among molecules the only consideration for the molecules to react with one another?

55. Why does an increase in temperature favor an increase in the speed of a reaction?

56. What does it mean to say that all chemical reactions are, to one extent or another, *reversible*?

57. What does it mean to say that chemical equilibrium is a *dynamic* process?

58. Why does increasing the temperature for an exothermic process tend to favor the conversion of products back to reactants?

59. Suppose $K = 4.5 \times 10^{-3}$ at a certain temperature for the reaction

$$PCl_5(g) \rightleftharpoons PCl_3(g) + Cl_2(g)$$

If it is found that the concentration of PCl_5 is twice the concentration of PCl_3, what must be the concentration of Cl_2 under these conditions?

60. How does the collision model account for the fact that a reaction proceeds faster when the concentrations of the reactants are increased?

61. How does an increase in temperature result in an increase in the number of successful collisions between reactant molecules? What does an increase in temperature mean on a molecular basis?

---

colliding and re-forming the solid increases. Eventually, an equilibrium is established in which the dissolving and re-forming of the solid occur at the same rate.

44. A given amount of solvent can "hold" only a certain amount of solute. Once this amount has been reached, adding more solid will not increase the concentration of dissolved solute in solution.

45. Stirring or grinding the solute increases the speed with which the solute dissolves. However, the amount of solute that dissolves is set by the equilibrium constant for that process.

46. (a) $NiS(s) \rightleftharpoons Ni^{2+}(aq) + S^{2-}(aq)$;
$K_{sp} = [Ni^{2+}(aq)][S^{2-}(aq)]$
(b) $CuCO_3(s) \rightleftharpoons$
$Cu^{2+}(aq) + CO_3{}^{2-}(aq)$;
$K_{sp} = [Cu^{2+}(aq)][CO_3{}^{2-}(aq)]$
(c) $BaCrO_4(s) \rightleftharpoons$
$Ba^{2+}(aq) + CrO_4{}^{2-}(aq)$;
$K_{sp} = [Ba^{2+}(aq)][CrO_4{}^{2-}(aq)]$
(d) $Ag_3PO_4(s) \rightleftharpoons$
$3Ag^+(aq) + PO_4{}^{3-}(aq)$;
$K_{sp} = [Ag^+(aq)]^3[PO_4{}^{3-}(aq)]$

47. (a) $PbBr_2(s) \rightleftharpoons$
$Pb^{2+}(aq) + 2Br^-(aq)$;
$K_{sp} = [Pb^{2+}(aq)][Br^-(aq)]^2$
(b) $Ag_2S(s) \rightleftharpoons$
$2Ag^+(aq) + S^{2-}(aq)$;
$K_{sp} = [Ag^+(aq)]^2[S^{2-}(aq)]$
(c) $PbCO_3(s) \rightleftharpoons$
$Pb^{2+}(aq) + CO_3{}^{2-}(aq)$;
$K_{sp} = [Pb^{2+}(aq)][CO_3{}^{2-}(aq)]$;
(d) $Sr_3(PO_4)_2(s) \rightleftharpoons$
$3Sr^{2+}(aq) + 2PO_4{}^{3-}(aq)$;
$K_{sp} = [Sr^{2+}(aq)]^3[PO_4{}^{3-}(aq)]^2$

48. $K_{sp} = 7.98 \times 10^{-13}$

49. $K_{sp} = 1.6 \times 10^{-11}$

50. 5.5×10^{-3} g/L

51. 1.7×10^{-4} g/L

52. $K_{sp} = 1.9 \times 10^{-4}$; 10. g/L

53. 6.9×10^{-7} M

54. No. The molecules must also possess sufficient energy to react with one another and they must have the proper orientation in space for a reaction to occur.

55. An increase in temperature increases the fraction of molecules with energy greater than the activation energy.

56. To say a reaction is reversible means that it may occur in either direction.

57. Even though the reaction appears macroscopically to have stopped, on a microscopic basis the forward and reverse reactions are still taking place at the same speed.

58. In an exothermic process heat can be considered a product of the reaction. Adding heat (by increasing the temperature) therefore works against the forward process.

59. 9.0×10^{-3} M

60. A higher concentration means that more molecules are present in a given volume, which results in a greater frequency of collisions between molecules.

61. At higher temperatures, the average kinetic energy of the reactant molecules is larger. Therefore, the probability that the molecules will have enough energy for a reaction to take place is greater. At the molecular level, a higher temperature means that a given molecule is moving faster.

62. The liquid begins to evaporate and produces molecules of vapor above the liquid. As the amount of vapor increases, the molecules collide and condense. Eventually, the opposite processes of evaporation and condensation occur at equal rates, and equilibrium is established.

63. (a) $K = [HBr(g)]^2/[H_2(g)][Br_2(g)]$
(b) $K = [H_2S(g)]^2/[H_2(g)]^2[S_2(g)]$
(c) $K = [HCN(g)]^2/[H_2(g)][C_2N_2(g)]$

64. (a) $K = 1/[O_2(g)]^3$
(b) $K = 1/[NH_3(g)][HCl(g)]$
(c) $K = 1/[O_2(g)]$

65. (a) shifts right
(b) shifts right
(c) no effect; Although this change increases the total pressure, it does not change the pressures of any of the gases involved in the reaction and thus no shift will occur.

66. $K_{sp} = 1.4 \times 10^{-8}$

67. $K = 1.00$

68. (b) The equilibrium position is shifted to the left and the value for K decreases.

69. (a) A catalyst speeds up a reaction without being used up. It does this by lowering the activation energy.
(b) The catalyzed reaction pathway is represented by the dotted line. This is because the activation energy is lower for this reaction.
(c) The double arrows represent the activation energy of the reactions.

---

62. Explain why the development of a vapor pressure above a liquid in a closed container represents an equilibrium. What are the opposing processes? How do we recognize when the system has reached a state of equilibrium?

63. Write the equilibrium expression for each of the following reactions.

a. $H_2(g) + Br_2(g) \rightleftharpoons 2HBr(g)$

b. $2H_2(g) + S_2(g) \rightleftharpoons 2H_2S(g)$

c. $H_2(g) + C_2N_2(g) \rightleftharpoons 2HCN(g)$

64. Write the equilibrium expression for each of the following heterogeneous equilibria.

a. $4Al(s) + 3O_2(g) \rightleftharpoons 2Al_2O_3(s)$

b. $NH_3(g) + HCl(g) \rightleftharpoons NH_4Cl(s)$

c. $2Mg(s) + O_2(g) \rightleftharpoons 2MgO(s)$

65. Suppose the reaction system

$$2NO(g) + O_2(g) \rightleftharpoons 2NO_2(g)$$

has already reached equilibrium. Predict the effect of each of the following changes on the position of the equilibrium. Tell whether the equilibrium will shift to the right, will shift to the left, or will not be affected.

a. Additional oxygen is injected into the system.

b. NO_2 is removed from the reaction vessel.

c. 1.0 mol of helium is injected into the system.

66. Approximately 0.14 g of nickel(II) hydroxide, $Ni(OH)_2(s)$, dissolves per liter of water at 20 °C. Calculate the K_{sp} for $Ni(OH)_2(s)$ at this temperature.

---

67. Consider the reaction as represented by the following equation.

$$N_2(g) + 3H_2(g) \rightleftharpoons 2NH_3(g)$$

Initially, $[N_2] = 5.00 M$ and $[H_2] = 4.00 M$. At equilibrium, $[H_2] = 1.00 M$ at a certain temperature. Determine the value for K for this reaction at this temperature.

68. Consider the combustion of methane (as represented by the following equation). This is the reaction that occurs for a Bunsen burner, which is a source of heat for chemical reactions in the laboratory.

$$CH_4(g) + 2O_2(g) \rightleftharpoons CO_2(g) + 2H_2O(g)$$

For the system at chemical equilibrium, which of the following explains what happens if the temperature is raised?

a. The equilibrium position is shifted to the right and the value for K decreases.

b. The equilibrium position is shifted to the left and the value for K decreases.

c. The equilibrium position is shifted to the left and the value for K increases.

d. The equilibrium position is shifted but the value for K stays constant.

69. Consider the figure below in answering the following questions.

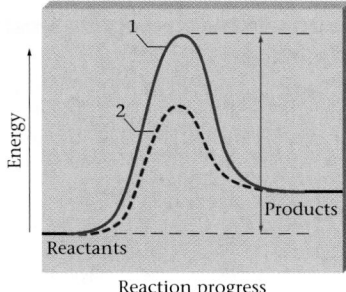

a. What does a catalyst do to a chemical reaction?

b. Which of the pathways in the figure is the catalyzed reaction pathway? How do you know?

c. What is represented by the double-headed arrow?

All Learners	Technology	Review & Assessment	Standards
TE Teaching Tips *p. 636*	**▶** Lab Generator CD **◉** EasyPlanner	**SE** Active Reading Question *p. 636* **SE** Practice Problem *p. 637* **TE** More Examples *p. 637* **SE** Key Terms *p. 661* **SE** Questions and Problems *p. 662*	**TE** **NSES** UCP1, A1, A2, B2, B3, E1, E2, G1, G2
TE Teaching Tips *pp. 637, 639* **RP** Team Learning Worksheet (Sec. 18.1)	**▤** Transparency: Rules for Assigning Oxidation States **◉** EasyPlanner	**SE** Active Reading Question *p. 638* **SE** Practice Problem *p. 640* **TE** More Examples *p. 640* **SE** Review Questions (18.1.A–18.1.B) *p. 641* **SE** Key Terms *p. 661* **SE** Questions and Problems *p. 662*	
TE Teaching Tips *p. 643*	**▶** Lab Generator CD **◉** EasyPlanner	**TE** More Examples *p. 644* **TE** More Examples *p. 644* **SE** Practice Problem *p. 645* **SE** Key Terms *p. 661* **SE** Questions and Problems *pp. 662–663*	**TE** **NSES** UCP1, UCP3, UCP5, A1, A2, B2, B3, E1, E2, F3, G1, G2, G3
TE Teaching Tips *pp. 646–647* **TE** Meeting Individual Needs *p. 648* **RP** Team Learning Worksheet (Sec. 18.2)	**▶** Lab Generator CD **◉** EasyPlanner	**SE** Active Reading Question *p. 646* **TE** More Examples *p. 648* **TE** More Examples *p. 650* **SE** Practice Problem *p. 651* **SE** Review Questions (18.2.A–18.2.B) *p. 651* **SE** Key Terms *p. 661* **SE** Questions and Problems *p. 663*	

Planning Guide

Section	Segment		Text Features and Components	Labs, Demonstrations, & Activities

18.3 Electrochemistry and Its Applications
 1.5 Blocks
 pp. 652–660
	A	**Electrochemistry: An Introduction**	(SE) Chemistry Explorers: Alessandro Volta *p. 654*	(TE) Teaching Support: Demonstration *pp. 652–653*
				 (LM) Experiment 82: Galvanic Cells, CBL
				     Lab Manual
				     Report Sheets
				     Teacher's Lab Guide

	B	**Batteries**	(SE) Top Ten Most Active Metals *p. 657*	

	C	**Corrosion**		(SE) Hands-On Chemistry: Lemon Power *p. 658*
				 (LM) Experiment 83: Corrosion of Iron, Traditional
				     Lab Manual
				     Report Sheets
				     Teacher's Lab Guide

	D	**Electrolysis**	(SE) Chemistry Explorers: Charles Martin Hall *p. 659*	

Key	(SE) Student Edition	(TE) Teacher Edition	(RP) Teacher Resource Package
	(AR) Additional Materials	(LM) Lab Materials	(≣) Transparencies
	(◉) DVD (▷) CD-ROM	(ℹ) classzone.com	

All Learners	Technology	Review & Assessment	Standards
(TE) Teaching Tip *p. 653*	(image) Transparency: Figure 18.2 (image) Animation: Electrochemical Half-Reactions in a Galvanic Cell (image) Animation: Galvanic (Voltaic) Cells (image) Animation: Voltaic Cell: Anode Reaction (image) Animation: Voltaic Cell: Cathode Reaction (image) Animation: Zinc/Copper Cells with Lemons (image) Lab Generator CD (image) EasyPlanner	(SE) Active Reading Question *p. 652* (SE) Active Reading Question *p. 653* (SE) Key Terms *p. 661* (SE) Questions and Problems *p. 663*	(TE) **NSES** UCP1, UCP3, UCP5, A1, A2, B2, B3, E1, E2, F3, F4, F6, G1, G2, G3
(TE) Teaching Tips *p. 655* (TE) Meeting Individual Needs *p. 656*	(image) Transparency: Figure 18.3 (image) Transparency: Figure 18.4 (image) Transparency: Figure 18.5 (image) EasyPlanner	(SE) Active Reading Question *p. 656* (SE) Key Terms *p. 661* (SE) Questions and Problems *p. 664*	
	(image) Lab Generator CD (image) EasyPlanner	(SE) Active Reading Question *p. 658* (SE) Key Terms *p. 661* (SE) Questions and Problems *p. 664*	
(TE) Teaching Tip *p. 658* (RP) Team Learning Worksheet (Sec. 18.3)	(image) Video: Electrolysis of Water (image) EasyPlanner	(SE) Critical Thinking *p. 659* (SE) Active Reading Question *p. 659* (SE) Review Questions (18.3.A–18.3.D) *p. 660* (SE) Key Terms *p. 661* (SE) Questions and Problems *p. 664*	

Resource Materials for Chapter 18

(SE) Chapter Review *p. 661*

(SE) Critical Thinking *p. 664*

(SE) Standardized Test Practice *p. 665*

(AR) English/Spanish Summaries

(image) English Summaries Audio

(image) Spanish Summaries Audio

(RP) Meeting Individual Needs Toolkit (MINT)
    Chapter Review Worksheets
    Chapter Summaries

(RP) Solutions Guide

(RP) Standardized Test Practice

(RP) Chapter Tests

(RP) Test Bank

(image) Test Generator

Chapter 18

Overview

In this chapter our goals are for students to:

- Learn about metal-nonmetal oxidation–reduction reactions

- Learn to assign oxidation states

- Understand oxidation and reduction in terms of oxidation states

- Learn to identify oxidizing and reducing agents

- Learn to balance oxidation–reduction equations using half reactions

- Understand the term *electrochemistry*

- Learn to identify the components of an electrochemical cell

- Learn about the composition and operation of commonly used batteries

- Understand the electrochemical nature of corrosion and to learn ways of preventing it

- Understand the process of electrolysis and learn about the commercial preparation of aluminum

A nickel electroplated with copper

634

IN YOUR LIFE

What do a forest fire, rusting steel, combustion in an automobile engine, and the metabolism of food in a human body have in common? All of these important processes involve oxidation–reduction reactions. In fact, virtually all of the processes that provide energy to heat buildings, power vehicles, and allow people to work and play depend on oxidation–reduction reactions. And every time you start your car, turn on your calculator, look at your digital watch, or listen to a radio at the beach, you are depending on an oxidation–reduction reaction to power the battery in each of these devices. In addition, because "pollution-free" vehicles have been promoted in California, hybrid cars are more common on U.S. roads. This will lead to increased reliance of our society on batteries and will spur the search for new, more efficient batteries.

The power generated by an alkaline AA battery and a mercury battery results from oxidation–reduction reactions.

WHAT DO YOU KNOW?

Prereading Questions

1. What is meant by the term *oxidation*? What is meant by the term *reduction*?

2. When forming compounds, do metals tend to gain or lose electrons? What about nonmetals?

3. What are the general trends for electronegativity across rows and down columns of the periodic table?

Oxidation–Reduction Reactions and Electrochemistry • Chapter 18 • **635**

SECTION 18.1
INTRODUCE

Student Preparation

Assign students to read Section 18.1 and to answer the Review Questions at the end of the section before coming to class.

 Active Learning
Team Learning Worksheet

After introducing the material in Section 18.1 in class, place students in groups and have them work together on **Section 18.1: Team Learning Worksheet.**

SECTION 18.1
GUIDE THE LEARNING

Homework

You may wish to assign these selected end-of-chapter problems as homework for this section: 1, 2, 3, 5, 6, 9, 11, 12

Additional end-of-chapter problems can be used for extra practice.

18.1.A Oxidation–Reduction Reactions

Objective To learn about metal-nonmetal oxidation–reduction reactions

 LABORATORY
EXPERIMENT 78:
Oxidation and Reduction, Microscale

LABORATORY
EXPERIMENT 79:
Activity Series

TEACHING TIPS

- An introduction to the terms *oxidation* and *reduction* is presented in this section. To assist students in remembering what happens in each type of reaction, many mnemonics are used. Some of the more common are OIL RIG (Oxidation Is Loss; Reduction Is Gain) or LEO (Loss Equals Oxidation) the lion says GER (Gain Equals Reduction).

- Remind students that these reactions are the same ones they studied earlier in the year.

SECTION 18.1
Electron Transfer Reactions

Key Terms

- Oxidation–reduction reactions (redox reactions)
- Oxidation
- Reduction
- Oxidation states

Objectives

- *To learn about metal-nonmetal oxidation–reduction reactions*
- *To learn to assign oxidation states*

A. Oxidation–Reduction Reactions

In Chapter 8 we discussed the chemical reactions between metals and nonmetals. For example, sodium chloride is formed by the reaction of elemental sodium and chlorine.

2Na(*s*) + Cl₂(*g*) → 2NaCl(*s*)
Sodium   Chlorine   Sodium chloride

Because elemental sodium and chlorine contain uncharged atoms and because sodium chloride is known to contain Na^+ and Cl^- ions, this reaction must involve a transfer of electrons from sodium atoms to chlorine atoms.

$$Na \xrightarrow{\quad e^- \quad} Cl$$

Oxidation–reduction reaction (redox reaction)
A chemical reaction involving the transfer of electrons

Oxidation
A loss of electrons; an increase in oxidation state

Reduction
A gain of electrons; a decrease in oxidation state

Reactions like this one, in which one or more electrons are transferred, are called **oxidation–reduction reactions**, *or* **redox reactions.** **Oxidation** is defined as a *loss of electrons.* **Reduction** is defined as a *gain of electrons.* In the reaction of elemental sodium and chlorine, each sodium atom loses one electron, forming a 1+ ion. Therefore, sodium is oxidized. Each chlorine atom gains one electron, forming a negative chloride ion, and is thus reduced. Whenever a metal reacts with a nonmetal to form an ionic compound, electrons are transferred from the metal to the nonmetal. So these reactions are always oxidation–reduction reactions where the metal is oxidized (loses electrons) and the nonmetal is reduced (gains electrons).

 Active Reading Question

Which element is oxidized and which element is reduced when a sodium metal reacts with chlorine gas?

Active Reading Question

Sodium metal is oxidized and chlorine gas is reduced.

EXAMPLE 18.1

Identifying Oxidation and Reduction in a Reaction

In the following reactions, identify which element is oxidized and which element is reduced.

a. $2Mg(s) + O_2(g) \rightarrow 2MgO(s)$ **b.** $2Al(s) + 3I_2(s) \rightarrow 2AlI_3(s)$

Solution

a. We have learned that Group 2 metals form 2+ cations and that Group 6 nonmetals form 2− anions, so we can predict that magnesium oxide contains Mg^{2+} and O^{2-} ions. This means that in the reaction given, each Mg loses two electrons to form Mg^{2+} and so is oxidized. Also each O gains two electrons to form O^{2-} and so is reduced.

b. Aluminum iodide contains the Al^{3+} and I^- ions. Thus aluminum atoms lose electrons (are oxidized). Iodine atoms gain electrons (are reduced).

Magnesium burns in air to give a bright, white flame.

 Practice Problem • Exercise 18.1

For the following reactions, identify the element oxidized and the element reduced.

a. $2Cu(s) + O_2(g) \rightarrow 2CuO(s)$ **b.** $2Cs(s) + F_2(g) \rightarrow 2CsF(s)$

Reactions Between Nonmetals Although we can identify reactions between metals and nonmetals as redox reactions, it is more difficult to decide whether a given reaction between nonmetals is a redox reaction. In fact, many of the most significant redox reactions involve only nonmetals. For example, combustion reactions such as methane burning in oxygen are oxidation–reduction reactions.

$$CH_4(g) + 2O_2(g) \rightarrow CO_2(g) + 2H_2O(g) + energy$$

Even though none of the reactants or products in this reaction is ionic, the reaction does involve a transfer of electrons from carbon to oxygen. To explain this, we must introduce the concept of oxidation states.

B. Oxidation States

The concept of **oxidation states** (sometimes called *oxidation numbers*) lets us keep track of electrons in oxidation–reduction reactions by assigning charges to the various atoms in a compound. Sometimes these charges are quite apparent. For example, in a binary ionic compound the ions have easily identified charges: in sodium chloride, sodium is +1 and chlorine is −1; in magnesium oxide, magnesium is +2 and oxygen is −2; and so on.

In such binary ionic compounds the oxidation states are simply the charges of the ions.

Ion	Oxidation State
Na^+	+1
Cl^-	−1
Mg^{2+}	+2
O^{2-}	−2

Oxidation state
A concept that allows us to keep track of electrons in oxidation–reduction reactions.

18.1 • Electron Transfer Reactions • **637**

EXAMPLE 18.1

More Examples

For the following reactions, identify which element is oxidized and which element is reduced.

1. $Cl_2(g) + Cu(s) \rightarrow CuCl_2(s)$
   Copper is oxidized and chlorine is reduced.

2. $O_2(g) + 2Ni(s) \rightarrow 2NiO(s)$
   Nickel is oxidized and oxygen is reduced.

3. $S(s) + 2Hg(l) \rightarrow Hg_2S(s)$
   Mercury is oxidized and sulfur is reduced.

 Answer to Practice Problem 18.1

a. CuO contains Cu^{2+} and O^{2-} ions, so copper is oxidized $(Cu \rightarrow Cu^{2+} + 2e^-)$ and oxygen is reduced $(O + 2e^- \rightarrow O^{2-})$.

b. CsF contains Cs^+ and F^- ions. Thus cesium is oxidized $(Cs \rightarrow Cs^+ + e^-)$ and fluorine is reduced $(F + e^- \rightarrow F^-)$.

18.1.B Oxidation States

Objective To learn how to assign oxidation states

🍎 TEACHING TIPS

• Some students wonder why the term *reduction* is used to describe a *gain* of electrons. When you discuss oxidation states, emphasize that when an atom is reduced, its oxidation state is reduced.

• It is easiest to introduce the oxidation states for ions before discussing covalent molecules. Since the charge on the ion is the same as the oxidation state, this approach makes sense to students. Emphasize that the charge on an ion is acquired from a transfer of electrons. This concept establishes the idea of assigning electrons to a particular atom. Then move to covalent molecules and begin assigning oxidation states.

Active Reading Question

Answers will vary. Sulfur has a negative oxidation state in hydrogen sulfide, H_2S (S has an oxidation state of -2). Sulfur has a positive oxidation state in sulfur dioxide, SO_2 (S has an oxidation state of $+4$).

In an uncombined element, all of the atoms are uncharged (neutral). For example, sodium metal contains neutral sodium atoms, and chlorine gas is made up of Cl_2 molecules, each of which contains two neutral chlorine atoms. Therefore, an atom in a pure element has no charge and is assigned an oxidation state of zero.

Oxidation States in Covalent Compounds In a covalent compound such as water, although no ions are actually present, chemists find it useful to assign imaginary charges to the elements in the compound. The oxidation states of the elements in these compounds are equal to the imaginary charges we determine by assuming that the most electronegative atom in a bond controls or possesses *both* of the shared electrons (see Chapter 12). For example, in the O—H bonds in water, it is assumed for purposes of assigning oxidation states that the much more electronegative oxygen atom controls both of the shared electrons in each bond. This gives the oxygen eight valence electrons.

$$
\begin{array}{c}
H \\
\diagdown \\
\ddot{O}: \xleftarrow{\ 2e^-\ } \\
\ddot{} \xleftarrow{\ 2e^-\ } \\
\diagup \\
H
\end{array}
$$

In effect we say that each hydrogen has lost its single electron to the oxygen. This gives each hydrogen an oxidation state of $+1$ and the oxygen an oxidation state of -2 (the oxygen atom has formally gained two electrons). In virtually all covalent compounds, oxygen is assigned an oxidation state of -2 and hydrogen is assigned an oxidation state of $+1$.

Because fluorine is so electronegative, it is always assumed to control any shared electrons. So fluorine is always assumed to have a complete octet of electrons and is assigned an oxidation state of -1. That is, for purposes of assigning oxidation states, fluorine is always imagined to be F^- in its covalent compounds.

The most electronegative elements are F, O, N, and Cl. In general, we give each of these elements an oxidation state equal to its charge as an anion: fluorine is -1, chlorine is -1, oxygen is -2, and nitrogen is -3. When two of these elements are found in the same compound, we assign them in order of electronegativity, starting with the element that has the largest electronegativity.

$$F > O > N > Cl$$

Largest   Least
electronegativity electronegativity

For example, in the compound NO_2, because oxygen has a greater electronegativity than nitrogen, we assign each oxygen an oxidation state of -2. This gives a total "charge" of -4 (2×-2) on the two oxygen atoms. Because the NO_2 molecule has zero overall charge, the N must be $+4$ to exactly balance the -4 on the oxygens. In NO_2, then, the oxidation state of *each* oxygen is -2 and the oxidation state of the nitrogen is $+4$.

 Active Reading Question

Provide an example when sulfur has a negative oxidation state in a compound, and an example when sulfur has a positive oxidation state in a compound.

The rules for assigning oxidation states are given below and are illustrated in **Table 18.1**. Application of these rules allows us to assign oxidation states in most compounds. The principles are illustrated by Example 18.2.

TECHNOLOGY

 Rules for Assigning Oxidation States

Rules for Assigning Oxidation States

1. The oxidation state of an atom in an uncombined element is 0.

2. The oxidation state of a monatomic ion is the same as its charge.

3. Oxygen is assigned an oxidation state of -2 in most of its covalent compounds. Important exception: peroxides (compounds containing the O_2^{2-} group), in which each oxygen is assigned an oxidation state of -1.

4. In its covalent compounds with nonmetals, hydrogen is assigned an oxidation state of $+1$.

5. In binary compounds, the element with the greater electronegativity is assigned a negative oxidation state equal to its charge as an anion in its ionic compounds.

6. For an electrically neutral compound, the sum of the oxidation states must be zero.

7. For an ionic species, the sum of the oxidation states must equal the overall charge.

 TEACHING TIPS

- Students need to learn the rules for assigning oxidation states. It is a good idea to give them a number of practice problems in which they must assign oxidation states to all of the elements in a compound.

- Students often become more concerned with the exceptions than with the compounds that follow the rules. For beginning students, focus on compounds that obey the rules. If students ask about exceptions, use examples such as H_2O_2 and NaH.

Table 18.1

Examples of Oxidation States

Substance	Oxidation States	Comments
sodium, metal, Na	Na, 0	rule 1
magnesium sulfide, MgS	Mg, $+2$ S, -2	rule 2 rule 2
carbon monoxide, CO	C, $+2$ O, -2	 rule 3
sulfur dioxide, SO_2	S, $+4$ O, -2	 rule 3
hydrogen peroxide, H_2O_2	H, $+1$ O, -1	 rule 3 (exception)
ammonia, NH_3	H, $+1$ N, -3	rule 4 rule 5
hydrogen sulfide, H_2S	H, $+1$ S, -2	rule 4 rule 5
sodium carbonate, Na_2CO_3	Na, $+1$ O, -2 C, $+4$	rule 2 rule 3 For CO_3^{-2}, the sum of the oxidation states is $+4 + 3(-2) = -2$. rule 7

EXAMPLE 18.2

More Examples

Assign oxidation states to all atoms in the following molecules or ions.

1. NF_3

nitrogen, $+3$; fluorine, -1

2. $HOCl$

hydrogen, $+1$; oxygen, -2; chlorine, $+1$

3. SO_4^{2-}

sulfur, $+6$; oxygen, -2

 Answer to Practice Problem 18.2

a. SO_3

Assign oxygen first. Each O has an oxidation state of -2, giving a total of -6 (3×-2) for the three O atoms. Because the molecule has zero charge overall, the sulfur must have an oxidation state of $+6$.
Check: $+6 + 3(-2) = 0$

b. SO_4^{2-}

As in part a, each oxygen is assigned an oxidation state of -2, giving a total of -8 (4×-2) on the four oxygen atoms. The anion has a net charge of -2, so the sulfur must have an oxidation state of $+6$.
Check: $+6 + 4(-2) = -2$
SO_4^{2-} has a charge of -2, so this is correct.

c. N_2O_5

We assign oxygen before nitrogen because oxygen is more electronegative. Each O has an oxidation state of -2, giving a total of -10 on the five oxygen atoms. Therefore, the oxidation states of the two nitrogen atoms must total $+10$, because N_2O_5 has no overall charge. Each N is assigned an oxidation state of $+5$.
Check: $2(+5) + 5(-2) = 0$

d. PF_3

Assign fluorine an oxidation state of -1, giving a total of -3 on the three fluorine atoms. Thus, P must have an oxidation state of $+3$.
Check: $+3 + 3(-1) = 0$

e. C_2H_6

It is best to recognize that hydrogen is always $+1$ in compounds with nonmetals. Thus, each H is assigned an oxidation state of $+1$ for a total of $+6$ ($6 \times +1$). Therefore, the two carbon atoms must account for -6,

and each carbon is assigned an oxidation state of -3.
Check: $2(-3) + 6(+1) = 0$

EXAMPLE 18.2

Assigning Oxidation States

Assign oxidation states to all atoms in the following molecules or ions.

a. CO_2

b. SF_6

c. NO_3^-

Solution

a. Rule 3 is most important here: oxygen is assigned an oxidation state of -2. We determine the oxidation state for carbon by recognizing that because CO_2 has no charge, the sum of the oxidation states for oxygen and carbon must be 0 (rule 6). Each oxygen is -2 and there are two oxygen atoms, so the carbon atom must be assigned an oxidation state of $+4$.

$$CO_2$$
$+4 \quad -2 \text{ for } each \text{ oxygen}$

Check: $+4 + 2(-2) = 0$

b. Because fluorine has the greater electronegativity, we assign its oxidation state first. Its charge as an anion is always -1, so we assign -1 as the oxidation state of each fluorine atom (rule 5). The sulfur must then be assigned an oxidation state of $+6$ to balance the total of -6 from the six fluorine atoms (rule 7).

$$SF_6$$
$+6 \quad -1 \text{ for } each \text{ fluorine}$

Check: $+6 + 6(-1) = 0$

c. Oxygen has a greater electronegativity than nitrogen, so we assign its oxidation state of -2 first (rule 5). Because the overall charge on NO_3^- is -1 and because the sum of the oxidation states of the three oxygens is -6, the nitrogen must have an oxidation state of $+5$.

$$NO_3^-$$
$+5 \quad -2 \text{ for } each \text{ oxygen gives } -6 \text{ total}$

Check: $+5 + 3(-2) = -1$

This is correct; NO_3^- has a -1 charge.

 Practice Problem • Exercise 18.2

Assign oxidation states to all atoms in the following molecules or ions.

a. SO_3

b. SO_4^{2-}

c. N_2O_5

d. PF_3

e. C_2H_6

CELEBRITY CHEMICAL — Hydrazine (N₂H₄)

Hydrazine, N_2H_4, is a colorless liquid with an ammonia-like odor that freezes at 2 °C and boils at 114 °C. This powerful reducing agent reacts with oxygen in a highly exothermic reaction,

$$N_2H_4(l) + O_2(g) \rightarrow N_2(g) + 2H_2O(g)$$

which produces 622 kJ of energy per mole of N_2H_4. Substituted hydrazines, where one or more of the hydrogen atoms are replaced by other groups, are useful as rocket fuels. For example, methylhydrazine ($CH_3N_2H_3$) is used with the oxidizing agent N_2O_4 (dinitrogen tetroxide) to power the U.S. space shuttle orbiter. The reaction is

$$5N_2O_4(l) + 4CH_3N_2H_3(l) \rightarrow$$
$$12H_2O(g) + 9N_2(g) + 4CO_2(g)$$

Because of the large number of gaseous molecules produced and the highly exothermic nature of this reaction, a very high value of thrust per gram of fuels is achieved. The reaction is also self-starting. That is, it begins immediately when the fuels are mixed—a useful characteristic for rocket engines that must be started and stopped frequently.

SECTION 18.1
REVIEW QUESTIONS

❶ In a reaction between a metal and a nonmetal which substance tends to be oxidized? Reduced? Why?

❷ How do oxidation states help us to decide whether an oxidation–reduction reaction has occurred?

❸ Assign oxidation states to all atoms in each of the following. Explain the order in which you determine the oxidation states for each element, if applicable.

   a. O_2

   b. HSO_4^-

   c. Na_2HPO_4

   d. $CrCl_3$

❹ Assign oxidation states for the two elements in the compound OF_2. Explain the rules that you use.

❺ For each of the following oxidation–reduction reactions of metals and nonmetals, identify the element that is oxidized and the element that is being reduced.

   a. $4Fe(s) + 3O_2(g) \rightarrow 2Fe_2O_3(s)$

   b. $Zn(s) + 2AgNO_3(aq) \rightarrow$
      $Zn(NO_3)_2(aq) + 2Ag(s)$

   c. $2K(s) + Cl_2(g) \rightarrow 2KCl(s)$

   d. $2Ca(s) + O_2(g) \rightarrow 2CaO(s)$

RESEARCH LINKS
CLASSZONE.COM

18.1 • Electron Transfer Reactions • **641**

SECTION 18.1
ASSESS

SECTION 18.1
Review Questions

1. The metal tends to be oxidized and the nonmetal tends to be reduced because metals have relatively low ionization energies compared to nonmetals.

2. If the oxidation state of an element changes in a chemical reaction, an oxidation–reduction reaction has occurred.

3. a. O, 0

   b. H, +1; S, +6; O, −2

   c. Na, +1; H, +1; P, +5; O, −2

   d. Cr, +3; Cl, −1

4. The oxidation state of F is −1 (rule 5). The oxidation state of O is +2 (rule 6).

5.

	Oxidized	Reduced
a.	Fe	O
b.	Zn	Ag
c.	K	Cl
d.	Ca	O

CELEBRITY CHEMICAL

Hydrazine (N₂H₄)

Hydrazine is merely one chemical used as rocket fuel. Ask students to use the Internet to learn more about other compounds used in rocket fuels. NASA's website is an excellent resource with many links to other interesting sites.

Most rocket fuels are combinations of oxidizing and reducing agents. The reactions involved are strongly exothermic and produce thrust through the formation of large amounts of rapidly expanding gases.

Student Preparation

Assign students to read Section 18.2 and to answer the Review Questions at the end of the section before coming to class.

 Active Learning
Team Learning Worksheet

After introducing the material in Section 18.2 in class, place students in groups and have them work together on **Section 18.2: Team Learning Worksheet**.

Homework

You may wish to assign these selected end-of-chapter problems as homework for this section: 14, 17, 18, 20, 22, 24, 26

Additional end-of-chapter problems can be used for extra practice.

18.2.A Oxidation–Reduction Reactions Between Nonmetals

Objective To understand oxidation and reduction in terms of oxidation states and learn to identify oxidizing and reducing agents

LABORATORY
EXPERIMENT 80:
Halogen Activity Series, CBL

Key Terms

- Oxidizing agent (electron acceptor)
- Reducing agent (electron donor)
- Half-reactions

Objectives

- *To understand oxidation and reduction in terms of oxidation states*
- *To learn to identify oxidizing and reducing agents*
- *To learn to balance oxidation–reduction equations using half reactions*

A. Oxidation–Reduction Reactions Between Nonmetals

We have seen that oxidation–reduction reactions are characterized by a transfer of electrons. In some cases, the transfer literally occurs to form ions, such as in the reaction

$$2Na(s) + Cl_2(g) \rightarrow 2NaCl(s)$$

We can use oxidation states to verify that electron transfer has occurred.

$$2Na(s) + Cl_2(g) \rightarrow 2NaCl(s)$$
Oxidation state: 0   0   +1 −1
            (element) (element) $(Na^+)(Cl^-)$

Thus in this reaction, we represent the electron transfer as follows:

e^- Na $\Rightarrow$ Na$^+$
    Cl   Cl$^-$

In other cases the electron transfer occurs in a different sense, such as in the combustion of methane (the oxidation state for each atom is given below each reactant and product).

$$CH_4(g) + 2O_2(g) \rightarrow CO_2(g) + 2H_2O(g)$$
Oxidation state: −4 +1 (each H)   0   +4 −2 (each O) +1 (each H) −2 (each O)

Note that the oxidation state of oxygen in O_2 is 0 because the oxygen is in elemental form. In this reaction there are no ionic compounds, but we can still describe the process in terms of the transfer of electrons. Note that carbon undergoes a change in oxidation state from −4 in CH_4 to +4 in CO_2. Such a change can be accounted for by a loss of eight electrons:

C (in CH_4) $\Rightarrow$ C (in CO_2)
    −4   Loss of 8e$^-$ +4

or, in equation form,

$$CH_4 \rightarrow CO_2 + 8e^-$$
      −4   +4

On the other hand, each oxygen changes from an oxidation state of 0 in O_2 to −2 in H_2O and CO_2, signifying a gain of two electrons per atom. Four oxygen atoms are involved, so this is a gain of eight electrons:

4O atoms (in $2O_2$) $\Rightarrow$ $4O^{2-}$ (in $2H_2O$ and CO_2)
              Gain of 8e$^-$

or, in equation form,

$$2O_2 + 8e^- \rightarrow CO_2 + 2H_2O$$
   0   4(−2) = −8

 nformation

CH_4
H = +1 (rule 4)
C = −4
−4 + 4(+1) = 0

CO_2
O = −2 (rule 3)
C = +4
+4 +(2(−2)) = 0

H_2O
H = +1 (rule 4)
O = −2 (rule 3)
2(+1) + 1(−2) = 0

Teaching Support
DEMONSTRATION

Floating Pennies

Materials
- Post-1982 penny
- File
- 6 *M* HCl
- Large Erlenmeyer flask
- Parafilm or watch glass

Presentation Place about 100 mL of HCl in the large flask. Using the file, make four or five notches in the edge of the penny, making sure you break through the copper covering on the penny. Place the penny into the acid. Cover the flask and let it remain undisturbed for several days (this activity is an excellent demonstration for a Friday). Eventually, the penny will float. Ask students to explain why.

Teaching Notes The penny floats because the zinc inside the copper plating reacts with HCl to produce hydrogen gas, which is trapped inside the penny and causes it to float to the surface. You can carefully pour out the HCl and retrieve the penny after washing it with water to remove the acid. It becomes evident that most of the penny has reacted, leaving only the "copper skin" of the penny. Have students write the oxidation–reduction equation for the reaction of zinc and HCl.

CHEMISTRY IN YOUR WORLD

Consumer Connections

U.S. Coins

We all use coins every day without thinking much about them. It turns out that some interesting chemistry is associated with the making of the coins used in the United States. For example, the "copper" penny is really mostly zinc with a coating of copper. The "nickel" coin contains much more copper than nickel—it's made of a copper/nickel alloy that is 75% copper and 25% nickel. All of the other coins used in the United States are clad—they have a pure copper core that is surrounded (sandwiched) by an alloy. The dime, the quarter, the half-dollar, and the Susan B. Anthony dollar all have a copper core sandwiched by a copper/nickel alloy. The Sacagawea dollar has a copper core surrounded by a special alloy containing copper, zinc, nickel, and manganese that gives it the same electromagnetic properties as the Anthony dollar so it will work in current vending machines.

The composition and physical properties of the coins are listed in the accompanying table.

Coin	Composition	Mass (g)	Diameter (mm)
Penny	Copper-plated zinc (97.5% Zn, 2.5% Cu)	2.5	19.1
Nickel	Copper/nickel alloy (75% Cu, 25% Zn)	5.0	21.2
Dime	Copper-nickel clad (91.7% Cu, 8.3% Ni)	2.3	17.9
Quarter	Copper-nickel clad (91.7% Cu, 8.3% Ni)	5.7	24.3
Half-dollar	Copper-nickel clad (91.7% Cu, 8.3% Ni)	11.3	30.6
Susan B. Anthony dollar	Copper-nickel clad (87.5% Cu, 12.5% Ni)	8.1	26.5
Sacagawea dollar	Manganese-brass clad (88.5% Cu, 6.0% Zn, 3.5% Mn, 2.0% Ni)	8.1	26.5

Note that eight electrons are required because four oxygen atoms are going from an oxidation state of 0 to -2. Each oxygen requires two electrons. No change occurs in the oxidation state of hydrogen, and it is not involved in the electron transfer process.

With this background, we can now define *oxidation* and *reduction* in terms of oxidation states. **Oxidation** is an *increase* in oxidation state (a loss of electrons). **Reduction** is a *decrease* in oxidation state (a gain of electrons). Thus in the reaction

$$2Na(s) + Cl_2(g) \rightarrow 2NaCl(s)$$

sodium is oxidized and chlorine is reduced. Cl_2 is called the **oxidizing agent (electron acceptor)** and Na is called the **reducing agent (electron donor)**. We can also define the *oxidizing agent* as the reactant containing the element that is reduced (gains electrons). The *reducing agent* can be defined similarly as the reactant containing the element that is oxidized (loses electrons).

Concerning the reaction

$$CH_4(g) + 2O_2(g) \rightarrow CO_2(g) + 2H_2O(g)$$
$$\substack{-4 \quad +1} \qquad \substack{0} \qquad \substack{+4 \quad -2} \qquad \substack{+1 \quad -2}$$

we can say the following:

> **Oxidizing agent**
> A reactant that accepts electrons from another reactant; the oxidizing agent is reduced since it gains one or more electrons.

> **Reducing agent**
> A reactant that donates electrons to another reactant; the reducing agent is oxidized since it donates one or more electrons.

TEACHING TIPS

- Use examples from earlier chapters, including single-displacement, synthesis, and decomposition reactions, to show students how many oxidation–reduction reactions they already know. Assign oxidation states to all of the elements in the reactants and products of these reactions to illustrate that in an oxidation–reduction reaction one substance is oxidized at the same time that another substance is reduced.

- Students need to practice determining the number of electrons gained or lost in a reaction. This is important for balancing oxidation–reduction reactions correctly. Students sometimes have trouble applying the rules of oxidation states to compounds. For example, oxygen has a -2 oxidation state. A compound such as SO_2 contains two oxygen atoms, however, which means that four electrons must have been transferred in $S + O_2 \rightarrow SO_2$.

Chemistry in Your World

U.S. Coins

Have students research the history of the composition of U.S. coins. Ask them to determine when the composition of each coin changed. Was a copper penny ever really copper? What are the implications of changing the composition of coins? Will they still work in various machines (such as vending machines)?

For an interesting demonstration of the composition of a penny, see the Teaching Support, "Floating Pennies."

EXAMPLE 18.3

More Examples

For the following reaction, identify the atoms that are oxidized and those that are reduced, and specify the oxidizing and reducing agents.

$$Fe_2O_3(s) + 3CO(g) \rightarrow 2Fe(l) + 3CO_2(g)$$

Iron is reduced and carbon is oxidized. $Fe_2O_3(s)$ is the oxidizing agent and $CO(g)$ is the reducing agent.

EXAMPLE 18.4

More Examples

For the following reaction, identify the atoms that are oxidized and those that are reduced, and specify the oxidizing and reducing agents.

$$Cl_2(g) + 2NaBr(aq) \rightarrow 2NaCl(aq) + Br_2(l)$$

Chlorine is reduced and bromine is oxidized. $Cl_2(g)$ is the oxidizing agent and $NaBr(aq)$ is the reducing agent.

information

In a redox reaction, an oxidizing agent is reduced (gains electrons) and a reducing agent is oxidized (loses electrons).

- Carbon is oxidized because there is an increase in its oxidation state (carbon has apparently lost electrons).
- The reactant CH_4 contains the carbon that is oxidized, so CH_4 is the reducing agent. It is the reactant that furnishes the electrons (those lost by carbon).
- Oxygen is reduced because there has been a decrease in its oxidation state (oxygen has apparently gained electrons).
- The reactant that contains the oxygen atoms is O_2, so O_2 is the oxidizing agent. That is, O_2 accepts the electrons.

Note that when the oxidizing or reducing agent is named, the *whole compound* is specified, not just the element that undergoes the change in oxidation state.

EXAMPLE 18.3

Identifying Oxidizing and Reducing Agents, I

When powdered aluminum metal is mixed with pulverized iodine crystals and a drop of water is added, the resulting reaction produces a great deal of energy. The mixture bursts into flames, and a purple smoke of I_2 vapor is produced from the excess iodine. The equation for the reaction is

$$2Al(s) + 3I_2(s) \rightarrow 2AlI_3(s)$$

For this reaction, identify the atoms that are oxidized and those that are reduced, and specify the oxidizing and reducing agents.

Solution

The first step is to assign oxidation states.

$$2Al(s) + 3I_2(s) \rightarrow 2AlI_3(s)$$

0	0	$+3$ $\quad -1$ (each I)
Free elements		$AlI_3(s)$ is a salt that contains Al^{3+} and I^- ions

Because each aluminum atom changes its oxidation state from 0 to +3 (an increase in oxidation state), aluminum is *oxidized* (loses electrons). On the other hand, the oxidation state of each iodine atom decreases from 0 to −1, and iodine is *reduced* (gains electrons). Because Al furnishes electrons for the reduction of iodine, it is the *reducing agent*. I_2 is the *oxidizing agent* (the reactant that accepts the electrons).

EXAMPLE 18.4

Identifying Oxidizing and Reducing Agents, II

Metallurgy, the process of producing a metal from its ore, always involves oxidation–reduction reactions. In the metallurgy of galena (PbS), the principal lead-containing ore, the first step is the conversion of lead sulfide to its oxide (a process called *roasting*).

$$2PbS(s) + 3O_2(g) \rightarrow 2PbO(s) + 2SO_2(g)$$

The oxide is then treated with carbon monoxide to produce the free metal.

$$PbO(s) + CO(g) \rightarrow Pb(s) + CO_2(g)$$

For each reaction, identify the atoms that are oxidized and those that are reduced, and specify the oxidizing and reducing agents.

644 • Chapter 18 • Oxidation–Reduction Reactions and Electrochemistry

Solution

For the first reaction, we can assign the following oxidation states:

$$PbS(s) + 3O_2(g) \rightarrow 2PbO(s) + 2SO_2(g)$$

+2 −2   0   +2 −2   +4 −2 (each O)

The oxidation state for the sulfur atom increases from −2 to +4, so sulfur is oxidized (loses electrons). The oxidation state for each oxygen atom decreases from 0 to −2. Oxygen is reduced (gains electrons). The oxidizing agent (electron acceptor) is O_2, and the reducing agent (electron donor) is PbS.

For the second reaction, we have

$$PbO(s) + CO(g) \rightarrow Pb(s) + CO_2(g)$$

+2 −2   +2 −2   0   +4 −2 (each O)

Lead is reduced (gains electrons; its oxidation state decreases from +2 to 0), and carbon is oxidized (loses electrons; its oxidation state increases from +2 to +4). PbO is the oxidizing agent (electron acceptor), and CO is the reducing agent (electron donor).

Practice Problem • Exercise 18.4

Ammonia, NH_3, which is widely used as a fertilizer, is prepared by reaction of the elements:

$$N_2(g) + 3H_2(g) \rightarrow 2NH_3(g)$$

Is this an oxidation–reduction reaction? If so, specify the oxidizing agent and the reducing agent.

CHEMISTRY IN YOUR WORLD

Science, Technology, and Society

Real Gold

Recently, a woman wrote to Annie's Mailbox complaining that the necklace her boyfriend had given her turned her neck green. Her concern was whether the necklace was "real gold." This leads to the question: What is "real gold"? To chemists, real gold is pure gold, called 24-carat gold by jewelers. Thus, when you see 24K (for "carat," which is also spelled "karat") on a piece of gold, it means that it is 100% gold. However, the woman's necklace was surely not 24K gold, because pure gold is too soft for making jewelry. Jewelry is usually made of 18K gold (which is 18/24 = 75% gold by mass) or 14K gold (14/24 = 58% gold). The carat system was invented by the British in about 1300 to provide a standard for the use of gold as currency.

In the United States, the lowest carat designation for gold is 10K. Because a 0.5-carat error is allowed, 10K gold is actually 9.5K or 39.6% gold by mass. So if 9.5K gold is only about 40% gold, what makes

up the rest of the "gold" jewelry? The metals most commonly used to form gold alloys are copper, silver, zinc, and nickel, depending on the specific use and color desired. For example, "yellow gold" typically contains Au, Cu, Ag, and Zn, whereas "white gold" contains Au, Cu, Ni, and Zn.

Now back to the woman's original question. Was her necklace "real gold"? Not likely. The necklace was probably mostly copper with a thin layer of gold plated on the surface. The woman's necklace turned green because copper "leaked" through cracks in the gold plating. Alloys of 14K gold do not behave in this way. She was right to worry about her friend's honesty.

Gold jewelry in a store in Thailand

We can tell whether this is an oxidation–reduction reaction by comparing the oxidation states of the elements in the reactants and products:

$$N_2 + 3H_2 \rightarrow 2NH_3$$

Oxidation states: 0   0   +1 (each H)   −3

Nitrogen goes from 0 to −3. Thus it gains three electrons and is reduced. Each hydrogen atom goes from 0 to +1 and is thus oxidized, so this is an oxidation–reduction reaction. The oxidizing agent is N_2 (it takes electrons from H_2). The reducing agent is H_2 (it gives electrons to N_2).

$$N_2 + 3H_2 \rightarrow 2NH_3$$
6e⁻

Chemistry in Your World

Real Gold

Gold is so unreactive that it is most commonly found in its elemental form. This lack of reactivity is useful when creating jewelry that does not interact with the chemicals on the skin. The only natural compounds that gold forms are those in combination with tellurium. The most common oxidation states for gold are +1 and +3.

Gold has reflective properties similar to those of silver and copper. These substances can all be used to make mirrors by depositing the metal on the surface of a piece of glass. Silver is most commonly used for this purpose because it does not color the reflection. You can demonstrate the silvering process (discovered in 1835 by Justus von Liebig, a German chemist) in class by using the Teaching Support, "A Silver Mirror."

Objective To learn to balance oxidation–reduction equations by using half-reactions

 LABORATORY

EXPERIMENT 81:
Analysis of Hydrogen Peroxide, Microscale

 TEACHING TIPS

- Use the concept of half-reactions to emphasize that oxidation cannot occur without reduction, and vice versa.

- Students may need help identifying the half-reactions. Writing half-reactions correctly requires assigning oxidation states in compounds.

Active Reading Question

In the oxidation half-reaction, an electron is a product.

B. Balancing Oxidation–Reduction Reactions by the Half-Reaction Method

Many oxidation–reduction reactions can be balanced readily by trial and error. That is, we use the procedure described in Chapter 7 to find a set of coefficients that give the same number of each type of atom on both sides of the equation.

However, the oxidation–reduction reactions that occur in aqueous solution are often so complicated that it becomes very tedious to balance them by trial and error. In this section we will develop a systematic approach for balancing the equations for these reactions.

To balance the equations for oxidation–reduction reactions that occur in aqueous solution, we separate the reaction into two half-reactions. **Half-reactions** are equations that have electrons as reactants or products. One half-reaction represents a reduction process and the other half-reaction represents an oxidation process.

In a reduction half-reaction, electrons are shown on the reactant side (electrons are gained by a reactant in the equation). In an oxidation half-reaction, the electrons are shown on the product side (electrons are lost by a reactant in the equation).

For example, consider the unbalanced equation for the oxidation–reduction reaction between the cerium(IV) ion and the tin(II) ion.

$$Ce^{4+}(aq) + Sn^{2+}(aq) \rightarrow Ce^{3+}(aq) + Sn^{4+}(aq)$$

This reaction can be separated into a half-reaction involving the substance being *reduced*:

$$e^- + Ce^{4+}(aq) \rightarrow Ce^{3+}(aq) \qquad \text{Reduction half-reaction}$$

and a half-reaction involving the substance being *oxidized*:

$$Sn^{2+}(aq) \rightarrow Sn^{4+}(aq) + 2e^- \qquad \text{Oxidation half-reaction}$$

Notice that Ce^{4+} must gain one electron to become Ce^{3+}, so one electron is shown as a reactant along with Ce^{4+} in this half-reaction. On the other hand, for Sn^{2+} to become Sn^{4+}, it must lose two electrons. This means that two electrons must be shown as products in this half-reaction.

 information

Ce^{4+} gains $1e^-$ to form Ce^{3+} and is thus reduced.

Sn^{2+} loses $2e^-$ to form Sn^{4+} and is thus oxidized.

Active Reading Question

In an oxidation half-reaction, is an electron a reactant or product?

The key principle in balancing oxidation–reduction reactions is that the number of electrons lost (from the reactant that is oxidized) must equal the number of electrons gained (from the reactant that is reduced).

Number of electrons lost	must be equal to	Number of electrons gained

In the half-reaction shown above, one electron is gained by each Ce^{4+} while two electrons are lost by each Sn^{2+}. We must equalize the number of electrons gained and lost. To do this, we first multiply the reduction half-reaction by 2.

$$2e^- + 2Ce^{4+} \rightarrow 2Ce^{3+}$$

A Silver Mirror

Materials
- 100-mL graduated cylinder
- 250-mL Erlenmeyer flask
- Small flask and stopper to fit
- 4 small beakers
- Sodium hydroxide
- Glucose

- Fructose
- Silver nitrate
- Ammonium nitrate
- Tartaric acid
- Ethanol
- Heating unit

Preparation Make the following solutions: To make solution A, dissolve 2.5 g glucose and 2.5 g fructose in 50 mL distilled water and add 0.6 g tartaric acid. Heat the solution to boiling; cool and then pour it into the 100-mL graduated cylinder. Add 10 mL of ethanol and dilute the solution to the 100-mL mark. Label it A. To make solution B, dissolve 4.0 g of silver nitrate in 50 mL water. Label it B. To make solution C, dissolve 6.0 g of ammonium nitrate in 50 mL water and label it C. To make solution D, dissolve 10 g NaOH in 50 mL water and label it D. Clean the small flask thoroughly with concentrated nitric acid.

Then we add this half-reaction to the oxidation half-reaction.

$$2e^- + 2Ce^{4+} \rightarrow 2Ce^{3+}$$

$$\underline{\hspace{3em} Sn^{2+} \rightarrow Sn^{4+} + 2e^- \hspace{3em}}$$

$$2e^- + 2Ce^{4+} + Sn^{2+} \rightarrow 2Ce^{3+} + Sn^{4+} + 2e^-$$

Finally, we cancel the $2e^-$ on each side to give the overall balanced equation

$$\cancel{2e^-} + 2Ce^{4+} + Sn^{2+} \rightarrow 2Ce^{3+} + Sn^{4+} + \cancel{2e^-}$$

$$2Ce^{4+} + Sn^{2+} \rightarrow 2Ce^{3+} + Sn^{4+}$$

Let's Review

Balancing Oxidation–Reduction Reactions In Aqueous Solution

1. Separate the reaction into an oxidation half-reaction and a reduction half-reaction.

2. Balance the half-reactions separately.

3. Equalize the number of electrons gained and lost.

4. Add the half-reactions together and cancel electrons to give the overall balanced equation.

It turns out that most oxidation–reduction reactions occur in solutions that are distinctly basic or distinctly acidic. We will cover only the acidic case in this text, because it is the most common. The detailed procedure for balancing the equations for oxidation–reduction reactions that occur in acidic solution is given below, and Example 18.5 illustrates the use of these steps.

The Half-Reaction Method for Balancing Equations for Oxidation–Reduction Reactions Occurring in Acidic Solution

Step 1 Identify and write the equations for the oxidation and reduction half-reactions.

Step 2 For each half-reaction:

    a. Balance all of the elements except hydrogen and oxygen.

    b. Balance oxygen using H_2O.

    c. Balance hydrogen using H^+.

    d. Balance the charge using electrons.

Step 3 If necessary, multiply one or both balanced half-reactions by an integer to equalize the number of electrons transferred in the two half-reactions.

Step 4 Add the half-reactions, and cancel identical species that appear on both sides.

Step 5 Check to be sure the elements and charges balance.

TEACHING TIPS

- Students should balance both atoms and charges in the half-reactions. A common error is for students to place the electrons on the wrong side of the half-reaction.

- Remind students that an equal number of electrons must be transferred. Students often forget to equalize this number when they begin to work with these equations. Explain that the electrons are transferred and so must be accounted for. That is, the number gained must equal the number lost.

- It takes time and practice to learn to balance these reactions. Students need to pay close attention to the details of the balancing process. Learning to use the method of half-reactions on relatively easy equations makes it easier to balance more difficult equations later.

(continued)

Presentation Place 30 mL of solution A into the clean flask. In a small beaker, mix 15 mL of solution B with 15 mL of solution C. Add this solution to the flask. Quickly add 30 mL of solution D to the flask and mix the flask with quick but gentle swirling motions. Make sure you cover the inside surface of the glass evenly while swirling. Continue swirling until the silver mirror forms inside the flask. Immediately pour out the remaining solution and deactivate the solution by adding lots of water. Rinse the silvered flask with distilled water.

Teaching Notes Do not mix solutions B and C until the demonstration is performed. They are potentially unstable after mixing. Metallic silver forms on the surface of the glass when the silver ions oxidize the aldehyde on the sugar molecule. If the silver doesn't stick to the glass, the glass was not completely clean.

EXAMPLE 18.5

More Examples

Balance each of the following oxidation–reduction reactions using the half-reaction method.

1. $Ce^{4+}(aq) + H_3AsO_3(aq) \rightarrow$
   $\quad Ce^{3+}(aq) + H_3AsO_4(aq)$

   $2Ce^{4+}(aq) + H_3AsO_3(aq) +$
   $\quad H_2O(l) \rightarrow 2Ce^{3+}(aq) +$
   $\quad H_3AsO_4(aq) + 2H^+(aq)$

2. $MnO_4^-(aq) + I^-(aq) \rightarrow$
   $\quad Mn^{2+}(aq) + I_2(s)$

   $2MnO_4^-(aq) + 10I^-(aq) +$
   $\quad 16H^+(aq) \rightarrow 2Mn^{2+}(aq) +$
   $\quad 5I_2(s) + 8H_2O(l)$

EXAMPLE 18.5

Balancing Oxidation–Reduction Reactions Using the Half-Reaction Method, I

A solution containing MnO_4^- ions (top) and a solution containing Fe^{2+} ions (bottom).

Balance the equation for the reaction between permanganate and iron(II) ions in acidic solution. The net ionic equation for this reaction is

$$MnO_4^-(aq) + Fe^{2+}(aq) \xrightarrow{\text{Acid}} Fe^{3+}(aq) + Mn^{2+}(aq)$$

This reaction is used to analyze iron ore for its iron content.

Solution

Step 1 *Identify and write equations for the half-reactions.*

The oxidation states for the half-reaction involving the permanganate ion show that manganese is reduced.

$$\underset{\substack{+7 \quad -2 \\ \text{(each O)}}}{MnO_4^-} \rightarrow \underset{+2}{Mn^{2+}}$$

Because manganese changes from an oxidation state of +7 to +2, it is reduced. So this is the *reduction half-reaction*. It will have electrons as reactants, although we will not write them yet. The other half-reaction involves the oxidation of iron(II) to the iron(III) ion and is the *oxidation half-reaction*.

$$\underset{+2}{Fe^{2+}} \rightarrow \underset{+3}{Fe^{3+}}$$

This reaction will have electrons as products, although we will not write them yet.

Step 2 *Balance each half-reaction.*

For the reduction reaction, we have

$$MnO_4^- \rightarrow Mn^{2+}$$

   a. The manganese is already balanced.

   b. We balance oxygen by adding $4H_2O$ to the right side of the equation.

$$MnO_4^- \rightarrow Mn^{2+} + 4H_2O$$

   c. Next we balance hydrogen by adding $8H^+$ to the left side.

$$8H^+ + MnO_4^- \rightarrow Mn^{2+} + 4H_2O$$

   d. All of the elements have been balanced, but we need to balance the charge using electrons. At this point we have the following charges for reactants and products in the reduction half-reaction.

$$\underset{\underset{7+}{\underbrace{8+ \quad + \quad 1-}}}{8H^+ + MnO_4^-} \rightarrow \underset{\underset{2+}{\underbrace{2+ \quad + \quad 0}}}{Mn^{2+} + 4H_2O}$$

We can equalize the charges by adding five electrons to the left side.

$$\underset{2+}{\underbrace{5e^- + 8H^+ + MnO_4^-}} \rightarrow \underset{2+}{\underbrace{Mn^{2+} + 4H_2O}}$$

> ℹ️ **information**
>
> The H^+ comes from the acidic solution in which the reaction is taking place.

> ℹ️ **information**
>
> Always add electrons to the side of the half-reaction with excess positive charge.

Meeting Individual Needs
INCLUSION STRATEGIES

For the practice and homework exercises that correspond with this section, encourage students to use colored pencils when they attempt to balance an equation. Students can use color, similar to the process shown in the example problems, to help organize each step when balancing oxidation–reduction equations. You may wish to allow students to use colored pencils during quizzes and tests.

Both the *elements* and the *charges* are now balanced, so this represents the balanced reduction half-reaction. The fact that five electrons appear on the reactant side of the equation makes sense, because five electrons are required to reduce MnO_4^- (in which Mn has an oxidation state of +7) to Mn^{2+} (in which Mn has an oxidation state of +2).

For the oxidation reaction,

$$Fe^{2+} \rightarrow Fe^{3+}$$

the elements are balanced, so all we have to do is balance the charge.

$$\underbrace{Fe^{2+}}_{2+} \rightarrow \underbrace{Fe^{3+}}_{3+}$$

One electron is needed on the right side to give a net 2+ charge on both sides.

$$\underbrace{Fe^{2+}}_{2+} \quad \rightarrow \quad \underbrace{Fe^{3+} + e^-}_{2+}$$

Step 3 *Equalize the number of electrons transferred in the two half-reactions.*

Because the reduction half-reaction involves a transfer of five electrons and the oxidation half-reaction involves a transfer of only one electron, the oxidation half-reaction must be multiplied by 5.

$$5Fe^{2+} \rightarrow 5Fe^{3+} + 5e^-$$

Step 4 *Add the half-reactions and cancel identical species.*

$$5e^- + 8H^+ + MnO_4^- \rightarrow Mn^{2+} + 4H_2O$$
$$\underline{ 5Fe^{2+} \rightarrow 5Fe^{3+} + 5e^-}$$
$$\cancel{5e^-} + 8H^+ + MnO_4^- + 5Fe^{2+} \rightarrow Mn^{2+} + 5Fe^{3+} + 4H_2O + \cancel{5e^-}$$

Note that the electrons cancel (as they must) to give the final balanced equation

$$5Fe^{2+}(aq) + MnO_4^-(aq) + 8H^+(aq) \rightarrow$$
$$5Fe^{3+}(aq) + Mn^{2+}(aq) + 4H_2O(l)$$

Note that we show the physical states of the reactants and products—(*aq*) and (*l*) in this case—only in the final balanced equation.

Step 5 *Check to be sure that elements and charges balance.*

Elements   5Fe, 1Mn, 4O, 8H → 5Fe, 1Mn, 4O, 8H

Charges   17+ → 17+

The equation is balanced.

nformation

The number of electrons gained in the reduction half-reaction must equal the number of electrons lost in the oxidation half-reaction.

EXAMPLE 18.6

More Examples

1. $MnO_4^-(aq) + C_2O_4^{2-}(aq) \rightarrow$
   $Mn^{2+}(aq) + CO_2(g)$

   $2MnO_4^-(aq) + 5C_2O_4^{2-}(aq)$
   $+ 16H^+(aq) \rightarrow 2Mn^{2+}(aq)$
   $+ 10CO_2(g) + 8H_2O(l)$

2. $BiO_3^-(aq) + Mn^{2+}(aq) \rightarrow$
   $Bi^{3+}(aq) + MnO_4^-(aq)$

   $5BiO_3^-(aq) + 2Mn^{2+}(aq) +$
   $14H^+(aq) \rightarrow 5Bi^{3+}(aq) +$
   $2MnO_4^-(aq) + 7H_2O(l)$

Answer to Practice Problem 18.6

The unbalanced equation for this reaction is

$Cu(s) + HNO_3(aq) \rightarrow Cu(NO_3)_2(aq) + H_2O(l) + NO(g)$

Copper Nitric acid Aqueous   Water Nitrogen
metal   copper(II)   monoxide
                         nitrate
                         (contains Cu^{2+})

Step 1 The oxidation half-reaction is

Oxidation states:
$$Cu + HNO_3 \rightarrow Cu(NO_3)_2$$
$$0 \quad +1 +5 -2 \quad +2 +5 -2$$
$$\text{(each O)} \quad \text{(each O)}$$

The copper goes from 0 to +2 and thus is oxidized. This reduction reaction is

Oxidation states:
$$HNO_3 \rightarrow NO$$
$$+1 +5 -2 \quad +2 -2$$
$$\text{(each O)}$$

In this case nitrogen goes from +5 in HNO_3 to +2 in NO and so is reduced. Notice two things about these reactions:

1. The HNO_3 must be included in the oxidation half-reaction to supply NO_3^- in the product $Cu(NO_3)_2$.

2. Although water is a product in the overall reaction, it does not need to be included in either half-reaction at the beginning. It will appear later as we balance the equation.

Step 2 Balance the oxidation half-reaction.

$Cu + HNO_3 \rightarrow Cu(NO_3)_2$

a. Balance nitrogen first.

$Cu + 2HNO_3 \rightarrow Cu(NO_3)_2$

b. Balancing nitrogen also caused oxygen to balance.

c. Balance hydrogen using H^+.

$Cu + 2HNO_3 \rightarrow$
$Cu(NO_3)_2 + 2H^+$

d. Balance the charge using e^-.

$Cu + 2HNO_3 \rightarrow$
$Cu(NO_3)_2 + 2H^+ + 2e^-$

EXAMPLE 18.6

Balancing Oxidation–Reduction Reactions Using the Half-Reaction Method, II

When an automobile engine is started, it uses the energy supplied by a lead storage battery. This battery uses an oxidation–reduction reaction between elemental lead (lead metal) and lead(IV) oxide to provide the power to start the engine. The unbalanced equation for a simplified version of the reaction is

$$Pb(s) + PbO_2(s) + H^+(aq) \rightarrow Pb^{2+}(aq) + H_2O(l)$$

Balance this equation using the half-reaction method.

Solution

ⓘ **information**

Because Pb^{2+} is the only lead-containing product, it must be the product in both half-reactions.

Step 1 First we identify and write the two half-reactions. One half-reaction must be $Pb \rightarrow Pb^{2+}$ and the other is $PbO_2 \rightarrow Pb^{2+}$.

The first reaction involves the oxidation of Pb to Pb^{2+}. The second reaction involves the reduction of Pb^{4+} (in PbO_2) to Pb^{2+}.

Step 2 Now we will balance each half-reaction separately.

The oxidation half-reaction

$$Pb \rightarrow Pb^{2+}$$

a–c. All the elements are balanced.

d. The charge on the left is zero and that on the right is 2+, so we must add $2e^-$ to the right to give zero overall charge.

$$Pb \rightarrow Pb^{2+} + 2e^-$$

This half-reaction is balanced.

The reduction half-reaction

$$PbO_2 \rightarrow Pb^{2+}$$

a. All elements are balanced except O.

b. The left side has two oxygen atoms and the right side has none, so we add $2H_2O$ to the right side.

$$PbO_2 \rightarrow Pb^{2+} + 2H_2O$$

c. Now we balance hydrogen by adding $4H^+$ to the left.

$$4H^+ + PbO_2 \rightarrow Pb^{2+} + 2H_2O$$

d. Because the left side has a 4+ overall charge and the right side has a 2+ charge, we must add $2e^-$ to the left side.

$$2e^- + 4H^+ + PbO_2 \rightarrow Pb^{2+} + 2H_2O$$

The half-reaction is balanced.

Step 3 Because each half-reaction involves $2e^-$, we can simply add the half-reactions as they are.

This is the balanced oxidation half-reaction.

Balance the reduction half-reaction.

$$HNO_3 \rightarrow NO$$

a. All elements are balanced except hydrogen and oxygen.

b. Balance oxygen using H_2O.

$HNO_3 \rightarrow NO + 2H_2O$

c. Balance hydrogen using H^+.

$3H^+ + HNO_3 \rightarrow NO + 2H_2O$

d. Balance the charge using e^-.

$3e^- + 3H^+ + HNO_3 \rightarrow$
$NO + 2H_2O$

This is the balanced reduction half-reaction.

Step 3 We equalize electrons by multiplying the oxidation half-reaction by 3:

$3 \times (Cu + 2HNO_3 \rightarrow$
$Cu(NO_3)_2 + 2H^+ + 2e^-)$

which gives

$3Cu + 6HNO_3 \rightarrow$
$3Cu(NO_3)_2 + 6H^+ + 6e^-$

Multiplying the reduction half-reaction by 2

$2 \times (3e^- + 3H^+ + HNO_3 \rightarrow$
$NO + 2H_2O)$

gives

$6e^- + 6H^+ + 2HNO_3 \rightarrow$
$2NO + 4H_2O$

Step 4

$$Pb \rightarrow Pb^{2+} + 2e^-$$

$$2e^- + 4H^+ + PbO_2 \rightarrow Pb^{2+} + 2H_2O$$

$$\overline{2e^- + 4H^+ + Pb + PbO_2 \rightarrow 2Pb^{2+} + 2H_2O + 2e^-}$$

Canceling electrons gives the balanced overall equation

$$Pb(s) + PbO_2(s) + 4H^+(aq) \rightarrow 2Pb^{2+}(aq) + 2H_2O(l)$$

where the appropriate states are also indicated.

Step 5 Both the elements and the charges balance.

Elements $2Pb, 2O, 4H \rightarrow 2Pb, 2O, 4H$

Charges $4+ \rightarrow 4+$

The equation is correctly balanced.

Copper metal reacting with concentrated nitric acid. The solution is colored by the presence of Cu^{2+} ions. The brown gas is NO_2.

 Practice Problem • Exercise 18.6

Copper metal reacts with dilute nitric acid, $HNO_3(aq)$, to give aqueous copper(II) nitrate, water, and nitrogen monoxide gas as products. Write and balance the equation for this reaction.

SECTION 18.2
REVIEW QUESTIONS

❶ Explain how you can determine the oxidizing agent and reducing agent in an oxidation–reduction reaction.

❷ For each of the following oxidation–reduction reactions of metals and nonmetals, identify the oxidizing agent and reducing agent.

  a. $Cu(s) + 2AgNO_3(aq) \rightarrow Cu(NO_3)_2(aq) + 2Ag(s)$

  b. $4Al(s) + 3O_2(g) \rightarrow 2Al_2O_3(s)$

  c. $C(s) + O_2(g) \rightarrow CO_2(g)$

❸ For each of the following reactions, is oxygen gas an oxidizing agent or a reducing agent? Does that mean oxygen is oxidized or reduced?

  a. $4Al(s) + 3O_2(g) \rightarrow 2Al_2O_3(s)$

  b. $C(s) + O_2(g) \rightarrow CO_2(g)$

❹ Write two definitions of oxidation. In the first definition, use the phrase *oxidation state*. In the second definition, use the term *electrons*.

❺ Write two definitions of reduction. In the first definition, use the phrase *oxidation state*. In the second definition, use the term *electrons*.

❻ Write the balanced half-reactions corresponding to each of the following:

  a. The reduction of $Br_2(l)$ to $Br^-(aq)$.

  b. The oxidation of $Zn(s)$ to $Zn^{2+}(aq)$.

❼ Each of the oxidation–reduction reactions place in acidic solution. Balance each reaction by using the half-reaction method.

  a. $NO_3^-(aq) + Br^-(aq) \rightarrow NO(g) + Br_2(l)$

  b. $Ni(s) + NO_3^-(aq) \rightarrow Ni^{2+}(aq) + NO_2(g)$

  c. $ClO_4^-(aq) + Cl^-(aq) \rightarrow ClO_3^-(aq) + Cl_2(g)$

RESEARCH LINKS
CLASSZONE.COM

SECTION 18.2
ASSESS

SECTION 18.2
Review Questions

1. The oxidizing agent is the species that is reduced. The reducing agent is the species that is oxidized.

2 **a.** Cu is the reducing agent. $AgNO_3$ is the oxidizing agent.

  b. Al is the reducing agent. O_2 is the oxidizing agent.

  c. C is the reducing agent. O_2 is the oxidizing agent.

3. Oxygen gas is an oxidizing agent. It is reduced.

4. Oxidation is an increase in oxidation state. Oxidation is the loss of one or more electrons.

5. Reduction is a decrease in oxidation state. Reduction is the gain of one or more electrons.

6. **a.** $Br_2(l) + 2e^- \rightarrow 2Br^-(aq)$

  b. $Zn(s) \rightarrow Zn^{2+}(aq) + 2e^-$

7. **a.** $8H^+(aq) + 2NO_3^-(aq) + 6Br^-(aq) \rightarrow 2NO(g) + 3Br_2(l) + 4H_2O(l)$

  b. $4H^+(aq) + Ni(s) + 2NO_3^-(aq) \rightarrow Ni^{2+}(aq) + 2NO_2(g) + 2H_2O(l)$

  c. $2H^+(aq) + ClO_4^-(aq) + 2Cl^-(aq) \rightarrow ClO_3^-(aq) + Cl_2(g) + H_2O(l)$

(continued)

Step 4 We can now add the balanced half-reactions, which both involve a six-electron change.

$$3Cu + 6HNO_3 \rightarrow 3Cu(NO_3)_2 + 6H^+ + 6e^-$$

$$6e^- + 6H^+ + 2HNO_3 \rightarrow 2NO + 4H_2O$$

$$\overline{6e^- + 6H^+ + 3Cu + 8HNO_3 \rightarrow}$$

$$3Cu(NO_3)_2 + 2NO + 4H_2O + 6H^+ + 6e^+$$

Canceling species common to both sides gives the balanced overall equation:

$$3Cu(s) + 8HNO_3(aq) \rightarrow$$
$$3Cu(NO_3)_2(aq) + 2NO(g) + 4H_2O(l)$$

Step 5 Check the elements and charges.

Elements $3Cu, 8H, 8N, 24O \rightarrow 3Cu, 8H, 8N, 24O$

Charges $0 \rightarrow 0$

SECTION 18.3
INTRODUCE

Student Preparation

Assign students to read Section 18.3 and to answer the Review Questions at the end of the section before coming to class.

 Active Learning
Team Learning Worksheet

After introducing the material in Section 18.3 in class, place students in groups and have them work together on **Section 18.3: Team Learning Worksheet**.

SECTION 18.3
GUIDE THE LEARNING

Homework

You may wish to assign these selected end-of-chapter problems as homework for this section: 28, 29, 31, 33, 34, 35, 38, 39, 41

Additional end-of-chapter problems can be used for extra practice.

18.3.A Electrochemistry: An Introduction

Objective To understand the term *electrochemistry* and learn to identify the components of an electrochemical (galvanic) cell

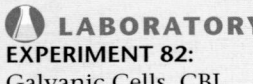 **LABORATORY**
EXPERIMENT 82:
Galvanic Cells, CBL

 Active Reading Question

The key is to separate the oxidizing agent from the reducing agent.

SECTION 18.3

Electrochemistry and Its Applications

Key Terms

- Electrochemistry
- Electrochemical battery (galvanic cell)
- Anode
- Cathode
- Electrolysis
- Lead storage battery
- Potential
- Dry cell batteries
- Corrosion
- Cathodic protection

Objectives

- *To understand the concept of electrochemistry*
- *To learn to identify the components of an electrochemical (galvanic) cell*
- *To learn about commonly used batteries*
- *To understand corrosion and ways of preventing it*
- *To understand electrolysis*
- *To learn about the commercial preparation of aluminum*

A. Electrochemistry: An Introduction

Our lives would be very different without batteries. We would have to crank the engines in our cars by hand, wind our watches, and buy very long extension cords if we wanted to listen to an MP3 player on a picnic. Indeed, our society sometimes seems to run on batteries. In this section and the next, we will find out how these important devices produce electrical energy.

A battery uses the energy from an oxidation–reduction reaction to produce an electric current. This is an important illustration of **electrochemistry**, *the study of the interchange of chemical and electrical energy.*

> **Electrochemistry**
> The study of the interchange of chemical and electrical energy

Electrochemistry involves two types of processes:
1. The production of an electric current from a chemical (oxidation-reduction) reaction
2. The use of an electric current to produce a chemical change

To understand how a redox reaction can be used to generate a current, let's reconsider the aqueous reaction between MnO_4^- and Fe^{2+} that we worked with in Example 18.5. We can break this redox reaction into the following half-reactions:

$$8H^+ + MnO_4^- + 5e^- \rightarrow Mn^{2+} + 4H_2O \qquad \text{Reduction}$$
$$Fe^{2+} \rightarrow Fe^{3+} + e^- \qquad \text{Oxidation}$$

When the reaction between MnO_4^- and Fe^{2+} occurs in solution, electrons are transferred directly as the reactants collide. No useful work is obtained from the chemical energy involved in the reaction. How can we harness this energy? The key is to *separate the oxidizing agent (electron acceptor) from the reducing agent (electron donor)*, thus requiring the electron transfer to occur through a wire. That is, to get from the reducing agent to the oxidizing agent, the electrons must travel through a wire. The current produced in the wire by this electron flow can be directed through a device, such as an electric motor, to do useful work.

> **DID YOU KNOW**
>
> The energy involved in a chemical reaction is customarily not shown in the balanced equation. In the reaction of MnO_4^- with Fe^{2+}, energy is released that can be used to do useful work.

> **Active Reading Question**
>
> **What is the key to getting useful energy from an oxidation–reduction reaction?**

652 • Chapter 18 • Oxidation–Reduction Reactions and Electrochemistry

---

Teaching Support
DEMONSTRATION

Making a Galvanic Cell

Materials
- Two 250-mL beakers
- Strips of zinc and copper metal (approximately 4 in. $\times \frac{1}{2}$ in.)
- 1 M $CuSO_4$
- 1 M $ZnSO_4$
- 1 M KNO_3
- Large piece of filter paper
- Voltmeter (one that projects on an overhead projector is ideal)
- Two wires with alligator clips at each end

Presentation Fill one beaker two-thirds full with $ZnSO_4$ solution and place the zinc electrode in it. Fill the second beaker two-thirds full of $CuSO_4$ and place the copper electrode in it. Connect a wire from each metal to the voltmeter. At this point, the voltmeter should register 0 volts. Ask

For example, consider the system illustrated in **Figure 18.1.** If our reasoning has been correct, electrons should flow through the wire from Fe^{2+} to MnO_4^-. However, when we construct the apparatus as shown, no flow of electrons occurs. Why? The problem is that if the electrons flowed from the right to the left compartment, the left compartment would become negatively charged and the right compartment would experience a build-up of positive charge. Creating a charge separation of this type would require large amounts of energy. Therefore, electron flow does not occur under these conditions.

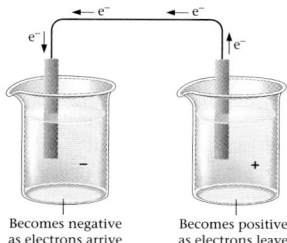

Becomes negative
as electrons arrive

Becomes positive
as electrons leave

We can, however, solve this problem very simply. The solutions must be connected (without allowing them to mix extensively) so that *ions* can also flow to keep the net charge in each compartment zero. This can be accomplished by using a salt bridge (a U-shaped tube filled with a strong electrolyte) or a porous disk in a tube connecting the two solutions (see **Figure 18.2**). Either of these devices allows ion flow but prevents extensive mixing

Ions need
to flow

of the solutions. When we make a provision for ion flow, the circuit is complete. Electrons flow through the wire from reducing agent to oxidizing agent, and ions in the two aqueous solutions flow from one compartment to the other to keep the net charge zero.

Wire

$MnO_4^-(aq)$
$H^+(aq)$

$Fe^{2+}(aq)$

Oxidizing agent
(electron acceptor)

Reducing agent
(electron donor)

Figure 18.1
Schematic of a method for separating the oxidizing and reducing agents in a redox reaction. (The solutions also contain other ions to balance the charge.) This cell is incomplete at this point.

Active Reading Question

What is the purpose of a salt bridge in an electrochemical cell?

Salt bridge

(a)

Porous disk

(b)

Figure 18.2
A salt bridge or a porous-disk connection allows ions to flow, completing the electric circuit.
(a) The salt bridge contains a strong electrolyte either as a gel or as a solution; both ends are covered with a membrane that allows only ions to pass.
(b) The porous disk allows ion flow but does not permit overall mixing of the solutions in the two compartments.

18.3 • Electrochemistry and Its Applications • **653**

TEACHING TIP

Explain to students that the reactions in electrochemical cells are different from ordinary oxidation–reduction reactions because the half-reactions are separated from each other. The arrangement of the half-cells can be accomplished in several ways, as shown in Figure 18.2.

Active Reading Question

The salt bridge allows ions to flow between the solutions in the anode and cathode to keep a charge separation from occurring. In addition, it does not allow the solutions to mix a great deal.

TECHNOLOGY

Figure 18.2

Animation
Electrochemical Half-Reactions in a Galvanic Cell

An electric car being charged

(continued)

students why. No voltage registers because the circuit is incomplete (the two beakers are not connected by a salt bridge). Roll up the filter paper and dip it into the KNO_3 solution, wetting the entire filter paper. Next, insert one end of the filter paper roll into each beaker, forming a salt bridge. The voltmeter should register about 1 volt. Electrons can now flow through the wire because ions can flow through the salt bridge.

Teaching Notes The solutions and electrodes can be stored safely and reused. If you don't have a voltmeter, you may be able to borrow one from the electronics classroom or purchase one at a local electronics store. Ask students to write the half-reaction equations and identify the cathode and the anode.

Galvanic cell (electrochemical battery)
A device in which chemical energy is converted to electrical energy by means of an oxidation–reduction reaction

Anode
The electrode in a galvanic cell where oxidation occurs

Cathode
The electrode in a galvanic cell where reduction occurs

Electrolysis
A process that involves forcing a current through a cell to cause a chemical reaction that would not otherwise occur

Thus an **electrochemical battery**, also called a **galvanic cell**, is a device powered by an oxidation–reduction reaction where the oxidizing agent is separated from the reducing agent so that the electrons must travel through a wire from the reducing agent to the oxidizing agent.

Notice that in a battery, the reducing agent loses electrons (which flow through the wire toward the oxidizing agent) and so is oxidized. The electrode where oxidation occurs is called the **anode**. At the other electrode, the oxidizing agent gains electrons and is thus reduced. The electrode where reduction occurs is called the **cathode**.

We have seen that an oxidation–reduction reaction can be used to generate an electric current. In fact, this type of reaction is used to produce electric currents in many space vehicles. An oxidation–reduction reaction that can be used for this purpose is hydrogen and oxygen reacting to form water.

$$2H_2(g) \; + \; O_2(g) \; \rightarrow \; 2H_2O(l)$$

Oxidation states: $\quad$ 0 $\qquad\qquad$ 0 $\qquad\qquad$ +1 $\quad$ −2
$\qquad\qquad\qquad\qquad\qquad\qquad\qquad\qquad\qquad$ (each H)

Notice from the changes in oxidation states that in this reaction, hydrogen is oxidized and oxygen reduced. The opposite process can also occur. We can *force* a current through water to produce hydrogen and oxygen gas.

$$2H_2O(l) \xrightarrow[\text{energy}]{\text{Electrical}} 2H_2(g) \; + \; O_2(g)$$

This process, where *electrical energy is used to produce a chemical change*, is called **electrolysis**.

In the remainder of this chapter, we will discuss both types of electrochemical processes. Next we will concern ourselves with the practical galvanic cells we know as batteries.

CHEMISTRY EXPLORERS
Alessandro Volta • 1745–1827

The name *galvanic cell* honors Luigi Galvani (1737–1798), an Italian scientist generally credited with the discovery of electricity. Galvani is most famous for his experiments on decapitated frogs. He assumed that the movement of the dead frog's legs when two dissimilar metals were attached was due to electricity stored in the tissue. Alessandro Volta, a professor of physics at the University of Pavia in Italy, disagreed with his friend Galvani's interpretation of the source of electricity. Volta believed that the current came from the metals, not the frog. He proved this in 1799 when he constructed a primitive battery consisting of alternating layers of zinc and copper separated by pieces of cloth dampened with acid. The battery could produce a current independent of any living tissue. The unit of electrical potential was named the *volt* to honor Volta for his discovery of the storage battery.

CHEMISTRY EXPLORERS
Alessandro Volta

Between 1776 and 1778, Volta discovered and isolated methane gas. In 1810, Napoleon gave Volta the title of count for this discovery. Volta also invented the electrophorus, a device that produces a static electric charge. In 2004, Toyota developed a hybrid automobile named the Alessandro Volta.

B. Batteries

In the previous section we saw that a galvanic cell is a device that uses an oxidation–reduction reaction to generate an electric current by separating the oxidizing agent from the reducing agent. In this section we will consider several specific galvanic cells and their applications.

Lead Storage Battery

Since about 1915, when self-starters were first used in automobiles, the **lead storage battery** has been a major factor in making the automobile a practical means of transportation. This type of battery can function for several years under temperature extremes ranging from -30 °F to 100 °F and under incessant punishment from rough roads. The fact that this same type of battery has been in use for so many years in the face of all of the changes in science and technology over that span of time attests to how well it does its job.

In the lead storage battery, the reducing agent is lead metal, Pb, and the oxidizing agent is lead(IV) oxide, PbO_2. We have already considered a simplified version of this reaction in Example 18.6. In an actual lead storage battery, sulfuric acid, H_2SO_4, furnishes the H^+ needed in the reaction; it also furnishes SO_4^{2-} ions that react with the Pb^{2+} ions to form solid $PbSO_4$. A schematic of one cell of the lead storage battery is shown in **Figure 18.3.**

In this cell the anode is constructed of lead metal, which is oxidized. In the cell reaction, lead atoms lose two electrons each to form Pb^{2+} ions, which combine with SO_4^{2-} ions present in the solution to give solid $PbSO_4$.

The cathode of this battery has lead(IV) oxide coated onto lead grids. Lead atoms in the +4 oxidation state in PbO_2 accept two electrons each (are reduced) to give Pb^{2+} ions that also form solid $PbSO_4$.

In the cell the anode and cathode are separated (so that the electrons must flow through an external wire) and bathed in sulfuric acid. The half-reactions that occur at the two electrodes and the overall cell reaction are shown below.

Anode reaction:

$$Pb + H_2SO_4 \rightarrow PbSO_4 + 2H^+ + 2e^- \qquad \text{Oxidation}$$

Cathode reaction:

$$PbO_2 + H_2SO_4 + 2e^- + 2H^+ \rightarrow PbSO_4 + 2H_2O \qquad \text{Reduction}$$

Overall reaction:

$$Pb(s) + PbO_2(s) + 2H_2SO_4(aq) \rightarrow 2PbSO_4(s) + 2H_2O(l)$$

Lead storage battery
A battery used in cars in which the anode is lead, the cathode is lead coated with lead(IV) oxide, and the electrolyte is sulfuric acid

 i n f o r m a t i o n

The oxidizing agent accepts electrons and the reducing agent furnishes electrons.

18.3.B Batteries
Objective To learn about the composition and operation of commonly used batteries

🍎 TEACHING TIPS

• The remainder of this chapter explains practical applications of electrochemistry. Now is an excellent time for students to make connections between chemistry and their own lives.

• If you can obtain an old lead storage battery, drain it, and saw it in half, you can make a good model to use in class when explaining how lead storage batteries work. The model can serve as a permanent one for the classroom.

TECHNOLOGY

 Figure 18.3

Figure 18.3
In a lead storage battery each cell consists of several lead grids that are connected by a metal bar. These lead grids furnish electrons (the lead atoms lose electrons to form Pb^{2+} ions, which combine with SO_4^{2-} ions to give solid $PbSO_4$). Because the lead is oxidized, it functions as the anode of the cell. The substance that gains electrons is PbO_2; it is coated onto lead grids, several of which are hooked together by a metal bar. The PbO_2 formally contains Pb^{4+}, which is reduced to Pb^{2+}, which in turn combines with SO_4^{2-} to form solid $PbSO_4$. The PbO_2 accepts electrons, so it functions as the cathode.

e^- flow

H_2SO_4 electrolyte solution

Pb metal grid (anode)

PbO_2 coated onto a lead grid (cathode)

18.3 • Electrochemistry and Its Applications • **655**

Active Reading Question

The reducing agent is lead metal. The oxidizing agent is lead(IV) oxide.

TECHNOLOGY

📖 Figure 18.4

Potential
The "pressure" on electrons to flow from the anode to the cathode in a battery

Dry cell battery
A battery that does not contain a liquid electrolyte; commonly used in calculators and watches

Cathode
(graphite rod)

Anode (zinc
inner case)

Paste of MnO_2,
NH_4Cl, and carbon

Figure 18.4
A common dry cell battery

What is the reducing agent in the lead storage battery? The oxidizing agent?

Electrical Potential The tendency for electrons to flow from the anode to the cathode in a battery depends on the ability of the reducing agent to release electrons and on the ability of the oxidizing agent to capture electrons. If a battery consists of a reducing agent that releases electrons readily and an oxidizing agent with a high affinity for electrons, the electrons are driven through the connecting wire with great force and can provide much electrical energy.

To understand this think of the analogy of water flowing through a pipe. The greater the pressure on the water, the more vigorously the water flows. The "pressure" on electrons to flow from one electrode to the other in a battery is called the **potential** of the battery and is measured in volts. For example, each cell in a lead storage battery produces about 2 volts of potential. In an actual automobile battery, six of these cells are connected to produce about 12 volts of potential.

Dry Cell Batteries

The calculators, electronic watches, personal music players that are so familiar to us are all powered by small, efficient **dry cell batteries**. They are called dry cells because they do not contain a liquid electrolyte. The common dry cell battery was invented more than 100 years ago by George Leclanché (1839–1882), a French chemist. In its *acid version,* the dry cell battery contains a zinc inner case that acts as the anode and a carbon (graphite) rod in contact with a moist paste of solid MnO_2, solid NH_4Cl, and carbon that acts as the cathode (see **Figure 18.4**). The half-cell reactions are complex but can be approximated as follows:

Anode reaction:

$$Zn \rightarrow Zn^{2+} + 2e^- \qquad \text{Oxidation}$$

Cathode reaction:

$$2NH_4^+ + 2MnO_2 + 2e^- \rightarrow Mn_2O_3 + 2NH_3 + H_2O \qquad \text{Reduction}$$

This cell produces a potential of about 1.5 volts.

In the *alkaline version* of the dry cell battery, the NH_4Cl is replaced with KOH or NaOH. In this case the half-reactions can be approximated as follows:
Anode reaction:

$$Zn + 2OH^- \rightarrow ZnO + H_2O + 2e^- \qquad \text{Oxidation}$$

Cathode reaction:

$$2MnO_2 + H_2O + 2e^- \rightarrow Mn_2O_3 + 2OH^- \qquad \text{Reduction}$$

The alkaline dry cell lasts longer, mainly because the zinc anode corrodes less rapidly under basic conditions than under acidic conditions.

656 • Chapter 18 • Oxidation–Reduction Reactions and Electrochemistry

Meeting Individual Needs

ADVANCED LEARNERS

Have students compare and contrast the functions and uses of a dry cell battery versus an alkaline battery.

Other types of dry cell batteries include the *silver cell,* which has a Zn anode and a cathode that employs Ag_2O as the oxidizing agent in a basic environment. *Mercury cells,* often used in calculators, have a Zn anode and a cathode involving HgO as the oxidizing agent in a basic medium (see **Figure 18.5**).

Cathode (steel)

Insulation

Anode (zinc container)

Paste of HgO (oxidizing agent) in a basic medium of KOH and $Zn(OH)_2$

Figure 18.5
A mercury battery of the type used in small calculators

An especially important type of dry cell is the *nickel-cadmium battery,* in which the electrode reactions are

Anode reaction:

$$Cd + 2OH^- \rightarrow Cd(OH)_2 + 2e^- \qquad \text{Oxidation}$$

Cathode reaction:

$$NiO_2 + 2H_2O + 2e^- \rightarrow Ni(OH)_2 + 2OH^- \qquad \text{Reduction}$$

In this cell, as in the lead storage battery, the products adhere to the electrodes. Therefore, a nickel–cadmium battery can be recharged an indefinite number of times, because the products can be turned back into reactants by the use of an external source of current.

C. Corrosion

Most metals are found in nature in compounds with nonmetals such as oxygen and sulfur. For example, iron exists as iron ore (which contains Fe_2O_3 and other oxides of iron).

Corrosion can be viewed as the process of returning metals to their natural state—the ores from which they were originally obtained. Corrosion involves oxidation of the metal. Because corroded metal often loses its strength and attractiveness, this process causes great economic loss. For example, approximately one-fifth of the iron and steel produced annually is used to replace rusted metal.

Self-Protecting Metals Because most metals react with O_2, we might expect them to corrode so fast in air that they wouldn't be useful. It is surprising, therefore, that the problem of corrosion does not virtually prevent the use of metals in air. Part of the explanation is that most metals develop a thin oxide coating, which tends to protect their internal atoms against further oxidation. The best example of this is aluminum. Aluminum readily loses electrons, so it should be very easily oxidized by O_2. Given this fact, why is aluminum so useful for building airplanes, bicycle frames, and so on? Aluminum is such a valuable structural material because it forms a thin adherent layer of aluminum oxide, Al_2O_3, which greatly inhibits further corrosion. Aluminum protects itself with this tough oxide coat. Many other metals, such as chromium, nickel, and tin, do the same thing.

Top Ten Most Active Metals (Best Reducing Agents in Water)
Li
K
Ba
Ca
Na
La
Mg
Al
Mn
Zn

Corrosion
The process by which metals are oxidized in the atmosphere

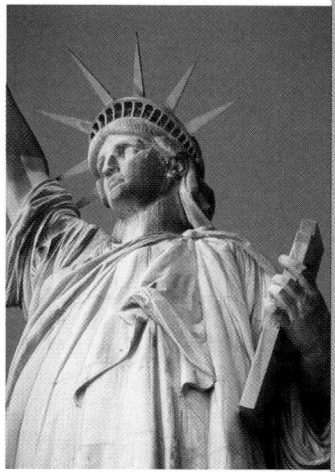

TOP TEN

Students can practice writing half-reactions and electrochemical equations by using the Top Ten. Have them write equations for the interaction of each element in the Top Ten with each of the other elements below it in the table. Students will need to know which metal is oxidized and which is reduced. They will then need to write the correct half-reactions and finally the chemical equation for the net reaction between the substances.

TECHNOLOGY

 Figure 18.5

18.3.C Corrosion

Objective To understand the electrochemical nature of corrosion and learn some ways of preventing it

LABORATORY
EXPERIMENT 83:
Corrosion of Iron, Traditional

Some metals (such as aluminum) develop a thin oxide coating that protects internal atoms in the metal sample from oxidizing further.

18.3.D Electrolysis
Objective To understand the process of electrolysis and learn about the commercial preparation of aluminum

 TEACHING TIP

Charging the lead storage battery is a practical example of electrolysis. Many students know that these batteries are "recharged" when the automobile engine runs. This point is a good starting place for a discussion about electrolysis.

HANDS-ON CHEMISTRY • MINI-LAB •

Lemon Power

Materials
- three lemons
- three galvanized nails
- three pennies
- alligator clips
- wire
- voltmeter

Procedure

1. Stick one nail and one penny into each lemon, making sure that they do not touch. Connect the penny from the first lemon to the nail of the second lemon using the alligator clips and a piece of wire. Connect the third lemon to the second lemon in the same way.

2. Connect the nail of the first lemon to a terminal of a voltmeter using an alligator clip and a piece of wire. Connect the penny of the third lemon to a terminal of a voltmeter in the same way. Determine the potential of the lemon battery.

Results/Analysis

1. Explain why this battery works.

 Active Reading Question

How do some metals protect themselves from corrosion?

 information

An alloy is a mixture of elements with metallic properties.

Cathodic protection
The connection of an active metal, such as magnesium, to steel to protect the steel from corrosion

Buried iron pipe

Connecting insulated wire

Magnesium

Figure 18.6
Cathodic protection of an underground pipe

Iron can also form a protective oxide coating. However, this oxide is not a very effective shield against corrosion, because it scales off easily, exposing new metal surfaces to oxidation. Under normal atmospheric conditions, copper forms an external layer of greenish copper sulfate or carbonate called *patina*. *Silver tarnish* is silver sulfide, Ag_2S, which in thin layers gives the silver surface a richer appearance. Gold shows no appreciable corrosion in air.

Preventing Corrosion Preventing corrosion is an important way of conserving our natural supplies of metals and energy. The primary means of protection is the application of a coating—most often paint or metal plating—to protect the metal from oxygen and moisture. Chromium and tin are often used to plate steel because they oxidize to form a durable, effective oxide coating.

Alloying is also used to prevent corrosion. *Stainless steel* contains chromium and nickel, both of which form oxide coatings that protect the steel.

Cathodic protection is the method most often employed to protect steel in buried fuel tanks and pipelines. A metal that furnishes electrons more easily than iron, such as magnesium, is connected by a wire to the pipeline or tank that is to be protected (see **Figure 18.6**). Because the magnesium is a better reducing agent than iron, electrons flow through the wire from the magnesium to the iron pipe. Thus the electrons are furnished by the magnesium rather than by the iron, keeping the iron from being oxidized. As oxidation of the magnesium occurs, the magnesium dissolves, so it must be replaced periodically.

D. Electrolysis

Unless it is recharged, a battery "runs down" because the substances in it that furnish and accept electrons (to produce the electron flow) are

658 • Chapter 18 • Oxidation–Reduction Reactions and Electrochemistry

---

Hands-On Chemistry
MINI-LAB

Lemon Power

Materials Each group will need 3 lemons, 3 pennies, 3 galvanized nails, 4 pieces of wire, 6 alligator clips, and access to a voltmeter. A small clock is optional.

Purpose Students will make a battery consisting of individual cells.

Discussion The juice in the lemon is acidic and contains many ions; therefore, it can carry a charge. In this battery, electrons flow from the iron nail to the copper penny. The lemon battery should be able to supply 1.5 V, enough to power a small clock.

consumed. For example, in the lead storage battery (see Section 18.3B), PbO_2 and Pb are consumed to form $PbSO_4$ as the battery runs.

$$PbO_2(s) + Pb(s) + 2H_2SO_4(aq) \rightarrow 2PbSO_4(s) + 2H_2O(l)$$

However, one of the most useful characteristics of the lead storage battery is that it can be recharged. *Forcing* current through the battery in the direction opposite to the normal direction reverses the oxidation–reduction reaction. That is, $PbSO_4$ is consumed and PbO_2 and Pb are formed in the charging process. This recharging is done continuously by the automobile's alternator, which is powered by the engine.

The process of **electrolysis** involves *forcing a current through a cell to produce a chemical change that would not otherwise occur.*

One important example of this type of process is the electrolysis of water. Water is a very stable substance that can be broken down into its elements by using an electric current.

$$2H_2O(l) \xrightarrow[\text{current}]{\substack{\text{Forced} \\ \text{electric}}} 2H_2(g) + O_2(g)$$

The electrolysis of water produces hydrogen gas at the cathode (on the left) and oxygen gas at the anode (on the right). A nonreacting strong electrolyte such as Na_2SO_4 is needed to furnish ions to allow the flow of current.

The electrolysis of water to produce hydrogen and oxygen occurs when a current is forced through an aqueous solution. Thus, when the lead storage battery is charged, or "jumped," potentially explosive mixtures of H_2 and O_2 are produced by the current flow through the solution in the battery. This is why it is very important not to produce a spark near the battery during these operations.

Electrolysis
A process involving forcing a current through a cell to produce a chemical change that would not otherwise occur

CRITICAL THINKING

The air we breathe is approximately 80% nitrogen and 20% oxygen.

What if our air was 80% oxygen and 20% nitrogen? How would it affect our lives?

Active Reading Question

Why is it important to avoid a spark near a car battery when you are jump-starting it?

CRITICAL THINKING ?

The oxygen in air is reactive, but the nitrogen is inert. The rate of a chemical reaction is dependent upon the concentrations of reactants. Therefore, with more oxygen, reactions would occur more quickly. These reactions include the spoiling of food, the rusting of cars, and the aging of our bodies.

Active Reading Question

Hydrogen gas and oxygen gas are products of the electrolysis of water, which occurs when current flows through the solution of the battery. A spark could ignite the hydrogen and oxygen mixture and cause an explosion.

TECHNOLOGY

Video
Electrolysis of Water

CHEMISTRY EXPLORERS
Charles Martin Hall • 1863–1914

Hall was a student at Oberlin College in Ohio when he first became interested in aluminum. One of his professors commented that anyone who could find a way to manufacture aluminum cheaply would make a fortune, and Hall decided to give it a try. The 21-year-old worked in a wooden shed near his house with an iron frying pan as a container, a blacksmith's forge as a heat source, and galvanic cells constructed from fruit jars. Using these crude galvanic cells, Hall found that he could produce aluminum by passing a current through a molten mixture of Al_2O_3 and Na_3AlF_6. By a strange coincidence, Paul Heroult, a French chemist who was born and died in the same years as Hall, made the same discovery at about the same time.

18.3 • Electrochemistry and Its Applications • **659**

CHEMISTRY EXPLORERS
Charles Martin Hall

In 1889, Hall and Alfred E. Hunt founded the Pittsburgh Reduction Company (which later became ALCOA). Hall enrolled in Oberlin College in 1880 after studying at the Oberlin Academy during high school. He graduated in 1885 with a degree in chemistry. Oberlin College now has a statue of Hall made of aluminum.

SECTION 18.3
Review Questions

1. In a galvanic cell, electric current is produced from an oxidation–reduction reaction. In an electrolytic cell, current is used to produce a chemical change.

2. a. The electrons (labeled as e) in the wire point from right to left.

   b. The anode is the electrode in the right cell and the cathode is the electrode in the left cell.

   c. Oxidation occurs in the right cell and reduction occurs in the left cell.

   d. Current would cease to flow without the salt bridge.

3. The "pressure" on electrons to flow from one electrode to the other in a battery is called the electrochemical potential.

4. The alkaline dry cell lasts longer mainly because the zinc anode corrodes less rapidly under basic conditions than under acidic conditions.

5. Corrosion involves the oxidation of metals. Generally, corroded metals lose their strength and attractiveness.

6. Three ways to protect against corrosion are coating, cathodic protection, and formation of alloys.

7. A battery is recharged by forcing an electric current through it in the opposite direction to the normal operation of the cell. This procedure reverses the oxidation–reduction reaction.

Production of Aluminum Another important use of electrolysis is in the production of metals from their ores. The metal produced in the greatest quantities by electrolysis is aluminum.

Aluminum is one of the most abundant elements on earth, ranking third behind oxygen and silicon. Because aluminum is a very reactive metal, it is found in nature as its oxide in an ore called *bauxite* (named after Les Baux, France, where it was discovered in 1821). Production of aluminum metal from its ore proved to be more difficult than the production of most other metals. In 1782 Lavoisier, the pioneering French chemist, recognized aluminum as a metal "whose affinity for oxygen is so strong that it cannot be overcome by any known reducing agent." As a result, pure aluminum metal remained unknown. Finally, in 1854, a process was found for producing metallic aluminum by using sodium, but aluminum remained a very expensive rarity. In fact, it is said that Napoleon III served his most honored guests with aluminum forks and spoons, while the others had to settle for gold and silver utensils!

The breakthrough came in 1886 when two men, Charles M. Hall in the United States and Paul Heroult in France, almost simultaneously discovered a practical electrolytic process for producing aluminum, which greatly increased the availability of aluminum for many purposes. **Table 18.2** shows how dramatically the price of aluminum dropped after this discovery. The effect of the electrolysis process is to reduce Al^{3+} ions to neutral Al atoms that form aluminum metal. The aluminum produced in this electrolytic process is 99.5% pure. To be useful as a structural material, aluminum is alloyed with metals such as zinc (for trailer and aircraft construction) and manganese (for cooking utensils, storage tanks, and highway signs). The production of aluminum consumes about 4.5% of all electricity used in the United States.

Table 18.2

The Price of Aluminum

Date	Price of Aluminum ($/lb)*
1855	$100,000
1885	100
1890	2
1895	0.50
1970	0.30
1980	0.80
1990	0.74
2005	0.92

*Note the huge drop in price after the discovery of the Hall-Heroult process in 1886.

SECTION 18.3
REVIEW QUESTIONS

① What is the difference between a galvanic cell and an electrolytic cell?

② Draw the galvanic cell shown in Figure 18.2b.

   a. Label the electrons in the wire as flowing from right to left.

   b. Label the anode and the cathode.

   c. Show where oxidation occurs. Show where reduction occurs.

   d. What would happen to the cell if you removed the salt bridge?

③ What is electrochemical potential?

④ Why does an alkaline battery last longer than an acid dry cell?

⑤ What is corrosion? Why do we want to prevent it?

⑥ What are three ways to protect against corrosion?

⑦ What happens to a battery when it is "recharged"?

RESEARCH LINKS
CLASSZONE.COM

Chapter 18 Review

Key Terms

18.1 **Oxidation–reduction reactions (redox reactions)**

Oxidation

Reduction

Oxidation states

18.2 **Oxidizing agent (electron acceptor)**

Reducing agent (electron donor)

Half-reactions

18.3 **Electrochemistry**

Electrochemical battery (galvanic cell)

Anode

Cathode

Electrolysis

Lead storage battery

Potential

Dry cell batteries

Corrosion

Cathodic protection

Key Ideas

18.1 Electron Transfer Reactions

■ Oxidation–reduction reactions involve electron transfer.
- Oxidation states are used to keep track of electrons.
- Oxidation—an increase in oxidation state (a loss of electrons)
- Reduction—a decrease in oxidation state (a gain of electrons)
- The oxidizing agent accepts electrons.
- The reducing agent furnishes electrons.

18.2 Balancing Oxidation–Reduction Reactions

■ Balancing oxidation–reduction reactions can be accomplished by two methods:
- Inspection (trial and error)
- Half-reactions

18.3 Electrochemistry and Its Applications

■ Electrochemistry is the study of the interchange of chemical and electrical energy.

■ A galvanic cell is a device for converting chemical energy to electrical energy.
- Consists of separate compartments for the oxidizing and reducing agents which are connected by a salt bridge and a wire
- Anode—electrode at which oxidation occurs
- Cathode—electrode at which reduction occurs
- Battery—a galvanic cell or a group of cells connected together

■ Corrosion is the oxidation of metals to form mainly oxides and sulfides.
- Some metals, such as aluminum, protect themselves with their oxide coating.
- Corrosion of iron can be prevented by coatings, by alloying, and cathodic protection.

■ Electrolysis is the use of electrical energy to produce a chemical change.

RESEARCH LINKS
CLASSZONE.COM

Meeting Individual Needs
CHAPTER REVIEW

Chapter 18 Review Worksheet at the appropriate level:
    Basic
    Standard
    Challenge

CHAPTER SUMMARY
A **Chapter Summary** that includes additional Active Reading Questions for Chapter 18 is available.

Assessment Resources
CHAPTER 18
Chapter 18 Test
TECHNOLOGY
Computerized Test Bank for Chapter 18

Chapter 18 Assessment

Left column (answers)

1. Oxidation can be defined as the loss of electrons by an atom, molecule, or ion. It may also be defined as an increase in oxidation state for an element. The following equation shows the oxidation of copper:

$$Cu(s) \rightarrow Cu^{2+}(aq) + 2e^-$$

2. Reduction can be defined as the gain of electrons by an atom, molecule, or ion. It may also be defined as a decrease in oxidation state for an element. The following equation shows the reduction of sulfur:

$$S(s) + 2e^- \rightarrow S^{2-}(aq)$$

3. (a) sodium is oxidized, nitrogen is reduced; (b) magnesium is oxidized, chlorine is reduced; (c) aluminum is oxidized, bromine is reduced; (d) iron is oxidized, oxygen is reduced

4. (a) magnesium is oxidized, bromine is reduced; (b) sodium is oxidized, sulfur is reduced; (c) bromide ion is oxidized, chlorine is reduced; (d) potassium is oxidized, nitrogen is reduced

5. The assignment of oxidation states is a bookkeeping method by which charges are assigned to the various atoms in a compound. This method allows us to keep track of electrons transferred between species in oxidation–reduction reactions.

6. For very electronegative elements (such as oxygen), we assign each of these elements an oxidation state equal to its charge when the element forms an anion. The most common exception to oxygen having an oxidation state of -2 occurs with the peroxide ion, in which each oxygen has an oxidation state of -1.

7. A neutral molecule has an overall charge of zero.

8. The sum of all the oxidation states of the atoms in a polyatomic ion must equal the overall charge on the ion.

9. (a) N, $+3$; Cl, -1; (b) S, $+6$; F, -1; (c) P, $+5$; Cl, -1; (d) Si, -4; H, $+1$

10. (a) H, $+1$; Br, -1; (b) H, $+1$; O, -2; Br, $+1$; (c) Br, 0; (d) H, $+1$; O, -2; Br, $+7$

11. (a) H, $+1$; O, -2; N, $+5$ (b) H, $+1$; O, -2; P, $+5$ (c) H, $+1$; O, -2; S, $+6$ (d) O, -1

Center column

All exercises with blue numbers have answers in the back of this book.

18.1 Electron Transfer Reactions

A. Oxidation–Reduction Reactions

1. How is *oxidation* defined? Write an equation showing an atom being *oxidized*.

2. How is *reduction* defined? Write an equation showing an atom being *reduced*.

3. For each of the following oxidation–reduction reactions of metals with nonmetals, identify which element is oxidized and which is reduced.

   a. $6Na(s) + N_2(g) \rightarrow 2Na_3N(s)$
   b. $Mg(s) + Cl_2(g) \rightarrow MgCl_2(s)$
   c. $2Al(s) + 3Br_2(l) \rightarrow 2AlBr_3(s)$
   d. $4Fe(s) + 3O_2(g) \rightarrow 2Fe_2O_3(s)$

4. For each of the following oxidation–reduction reactions, identify which element is oxidized and which is reduced.

   a. $Mg(s) + Br_2(l) \rightarrow MgBr_2(s)$
   b. $2Na(s) + S(s) \rightarrow Na_2S(s)$
   c. $Cl_2(g) + 2NaBr(aq) \rightarrow Br_2(l) + 2NaCl(aq)$
   d. $6K(s) + N_2(g) \rightarrow 2K_3N(s)$

B. Oxidation States

5. What is an oxidation state? Why is this concept useful?

6. Explain why, although it is not an ionic compound, we assign oxygen an oxidation state of -2 in water, H_2O. Give an example of a compound in which oxygen is *not* in the -2 oxidation state.

7. Why must the sum of all the oxidation states of the atoms in a neutral molecule be zero?

8. What must be the sum of the oxidation states of all the atoms in a polyatomic ion?

9. Assign oxidation states to all of the atoms in each of the following:

   a. NCl_3 c. PCl_5
   b. SF_6 d. SiH_4

10. Assign oxidation states to all of the atoms in each of the following:

    a. HBr   c. Br_2
    b. HOBr   d. $HBrO_4$

Right column

11. Assign oxidation states to all of the atoms in each of the following:

    a. HNO_3 c. HSO_4^-
    b. HPO_4^{2-} d. O_2^{2-}

12. Assign oxidation states to all of the atoms in each of the following:

    a. $CuCl_2$ c. $HCrO_4^-$
    b. $CrCl_3$ d. Cr_2O_3

13. Assign oxidation states to all of the atoms in each of the following:

    a. CH_4 c. $KHCO_3$
    b. Na_2CO_3 d. CO

18.2 Balancing Oxidation–Reduction Reactions

A. Oxidation–Reduction Reactions Between Nonmetals

14. Oxidation can be defined as a loss of electrons or as an increase in oxidation state. Explain why the two definitions mean the same thing, and give an example to support your explanation.

15. Reduction can be defined as a gain of electrons or as a decrease in oxidation state. Explain why the two definitions mean the same thing, and give an example to support your explanation.

16. Is an oxidizing agent itself oxidized or reduced? Is a reducing agent itself oxidized or reduced?

17. Does an oxidizing agent increase or decrease its own oxidation state when it acts on another atom? Does a reducing agent increase or decrease its own oxidation state when it acts on another substance?

18. In each of the following reactions, identify which element is oxidized and which is reduced by assigning oxidation numbers.

    a. $Zn(s) + 2HNO_3(aq) \rightarrow Zn(NO_3)_2(aq) + H_2(g)$
    b. $H_2(g) + CuSO_4(aq) \rightarrow Cu(s) + H_2SO_4(aq)$
    c. $N_2(g) + 3Br_2(l) \rightarrow 2NBr_3(g)$
    d. $2KBr(aq) + Cl_2(g) \rightarrow 2KCl(aq) + Br_2(l)$

19. In each of the following reactions, identify which element is oxidized and which is reduced by assigning oxidation states.

    a. $Cu(s) + 2AgNO_3(aq) \rightarrow 2Ag(s) + Cu(NO_3)_2(aq)$
    b. $N_2(g) + 3F_2(g) \rightarrow 2NF_3(g)$
    c. $2Fe_2O_3(s) + 3S(s) \rightarrow 4Fe(s) + 3SO_2(g)$
    d. $2H_2O_2(l) \rightarrow 2H_2O(l) + O_2(g)$

Bottom section (answers continued)

12. (a) Cu, $+2$; Cl, -1
    (b) Cr, $+3$; Cl, -1
    (c) H, $+1$; O, -2; Cr, $+6$
    (d) Cr, $+3$; O, -2

13. (a) H, $+1$; C, -4;
    (b) Na, $+1$; O, -2; C, $+4$;
    (c) K, $+1$; H, $+1$; C, $+4$;
    O, -2; (d) O, -2; C, $+2$

14. Consider the reaction: $Na \rightarrow Na^+ + e^-$. The sodium atom on the left side of the equation is losing an electron. Because electrons are negatively charged, the oxidation state is increasing (from 0 to $+1$).

15. When an atom gains an electron, it gains a negative charge, which will lower its oxidation state. In $Cl + e^- \rightarrow Cl^-$, the oxidation state goes from 0 to -1.

16. An oxidizing agent causes another species to be oxidized (to lose electrons). To do this, the oxidizing agent must take in electrons (be reduced). Thus an oxidizing agent is reduced (and a reducing agent is oxidized).

17. An oxidizing agent decreases its oxidation state. A reducing agent increases its oxidation state.

18. (a) zinc is oxidized (0 to $+2$); hydrogen is reduced ($+1$ to 0); (b) hydrogen is oxidized (0 to $+1$); copper is reduced ($+2$ to 0); (c) nitrogen is

20. In ordinary photography, the light-sensitive portion of the film is a thin coating of a silver halide (usually silver bromide). When the film is exposed to light, the reaction

$$2AgBr(s) \rightarrow 2Ag(s) + Br_2(g)$$

occurs. Identify which element is reduced and which is oxidized.

21. Although magnesium metal does not react with water at room temperature, it does react vigorously with steam at higher temperatures, releasing elemental hydrogen gas from the water.

$$Mg(s) + 2H_2O(g) \rightarrow Mg(OH)_2(s) + H_2(g)$$

Identify which element is being oxidized and which is being reduced.

B. Balancing Oxidation–Reduction Reactions by the Half-Reaction Method

22. In what *two* respects must oxidation–reduction reactions be balanced?

23. Why must the number of electrons lost in the oxidation equal the number of electrons gained in the reduction? Is it possible to have "leftover" electrons in a reaction?

24. Balance each of the following half-reactions.

a. $N_2(g) \rightarrow N_3^-(aq)$
b. $O_2^{2-}(aq) \rightarrow O_2(g)$
c. $Zn(s) \rightarrow Zn^{2+}(aq)$
d. $F_2(g) \rightarrow F^-(aq)$

25. Balance each of the following half-reactions, which take place in acidic solution.

a. $O_2(g) \rightarrow H_2O(l)$
b. $IO_3^-(aq) \rightarrow I_2(s)$
c. $VO^{2+}(aq) \rightarrow V^{3+}(aq)$
d. $BiO^+(aq) \rightarrow Bi(s)$

26. Balance each of the following oxidation–reduction reactions, which take place in acidic solution, by using the half-reaction method.

a. $MnO_4^-(aq) + Zn(s) \rightarrow Mn^{2+}(aq) + Zn^{2+}(aq)$
b. $Sn^{4+}(aq) + H_2(g) \rightarrow Sn^{2+}(aq) + H^+(aq)$
c. $Zn(s) + NO_3^-(aq) \rightarrow Zn^{2+}(aq) + NO_2(g)$
d. $H_2S(g) + Br_2(l) \rightarrow S(s) + Br^-(aq)$

27. Iodide ion, I^-, is one of the most easily oxidized species. Balance each of the following oxidation–reduction reactions, which take place in acidic solution, by using the half-reaction method.

a. $IO_3^-(aq) + I^-(aq) \rightarrow I_2(aq)$
b. $Cr_2O_7^{2-}(aq) + I^-(aq) \rightarrow Cr^{3+}(aq) + I_2(aq)$
c. $Cu^{2+}(aq) + I^-(aq) \rightarrow CuI(s) + I_2(aq)$

18.3 Electrochemistry and Its Applications

A. Electrochemistry: An Introduction

28. How is an oxidation–reduction reaction set up as a galvanic cell (battery)? How is the transfer of electrons between reducing agent and oxidizing agent made useful?

29. What is a salt bridge? Why is a salt bridge necessary in a galvanic cell? Can a different method be used in place of the salt bridge?

30. In which direction do electrons flow in a galvanic cell, anode to cathode, or vice versa?

31. Consider the oxidation–reduction reaction

$$Al(s) + Ni^{2+}(aq) \rightarrow Al^{3+}(aq) + Ni(s)$$

Sketch a galvanic cell that makes use of this reaction. Which metal ion is reduced? Which metal is oxidized? What half-reaction takes place at the anode in the cell? What half-reaction takes place at the cathode?

32. Consider the oxidation–reduction reaction

$$Zn(s) + Pb^{2+}(aq) \rightarrow Zn^{2+}(aq) + Pb(s)$$

Sketch a galvanic cell that uses this reaction. Which metal ion is reduced? Which metal is oxidized? What half-reaction takes place at the anode in the cell? What half-reaction takes place at the cathode?

reduced (0 to −3); bromine is oxidized (0 to +1); (d) bromine is oxidized (−1 to 0); chlorine is reduced (0 to −1)

19. (a) copper is oxidized (0 to +2); silver is reduced (+1 to 0); (b) nitrogen is oxidized (0 to +3); fluorine is reduced (0 to −1); (c) sulfur is oxidized (0 to +4); iron is reduced (+3 to 0); oxygen is both oxidized (−1 to 0) and reduced (−1 to −2)

20. silver is reduced [+1 in $AgBr(s)$, 0 in $Ag(s)$]; bromine is oxidized [−1 in $AgBr(s)$, 0 in $Br_2(g)$]

21. magnesium is oxidized [0 in $Mg(s)$, +2 in $Mg(OH)_2(s)$]; hydrogen is reduced [+1 in $H_2O(l)$, 0 in $H_2(g)$]

22. Oxidation–reduction reactions must be balanced with respect to mass and charge.

23. Under ordinary conditions it is impossible to have "free" electrons that are not part of some atom, ion, or molecule. Consequently, the total number of electrons lost by the species being oxidized must equal the total number of electrons gained by the species being reduced.

24. (a) $N_2(g) + 6e^- \rightarrow 2N^{3-}(aq)$; (b) $O_2^{2-}(aq) \rightarrow O_2(g) + 2e^-$; (c) $Zn(s) \rightarrow Zn^{2+}(aq) + 2e^-$; (d) $F_2(g) + 2e^- \rightarrow 2F^-(aq)$

25. (a) $4e^- + 4H^+(aq) + O_2(g) \rightarrow 2H_2O(l)$; (b) $10e^- + 12H^+(aq) + 2IO_3^-(aq) \rightarrow I_2(s) + 6H_2O(l)$; (c) $e^- + 2H^+(aq) + VO^{2+}(aq) \rightarrow V^{3+}(aq) + H_2O(l)$; (d) $3e^- + 2H^+(aq) + BiO^+(aq) \rightarrow Bi(s) + H_2O(l)$

26. (a) $2MnO_4^-(aq) + 16H^+(aq) + 5Zn(s) \rightarrow 2Mn^{2+}(aq) + 8H_2O(l) + 5Zn^{2+}(aq)$; (b) $H_2(g) + Sn^{4+}(aq) \rightarrow 2H^+(aq) + Sn^{2+}(aq)$; (c) $2NO_3^-(aq) + 4H^+(aq) + Zn(s) \rightarrow 2NO_2(g) + 2H_2O(l) + Zn^{2+}(aq)$; (d) $H_2S(g) + Br_2(l) \rightarrow S(s) + 2H^+(aq) + 2Br^-(aq)$

27. (a) $IO_3^-(aq) + 6H^+(aq) + 5I^-(aq) \rightarrow 3I_2(aq) + 3H_2O(l)$; (b) $6I^-(aq) + Cr_2O_7^{2-}(aq) + 14H^+(aq) \rightarrow 3I_2(aq) + 2Cr^{3+}(aq) + 7H_2O(l)$; (c) $2Cu^{2+}(aq) + 4I^-(aq) \rightarrow 2CuI(s) + I_2(aq)$

28. An oxidation–reduction reaction is made useful as a galvanic cell (battery) by physically separating the oxidation half-reaction from the reduction half-reaction and by causing the electrons to be transferred through a wire connecting the two. The passage of electrons through the wire represents an electrical current, which might be used to drive a motor or some other device.

29. A salt bridge completes the electrical circuit in a cell. It does so by allowing ion flow from one half of the cell to the other half without allowing bulk mixing of the solutions. It is typically a U-shaped tube filled with an electrolyte that is not involved in the oxidation–reduction reaction. Any method that allows ion flow without large-scale mixing of solutions (such as a porous cup or frit) can be used in place of a salt bridge.

30. In a galvanic cell, electrons flow from the anode (where oxidation occurs) to the cathode (where reduction occurs).

31. See the *Solutions Guide*.

32. See the *Solutions Guide*.

33. The overall reaction is $Pb(s) + PbO_2(s) + 2H_2SO_4(aq) \rightarrow 2PbSO_4(s) + 2H_2O(l)$, in which lead is both oxidized (0 to +2) and reduced (+4 to +2). The battery can be recharged because the reaction can be reversed by the electrolysis of the mixture of water and solid lead(II) sulfate.

34. Both normal and alkaline cells contain zinc as an electrode; zinc corrodes more slowly under alkaline (basic) conditions than in a normal dry cell (which is acidic). Anode: $Zn(s) + 2OH^-(aq) \rightarrow ZnO(s) + H_2O(l) + 2e^-$. Cathode: $2MnO_2(s) + H_2O(l) + 2e^- \rightarrow Mn_2O_3(s) + 2OH^-(aq)$.

35. Corrosion returns metals to their natural state (ore) and involves oxidation of the metal. It is undesirable because as the metal is converted to its oxide, the bulk of the metal loses strength, flexibility, and other metallic properties.

36. Aluminum reacts very quickly with the oxygen in air to form a thin coating of Al_2O_3 on its surface. This coating is transparent and clings tightly to the aluminum. In addition, the aluminum oxide is much less reactive than aluminum and protects the surface from further reaction.

37. Most steels contain additives such as chromium or nickel. These additives are able to form protective oxide coatings on the surface of the steel to prevent further oxidation.

38. In the cathodic protection of steel tanks and pipes, a more reactive metal than iron is connected to the item to be protected. The active metal is then oxidized instead of the iron of the tank or pipe.

39. Electrolysis is the process of forcing an electrical current through a cell to produce a chemical change that would otherwise not occur.

40. The main recharging reaction for the lead storage battery is $2PbSO_4(s) + 2H_2O(l) \rightarrow Pb(s) + PbO_2(s) + H_2SO_4(aq)$. A major side reaction is the electrolysis of water, $2H_2O(l) \rightarrow 2H_2(g) + O_2(g)$.

41. Aluminum combines readily with oxygen, so it cannot be produced by electrolysis of aqueous solutions of an aluminum salt. Aluminum is most commonly prepared by the Hall process, which is the electrolysis of a molten mixture of Al_2O_3 and Na_3AlF_6.

42. The item to be plated should be made the cathode in a cell containing a solution of ions of the desired plating metal.

B. Batteries

33. Write the chemical equation for the overall cell reaction that occurs in a lead storage automobile battery. What species is oxidized in such a battery? What species is reduced? Why can such a battery be "recharged"?

34. Why does an alkaline dry cell battery typically last longer than a normal dry cell? Write the chemical equation for the overall cell reaction in an alkaline dry cell.

C. Corrosion

35. What process is represented by the *corrosion* of a metal? Why is corrosion undesirable?

36. Explain how some metals, notably aluminum, naturally resist complete oxidation by the atmosphere.

37. Pure iron ordinarily rusts quickly, but steel does not corrode nearly as fast. How does steel resist corrosion?

38. What is *cathodic protection,* and how is it applied to prevent oxidation of steel tanks and pipes?

D. Electrolysis

39. What is *electrolysis?* What types of reactions is electrolysis capable of causing?

40. What reactions go on during the recharging of an automobile battery?

41. How is aluminum metal produced by electrolysis? Why can't simpler chemical reduction methods be used?

42. Jewelry is often manufactured by plating an expensive metal such as gold over a cheaper metal. How might such a process be set up as an electrolysis reaction?

Critical Thinking

43. An oxidizing agent causes the (oxidation/reduction) of another species, and the oxidizing agent itself is (oxidized/reduced).

44. To function as a good reducing agent, a species must _____ electrons easily.

45. Jump-starting a dead automobile battery can be dangerous if precautions are not taken, because of the production of an explosive mixture of _____ and _____ gases in the battery.

46. For each of the following unbalanced oxidation–reduction chemical equations, balance the equation by inspection, and identify which species is undergoing oxidation and which is undergoing reduction.

   a. $Fe(s) + O_2(g) \rightarrow Fe_2O_3(s)$
   b. $Al(s) + Cl_2(g) \rightarrow AlCl_3(s)$
   c. $Mg(s) + P_4(s) \rightarrow Mg_3P_2(s)$

47. Balance each of the following oxidation–reduction reactions, which take place in acidic solution.

   a. $MnO_4^-(aq) + H_2O_2(aq) \rightarrow Mn^{2+}(aq) + O_2(g)$
   b. $BrO_3^-(aq) + Cu^+(aq) \rightarrow Br^-(aq) + Cu^{2+}(aq)$
   c. $HNO_2(aq) + I^-(aq) \rightarrow NO(g) + I_2(aq)$

48. For each of the following oxidation–reduction reactions of metals with nonmetals, identify which element is oxidized and which is reduced.

   a. $3Zn(s) + N_2(g) \rightarrow Zn_3N_2(s)$
   b. $Co(s) + S(s) \rightarrow CoS(s)$
   c. $4K(s) + O_2(g) \rightarrow 2K_2O(s)$
   d. $4Ag(s) + O_2(g) \rightarrow 2Ag_2O(s)$

49. Assign oxidation states to all of the atoms in each of the following:

   a. MnO_2
   b. $BaCrO_4$
   c. H_2SO_3
   d. $Ca_3(PO_4)_2$

50. In each of the following reactions, identify which element is oxidized and which is reduced by assigning oxidation states.

   a. $2B_2O_3(s) + 6Cl_2(g) \rightarrow 4BCl_3(l) + 3O_2(g)$
   b. $GeH_4(g) + O_2(g) \rightarrow Ge(s) + 2H_2O(g)$
   c. $C_2H_4(g) + Cl_2(g) \rightarrow C_2H_4Cl_2(l)$
   d. $O_2(g) + 2F_2(g) \rightarrow 2OF_2(g)$

51. Consider the oxidation–reduction reaction

   $$Mg(s) + Cu^{2+}(aq) \rightarrow Mg^{2+}(aq) + Cu(s)$$

   Sketch a galvanic cell that uses this reaction. Which metal ion is reduced? Which metal is oxidized? What half-reaction takes place at the anode in the cell? What half-reaction takes place at the cathode?

43. oxidation; reduced

44. lose

45. hydrogen; oxygen

46. (a) $4Fe(s) + 3O_2(g) \rightarrow 2Fe_2O_3(s)$; iron is oxidized, oxygen is reduced; (b) $2Al(s) + 3Cl_2(g) \rightarrow 2AlCl_3(s)$; aluminum is oxidized, chlorine is reduced; (c) $6Mg(s) + P_4(s) \rightarrow 2Mg_3P_2(s)$; magnesium is oxidized, phosphorus is reduced

47. (a) $2MnO_4^-(aq) + 6H^+(aq) + 5H_2O_2(aq) \rightarrow 2Mn^{2+}(aq) + 8H_2O(l) + 5O_2(g)$; (b) $6Cu^+(aq) + 6H^+(aq) + BrO_3^-(aq) \rightarrow 6Cu^{2+}(aq) + Br^-(aq) + 3H_2O(l)$; (c) $2HNO_2(aq) + 2H^+(aq) + 2I^-(aq) \rightarrow 2NO(g) + 2H_2O(l) + I_2(aq)$

48. (a) zinc is oxidized, nitrogen is reduced; (b) cobalt is oxidized, sulfur is reduced; (c) potassium is oxidized, oxygen is reduced; (d) silver is oxidized, oxygen is reduced

49. (a) Mn, +4; O, −2
   (b) Ba, +2; Cr, +6; O, −2
   (c) H, +1; S, +4; O, −2
   (d) Ca, +2; P, +5; O, −2

50. (a) oxygen is oxidized, chlorine is reduced; (b) germanium is oxidized, oxygen is reduced; (c) carbon is oxidized, chlorine is reduced; (d) oxygen is oxidized, fluorine is reduced

51. See the *Solutions Guide.*

1 In the following reaction, identify which element is oxidized, and which element is reduced.

$$2Ca(s) + O_2(g) \rightarrow 2CaO(s)$$

A Calcium is oxidized and oxygen is reduced.

B Oxygen is oxidized and calcium is reduced.

C One of the oxygen atoms is oxidized, and the other oxygen atom is oxidized.

D The reaction above is not an oxidation–reduction reaction.

2 In which of the following compounds or ions is the oxidation state for nitrogen -3?

A N_2

B NI_3

C NO_2

D NH_3

3 Which of the following is not an oxidation reduction reaction?

A $2Al(s) + 3I_2(s) \rightarrow 2AlI_3(s)$

B $Mg(s) + 2HCl(aq) \rightarrow MgCl_2(aq) + H_2(g)$

C $HCl(aq) + NaOH(aq) \rightarrow NaCl(aq) + H_2O(l)$

D $CH_4(g) + 2O_2(g) \rightarrow CO_2(g) + 2H_2O(l)$

4 In the following reaction, identify the oxidizing agent and the reducing agent.

$$Cl_2(g) + 2NaBr(s) \rightarrow Br_2(g) + 2NaCl(s)$$

A Cl_2 = oxidizing agent, NaBr = reducing agent

B NaBr = oxidizing agent, Cl_2 = reducing agent

C Cl_2 = oxidizing agent, Br_2 = reducing agent

D NaCl = oxidizing agent, NaBr = reducing agent

5 Which of the following is true concerning the following equation?

$$Ag^+(aq) + Cu(s) \rightarrow Cu^{2+}(aq) + Ag(s)$$

A When the equation is balanced in standard form, the coefficient in front of the Cu and Cu^{2+} is 2.

B When the equation is balanced in standard form, the coefficient in front of the Ag and Ag^+ is 2.

C When the equation above is balanced in standard form, electrons need to appear in the equation.

D The equation as written above is balanced in standard form.

6 The oxidizing agent in the lead storage battery is

A Pb

B PbO_2

C H_2SO_4

D $PbSO_4$

7 The process in which electrical energy is used to produce chemical energy is called

A cathodic protection.

B electrolysis.

C corrosion.

D electrochemistry.

8 Label the following parts of the galvanic cell.

anode

cathode

reducing agent

oxidizing agent

9 The reaction $Cu(s) + NO_3^-\ (aq) \rightarrow Cu^{2+}(aq) + NO(g)$ takes place in acidic solution.

a Write the balanced oxidation half-reaction.

b Write the balanced reduction half-reaction.

c Write the overall balanced reaction.

d Label the oxidizing agent and the reducing agent.

Chapter 18
Standardized Test Practice

1. A

2. D

3. C

4. A

5. B

6. B

7. B

8. Anode: C

Cathode: A

Reducing agent: D

Oxidizing agent: B

9. a. $Cu(s) \rightarrow Cu^{2+}(aq) + 2e^-$

b. $3e^- + 4H^+ + NO_3^-(aq) \rightarrow NO(g) + 2H_2O$

c. $8H^+ + 3Cu(s) + 2NO_3^-(aq) \rightarrow 3Cu^{2+}(aq) + 2NO(g) + 4H_2O$

d. The oxidizing agent is $NO_3^-(aq)$ and the reducing agent is $Cu(s)$.

Test Taking Strategy

Encourage students to take time to read all information given with a test item, especially a chemical equation. Tell students to read the equation closely, first checking whether it is balanced, and then extracting as much information as necessary to answer the test question. Point out that an equation may also provide some insight to another question that appears elsewhere on the test.

Assessment Resources
CHAPTER 18

For additional practice with standardized testing, see *Standardized Test Practice* located in the *Teacher Resources*.

Planning Guide

Section	Segment		Text Features and Components	Labs, Demonstrations, & Activities
19.1 Radioactivity **1 Block** pp. 668–678	A	**Radioactive Decay**	(SE) Chemistry Explorers: Marie Curie *p. 672*	(LM) Experiment 84: Investigating Radioactivity, CBL Lab Manual Report Sheets Teacher's Lab Guide
	B	**Nuclear Transformations**		
	C	**Detection of Radioactivity and the Concept of Half-life**	(SE) Chemistry Explorers: Darleane Hoffman *p. 678*	(TE) Mini-Demo *p. 676* (LM) Experiment 85: Half-life of Pennies, Traditional Lab Manual Report Sheets Teacher's Lab Guide
19.2 Application of Radioactivity **0.5 Block** pp. 679–682	A	**Dating by Radioactivity**	(SE) Chemistry in Your World: Dating Diamonds *p. 680*	
	B	**Medical Applications of Radioactivity**		
	continued on next page			

Key					
(SE) Student Edition	(TE) Teacher Edition	(RP) Teacher Resource Package			
(AR) Additional Materials	(LM) Lab Materials	(📖) Transparencies			
(●) DVD	(▶) CD-ROM	(ℹ) classzone.com			

All Learners	Technology	Review & Assessment	Standards
TE Teaching Tips *pp. 669–670* **TE** Meeting Individual Needs *p. 671*	**⊙** Animation: Nuclear Particles **▣** Transparency: Figure 19.1 **▮** Lab Generator CD **⊙** EasyPlanner	**SE** Active Reading Question *p. 669* **SE** Active Reading Question *p. 670* **TE** More Examples *p. 672* **SE** Practice Problem *p. 673* **SE** Practice Problem *p. 674* **TE** More Examples *p. 674* **SE** Key Terms *p. 692* **SE** Questions and Problems *p. 694*	**TE** **NSES** UCP1, UCP3, A1, A2, B1, B2, D3, E1, E2, F1, F6, G1, G2, G3
TE Teaching Tips *p. 674* **TE** Meeting Individual Needs *p. 675*	**⊙** EasyPlanner	**SE** Key Terms *p. 692* **SE** Questions and Problems *p. 694*	
TE Teaching Tips *pp. 676–677* **TE** Misconception *p. 676* **RP** Team Learning Worksheet (Sec. 19.1)	**⊙** Animation: Geiger Counter **⊙** Animation: Half-life of Reactions **⊙** Animation: Half-life of Nuclear Decay **▮** Lab Generator CD **⊙** EasyPlanner	**SE** Active Reading Question *p. 676* **SE** Practice Problem *p. 677* **TE** More Examples *p. 677* **SE** Review Questions (19.1.A–19.1.C) *p. 678* **SE** Key Terms *p. 692* **SE** Questions and Problems *pp. 694–695*	
TE Teaching Tips *p. 679*	**⊙** EasyPlanner	**SE** Active Reading Question *p. 679* **SE** Key Terms *p. 692* **SE** Questions and Problems *p. 695*	**TE** **NSES** UCP1, UCP3, UCP5, A1, A2, B1, B2, D3, E1, E2, F1, F3, F6, G1, G2, G3
TE Teaching Tips *pp. 680–681* **RP** MINT: Challenge Projects *TE p. 681*	**⊙** EasyPlanner	**SE** Active Reading Question *p. 682* **SE** Review Questions (19.2.A–19.2.B) *p. 682* **SE** Key Terms *p. 692* **SE** Questions and Problems *p. 695*	

Planning Guide

Section	Segment	Text Features and Components	Labs, Demonstrations, & Activities
19.3 Using the Nucleus as a Source of Energy **1 Block** pp. 683–691	**A** **Nuclear Energy**		
	B **Nuclear Fission**	**SE** Top Ten Countries Producing Electricity by Nuclear Power *p. 684*	
	C **Nuclear Reactors**	**SE** Celebrity Chemical: Uranium *p. 686* **SE** Chemistry in Your World: Making Elements in Stars *p. 687*	
	D **Nuclear Fusion**	**SE** Top Ten Elements in the Sun *p. 688*	
	E **Effects of Radiation**	**SE** Chemistry in Your World: Nuclear Waste Disposal *p. 689* **TE** Teaching Support: Historical Note *p. 690*	

Key	**SE** Student Edition	**TE** Teacher Edition	**RP** Teacher Resource Package
	AR Additional Materials	**LM** Lab Materials	Transparencies
	DVD	CD-ROM	classzone.com

All Learners	Technology	Review & Assessment	Standards
	💿 EasyPlanner	SE Key Terms *p. 693* SE Questions and Problems *p. 695*	TE **NSES** UCP1, UCP3, UCP5, A1, A2, B1, B2, D3, D4, E1, E2, F3, F4, F6, G1, G2, G3
TE Teaching Tip *p. 683*	🔵 Animation: Nuclear Fission 💿 EasyPlanner	SE Critical Thinking *p. 683* SE Active Reading Question *p. 684* SE Key Terms *p. 693* SE Questions and Problems *p. 695*	
TE Meeting Individual Needs *p. 685*	📠 Transparency: Figure 19.4 💿 EasyPlanner	SE Key Terms *p. 693* SE Questions and Problems *pp. 695–696*	
	🔵 Animation: Nuclear Fusion 💿 EasyPlanner	SE Key Terms *p. 693* SE Questions and Problems *p. 696*	
TE Teaching Tips *pp. 688, 690–691* RP Team Learning Worksheet (Sec. 19.2–19.3)	💿 EasyPlanner	SE Active Reading Question *p. 690* SE Review Questions (19.3.A–19.3.E) *p. 691* SE Questions and Problems *p. 696*	

Resource Materials for Chapter 19

SE Chapter Review *pp. 692–693*

SE Critical Thinking *p. 696*

SE Standardized Test Practice *p. 697*

AR English/Spanish Summaries

🔊 English Summaries Audio

🔊 Spanish Summaries Audio

RP Meeting Individual Needs Toolkit (MINT)
  Challenge Projects
  Chapter Review Worksheets
  Chapter Summaries

RP Solutions Guide

RP Standardized Test Practice

RP Chapter Tests

RP Test Bank

🖥 Test Generator

Chapter 19
Overview

In this chapter our goals are for students to:

- Learn the types of radioactive decay
- Learn to write nuclear equations
- Learn how one element can be changed into another by particle bombardment
- Learn about instruments for detecting radiation
- Understand half-life
- Learn how objects can be dated by radioactivity
- Discuss the use of radiotracers in medicine
- Introduce fusion and fission as producers of nuclear energy
- Learn about nuclear fission
- Understand how a nuclear reactor works
- Learn about nuclear fusion
- See how radiation damages human tissue

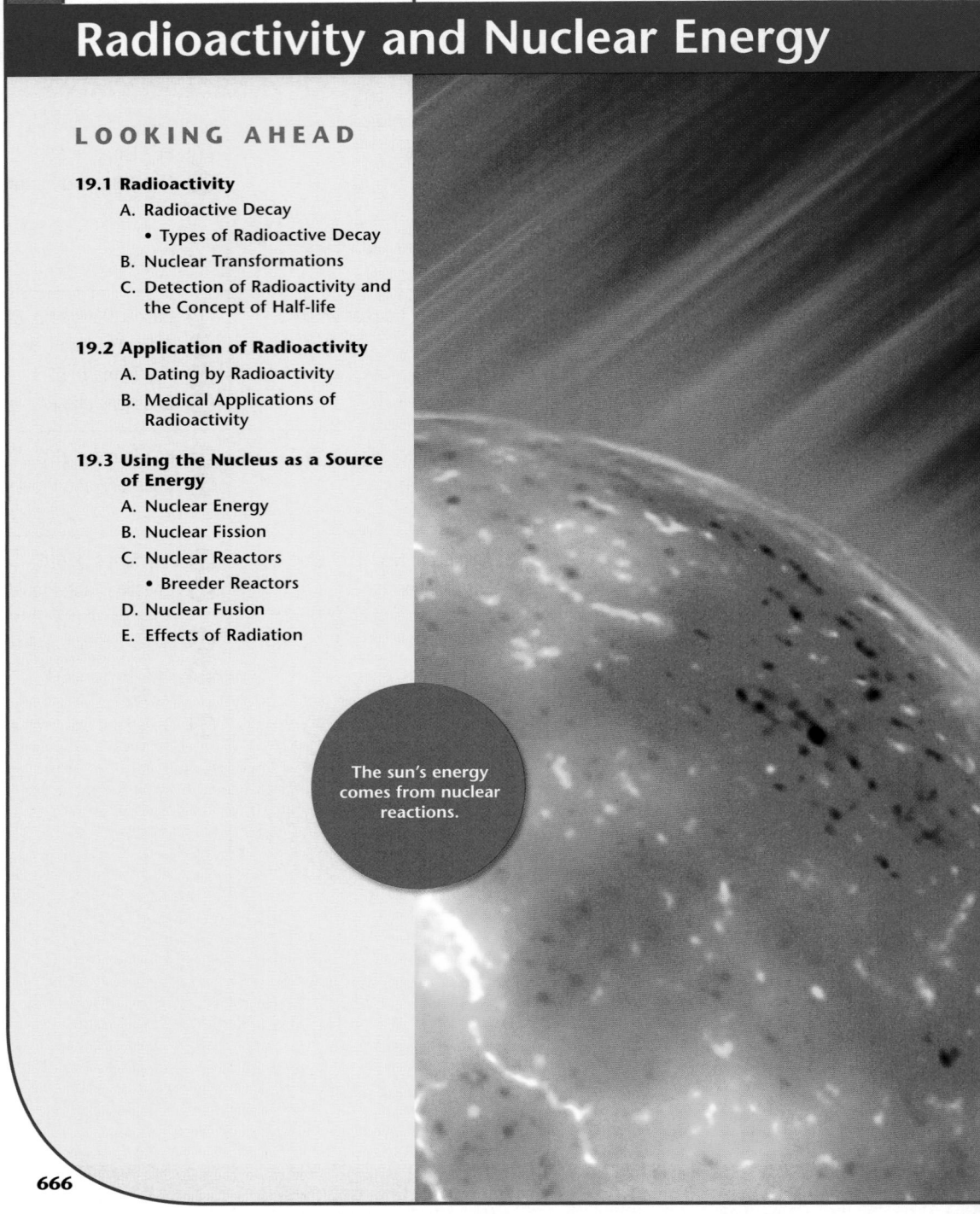

Chapter 19
Radioactivity and Nuclear Energy

LOOKING AHEAD

The sun's energy comes from nuclear reactions.

666

IN YOUR LIFE

Although the electrons are the part of the atom that mostly determines its chemical properties, the nucleus is very important in all of our lives. The high energy radiation produced by radioactive nuclides can be very harmful to us, but it is also used in many types of medical tests. Called radiotracers, certain radioactive nuclides are introduced into the body to analyze biological functions and to provide images of organs such as the thyroid and the heart.

The nucleus is also a very important, though controversial, source of energy in our society. For example, France uses nuclear energy as a source for about 80% of its electrical power. In the United States nuclear energy produces over 20% of our electrical power. Although the production of energy in nuclear reactors has some safety issues, nuclear energy production is likely to become more important in the future because it does not result in the release of "greenhouse gases" such as carbon dioxide.

Nuclear processes are also important to geologists and archeologists who use radioactivity to find the age of rocks and other artifacts.

Wooden artifacts from Easter Island can be dated by carbon-14 analysis.

WHAT DO YOU KNOW?

Prereading Questions

1. What is meant by the term *atomic number*? What is meant by the term *mass number*?

2. What are isotopes?

3. What comes to mind when you hear the term *radioactive*?

4. Have you heard of carbon dating? What do you know about it?

Radioactivity and Nuclear Energy • Chapter 19 • **667**

Prereading Questions

1. An atomic number represents the number of protons in the nucleus of an atom. A mass number is the number of protons and neutrons in the nucleus of an atom.

2. Isotopes are atoms of the same element that have different numbers of neutrons.

3. *Answers will vary.* An atom is radioactive if it spontaneously decomposes to form a different atom.

4. *Answers will vary.* Carbon dating is a technique used to determine the age of artifacts made of wood or cloth.

TECHNOLOGY IN THE CLASSROOM

 Transparencies
Figures: 19.1, 19.4

 Power Presentation DVD
PowerPoint Slides
Animations
  Nuclear Particles
  Geiger Counter
  Half-life of Reactions
  Half-life of Nuclear
    Decay
  Nuclear Fission
  Nuclear Fusion
eEdition
EasyPlanner

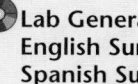 **Lab Generator CD**
English Summaries CD
Spanish Summaries CD
ML Test Generator

 classzone.com

Student Preparation

Assign students to read Section 19.1 and to answer the Review Questions at the end of the section before coming to class.

 Active Learning
Team Learning Worksheet

After introducing the material in Section 19.1 in class, place students in groups and have them work together on **Section 19.1: Team Learning Worksheet.**

Homework

You may wish to assign these selected end-of-chapter problems as homework for this section:
1, 2, 4, 6, 7, 8, 12a–b, 13, 14a–b, 15a–b, 17, 19, 20, 21, 25

Additional end-of-chapter problems can be used for extra practice.

19.1.A Radioactive Decay

Objective To learn the types of radioactive decay and learn to write nuclear equations that describe radioactive decay

LABORATORY
EXPERIMENT 84:
Investigating Radioactivity, CBL

Key Terms

- Nucleons (protons and neutrons)
- Atomic number (*Z*)
- Mass number (*A*)
- Isotopes
- Nuclide
- Radioactive
- Beta particle
- Nuclear equation
- Alpha particle
- Alpha-particle production
- Beta-particle production
- Gamma ray
- Positron
- Positron production
- Electron capture
- Decay series
- Nuclear transformation
- Transuranium elements
- Geiger–Müller counter
- Scintillation counter
- Half-life

Objectives

- *To learn the types of radioactive decay*
- *To learn to write nuclear equations for radioactive decay*
- *To learn how one element may be changed to another by particle bombardment*
- *To learn about radiation detection instruments*
- *To understand half-life*

Several facts about the nucleus are immediately impressive: its very small size, its very large density, and the energy that holds it together. The radius of a typical nucleus is about 10^{-13} cm, only a hundred-thousandth the radius of a typical atom. In fact, if the nucleus of the hydrogen atom were the size of a ping-pong ball, the electron in the 1*s* orbital would be, on the average, 0.5 km (0.3 mile) away. The density of the nucleus is equally impressive; it is approximately 1.6×10^{14} g/cm^3. A sphere of nuclear material the size of a ping-pong ball would have a mass of 2.5 *billion tons!* Finally, the energies involved in nuclear processes are typically millions of times larger than those associated with normal chemical reactions, a fact that makes nuclear processes potentially attractive for generating energy.

The nucleus is believed to be made of particles called **nucleons (neutrons** and **protons**). Recall from Chapter 3 that the number of protons in a nucleus is called the **atomic number (*Z*)** and that the sum of the numbers of neutrons and protons is the **mass number (*A*)**. Atoms that have identical atomic numbers but different mass numbers are called **isotopes.** The general term **nuclide** is applied to each unique atom, and we represent it as follows:

where X represents the symbol for a particular element. For example, the following nuclides constitute the common isotopes of carbon: carbon-12, $^{12}_{6}$C; carbon-13, $^{13}_{6}$C; and carbon-14, $^{14}_{6}$C. Notice that all of the carbon nuclides have six protons ($Z = 6$) and that they have six, seven, and eight neutrons, respectively.

A. Radioactive Decay

Many nuclei are **radioactive**; that is, they spontaneously decompose, forming a different nucleus and producing one or more particles. An example is carbon-14, which decays as shown in the equation

$$^{14}_{6}\text{C} \rightarrow {}^{14}_{7}\text{N} + {}^{0}_{-1}\text{e}$$

where $^{0}_{-1}$e represents an electron, which in nuclear terminology is called a **beta particle**, or **β particle**. This **nuclear equation**, which is typical of those representing radioactive decay, is quite different from the chemical equations we have written before. Recall that in a balanced chemical equation the atoms must be conserved.

---

information

The atomic number (*Z*) represents the number of protons in a nucleus; the mass number (*A*) represents the sum of the numbers of protons and neutrons in a nucleus.

DID YOU KNOW

Over 85% of all known nuclides are radioactive.

In a nuclear equation both the atomic number (*Z*) and the mass number (*A*) must be conserved.

That is, the sums of the *Z* values on both sides of the arrow must be equal, and the same restriction applies to the *A* values. For example, in the equation on the previous page, the sum of the *Z* values is 6 on both sides of the arrow (6 and 7 − 1), and the sum of the *A* values is 14 on both sides of the arrow (14 and 14 + 0). Notice that the mass number for the β particle is zero; the mass of the electron is so small that it can be neglected here. Of the approximately 2000 known nuclides, only 279 do not undergo radioactive decay. Tin has the largest number of nonradioactive isotopes—ten.

 Active Reading Question

What is the difference between a chemical equation and a nuclear equation?

Types of Radioactive Decay

There are several different types of radioactive decay. One frequently observed decay process involves production of an **alpha (α) particle**, which is a helium nucleus ($^4_2$He). **Alpha-particle production** is a very common mode of decay for heavy radioactive nuclides. For example, $^{222}_{88}$Ra, radium-222, decays by α-particle production to give radon-218.

$$^{222}_{88}\text{Ra} \rightarrow {}^4_2\text{He} + {}^{218}_{86}\text{Rn}$$

Notice in this equation that the mass number is conserved (222 = 4 + 218) and the atomic number is conserved (88 = 2 + 86). Another α-particle producer is $^{230}_{90}$Th:

$$^{230}_{90}\text{Th} \rightarrow {}^4_2\text{He} + {}^{226}_{88}\text{Ra}$$

Notice that the production of an α particle results in a loss of 4 in mass number (*A*) and a loss of 2 in atomic number (*Z*).

Beta-particle production is another common decay process. For example, the thorium-234 nuclide produces a β particle as it changes to protactinium-234.

$$^{234}_{90}\text{Th} \rightarrow {}^{234}_{91}\text{Pa} + {}^{\ \ 0}_{-1}\text{e}$$

Iodine-131 is also a β-particle producer.

$$^{131}_{53}\text{I} \rightarrow {}^{\ \ 0}_{-1}\text{e} + {}^{131}_{54}\text{Xe}$$

Recall that the β particle is assigned mass number 0, because its mass is tiny compared to that of a proton or neutron. The value of *Z* is −1 for the β particle, so the atomic number for the new nuclide is greater by 1 than the atomic number for the original nuclide. Therefore, *the net effect of β-particle production is to change a neutron to a proton.*

Production of a β particle results in no change in mass number (*A*), and an increase of 1 in atomic number (*Z*).

Alpha particle (α particle)
A helium nucleus produced in radioactive decay

Alpha-particle production
A common mode of decay for heavy radioactive nuclides resulting in a loss of 4 in mass number and a loss of 2 in atomic number

Beta-particle production
A decay process for radioactive nuclides in which the mass number does not change and the atomic number increases by 1

 information

α-particle production

$\Delta A = -4$
$\Delta Z = -2$

 information

Notice that both *Z* and *A* balance in each of these nuclear equations.

 information

β-particle production

$\Delta A = 0$
$\Delta Z = +1$

 TEACHING TIPS

- Balancing nuclear equations provides an excellent opportunity to review balancing by atoms and by charge and to review the meanings of the mass number and atomic number in element notation.

- Students should be aware that in a nuclear decay, the product is a different element. Therefore we cannot balance the equation by balancing the atoms.

- Remind students that when forming ions, the number of electrons changes but the number of protons (and therefore the type of atom) remains the same. In nuclear equations, if the number of protons changes, the atom's identity also changes.

 Active Reading Question

In a chemical equation, atoms must be conserved. In a nuclear equation, atomic number and mass number must be conserved.

TECHNOLOGY

Animation
Nuclear Particles

Active Reading Question

positron production, electron capture, and α-particle production

The $_0^0\gamma$ notation indicates $Z = 0$ and $A = 0$ for a γ ray. A gamma ray is often simply indicated by γ.

Positron production

$\Delta A = 0$
$\Delta Z = -1$

Gamma ray (γ ray)
A high-energy photon produced in radioactive decay

Positron
A particle with the same mass as an electron but opposite in charge

A **gamma ray**, or **γ ray**, is a high-energy photon of light. A nuclide in an excited nuclear energy state can release excess energy by producing a gamma ray, and γ-ray production often accompanies nuclear decays of various types. For example, in the α-particle decay of $_{92}^{238}$U,

$$_{92}^{238}\text{U} \rightarrow {}_2^4\text{He} + {}_{90}^{234}\text{Th} + 2{}_0^0\gamma$$

two γ rays of different energies are produced in addition to the α particle ($_2^4$He). Gamma rays are photons of light and so have zero charge and zero mass number.

Production of a γ ray results in no change in mass number (*A*), and no change in atomic number (*Z*).

The **positron** is a particle with the same mass as the electron but opposite charge. An example of a nuclide that decays by **positron production** is sodium-22.

$$_{11}^{22}\text{Na} \rightarrow {}_1^0\text{e} + {}_{10}^{22}\text{Ne}$$

Note that the production of a positron has the effect of changing a proton to a neutron.

Production of a positron results in no change in mass number (*A*), and a decrease of 1 in atomic number (*Z*).

Electron capture is a process in which one of the inner-orbital electrons is captured by the nucleus, as illustrated by the process

$$_{80}^{201}\text{Hg} + {}_{-1}^0\text{e} \rightarrow {}_{79}^{201}\text{Au} + {}_0^0\gamma$$
$$\uparrow$$
$$\text{Inner-orbital electron}$$

This reaction would have been of great interest to the alchemists, but unfortunately it does not occur often enough to make it a practical means of changing mercury to gold. Gamma rays are always produced along with electron capture.

Active Reading Question

For which radioactive processes does the reactant have a greater atomic number than the product?

Bone scintigraph of a patient's cranium following administration of the radiopharmaceutical technetium-99

Table 19.1 lists the common types of radioactive decay, with examples.

Table 19.1	
Various Types of Radioactive Processes	
Process	**Example**
β-particle (electron) production	$^{227}_{89}\text{Ac} \rightarrow ^{227}_{90}\text{Th} + ^{0}_{-1}\text{e}$
positron production	$^{13}_{7}\text{N} \rightarrow ^{13}_{6}\text{C} + ^{0}_{1}\text{e}$
electron capture	$^{73}_{33}\text{As} + ^{0}_{-1}\text{e} \rightarrow ^{73}_{32}\text{Ge}$
α-particle production	$^{210}_{84}\text{Po} \rightarrow ^{206}_{82}\text{Pb} + ^{4}_{2}\text{He}$
γ-ray production	excited nucleus → ground-state nucleus + $^{0}_{0}\gamma$
	excess energy lower energy

Often a radioactive nucleus cannot achieve a stable (nonradioactive) state through a single decay process. In such a case, a **decay series** occurs until a stable nuclide is formed. A well-known example is the decay series that starts with $^{238}_{92}\text{U}$ and ends with $^{206}_{82}\text{Pb}$, as shown in **Figure 19.1**. Similar series exist for $^{235}_{92}\text{U}$:

$$^{235}_{92}\text{U} \xrightarrow[\text{decays}]{\text{Series of}} ^{207}_{82}\text{Pb}$$

and for $^{232}_{90}\text{Th}$:

$$^{232}_{90}\text{Th} \xrightarrow[\text{decays}]{\text{Series of}} ^{208}_{82}\text{Pb}$$

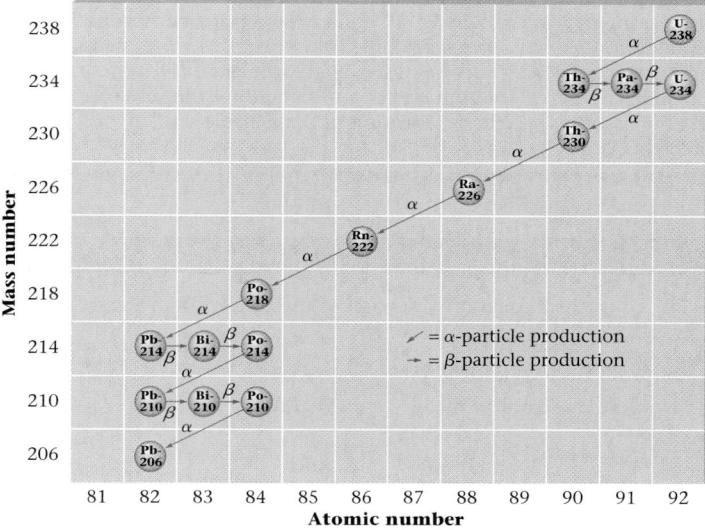

Figure 19.1
The decay series from $^{238}_{92}\text{U}$ to $^{206}_{82}\text{Pb}$. Each nuclide in the series except $^{206}_{82}\text{Pb}$ is radioactive, and the successive transformations (shown by the arrows) continue until $^{238}_{82}\text{Pb}$ is finally formed. The horizontal red arrows indicate β-particle production (Z increases by 1 and A is unchanged). The diagonal blue arrows signify α-particle production (both A and Z decrease).

19.1 • Radioactivity • **671**

EXAMPLE 19.1

More Examples

Write balanced nuclear equations for each of the following processes.

1. $^{116}_{47}\text{Ag}$ produces a beta particle.

$$^{116}_{47}\text{Ag} \rightarrow {}^{0}_{-1}\text{e} + {}^{116}_{48}\text{Cd}$$

2. $^{211}_{83}\text{Bi}$ produces an alpha particle.

$$^{211}_{83}\text{Bi} \rightarrow {}^{4}_{2}\text{He} + {}^{207}_{81}\text{Tl}$$

CHEMISTRY EXPLORERS
Marie Curie • 1867–1934

Marie Sklodowska Curie, one of the truly monumental figures of modern science, was born in Warsaw, Poland, on November 7, 1867.

Marie emigrated to Paris in 1891 at the age of 24, where she decided to pursue a degree in science at the Sorbonne Institute. While studying there, Marie met Pierre Curie, a well-respected physicist, and they were married in 1895, after which Marie decided to pursue a doctorate in physics. As the subject of her doctoral thesis, she studied the strange radiation emitted by uranium ore, which had been accidentally discovered by Henri Becquerel. In her studies, Madame Curie noticed that pitchblende produced more radiation than uranium, and she became convinced that an as-yet-unknown element in pitchblende was responsible for this "radioactivity"—a term that she coined.

The next step was to identify and isolate the radioactive element or elements in pitchblende. Pierre interrupted his own research—he thought it would be for just a few weeks—to collaborate with his wife on the project.

They convinced the Austrian government to send them one ton of pitchblende from the mines at Joachimsthal. After receiving this 5-cubic-foot pile of "sand" from Austria, the Curies worked to chemically digest the ore. In this process they worked with batches as large as 40 pounds in an improvised laboratory with a leaky roof. Working through the bitter winter of 1896 and all through 1897 (in which they had their first daughter, Iréne, who also became a prominent scientist), in July 1898 the Curies finally isolated a previously unknown element they named polonium after Marie's homeland. Although most people would be satisfied by discovering a new element 400 times more radioactive than uranium, the Curies kept working. By this time, the one ton of pitchblende had been concentrated to an amount that would fit into an ordinary flask. Marie continued to extract and crystallize increasingly smaller amounts of material. Finally, in November 1898 she obtained crystals of the salt of another new element that the Curies named radium, which turned out to be 900 times more radioactive than uranium.

For their work the Curies were awarded the Nobel Prize in Physics in 1903, sharing the award with Henri Becquerel.

In 1911, Marie was awarded her second Nobel Prize—this time in chemistry, for the chemical processes discovered in the identification of radium and polonium and for the subsequent characterization of these elements.

EXAMPLE 19.1

Writing Nuclear Equations, I

Write balanced nuclear equations for each of the following processes.

a. $^{11}_{6}\text{C}$ produces a positron.

b. $^{214}_{83}\text{Bi}$ produces a β particle.

c. $^{237}_{93}\text{Np}$ produces an α particle.

Solution

a. We must find the product nuclide represented by $^{A}_{Z}\text{X}$ in the following equation:

$$^{11}_{6}\text{C} \rightarrow \underset{\underset{\text{Positron}}{\uparrow}}{^{0}_{1}\text{e}} + {}^{A}_{Z}\text{X}$$

CHEMISTRY EXPLORERS
Marie Curie

Soon after its discovery, radium was used to treat malignant tumors. Curie helped to persuade the French government and the Pasteur Foundation to fund the Radium Institute to use radioactivity for medical purposes. When Germany invaded France, almost all of Curie's staff enlisted in the war effort. Curie took the initiative to help soldiers. She prepared tiny glass tubes containing the radioactive radon gas. Doctors inserted the tubes into soldiers in areas of the body where the radiation would destroy diseased tissue.

The key to solving this problem is to recognize that both A and Z must be conserved. That is, we can find the identity of $_Z^A X$ by recognizing that the sums of the Z and the A values must be the same on both sides of the equation. Thus for X, Z must be 5 because $Z + 1 = 6$. A must be 11 because $11 + 0 = 11$. Therefore, $_Z^A X$ is $_5^{11}B$. (The fact that Z is 5 tells us that the nuclide is boron. See the periodic table on the inside back cover of the book.) So the balanced equation is $_6^{11}C \rightarrow _1^0 e + _5^{11}B$.

Check: **Left Side**   **Right Side**

$$Z = 6 \qquad Z = 5 + 1 = 6$$
$$\rightarrow$$
$$A = 11 \qquad A = 11 + 0 = 11$$

b. Knowing that a β particle is represented by $_{-1}^0 e$, we can write

$$_{83}^{214}Bi \rightarrow _{-1}^0 e + _Z^A X$$

where $Z - 1 = 83$ and $A + 0 = 214$. This means $Z = 84$ and $A = 214$.

We can now write

$$_{83}^{214}Bi \rightarrow _{-1}^0 e + _{84}^{214}X$$

Using the periodic table, we find that $Z = 84$ for the element polonium, so $_{84}^{214}X$ must be $_{84}^{214}Po$.

Check: **Left Side**   **Right Side**

$$Z = 83 \qquad Z = 84 - 1 = 83$$
$$\rightarrow$$
$$A = 214 \qquad A = 214 + 0 = 214$$

c. Because an α particle is represented by $_2^4 He$, we can write

$$_{93}^{237}Np \rightarrow _2^4 He + _Z^A X$$

where $A + 4 = 237$ or $A = 237 - 4 = 233$, and $Z + 2 = 93$ or $Z = 93 - 2 = 91$. Thus $A = 233$, $Z = 91$, and the balanced equation must be

$$_{93}^{237}Np \rightarrow _2^4 He + _{91}^{233}Pa$$

Check: **Left Side**   **Right Side**

$$Z = 93 \qquad Z = 91 + 2 = 93$$
$$\rightarrow$$
$$A = 237 \qquad A = 133 + 4 = 237$$

✔ Practice Problem • Exercise 19.1

The decay series for $_{92}^{238}U$ is represented in Figure 19.1. Write the balanced nuclear equation for each of the following radioactive decays.

  a. Alpha-particle production by $_{88}^{226}Ra$

  b. Beta-particle production by $_{82}^{214}Pb$

✔ Answer to Practice Problem 19.1

a. An alpha particle is a helium nucleus, $_2^4 He$. We can initially represent the production of an α particle by $_{88}^{226}Ra$ as follows:
$$_{88}^{226}Ra \rightarrow _2^4 He + _Z^A X$$

Because we know that both A and Z are conserved, we can write

$A + 4 = 226$ and

$Z + 2 = 88$

Solving for A gives 222 and for Z gives 86, so $_Z^A X$ is $_{86}^{222}X$. Because Rn has $Z = 86$, $_Z^A X$ is $_{86}^{222}Rn$. The overall balanced equation is
$$_{88}^{226}Ra \rightarrow _2^4 He + _{86}^{226}Rn$$
Check: $Z = 88 \rightarrow$
$$Z = 86 + 2 = 88$$

$A = 226 \rightarrow$
$$A = 222 + 4 = 226$$

b. Using a similar strategy, we have
$$_{82}^{214}Pb \rightarrow _{-1}^0 e + _Z^A X$$

Because $Z - 1 = 82$, $Z = 83$, and because $A + 0 = 214$, $A = 214$. Therefore, $_Z^A X = _{83}^{214}Bi$. The balanced equation is

$$_{82}^{214}Pb \rightarrow _{-1}^0 e + _{83}^{214}Bi$$

Check: $Z = 82 \rightarrow$
$$Z = 83 - 1 = 82$$

$A = 214 \rightarrow$
$$A = 214 + 0 = 214$$

EXAMPLE 19.2

More Examples

In each of the following nuclear reactions, supply the missing particle.

1. $^{210}_{89}\text{Ac} \rightarrow {}^{4}_{2}\text{He} + ?$
   $^{206}_{87}\text{Fr}$

2. $^{131}_{53}\text{I} \rightarrow {}^{131}_{54}\text{Xe} + ?$
   $^{0}_{-1}\text{e}$

3. $^{88}_{35}\text{Br} \rightarrow {}^{87}_{35}\text{Br} + ?$
   $^{1}_{0}\text{n}$

Answer to Practice Problem 19.2

a. The missing particle must be $^{4}_{2}\text{He}$ (an α particle), because
$$^{226}_{86}\text{Rn} \rightarrow {}^{218}_{84}\text{Po} + {}^{4}_{2}\text{He}$$
is a balanced equation.

Check: $Z = 86 \rightarrow$
$Z = 84 + 2 = 86$

$A = 222 \rightarrow$
$A = 218 + 4 = 222$

b. The missing species must be $^{15}_{7}\text{X}$ or $^{15}_{7}\text{N}$, because the balanced equation is
$$^{15}_{8}\text{O} \rightarrow {}^{15}_{7}\text{N} + {}^{0}_{1}\text{e}$$

Check: $Z = 8 \rightarrow$
$Z = 7 + 1 = 8$

$A = 15 \rightarrow$
$A = 15 + 0 = 15$

19.1.B Nuclear Transformations

Objective To learn how one element may be changed into another by particle bombardment

 TEACHING TIPS

- Nuclear transformations are balanced in the same way as nuclear decay reactions.

- Radioisotopes are found in many household devices. Some examples are starters for fluorescent lamps and appliances (promethium-147, krypton-85, and thorium-232), antistatic devices (polonium-210), and smoke detectors (americium-241).

EXAMPLE 19.2

Writing Nuclear Equations, II

In each of the following nuclear reactions, supply the missing particle.

a. $^{195}_{79}\text{Au} + ? \rightarrow {}^{195}_{78}\text{Pt}$
b. $^{38}_{19}\text{K} \rightarrow {}^{38}_{18}\text{Ar} + ?$

Solution

a. A does not change and Z for Pt is 1 lower than Z for Au, so the missing particle must be an electron.
$$^{195}_{79}\text{Au} + {}^{0}_{-1}\text{e} \rightarrow {}^{195}_{78}\text{Pt}$$

Check: **Left Side** **Right Side**
$Z = 79 - 1 = 78$ $Z = 78$
$\rightarrow$
$A = 195 + 0 = 195$ $A = 195$

This is an example of electron capture.

b. For Z and A to be conserved, the missing particle must be a positron.
$$^{38}_{19}\text{K} \rightarrow {}^{38}_{18}\text{Ar} + {}^{0}_{1}\text{e}$$

Check: **Left Side** **Right Side**
$Z = 19$ $Z = 18 + 1 = 19$
$\rightarrow$
$A = 38$ $A = 38 + 0 = 38$

Potassium-38 decays by positron production.

Practice Problem • Exercise 19.2

Supply the missing species in each of the following nuclear equations.

a. $^{222}_{86}\text{Rn} \rightarrow {}^{218}_{84}\text{Po} + ?$ b. $^{15}_{8}\text{O} \rightarrow ? + {}^{0}_{1}\text{e}$

B. Nuclear Transformations

Nuclear transformation
The change of one element into another

In 1919 Lord Rutherford observed the first **nuclear transformation**, *the change of one element into another*. He found that bombarding $^{14}_{7}\text{N}$ with α particles produced the nuclide $^{17}_{8}\text{O}$,
$$^{14}_{7}\text{N} + {}^{4}_{2}\text{He} \rightarrow {}^{17}_{8}\text{O} + {}^{1}_{1}\text{H}$$

with a proton ($^{1}_{1}\text{H}$) as another product. Fourteen years later, Irene Curie and her husband Frederick Joliot observed a similar transformation from aluminum to phosphorus:
$$^{27}_{13}\text{Al} + {}^{4}_{2}\text{He} \rightarrow {}^{30}_{15}\text{P} + {}^{1}_{0}\text{n}$$

where $^{1}_{0}\text{n}$ represents a neutron that is produced in the process.

Notice that in both of these cases the bombarding particle is a helium nucleus (an α particle). Other small nuclei, such as $^{12}_{6}C$ and $^{15}_{7}N$, can also be used to bombard heavier nuclei and cause transformations. However, because these positive bombarding ions are repelled by the positive charge of the target nucleus, the bombarding particle must be moving at a very high speed to penetrate the target. These high speeds are achieved in various types of *particle accelerators*.

Neutrons are also employed as bombarding particles to effect nuclear transformations. However, because neutrons are uncharged (and thus not repelled by a target nucleus), they are readily absorbed by many nuclei, producing new nuclides. The most common source of neutrons for this purpose is a fission reactor (see Section 19.3).

By using neutron and positive-ion bombardment, scientists have been able to extend the periodic table—that is, to produce chemical elements that are not present naturally. Prior to 1940, the heaviest known element was uranium ($Z = 92$), but in 1940, neptunium ($Z = 93$) was produced by neutron bombardment of $^{238}_{92}U$. The process initially gives $^{239}_{92}U$, which decays to $^{239}_{93}Np$ by β-particle production

$$^{238}_{92}U + ^{1}_{0}n \rightarrow ^{239}_{92}U \rightarrow ^{239}_{93}Np + ^{0}_{-1}e$$

Irene Curie and Frederick Joliot

In the years since 1940, the elements with atomic numbers 93 through 112, called the **transuranium elements**, have been synthesized. **Table 19.2** gives some examples of these processes.

Table 19.2

Syntheses of Some of the Transuranium Elements

Neutron Bombardment	neptunium ($Z = 93$)	$^{238}_{92}U + ^{1}_{0}n \rightarrow ^{239}_{92}U \rightarrow ^{239}_{93}Np + ^{0}_{-1}e$
	americium ($Z = 95$)	$^{239}_{94}Pu + 2\,^{1}_{0}n \rightarrow ^{241}_{94}Pu \rightarrow ^{241}_{95}Am + ^{0}_{-1}e$
Positive-Ion Bombardment	curium ($Z = 96$)	$^{239}_{94}Pu + ^{4}_{2}He \rightarrow ^{242}_{96}Cm + ^{1}_{0}n$
	californium ($Z = 98$)	$^{242}_{96}Cm + ^{4}_{2}He \rightarrow ^{245}_{98}Cf + ^{1}_{0}n$ or
		$^{238}_{92}U + ^{12}_{6}C \rightarrow ^{246}_{98}Cf + 4\,^{1}_{0}n$
	rutherfordium ($Z = 104$)	$^{249}_{98}Cf + ^{12}_{6}C \rightarrow ^{257}_{104}Rf + 4\,^{1}_{0}n$
	dubnium ($Z = 105$)	$^{249}_{98}Cf + ^{15}_{7}N \rightarrow ^{260}_{105}Db + 4\,^{1}_{0}n$
	seaborgium ($Z = 106$)	$^{249}_{98}Cf + ^{18}_{8}O \rightarrow ^{263}_{106}Sg + 4\,^{1}_{0}n$

19.1 • Radioactivity • **675**

Objective To learn about radiation detection instruments and understand half-life

 LABORATORY

EXPERIMENT 85:
Half-life of Pennies, Traditional

 TEACHING TIPS

- The Half-life of Pennies Laboratory will allow students to get a better understanding of the concept of half-life.

- This section offers an excellent opportunity to connect with the math program. Ask students to find a function in math that operates in the same way as half-life.

MISCONCEPTION
Chemistry

Students have difficulty with the concept of half-life. They often believe that after two half-lives, all of the material should be decayed because $2 \times \frac{1}{2} = 1$. You may want to relate the story of the tortoise that always travels half the distance to the finish line in each minute. How long will it take for the turtle to reach the finish line?

 Active Reading Question

The probe of the Geiger counter contains argon gas. When high speed particles from nuclear decay collide with argon atoms, electrons come off the atoms. A sample of argon ions and electrons will allow a current to flow. The Geiger counter detects this current.

TECHNOLOGY

 Animations
Geiger Counter
Half-life of Reactions
Half-life of Nuclear Decay

Geiger–Müller counter (Geiger counter)
An instrument that measures the rate of radioactive decay by registering the ions and electrons produced as a radioactive particle passes through a gas-filled chamber

DID YOU KNOW

Geiger counters are commonly called survey meters.

Figure 19.2
A schematic representation of a Geiger–Müller counter. The high-speed particle knocks electrons off argon atoms to form ions,
$$Ar \xrightarrow{Particle} Ar^+ + e^-$$
and a pulse of current flows.

Scintillation counter
An instrument that measures the rate of radioactive decay by sensing flashes of light that the radiation produces in a detector

Half-life
The time required for half of the original sample of radioactive nuclides to decay

MINI-DEMO

If you have access to a Geiger counter, bring it to class for demonstration. A typical mantle from a gas camping lantern or a piece of orange Fiesta dinnerware pottery can be used as a source of radioactive material.

C. Detection of Radioactivity and the Concept of Half-life

The most familiar instrument for measuring radioactivity levels is the **Geiger–Müller counter**, or **Geiger counter** (see **Figure 19.2**). High-energy particles from radioactive decay produce ions when they travel through matter. The probe of the Geiger counter contains argon gas. The argon atoms have no charge, but they can be ionized by a rapidly moving particle.

$$Ar(g) \xrightarrow[\text{particle}]{\text{High-energy}} Ar^+(g) + e^-$$

That is, the fast-moving particle "knocks" electrons off some of the argon atoms. Although a sample of uncharged argon atoms does not conduct a current, the ions and electrons formed by the high-energy particle allow a current to flow momentarily, so a "pulse" of current flows every time a particle enters the probe. The Geiger counter detects each pulse of current, and these events are counted.

Active Reading Question

How does a Geiger counter work?

Speaker gives "click" for each particle

Window

Particle path

Argon atoms

A **scintillation counter** is another instrument often employed to detect radioactivity. This device uses a substance, such as sodium iodide, that gives off light when it is struck by a high-energy particle. A detector senses the flashes of light and counts the decay events.

Half-Life One important characteristic of a given type of radioactive nuclide is its half-life. The **half-life** is the *time required for half of the original sample of nuclei to decay*. For example, if a certain radioactive sample contains 1000 nuclei at a given time and 500 nuclei (half of the original number) 7.5 days later, this radioactive nuclide has a half-life of 7.5 days.

A given type of radioactive nuclide always has the same half-life. However, the various radioactive nuclides have half-lives that cover a tremendous range. For example, $^{234}_{91}Pa$, protactinium-234, has a half-life of 1.2 minutes, and $^{238}_{92}U$, uranium-238, has a half-life of 4.5×10^9 (4.5 billion) years. This means that a sample containing 100 million $^{234}_{91}Pa$ nuclei will have only 50 million $^{234}_{91}Pa$ nuclei in it (half of 100 million) after 1.2 minutes have passed. In another

1.2 minutes, the number of nuclei will decrease to half of 50 million, or 25 million nuclei.

$$100 \text{ million } ^{234}_{91}\text{Pa} \xrightarrow[\text{minutes}]{1.2} 50 \text{ million } ^{234}_{91}\text{Pa} \xrightarrow[\text{minutes}]{1.2} 25 \text{ million } ^{234}_{91}\text{Pa}$$
(50 million decays)   (25 million decays)

This means that a sample of $^{234}_{91}\text{Pa}$ with 100 million nuclei will show 50 million decay events (50 million $^{234}_{91}\text{Pa}$ nuclei will decay) over a time of 1.2 minutes. By contrast, a sample containing 100 million $^{238}_{92}\text{U}$ nuclei will undergo 50 million decay events over 4.5 billion years. Therefore, $^{234}_{91}\text{Pa}$ shows much greater activity than $^{238}_{92}\text{U}$. We sometimes say that $^{234}_{91}\text{Pa}$ is "hotter" than $^{238}_{92}\text{U}$.

Thus, at a given moment, a radioactive nucleus with a short half-life is much more likely to decay than one with a long half-life.

EXAMPLE 19.3

Understanding Half-life

Table 19.3 lists various radioactive nuclides of radium.

   a. Order these nuclides in terms of activity (from most to least decays per day).

   b. How long will it take for a sample containing 1.00 mol of $^{223}_{88}\text{Ra}$ to reach a point where it contains only 0.25 mol of $^{223}_{88}\text{Ra}$?

Solution

   a. The shortest half-life indicates the greatest activity (the most decays over a given period of time). Therefore, the order is

Most activity   Least activity
(shortest half-life)   (longest half-life)

$$^{224}_{88}\text{Ra} > \; ^{223}_{88}\text{Ra} > \; ^{225}_{88}\text{Ra} > \; ^{228}_{88}\text{Ra} > \; ^{226}_{88}\text{Ra}$$
3.6 days   12 days   15 days   6.7 years   1600 years

   b. In one half-life (12 days), the sample will decay from 1.00 mol of $^{223}_{88}\text{Ra}$ to 0.50 mol of $^{223}_{88}\text{Ra}$. In the next half-life (another 12 days), it will decay from 0.50 mol of $^{223}_{88}\text{Ra}$ to 0.25 mol of $^{223}_{88}\text{Ra}$.

$$1.00 \text{ mol } ^{223}_{88}\text{Ra} \xRightarrow{\text{12 days}} 0.50 \text{ mol } ^{223}_{88}\text{Ra} \xRightarrow{\text{12 days}} 0.25 \text{ mol } ^{223}_{88}\text{Ra}$$

Therefore, it will take 24 days (two half-lives) for the sample to change from 1.00 mol of $^{223}_{88}\text{Ra}$ to 0.25 mol of $^{223}_{88}\text{Ra}$.

Table 19.3	
The Half-lives for Some of the Radioactive Nuclides of Radium	
Nuclide	**Half-life**
$^{223}_{88}\text{Ra}$	12 days
$^{224}_{88}\text{Ra}$	3.6 days
$^{225}_{88}\text{Ra}$	15 days
$^{226}_{88}\text{Ra}$	1600 years
$^{228}_{88}\text{Ra}$	6.7 years

✒ Practice Problem • Exercise 19.3

Watches with numerals that "glow in the dark" were formerly made by including radioactive radium in the paint used to letter the watch faces. Assume that to make the numeral 3 on a given watch, a sample of paint containing 8.0×10^{-7} mol of $^{228}_{88}\text{Ra}$ was used. This watch was then put in a drawer and forgotten. Many years later someone finds the watch and wishes to know when it was made. Analyzing the paint, this person finds 1.0×10^{-7} mol of $^{228}_{88}\text{Ra}$ in the numeral 3. How much time elapsed between the making of the watch and the finding of the watch?

Hint: Use the half-life of $^{228}_{88}\text{Ra}$ from Table 19.3.

A watch dial with radium paint

19.1 • Radioactivity • **677**

🍎 **TEACHING TIP**

Now is a good time to plot the amount of a radionuclide present versus time on the board to show students the progression of its decay over time. You can use data from Table 19.3 to do so.

EXAMPLE 19.3

More Examples

1. Gold-198, which has a half-life of 2.7 days, is used as an implant for cancer therapy. For an implant containing 50 µg of Au-198, approximately how much Au-198 remains after 1 week?

   Just over 6 µg. After 8.1 days, or 4 half-lives, 6.25 µg remains.

2. Krypton-76 has a half-life of 14.8 hr. About how long will it take to reach a point where a sample contains about 10% of its original Kr-76?

   About 2 days. After 3 half-lives (around 44 hours), approximately 12.5% of the Kr-76 will remain.

✒ Answer to Practice Problem 19.3

Let's do this problem by thinking about the number of half-lives required to go from 8.0×10^{-7} mol to 1.0×10^{-7} mol of $^{228}_{88}\text{Ra}$.

$$8.0 \times 10^{-7} \text{ mol} \rightarrow$$
First half-life

$$4.0 \times 10^{-7} \text{ mol} \rightarrow$$
Second half-life

$$2.0 \times 10^{-7} \text{ mol} \rightarrow$$
Third half-life

$$1.0 \times 10^{-7} \text{ mol}$$

It takes three half-lives, then, for the sample to go from 8.0×10^{-7} mol of $^{228}_{88}\text{Ra}$ to 1.0×10^{-7} mol of $^{228}_{88}\text{Ra}$. From Table 19.3, we know that the half-life of $^{228}_{88}\text{Ra}$ is 6.7 years. Therefore, the elapsed time is $3(6.7 \text{ years}) = 20.1$ years, or 2.0×10^{1} years when we use the correct number of significant figures.

SECTION 19.1
Review Questions

1. Mass and charge must be conserved when balancing nuclear equations. In other chemistry equations, atoms and charge are conserved.

2. a. Mass number decreases by 4; atomic number decreases by 2.

   b. Mass number stays the same; atomic number increases by 1.

   c. Mass number stays the same; atomic number decreases by 1.

   d. Mass number stays the same; atomic number decreases by 1.

3. a. $^{28}_{13}\text{Al} \rightarrow ^{0}_{-1}\text{e} + ^{28}_{14}\text{Si}$

   b. $^{56}_{24}\text{Cr} \rightarrow ^{0}_{-1}\text{e} + ^{56}_{25}\text{Mn}$

   c. $^{72}_{30}\text{Zn} \rightarrow ^{0}_{-1}\text{e} + ^{72}_{31}\text{Ga}$

4. In nuclear decay, one particle emits smaller particles and becomes another element. In nuclear transformations, an element is bombarded with a particle and is transformed into another element.

5. At the end of the first half-life, one-half of the original sample remains. At the end of the second half-life, half of this sample still remains. This is one-half of the half of the original sample, or one-fourth of the original sample.

6. about 1.5% (1/64 × 100% = 1.56%)

CHEMISTRY EXPLORERS
Darleane Hoffman • 1926–

Darleane Hoffman was born on November 8, 1926, in Terril, Iowa. She began her college career at Iowa State College (now University) as an art major. She decided to switch her major from art to chemistry in part because of the influence of her first chemistry professor, also a woman.

Dr. Hoffman worked at Los Alamos National Laboratory for 31 years where she was part of the team that discovered plutonium-244 in nature, discovered element 100 (fermium), and confirmed the discovery of element 106 (which is named seaborgium after Hoffman's colleague Glenn Seaborg). She was awarded the prestigious Priestly Medal by the American Chemical Society in March 2000, the highest honor of the society, and is the only woman to receive the ACS Award for Nuclear Chemistry.

SECTION 19.1
REVIEW QUESTIONS

① When balancing a nuclear equation, what two quantities must be conserved? How is this different from balancing other chemistry equations?

② Determine the net result to mass number and atomic number for each of the following processes.

   a. alpha-particle production

   b. beta-particle production

   c. electron capture

   d. positron production

③ Complete each of the following nuclear equations by supplying the missing particle.

   a. $^{23}_{13}\text{Al} \rightarrow ? + ^{28}_{14}\text{Si}$

   b. $^{56}_{24}\text{Cr} \rightarrow ^{0}_{-1}\text{e} + ?$

   c. $^{72}_{30}\text{Zn} \rightarrow ^{0}_{-1}\text{e} + ?$

④ What is the difference between nuclear decay and nuclear transformation reactions?

⑤ Explain why one fourth of a given radioactive sample still remains at the end of two half-lives.

⑥ The half-life of radium-255 is 15 days. Approximately what percentage of radium-255 is left after 3 months?

RESEARCH LINKS
CLASSZONE.COM

678 • Chapter 19 • Radioactivity and Nuclear Energy

CHEMISTRY EXPLORERS
Darleane Hoffman

Like her colleague Glenn Seaborg, Hoffman has been honored with the National Medal of Science (the U.S. equivalent to the Nobel Prize). Hoffman led the development of a technique called "one-atom-at-a-time" chemistry. In this process, chemical properties of short-lived elements are studied by measuring the rate of radioactive decay of individual atoms, combining the results, and comparing these properties to other known elements.

Application of Radioactivity

Objectives

- *To learn how objects can be dated by radioactivity*
- *To understand the use of radiotracers in medicine*

Key Terms

- Radiocarbon dating (Carbon-14 dating)
- Radiotracers

A. Dating by Radioactivity

Archaeologists, geologists, and others involved in reconstructing the ancient history of the earth rely heavily on the half-lives of radioactive nuclei to provide accurate dates for artifacts and rocks. A method for dating ancient articles made from wood or cloth is **radiocarbon dating**, or **carbon-14 dating**, a technique originated in the 1940s by Willard Libby, an American chemist who received the Nobel Prize for his efforts.

Radiocarbon dating is based on the radioactivity of $^{14}_{6}C$, which decays by β-particle production.

$$^{14}_{6}C \rightarrow {^{0}_{-1}e} + {^{14}_{7}N}$$

Carbon-14 is continuously produced in the atmosphere when high-energy neutrons from space collide with nitrogen-14.

$$^{14}_{7}N + {^{1}_{0}n} \rightarrow {^{14}_{6}C} + {^{1}_{1}H}$$

Just as carbon-14 is continuously produced by this process, it continuously decomposes through β-particle production. Over the years, these two opposing processes have come into balance, causing the amount of $^{14}_{6}C$ present in the atmosphere to remain approximately constant.

Carbon-14 can be used to date wood and cloth artifacts because the $^{14}_{6}C$, along with the other carbon isotopes in the atmosphere, reacts with oxygen to form carbon dioxide. A living plant consumes this carbon dioxide in the photosynthesis process and incorporates the carbon, including $^{14}_{6}C$, into its molecules. As long as the plant lives, the $^{14}_{6}C$ content in its molecules remains the same as in the atmosphere because of the plant's continuous uptake of carbon. However, as soon as a tree is cut to make a wooden bowl or a flax plant is harvested to make linen, it stops taking in carbon. There is no longer a source of $^{14}_{6}C$ to replace that lost to radioactive decay, so the material's $^{14}_{6}C$ content begins to decrease.

Because the half-life of $^{14}_{6}C$ is known to be 5730 years, a wooden bowl found in an archaeological dig that shows a $^{14}_{6}C$ content of half that found in currently living trees is approximately 5730 years old. That is, because half of the $^{14}_{6}C$ present when the tree was cut has disappeared, the tree must have been cut one half-life of $^{14}_{6}C$ ago.

Active Reading Question

What must we assume about the atmospheric content of carbon-14 when using carbon dating?

> **Radiocarbon dating (carbon-14 dating)**
> A method for dating ancient wood or cloth on the basis of the radioactive decay of the carbon-14 nuclide

Brigham Young researcher Scott Woodward takes a bone sample for carbon-14 dating at an archeological site in Egypt.

TEACHING TIP

The useful properties of radiotracers depend on their half-lives. Have students compare the half-lives of radiotracers with carbon-14.

CHEMISTRY IN YOUR WORLD

Science, Technology, and Society

Dating Diamonds

While connoisseurs of gems value the clearest possible diamonds, geologists learn the most from impure diamonds. Diamonds are formed in the earth's crust at depths of about 200 kilometers, where the high pressures and temperatures favor the most dense form of carbon. As the diamond is formed, impurities are sometimes trapped and these can be used to determine the diamond's date of "birth." One valuable dating impurity is $^{238}_{92}U$, which is radioactive and decays in a series of steps to $^{206}_{82}Pb$, which is stable (nonradioactive). Because the rate at which $^{238}_{92}U$ decays is known, determining how much $^{238}_{92}U$ has been converted to $^{206}_{82}Pb$ tells scientists the amount of time that has elapsed since the $^{238}_{92}U$ was trapped in the diamond as it was formed.

Using these dating techniques, Peter D. Kinney of Curtin University of Technology in Perth, Australia, and Henry O. A. Meyer of Purdue University in West Lafayette, Indiana, have recently identified the youngest diamond ever found. Discovered in Mbuji Mayi, Zaire, the diamond is 628 million years old,

far younger than all previously dated diamonds, which range from 2.4 to 3.2 billion years old.

The great age of all previously dated diamonds had caused some geologists to speculate that all diamond formation occurred billions of years ago. However, this "youngster" suggests that diamonds have formed throughout geologic time and are probably being formed right now in the earth's crust. These diamonds won't be seen for a long time, because diamonds typically remain deeply buried in the earth's crust for millions of years until they are brought to the surface by volcanic blasts called kimberlite eruptions.

It's good to know that eons from now there will be plenty of diamonds to mark the engagements of future couples.

The Hope Diamond

B. Medical Applications of Radioactivity

Although we owe the rapid advances of the medical sciences in recent decades to many causes, one of the most important has been the discovery and use of **radiotracers**—radioactive nuclides that can be introduced into organisms in food or drugs and subsequently *traced* by monitoring their radioactivity. For example, the incorporation of nuclides such as $^{14}_{6}C$ and $^{32}_{15}P$ into nutrients has yielded important information about how these nutrients are used to provide energy for the body.

Radiotracer
A radioactive nuclide introduced into an organism and traced (followed) for diagnostic purposes

Chemistry in Your World

Dating Diamonds

New techniques for distinguishing diamonds have recently been developed by the major diamond traders to maintain their control over the price and quality of diamonds. Students can use the Internet to investigate how this identification is made and learn more about the chemistry involved.

Iodine-131 has proved very useful in the diagnosis and treatment of illnesses of the thyroid gland. Patients drink a solution containing a small amount of NaI that includes ^{131}I, and the uptake of the iodine by the thyroid gland is monitored with a scanner **(Figure 19.3)**.

DID YOU KNOW

Nuclides used as radiotracers have short half-lives so that they disappear rapidly from the body.

Figure 19.3
After consumption of Na^{131}I, the patient's thyroid is scanned for radioactivity levels to determine the efficiency of iodine absorption. (a) Scan of radioactive iodine in a normal thyroid (b) Scan of an enlarged thyroid

Thallium-201 can be used to assess the damage to the heart muscle in a person who has suffered a heart attack, because thallium becomes concentrated in healthy muscle tissue. Technetium-99, which is also taken up by normal heart tissue, is used for damage assessment in a similar way.

Radiotracers provide sensitive and nonsurgical methods for learning about biological systems, for detecting disease, and for monitoring the action and effectiveness of drugs. Some useful radiotracers are listed in **Table 19.4**.

Table 19.4

Some Radioactive Nuclides, Their Half-lives, and Their Medical Applications as Radiotracers*

Nuclide	Half-Life	Area of the Body Studied
^{131}I	8.1 days	thyroid
^{59}Fe	45.1 days	red blood cells
^{99}Mo	67 hours	metabolism
^{32}P	14.3 days	eyes, liver, tumors
^{51}Cr	27.8 days	red blood cells
^{87}Sr	2.8 hours	bones
^{99}Tc	6.0 hours	heart, bones, liver, lungs
^{133}Xe	5.3 days	lungs
^{24}Na	14.8 hours	circulatory system
*Z is sometimes not written when listing nuclides.		

19.2 • Application of Radioactivity • **681**

TEACHING TIP

Students can be assigned projects in which they learn more about the applications in Table 19.4. They can create oral reports to share their information with the class.

Meeting Individual Needs

CHALLENGE PROJECTS

For a project that requires students to research outside sources, see *Medical Treatment by Radioisotopes* located in the *Teacher Resources*.

Active Reading Question

Generally, the half-lives of
radiotracers are much shorter
than the half-lives of some
of the radioactive nuclides
of radium.

SECTION 19.2
ASSESS

SECTION 19.2
Review Questions

1. Radiocarbon dating is based
on the fact that carbon-14
is a radioactive isotope of
carbon. It is produced in the
atmosphere from nitrogen
and also decomposes to form
nitrogen. We assume then,
that the amount of carbon-14
present in the atmosphere is
constant. A tree incorporates
both carbon-12 and carbon-14
into its molecules. When the
tree is cut down to make a
wood artifact, for example,
the carbon-14 decomposes
but is not replaced. By
comparing the amount of
carbon-14 in the artifact
with the carbon-14 in the
atmosphere (and knowing
the half-life of carbon-14)
we can date the object.

2. Carbon dating is used to date
objects that come from a
once-living organic source.
Once the object dies, the
resource for carbon-14 is no
longer available, and the
carbon-14 content begins to
decrease. In diamonds, the
source for carbon is not living
tissue, so they cannot be
dated using the carbon-14
method. Instead, the decay
of the uranium tells us when
the diamond was formed.

3. Tracers have a much shorter
half-life than carbon-14.
When using a radioactive
substance in medicine, the
most common goal is to
have the substance become
inactive and "safe" within a
short time.

Active Reading Question

In general, how do the half-lives of radiotracers compare to the half-
lives of some of the radioactive nuclides of radium?

SECTION 19.2
REVIEW QUESTIONS

❶ Explain the basic ideas of radiocarbon dating
in your own words.

❷ Diamonds are made of carbon. In "Chemistry
In Your World: Dating Diamonds," however, it
is stated that uranium and not carbon is used
to determine when a diamond was formed.
Why don't scientists use carbon dating to
determine this date?

❸ How do half-lives of tracers compare to the
half-life of carbon-14? Why would these
nuclides be a better choice for medical
applications than carbon-14?

❹ Use the graph to answer the following
questions.

a. Which radiotracer has the shortest
half-life?

b. Which radiotracer has a half-life equal to
the sum of the half-lives of Xe-133 and
Mo-99?

c. If we started with equal amounts of each
radiotracer, which would be present in the
least amount after 15 days? Explain your
answer.

d. If we started with equal amounts of each
radiotracer, which would be present in the
greatest amount after 15 days? Explain
your answer.

Half-lives of Some Radiotracers

(Bar graph: Half-life (days) on y-axis from 0 to 16; radiotracers I-131, Mo-99, P-32, Xe-133 on x-axis. I-131 ≈ 8, Mo-99 ≈ 2.5, P-32 ≈ 14, Xe-133 ≈ 5.)

 RESEARCH LINKS
CLASSZONE.COM

682 • Chapter 19 • Radioactivity and Nuclear Energy

4. a. Mo-99

b. I-131

c. Mo-99, because it has
the shortest half-life. The
half-life is about 2.5 days,
so after 15 days there
would be about 1.5% left.

d. P-32, because it has the
longest half-life. The half-
life is about 14 days, so
after 15 days there would
be just over 50% left.

Using the Nucleus as a Source of Energy

Objectives

- *To introduce fusion and fission as sources of energy*
- *To learn about nuclear fission*
- *To understand how a nuclear reactor works*
- *To learn about nuclear fusion*
- *To see how radiation damages human tissue*

Key Terms

- Fusion
- Fission
- Chain reaction
- Critical mass
- Breeder reactors

A. Nuclear Energy

The protons and the neutrons in atomic nuclei are bound together with forces that are much greater than the forces that bind atoms together to form molecules. In fact, the energies associated with nuclear processes are more than a million times those associated with chemical reactions. This potentially makes the nucleus a very attractive source of energy.

Because medium-sized nuclei contain the strongest binding forces ($_{26}^{56}$Fe has the strongest binding forces of all), there are two types of nuclear processes that produce energy:
1. Combining two light nuclei to form a heavier nucleus. This process is called **fusion**.
2. Splitting a heavy nucleus into two nuclei with smaller mass numbers. This process is called **fission**.

As we will see, these two processes can supply amazing quantities of energy with relatively small masses of materials consumed.

B. Nuclear Fission

Nuclear fission was discovered in the late 1930s when $_{92}^{235}$U nuclides bombarded with neutrons were observed to split into two lighter elements.

$$_{0}^{1}n + _{92}^{235}U \rightarrow _{56}^{141}Ba + _{36}^{92}Kr + 3\,_{0}^{1}n$$

This process, shown below, releases 2.1×10^{13} joules of energy per mole of $_{92}^{235}$U. Compared with what we get from typical fuels, this is a huge amount of energy. For example, the fission of 1 mol of $_{92}^{235}$U produces about *26 million times* as much energy as the combustion of 1 mol of methane.

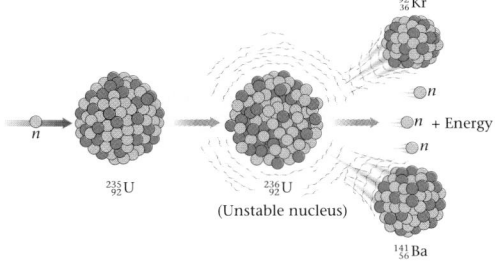

$_{0}^{1}n$
$_{92}^{235}U$
$_{92}^{236}U$
(Unstable nucleus)
$_{56}^{141}Ba$
$_{36}^{92}Kr$
n
n + Energy
n

Fusion
The process of combining two light nuclei to form a heavier, more stable nucleus

Fission
The process of splitting a heavy nucleus into two more stable nuclei with smaller mass numbers

 CRITICAL THINKING

Nuclear fission processes can provide useful energy but can also be dangerous.

What if Congress decided to outlaw all processes that involve fission? How would it change our society?

The critical mass is the minimal amount of fissionable material required to allow a chain reaction to occur.

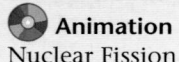
Upon capturing a neutron, the $^{235}_{92}U$ nucleus undergoes fission to produce two lighter nuclides, more neutrons (typically three), and a large amount of energy.

The process shown on the previous page is only one of the many fission reactions that $^{235}_{92}U$ can undergo. In fact, over 200 different isotopes of 35 different elements have been observed among the fission products of $^{235}_{92}U$.

In addition to the product nuclides, neutrons are produced in the fission reactions of $^{235}_{92}U$. As these neutrons fly through the solid sample of uranium, they may collide with other $^{235}_{92}U$ nuclei, producing additional fission events. Each of these fission events produces more neutrons that can, in turn, produce the fission of more $^{235}_{92}U$ nuclei. Because each fission event produces neutrons, the process can be self-sustaining. We call it a **chain reaction**.

Chain reaction
A self-sustaining fission process caused by the production of neutrons that proceed to split other nuclei

Critical mass
The mass of fissionable material required to produce a chain reaction

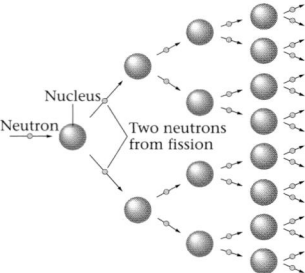

Nucleus

Neutron

Two neutrons from fission

For the fission process to be self-sustaining, at least one neutron from each fission event must go on to split another nucleus. If, on the average, *less than one* neutron causes another fission event, the process dies out. If *exactly one* neutron from each fission event causes another fission event, the process sustains itself at the same level and is said to be *critical*. If *more than one* neutron from each fission event causes another fission event, the process rapidly escalates and the heat build-up causes a violent explosion.

To achieve the critical state, a certain mass of fissionable material, called the **critical mass**, is needed. If the sample is too small, too many neutrons escape before they have a chance to cause a fission event, and the process stops.

 Active Reading Question

What is the relationship between *critical mass* and *chain reaction*?

During World War II, the United States carried out an intense research effort called the Manhattan Project to build a bomb based on the principles of nuclear fission. This program produced the fission bomb, which was used with devastating effect on the cities of Hiroshima and Nagasaki in 1945. Basically, a fission bomb operates by suddenly combining subcritical masses, which results in rapidly escalating fission events that produce an explosion of incredible intensity.

Top Ten Countries Producing Electricity by Nuclear Power (in order of total nuclear output)	
Country	Percentage of Country's Total Power Production
United States	21.9
France	77.4
Japan	34.0
Germany	30.3
Russia	13.1
Canada	16.0
Ukraine	43.8
United Kingdom	26.0
Sweden	52.4
South Korea	35.8

19

19.3.C Nuclear Reactors
Objective To understand how
a nuclear reactor works

C. Nuclear Reactors

Because of the tremendous energies involved, fission has been developed as an energy source to produce electricity in reactors where controlled fission can occur. The resulting energy is used to heat water to produce steam that runs turbine generators, in much the same way that a coal-burning power plant generates energy by heating water to produce steam. A schematic diagram of a nuclear power plant is shown in **Figure 19.4.**

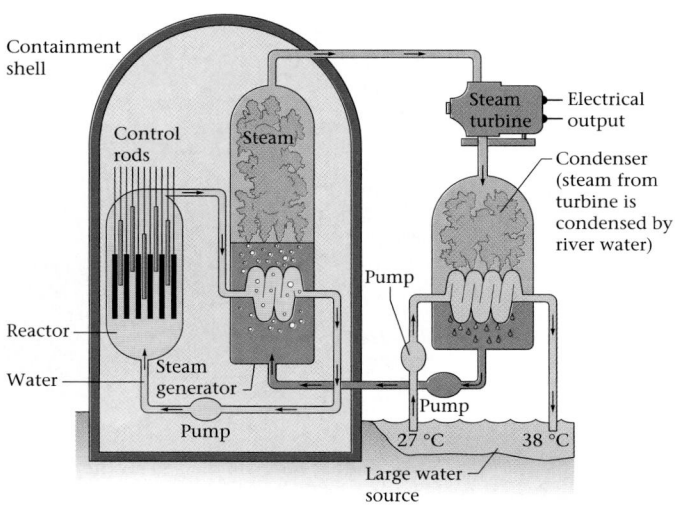

Figure 19.4
A schematic diagram of a nuclear power plant. The energy from the fission process is used to boil water, producing steam for use in a turbine-driven generator. Cooling water from a lake or river is used to condense the steam after it leaves the turbine.

In the reactor core (see **Figure 19.5**), uranium that has been enriched to approximately 3% $^{235}_{92}U$ (natural uranium contains only 0.7% $^{235}_{92}U$) is housed in metal cylinders. A *moderator* surrounding the cylinders slows down the neutrons so that the uranium fuel can capture them more efficiently. *Control rods*, composed of substances (such as cadmium) that absorb neutrons, are used to regulate the power level of the reactor. The reactor is designed so that if a malfunction occurs, the control rods are automatically inserted into the core to absorb neutrons and stop the reaction. A liquid (usually water) is circulated through the core to extract the heat generated by the energy of fission. This heat energy is then used to change water to steam, which runs turbines that in turn run electrical generators.

Figure 19.5
A schematic of the reactor core

19.3 • Using the Nucleus as a Source of Energy • **685**

Uranium was first discovered in 1789 as a component of pitchblende. Its name came from the planet Uranus, which had been discovered only shortly before. Uranium, which is not a rare element in the earth's crust (it is more abundant than tin), is widely scattered on earth. The most easily accessible deposits of uranium are found in the United States, Canada, South Africa, and Australia. Although uranium is used in small amounts as a coloring agent for glass and ceramics, its major use is as a nuclear fuel in fission reactors.

Uranium consists principally of $^{238}_{92}U$ mixed with smaller amounts of $^{235}_{92}U$. Both isotopes are radioactive, although ^{235}U decays more rapidly than ^{238}U by about a factor of six. The ^{235}U isotope splits into two smaller nuclei (fission) when it is bombarded by neutrons, which makes it useful for producing energy in nuclear reactions.

Because fission of ^{235}U requires carefully controlled conditions, scientists were shocked to find that a natural nuclear reactor existed millions of years ago in Oklo, Gabon. Apparently, conditions were just right in a uranium deposit at Oklo to allow natural fission to occur. Water that was trapped in clay mixed with the ore and acted as the moderator, slowing down the neutrons to promote efficient fission. As the "reactor" heated up, it apparently drove off some of the water. This loss caused the fission to slow down, thus preventing an explosion. As the area cooled down, the water returned, leading to an increase in fission again. This speeding up and slowing down of the natural reactor apparently occurred repeatedly over many years until conditions changed enough to cause the reactor to stop. It seems clear that nature invented the nuclear reactor millions of years before humans thought of the idea.

Uranium-238 kernels for use in a reactor

Although the concentration of $^{235}_{92}U$ in the fuel elements is not great enough to allow an explosion such as that which occurs in a fission bomb, a failure of the cooling system can lead to temperatures high enough to melt the reactor core. This means that the building housing the core must be designed to contain the core even in the event of such a "melt-down." A great deal of controversy now exists about the efficiency of the safety systems in nuclear power plants. Accidents such as the one at the Three Mile Island facility in Pennsylvania in 1979 and the one at Chernobyl in the Soviet Union in 1986 have led many people to question the wisdom of continuing to build fission-based power plants.

Breeder Reactors

Breeder reactor
A nuclear reactor in which fissionable fuel is produced while the reactor runs

One potential problem facing the nuclear power industry is the limited supply of $^{235}_{92}U$. Some scientists believe we have nearly depleted the uranium deposits that are rich enough in $^{235}_{92}U$ to make the production of fissionable fuel economically feasible. Because of this possibility, reactors have been developed in which fissionable fuel is actually produced while the reactor runs. In these **breeder reactors**, the major component of natural uranium, nonfissionable $^{238}_{92}U$, is changed to fissionable $^{239}_{94}Pu$. The reaction involves absorption of a neutron, followed by production of two β particles.

CELEBRITY CHEMICAL

Uranium (U)

Ores that contain uranium contain very small amounts. To obtain uranium in larger amounts, the uranium oxide must be milled first. Then, sulfuric acid is used to leach out the uranium. The result (after filtering and drying) is a coarse powder known as yellowcake. The oxidized uranium (U_3O_8) must be converted to UF_6 before being enriched. Uranium hexafluoride is ideal because it vaporizes easily.

$$_0^1n + _{92}^{238}U \rightarrow _{92}^{239}U$$
$$_{92}^{239}U \rightarrow _{93}^{239}Np + _{-1}^0e$$
$$_{93}^{239}Np \rightarrow _{94}^{239}Pu + _{-1}^0e$$

As the reactor runs and $_{92}^{235}U$ is split, some of the excess neutrons are absorbed by $_{92}^{238}U$ to produce $_{94}^{239}Pu$. The $_{94}^{239}Pu$ is then separated out and used to fuel another reactor. Such a reactor thus "breeds" nuclear fuel as it operates.

Although breeder reactors are now used in Europe, the United States is proceeding slowly with their development because much controversy surrounds their use. One problem involves the hazards that arise in handling plutonium, which is very toxic and flames on contact with air.

CHEMISTRY IN YOUR WORLD

Connection to Astronomy

Making Elements in Stars

How did all the matter around us originate? One scientific answer to this question is a theory called *stellar nucleosynthesis*—the formation of nuclei in stars.

Many scientists believe that our universe originated as a cloud of neutrons that became unstable and produced an immense explosion, giving this model its name: *the big bang theory.* The model postulates that after the initial explosion, neutrons decomposed into protons and electrons,

$$_0^1n \rightarrow _1^1H + _{-1}^0e$$

which eventually combined to form clouds of hydrogen. Over the eons, gravitational forces caused many of these hydrogen clouds to contract and heat up sufficiently to reach temperatures at which proton fusion began to occur, releasing large quantities of energy. When the tendency to expand in response to the heat from fusion and the tendency to contract in response to the forces of gravity are balanced, a stable young star such as our sun can form.

Eventually, when the star's supply of hydrogen is exhausted, the core of the star again contracts, with further heating, until it reaches temperatures at which fusion of helium nuclei can occur, leading to the formation of $_6^{12}C$ and $_8^{16}O$ nuclei. In turn, when the supply of helium nuclei runs out, further contraction and heating occur, until the fusion of heavier nuclei takes place. This process occurs

repeatedly, forming heavier and heavier nuclei, until iron nuclei are formed. Because the iron nucleus has the greatest binding forces of all, iron nuclei do not release excess energy when they fuse to form heavier nuclei. This means that there is no further fusion energy to sustain the star, and it cools to a small, dense *white dwarf.*

The evolution just described is characteristic of small and medium-sized stars. Much larger stars, however, become unstable at some time during their evolution and undergo a *supernova explosion.* In this explosion, nuclei with medium mass numbers are fused to produce heavy elements. Also in the explosion, light nuclei capture neutrons. These neutron-rich nuclei then produce β particles, increasing their atomic number with each β decay. This eventually leads to nuclei with large atomic numbers. In fact, almost all nuclei beyond iron are thought to originate in supernova explosions. The debris of such an explosion contains a wide variety of elements, and it is thought that this debris might eventually form a solar system such as our own.

A view of a portion of the Cygnus Loop supernova remnant taken by the Hubble Space Telescope

19.3 • Using the Nucleus as a Source of Energy • **687**

Chemistry in Your World

Making Elements in Stars

Use this Chemistry in Your World to connect with astronomy. Have students investigate the connections between chemistry and the formation of the stars and other celestial objects.

D. Nuclear Fusion

The process of combining two light nuclei—called **nuclear fusion**—produces even more energy per mole than does nuclear fission. In fact, stars produce their energy through nuclear fusion. Our sun, which presently consists of 73% hydrogen, 26% helium, and 1% other elements, gives off vast quantities of energy from the fusion of protons to form helium. One possible scheme for this process is

$$^1_1H + {}^1_1H \rightarrow {}^2_1H + {}^0_1e + \text{energy}$$

$$^1_1H + {}^2_1H \rightarrow {}^3_2He + \text{energy}$$

$$^3_2He + {}^3_2He \rightarrow {}^4_2He + 2\,{}^1_1H + \text{energy}$$

$$^3_2He + {}^1_1H \rightarrow {}^4_2He + {}^0_1e + \text{energy}$$

 nformation

^2_1H particles are called deuterons.

Intense efforts are under way to develop a feasible fusion process because of the ready availability of many light nuclides (deuterium, ^2_1H, in seawater, for example) that can serve as fuel in fusion reactors. However, initiating the fusion process is much more difficult than initiating fission. The forces that bind nucleons together to form a nucleus become effective only at *very small* distances (approximately 10^{-13} cm), so for two protons to bind together and thereby release energy, they must get very close together. But protons, because they are identically charged, repel each other. This suggests that to get two protons (or two deuterons) close enough to bind together (the strong nuclear binding force is *not* related to charge), they must be "shot" at each other at speeds high enough to overcome their repulsion from each other. The repulsive forces between two ^2_1H nuclei are so great that temperatures of about 40 million K are thought to be necessary. Only at these temperatures are the nuclei moving fast enough to overcome the repulsions.

Currently, scientists are studying two types of systems to produce the extremely high temperatures required: high-powered lasers and heating by electric currents. At present many technical problems remain to be solved, and it is not clear whether either method will prove useful.

Top Ten Elements in the Sun (by mass)
Hydrogen
Helium
Oxygen
Carbon
Iron
Neon
Nitrogen
Silicon
Magnesium
Sulfur

E. Effects of Radiation

Everyone knows that being hit by a train is a catastrophic event. The energy transferred in such a collision is very large. In fact, any source of energy is potentially harmful to organisms. Energy transferred to cells can break chemical bonds and cause malfunctioning of the cell systems. This fact is behind our present concern about maintaining the ozone layer in the earth's upper atmosphere, which screens out high-energy ultraviolet radiation arriving from the sun.

Radioactive elements, which are sources of high-energy particles, are also potentially hazardous. However, the effects are usually quite subtle, because even though high-energy particles are involved, the quantity of energy actually deposited in tissues *per decay event* is quite small. The resulting damage is no less real, but the effects may not be apparent for years.

A solar flare erupts from the surface of the sun.

CHEMISTRY IN YOUR WORLD

Science, Technology, and Society

Nuclear Waste Disposal

Our society does not have an impressive record for safe disposal of industrial wastes. We have polluted our water and air, and some land areas have become virtually uninhabitable because of the improper burial of chemical wastes. As a result, many people are wary about the radioactive wastes from nuclear reactors. The potential threats of cancer and genetic mutations make these materials especially frightening.

Because of its controversial nature, most of the nuclear waste generated over the past 50 years has been placed in temporary storage. However, in 1982 the U.S. Congress passed the Nuclear Waste Policy Act, which established a timetable for choosing and preparing sites for the deep underground disposal of radioactive materials.

The tentative disposal plan calls for incorporation of the spent nuclear fuel into blocks of glass that will be packed in corrosion-resistant metal containers and then buried in a deep, stable rock formation indicated by the rock layers in **Figure 19.6.**

There are indications that this method will isolate the waste until the radioactivity decays to safe levels. Some reassuring evidence comes from the natural fission "reactor" that was discovered at Oklo in Gabon, Africa (see "Celebrity Chemical: Uranium" on page 686). Spawned about 2 billion years ago when uranium in ore deposits there formed a critical mass, this "reactor" produced fission and fusion products for several thousand years. Although some of these products have migrated away from the site in the intervening 2 billion years, most have stayed in place.

In 1999 the Waste Isolation Pilot Plant (WIPP) in New Mexico began receiving nuclear waste. This facility employs tunnels carved into the salt beds of an ancient ocean. Once a repository room becomes full, the salt will collapse around the waste, encapsulating it forever.

Another waste depository, under Yucca Mountain in Nevada, is being contemplated. For nearly two decades, this area has been studied to determine its suitability for storage of high-level radioactive wastes. At present it looks to be a long time before this issue is settled.

Figure 19.6
A schematic diagram for the tentative plan for deep underground isolation of nuclear waste. The disposal system would consist of a waste package buried in tunnels like the one shown above.

Chemistry in Your World

Nuclear Waste Disposal

Have students investigate the waste products from nuclear reactors. How do we store our radioactive waste? How long will it be before the material is "safe"?

Radiation damage to organisms can be classified as somatic or genetic damage. *Somatic damage* is damage to the organism itself, resulting in sickness or death. The effects may appear almost immediately if a massive dose of radiation is received; for smaller doses, damage may appear years later, usually in the form of cancer. *Genetic damage* is damage to the genetic machinery of reproductive cells, creating problems that often afflict the offspring of the organism.

The Factors Determining Biological Effects of Radiation

1. *The energy of the radiation.* The higher the energy content of the radiation, the more damage it can cause.

2. *The penetrating ability of the radiation.* The particles and rays produced in radioactive processes vary in their ability to penetrate human tissue: γ rays are highly penetrating, β particles can penetrate approximately 1 cm, and α particles are stopped by the skin (see **Figure 19.7**).

3. *The ionizing ability of the radiation.* Because ions behave quite differently from neutral molecules, radiation that removes electrons from molecules in living tissues seriously disturbs their functions. The ionizing ability of radiation varies dramatically. For example, γ rays penetrate very deeply but cause only occasional ionization. On the other hand, α particles, although they are not very penetrating, are very effective at causing ionization and produce serious damage. Therefore, the ingestion of a producer of α particles, such as plutonium, is particularly damaging.

4. *The chemical properties of the radiation source.* When a radioactive nuclide is ingested, its capacity to cause damage depends on how long it remains in the body. For example, both $^{85}_{36}Kr$ and $^{90}_{38}Sr$ are β-particle producers. Because krypton, being a noble gas, is chemically inert, it passes through the body quickly and does not have much time to do damage. Strontium, on the other hand, is chemically similar to calcium. It can collect in bones, where it may cause leukemia and bone cancer.

Figure 19.7
Radioactive particles and rays vary greatly in penetrating power. Gamma rays are by far the most penetrating.

Rem
A unit of radiation dosage that accounts for both the energy of the dose and its effectiveness in causing biological damage

Because of the differences in the behavior of the particles and rays produced by radioactive decay, we have invented a unit called the **rem** that indicates the danger the radiation poses to humans.

Table 19.5 shows the physical effects of short-term exposure to various doses of radiation, and **Table 19.6** gives the sources and amounts of the radiation to which a typical person in the United States is exposed each year. Note that natural sources contribute about twice as much as human activities do to the total exposure. However, although the nuclear industry contributes only a small percentage of the total exposure, controversy surrounds nuclear power plants because of their *potential* for creating radiation hazards. These hazards arise mainly from two sources: accidents allowing the release of radioactive materials, and improper disposal of the radioactive products in spent fuel elements.

 Active Reading Question

What human activity typically exposes people to the greatest amount of radiation per year?

Table 19.5

Effects of Short-Term Exposures to Radiation

Dose (rem)	Clinical Effect
0–25	nondetectable
25–50	temporary decrease in white blood cell counts
100–200	strong decrease in white blood cell counts
500	death of half the exposed population within 30 days after exposure

Table 19.6

Typical Radiation Exposures for a Person Living in the United States (1 millirem = 10^{-3} rem)

Source	Exposure (millirems/year)
cosmic	50
from the earth	47
from building materials	3
in human tissues	21
inhalation of air	5
Total from natural sources	126
X-ray diagnosis	50
radiotherapy X rays, radioisotopes	10
internal diagnosis and therapy	1
nuclear power industry	0.2
luminous watch dials, TV tubes, industrial wastes	2
radioactive fallout	4
Total from human activities	97
Total	193 = 0.193 rems

SECTION 19.3
REVIEW QUESTIONS

❶ What is the difference between fission and fusion?

❷ If there is no danger of a nuclear power plant having a nuclear explosion (if the reaction got out of control), why do we need to build containment buildings for the core?

❸ Explain the role of *critical mass* for a chain reaction.

❹ How is a typical nuclear power plant in the United States different from a breeder reactor commonly used in Europe?

❺ Why is initiating fusion much more difficult than initiating fission?

❻ What are the factors that determine the biological effects of radiation?

RESEARCH LINKS
CLASSZONE.COM

19.3 • Using the Nucleus as a Source of Energy • **691**

 TEACHING TIPS

• Table 19.6 gives sources and amounts of radiation exposure for humans. This information can be used in a discussion of the natural sources of radioactivity and exposure to radioactivity expected in our lives.

• The use of nuclear imaging techniques is a good starting point for a discussion about the hazards and benefits of nuclear medicine.

SECTION 19.3
ASSESS

 SECTION 19.3
Review Questions

1. Fission is the splitting of an atom into lighter atoms. Fusion is the formation of a heavier nucleus from smaller nuclei.

2. The containment buildings are designed to hold the radioactive material and prevent it from leaking into the environment.

3. For a chain reaction to occur, there must be a minimal amount of fissionable material present to sustain the reaction. This is the critical mass.

4. U.S. power plants do not make fuel in the course of the reaction. Breeder reactors make fuel that can then be used in the reactor.

5. To initiate fusion, two protons most be very close together. However, protons are positively charged and therefore repel each other. The energy required to get the protons together is very great.

6. The factors determining the effects of radiation are the energy of the radiation, its penetrating ability, its ionizing ability, and the chemical properties of the radiation source.

Chapter 19 Review

Key Terms

19.1 Nucleons (protons and neutrons)

Atomic number (Z)

Mass number (A)

Isotopes

Nuclide

Radioactive

Beta particle

Nuclear equation

Alpha particle

Alpha-particle production

Beta-particle production

Gamma ray

Positron

Positron production

Electron capture

Decay series

Nuclear transformation

Transuranium elements

Geiger–Müller counter

Scintillation counter

Half-life

19.2 Radiocarbon dating (Carbon-14 dating)

Radiotracers

Key Ideas

19.1 Radioactivity

- Radioactivity is the spontaneous decomposition of a nucleus to form another nucleus.

  - Atomic number (Z) and atomic mass number (A) are both conserved in a radioactive decay.

$$\text{Mass number} \downarrow$$
$$^{A}_{Z}X \leftarrow \text{Element symbol}$$
$$\uparrow$$
$$\text{Atomic number}$$

  - Types of radioactive decay
    - ◆ Alpha (α) particle production
    - ◆ Beta (β) particle production
    - ◆ Gamma (γ) ray production
    - ◆ Electron capture
    - ◆ Positron (β⁺) production
  - Often a series of decays occurs until a stable nucleus is formed.
  - Radioactivity is detected by instruments such as the Geiger–Müller counter.
  - Half-life for a radioactive nucleus is the time required for half of the sample to decay.
- Nuclear transformations change one atom into another by particle bombardment.

19.2 Application of Radioactivity

- Radiocarbon or carbon-14 dating—objects containing carbon can be dated by measuring their $^{14}_{6}C$ content.
- Radiotracers are radioactive nuclides that can be introduced into an organism and traced by observing their radioactive decay.

RESEARCH LINKS
CLASSZONE.COM

Meeting Individual Needs
CHAPTER REVIEW

Chapter 19 Review Worksheet at the appropriate level:
  Basic
  Standard
  Challenge

CHAPTER SUMMARY

A **Chapter Summary** that includes additional Active Reading Questions for Chapter 19 is available.

Assessment Resources
CHAPTER 19

Chapter 19 Test

TECHNOLOGY

 Computerized Test Bank for Chapter 19

19.3 Using the Nucleus as a Source of Energy

■ Energy can be obtained from the nucleus in two ways.

  • Fusion is the combining of two light nuclei to form a heavier nucleus.

  • Fission is the splitting of a heavy nucleus into two lighter nuclei.

    ◆ Current nuclear reactors use fission to produce electrical energy.

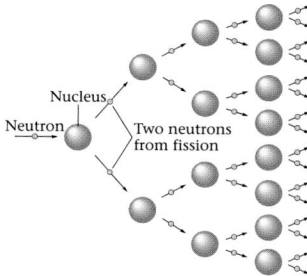

■ Nuclear radiation can cause damage.

  • Somatic—damage to an organism

  • Genetic—damage to an organism's offspring

  • Biological effects of radiation depend on the following:

    ◆ Its energy

    ◆ Its penetrating ability

    ◆ The chemical properties of the source

RESEARCH LINKS
CLASSZONE.COM

Chapter 19 • Review • **693**

Chapter 19 Assessment

1. The nucleus of an atom has little or no effect on the atom's chemical properties. The chemical properties are determined by the number and arrangement of the electrons (which are outside the nucleus).

2. The radius of a typical atomic nucleus is on the order of 10^{-13} cm, or roughly 100,000 times smaller than the overall radius of the atom.

3. The atomic number (Z) represents the number of protons in the nucleus. The mass number (A) represents the total number of protons and neutrons in the nucleus. For example, for $^{13}_{6}C$, with six protons and seven neutrons, we have $Z = 6$ and $A = 13$.

4. Isotopes are atoms of the same element that differ in the number of neutrons present in the nuclei. Since the isotopes are atoms of the same element, they have the same number of protons, and thus the same atomic number. Since the number of neutrons differs, isotopes of the same element have different mass numbers.

5. The atomic number (Z) is written as a left subscript; the mass number (A) is written as a left superscript. The general symbol for a nuclide is $^{A}_{Z}X$. As an example, the isotope of oxygen with 8 neutrons would be $^{16}_{8}O$.

6. When a nucleus produces an alpha particle, the atomic number of the parent nucleus decreases by two units.

7. When a nucleus produces a beta particle, the atomic number of the parent nucleus increases by one unit.

8. Gamma rays are high-energy photons of electromagnetic radiation; they are not normally considered to be particles. When a nucleus produces only gamma radiation, the atomic number and mass number are the same.

All exercises with blue numbers have answers in the back of this book.

19.1 Radioactivity

A. Radioactive Decay

1. Does the nucleus of an atom have much of an effect on the atom's chemical properties? Explain.

2. How large is a typical atomic nucleus, and how does the size of the nucleus of an atom compare with the overall size of the atom?

3. What do the *atomic number* and the *mass number* of a nucleus represent? Use a specific element as an example to illustrate your answer.

4. What are *isotopes*? Do the isotopes of an element have the same atomic number? Do they have the same mass number? Explain.

5. Using Z to represent the atomic number and A to represent the mass number, give the general symbol for a nuclide of element X. Give also a specific example of the use of such symbolism.

6. When an unstable nucleus produces an alpha particle, by how many units does the atomic number of the nucleus change? Does the atomic number increase or decrease?

7. When an unstable nucleus produces a beta particle, by how many units does the atomic number of the nucleus change? Does the atomic number increase or decrease?

8. What does a *gamma ray* represent? Is a gamma ray a particle? Is there a change in mass or atomic number when a nucleus produces only a gamma ray?

9. What is a *positron*? What are the mass number and charge of a positron? How do the mass number and atomic number of a nucleus change when the nucleus produces a positron?

10. What do we mean when we say a nucleus has undergone an *electron capture* process? What type of electron is captured by the nucleus in this process?

11. Naturally occurring magnesium consists primarily of three isotopes, of mass numbers 24, 25, and 26. How many protons does each of these nuclides contain? How many neutrons does each of these nuclides contain? Write nuclear symbols for each of these isotopes.

---

12. Complete each of the following nuclear equations by supplying the missing particle.

a. $^{196}_{85}At \rightarrow {}^{4}_{2}He + ?$

b. $^{208}_{84}Po \rightarrow {}^{4}_{2}He + ?$

c. $^{210}_{86}Rn \rightarrow {}^{4}_{2}He + ?$

13. Complete each of the following nuclear equations by supplying the missing particle.

a. $^{201}_{80}Hg + ? \rightarrow {}^{201}_{79}Au$

b. $^{210}_{82}Pb \rightarrow {}^{210}_{83}Bi + ?$

c. $? \rightarrow {}^{210}_{84}Po + {}^{0}_{-1}e$

14. Write a balanced nuclear equation for the decay of each of the following nuclides to produce a beta particle.

a. $^{136}_{53}I$

b. $^{133}_{51}Sb$

c. $^{117}_{49}In$

15. Write a balanced nuclear equation for the decay of each of the following nuclides to produce an alpha particle.

a. $^{226}_{88}Ra$ c. $^{239}_{94}Pu$

b. $^{222}_{86}Rn$ d. $^{8}_{4}Be$

B. Nuclear Transformations

16. What does a *nuclear transformation* represent? How is a nuclear transformation performed?

17. Why are particle accelerators needed for bombardment processes?

18. What are the elements with atomic numbers greater than 92 called? How have these elements been prepared?

19. Write a balanced nuclear equation for the bombardment of $^{27}_{13}Al$ with alpha particles to produce $^{30}_{15}P$ and a neutron.

C. Detection of Radioactivity and the Concept of Half-life

20. Describe the operation of a Geiger counter. How does a Geiger counter detect radioactive particles? How does a scintillation counter differ from a Geiger counter?

Speaker gives "click" for each particle

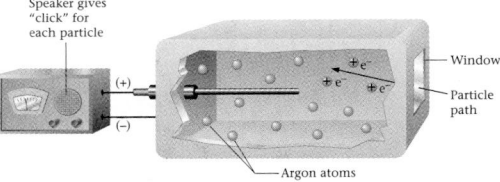

Window — Particle path — Argon atoms

---

9. A positron is a particle with the same mass as an electron, but with the opposite charge (a positive charge). The mass number of a positron is zero. When an unstable nucleus produces a positron, the mass number of the original nucleus is unchanged, but the atomic number decreases by 1.

10. Electron capture occurs when one of the inner orbital electrons is pulled into, and becomes part of, the nucleus.

11. Each contains 12 protons. Magnesium-24 contains 12 neutrons, magnesium-25 contains 13 neutrons, and magnesium-26 contains 14 neutrons.

12. (a) $^{192}_{83}Bi$; (b) $^{204}_{82}Pb$; (c) $^{206}_{84}Po$

13. (a) $^{0}_{-1}e$; (b) $^{0}_{-1}e$; (c) $^{210}_{83}Bi$

14. (a) $^{136}_{53}I \rightarrow {}^{0}_{-1}e + {}^{136}_{54}Xe$

(b) $^{133}_{51}Sb \rightarrow {}^{0}_{-1}e + {}^{133}_{52}Te$

(c) $^{117}_{49}In \rightarrow {}^{0}_{-1}e + {}^{117}_{50}Sn$

15. (a) $^{226}_{88}Ra \rightarrow {}^{222}_{86}Rn + {}^{4}_{2}He$

(b) $^{222}_{86}Rn \rightarrow {}^{218}_{84}Po + {}^{4}_{2}He$

(c) $^{239}_{94}Pu \rightarrow {}^{235}_{92}Pu + {}^{4}_{2}He$

(d) $^{8}_{4}Be \rightarrow {}^{4}_{2}He + {}^{4}_{2}He$

21. What is the *half-life* of a radioactive nucleus? Does a given type of nucleus always have the same half-life? Do nuclei of different elements have the same half-life?

22. What do we mean when we say that one radioactive nucleus is "hotter" than another? Which element would have more decay events over a given period of time?

23. The following isotopes (listed with their half-lives) have been used in the medical and biological sciences. Arrange these isotopes in order of their relative decay activities: ^3H (12.2 years), ^{24}Na (15 hours), ^{131}I (8 days), ^{60}Co (5.3 years), ^{14}C (5730 years).

24. A list of several important radioactive nuclides is given in Table 19.4. Arrange these nuclides in order of their relative decay activities.

25. For the first three isotopes of radium listed in Table 19.3, given a starting amount of 1000 mg, *estimate* the approximate amount of each isotope remaining after 1 month.

26. Technetium-99 has been used as a radiographic agent in bone scans ($^{99}_{43}Tc$ is absorbed by bones). If $^{99}_{43}Tc$ has a half-life of 6.0 hours, what fraction of an administered dose of 100 μg of $^{99}_{43}Tc$ remains in a patient's body after 2.0 days?

19.2 Applications of Radioactivity

A. Dating by Radioactivity

27. What nuclide is commonly used in the dating of artifacts?

28. How is $^{14}_{6}C$ produced in the atmosphere? Write a balanced equation for this process.

29. Why is it assumed that the amount of $^{14}_{6}C$ in the atmosphere remains constant?

30. Why does an ancient wood or cloth artifact contain less $^{14}_{6}C$ than contemporary or more recently fabricated articles made of similar materials?

B. Medical Applications of Radioactivity

31. What is a *radiotracer*? Which tracers have been used to study the conversion of nutrients into energy in living cells?

32. List four radioisotopes used in medical diagnosis or treatment, and give their nuclear symbols. Discuss why the isotopes you choose are particularly well suited to their uses.

19.3 Using the Nucleus as a Source of Energy

A. Nuclear Energy

33. How do the forces that hold an atomic nucleus together compare in strength with the forces between atoms in a molecule?

34. Define the terms *nuclear fission* and *nuclear fusion*. Which process results in the production of a heavier nucleus? Which results in the production of smaller nuclei?

B. Nuclear Fission

35. How do the energies released by nuclear processes compare in magnitude with the energies of ordinary chemical processes?

36. Write an equation for the fission of $^{235}_{92}U$ by bombardment with neutrons.

37. How is it possible for the fission of $^{235}_{92}U$, once started, to lead to a chain reaction?

38. What does it mean to say that fissionable material possesses a *critical mass*? Can a chain reaction occur when a sample has less than the critical mass?

C. Nuclear Reactors

39. Describe the purpose of each of the major components of a nuclear reactor (moderator, control rods, containment, cooling liquid, and so on).

40. Can a nuclear explosion take place in a reactor? Is the concentration of fissionable material used in reactors large enough for this?

41. What is a *melt-down* and how can it occur? Most nuclear reactors use water as the cooling liquid. Is there any danger of a steam explosion if the reactor core becomes overheated?

will be passed through the argon each time a high-energy particle strikes the argon gas probe (an ionization event). The Geiger counter detects each pulse of current, and these pulses are counted and displayed on the meter of the device. A scintillation counter uses a substance like sodium iodide, which emits light when struck by a high-energy particle from radioactive decay. A detector senses the flashes of light, which are counted and displayed on the meter of the device.

21. The half-life for a nucleus is the time required for one-half of the original sample of nuclei to decay. A given isotope of an element always has the same half-life. Different isotopes of the same element may have very different half-lives. Nuclei of different elements have different half-lives.

22. The "hot" nucleus undergoes more decay events per time period.

23. From highest to lowest activity: $^{24}Na > ^{131}I > ^{60}Co > ^3H > ^{14}C$

24. From highest to lowest activity: $^{87}Sr > ^{99}Tc > ^{24}Na > ^{99}Mo > ^{133}Xe > ^{131}I > ^{32}P > ^{51}Cr > ^{59}Fe$

25. For ^{223}Ra, approximately 125 mg (after 36 days or 3 half-lives); for ^{224}Ra, approximately 4 mg (after 29 days or 8 half-lives); for ^{225}Ra, approximately 250 mg (after 30 days, or 2 half-lives)

26. On a percentage basis, less than 0.4% of the original radioisotope remains.

27. Carbon-14 ($^{14}_{6}C$) is most commonly used.

28. Carbon-14 is produced in the upper atmosphere by the bombardment of nitrogen with neutrons from space:

$$^{14}_{7}N + ^1_0n \rightarrow ^{14}_{6}C + ^1_1H.$$

29. The quantity of $^{14}_{6}C$ in the atmosphere is assumed to remain constant because a balance exists between its production (from

16. A nuclear transformation represents the change of one element into another. It is accomplished by bombardment of a target nucleus with some small energetic particle.

17. The target nucleus and the bombarding particles often repel each other greatly, especially when the bombarding particles are positively charged.

Accelerators are needed to speed up the particles to overcome this repulsion.

18. The elements with atomic numbers greater than 92 are referred to as transuranium elements. The transuranium elements have been prepared by bombardment reactions of other nuclei.

19. $^{27}_{13}Al + ^4_2He \rightarrow ^{30}_{15}P + ^1_0n$

20. Geiger counters contain a probe that holds argon gas. The argon atoms have no charge but can be ionized by high-energy particles from a radioactive decay process. Ionized argon gas will conduct a current briefly. If an electrical field is applied to the argon gas probe, a brief pulse of electricity

bombardment of nitrogen in the upper atmosphere by cosmic rays) and its decay through beta particle production.

30. When a plant dies, it no longer replenishes itself with carbon-14 from the atmosphere. As the carbon-14 in the plant undergoes decay, the amount decreases over time. This process assumes that the concentration of carbon-14 in the atmosphere remains constant over time.

31. A radiotracer is a radioactive nuclide that can be introduced into an organism via food or drugs, whose pathway through the body can then be traced by monitoring the radioactivity of the nuclide. Carbon-14 and phosphorus-32 have been used to study the conversion of nutrients into energy by living cells.

32. These isotopes are listed in Table 19.4.

33. The forces that hold protons and neutrons together in the nucleus are much greater than the forces that bind atoms together in molecules.

34. Nuclear fusion is the combining of two light nuclei to form a heavier, more stable nucleus. Splitting a heavy nucleus into nuclei with smaller mass numbers is nuclear fission.

35. The energies released by nuclear processes are on the order of 106 times more powerful than those associated with ordinary chemical reactions.

36. $^{1}_{0}n + ^{235}_{92}U \rightarrow ^{142}_{56}Ba + ^{91}_{36}Kr + 3\,^{1}_{0}n$

37. For every nucleus of $^{235}_{92}U$ that decays, three neutrons are produced. Once the reaction has been started (with neutrons from an outside source), the neutrons generated by the decay cause the reaction to continue.

38. A critical mass of fissionable material is the amount needed to sustain a chain reaction. Enough neutrons must be produced to cause a constant fission of more material. A sample with less than the critical mass is still radioactive, but cannot sustain a chain reaction.

39. The moderator surrounds the fuel rods and slows down the neutrons produced by the uranium decay process so that they can be absorbed more easily by other uranium atoms. The control rods absorb neutrons and are used to control the power level of the reactor. The containment is the building in which the reactor is located, which is designed to contain the radioactive core in case of a nuclear accident. A cooling liquid (usually water) is circulated throughout the reactor to draw off heat produced by the nuclear reaction; this heat energy is converted to electrical energy in the power plant's turbines.

40. The type of nuclear explosion produced by a nuclear weapon cannot occur in a nuclear reactor, because the concentration of fissionable materials is not sufficient to form a supercritical mass.

42. In a *breeder* nuclear reactor, nonfissionable $^{238}_{92}U$ is converted to fissionable $^{239}_{94}Pu$. Write nuclear equations showing this transformation.

D. Nuclear Fusion

43. What is the nuclear *fusion* of small nuclei? How does the energy released by fusion compare in magnitude with that released by fission?

44. What are some reasons why a practical fusion reactor has not yet been developed?

45. Why is the development of nuclear fusion reactors desirable?

E. Effects of Radiation

46. Although the energy transferred per event when a living creature is exposed to radiation is small, why is such exposure dangerous?

47. Explain the difference between *somatic* damage from radiation and *genetic* damage. Which type causes immediate damage to the exposed individual?

48. Describe the relative penetrating powers of alpha, beta, and gamma radiation.

49. Explain why, although gamma rays are far more penetrating than alpha particles, the latter are actually more likely to cause damage to an organism. Which radiation is more effective at causing ionization of biomolecules?

50. How do the *chemical properties* of radioactive nuclei (as opposed to the nuclear decay they undergo) influence the degree of damage they do to an organism?

51. Although radiation has been measured in many terms, the *rem* is most commonly used in discussions of the exposure of human beings to radiation. Using Table 19.6, discuss the sources of radiation to which humans are exposed naturally, and indicate how the total exposure compares with the "acceptable" (nondetectable clinical effect) level of exposure given in Table 19.5.

Critical Thinking

52. The decay series from uranium-238 to lead-206 is indicated in Figure 19.1. For each step of the process indicated in the figure, specify what type of particle is produced by the particular nucleus involved at that point in the series.

53. Each of the following isotopes has been used medically for the purpose indicated. Suggest reasons why the particular element might have been chosen for this purpose.

    a. cobalt-57, for study of the body's use of vitamin B_{12}

    b. calcium-47, for study of bone metabolism

    c. iron-59, for study of red blood cell function

    d. mercury-197, for brain scans before the CAT scan became available

54. Discuss some of the problems associated with the storage and disposal of the waste products of the nuclear industry.

55. Aluminum exists in several isotopic forms, including $^{27}_{13}Al$, $^{28}_{13}Al$, and $^{29}_{13}Al$. Indicate the number of protons and the number of neutrons in each of these isotopes.

56. How have $^{131}_{53}I$ and $^{201}_{81}Tl$ been used in medical diagnosis? Why are these particular nuclides especially well suited for this purpose?

57. What is a *breeder* nuclear reactor? What difficulties with such reactors have led to their not yet being used in the United States for the generation of electricity?

(continued on page 697a)

1 Atoms with identical atomic numbers but different mass numbers are termed

A   neutrons.

B   nucleons.

C   isotopes.

D   alpha particles.

2 Complete the nuclear equation by supplying the missing particle.

$$^{65}_{29}Cu + ^{12}_{6}C \rightarrow 3\ ^{1}_{0}n + ?$$

A $^{74}_{32}Ge$

B $^{76}_{32}Ge$

C $^{76}_{35}Br$

D $^{74}_{35}Br$

3 The nuclide ^{99}Tc has a half-life of 6.0 hours. How much of a 200.0 g sample remains after 1 day?

A   100.0 g

B   50.00 g

C   25.00 g

D   12.50 g

4 Nuclides used in medicine that can be useful in diagnosis and treatment of areas of the body are called

A   gamma rays.

B   radiotracers.

C   positrons.

D   rems.

5 Splitting a heavy nuclide into two nuclei with smaller mass numbers is called

A   critical mass.

B   fusion.

C   fission.

D   electron capture.

Write balanced nuclear equations for each of the processes in Questions 6–8.

6 $^{232}_{90}Th$ produces an alpha particle.

7 $^{234}_{91}Pa$ produces a beta particle.

8 $^{30}_{15}P$ produces a positron.

For questions 9–11, use the following figure.

9 Which of the following must occur for transformation 2 in the figure?

A   alpha-particle production

B   beta-particle production

C   electron capture

10 Which of the following must occur for transformation 1 in the figure?

A   alpha-particle production

B   beta-particle prodcution

C   electron capture

11 Which of the following must occur for transformation 3 in the figure?

A   alpha-particle production

B   beta-particle production

C   electron-capture

12 Carbon-14 dating is a technique which can provide accurate dates for artifacts and rocks. Answer the following questions concerning carbon-14 dating.

a.   Carbon-14 decays by beta particle production. Write the nuclear equation for this process.

b.   Carbon-14 is produced in the atmosphere when high-energy neutrons collide with nitrogen-14 (in a 1:1 mol ratio), also producing a hydrogen nucleus. Write the nuclear equation for this process.

c.   Explain how carbon-14 is used to determine the dates of wooden artifacts.

1. C

2. D

3. D

4. B

5. C

6. $^{232}_{90}Th \rightarrow ^{228}_{88}Ra + ^{4}_{2}He$

7. $^{234}_{91}Pa \rightarrow ^{234}_{92}U + ^{0}_{-1}e$

8. $^{30}_{15}P \rightarrow ^{30}_{14}Si + ^{0}_{1}e$

9. B

10. A

11. B

12. a. $^{14}_{6}C \rightarrow ^{14}_{7}N + ^{0}_{-1}e$

   b. $^{14}_{7}N + ^{1}_{0}n \rightarrow ^{14}_{6}C + ^{1}_{1}H$

   c. All isotopes of carbon react with oxygen in the atmosphere to form carbon dioxide. A living plant taking in this carbon dioxide incorporates the carbon into its molecules. As long as the plant is alive, the carbon-14 content of the plant remains the same as that in the atmosphere. Once the plant is cut or harvested, it stops taking in carbon. The carbon-14 content decreases since carbon-14 is radioactive and decays. By knowing the half-life of carbon-14 and comparing the content of carbon-14 in the plant to that in the atmosphere, we can date the plant.

Test Taking Strategy

Point out that the diagram above question 9 is to be used for questions 9, 10, and 11. Emphasize the importance of taking time to read direction lines.

Assessment Resources
CHAPTER 19

For additional practice with standardized testing, see *Standardized Test Practice* located in the *Teacher Resources*.

(continued from page 696)

41. If the system used to cool a reactor core fails, the reactor may reach temperatures high enough to melt the core itself. It could become hot enough to melt through the bottom of the reactor and into the earth. A steam explosion is possible if the cooling system becomes blocked.

42. $_0^1 n + {_{92}^{238}}U \rightarrow {_{92}^{239}}U$;
$_{92}^{239}U \rightarrow {_{93}^{239}}Np + {_{-1}^{0}}e$;
$_{93}^{239}Np \rightarrow {_{94}^{239}}Pu + {_{-1}^{0}}e$

43. Nuclear fusion is the process of combining two light nuclei into a larger nucleus, with an energy release larger even than that provided by the fission process.

44. The hydrogen nuclei are positively charged and therefore repel each other. Extremely high temperatures are needed to overcome this repulsion as they are shot into each other.

45. Fusion provides an enormous amount of energy per gram of fused material. If hydrogen can be fused, the earth possesses a large supply of needed raw materials in the oceans. In addition, the product nuclei from the fusion of hydrogen (which are helium isotopes) are far less dangerous that those produced by the fission process.

46. Although the energy is small, it is enough to break chemical bonds, which may cause malfunctioning of cellular systems.

47. Somatic damage is damage directly to the organism itself. It causes nearly immediate sickness or death. Genetic damage is damage to the genetic machinery of the organism. It causes defects in future generations of offspring.

48. Alpha particles are stopped by the outermost layers of the skin; beta particles penetrate only about 1 cm into the body; gamma rays are deeply penetrating.

49. Alpha particles are much heavier than gamma rays, so they can ionize biological materials very effectively. Gamma rays can penetrate long distances but seldom cause ionization.

50. Nuclei of atoms that are chemically inert, or that are not ordinarily found in the body, tend to be excreted from the body quickly and do little damage. Nuclei of atoms that form a part of the body's structure or normal metabolic processes are likely to be incorporated into the body.

51. The exposure limits listed in Table 19.5 as causing no detectable clinical effects are in the range of 0–25 rem. The total yearly exposures from natural and human-induced radioactive sources are estimated in Table 19.6 as less than 200 millirem (0.2 rem)—well within the acceptable limits.

52. alpha, beta, beta, alpha, alpha, alpha, alpha, alpha, beta, beta, alpha, beta, beta, alpha

53. (a) Cobalt is a component of vitamin B_{12}.
(b) Bones consist partly of calcium phosphate.
(c) Red blood cells contain hemoglobin, an iron-protein compound.
(d) Mercury is absorbed by substances in the brain (this is part of the reason why mercury is so hazardous in the environment).

54. Nuclear waste has been generated for more than 40 years but no permanent disposal plan has been implemented yet. A major problem is that nuclear material has long half-lives, and we have not yet come up with equally long-lasting storage devices.

55. Al-27: 13 protons, 14 neutrons; Al-28: 13 protons, 15 neutrons; Al-29: 13 protons, 16 neutrons

56. ^{131}I is used in the diagnosis and treatment of thyroid cancer and other dysfunctions of the thyroid gland. The thyroid gland is the only organ in the human body that uses and stores iodine. ^{131}I that is administered concentrates in the thyroid gland and can be used to create an image on a scanner or X-ray film. In higher doses it can selectively destroy cancer cells in the thyroid. ^{201}Tl concentrates in healthy muscle cells when administered and can be used to detect and assess damage to heart muscles after a heart attack; the damaged muscles show a lower uptake of ^{201}Tl than normal muscles do.

57. Breeder reactors convert nonfissionable U-238 into fissionable Pu-239. A combination of U-238 and U-235 is used. Excess neutrons from the U-235 fission are absorbed by the U-238, converting it to Pu-239. The chemical and physical properties of Pu-239 make it very expensive and difficult to handle.

Planning Guide

Section	Segment		Text Features and Components	Labs, Demonstrations, & Activities
20.1 Saturated Hydrocarbons 1.5 Blocks pp. 700–717	A	Carbon Bonding		
	B	Alkanes		
	C	Structural Formulas and Isomerism	**SE** Chemistry in Your World: Plastic Tasters *p. 705*	**RP** Classroom Activities and Projects *TE p. 704*
	D	Naming Alkanes	**SE** Chemistry in Your World: www.Dot.Safety *p. 710*	
	E	Petroleum		**TE** Mini-Demo *p. 715*
	F	Reactions of Alkanes		
20.2 Unsaturated Hydrocarbons 1 Block pp. 718–726	A	Alkenes and Alkynes		**TE** Mini-Demo *p. 720*
	B	Aromatic Hydrocarbons		
	continued on next page			

Key **SE** Student Edition **TE** Teacher Edition **RP** Teacher Resource Package
AR Additional Materials **LM** Lab Materials Transparencies
DVD CD-ROM classzone.com

All Learners	Technology	Review & Assessment	Standards
(TE) Teaching Tips *p. 701* (TE) Meeting Individual Needs *p. 701*	(◉) EasyPlanner	(SE) Key Terms *p. 742* (SE) Questions and Problems *p. 744*	(TE) **NSES** UCP1, UCP2, UCP5, A1, A2, B1, B2, B3, C5, E1, F1, F3, F4, F5, F6, G1, G2, G3
(TE) Teaching Tips *p. 702*	(◉) EasyPlanner	(SE) Active Reading Question *p. 702* (SE) Practice Problem *p. 703* (TE) More Examples *p. 703* (TE) More Examples *p. 704* (SE) Key Terms *p. 742* (SE) Questions and Problems *p. 744*	
(TE) Teaching Tips *pp. 704, 707* (TE) Meeting Individual Needs *p. 704* (TE) Meeting Individual Needs *p. 707*	(◉) EasyPlanner	(SE) Active Reading Question *p. 704* (TE) More Examples *p. 706* (SE) Key Terms *p. 742* (SE) Questions and Problems *p. 744*	
(TE) Teaching Tips *pp. 708, 711* (TE) Meeting Individual Needs *p. 712*	(▣) Transparency: Table 20.2 (◉) EasyPlanner	(SE) Active Reading Question *p. 710* (TE) More Examples *p. 711* (SE) Practice Problem *p. 713* (SE) Practice Problem *p. 714* (TE) More Examples *p. 714* (SE) Questions and Problems *p. 744*	
	(◉) EasyPlanner	(SE) Critical Thinking *p. 715* (SE) Key Terms *p. 742* (SE) Questions and Problems *p. 745*	
(TE) Teaching Tips *p. 716* (RP) Team Learning Worksheet (Sec. 20.1)	(◉) EasyPlanner	(SE) Active Reading Question *p. 716* (SE) Review Questions (20.1.A–20.1.F) *p. 717* (SE) Key Terms *p. 742* (SE) Questions and Problems *p. 745*	
(TE) Teaching Tips *pp. 718–719*	(◉) EasyPlanner	(SE) Practice Problem *p. 719* (TE) More Examples *p. 719* (SE) Active Reading Question *p. 720* (SE) Key Terms *p. 742* (SE) Questions and Problems *p. 745*	(TE) **NSES** UCP1, UCP2, UCP5, A1, A2, B2, B3, C6
(TE) Teaching Tips *p. 720*	(◉) EasyPlanner	(SE) Key Terms *p. 742* (SE) Questions and Problems *p. 745*	

Planning Guide

Section	Segment		Text Features and Components	Labs, Demonstrations, & Activities
20.2 (continued)	C	Naming Aromatic Compounds	**SE** Chemistry in Your World: Termite Mothballing p. 726	
20.3 Introduction to Functional Groups and Alcohols **1 Block** pp. 727–731	A	Functional Groups		**TE** Mini-Demo p. 727
	B	Alcohols		**TE** Mini-Demo p. 728
	C	Properties and Uses of Alcohols		
20.4 Additional Organic Compounds **3 Blocks** pp. 732–741	A	Aldehydes and Ketones		**TE** Mini-Demo p. 732
	B	Naming Aldehydes and Ketones		
	continued on next page			

continued on next page

Key
SE Student Edition   **TE** Teacher Edition   **RP** Teacher Resource Package
AR Additional Materials   **LM** Lab Materials   Transparencies
DVD   CD-ROM   classzone.com

All Learners	Technology	Review & Assessment	Standards
TE Teaching Tips *pp. 721, 723* **TE** Meeting Individual Needs *p. 722* **TE** Meeting Individual Needs *p. 724* **RP** Team Learning Worksheet (Sec. 20.2)	**●** EasyPlanner	**SE** Active Reading Question *p. 723* **SE** Practice Problem *p. 725* **TE** More Examples *p. 725* **SE** Review Questions (20.2.A–20.2.C) *p. 726* **SE** Key Terms *p. 742* **SE** Questions and Problems *pp. 745–746*	
TE Teaching Tip *p. 727*	**▣** Transparency: Table 20.6 **●** EasyPlanner	**SE** Key Terms *p. 742* **SE** Questions and Problems *p. 746*	**TE** **NSES** UCP2, UCP3, UCP5, A1, A2, B2, B3
TE Meeting Individual Needs *p. 728* **TE** Teaching Tip *p. 729*	**●** EasyPlanner	**SE** Active Reading Question *p. 729* **TE** More Examples *p. 729* **SE** Practice Problem *p. 730* **SE** Key Terms *p. 742* **SE** Questions and Problems *p. 746*	
TE Teaching Tip *p. 730* **TE** Meeting Individual Needs *p. 730* **RP** Team Learning Worksheet (Sec. 20.3)	**●** EasyPlanner	**SE** Review Questions (20.3.A–20.3.C) *p. 731* **SE** Questions and Problems *p. 746*	
	● EasyPlanner	**SE** Key Terms *p. 743* **SE** Questions and Problems *p. 746*	**TE** **NSES** UCP1, UCP3, UCP5, A1, A2, B2, B3, E1, E2, F6, G1, G2, G3
TE Teaching Tips *p. 733* **TE** Meeting Individual Needs *p. 734*	**●** EasyPlanner	**SE** Active Reading Question *p. 734* **SE** Practice Problem *p. 735* **TE** More Examples *p. 735* **SE** Questions and Problems *p. 747*	

Planning Guide

Section	Segment	Text Features and Components	Labs, Demonstrations, & Activities

20.4 (continued)	**C** Carboxylic Acids and Esters		**TE** Mini-Demo *p. 737*
			 LM Experiment 86: Ester Synthesis, Microscale
			    Lab Manual
			    Report Sheets
			    Teacher's Lab Guide
			 LM Experiment 87: Saponification, Traditional
			    Lab Manual
			    Report Sheets
			    Teacher's Lab Guide

	D Polymers		**TE** Group Activity *p. 739*
			 TE Teaching Support: Demonstration *p. 740*
			 SE Hands-On Chemistry: Guar Gum Slime *p. 741*
			 LM Experiment 88: Slime, Traditional
			    Lab Manual
			    Report Sheets
			    Teacher's Lab Guide
			 LM Experiment 89: Gluep
			    Lab Manual
			    Report Sheets
			    Teacher's Lab Guide

Key

SE Student Edition	**TE** Teacher Edition	**RP** Teacher Resource Package	
AR Additional Materials	**LM** Lab Materials	Transparencies	
DVD	CD-ROM	classzone.com	

All Learners	Technology	Review & Assessment	Standards
TE Meeting Individual Needs *p. 736* **TE** Teaching Tips *pp. 737–738*	**■** Lab Generator CD **◉** EasyPlanner	**SE** Key Terms *p. 743* **SE** Questions and Problems *p. 747*	
TE Teaching Tips *p. 738* **RP** Team Learning Worksheet (Sec. 20.4)	**◉** Video: Nylon **■** Lab Generator CD **◉** EasyPlanner	**SE** Active Reading Question *p. 740* **SE** Active Reading Question *p. 741* **SE** Key Terms *p. 743* **SE** Questions and Problems *p. 747*	

Resource Materials for Chapter 20

SE Chapter Review *pp. 742–743*	**RP** Meeting Individual Needs Toolkit (MINT)
	    Chapter Review Worksheets
	    Chapter Summaries

SE Critical Thinking *p. 748*	
SE Standardized Test Practice *p. 749*	**RP** Solutions Guide
AR English/Spanish Summaries	**RP** Standardized Test Practice
■ English Summaries Audio	**RP** Chapter Tests
■ Spanish Summaries Audio	**RP** Test Bank
	🔧 Test Generator

Chapter 20

Overview

In this chapter our goals are for students to:

- Understand the types of bonds formed by the carbon atom
- Learn about alkanes
- Learn about structural isomers
- Learn the system of naming alkanes and substituted alkanes
- Learn about the composition and uses of petroleum
- Learn various types of chemical reactions that alkanes undergo
- Learn to name alkenes and alkynes
- Understand addition reactions
- Learn about aromatic hydrocarbons and how to name them
- Learn the common functional groups in organic molecules
- Learn how some alcohols are made and used
- Learn the general formulas for aldehydes and ketones and some of their uses
- Learn the system for naming aldehydes and ketones
- Learn the structures and names of the common carboxylic acids
- Learn about some common polymers

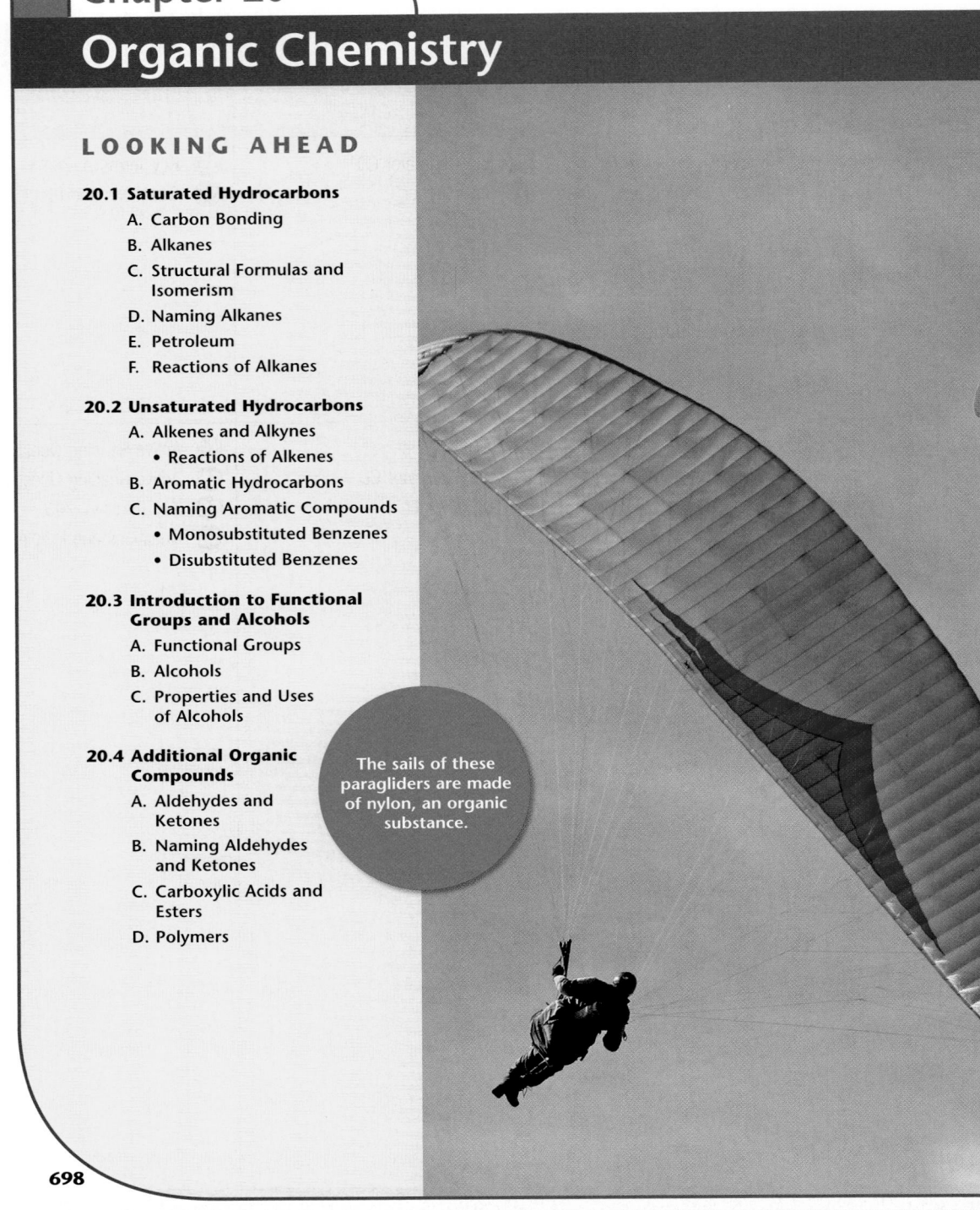

Chapter 20

Organic Chemistry

LOOKING AHEAD

The sails of these paragliders are made of nylon, an organic substance.

698

Prereading Questions

1. *Answers will vary.* Methane (CH$_4$) is the main component of natural gas. Propane (C$_3$H$_8$) is used in propane torches and gas grills. Butane (C$_4$H$_{10}$) is used in lighters.

2. Petroleum products include gasoline, kerosene, jet fuel, diesel fuel, heating oil, lubricating oil, and asphalt.

3. *Answers will vary.* Students may know that plastics are made of polymers.

IN YOUR LIFE

The study of carbon-containing compounds and their properties is called **organic chemistry**. The industries based on organic substances have truly revolutionized our lives. In particular, the development of polymers, such as nylon for fabrics; Velcro for fasteners; Kevlar for the composites used in exotic cars, airplanes, and bicycles; and polyvinyl chloride (PVC) for pipes, siding, and toys has produced a wondrous new world.

Organic chemistry plays a vital role in our quest to understand living systems. Beyond that, the synthetic fibers, plastics, artificial sweeteners, and medicines that we take for granted are products of industrial organic chemistry. Finally, the energy which we rely on so heavily to power our civilization is based mostly on the combustion of organic materials found in coal and petroleum.

A close-up photo of Velcro, a synthetic organic material used for fasteners

WHAT DO YOU KNOW?

Prereading Questions

1. What do you know about methane, propane, and butane?

2. What are some uses for petroleum?

3. What first comes to mind when you hear the term *polymer*?

Organic Chemistry • Chapter 20 • **699**

TECHNOLOGY IN THE CLASSROOM

 Transparencies
Tables: 20.2, 20.6

 Power Presentation DVD
   PowerPoint Slides
   Video
      Nylon
   eEdition
   EasyPlanner

Lab Generator CD
English Summaries CD
Spanish Summaries CD
ML Test Generator

 classzone.com

Student Preparation

Assign students to read Section 20.1 and to answer the Review Questions at the end of the section before coming to class.

 Active Learning
Team Learning Worksheet

After introducing the material in Section 20.1 in class, place students in groups and have them work together on **Section 20.1: Team Learning Worksheet.**

SECTION 20.1
GUIDE THE LEARNING

Homework

You may wish to assign these selected end-of-chapter problems as homework for this section: 1, 2, 4, 5, 6, 7, 9, 11, 12, 15, 16a–b, 17a–b, 18, 20, 21, 22, 25, 26

Additional end-of-chapter problems can be used for extra practice.

SECTION 20.1

Saturated Hydrocarbons

Key Terms

- Organic chemistry
- Biomolecule
- Hydrocarbons
- Saturated
- Unsaturated
- Alkanes
- Unbranched hydrocarbons (normal or straight chain)
- Structural isomerism
- Petroleum
- Natural gas
- Combustion reactions
- Substitution reactions
- Dehydrogenation reactions

Biomolecule
A molecule that functions in maintaining and/or reproducing life

Objectives

- *To understand the types of bonds formed by the carbon atom*
- *To learn about the alkanes*
- *To learn about structural isomers*
- *To learn to draw structural formulas*
- *To learn to name alkanes and substituted alkanes*
- *To learn about the composition and uses of petroleum*
- *To learn about the chemical reactions of alkanes*

Two Group 4 elements, carbon and silicon, form the basis of most natural substances. Silicon, with its great affinity for oxygen, forms chains and rings containing $Si-O-Si$ bonds to produce the silica and silicates that form the basic structures for most rocks, sands, and soils. Therefore, silicon compounds are the fundamental inorganic materials of the earth. What silicon is to the geological world, carbon is to the organic or biological world.

Carbon has the unusual ability to bond strongly to itself, forming long chains or rings of carbon atoms. In addition, carbon forms strong bonds to other nonmetals such as hydrogen, nitrogen, oxygen, sulfur, and the halogens. Because of these bonding properties, an extraordinary number of carbon compounds exists; several million are now known, and the number continues to grow rapidly. Among these many compounds are the **biomolecules**, those molecules that make possible the maintenance and reproduction of life.

Although a few compounds of carbon, such as the oxides of carbon and carbonates, are considered to be inorganic substances, the vast majority of carbon compounds are designated as organic compounds; compounds that typically contain chains or rings of carbon atoms. Originally, the distinction between inorganic and organic substances was based on whether they were produced by living systems. For example, until the early nineteenth century, it was believed that organic compounds had some kind of "life force" and could be synthesized only by living organisms. This misconception was dispelled in 1828 when the German chemist Friedrich Wöhler (1800–1882) prepared urea from the inorganic salt ammonium cyanate by simple heating.

$$NH_4OCN \xrightarrow{\text{Heat}} N_2H-\overset{\displaystyle O}{\underset{\displaystyle \|}{C}}-NH_2$$

Ammonium cyanate   Urea

Urea is a component of urine, so it is clearly an organic material formed by living things, yet here was clear evidence that it could be produced in the laboratory as well.

Because organic chemistry is such a vast subject, we can introduce it only briefly in this text. We will begin with the simplest class of organic compounds, the hydrocarbons, and then show how most other organic compounds can be considered to be derived from hydrocarbons.

A. Carbon Bonding

The reason so many carbon-containing compounds exist is because carbon forms strong bonds to itself and to many other elements. A carbon atom can form bonds to a maximum of four other atoms; these can be either carbon atoms or atoms of other elements. One of the hardest, toughest materials known is diamond, a form of pure carbon in which each carbon atom is bound to four other carbon atoms.

One of the most familiar compounds of carbon is methane, CH_4, the main component of natural gas. The methane molecule consists of a carbon atom with four hydrogen atoms bound to it in a tetrahedral fashion. That is, as predicted by the VSEPR model (see Chapter 12), the four pairs of bonding electrons around the carbon have minimum repulsions when they are located at the corners of a tetrahedron.

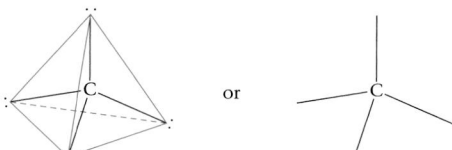

This leads to the structure for CH_4 shown in **Figure 20.1.**

> When carbon has four atoms bound to it, these atoms will always have a tetrahedral arrangement about the carbon.

Carbon can bond to fewer than four elements by forming one or more multiple bonds. Recall that a multiple bond involves the sharing of more than one pair of electrons. For example, a *double bond* involves sharing two pairs of electrons, as in carbon dioxide:

$$\ddot{O}=C=\ddot{O}$$

A *triple bond* involves sharing three pairs of electrons, as in carbon monoxide:

$$:C\equiv O:$$

Note that carbon is bound to two other atoms in CO_2 and to only one other atom in CO.

Multiple bonding also occurs in organic molecules. Ethylene, C_2H_4, has a double bond:

In this case each carbon is bound to three other atoms (one C atom and two H atoms). A molecule with a triple bond is acetylene, C_2H_2:

$$H-C\equiv C-H$$

Here each carbon is bound to two other atoms (one carbon atom and one hydrogen atom).

More than any other element, carbon has the ability to form chains of atoms, as illustrated by the structures of propane and butane shown in **Figure 20.3.** In these compounds each carbon atom is bound to four atoms in a tetrahedral fashion.

Figure 20.1
Methane is a tetrahedral molecule.

i n f o r m a t i o n

CO_2 and CO are classed as inorganic substances.

Objective To understand the types of bonds formed by the carbon atom

🍎 TEACHING TIPS

- To introduce the topic of organic chemistry and its impact on our lives, ask students what the classroom would look like without carbon-containing compounds. You will need to assist them in figuring out which items contain carbon, but it will not be long before they appreciate how many of the objects surrounding us are organic compounds.

- You will find a good set of three-dimensional models very helpful in presenting this material. Use the models to illustrate the shapes of the molecules discussed in this section. The tetrahedral shape of methane, for instance, is difficult to visualize without a model.

- This section provides an excellent opportunity to review the concept of covalent bonding.

Meeting Individual Needs
VISUAL LEARNERS

Inexpensive classroom-sized models of organic molecules can be built from painted Styrofoam balls and wooden dowels (or old Tinkertoys). Students can create models to help them gain a greater understanding of organic structures.

Objective To learn about the alkanes—compounds that contain saturated carbon atoms

 TEACHING TIPS

- Work slowly through this section with students. Build the alkanes one at a time using the three-dimensional molecular models. Make sure that students see how the nomenclature and the structures are connected.

- By the time you construct a four-carbon molecule, students should be able to see clearly that the carbon chain is not linear and that the hydrogen atoms can exist in many different orientations with respect to each other.

 Active Reading Question

two carbons (C_2H_4)

Hydrocarbon
A compound consisting only of hydrogen and carbon

Saturated
Describes a hydrocarbon in which all carbon–carbon bonds are single bonds

Unsaturated
Describes a hydrocarbon containing carbon–carbon multiple bonds

Alkane
Another name for saturated hydrocarbons; alkanes have the general formula C_nH_{2n+2}.

(a)

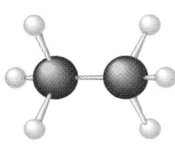

(b)

(c)

Figure 20.2
(a) The Lewis structure of ethane, C_2H_6. The molecular structure of ethane represented by (b) a space-filling model and (c) a ball-and-stick model.

B. Alkanes

Hydrocarbons, as the name indicates, are compounds composed of carbon and hydrogen. Those whose carbon–carbon bonds are all single bonds are said to be **saturated**, because each carbon is bound to four atoms, the maximum number. Hydrocarbons containing carbon–carbon multiple bonds are described as being **unsaturated**, because the carbon atoms involved in a multiple bond can bond to one or more additional atoms. This is shown by the *addition* of hydrogen to ethylene.

$$H_2C=CH_2 + H_2 \rightarrow H_3C-CH_3$$

Note that each carbon in ethylene is bonded to three atoms (one carbon and two hydrogens) but can bond to one additional atom after one bond of the carbon–carbon double bond is broken. This leads to ethane, a saturated hydrocarbon (each carbon atom is bonded to four atoms).

Active Reading Question

What is the fewest number of carbons an unsaturated hydrocarbon may have?

Saturated hydrocarbons are called **alkanes**. The simplest alkane is *methane*, CH_4, which has a tetrahedral structure (see Figure 20.1). The next alkane, the one containing two carbon atoms, is *ethane*, C_2H_6, shown in **Figure 20.2**. Note that each carbon atom in ethane is bonded to four atoms.

The next two members of the series are *propane*, with three carbon atoms and the formula C_3H_8, and *butane*, with four carbon atoms and the formula C_4H_{10}. These molecules are shown in **Figure 20.3**. Again, these are saturated hydrocarbons (alkanes); each carbon is bonded to four atoms.

(a) Propane   (b) Butane

Figure 20.3
The structures of (a) propane and (b) butane

Alkanes in which the carbon atoms form long "strings" or chains are called **normal**, **straight-chain**, or **unbranched hydrocarbons**. As Figure 20.3 illustrates, the chains in normal alkanes are not really straight but zig-zag, because the tetrahedral C—C—C angle is 109.5°. The normal alkanes can be represented by the structure:

where *m* is a whole number. Note that each member is obtained from the previous one by insertion of a *methylene*, CH_2, group. We can condense the structural formulas by omitting some of the C—H bonds. For example, the general formula for normal alkanes shown above can be condensed to:

$$CH_3—(CH_2)_m—CH_3$$

EXAMPLE 20.1

Writing Formulas for Alkanes

Give the formulas for the normal (or straight-chain) alkanes with six and eight carbon atoms.

Solution

Six Atoms: The alkane with six carbon atoms can be written as

$$CH_3CH_2CH_2CH_2CH_2CH_3$$

which can be condensed to

$$CH_3—(CH_2)_4—CH_3$$

Notice that the molecule contains fourteen hydrogen atoms in addition to the six carbon atoms. Therefore, the formula is C_6H_{14}.

Eight Atoms: The alkane with eight carbons is

$$\begin{array}{cccccccc} 1 & 2 & 3 & 4 & 5 & 6 & 7 & 8 \end{array}$$
$$CH_3CH_2CH_2CH_2CH_2CH_2CH_2CH_3$$

which can be written in condensed form as

$$CH_3—(CH_2)_6—CH_3$$

This molecule has eighteen hydrogens. The formula is C_8H_{18}.

 Practice Problem • Exercise 20.1

Give the molecular formulas for the alkanes with 10 and 15 carbon atoms.

The first ten straight-chain alkanes are shown in **Table 20.1.** Note that all alkanes can be represented by the general formula C_nH_{2n+2}, where *n* represents the number of carbon atoms. For example, nonane, which has nine carbon atoms, is represented by $C_9H_{(2×9)+2}$, or C_9H_{20}. The formula C_nH_{2n+2} reflects the fact that each carbon in the chain has two hydrogen atoms except the two end carbons, which have three each. Thus the number of hydrogen atoms present is twice the number of carbon atoms plus two (for the extra two hydrogen atoms on the ends).

20.1 • Saturated Hydrocarbons • **703**

EXAMPLE 20.1

More Examples

Give the formulas for the normal (or straight-chain) alkanes with 5 and 12 carbons.

$$CH_3CH_2CH_2CH_2CH_3,$$
$$C_5H_{12};$$
$$CH_3CH_2CH_2CH_2CH_2CH_2CH_2CH_2CH_2CH_2CH_2CH_3,$$
$$C_{12}H_{26}$$

Answer to Practice Problem 20.1

The alkane with 10 carbon atoms can be represented as $CH_3—(CH_2)_8—CH_3$ and its formula is $C_{10}H_{22}$. The alkane with 15 carbons, $CH_3—(CH_2)_{13}—CH_3$ has the formula $C_{15}H_{32}$.

EXAMPLE 20.2

More Examples

Determine the number of hydrogens on an alkane with

a. 8 carbons

18

b. 22 carbons

46

20.1.C Structural Formulas and Isomerism

Objective To learn about structural isomers and how to draw their structural formulas

 TEACHING TIP

Use the board to draw structural isomers with students. Show them that structural isomers actually have a different order of atoms. Rotating a carbon to point up or down on the end of a chain, for instance, does not produce a new structure.

 Active Reading Question

Methane, ethane, and propane cannot have structural isomers. Ethane and propane can exist only as straight-chain molecules.

Active Learning
Classroom Activities and Projects

For a group activity to help students understand structural isomerism, see *Structural Isomers* located in the *Teacher Resources.*

Table 20.1

Formulas of the First Ten Straight-Chain Alkanes

Name	Condensed Formula (C_nH_{2n+2})	Extended Formula
methane	CH_4	CH_4
ethane	C_2H_6	CH_3CH_3
propane	C_3H_8	$CH_3CH_2CH_3$
n-butane	C_4H_{10}	$CH_3CH_2CH_2CH_3$
n-pentane	C_5H_{12}	$CH_3CH_2CH_2CH_2CH_3$
n-hexane	C_6H_{14}	$CH_3CH_2CH_2CH_2CH_2CH_3$
n-heptane	C_7H_{16}	$CH_3CH_2CH_2CH_2CH_2CH_2CH_3$
n-octane	C_8H_{18}	$CH_3CH_2CH_2CH_2CH_2CH_2CH_2CH_3$
n-nonane	C_9H_{20}	$CH_3CH_2CH_2CH_2CH_2CH_2CH_2CH_2CH_3$
n-decane	$C_{10}H_{22}$	$CH_3CH_2CH_2CH_2CH_2CH_2CH_2CH_2CH_2CH_3$

EXAMPLE 20.2

Using the General Formula for Alkanes

Show that the alkane with 15 carbon atoms can be represented in terms of the general formula C_nH_{2n+2}.

Solution
In this case $n = 15$. The formula is $C_{15}H_{2(15)+2}$, or $C_{15}H_{32}$.

C. Structural Formulas and Isomerism

Structural isomerism
Describes what occurs when two molecules have the same atoms but different bonds

Butane and all larger alkanes exhibit structural isomerism. **Structural isomerism** occurs when two molecules have the same atoms but different bonds. That is, the molecules have the same formulas but different arrangements of the atoms. For example, butane can exist as a straight-chain molecule (normal butane, or *n*-butane) or with a branched-chain structure (called isobutane), as shown in **Figure 20.4.** Because of their different structures, these structural isomers have different properties.

Active Reading Question

Which alkanes cannot have structural isomers? Why?

704 • Chapter 20 • Organic Chemistry

Meeting Individual Needs

VISUAL LEARNERS

Use strings of children's pop beads to illustrate that bending or twisting the string does not produce a change in the structure. To create a different order of beads, you must take the chain apart and put it together differently.

CHEMISTRY IN YOUR WORLD

Science, Technology, and Society

Plastic Tasters

The scene: A lab near Brussels, Belgium; room temperature 21 °C; humidity 60%. A woman in a white lab coat is sitting in a private cubicle in front of a row of glasses each filled with a liquid. The woman rinses out her mouth with pure water and then begins the tasting. Exotic coffees? Premium teas? No. The woman is tasting water that has had various plastics soaking in it.

What is going on here? This scene takes place every Tuesday through Friday at Exxon Chemicals' Machelen Research Center in Belgium, where trained tasters (called *organolepticians*) sniff and taste plastic-marinated water. Their job is to make sure that you never detect the taste or smell of plastic in your favorite cheese, meat, pizza, or other packaged foods. Today's shoppers expect clear plastic wrapping and plastic containers that keep food fresh, safe, and ready to use right out of the package. They also expect it to taste just like it came from the farm or from mom's kitchen.

Ensuring that plastic packaging does not impart a taste to the food stored inside is quite a challenge. That's where organoleptics—the art and science of tasting and smelling—comes in. To test a new type of plastic, the material is sealed into an aluminum bag with mineral water. After about a week the water is tasted by a panel of highly trained organolepticians. The sample is also checked for odors. Although highly sophisticated instruments are used to test the samples as well, the human nose and tongue have been found to be the most sensitive and reliable detectors of odors and tastes. For the plastic manufacturers, no taste means good business.

Produce wrapped in plastic

	Ball-and-stick structure	Space-filling structure	Lewis structure
n-butane			
isobutane			Side chain (branch) / Main carbon chain

Figure 20.4
The structural isomers of C_4H_{10}

Chemistry in Your World

Plastic Tasters

Discuss the effects of smell and taste on marketing a product. What products have pleasing smells added to them? Why? Should people with allergies have products available without smells? What colors are pleasing to people in foods? How do manufacturers determine the preferences of people for their products?

EXAMPLE 20.3

More Examples

Draw three structural isomers of heptane, C_7H_{16}.

a.

```
    H  H  H  H  H  H  H
    |  |  |  |  |  |  |
H—C—C—C—C—C—C—C—H
    |  |  |  |  |  |  |
    H  H  H  H  H  H  H
```

b.

```
    H  H  H  H  H  H
    |  |  |  |  |  |
H—C—C—C—C—C—C—H
    |     |  |  |  |
    H     H  H  H  H

    H—C—H
       |
       H
```

c.

```
    H  H  H  H  H  H
    |  |  |  |  |  |
H—C—C—C—C—C—C—H
    |  |     |  |  |
    H  H     H  H  H

       H—C—H
          |
          H
```

d.

```
    H           H
    |           |
H—C—H     H—C—H
    H           H  H
    |           |  |
H—C—C           C—C—C—H
    |  |        |  |  |
    H  H        H  H  H
```

e.

```
    H  H  H     H  H
    |  |  |     |  |
H—C—C—C     C—C—H
    |     |     |  |
    H     H     H

    H—C—H  H—C—H
       |     |
       H     H
```

f.

```
              H
              |
           H—C—H

    H  H              H
    |  |              |
H—C—C           C—C—H
    |  |           |  |
    H  H           H

    H—C—H  H—C—H
       |     |
       H     H
```

g.

```
       H
       |
    H—C—H

    H  |  H  H  H
    |  |  |  |  |
H—C—C—C—C—C—H
    |  |  |  |  |
    H  |  H  H  H

    H—C—H
       |
       H
```

EXAMPLE 20.3

Drawing Structural Isomers of Alkanes

Draw the structural isomers of pentane, C_5H_{12}.

Solution

To find the isomeric structures for pentane, C_5H_{12}, we first write the straight carbon chain and then add the hydrogen atoms.

1. The straight-chain structure has the five carbon atoms in a row.

    C—C—C—C—C

    We can now add the H atoms.

```
    H  H  H  H  H
    |  |  |  |  |
H—C—C—C—C—C—H
    |  |  |  |  |
    H  H  H  H  H
```

    This can be written in shorthand form as

    CH_3—CH_2—CH_2—CH_2—CH_3 or CH_3—$(CH_2)_3$—CH_3

    and is called *n*-pentane.

n-Pentane

2. Next we remove one C atom from the main chain and bond it to the second carbon in the chain.

```
       C
       |
C—C—C—C
```

    Then we put on the H atoms, so that each carbon has four bonds.

```
              H
              |
        H—C—H

    H           H  H
    |           |  |
H—C        C        C—C—H
    |        |        |  |
    H        H        H  H
```

    This structure can be represented as

```
           CH_3
            |
CH_3—CH—CH_2—CH_3
```

    and is called isopentane.

Isopentane

TEACHING TIP

This example is important for showing students that the three structures with four carbons in the chain and one branch are identical.

3. Finally, we take two carbons out of the chain to give the arrangement

```
    C
    |
C—C—C
    |
    C
```

Adding the H atoms gives

```
        H
        |
    H—C—H
  H     H
  |     |
H—C—  C  —C—H
  H   |   H
    H—C—H
        H
```

which can be written in shorthand form as

```
      CH3
      |
CH3—C—CH3
      |
      CH3
```

Neopentane

This molecule is called neopentane.

The space-filling models for these molecules are shown in the margin.

Note that all of these molecules have the formula C_5H_{12}, as required. Also note that the structures

```
              CH3
              |
CH3—CH2—CH—CH3   CH3—CH—CH2—CH3   CH3—CH2—CH—CH3
                      |                   |
                      CH3                 CH3
```

which might at first appear to be additional isomers, are actually identical to structure 2. All three of these structures have exactly the same skeleton of carbons as the structure shown in part 2. All of these structures have four carbons in the chain with one carbon on the side:

```
C—C—C—C
    |
    C
```

Meeting Individual Needs
READING STRATEGIES

Have students look up the meaning of the prefix *iso-* and then compare and contrast the meanings of the words *isotope* and *isomer*.

Objective To learn the system for naming alkanes and substituted alkanes

 TEACHING TIPS

- Organic nomenclature can seem overwhelming at first. It is not possible to memorize all of the names and formulas for organic molecules. Students need to learn the names for the basic roots and substituents, however. Once these are learned, naming organic compounds becomes a problem-solving activity.

- Make sure you include some examples where the longest carbon chain is not horizontal. Students find it difficult to understand that a carbon chain with several bends in it is not branched. Tell students that the longest chain is the one that they can follow without lifting their pencils along the line of carbons or retracing lines.

- Circling or highlighting the longest chain of carbons can help when you are teaching students to identify the substituents.

D. Naming Alkanes

Because there are literally millions of organic compounds, it would be impossible to remember common names for all of them. Just as we did in Chapter 4 for inorganic compounds, we must learn a systematic method for naming organic compounds. We will first consider the principles applied in naming alkanes and then summarize them as a set of rules.

1. The first four members of the alkane series are called methane, ethane, propane, and butane. The names of the alkanes beyond butane are obtained by adding the suffix *-ane* to the Greek root for the number of carbon atoms.

Number	Greek Root
5	*pent*
6	*hex*
7	*hept*
8	*oct*
9	*non*
10	*dec*

 nformation

The complete name for this alkane is *n*-octane, the *n* indicating a straight-chain alkane.

Therefore, the alkane

$$CH_3CH_2CH_2CH_2CH_2CH_2CH_2CH_3$$

which has eight carbons in the chain, is called octane.

oct   –   ane

Tells us there are eight carbons   Tells us it is an alkane

2. For a branched hydrocarbon, the longest continuous chain of carbon atoms gives the root name for the hydrocarbon. For example, in the alkane

$$\begin{array}{c} CH_3 \\ | \\ CH_2 \\ | \\ CH_2 \\ | \\ CH_3-CH_2-CH-CH_2-CH_3 \end{array}$$

Six carbons

Five carbons

the longest continuous chain contains six carbon atoms. The specific name of this compound is not important at this point, but it will be named as a hexane (indicating a six-carbon chain).

3. Alkanes lacking one hydrogen atom can be attached to a hydrocarbon chain in place of one hydrogen atom. For example, the molecule

$$\begin{array}{c} \text{H} \quad \text{H} \quad \text{H} \quad \text{H} \quad\quad \text{H} \\ | \quad\ | \quad\ | \quad\ | \quad\quad | \\ \text{H}-\text{C}-\text{C}-\text{C}-\text{C}-\!-\!\text{C}-\text{H} \\ | \quad\ | \quad\ | \quad\ | \quad\quad | \\ \text{H} \quad \text{H} \quad \text{H} \quad (\text{CH}_3) \quad \text{H} \end{array}$$

CH_3 substituted for H

can be viewed as a pentane (five-carbon chain) in which one hydrogen atom has been replaced by a —CH_3 group, which is a methane, CH_4, molecule with a hydrogen removed.

When a group is substituted for a hydrogen on an alkane chain, we call this group a *substituent*. To name the $-CH_3$ substituent, we start with the name of its parent alkane, drop the *-ane*, and add *-yl*. Therefore, $-CH_3$ is called *methyl*. Likewise, when we remove one hydrogen from ethane, CH_3CH_3, we get $-CH_2CH_3$. Dropping the *-ane* ending and adding *-yl* gives this group the name *ethyl*. Removal of a hydrogen from the end carbon of propane, $CH_3CH_2CH_3$, yields $-CH_2CH_2CH_3$, which is called the *propyl* group.

There are two ways in which the propyl group can be attached as a substituent. A hydrogen can be removed from an end carbon to give the propyl group or from the middle carbon to give the isopropyl group.

Name: Propyl   Isopropyl

When a hydrogen is removed from butane, $CH_3CH_2CH_2CH_3$, we get a butyl substituent. In the case of the butyl group, there are four ways in which the atoms can be arranged. These are shown, with their respective names, in **Table 20.2.**

The general name for an alkane when it functions as a substituent is *alkyl*. All of the common alkyl groups are shown in Table 20.2.

4. We specify the positions of substituent groups by numbering sequentially the carbons in the longest chain of carbon atoms, starting at the end closest to the branching (the place where the first substituent occurs). For example, the compound

Methyl substituent

	CH₃—CH₂—CH—CH₂—CH₂—CH₃
Correct numbering	1 2 3 4 5 6
Incorrect numbering	6 5 4 3 2 1

is called 3-methylhexane. Note that the top set of numbers is correct; the left end of the molecule is closest to the branching, and this gives the smallest number for the position of the substituent. Also note that a hyphen is written between the number and the name of the substituent.

5. When a given type of substituent occurs more than once, we indicate this by using a prefix. The prefix *di-* indicates two identical substituents, and *tri-* indicates three. For example, the compound

has the root name pentane (five carbons in the longest chain). We use *di-* to indicate the two methyl substituents and use numbers to locate them on the chain. The name is 2,3-dimethylpentane.

Table 20.2

The Most Common Alkyl Substituents and Their Names

Structure*	Name
$-CH_3$	methyl
$-CH_2CH_3$	ethyl
$-CH_2CH_2CH_3$	propyl
$CH_3\overset{\mid}{C}HCH_3$	isopropyl
$-CH_2CH_2CH_2CH_3$	butyl
$CH_3\overset{\mid}{C}HCH_2CH_3$	*sec*-butyl
$-CH_2-\overset{\overset{H}{\mid}}{C}-CH_3$ $\underset{\mid}{CH_3}$	isobutyl
$-\overset{\overset{CH_3}{\mid}}{C}-CH_3$ $\underset{\mid}{CH_3}$	*tert*-butyl

*The bond with one end open shows the point of attachment of the substituent.

The suffix *-yl* signifies that a hydrocarbon substituent (an alkyl group) has replaced a hydrogen.

Active Reading Question

What does the suffix *-yl* mean when naming an organic compound?

Let's Review

Rules for Naming Alkanes

1. Find the longest continuous chain of carbon atoms. This chain (called the parent chain) determines the base alkane name.

2. Number the carbons in the parent chain, starting at the end closest to any branching (the first alkyl substituent). When a substituent occurs the same number of carbons from each end, use the next substituent (if any) to determine from which end to start numbering.

3. Using the appropriate name for each alkyl group, specify its position on the parent chain with a number.

4. When a given type of alkyl group occurs more than once, attach the appropriate prefix (*di-* for two, *tri-* for three, and so on) to the alkyl name.

5. The alkyl groups are listed in alphabetical order, *disregarding any prefix*.

CHEMISTRY IN YOUR WORLD

Consumer Connection

www.Dot.Safety

Elbert Dysart Botts may have saved your life, even though you have probably never heard of him. Botts, who was born in rural Missouri in 1893, was a chemist who specialized in paints and who taught chemistry at San Jose State University in California. Eventually he went to work for the California Department of Transportation (Caltrans), where he tried unsuccessfully to find a paint for road stripes that would be both durable and visible even on rainy, gloomy nights. Discouraged by his failure, Botts decided that a reflective pavement marker might be a better solution. He and his team came up with a glass-and-ceramic marker that was visible at night for over 100 meters. The biggest problem was how to attach the markers to the pavement. Eventually Botts settled on a fast-setting epoxy developed by one of his former chemistry students, which would bond the reflectors to virtually any solid surface.

The first "Botts Dots" were put in service in California in 1966. Today, hundreds of millions of them all over the world protect drivers from straying out of their lanes.

"Botts Dots" highlight traffic lanes.

Chemistry in Your World

www.Dot.Safety

Have students investigate the number of highways in your state that use these dots for safety. In some states, a special blue dot is used to demark fire hydrants on the roadside. If the dots are not in use in your area, students can write their state representatives to urge their use. Look on the Internet to discover the safety records on roads that have the dots versus the safety records on similar roads without the dots.

The dots protect drivers from wandering into another lane at night and during poor visibility conditions.

EXAMPLE 20.4

Naming Isomers of Alkanes

Draw the structural isomers for the alkane C_6H_{14}, and give the systematic name for each one.

Solution

We proceed systematically, starting with the longest chain and then rearranging the carbons to form the shorter, branched chains.

1. 1   2   3   4   5   6
$CH_3CH_2CH_2CH_2CH_2CH_3$

This alkane has six carbons all in the same continuous chain, so we call it hexane or, more properly, *n*-hexane, indicating that all of the carbon atoms are in the same chain.

2. We now take one carbon out of the main chain and make it a methyl substituent. This gives the molecule

$CH_3CHCH_2CH_2CH_3$
    ↑
    CH_3

The carbon skeleton is as follows:

  1 2 3 4 5
C—C—C—C—C
    |
    C

Because the longest chain has five carbons, the base name is pentane. We have numbered the chain from the left, starting closest to the substituent, a methyl group. We indicate the position of the methyl group on the chain by the number 2, the number of the carbon to which it is attached. So the name is 2-methylpentane. Note that if we numbered the chain from the right end, the methyl group would be on carbon 4. We want the smallest possible number, so the numbering shown is correct.

3. The methyl substituent can also be on the number-3 carbon:

  1   2   3 4   5
$CH_3CH_2CHCH_2CH_3$
         |
         CH_3

The name is 3-methylpentane. We have now exhausted all possibilities for placing a single methyl group on pentane.

4. Next we take two carbons out of the original six-member chain.

$CH_3CH—CHCH_3$
    | |
    CH_3 CH_3

The carbon skeleton is

  1 2 3 4
C—C—C—C
    | |
    C C

information

Note that placing the —CH_3 group on carbon 4 gives the same molecule as placing it on carbon 2.

EXAMPLE 20.4

More Examples

Name three structural isomers of heptane, C_7H_{16}.

   n-heptane
   2-methylhexane
   3-methylhexane
   2,3-dimethylpentane
   2,4-dimethylpentane
   2,2,3-trimethylbutane
   2,2-dimethylpentane

🍎 TEACHING TIP

It is helpful to show students how to think about these isomer problems. An organized approach to drawing and naming isomers makes the process much simpler. Start with the longest carbon chain, remove one methyl group at a time, and try to place the group on as many new carbons as possible without producing duplicates. Naming each molecule will help to eliminate duplicates. If the names are the same, then the molecules are the same even if they look different in the drawing.

The longest chain of this molecule has four carbons, so the root name is butane. Because there are two methyl groups (on carbons 2 and 3), we use the prefix *di-*. The name of the molecule is 2,3-dimethylbutane. Note that when two or more numbers are used, they are separated by a comma.

5. Two methyl groups can also be attached to the same carbon atom in the four-carbon chain to give the following molecule:

$$CH_3 - \underset{\underset{CH_3}{|}}{\overset{\overset{CH_3}{|}}{C}} - CH_2CH_3$$

The carbon skeleton is

$$\underset{\underset{C}{|}}{C} - \underset{\overset{|}{C}}{\overset{\overset{C}{|}}{C}} - C - C$$

The root name is butane, and there are two methyl groups on the number-2 carbon. The name is 2,2-dimethylbutane.

6. As we search for more isomers, we might try to place an ethyl substituent on the four-carbon chain to give the molecule

$$CH_3 - \underset{\underset{CH_3}{\underset{|}{CH_2}}}{\overset{|}{CH}}CH_2CH_3$$

The carbon skeleton is

$$C - \underset{\underset{C}{\underset{|}{C}}}{\overset{|}{C}} - C - C$$

We might be tempted to name this molecule 2-ethylbutane, but this is incorrect. Notice that there are five carbon atoms in the longest chain.

$$C - \underset{\underset{C_1}{\underset{|}{C_2}}}{\overset{|}{C_3}} - C_4 - C_5$$

We can rearrange this carbon skeleton to give

$$\underset{1 \quad 2 \quad 3 \quad 4 \quad 5}{C - C - \overset{\overset{C}{|}}{C} - C - C}$$

This molecule is in fact a pentane (3-methylpentane), because the longest chain has five carbon atoms, so it is not a new isomer.

Meeting Individual Needs
ADVANCED LEARNERS

Pair advanced students with learners who are having difficulty grasping this content. Advanced learners can help to guide others through the steps to solve problems. In addition, advanced students will solidify their mastery of the subject matter.

In searching for more isomers, we might try a structure such as

$$CH_3-\underset{\underset{\underset{CH_3}{|}}{\underset{CH_2}{|}}{\overset{\overset{CH_3}{|}}{C}}}-CH_3$$

As we have drawn it, this molecule might appear to be a propane. However, the molecule has a longest chain of four atoms (look vertically), so the correct name is 2,2-dimethylbutane.

Thus there are five distinct structural isomers of C_6H_{14}: *n*-hexane, 2-methylpentane, 3-methylpentane, 2,3-dimethylbutane, and 2,2-dimethylbutane.

Practice Problem • Exercise 20.4

Name the following molecules.

a. $CH_3-CH_2-\underset{\underset{CH_3}{|}}{CH}-CH_2-\underset{\underset{\underset{CH_3}{|}}{CH_2}}{CH}-CH_2-CH_2-CH_3$

b. $CH_3-CH_2-\underset{\underset{\underset{CH_3}{|}}{CH_2}}{CH}-CH_2-\underset{\underset{\underset{CH_3}{|}}{CH_2}}{CH}-CH_3$

So far we have learned how to name a compound by examining its structural formula. We must also be able to do the reverse: to write the structural formula from the name.

a.

$$\overset{1}{CH_3}-\overset{2}{CH_2}-\overset{3}{CH}-\overset{4}{CH_2}-\overset{5}{CH}-\overset{6}{CH_2}-\overset{7}{CH_2}-\overset{8}{CH_3}$$

Methyl   Ethyl

This molecule is 5-ethyl-3-methyloctane.

b.
$$\overset{7}{CH_3}-\overset{6}{CH_2}-\overset{5}{CH}-\overset{4}{CH_2}-\overset{3}{CH}-\overset{}{CH_3}$$ Methyl

Ethyl

This molecule is 5-ethyl-3-methylheptane.

Note that this chain could be numbered from the opposite direction to give the name 3-ethyl-5-methylheptane. These two names are equally correct.

EXAMPLE 20.5

More Examples

Draw the structural formula for each of the following compounds.

1. 3-methylheptane

2. 2, 4-dimethylheptane

Answer to Practice Problem 20.5

The root name decane indicates a ten-carbon chain. There is a methyl group attached to carbon 4 and an isopropyl group attached to carbon 5. The structural formula is

---

EXAMPLE 20.5

Writing Structural Isomers from Names

Write the structural formula for each of the following compounds.

   a. 4-ethyl-3,5-dimethylnonane

   b. 4-*tert*-butylheptane

Solution

   a. The root name nonane signifies a nine-carbon chain. Therefore, we have the following main chain of carbons:

$$\overset{1}{C}-\overset{2}{C}-\overset{3}{C}-\overset{4}{C}-\overset{5}{C}-\overset{6}{C}-\overset{7}{C}-\overset{8}{C}-\overset{9}{C}$$

The name indicates an ethyl group attached to carbon 4 and two methyl groups, one on carbon 3 and one on carbon 5. This gives the following carbon skeleton:

When we add the hydrogen atoms, we get the final structure

   b. Heptane signifies a seven-carbon chain, and the *tert*-butyl group (see Table 20.2) is

Thus we have the molecule

Practice Problem • Exercise 20.5

Write the structural formula for 5-isopropyl-4-methyldecane.

E. Petroleum

Woody plants, coal, petroleum, and natural gas provide a vast resource of energy that originally came from the sun. By the process of photosynthesis, plants store energy that we can claim by burning the plants themselves or, more commonly, burning the decay products that have been converted to fossil fuels. Although the United States currently depends heavily on petroleum for energy, this dependency is a relatively recent phenomenon (see **Figure 20.5**).

| Wood | Coal | Petroleum/natural gas | Hydro and nuclear |

Figure 20.5
Energy sources used in the United States

Petroleum and natural gas deposits probably formed from the remains of marine organisms that lived approximately 500 million years ago. **Petroleum** is a thick, dark liquid composed largely of hydrocarbons containing from 5 to more than 25 carbon atoms. **Natural gas**, which is usually associated with petroleum deposits, consists mostly of methane but also contains significant amounts of ethane, propane, and butane.

To be used efficiently, petroleum must be separated by boiling or distilled into portions called fractions. The smaller hydrocarbons can be boiled off at relatively low temperatures; the larger molecules require successively higher temperatures. The major uses of various petroleum fractions are shown in **Table 20.3**.

Table 20.3

Uses of the Various Petroleum Fractions

Petroleum Fraction*	Major Uses
$C_5 \rightarrow C_{12}$	gasoline
$C_{10} \rightarrow C_{18}$	kerosene jet fuel
$C_{15} \rightarrow C_{25}$	diesel fuel heating oil lubricating oil
$> C_{25}$	asphalt

*Shows the chain lengths present in each fraction.

CRITICAL THINKING

Petroleum is a very valuable raw material for the synthesis of polymers.

What if Congress decided that petroleum must be conserved as a raw material and could not be used as fuel? What might our society use as alternative sources of energy?

Petroleum
A thick, dark liquid composed mostly of hydrocarbon compounds

Natural gas
A gaseous fossil fuel, mostly consisting of methane (with some ethane, propane, and butane) and usually associated with petroleum deposits

---

20.1.E Petroleum

Objective To learn about the composition and uses of petroleum

CRITICAL THINKING

More than 90% of all petroleum currently produced is used for fuels. If we could not use petroleum for fuels, we would need to develop technologies that utilize resources such as the sun, wind, water, and nuclear fission.

MINI-DEMO

If you can obtain a sample of crude oil, bring it to class along with a sample of gasoline to show students the differences between the two.

20.1 • Saturated Hydrocarbons • **715**

Objective To learn various types of chemical reactions that alkanes undergo

 TEACHING TIPS

- Classifying reactions is a new skill for students. It is important to help them practice classifying organic reactions. Explain how you think about each reaction so as to classify it.

- In substitution reactions, any one of the hydrogens can be substituted. Not all substitutions will produce different products. This idea may be confusing to students. Use three-dimensional models to illustrate this concept, one molecule at a time.

- For dehydrogenation reactions, point out that a hydrogen is removed from each of two adjacent carbons and that these two carbons form a double bond.

 Active Reading Question

The other reactant is oxygen gas (O_2). The products are carbon dioxide and water (carbon monoxide may be a product when oxygen is limiting).

Combustion reaction
A chemical reaction involving oxygen as one of the reactants that produces enough heat so that a flame results

Substitution reaction
A reaction in which an atom (such as a halogen) replaces a hydrogen atom in a hydrocarbon

---

information

The symbol *hv* signifies ultraviolet light used to furnish energy for the reaction.

F. Reactions of Alkanes

At low temperatures alkanes are not very reactive because the C—C and C—H bonds in alkanes are relatively strong. For example, at 25 °C alkanes do not react with acids, bases, or strong oxidizing agents. This chemical inertness makes alkanes valuable as lubricating materials and as the backbone for structural materials such as plastics.

At sufficiently high temperatures, however, alkanes *react vigorously with oxygen.* These **combustion reactions** are the basis for the alkanes' widespread use as fuels. For example, the combustion reaction of butane with oxygen is

$$2C_4H_{10}(g) + 13O_2(g) \rightarrow 8CO_2(g) + 10H_2O(g)$$

Active Reading Question

When hydrocarbons undergo combustion, what is the other reactant? What are the products?

The alkanes can also undergo **substitution reactions**—reactions in which *one or more hydrogen atoms of the alkane are replaced* (substituted) *by different atoms.* We can represent the substitution reaction of an alkane with a halogen molecule as follows:

$$R—H + X_2 \rightarrow R—X + HX$$

where R represents an alkyl group and X represents a halogen atom. For example, methane can react successively with chlorine as follows:

$$CH_4 \quad + Cl_2 \xrightarrow{hv} \quad CH_3Cl \quad + HCl$$
Chloromethane

$$CH_3Cl \quad + Cl_2 \xrightarrow{hv} \quad CH_2Cl_2 \quad + HCl$$
Dichloromethane

$$CH_2Cl_2 + Cl_2 \xrightarrow{hv} \quad CHCl_3 \quad + HCl$$
Trichloromethane (chloroform)

$$CHCl_3 \quad + Cl_2 \xrightarrow{hv} \quad CCl_4 \quad + HCl$$
Tetrachloromethane (carbon tetrachloride)

The *hv* above each arrow signifies that ultraviolet light is needed to furnish the energy to break the Cl—Cl bond to produce chlorine atoms:

$$Cl_2 \xrightarrow{hv} Cl \cdot + Cl \cdot$$

A chlorine atom has an unpaired electron, indicated by the dot, which makes it very reactive and able to disrupt the C—H bond.

Notice that each step in the process involves replacement of a C—H bond by a C—Cl bond. That is, a chlorine atom *substitutes* for a hydrogen atom. The names of the products of these reactions use the term *chloro* for the chlorine substituents with a prefix that gives the number of chlorine atoms present: *di-* for two, *tri-* for three, and *tetra-* for four. No number is used to describe the chlorine positions in this case, because methane has only one carbon atom. Note that the products of the last two reactions have two names, the systematic name and the common name in parentheses.

Besides substitution reactions, alkanes can undergo **dehydrogenation reactions** in which *hydrogen atoms are removed* and the product is an unsaturated hydrocarbon. For example, in the presence of a catalyst, such as chromium(III) oxide, at high temperatures, ethane can be dehydrogenated, yielding ethylene, C_2H_4.

$$CH_3CH_3 \xrightarrow[500\ °C]{Cr_2O_3} CH_2{=}CH_2 + H_2$$
Ethylene

> **Dehydrogenation reaction**
> A reaction in which hydrogen atoms are removed from an alkane and the result is an unsaturated hydrocarbon

SECTION 20.1
REVIEW QUESTIONS

❶ How is carbon and its bonding unusual compared to other elements?

❷ Determine the shape of each of the following molecules (assume C is the central atom):

  a. CH_4

  b. H_2CO

  c. C_2H_2

❸ How is a saturated carbon compound different from an unsaturated one?

❹ Draw the structural formulas for at least five isomeric alkanes having the formula C_8H_{18}.

❺ What are some of the uses of petroleum?

❻ Write a balanced equation for the combustion of propane.

❼ How is substitution reaction in alkanes different from a dehydrogentation reaction since both involve removing a hydrogen atom from the molecule?

❽ Give the systematic name for each of the following alkanes.

  a. $CH_3{-}CH{-}CH_2{-}CH_2{-}CH_2{-}CH_3$
     $\qquad\quad |$
     $\qquad\; CH_2{-}CH_3$

  b. $CH_3{-}CH{-}CH{-}CH_3$
     $\qquad\quad |\quad\;\; |$
     $\qquad\;\; CH_3\; CH_3$

  c. $CH_3{-}CH{-}CH{-}CH_3$
     $\qquad\qquad\;\; |$
     $\qquad\qquad\; CH_3$
     (with CH_3 above)

  d. $CH_3{-}CH_2{-}CH_2{-}CH{-}CH{-}CH{-}CH_3$
     $\qquad\qquad\qquad\;\; |\quad\; |\quad\; |$
     $\qquad\qquad\qquad CH_3\; CH_3\; CH_3$

RESEARCH LINKS
CLASSZONE.COM

  e. $CH_3CHCH_2CH_2CHCH_3$
     $\qquad\; |\qquad\qquad |$
     $\qquad CH_3\qquad\;\; CH_3$

  f. $CH_3CH_2CHCHCH_2CH_3$
     $\qquad\qquad\;\; |$
     $\qquad\qquad CH_3$
     (with CH_3 below)

  g. $CH_3CHCH_2CHCH_2CH_3$
     $\qquad\; |\qquad\;\; |$
     $\qquad CH_3\quad CH_3$

  h. $CH_3CHCH{-}CHCH_3$
     $\qquad\; |\qquad |\;\; |$
     $\qquad\;\;\;\;\; CH_3\; CH_3$
     (with CH_3 below left)

  i. $\qquad\qquad CH_3$
     $\qquad\qquad\;\; |$
     $CH_3{-}C{-}CH_2CHCH_3$
     $\qquad\; |\qquad\qquad |$
     $\qquad CH_3\qquad\; CH_3$

  j. $\qquad\qquad CH_3$
     $\qquad\qquad\;\; |$
     $CH_3{-}C{-}CH{-}CH_2CH_3$
     $\qquad\; |\qquad |$
     $\qquad CH_3\; CH_3$

  k. $\qquad\qquad CH_3$
     $\qquad\qquad\;\; |$
     $CH_3CHCHCH_2CH_2CH_3$
     $\qquad\; |$
     $\qquad CH_3$

  l. $\qquad\qquad CH_3$
     $\qquad\qquad\;\; |$
     $CH_3CHCCH_2CH_3$
     $\qquad\qquad\;\; |$
     $\qquad\qquad CH_3$
     (with CH_3 below)

  m. $\qquad CH_3\;\; CH_3$
     $\qquad\; |\qquad |$
     $CH_3C{-}C{-}CH_3$
     $\qquad\; |\qquad |$
     $\qquad CH_3\;\; CH_3$

5. Petroleum products include gasoline, kerosene, jet fuel, diesel fuel, heating oil, lubricating oil, and asphalt.

6. $C_3H_8(l) + 5O_2(g) \rightarrow$
$\qquad 3CO_2(g) + 4H_2O(g)$

7. In a substitution reaction, a hydrogen is replaced by another atom. In a dehydrogenation reaction, hydrogen atoms are removed from adjacent carbons to create a double bond between carbon atoms.

8.a. 3-methylheptane

  b. 2,3-dimethylbutane

  c. 2,3-dimethylbutane

  d. 2,3,4-trimethylheptane

SECTION 20.1
ASSESS

SECTION 20.1
Review Questions

1. Carbon atoms form four bonds with other atoms and carbon can form molecules with long chains of carbon atoms.

2.a. tetrahedral

  b. trigonal planar

  c. linear

3. A saturated carbon compound contains only single bonds. An unsaturated compound contains both single and multiple bonds among the carbon atoms.

4. Selected structural isomers follow:

  a. $CH_3CH_2CH_2CH_2CH_2CH_2CH_2CH_3$

  b. $CH_3CHCH_2CH_2CH_2CH_2CH_3$
     $\qquad\; |$
     $\qquad CH_3$

  c. $CH_3CH_2CHCH_2CH_2CH_2CH_3$
     $\qquad\qquad\; |$
     $\qquad\qquad CH_3$

  d. $CH_3CH_2CH_2CHCH_2CH_2CH_3$
     $\qquad\qquad\qquad\; |$
     $\qquad\qquad\qquad CH_3$

SECTION 20.2
INTRODUCE

Student Preparation

Assign students to read Section 20.2 and to answer the Review Questions at the end of the section before coming to class.

 Active Learning
Team Learning Worksheet

After introducing the material in Section 20.2 in class, place students in groups and have them work together on **Section 20.2: Team Learning Worksheet.**

SECTION 20.2
GUIDE THE LEARNING

Homework

You may wish to assign these selected end-of-chapter problems as homework for this section: 27, 28, 29, 30, 32, 35, 36, 37

Additional end-of-chapter problems can be used for extra practice.

20.2.A Alkenes and Alkynes

Objective To learn to name hydrocarbons with double bonds (alkenes) and triple bonds (alkynes) and understand addition reactions

 TEACHING TIP

Use models to show the shapes of alkene and alkyne molecules around single and multiple bonds.

Key Terms

- Alkenes
- Alkynes
- Addition reactions
- Hydrogenation reactions
- Halogenation
- Polymerization
- Aromatic hydrocarbons
- Benzene
- Phenyl group

Objectives

- *To learn to name hydrocarbons with double and triple bonds*
- *To understand addition reaction*
- *To learn about the aromatic hydrocarbons*
- *To learn to name aromatic compounds*

A. Alkenes and Alkynes

We have seen that alkanes are saturated hydrocarbons—each of the carbon atoms is bound to four atoms by single bonds. Hydrocarbons that contain carbon–carbon *double bonds* are called **alkenes**. Hydrocarbons with carbon–carbon *triple bonds* are called **alkynes**. Alkenes and alkynes are unsaturated hydrocarbons.

Multiple carbon–carbon bonds result when hydrogen atoms are removed from alkanes. Alkenes that contain one carbon–carbon double bond have the general formula C_nH_{2n}. The simplest alkene, C_2H_4, commonly known as *ethylene*, has the structure

The system for naming alkenes and alkynes is similar to the one we have used for alkanes. The following rules are useful.

Alkene
An unsaturated hydrocarbon containing a carbon–carbon double bond; alkenes have the general formula C_nH_{2n}.

Alkyne
An unsaturated hydrocarbon containing a carbon–carbon triple bond; alkenes have the general formula C_nH_{2n-2}.

*i*nformation

In writing shorthand formulas, the hydrogen atoms are often written just after the carbon to which they are attached. For example, the formula for H—C≡C—H is often written as CH≡CH.

Rules for Naming Alkenes and Alkynes

1. Select the longest continuous chain of carbon atoms that contains the double or triple bond.

2. For an alkene, the root name of the carbon chain is the same as for the alkane, except that the *-ane* ending is replaced by *-ene*. For an alkyne, the *-ane* is replaced by *-yne*. For example, for a two-carbon chain we have

   CH_3CH_3 $CH_2\!=\!CH_2$ $CH\!\equiv\!CH$
   Ethane   Ethene   Ethyne

3. Number the parent chain, starting at the end closest to the double or triple bond. The location of the multiple bond is given by the lowest-numbered carbon involved in the bond. For example,

   $\underset{1\ \ \ 2\ \ \ 3\ \ \ 4}{CH_2\!=\!CHCH_2CH_3}$

   is called 1-butene and

   $\underset{1\ \ \ 2\ \ \ 3\ \ \ 4}{CH_3CH\!=\!CHCH_3}$

   is called 2-butene.

4. Substituents on the parent chain are treated the same way as in naming alkanes. For example, the molecule $ClCH\!=\!CHCH_2CH_3$ is called 1-chloro-1-butene.

718 • Chapter 20 • Organic Chemistry

EXAMPLE 20.6

Naming Alkenes and Alkynes

Name each of the following molecules.

a. CH₃CH₂CHCH=CHCH₃
     |
     CH₃

b. CH₃CH₂C≡CCHCH₂CH₃
              |
              CH₂
              |
              CH₃

Solution

a. The longest chain contains six carbon atoms, and we number the carbons starting from the end closest to the double bond.

   6   5   4   3   2   1
   CH₃CH₂CHCH=CHCH₃
            |
            CH₃

   Thus the root name for the hydrocarbon is 2-hexene. Remember to use the lower number of the two carbon atoms involved in the double bond. There is a methyl group attached to the number-4 carbon. Therefore, the name of the compound is 4-methyl-2-hexene.

b. The longest chain of carbon atoms is seven carbons long, and the chain is numbered as shown (starting from the end closest to the triple bond).

   1   2   3   45   6   7
   CH₃CH₂C≡CCHCH₂CH₃
              |
              CH₂
              |
              CH₃

   The hydrocarbon is a 3-heptyne (we use the lowest-numbered carbon in the triple bond). Because there is an ethyl group on carbon number 5, the full name is 5-ethyl-3-heptyne.

Practice Problem • Exercise 20.6

Name the following molecules.

a. CH₃CH₂CH₂CH₂CH=CHCHCH₃
                          |
                          CH₃

b. CH₃CH₂CH₂C≡CH

EXAMPLE 20.6

More Examples

Name each of the following molecules.

1. CH₃CH=CHCH₂CH₂CH₂CH₂CH₂CH₃
   2-decene

2. CH₃CH₂C≡CCH₃
   2-pentyne

Answer to Practice Problem 20.6

a. The longest chain has eight carbon atoms with a double bond, so the root name is octene. The double bond exists between carbons 3 and 4, so the name is 3-octene. There is a methyl group on the number 2 carbon. The name is 2-methyl-3-octene.

b. The carbon chain has five carbons with a triple bond between carbons 1 and 2. The name is 1-pentyne.

TEACHING TIP

Molecules that have the same number of carbons and hydrogens but have double or triple bonds between different carbons are isomers. Students can identify which molecules are the same and which are structural isomers by noting the different locator numbers for the double and triple bonds in the names of the compounds.

You can show an addition reaction in class by adding a small amount of bromine dissolved in an inert solvent (such as trichloromethane) to some cyclohexene. The red color of the bromine disappears as the reaction occurs. Compare this reaction to the reaction that occurs when you add some of the bromine to a liquid alkane (such as hexane). The red color does not disappear in the latter reaction.

 Active Reading Question

In a substitution reaction of an alkane involving a halogen, one halogen atom replaces a hydrogen atom in the alkane. In a halogenation reaction of an alkene, two halogen atoms are added to an unsaturated hydrocarbon.

20.2.B Aromatic Hydrocarbons

Objective To learn about the aromatic hydrocarbons

 TEACHING TIPS

• A model that shows the difference between cyclohexane (a puckered ring) and benzene (a flat ring) would be useful in helping students understand aromatic hydrocarbons.

• You may wish to discuss the delocalization of the electrons in the benzene ring as an example of a limitation of our bonding model. Drawing the benzene ring structure with the circle inside the hexagon reminds us that benzene behaves differently than a carbon molecule with a double bond.

Addition reaction
A reaction in which new atoms form single bonds to the carbon atoms in unsaturated hydrocarbons that were involved in double or triple bonds

Hydrogenation reaction
An addition reaction in which H_2 is a reactant

Halogenation
An addition reaction in which a halogen is a reactant

Polymerization
A process in which many small molecules (monomers) are joined together to form a large molecule

---

Aromatic hydrocarbon
One of a special class of cyclic unsaturated hydrocarbons, the simplest of which is benzene

---

Reactions of Alkenes

Because alkenes and alkynes are unsaturated, their most important reactions are **addition reactions**.

> In addition reactions, new atoms form single bonds to the carbons formerly involved in the double or triple bonds.

An addition reaction for an alkene changes the carbon–carbon double bond to a single bond, giving a saturated hydrocarbon (each carbon bonded to four atoms). For example, **hydrogenation reactions**, which use H_2 as a reactant, lead to the addition of a hydrogen atom to each carbon formerly involved in the double bond.

$$CH_2{=}CHCH_3 + H_2 \xrightarrow{\text{Catalyst}} CH_3CH_2CH_3$$
1-Propene   Propane

Hydrogenation of molecules with double bonds is an important industrial process, particularly in the manufacture of solid shortenings. Unsaturated fats (fats containing double bonds) are generally liquids at room temperatures, whereas saturated fats (those containing C—C single bonds) are solids. The liquid unsaturated fats are converted to solid saturated fats by hydrogenation.

Halogenation of unsaturated hydrocarbons involves the addition of halogen atoms. Here is an example:

$$CH_2{=}CHCH_2CH_2CH_3 + Br_2 \rightarrow CH_2BrCHBrCH_2CH_2CH_3$$
1-Pentene   1,2-Dibromopentane

Another important reaction of certain unsaturated hydrocarbons is **polymerization**, a process in which many small molecules are joined together to form a large molecule. Polymerization will be discussed later in the chapter.

 Active Reading Question

> What is the difference between a substitution reaction of an alkane that involves a halogen, and a halogenation reaction of an alkene?

B. Aromatic Hydrocarbons

When mixtures of hydrocarbons from natural sources, such as petroleum or coal, are separated, certain of the compounds that emerge have pleasant odors and are thus known as **aromatic hydrocarbons**. When these substances, which include wintergreen, cinnamon, and vanillin, are examined, they are all found to contain a common feature: a six-membered ring of carbon atoms called the benzene ring. **Benzene** has the formula C_6H_6 and a planar (flat) structure in which all of the bond angles are 120°.

H
|
H — C_{120°} C_{120°} H
C   120°   C
H — C   C — H
|
H

When we examine the bonding in the benzene ring, we find that more than one Lewis structure can be drawn. That is, the double bonds can be located in different positions, as shown below.

Because the actual bonding is a combination of the structures represented above, the benzene ring is usually shown with a circle.

C. Naming Aromatic Compounds

Substituted benzene molecules are formed by replacing one or more of the H atoms on the benzene ring with other atoms or groups of atoms. We will consider benzene rings with one substituent, called monosubstituted benzenes, first.

Monosubstituted Benzenes

The systematic method for naming monosubstituted benzenes uses the substituent name as a prefix of benzene. For example, the molecule

is called chlorobenzene, and the molecule

is called ethylbenzene.

Sometimes monosubstituted benzene compounds have special names. For example, the molecule

has the systematic name methylbenzene. However, for convenience it is given the name toluene. Likewise, the molecule

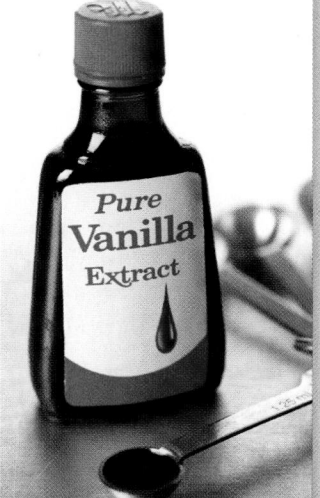

TEACHING TIPS

- Students need to learn the basic monosubstituted benzene molecule names because they are used repeatedly.

- Many students forget that when benzene is a substituent the correct name for the group is *phenyl-*, not *benzyl-*.

which might be called hydroxybenzene, has the special name phenol. Several examples of monosubstituted benzenes are shown in **Table 20.4.**

Table 20.4
Common Monosubstituted Benzenes

Name	Structure
Chlorobenzene	Cl — benzene ring
Toluene	CH_3 — benzene ring
Bromobenzene	Br — benzene ring
Phenol	OH — benzene ring
Nitrobenzene	NO_2 — benzene ring
Styrene	$CH=CH_2$ — benzene ring

Sometimes it is more convenient to name compounds if we view the benzene ring itself as a substituent. For example, the compound

$$\overset{4}{C}H_3\overset{3}{C}H\overset{2}{C}H=\overset{1}{C}H_2$$

is most easily named as a 1-butene with a benzene ring as a substituent on the number-3 carbon. When the benzene ring is used as a substituent, it is called the **phenyl** (pronounced fen´-ill) **group**. So the name of this compound is 3-phenyl-1-butene. As another example, the compound

is named 4-chloro-2-phenylhexane. Remember, we start to number the chain from the end closest to the first substituent and name the substituents in alphabetical order (chloro before phenyl).

Active Reading Questions

Numbers can indicate substituent positions. Also, the terms *ortho, meta,* and *para* indicate the relative positions of the substiuents.

 Active Reading Question

What are the two ways of naming monosubstituted benzenes?

Disubstituted Benzenes

When there is more than one substituent on the benzene ring, numbers are used to indicate substituent position. For example, the compound

is named 1,2-dichlorobenzene. Another naming system uses the prefix *ortho-* *(o-)* for two adjacent substituents, *meta- (m-)* for two substituents with one carbon between them, and *para- (p-)* for two substituents opposite each other. This means that 1,2-dichlorobenzene can also be called *ortho*-dichlorobenzene or *o*-dichlorobenzene. Likewise, the compound

can be called 1,3-dichlorobenzene or *m*-dichlorobenzene. The compound

is named 1,4-dichlorobenzene or *p*-dichlorobenzene.

Benzenes that have two methyl substituents have the special name xylene. So the compound

which might be called 1,3-dimethylbenzene, is instead called *m*-xylene (*meta*-xylene).

 nformation

Ortho- (o-) means two adjacent substituents.

Para- (p-) means two substituents directly across the ring from each other.

Meta- (m-) means two substituents with one carbon between them.

TEACHING TIPS

• When naming disubstituted benzenes, give the names in both naming systems. Students tend to find the system using numbers easier than the older (*ortho-, meta-, para-*) system.

• Naming disubstituted benzenes can be complicated. When both substituents use the same two numbers as locators, but the substituents are different, only one number is used because we assume that the first substituent is on the number 1 carbon. You will need to help students understand this distinction.

When two different substituents are present on the benzene ring, one is always assumed to be at carbon number 1, and this number is not often specified in the name. For example, the compound

is named 2-bromochlorobenzene, not 2-bromo-1-chlorobenzene. Various examples of disubstituted benzenes are shown below.

1,2-Dibromobenzene (*o*-dibromobenzene)	1,3-Dibromobenzene (*m*-dibromobenzene)	1,4-Dibromobenzene (*p*-dibromobenzene)
1,4-Dimethylbenzene (*p*-xylene)	1,2-Dimethylbenzene (*o*-xylene)	1,3-Dimethylbenzene (*m*-xylene)
2-Nitrotoluene (*o*-nitrotoluene)	3-Bromonitrobenzene (*m*-bromonitrobenzene)	3-Chlorotoluene (*m*-chlorotoluene)

Benzene is the simplest aromatic molecule. More complex aromatic systems can be viewed as consisting of a number of "fused" benzene rings. Some examples are given in **Table 20.5.**

Table 20.5

More Complex Aromatic Molecules

Structural Formula	Name	Use
	naphthalene	
	anthracene	dyes
	phenanthrene	dyes, explosives, and synthesis of drugs

EXAMPLE 20.7

Naming Aromatic Compounds

Name the following compounds.

a. CH₂CH₃ / CH₂CH₃ (on benzene ring, 1,3 positions)

c. CH₃—CH—C≡CH (with phenyl substituent)

b. CH₃ (on benzene ring with Br)

d. CH₃ with O₂N, NO₂ and NO₂ on benzene ring

Solution

a. There are ethyl groups in the 1 and 3 (or *meta*-) positions, so the name is 1,3-diethylbenzene or *m*-diethylbenzene.

b.

The (benzene ring) group is called toluene. The bromine is in the 4 (or *para*-) position. The name is 4-bromotoluene or *p*-bromotoluene.

c. In this case we name the compound as a butyne with a phenyl substituent. The name is 3-phenyl-1-butyne.

d. We name this compound as a substituted toluene (with the —CH₃ group assumed to be on carbon number 1). So the name is 2,4,6-trinitrotoulene. This compound is more commonly known as TNT, a component of high explosives.

✔ Practice Problem • Exercise 20.7

Name the following compounds.

a. NO₂ / Cl (on benzene ring)

b. CH₃CH₂CH—CH=CHCH₃ (with phenyl substituent)

EXAMPLE 20.7

More Examples

Name the following compounds.

1.
CH₃
CH
CH₃

2-phenylpropane

2.
Cl
Br

3-bromochlorobenzene

✔ Answer to Practice Problem 20.7

a. 2-chloronitrobenzene or *o*-chloronitrobenzene

b. 4-phenyl-2-hexene

SECTION 20.2
Review Questions

1.a.

CH₃C—C=C—C—CH₃ with H H above and CH₃ H CH₃ below

$CH_3C-C=C-C-CH_3$

b.

$CH_3-C=C-C-CH_3$

c. $H-C\equiv C-I$

d. $H-C\equiv C-CH-CH_2CH_3$ with CH_3 below

2. Alkanes contain only single bonds. For an addition reaction to occur, a double or triple bond must be present on which atoms can be added.

3. In both cases a diatomic molecule is added across a double or triple bond.

4. a benzene ring

5. The structures are

(two ring structures shown: one cyclohexane with all C and H labeled, one benzene ring with H labeled)

a. cyclohexane and benzene

b. Both molecules contain six carbons linked in a ring.

c. Cyclohexane contains no double bonds and twice the number of hydrogen atoms as benzene. Benzene contains three double bonds and half as many hydrogen atoms as cyclohexane.

d. This is a substitution reaction because there are no double bonds.

6.a. *ortho*-dimethylbenzene or 1,2-dimethylbenzene or 2-methyltoluene

b. 1,3,5-tribromobenzene

c. 2-chloronitrobenzene or 2-nitrochlorobenzene

d. naphthalene

CHEMISTRY IN YOUR WORLD

Science, Technology, and Society

Termite Mothballing

Termites typically do not get much respect. They are regarded as lowly, destructive insects. However, termites are the first insects known to fumigate their nests with naphthalene, a chemical long used by humans to prevent moths from damaging wool garments. Although termites are not concerned about holes in their sweaters, they may use naphthalene to ward off microbes and predatory ants, among other pests.

Gregg Henderson and Jian Chen, of the Louisiana State University Agricultural Center in Baton Rouge, have observed that Formosan termites are unusually resistant to naphthalene. In fact these insects build their underground galleries from chewed wood glued together with saliva and excrement. This

"glue" (called *carton*) contains significant amounts of naphthalene, which evaporates and permeates the air in the underground tunnels. The source of the naphthalene is unknown—it might be a metabolite from a food source of the termites or it might be produced from the carton by organisms present in the nest. Whatever the source of the naphthalene, this interesting example shows how organisms use chemistry to protect themselves.

Naphthalene

Formosan subterranean termites

SECTION 20.2
REVIEW QUESTIONS

❶ Draw structural formulas for the following:

a. 2,5-dimethyl-3-hexene

b. 4-methyl-2-pentene

c. iodoethyne

d. 3-methylpentyne

❷ Why do alkenes and alkynes react by addition reactions whereas alkanes do not?

❸ How is a halogenation reaction similar to a hydrogenation reaction?

❹ What is the common feature of an aromatic compound?

❺ Draw the structure for the ring compounds with formulas C_6H_{12} and C_6H_6.

a. Name each compound.

b. How are they similar?

c. How are they different?

d. Would C_6H_{12} react by addition or substitution reactions? Why?

❻ Name each of the following aromatic or substituted aromatic compounds.

a. (benzene ring with two CH₃ groups)

b. (benzene ring with three Br groups)

c. (benzene ring with NO₂ and Cl)

d. (naphthalene structure)

RESEARCH LINKS
CLASSZONE.COM

Chemistry in Your World

Termite Mothballing

Have students investigate other animals and plants that use chemical means to protect their environments. Many excellent biological examples of this phenomenon exist. This Chemistry in Your World makes an excellent connection to biology.

Introduction to Functional Groups and Alcohols

Objectives

- *To learn the common functional groups in organic molecules*
- *To learn about simple alcohols and how to name them*
- *To learn about how some alcohols are made and used*

Key Terms

- Functional groups
- Alcohols

A. Functional Groups

The vast majority of organic molecules contain elements in addition to carbon and hydrogen. Most of these substances are fundamentally hydrocarbons that have additional atoms or groups of atoms called **functional groups**. The common functional groups are listed in **Table 20.6**; one example of a compound that contains that functional group is given for each.

Table 20.6

The Common Functional Groups

Class	Functional Group	General Formula*	Example
halohydrocarbons[†]	—X (F, Cl, Br, I)	R—X	CH_3I
alcohols	—OH	R—OH	CH_3OH
ethers	—O—	R—O—R′	$CH_3—O—CH_3$
aldehydes	$\overset{O}{\overset{\|}{-C-H}}$	$\overset{O}{\overset{\|}{R-C-H}}$	$\overset{O}{\overset{\|}{H-C-H}}$
ketones	$\overset{O}{\overset{\|}{-C-}}$	$\overset{O}{\overset{\|}{R-C-R'}}$	$\overset{O}{\overset{\|}{CH_3-C-CH_3}}$
carboxylic acids	$\overset{O}{\overset{\|}{-C-OH}}$	$\overset{O}{\overset{\|}{R-C-OH}}$	$\overset{O}{\overset{\|}{CH_3-C-OH}}$
esters	$\overset{O}{\overset{\|}{-C-O-}}$	$\overset{O}{\overset{\|}{R-C-O-R'}}$	$\overset{O}{\overset{\|}{CH_3-C-OCH_2CH}}$
amines	$—NH_2$	$R—NH_2$	CH_3NH_2

*R and R′ represent hydrocarbon fragments, which may be the same or different.

[†]These substances are also called alkyl halides.

Functional group
An atom or group of atoms in a hydrocarbon derivative that contains elements in addition to carbon and hydrogen

---

Student Preparation

Assign students to read Section 20.3 and to answer the Review Questions at the end of the section before coming to class.

 Active Learning
Team Learning Worksheet

After introducing the material in Section 20.3 in class, place students in groups and have them work together on **Section 20.3: Team Learning Worksheet.**

SECTION 20.3
GUIDE THE LEARNING

Homework

You may wish to assign these selected end-of-chapter problems as homework for this section: 38, 39, 42, 43, 46, 47

Additional end-of-chapter problems can be used for extra practice.

20.3.A Functional Groups

Objective To learn the common functional groups in organic molecules

 TEACHING TIP

You may wish to spend some time drawing organic molecules on the board or overhead projector, with students circling the functional groups. Learning to identify the functional group is the first step in being able to predict the organic reaction that occurs when chemicals are mixed.

TECHNOLOGY

 Table 20.6

The Common Functional Groups can be used in class to help students recognize the functional groups and learn to draw their structures correctly.

MINI-DEMO

If you have samples of molecules containing the functional groups you plan to discuss, bring them to class. These chemicals have interesting odors and physical properties.

Objective To learn about simple alcohols and explain how to name them

Bring samples of rubbing alcohol, methanol, and ethylene glycol (antifreeze) to class as examples of alcohols.

Alcohol
A hydrocarbon derivative in which the hydroxyl group (−OH) is the functional group

B. Alcohols

Alcohols are characterized by the presence of the —OH group. Some common alcohols are listed in **Table 20.7.** The systematic name for an alcohol is obtained by replacing the final *-e* of the parent hydrocarbon name with *-ol*. The position of the —OH group is specified by a number (where necessary) chosen such that it is the smallest of the substituent numbers.

Table 20.7

Some Common Alcohols

Formula	Systematic Name	Common Name
CH_3OH	methanol	methyl alcohol
CH_3CH_2OH	ethanol	ethyl alcohol
$CH_3CH_2CH_2OH$	1-propanol	*n*-propyl alcohol
CH_3CHCH_3 OH	2-propanol	isopropyl alcohol

The rules for naming alcohols follow.

Rules for Naming Alcohols

1. Select the longest chain of carbon atoms containing the —OH group.
2. Number the chain such that the carbon with the —OH group gets the lowest possible number.
3. Obtain the root name from the name of the parent hydrocarbon chain by replacing the final *-e* with *-ol*.
4. Name any other substituents as usual.

For example, the compound

$$CH_3CHCH_2CH_2CH_3$$
$$|$$
$$OH$$

is called 2-pentanol because the parent carbon chain is pentane. The compound

$$CH_3CH_2CHCH_2CH_2CH_3$$
$$|$$
$$OH$$

is called 3-hexanol.

Meeting Individual Needs
ENGLISH LANGUAGE LEARNERS

As you introduce each type of common alcohol, explain the real-world application of each. Refer to part C of this section for ideas. Also, when explaining hydrocarbon fragments, explain that the terms *primary*, *secondary*, and *tertiary* refer to the numbers 1, 2, and 3.

Alcohols are classified according to the number of hydrocarbon fragments (alkyl groups) bonded to the carbon where the —OH group is attached. Thus we have

$R—CH_2OH$ Primary alcohol (one R group)

$\underset{R'}{\overset{R}{\diagdown}}CHOH$ Secondary alcohol (two R groups)

$R'—\underset{R''}{\overset{R}{C}}OH$ Tertiary alcohol (three R groups)

where R, R′, and R″ (which may be the same or different) represent hydrocarbon fragments (alkyl groups).

Active Reading Question

What is the difference among primary, secondary, and tertiary alcohols?

EXAMPLE 20.8
Naming Alcohols

Give the systematic name for each of the following alcohols, and specify whether the alcohol is primary, secondary, or tertiary.

a. $CH_3CHCH_2CH_3$
   |
   OH

b. $ClCH_2CH_2CH_2OH$

c. CH_3
   |
   $CH_3CCH_2CH_2CH_2CH_2Br$
   |
   OH

Solution

a. The chain is numbered as follows:

$\overset{1}{C}H_3\overset{2}{C}H\overset{3}{C}H_2\overset{4}{C}H_3$
      |
      OH

The compound is called 2-butanol, because the —OH group is located at the number-2 position of a four-carbon chain. Note that the carbon to which the —OH is attached also has two R groups (—CH_3 and —CH_2CH_3) attached. Therefore, this is a *secondary* alcohol.

$\underset{R}{(CH_3)}—\underset{OH}{\overset{H}{C}}—\underset{R'}{(CH_2CH_3)}$

b. The chain is numbered as follows:

$Cl—\overset{3}{C}H_2—\overset{2}{C}H_2—\overset{1}{C}H_2—OH$

20.3 • Introduction to Functional Groups and Alcohols • **729**

Active Reading Question

A primary alcohol has the —OH group bonded to a carbon atom that is bonded to one other carbon atom. A secondary alcohol is one in which the —OH group is bonded to a carbon atom that is bonded to two other carbon atoms. A tertiary alcohol has the —OH group bonded to a carbon atom that is bonded to three other carbon atoms.

EXAMPLE 20.8

More Examples

Give the systematic names for each of the following alcohols, and specify whether the alcohol is primary, secondary, or tertiary.

1. OH
        |
   $CH_3—CCH_2CH_3$
        |
        CH_3

   2-methyl-2-butanol; tertiary alcohol

2. $CH_3CH_2CH_2CHCH_2OH$
                |
                CH_3

   2-methyl-1-pentanol; primary alcohol

🍎 TEACHING TIP

When determining whether an alcohol is primary, secondary, or tertiary, focus on the carbon where the —OH is attached. Students often erroneously focus on the —OH group itself, which does not reveal anything about the classification.

20.3 • Introduction to Functional Groups and Alcohols • **729**

Answer to Practice Problem 20.8

a. 1-pentanol; primary alcohol

b. 2-methyl-2-propanol (but this alcohol is usually called tertiary butyl alcohol or t-butyl alcohol); tertiary alcohol

c. 5-bromo-2-hexanol; secondary alcohol

20.3.C Properties and Uses of Alcohols

Objective To learn about how some alcohols are made and used

 TEACHING TIP

You may want to compare the toxicities of methanol, ethanol, and ethylene glycol.

Remember that in naming an alcohol, we give the carbon with the —OH attached the lowest possible number. The name is 3-chloro-1-propanol. This is a *primary* alcohol.

$$Cl-CH_2CH_2-\overset{\overset{\displaystyle H}{|}}{\underset{\underset{\displaystyle H}{|}}{C}}-OH$$

One R group attached to the carbon with the —OH group

c. The chain is numbered as follows:

$$\overset{1}{CH_3}-\overset{2}{\underset{\underset{\displaystyle OH}{|}}{C}}-\overset{3}{CH_2}-\overset{4}{CH_2}-\overset{5}{CH_2}-\overset{6}{CH_2Br}$$
$$\overset{|}{CH_3}$$

The name is 6-bromo-2-methyl-2-hexanol. This is a tertiary alcohol, because the carbon where the —OH is attached also has three R groups attached.

Practice Problem • Exercise 20.8

Name each of the following alcohols, and specify whether it is primary, secondary, or tertiary.

a. $CH_3CH_2CH_2CH_2CH_2OH$

c.
$$\overset{Br}{CH_3-\underset{\underset{\displaystyle OH}{|}}{CH}-CH_2CH_2\overset{|}{C}HCH_3}$$

b.
$$CH_3-\overset{\overset{\displaystyle CH_3}{|}}{\underset{\underset{\displaystyle OH}{|}}{C}}-CH_3$$

C. Properties and Uses of Alcohols

Although there are many important alcohols, the simplest ones, methanol and ethanol, have the greatest commercial value. Methanol, also known as *wood alcohol* because it was formerly obtained by heating wood in the absence of air, is prepared industrially (over 20 million tons per year in the United States) by the hydrogenation of carbon monoxide (catalyzed by a ZnO/Cr_2O_3 mixture).

$$CO + 2H_2 \xrightarrow[ZnO/Cr_2O_3]{400\ °C} CH_3OH$$

Methanol Methanol is used as a starting material for the synthesis of acetic acid and many types of adhesives, fibers, and plastics. It also can be used as a motor fuel. In fact, pure methanol has been used for many years in the engines of the cars that are driven in the Indianapolis 500 and similar races. Methanol is especially useful in racing engines because of its resistance to knocking. It is advantageous for regular cars because it produces less carbon monoxide (a toxic gas) in the exhaust than does gasoline. Methanol is highly toxic to humans, and swallowing it can lead to blindness and death.

730 • Chapter 20 • Organic Chemistry

Meeting Individual Needs
ADVANCED LEARNERS

Have students research the U.S. government's current views regarding ethanol as an energy source. Students should use their research to write a persuasive argument supporting or rejecting the use of ethanol as an energy source.

Ethanol Ethanol, which is used in the production of some beverages, is produced by the fermentation of the sugar glucose in corn, barley, grapes, and so on.

$$C_6H_{12}O_6 \xrightarrow{\text{Yeast}} 2CH_3CH_2OH + 2CO_2$$
Glucose   Ethanol

This reaction is catalyzed by the enzymes (biological catalysts) found in yeast, and it can proceed only until the alcohol content reaches approximately 13%, at which point the yeast can no longer survive. Beverages with higher alcohol content are made by distilling the fermentation mixture.

Ethanol, like methanol, can be burned in the internal combustion engines of automobiles and is now commonly added to gasoline to form gasohol. It is also used in industry as a solvent and for the preparation of acetic acid. The commercial production of ethanol (half a million tons per year in the United States) is carried out by reaction of water with ethylene.

$$CH_2{=}CH_2 + H_2O \xrightarrow[\text{Catalyst}]{\text{Acid}} CH_3CH_2OH$$

Other Alcohols Many alcohols are known that contain more than one —OH group. The one that is the most important commercially is ethylene glycol,

$$\begin{aligned} H_2C&-OH \\ | \\ H_2C&-OH \end{aligned}$$

a toxic substance that is the major constituent of most automobile antifreezes.

The simplest aromatic alcohol is

OH

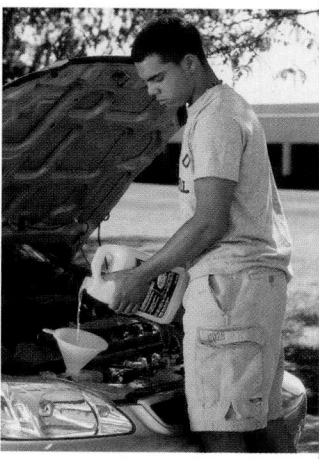

Ethylene glycol is a component of antifreeze, which is used to protect the cooling systems of automobiles.

commonly called **phenol**. Most of the 1 million tons of phenol produced annually in the United States is used to produce polymers for adhesives and plastics.

 SECTION 20.3
REVIEW QUESTIONS

❶ How are aldehydes and ketones similar? How can you distinguish an aldehyde from a ketone? (See Table 20.6.)

❷ How are carboxylic acids and esters similar? How can you distinguish a carboxylic acid from an ester? (See Table 20.6.)

❸ Name the following compounds:
   a. $CH_3CH_2CH_2CH_2OH$
   b. $\underset{\underset{OH}{|}}{CHCHCH_3}$
   c. $HOCH_2\underset{\underset{CH_3}{|}}{CHCHCH_2}CH_2OH$

❹ Draw a structural formula for each of the following alcohols. Indicate whether the alcohol is primary, secondary, or tertiary.
   a. 2-propanol
   b. 2-methyl-2-propanol
   c. 4-isopropyl-2-heptanol
   d. 2,3-dichloro-1-pentanol

❺ Why is methanol important commercially?

 RESEARCH LINKS
CLASSZONE.COM

20.3 • Introduction to Functional Groups and Alcohols • **731**

SECTION 20.3
Review Questions

1. The most important structural characteristic is the carbonyl group. In ketones, the carbonyl group is located between two other carbons, while in aldehydes, the carbonyl group is an end carbon.

2. Carboxylic acids and esters both have a carbon atom double bonded to one oxygen atom and singly bonded to a different oxygen atom. For carboxylic acids, the singly bonded oxygen atom is bonded to a hydrogen atom. For esters, the singly bonded oxygen atom is bonded to another carbon atom.

3. a. butanol
   b. isopropanol or 2-propanol
   c. 2,3-dimethyl-1,5-pentanadiol

4. a.
   $$CH_3-\underset{\underset{H}{|}}{\overset{\overset{OH}{|}}{C}}-CH_3$$
   secondary alcohol

   b.
   $$CH_3-\underset{\underset{CH_3}{|}}{\overset{\overset{OH}{|}}{C}}-CH_3$$
   tertiary alcohol

   c.
   $$CH_3-\underset{\underset{OH}{|}}{\overset{\overset{H}{|}}{C}}-CH_2\underset{\underset{H}{|}}{\overset{\overset{CH_3\ \ CH_3}{\diagdown | \diagup}}{C}}CH_2CH_2CH_3$$
   secondary alcohol

   d.
   $$CH_3CH_2\underset{\underset{Cl}{|}}{\overset{\overset{Cl}{|}}{C}}HCHCH_2OH$$
   primary alcohol

5. Methanol is the starting material for the synthesis of acetic acid, adhesives, fibers, and plastics. It can also be used as a motor fuel.

732 • Chapter 20 • Organic Chemistry

Student Preparation

Assign students to read Section 20.4 and to answer the Review Questions at the end of the section before coming to class.

 Active Learning
Team Learning Worksheet

After introducing the material in Section 20.4 in class, place students in groups and have them work together on **Section 20.4: Team Learning Worksheet**.

Homework

You may wish to assign these selected end-of-chapter problems as homework for this section: 49, 50a–c, 51a–c, 52, 54a–b, 55a–c, 57, 58

Additional end-of-chapter problems can be used for extra practice.

20.4.A Aldehydes and Ketones

Objective To learn the general formulas for aldehydes and ketones and some of their uses

MINI-DEMO

Some interesting aldehydes and ketones to bring to class include cinnamaldehyde, citral (lemon), and vanillin. All of these compounds have a strong odor, so only a small amount is needed.

Key Terms

- Carbonyl group
- Ketones
- Aldehydes
- Carboxylic acids
- Carboxyl group
- Ester
- Polymer
- Addition polymerization
- Condensation polymerization
- Copolymer
- Homopolymer
- Dimer
- Polyester

Ketone
A hydrocarbon derivative containing the carbonyl group bonded to two carbon atoms

Aldehyde
A hydrocarbon derivative containing the carbonyl group at the end of the hydrocarbon chain

Objectives

- *To learn about aldehydes and ketones*
- *To learn to name aldehydes and ketones*
- *To learn about some common carboxylic acids and esters*
- *To learn about some common polymers*

A. Aldehydes and Ketones

Aldehydes and ketones contain the **carbonyl group**

$$-\underset{\underset{O}{\|}}{C}-$$

In **ketones** this group is bonded to two carbon atoms; an example is acetone:

$$CH_3-\underset{\underset{O}{\|}}{C}-CH_3$$

The general formula for a ketone is

$$R-\underset{\underset{O}{\|}}{C}-R'$$

where R and R′ are alkyl groups that may or may not be the same. In a ketone the carbonyl group is never at the end of the hydrocarbon chain. (If it were, it would be an aldehyde.)

In **aldehydes** the carbonyl group always appears at the end of the hydrocarbon chain. There is always at least one hydrogen bonded to the carbonyl carbon atom. An example of an aldehyde is acetaldehyde:

$$CH_3-\underset{\underset{O}{\|}}{C}-H$$

The general formula for an aldehyde is

$$R-\underset{\underset{O}{\|}}{C}-H$$

We often use compact formulas for aldehydes and ketones. For example, formaldehyde (where R = H) and acetaldehyde (where R = CH_3) are usually represented as HCHO and CH_3CHO, respectively. Acetone is often written as

$$CH_3COCH_3 \text{ or } (CH_3)_2CO.$$

Many ketones have useful solvent properties (acetone is often found in nail polish remover, for example) and are frequently used in industry for this purpose. Aldehydes typically have strong odors. Vanillin is responsible for the pleasant odor of vanilla beans; cinnamaldehyde produces the characteristic odor of cinnamon. On the other hand, the unpleasant odor of rancid butter arises from the presence of butyraldehyde and butyric acid. (See **Table 20.8** for the structures of these compounds.)

Aldehydes and ketones are most often produced commercially by the oxidation of alcohols. Oxidation of a *primary* alcohol gives the corresponding aldehyde, for example,

$$CH_3CH_2OH \xrightarrow{\text{Oxidation}} CH_3C\begin{smallmatrix}O\\\\H\end{smallmatrix} \qquad R{-}OH \longrightarrow R{-}C\begin{smallmatrix}O\\\\H\end{smallmatrix}$$

Oxidation of a *secondary* alcohol results in a ketone:

$$CH_3\underset{OH}{C}HCH_3 \xrightarrow{\text{Oxidation}} CH_3\underset{O}{C}CH_3 \qquad R{-}\underset{OH}{\overset{H}{C}}{-}R' \longrightarrow R{-}\underset{O}{C}{-}R'$$

B. Naming Aldehydes and Ketones

We obtain the systematic name for an aldehyde from the parent alkane by removing the final *-e* and adding *-al*. For ketones the final *-e* is replaced by *-one*, and a number indicates the position of the carbonyl group where necessary. The carbon chain in ketones is numbered such that the

$$-\underset{O}{\overset{\|}{C}}-$$

carbon gets the lowest possible number. In aldehydes the

$$-\underset{O}{\overset{\|}{C}}-H$$

is always at the end of the chain and is always assumed to be carbon number 1. The positions of other substituents are specified by numbers, as usual. The following examples illustrate these principles.

$$H{-}\overset{O}{\overset{\|}{C}}{-}H \qquad CH_3{-}\overset{O}{\overset{\|}{C}}{-}H \qquad CH_3{-}\overset{O}{\overset{\|}{C}}{-}CH_3$$

Methanal (formaldehyde)   Ethanal (acetaldehyde)   Propanone (acetone)

$$CH_3{-}\overset{O}{\overset{\|}{C}}{-}CH_2CH_2CH_3 \qquad CH_3\underset{Cl}{\overset{|}{C}}HCH_2\overset{O}{\overset{\|}{C}}{-}H$$

2-Pentanone   3-Chlorobutanal

The names in parentheses are common names that are used much more often than the systematic names.

Table 20.8

Common Aldehydes

Name	Structure
Vanillin	(structure of vanillin)
Cinnamaldehyde	$CH{=}CH{-}C\begin{smallmatrix}O\\\\H\end{smallmatrix}$ (with benzene ring)
Butyraldehyde	$CH_3CH_2CH_2C\begin{smallmatrix}O\\\\H\end{smallmatrix}$

20.4.B Naming Aldehydes and Ketones

Objective To learn the systems for naming aldehydes and ketones

 TEACHING TIPS

- It is difficult to distinguish between *-ol* and *-al* in spoken language. Be sure to write the structure, say the name, and write the name when discussing these compounds in class. This effort will help students clearly distinguish among the molecules.

- The aldehyde and ketone groups seem very similar to beginning students. Make sure you show them that the carbonyl group is located between two other carbons in ketones, whereas the carbonyl group is an end carbon in aldehydes.

Active Reading Question

A ketone can be named by removing the final -*e* from the parent alkane and replacing it with -*one*. For example, 2-butanone. A ketone can also be named by specifying the substituents attached to the C=O group. For example, methyl ethyl ketone.

Another common aldehyde is benzaldehyde (an aromatic aldehyde), which has the structure

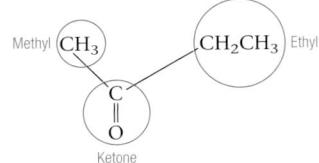

Benzaldehyde

An alternative system for naming ketones specifies the substituents attached to the C=O group. For example, the compound

$CH_3CCH_2CH_3$

is called 2-butanone when we use the system just described. However, this molecule can also be named methyl ethyl ketone and is commonly referred to in industry as MEK (*m*ethyl *e*thyl *k*etone):

Another example is the use of the name ketone for the compound

which is commonly called methyl phenyl ketone.

Active Reading Question

What are two ways of naming ketones?

Meeting Individual Needs

INCLUSION STRATEGIES

Since many compounds have more than one naming convention, have students keep track of these compounds in a separate table in their notebooks.

EXAMPLE 20.9

Naming Aldehydes and Ketones

Name the following molecules.

a. CH_3 (Give two names.)   c. CH_3CH_2

$$CH_3C-CHCH_3$$
$$\underset{O}{\|}$$

c. CH_3CH_2, $C=O$ attached to benzene ring

b. H, $C=O$ attached to benzene ring with NO_2

d. $CH_3CHCH_2CH_2CHO$
$$\underset{Cl}{|}$$

Solution

a. We can name this molecule as a 2-butanone because the longest chain has four carbon atoms (butane root) with the

$$\diagup C=O$$

group in the number 2 position (the lowest possible number). Because the methyl group is in the number 3 position, the name is 3-methyl-2-butanone. We can also name this compound methyl isopropyl ketone.

b. We name this molecule as a substituted benzaldehyde (the nitro group is in the number 3 position): 3-nitrobenzaldehyde. It might also be named *m*-nitrobenzaldehyde.

c. We name this molecule as a ketone: ethyl phenyl ketone.

d. The name is 4-chloropentanal. Note that an aldehyde group is always at the end of the chain and is automatically assigned as the number 1 carbon.

✓ Practice Problem • Exercise 20.9

Name the following molecules.

a. $$CH_3CH_2\underset{\underset{CH_2CH_3}{|}}{\overset{\overset{O}{\|}}{C}}CHCH_2CH_3$$

b. $$CH_3CH_2CH_2\underset{\underset{CH_3CHCH_3}{|}}{C}HCH_2CH_2CH_2CH_2CH_2CHO$$

EXAMPLE 20.9

More Examples

Name the following molecules.

1. $$CH_3\underset{\underset{CH_3}{|}}{\overset{\overset{H}{|}}{C}}\overset{\overset{O}{\|}}{C}-CH_2CH_2CH_3$$

2-methyl-3-hexanone

2. $$CH_3CH_2\underset{\underset{H}{|}}{\overset{\overset{CH_3}{|}}{C}}-CH_2\overset{\overset{O}{\|}}{C}-H$$

3-methylpentanal

✓ Answer to Practice Problem 20.9

a. 4-ethyl-3-hexanone
Because the compound is named as a hexanone, the carbonyl group is assigned the lowest possible number.

b. 7-isopropyldecanal

Objective To learn the structures and names of the common carboxylic acids

 LABORATORY
EXPERIMENT 86:
Ester Synthesis, Microscale

LABORATORY
EXPERIMENT 87:
Saponification, Traditional

Carboxylic acid
A hydrocarbon derivative containing the carboxyl group (−COOH)

C. Carboxylic Acids and Esters

Carboxylic acids are characterized by the presence of the **carboxyl group**, −COOH, which has the structure

$$-C\begin{array}{c} O \\ \\ O-H \end{array}$$

The general formula of a carboxylic acid is RCOOH, where R represents the hydrocarbon fragment. These molecules typically are weak acids in aqueous solution. That is, the dissociation (ionization) equilibrium

$$RCOOH(aq) + H_2O(l) \rightleftharpoons H_3O^+(aq) + RCOO^-(aq)$$

lies far to the left—only a small percentage of the RCOOH molecules are ionized.

We name carboxylic acids by dropping the final *-e* from the parent alkane (the longest chain containing the −COOH group) and adding *-oic*. Carboxylic acids are frequently known by their common names. For example, CH_3COOH, often written $HC_2H_3O_2$ and commonly called acetic acid, has the systematic name ethanoic acid because the parent alkane is ethane. Several carboxylic acids, their systematic names, and their common names are given in **Table 20.9**. Other examples of carboxylic acids are shown below.

COOH

Benzoic acid

COOH

NO_2

p-Nitrobenzoic acid

$CH_3CHCH_2CH_2COOH$
|
Br

4-Bromopentanoic acid

CH_2CH_2COOH
|
Cl

3-Chloropropanoic acid

Note that the −COOH group is always assigned the number 1 position in the chain.

Carboxylic acids can be produced by oxidizing primary alcohols with a strong oxidizing agent. For example, we can oxidize ethanol to acetic acid by using potassium permanganate.

$$CH_3CH_2OH \xrightarrow{KMnO_4(aq)} CH_3COOH$$

Table 20.9

Several Carboxylic Acids, Their Systematic Names, and Their Common Names

Formula	Systematic Name	Common Name
HCOOH	methanoic acid	formic acid
CH_3COOH	ethanoic acid	acetic acid
CH_3CH_2COOH	propanoic acid	propionic acid
$CH_3CH_2CH_2COOH$	butanoic acid	butyric acid
$CH_3CH_2CH_2CH_2COOH$	pentanoic acid	valeric acid

Meeting Individual Needs
INCLUSION STRATEGIES

Encourage students to refer back to Table 20.6 each time you introduce a new class of functional groups. Students can use this table as a beginning point to organize information about each group as it becomes available.

Esters A carboxylic acid reacts with an alcohol to form an ester and a water molecule. For example, the reaction of acetic acid and ethanol produces the ester ethyl acetate and water.

$$CH_3\overset{O}{\overset{\|}{C}}-(OH + H)-OCH_2CH_3 \rightarrow CH_3\overset{O}{\overset{\|}{C}}-OCH_2CH_3 + H_2O$$

React to
form water

This reaction can be represented in general as follows:

$$RCOOH + R'OH \rightarrow RCOOR' + H_2O$$

Acid   Alcohol   Ester   Water

An **ester** has the following general formula:

$$R-\overset{O}{\overset{\|}{C}}\underset{O-R'}{}$$

From the acid   From the alcohol

Esters often have a sweet, fruity odor that contrasts markedly with the often-pungent odors of the parent carboxylic acids. For example, the odor of bananas derives from *n*-amyl acetate:

$$CH_3\overset{O}{\overset{\|}{C}}\underset{OCH_2CH_2CH_2CH_2CH_3}{}$$

and that of oranges from *n*-octyl acetate:

$$CH_3\overset{}{C}-OC_8H_{17}$$
$$\underset{O}{\overset{\|}{}}$$

Like carboxylic acids, esters are often referred to by their common names. The name consists of the alkyl name from the alcohol followed by the acid name, where the *-ic* ending is replaced by *-ate*. For example, the ester

$$CH_3\overset{O}{\overset{\|}{C}}\underset{O-CH\underset{CH_3}{\overset{CH_3}{}}}{}$$

is made from acetic acid, CH_3COOH, and isopropyl alcohol,

$$CH_3CHCH_3$$
$$\underset{OH}{\overset{|}{}}$$

and is called isopropyl acetate. The systematic name for this ester is isopropylethanoate (from ethanoic acid, the systematic name for acetic acid).

The smell of bananas results from an aromatic ester.

information

Amyl is a common name for $CH_3CH_2CH_2CH_2CH_2-$.

TEACHING TIP

When students look at the formula for an ester, they often find it difficult to tell which part of the molecule is derived from the acid and which part is derived from the alcohol. To help students figure this out, you can draw the formula so that the alcohol part of the molecule is below the main line for the formula.

MINI-DEMO

If you have some available, bring samples of esters to class. Good examples include isobutyl formate (raspberries), octyl acetate (orange), and ethyl butyrate (pineapple). You may be able to obtain samples from a health food store or an aromatherapy store.

A very important ester is formed from the reaction of salicylic acid and acetic acid.

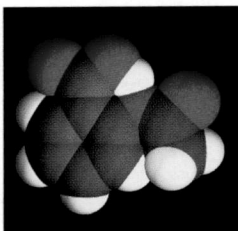

Computer-generated space-filled model of acetylsalicylic acid (aspirin)

The product is acetylsalicylic acid, commonly known as *aspirin*, which is manufactured in huge quantities and is widely used as an analgesic (painkiller).

Polymers
A large, usually chainlike molecule made from small molecules called monomers

Addition polymerization
The process in which monomers simply "add together" to form polymers

D. Polymers

Polymers are large, usually chainlike molecules that are built from small molecules called *monomers*. Polymers form the basis for synthetic fibers, rubbers, and plastics and have played a leading role in the revolution brought about in our lives by chemistry during the past 50 years. (Many important biomolecules are also polymers.)

The simplest and one of the best-known synthetic polymers is *polyethylene*, which is constructed from ethylene monomers. Its structure is

where *n* represents a large number (usually several thousand). Polyethylene is a tough, flexible plastic used for piping, bottles, electrical insulation, film for packaging, garbage bags, and many other purposes. Its properties can be varied by using substituted ethylene monomers. For example, when tetra-fluoroethylene is the monomer, the polymer Teflon is obtained.

Because of the resistance of the strong C—F bonds to chemical attack, Teflon is an inert, tough, and nonflammable material that is widely used for electrical insulation, nonstick coatings for cooking utensils, and bearings for low-temperature applications.

Other similar polyethylene-type polymers are made from monomers containing chloro, methyl, cyano, and phenyl substituents (see **Table 20.10**). In each case, the carbon–carbon double bond in the substituted ethylene monomer becomes a single bond in the polymer. The different substituents lead to a wide variety of properties.

The polyethylene polymers illustrate one of the major types of polymerization reactions, called **addition polymerization**, in which the monomers simply "add together" to form the polymer and there are no other products.

Table 20.10

Some Common Synthetic Polymers, Their Monomers, and Applications

Monomer Name and Formula	Polymer Name and Formula	Applications
ethylene $H_2C{=}CH_2$	polyethylene $-(CH_2-CH_2)_n$	plastic piping, bottles, electrical insulation, toys
propylene $H_2C{=}\overset{\overset{H}{\vert}}{\underset{\underset{CH_3}{\vert}}{C}}$	polypropylene $-(CH-CH_2CH-CH_2)_n$ $\quad\vert\qquad\vert$ $\quad CH_3\quad CH_3$	film for packaging, carpets, lab wares, toys
vinyl chloride $H_2C{=}\overset{\overset{H}{\vert}}{\underset{\underset{Cl}{\vert}}{C}}$	polyvinyl chloride (PVC) $-(CH_2-CH)_n$ $\qquad\quad\vert$ $\qquad\quad Cl$	piping, siding, floor tile, clothing, toys
acrylonitrile $H_2C{=}\overset{\overset{H}{\vert}}{\underset{\underset{CN}{\vert}}{C}}$	polyacrylonitrile (PAN) $-(CH_2-CH)_n$ $\qquad\quad\vert$ $\qquad\quad CN$	carpets, fabrics
tetrafluoroethylene $F_2C{=}CF_2$	Teflon $-(CF_2-CF_2)_n$	coating for cooking utensils, electrical insulation, bearings
styrene $H_2C{=}C$	polystyrene $-(CH_2CH)_n$	containers, thermal insulation, toys
butadiene $H_2C{=}C-C{=}CH_2$	polybutadiene $-(CH_2CH{=}CHCH_2)_n$	tire tread, coating resin
butadiene and styrene (see above)	styrene–butadiene rubber $(CH-CH_2-CH_2-CH{=}CH-CH_2)_n$	synthetic rubber

TECHNOLOGY

Video
Nylon

Another common type of polymerization is **condensation polymerization**, in which a small molecule, such as water, is formed for each extension of the polymer chain. The most familiar polymer produced by condensation is *nylon*. Nylon is a **copolymer**, because two different types of monomers combine to form the chain (a **homopolymer**, by contrast, results from the polymerizing of a single type of monomer). One common form of nylon is produced when hexamethylenediamine and adipic acid react by splitting out a water molecule to form a C—N bond:

$$\underset{\text{Hexamethylenediamine}}{\overset{\text{H}}{\underset{\text{H}}{\text{N}}}-(\text{CH}_2)_6-\overset{\text{H}}{\text{N}}\boxed{\text{H}\quad\text{H}-\text{O}}} \quad \underset{\text{Adipic acid}}{\overset{\text{O}}{\text{C}}-(\text{CH}_2)_4-\overset{\text{O}}{\text{C}}\underset{\text{O}-\text{H}}{}} \longrightarrow \overset{\text{H}}{\underset{\text{H}}{\text{N}}}-(\text{CH}_2)_6-\overset{\text{H}}{\text{N}}-\overset{\text{O}}{\text{C}}-(\text{CH}_2)_4-\overset{\text{O}}{\text{C}}\underset{\text{O}-\text{H}}{} + \text{H}_2\text{O}$$

Active Reading Question

Is Teflon a copolymer or a homopolymer?

Condensation polymerization

The process in which a small molecule such as water is produced for each extension of the polymer chain

Copolymer
A polymer consisting of two different types of monomers

Homopolymer
A polymer consisting of a single type of monomer

Dimer
A molecule consisting of two monomers joined together

The molecule formed, which is called a **dimer** (two monomers joined), can undergo further condensation reactions because it has an amino group at one end and a carboxyl group at the other. Thus both ends are free to react with another monomer. Repetition of this process leads to a long chain of the type

$$\left(\overset{\text{H}}{\underset{}{\text{N}}}-(\text{CH}_2)_6-\overset{\text{H}}{\text{N}}-\overset{\text{O}}{\text{C}}-(\text{CH}_2)_4-\overset{\text{O}}{\text{C}}\right)_n$$

which is the general structure of nylon. The reaction to form nylon occurs quite readily and is often used as a classroom demonstration (see **Figure 20.6**). The properties of nylon can be varied by changing the number of carbon atoms in the chain of the acid or amine monomers.

More than 1 million tons of nylon are produced annually in the United States for use in clothing, carpets, rope, and so on. Many other types of condensation polymers are also produced. For example, Dacron is a copolymer formed from the condensation reaction of ethylene glycol (a dialcohol) and *p*-terephthalic acid (a dicarboxylic acid).

$$\underset{\substack{\text{Ethylene}\\\text{glycol}}}{\text{HOCH}_2\text{CH}_2\text{O}-\text{H}} \quad \underset{\text{H}_2\text{O}}{\text{HO}} \quad \underset{\substack{p\text{-Terephthalic}\\\text{acid}}}{\overset{\text{O}}{\text{C}}\qquad\qquad\overset{\text{O}}{\text{C}}-\text{O}-\text{H}}$$

Figure 20.6
The reaction to form nylon can be carried out at the interface of two immiscible liquid layers in a beaker. The bottom layer contains adipoyl chloride,

$$\text{Cl}-\overset{\text{O}}{\underset{\text{O}}{\text{C}}}-(\text{CH}_2)_4-\overset{\text{O}}{\underset{\text{O}}{\text{C}}}-\text{Cl}$$

dissolved in CCl_4, and the top layer contains hexamethylenediamine,

$$\text{H}_2\text{N}-(\text{CH}_2)_6-\text{NH}_2$$

dissolved in water. A molecule of HCl is formed as each C—N bond forms. This is a variation of the reaction to form nylon discussed in the text.

Teaching Support

DEMONSTRATION

Making Nylon

Materials
- 250-mL beaker
- 1,6-hexanediamine
- Sebacoyl chloride
- 1,1,1-trichloroethanine
- Large test tube
- Copper wire
- 0.4 *M* NaOH

Preparation Dissolve 1.15 g of 1,6-hexanediamine in 25 mL of

0.4 *M* NaOH. Dissolve 2.3 g of sebacoyl chloride in 25 mL of 1,1,1-trichloroethane.

Presentation Pour the sebacoyl chloride solution into the 250-mL beaker. Carefully pour the 1,6-hexanediamine solution down the side of the beaker so that it floats on the sebacoyl chloride solution. Nylon forms at the interface of the two solutions. Bend the copper wire into a hook and use it to grasp the nylon. Pull the nylon

strand out of the solution and wind it around the outside of the large test tube. It is possible to obtain several feet of nylon from the interface of the solutions.

Teaching Notes Be careful when handling the nylon, which is coated with HCl until it has been neutralized with $NaHCO_3(aq)$. Make sure you dispose of all excess chemicals as required.

The repeating unit of Dacron is

$$\left(\!\!\begin{array}{c} \text{OCH}_2\text{CH}_2-\text{O}-\overset{\displaystyle \text{O}}{\underset{\displaystyle \|}{\text{C}}}-\!\!\bigcirc\!\!-\overset{\displaystyle \text{O}}{\underset{\displaystyle \|}{\text{C}}} \end{array}\!\!\right)_{\!\!n}$$

Note that this polymerization involves a carboxylic acid and an alcohol to form an ester group,

$$-\text{O}-\overset{\displaystyle \text{O}}{\underset{\displaystyle \|}{\text{C}}}-$$

Thus Dacron is called a **polyester**. By itself or blended with cotton, Dacron is widely used in fibers for the manufacture of clothing.

Active Reading Question

What is meant by the term *polyester*?

HANDS-ON CHEMISTRY • MINI-LAB •

Guar Gum Slime

Materials
- 5-ounce paper cup
- graduated cylinder
- food coloring
- water
- guar gum
- 4% borax solution
- spoon
- plastic bag

Procedure
1. Measure 100 mL of water and pour it into a 5-ounce paper cup.
2. Add 2–3 drops of food coloring to the water.
3. Add 0.5 g $\left(\frac{1}{8}\text{ teaspoon}\right)$ guar gum to the water and stir until dissolved. The mixture will thicken slightly as the guar gum dissolves.
4. Add 5 mL 4% borax solution to the cup and stir. The mixture should change in 1–2 minutes.
5. Store the slime in a plastic bag to prevent it from drying out.

SECTION 20.4 REVIEW QUESTIONS

❶ Complete: Oxidation of a _____ alcohol results in a ketone. Oxidation of a _____ alcohol results in an aldehye.

❷ Draw a structural formula for each of the following:
a. 3-methylpentanal
b. 3-methyl-2-pentanone
c. methyl phenyl ketone
d. 2-hydroxybutanal
e. propanal

❸ Why is it more common for organic chemists to write the formula for acetic acid as CH_3COOH instead of $HC_2H_3O_2$?

❹ a. To make an ester, a carboxylic acid reacts with an alcohol. Water is removed to form the new ester. Circle the water that is removed in the reaction below and draw the ester which results:

$$CH_3CH_2C-OH + H-OCH_3$$

b. Name each of the compounds in your reaction.

❺ Do all of the monomers in a polymer have to be the same? Give examples to support your answer.

RESEARCH LINKS
CLASSZONE.COM

20.4 • Additional Organic Compounds • **741**

Hands-On Chemistry
MINI-LAB

Guar Gum Slime

Materials Each group will need water, food coloring, a paper cup, 0.5 g of guar gum, 5 mL of 4% borax solution, a stirring rod, and a plastic bag.

Purpose The purpose is to make a polymer.

Discussion Prepare the 4% borax solution by adding 4 g of borax to 100 mL of water. The slime will gel within a couple of minutes.

Guar gum is made from the ground endosperms of the bean plant *Cyamopsis tetragonolobus* and has a molar mass of about 220,000 g. It has five to eight times the thickening power of starch. Guar gum is used as a thickening agent in foods and cosmetics.

None of the substances used here are considered hazardous, but students should wash their hands thoroughly after completing this activity. Also, the guar gum slime should be kept off clothing, upholstery, and wood surfaces because it will stain them.

Active Reading Question

A polyester is a polymer in which the monomer contains an ester group.

SECTION 20.4 ASSESS

SECTION 20.4 Review Questions

1. secondary; primary

2. a.
$$\underset{\displaystyle \underset{\displaystyle \text{H}}{|}}{CH_3CH_2C}\overset{\displaystyle \overset{\displaystyle CH_3}{|}}{H}\overset{\displaystyle \text{O}}{\underset{\displaystyle \|}{\text{C}}}-\text{H}$$

b.
$$CH_3CH_2-\overset{\displaystyle \overset{\displaystyle CH_3}{|}}{\underset{\displaystyle |}{C}}\overset{}{\underset{\displaystyle \underset{\displaystyle \text{H}}{|}}{C}}\overset{}{\underset{\displaystyle \underset{\displaystyle \text{O}}{\|}}{}}-CH_3$$

c.
$$CH_3-\overset{\displaystyle \text{O}}{\underset{\displaystyle \|}{\text{C}}}-\bigcirc$$

d.
$$CH_3\overset{\displaystyle \overset{\displaystyle \text{H}}{|}}{\underset{\displaystyle \underset{\displaystyle \text{H}}{|}}{C}}\overset{\displaystyle \overset{\displaystyle \text{H}}{|}}{\underset{\displaystyle \underset{\displaystyle \text{OH}}{|}}{C}}\overset{\displaystyle \text{O}}{\underset{\displaystyle \|}{C}}-\text{H}$$

e.
$$CH_3CH_2\overset{\displaystyle \text{O}}{\underset{\displaystyle \|}{C}}-\text{H}$$

3. Organic chemists write the formula CH_3COOH because it tells us on sight that the compound is a carboxylic acid. The structure of the compound is given in the formula.

4. a.

$$CH_3CH_2\overset{\displaystyle \text{O}}{\underset{\displaystyle \|}{C}}-\text{OCH}_3$$

b. propanoic acid + methanol yields methylpropanoate

5. Not all of the monomers in a polymer have to be the same. An example where they are not the same is synthetic rubber.

Key Terms

20.1 Organic chemistry

Biomolecule

Hydrocarbons

Saturated

Unsaturated

Alkanes

Unbranched hydrocarbons
(normal or straight chain)

Structural isomerism

Petroleum

Natural gas

Combustion reactions

Substitution reactions

Dehydrogenation reactions

20.2 Alkenes

Alkynes

Addition reactions

Hydrogenation reaction

Halogenation

Polymerization

Aromatic hydrocarbons

Benzene

Phenyl group

20.3 Functional groups

Alcohols

Key Ideas

20.1 Saturated Hydrocarbons

- Organic chemistry is the study of carbon-containing compounds and their properties.

- Most organic compounds contain chains or rings of carbon atoms.

- Hydrocarbons are organic compounds composed of carbon and hydrogen.
  - Alkanes are called saturated hydrocarbons because they have four single bonds (the maximum possible) to each carbon.
    - ◆ General formula C_nH_{2n+2}
    - ◆ Exhibit structural isomerism: molecules with the same atoms but different arrangements of atoms
    - ◆ Undergo substitution reactions
  - Petroleum is a mixture of hydrocarbons formed by decay of ancient marine organisms which is used as a source of energy.

20.2 Unsaturated Hydrocarbons

- Alkenes are unsaturated hydrocarbons which contain one or more double carbon–carbon bonds.
  - Named as alkanes with the final -*ane* replaced by -*ene*

- Alkynes are unsaturated hydrocarbons which contain one or more triple carbon–carbon bonds.
  - Named as alkanes with the final -*ane* replaced by -*yne*

- Undergo addition reactions

- Some alkenes form special aromatic rings that are unusually stable.

20.3 Introduction to Functional Groups and Alcohols

- Alcohols contain one or more —OH groups

- Alcohols are named by using the root name of the parent alkane and replacing the final -*e* with -*ol*.

RESEARCH LINKS
CLASSZONE.COM

Meeting Individual Needs

CHAPTER REVIEW

Chapter 20 Review Worksheet at the appropriate level:
Standard
Challenge

CHAPTER SUMMARY

A **Chapter Summary** that includes additional Active Reading Questions for Chapter 20 is available.

Assessment Resources

CHAPTER 20

Chapter 20 Test

TECHNOLOGY

 Computerized Test Bank for Chapter 20

20.4 Additional Organic Compounds

■ Aldehydes and ketones

• Contain the carbonyl $-\overset{\underset{\|}{O}}{C}-$ groups

• Aldehyde $R-\overset{\underset{\|}{O}}{C}-H$

♦ Are named by using the parent alkane root and *-al* ending

• Ketone $R-\overset{\underset{\|}{O}}{C}-R'$

♦ Are named by using the parent alkane root and *-al* ending

■ Carboxylic acids

• Contain the carbonyl $-C\overset{O}{\underset{O-H}{\diagdown}}$ group

• Named by dropping the *-e* from the parent alkane and adding
-oic and the word *acid*

• React with alcohols to form esters

• Esters are sweet smelling compounds named by using the alkyl
name from the alcohol followed by the acid name in which the
-ic ending is replaced by *-ate*

■ Polymers

• Large molecules made by hooking small molecules (monomers)
together

• Types of polymerization reactions

♦ Addition: where monomers simply add together

♦ Condensation: in which a small molecule (often water)
is formed for each extension of the polymer chain

RESEARCH LINKS
CLASSZONE.COM

Chapter 20 Assessment

1. Carbon has the unusual ability to bond strongly to itself, forming long chains or rings of carbon atoms. There are many possible arrangements for a long chain of carbon atoms, so there are many possible carbon compounds.

2. Four. Carbon atoms have four valence electrons. By making four bonds, carbon atoms complete their valence octet.

3. A double bond represents the sharing of an extra pair of electrons between two bonded atoms. Two examples are

```
H   H              H   H   H
 \ /                \  |  /
  C=C     and        C=C—C—H
 / \                /      \
H   H              H        H
```

4. four; tetrahedral

5. A saturated hydrocarbon is one in which all carbon–carbon bonds are single bonds, with each carbon atom forming bonds to four other atoms. The saturated hydrocarbons are called alkanes.

6. The geometry around each carbon is a tetrahedral, making the angles 109.5°. To be "straight," the angles would have to be 180°.

7. (a)

```
  H  H  H  H  H  H  H
  |  |  |  |  |  |  |
H—C—C—C—C—C—C—C—H
  |  |  |  |  |  |  |
  H  H  H  H  H  H  H
```

heptane,
$CH_3CH_2CH_2CH_2CH_2CH_2CH_3$

(b)

```
  H  H  H  H  H  H  H  H  H
  |  |  |  |  |  |  |  |  |
H—C—C—C—C—C—C—C—C—C—H
  |  |  |  |  |  |  |  |  |
  H  H  H  H  H  H  H  H  H
```

nonane,
$CH_3CH_2CH_2CH_2CH_2CH_2CH_2CH_2CH_3$

(c)

```
  H  H  H
  |  |  |
H—C—C—C—H
  |  |  |
  H  H  H
```

propane, $CH_3CH_2CH_3$

(d)

```
  H  H  H  H  H  H  H  H  H  H
  |  |  |  |  |  |  |  |  |  |
H—C—C—C—C—C—C—C—C—C—C—H
  |  |  |  |  |  |  |  |  |  |
  H  H  H  H  H  H  H  H  H  H
```

All exercises with blue numbers have answers in the back of this book.

20.1 Saturated Hydrocarbons

A. Carbon Bonding

1. What makes carbon able to form so many different compounds?

2. What is the maximum number of other atoms to which a given carbon atom can be attached? Why?

3. What does a double bond represent? Give two examples of molecules in which double bonds occur, and draw the Lewis structures of those molecules.

4. Structural representations of the hydrocarbon ethane are shown in Figure 20.2. To how many other atoms is each carbon atom bonded in ethane? What is the geometry around each carbon atom in ethane?

B. Alkanes

5. What does it mean to say that a hydrocarbon is *saturated*? To how many other atoms is each carbon atom in a saturated hydrocarbon bonded? What name is given to the family of saturated hydrocarbons?

6. Figure 20.3 shows the structures of the hydrocarbons propane and butane. Alkanes that contain an unbranched chain of carbon atoms are often called straight-chain alkanes. Why is such an unbranched chain not really "straight"? What are the bond angles between the carbon atoms in propane and butane?

7. For each of the following straight-chain alkanes, draw the structural formula.
   a. heptane
   b. nonane
   c. propane
   d. decane

8. Draw the structural formula for each of the following straight-chain alkanes.
   a. butane
   b. octane
   c. pentane
   d. hexane

C. Structural Formulas and Isomerism

9. What are structural *isomers*? What is the smallest alkane that has a structural isomer? Draw structures to illustrate the isomers.

10. What is a small chain of carbon atoms called when it is attached to a longer chain of carbon atoms?

11. Draw structural formulas for at least *five* isomeric alkanes having the formula C_6H_{14}.

D. Naming Alkanes

12. Give the *root names* for the alkanes with five through ten carbon atoms.

13. To what does the root name for a *branched* hydrocarbon correspond?

14. How is the *position* of substituents along the longest chain of a hydrocarbon indicated?

15. In giving the name of a hydrocarbon with several substituents, in what order do we list the substituents?

16. Give the systematic name for each of the following alkanes.

   a. CH_3—CH_2—CH—CH_2—CH_3
          |
          CH_2—CH_3

   b. CH_3
                |
        CH_3—C—CH_3
                |
                CH_2—CH_3

   c. CH_3 CH_3
          \   /
            C
          /   \
      CH_3 CH_3

   d. CH_3—CH—CH—CH—CH_3
              | | |
           CH_3 CH_3 CH_3

17. Draw structural formulas for each of the following compounds.
   a. 2-methylhexane
   b. 3-methylhexane
   c. 2,2-dimethylhexane
   d. 2,3-dimethylhexane
   e. 3,3-dimethylhexane

---

decane,
$CH_3CH_2CH_2CH_2CH_2CH_2CH_2CH_2CH_2CH_3$

8. (a)

```
  H  H  H  H
  |  |  |  |
H—C—C—C—C—H
  |  |  |  |
  H  H  H  H
```

(b)

```
  H  H  H  H  H  H  H  H
  |  |  |  |  |  |  |  |
H—C—C—C—C—C—C—C—C—H
  |  |  |  |  |  |  |  |
  H  H  H  H  H  H  H  H
```

(c)

```
  H  H  H  H  H
  |  |  |  |  |
H—C—C—C—C—C—H
  |  |  |  |  |
  H  H  H  H  H
```

(d)

```
  H  H  H  H  H  H
  |  |  |  |  |  |
H—C—C—C—C—C—C—H
  |  |  |  |  |  |
  H  H  H  H  H  H
```

9. Structural isomerism occurs when two molecules have the same atoms present, but those atoms are bonded differently. The molecules have the same formulas but different arrangements of the atoms. Butane and 2-methylpropane are examples.

$CH_3CH_2CH_2CH_3$ CH_3CHCH_3
                              |
                           CH_3
Butane   2-Methylpropane

E. Petroleum

18. What are the major constituents of crude petroleum? What is the major constituent of natural gas? How were these mixtures formed?

19. List several petroleum fractions and tell how each fraction is primarily used.

20. How is petroleum separated into its fractions?

21. What source of energy is the United States most dependent on today? How does this compare to 100 years ago?

F. Reactions of Alkanes

22. Explain why alkanes are relatively unreactive.

23. What is a *combustion* reaction? How have we made use of the combustion reactions of alkanes?

24. What is a *substitution* reaction? Give an example of a reactive molecule that is able to replace the hydrogen atoms of an alkane.

25. What is a *dehydrogenation* reaction? What results when an alkane is dehydrogenated?

26. Complete and balance each of the following chemical equations.

a. $C_6H_{14}(l) + O_2(g) \rightarrow$

b. $CH_4(g) + Cl_2(g) \rightarrow$

c. $CHCl_3(l) + Cl_2(g) \rightarrow$

20.2 Unsaturated Hydrocarbons

A. Alkenes and Alkynes

27. What is an alkene? What structural feature characterizes alkenes? Give the general formula for alkenes.

28. What is an alkyne? What structural feature characterizes alkynes? Give the general formula for alkynes.

29. Complete each of the following chemical equations:

a. $CH \equiv C - CH_3(g) + H_2(g) \rightarrow ?$

b. $CH_3 - CH = CH - CH_3(l) + Br_2(l) \rightarrow ?$

c. $CH_3 - C \equiv C - CH_3(l) + O_2(g) \rightarrow ?$

30. Give the systematic name for each of the following unsaturated hydrocarbons and substituted unsaturated compounds.

a. $CH_3 - CH = CH - CH_3$

b. $CH_3 - CH - CH = CH_2$
$\quad\quad\quad\; | $
$\quad\quad\quad CH_3$

c. $CH \equiv C - CH_2 - CH_3$

d. $CH_2 = CH - CH - CH_3$
$\quad\quad\quad\quad\quad | $
$\quad\quad\quad\quad\; Cl$

31. Draw structural formulas, and give the systematic names, for at least *four* isomeric hydrocarbons containing seven carbon atoms and one double bond.

B. Aromatic Hydrocarbons

32. What structure do all aromatic hydrocarbons have in common?

33. Benzene exhibits resonance. Explain this statement in terms of the different Lewis structures that can be drawn for benzene.

C. Naming Aromatic Compounds

34. How is a monosubstituted benzene named? Give the structures and names of two examples. Also give two examples of monosubstituted benzenes that have special names.

35. What do the prefixes *ortho-*, *meta-*, and *para-* refer to in terms of the relative location of substituents in a disubstituted benzene?

36. Draw a structural formula for each of the following aromatic or substituted aromatic compounds.

a. naphthalene

b. 2-bromophenol

c. 3-methylstyrene

d. 4-nitrochlorobenzene

e. 1,3-dinitrobenzene

Chapter 20 • Assessment • **745**

13. The root name is derived from the number of carbon atoms in the longest continuous chain of carbon atoms.

14. The position of a substituent is indicated by a number that corresponds to the carbon atom in the longest chain to which the substituent is attached.

15. Multiple substituents are listed in alphabetical order, disregarding any prefix.

16. (a) 3-ethylpentane
(b) 2,2-dimethylbutane
(c) 2,2-dimethylpropane
(d) 2,3,4-trimethylpentane

17. (a)
$CH_3 - CH - CH_2 - CH_2 - CH_2 - CH_3$
$\quad\quad\quad | $
$\quad\quad CH_3$

(b)
$CH_3 - CH_2 - CH - CH_2 - CH_2 - CH_3$
$\quad\quad\quad\quad\quad | $
$\quad\quad\quad\quad CH_3$

(c)
$\quad\quad\quad CH_3$
$\quad\quad\quad | $
$CH_3 - C - CH_2 - CH_2 - CH_2 - CH_3$
$\quad\quad\quad | $
$\quad\quad\quad CH_3$

(d)
$CH_3 - CH - CH - CH_2 - CH_2 - CH_3$
$\quad\quad\quad | \quad\quad | $
$\quad\quad CH_3 \;\; CH_3$

(e)
$\quad\quad\quad\quad\quad CH_3$
$\quad\quad\quad\quad\quad | $
$CH_3 - CH_2 - C - CH_2 - CH_2 - CH_3$
$\quad\quad\quad\quad\quad | $
$\quad\quad\quad\quad\quad CH_3$

18. Petroleum is a thick, dark liquid composed mainly of hydrocarbons containing from 5 to more than 25 carbon atoms. Natural gas consists mostly of methane, but may also contain significant amounts of ethane, propane, and butane. These substances were formed over the eons from the decay of living organisms.

10. a branch or substituent

11. With six carbon atoms, there are five isomers possible. Here are the carbon skeletons:

$C-C-C-C-C-C$

$C-C-C-C-C$
$\quad\; | $
$\quad\; C$

$C-C-C-C-C$
$\quad\quad\; | $
$\quad\quad\; C$

$C-C-C-C$
$\quad | \quad | $
$\quad C \quad C$

$\quad\quad C$
$\quad\quad | $
$C-C-C-C$
$\quad\; | $
$\quad\; C$

12.

Number of Carbons	Root Name
5	pentane (*pent-*)
6	hexane (*hex-*)
7	heptane (*hept-*)
8	octane (*oct-*)

19.

Number of Carbon Atoms	Use
5–12	gasoline
10–18	kerosene, jet fuel
15–25	diesel fuel, heating oil

Chapter 20 • Assessment • **745**

20. Petroleum is separated into its fractions by boiling or distilling.

21. The United States is most dependent on petroleum and natural gas today. 100 years ago, the United States was most dependent on wood.

22. Alkanes are relatively unreactive because the C—C and C—H bonds that characterize these substances are relatively strong and difficult to break.

23. Combustion represents the vigorous reaction of a hydrocarbon (or other substance) with oxygen. Combustion has been used as a source of heat and light.

24. In a substitution reaction, one or more hydrogen atoms in an alkane are replaced by another type of atom. Because of the unreactivity of alkanes, only very vigorous reactants (such as the halogens) are able to substitute for the hydrogen atoms of alkanes.

25. Dehydrogenation reactions involve the removal of hydrogen atoms from adjacent carbon atoms in an alkane (or other substance). When two hydrogen atoms are removed from an alkane, a double bond is formed.

26. (a) $2C_6H_{14}(l) + 19O_2(g) \rightarrow 12CO_2(g) + 14H_2O(g)$
(b) $CH_4(g) + Cl_2(g) \rightarrow CH_3Cl(l) + HCl(g)$
(c) $CHCl_3(l) + Cl_2(g) \rightarrow CCl_4(l) + HCl(g)$

27. Alkenes are hydrocarbons that contain a carbon–carbon double bond. The general formula for alkenes is C_nH_{2n} where n is the number of carbon atoms present.

28. An alkyne is a hydrocarbon containing a carbon–carbon triple bond. The general formula is CnH_{2n-2} where n is the number of carbon atoms present.

---

37. Name each of the following aromatic or substituted aromatic compounds.

a.

b.

c.

d.

20.3 Introduction to Functional Groups and Alcohols

A. Functional Groups

38. On the basis of the functional groups listed in Table 20.6, identify the family of organic compounds to which each of the following belongs.

a. $CH_3—CH_2—CH_2—CH_2—CH_2—OH$
b. $CH_3—CH_2—C=O$ with $CH_2—CH_3$
c. $H_2N—CH_2—CH_2—CH_3$
d. $CH_3—CH_2—CH_2—C=O$ with H

39. On the basis of the functional groups listed in Table 20.5, identify the family of organic compounds to which each of the following belongs.

a. $CH_3CH_2—O—CH_2CH_2CH_3$
b. $CH_3CH_2CH_2CH_2—OH$
c. $CH_3CH_2CHCH_3$ with OH
d. $CH_3CH_2CH_2CH_2COOH$

B. Alcohols

40. What functional group characterizes an alcohol? What ending is added to the name of the parent hydrocarbon to show that a molecule is an alcohol?

---

41. Distinguish among primary, secondary, and tertiary alcohols. Give a structural formula for an example of each type.

42. Give the systematic name for each of the following alcohols. Indicate whether the alcohol is primary, secondary, or tertiary.

a. $CH_3CH_2CH_2CH_2CH_2—OH$
b.
CH_3
$CH_3CCH_2CH_3$
OH
c. $CH_3CH_2CHCH_2CH_3$ with OH
d. $CH_3CH_2CH_2—OH$

43. Draw structural formulas for each of the following alcohols. Indicate whether the alcohol is primary, secondary, or tertiary.

a. 1-pentanol
b. 2-pentanol
c. 3-pentanol
d. 3-methyl-3-pentanol

C. Properties and Uses of Alcohols

44. Why is methanol sometimes called wood alcohol? Describe the modern synthesis of methanol. What are some uses of methanol?

45. Write the equation for the fermentation of glucose to form ethanol. Why can't ethanol solutions of greater than about 13% concentration be made directly by fermentation? How can the ethanol content be increased beyond this level in beverages?

46. Write the equation for the synthesis of ethanol from ethylene. What are some commercial uses of ethanol made by this process?

47. Give the names and structural formulas of two other commercially important alcohols. Cite the major use of each.

20.4 Additional Organic Compounds

A. Aldehydes and Ketones

48. What functional group is *common* to both aldehydes and ketones?

49. What structural feature *distinguishes* aldehydes from ketones?

---

29. (a) $CH_3CH_2CH_3(g)$
(b) $CH_3CHBrCHBrCH_3(g)$
(c) $CO_2(g)$ and $H_2O(g)$ (coefficients of 8 and 6, respectively)

30. (a) 2-butene
(b) 3-methyl-1-butene
(c) 1-butyne
(d) 3-chloro-1-butene

31. The most obvious choices would be the *normal* alkenes with seven carbon atoms:

$CH_2=CH—CH_2—CH_2—CH_2—CH_2—CH_3$
1-Heptene

$CH_3—CH=CH—CH_2—CH_2—CH_2—CH_3$
2-Heptene

$CH_3—CH_2—CH=CH—CH_2—CH_2—CH_3$
3-Heptene

Additional choices are shorter-chain alkenes with branches, such as

$CH_2=C—CH_2—CH_2—CH_2—CH_3$ with CH_3
2-Methyl-1-hexene

$CH_3—C=CH—CH_2—CH_2—CH_3$ with CH_3
2-Methyl-2-hexene

32. Aromatic hydrocarbons all contain a benzene ring (phenyl group).

B. Naming Aldehydes and Ketones

50. Give the systematic name for each of the following:

a. $CH_3-CH_2-CH_2-C=O$
  with CH_2-CH_3 below the C

b. $CH_3-CH-CH-C=O$
  with Cl, Cl, H below

c.
  $CH_3-CH-CH-CH_2-C=O$
  with CH_3 above the first CH, CH_3 below, H below the C=O

d.
  $CH_3-CH-C=O$
  with CH_3 above, H below

e. $CH_3-CH_2-C=O$
  with phenyl ring below

51. Draw a structural formula for each of the following:

a. phenyl methyl ketone
b. butanal
c. butanone
d. dipropylketone
e. 4-heptanone

C. Carboxylic Acids and Esters

52. Are carboxylic acids typically strong acids or weak acids? Write an equation showing the acid CH_3CH_2COOH ionizing in water.

53. Draw the structure of acetylsalicylic acid, and circle the portion of the molecule that shows that it is an ester. From what acid and alcohol is acetylsalicylic acid synthesized?

54. Give the systematic name for each of the following:

a. $CH_3-CH-CH_2-COOH$
  with CH_3 below

b. phenyl ring$-COOH$

c. $CH_3-CH-COOH$
  with OH below

d. $CH_3-CH_2-CH-CH-CH_2-COOH$
  with CH_3 above, CH_3 below

55. Draw a structural formula for each of the following:

a. 3-methylpentanoic acid
b. ethyl methanoate
c. methyl benzoate
d. 2-bromobutanoic acid
e. 3-chloro-2,4-dimethylhexanoic acid

D. Polymers

56. What, in general terms, is a polymer? What is a monomer?

57. What is a polyester? What structural feature characterizes polyesters? Give an example of a common polyester.

58. Draw the structures of acrylonitrile and butadiene. Also draw the structures of the basic repeating units when each of these substances polymerizes. Give several uses of each polymeric substance.

59. For the polymeric substances nylon and Dacron, sketch representations of the repeating unit in each.

33. A set of equivalent Lewis structures can be drawn for benzene. Each structure differs only in the location of the three double bonds in the ring. Experimentally, benzene does not have the chemical properties expected for molecules having double bonds.

34. The systematic method for naming monosubstituted benzenes uses the substituent name as a *prefix* for the word *benzene*. Examples are

Cl on benzene ring — Chlorobenzene

CH_2CH_3 on benzene ring — Ethylbenzene

Two monosubstituted benzenes with their own special names are

CH_3 on benzene ring — Toluene (methylbenzene)

OH on benzene ring — Phenol (hydroxybenzene)

35. *ortho*-: adjacent substituents (1,2-);
meta-: two substituents with one unsubstituted carbon between them (1,3-);
para-: two substituents with two unsubstituted carbon atoms between them (1,4-)

36. (a) naphthalene structure

(b) OH and Br on benzene ring

(c) $CH=CH_2$ and CH_3 on benzene ring

(d) Cl and NO_2 on benzene ring

(e) NO_3 and NO_3 on benzene ring

37. (a) 1,2-dimethylbenzene (*o*-xylene is the common name)
(b) 1,2,3,4,5,6-hexachlorobenzene
(c) anthracene
(d) 3,5-dichloro-1-methylbenzene (3,5-dichlorotoluene)

38. (a) alcohol (primary)
(b) ketone
(c) amine
(d) aldehyde

39. (a) ether
(b) alcohol (primary)
(c) alcohol (secondary)
(d) organic (carboxylic) acid

40. Alcohols are characterized by the presence of the hydroxyl group, —OH. To name an alcohol, the final -*e* is dropped from the name of the parent hydrocarbon and the ending -*ol* is added. A locator may also be necessary to indicate the location of the hydroxyl group.

41. Primary alcohols have one hydrocarbon fragment (alkyl group) bonded to the carbon atom where the —OH group is attached. Secondary alcohols have two alkyl groups attached, and tertiary alcohols contain three alkyl groups. Examples are

Ethanol (primary) $CH_3—CH_2—OH$

2-Propanol (secondary) $CH_3—CH—CH_3$
  |
  OH

2-Methyl-2-propanol (tertiary)
  CH_3
  |
$CH_3—C—CH_3$
  |
  OH

42. (a) 1-pentanol (primary)
(b) 2-methyl-2-butanol (tertiary)
(c) 3-pentanol (secondary)
(d) 1-propanol (primary)

43. (a) $CH_3—CH_2—CH_2—CH_2—CH_2—OH$
(primary)

(b) $CH_3—CH_2—CH_2—CH—CH_3$
  |
  OH
(secondary)

(c) $CH_3—CH_2—CH—CH_2—CH_3$
  |
  OH
(secondary)

(d)
  CH_3
  |
$CH_3—CH_2—C—CH_2—CH_3$
  |
  OH
(tertiary)

44. Methanol is sometimes called wood alcohol because it was formerly obtained by heating wood in the absence of air (also called destructive distillation of wood). Currently it is prepared by the catalyzed hydrogenation of carbon monoxide. Methanol is an important industrial chemical produced in large amounts every year. It is used as a starting material for the synthesis of acetic acid and of many other important substances. Methanol is also used as a motor fuel for high-performance engines.

45. $C_6H_{12}O_6 \rightarrow 2CH_3CH_2OH + 2CO_2$ (yeast is a catalyst). The yeast are killed if the concentration of alcohol is greater than 13%. To make more concentrated ethanol solutions, distillation is needed.

---

60. Write the *general* formula for a normal alkane. How does a given alkane differ from the previous or the following member of the series?

61. Draw structural formulas for all isomeric alkanes having the general formula C_5H_{12}.

62. Give the systematic name of each of the following substituted alkanes.

a. $CH_3—CH—CH_2—CH_3$
  |
  Cl

b. $CH_2—CH_2$
  | |
  Br   Br

c. CHI_3

d. $CH_3—CH—CH—CH—CH_3$
  | | |
  Cl   Cl   Cl

e.
  Cl
  |
$CH_3—C—CH_2—CH—CH_2—CH_2—CH_3$
  | |
  Cl $CH_3—CH—CH_3$

63. Write a structural formula for each of the following compounds.

a. 2,3-dimethylheptane
b. 2,2-dimethyl-3-chloro-1-octanol
c. 2-chloro-1-hexene
d. 1-chloro-2-hexene
e. 2-methylphenol

64. Draw the structural formula(s) for, and give the name(s) of, the organic product(s) of each of the following reactions. If a mixture of several, similar products is expected, indicate the type of product expected.

a. $CH_3—CH_3 + Cl_2 \xrightarrow{\text{Light}}$

b. $CH_3—CH{=}CH—CH_3 + H_2 \xrightarrow{\text{Pt}}$

c. $CH_3—CH_2$
        \
          $C{=}CH—CH_3 + Br_2 \longrightarrow$
        /
$CH_3—CH_2$

---

65. The alcohol glycerol (glycerine), which is produced in the human body by the digestion of fats, has the following structure. Give the systematic name of glycerol.

$CH_2—CH—CH_2$
  | | |
  OH   OH   OH

66. The sugar glucose could conceivably be given the name 2,3,4,5,6-pentahydroxyhexanal (though this name is never used, because the actual sugar glucose is only one possible isomer having this name). Draw the structure implied by this name.

67. Draw a structure corresponding to each of the following names.

a. 2-methylpentanal
b. 3-hydroxybutanoic acid
c. 2-aminopropanal
d. 2,4-hexanedione
e. 3-methylbenzaldehyde

68. On the basis of the functional groups listed in Table 20.6, identify the family of organic compounds to which each of the following belongs.

a.
  (benzene ring)$—CH_2—CH_2—C{=}O$
                              |
                              OH

b. $CH_3—CH_2—CH_2—C{=}O$
                      |
                  (benzene ring)

c. $CH_3—CH_2—C{=}O$
                |
              $O—CH_2—CH_2—$(benzene ring)

d.
  (benzene ring)$—OH$
                $—CH_2—CH_3$

---

46. Although much ethanol is produced each year by means of the fermentation process, this compound is also produced synthetically by hydration of ethene (ethylene).

$CH_2{=}CH_2 + H_2O \rightarrow CH_3—CH_2OH$

Ethanol is used in industry as a solvent and as a starting material for the synthesis of more complicated molecules. Mixtures of ethanol and gasoline are used as automobile motor fuels (gasohol).

47. Methanol (CH_3OH): starting material for synthesis of acetic acid and many plastics; isopropyl alcohol (2-propanol, $CH_3—CH(OH)—CH_3$): rubbing alcohol

48. Aldehydes and ketones both contain the carbonyl functional group.

49. The location of the carbonyl group ($C{=}O$). Aldehydes contain the carbonyl group at the end of a hydrocarbon chain. Ketones contain the carbonyl group in the interior of a hydrocarbon chain.

(continued on page 749a)

1 Which of the following is a saturated hydrocarbon?

A C_3H_6

B C_2H_4

C C_4H_{10}

D C_5H_{10}

2 While studying together, your friend names a molecule 3-methyl-4-isopropylpentane. You point out that although the correct structure could be drawn from this name, the name did not follow systematic rules. What is the correct systematic name for the molecule?

A   3,4,5-trimethylhexane

B   2,3,4-trimethylhexane

C   2-isopropyl-3-methylpentane

D   1,1,2,3-tetramethylpentane

3 Which of the following names is a **correct** one?

A   3,4-dichloropentane

B   1,1-dimethyl-2,2-diethylbutane

C   4-pentene

D   2-bromo-1-chloro-4,4-diethyloctane

4 The name for the alkene with the skeletal structure C—C—C=C is

A   3-butene, because the double bond is after the third carbon.

B   2-butene because in this case you count from the right, and the double bond is before the second carbon.

C   1-butene because in this case you count from the right, and the double bond is after the first carbon.

D   4-butene, because the double bond is on a molecule with 4 carbon atoms.

5 Which of the following has a C=O bond?

A   ester, aldehyde, secondary alcohol, ketone

B   secondary alcohol, ketone, aldehyde

C   ester, aldehyde, ketone

D   carboxylic acid, ether, tertiary alcohol

6 How many isomers does pentane have?

A   4

B   3

C   2

D   1

7 What functional groups are present in aspirin (acetylsalicylic acid) as shown below?

A   carboxylic acid, alcohol

B   ether, alcohol

C   carboxylic acid, ester

D   ketone, ether

8 Name each of the following molecules.

a.

b. CH_3CHCH_2OH
         |
        CH_3

c. CH_3CH_2C—H
            ‖
           O

d. $CH_3CCH_2CH_3$
          ‖
          O

9 There are two isomers with the formula C_2H_6O.

a.   Draw Lewis structures for each of these molecules.

b.   Circle and label the functional group for each of the molecules.

c.   Which of the molecules would exhibit the stronger intermolecular forces? Explain your answer.

---

1. C

2. B

3. D

4. C

5. C

6. B

7. C

8. a. 1,3-dinitrobenzene, or *m*-dinitrobenzene

    b. 2-methyl-1-propanol

    c. propanal

    d. 2-butanone

9. a,b.

    c. Ethanol (the molecule on the left) would exhibit stronger intermolecular forces than dimethyl ether (the molecule on the right). This is because ethanol exhibits hydrogen bonding because of the —OH group.

Test Taking Strategy

Remind students to read each answer choice of an organic chemistry question carefully, as they just learned in this chapter how closely related the naming of various compounds are. Encourage students to highlight or circle the part of a chemical name that is the most important to avoid making quick careless errors.

Assessment Resources
CHAPTER 20

For additional practice with standardized testing, see *Standardized Test Practice* located in the *Teacher Resources*.

(continued from page 748)

50. (a) 3-hexanone (ethyl propyl ketone)
(b) 2,3-dichlorobutanal (2,3-dichlorobutyraldehyde)
(c) 3,4-dimethylpentanal
(d) 2-methylpropanal
(e) ethyl phenyl ketone

51. (a)

Ø—C—CH₃ (Ø = phenyl group)
║
O

(b)

CH₃—CH₂—CH₂—C—H
                        ‖
                        O

(c)

CH₃—CH₂—C—CH₃
              ‖
              O

(d)

CH₃—CH₂—CH₂—C—CH₂—CH₂—CH₃
                        ‖
                        O

(e)

CH₃—CH₂—CH₂—C—CH₂—CH₂—CH₃
                        ‖
                        O

52. Carboxylic acids are typically weak acids.

$$CH_3CH_2COOH + H_2O \rightleftharpoons$$
$$CH_3CH_2COO^- + H_3O^+$$

53. Acetylsalicylic acid is synthesized from salicylic acid (behaving as an alcohol through its —OH group) and acetic acid.

54. (a) 3-methylbutanoic acid
(b) benzoic acid
(c) 2-hydroxypropanoic acid
(d) 3,4-dimethylhexanoic acid

55. (a)

CH₃—CH₂—CH—CH₂—COOH
                    |
                    CH₃

(b)

H—C=O
        |
        O—CH₂—CH₃

(c)

Ø—C=O   (Ø = phenyl group)
      |
      O—CH₃

(d)

CH₃—CH₂—CH—COOH
                |
                Br

(e)

CH₃—CH₂—CH—CH—CH—COOH
                | | |
                CH₃ Cl   CH₃

56. Polymers are large, usually chainlike, molecules that are built from smaller molecules. The smaller molecules may combine and repeat in the chain of the polymer hundreds or thousands of times. The small molecules from which polymers are constructed are called monomers.

57. A polyester is a polymer in which the polymerization forms an ester group. The repeating unit is an ester; thus there are many esters, or "polyesters." Dacron is an example.

58. Carpets, fabrics

Acrylonitrile

        H
        |
H₂C=C
        |
        CN

Polyacrylnitrile (PAN)

$-(CH_2-CH)_{\overline{n}}$
            |
            CN

Tire tread, coating resin

Butadiene

        H H
        | |
H₂C=C—C=CH₂

Polybutadiene

$-(CH_2CH=CHCH_2)_{\overline{n}}$

59. Nylon

$$-\left(\overset{H}{N}-(CH_2)_6-\overset{H}{N}-\overset{O}{C}-(CH_2)_4-\overset{O}{C}\right)-$$

Dacron

$$-\left(O-CH_2-CH_2-O-\overset{O}{C}-\underset{}{\bigcirc}-\overset{O}{C}\right)-$$

60. The general formula is C_nH_{2n+2}. Each successive alkane differs from the preceding or following alkane by CH_2 (a methylene unit).

61. The carbon skeletons are

C—C—C—C—C

C—C—C—C
       |
       C

C—C—C
   |
   C
   |
   C

62. (a) 2-chlorobutane
(b) 1,2-dibromoethane
(c) triiodomethane (common name: iodoform)
(d) 2,3,4-trichloropentane
(e) 2,2-dichloro-4-isopropylheptane

63. (a)

$$CH_3-\underset{\underset{CH_3}{|}}{CH}-\underset{\underset{CH_3}{|}}{CH}-CH_2-CH_2-CH_2-CH_3$$

(b)

$$CH_3-CH_2-CH_2-CH_2-CH_2-CH-\underset{\underset{CH_3}{|}}{\overset{\overset{CH_3}{|}}{C}}-CH_2-OH$$
(with Cl below the C)

$$CH_3-CH_2-CH_2-CH_2-CH_2-\underset{\underset{Cl}{|}}{CH}-\underset{\underset{CH_3}{|}}{\overset{\overset{CH_3}{|}}{C}}-CH_2-OH$$

(c)

$$CH_3-CH_2-CH_2-CH_2-\underset{\underset{Cl}{|}}{C}=CH_2$$

(d) $CH_3-CH_2-CH_2-CH=CH-CH_2-Cl$

(e)

$$\underset{}{\bigcirc}\overset{OH}{\underset{CH_3}{}}$$

64. (a) CH_3-CH_2Cl, chloroethane, CH_2Cl-CH_2Cl, 1,2-dichloroethane, and various other chlorosubstituted ethanes
(b) $CH_3-CH_2-CH_2-CH_3$, butane
(c)

$$\underset{CH_3-CH_2}{\overset{CH_3-CH_2}{}}CBr-CHBr-CH_3,\ 2,2\text{-dibromo-3-ethylpentane}$$

65. 1,2,3-trihydroxypropane (1,2,3-propanetriol)

66.

$$CH_2-CH-CH-CH-CH-C=O$$
$$\ \ |\ \ \ \ |\ \ \ \ |\ \ \ \ |\ \ \ \ |\ \ \ \ \ |$$
$$OH\ \ OH\ \ OH\ \ OH\ \ OH\ \ H$$

67. (a)

$$CH_3-CH_2-CH_2-\underset{\underset{CH_3}{|}}{CH}-\overset{\overset{H}{|}}{C}=O$$

(b) $CH_3-\underset{\underset{OH}{|}}{CH}-CH_2-COOH$

(c)

$$CH_3-\underset{\underset{NH_2}{|}}{CH}-\overset{\overset{H}{|}}{C}=O$$

(d)

$$CH_3-\underset{\underset{O}{||}}{C}-CH_2-\underset{\underset{O}{||}}{C}-CH_2-CH_3$$

(e)

$$H\underset{}{\overset{C=O}{\diagdown}}\ \underset{}{\bigcirc}\overset{}{\underset{CH_3}{}}$$

68. (a) carboxylic acid
(b) ketone
(c) ester
(d) alcohol (phenol)

Planning Guide

Section	Segment		Text Features and Components	Labs, Demonstrations, & Activities
21.1 **Introduction to Proteins** 2 Blocks pp. 752–761	A	Proteins		
	B	Primary Structure of Proteins		**TE** Mini-Demo *p. 755*
	C	Secondary Structure of Proteins		
	D	Tertiary Structure of Proteins		**TE** Mini-Demo *p. 758*
	E	Functions of Proteins		**TE** Mini-Demo *p. 758*
	F	Enzymes	**SE** Chemistry in Your World: Urine Farming *p. 761*	**LM** Experiment 90: Enzymes in Food Lab Manual Report Sheets Teacher's Lab Guide
21.2 **Carbohydrates, Nucleic Acids, and Lipds** 2 Blocks pp. 762–775	A	Carbohydrates	**SE** Top Ten Sugar-Consuming Countries *p. 763* **SE** Celebrity Chemical: Aspartame *p. 765*	**LM** Experiment 91: Vitamin C in Juices, Microscale Lab Manual Report Sheets Teacher's Lab Guide
	B	Nucleic Acids		
	C	Lipids	**SE** Chemistry Explorers: Percy Julian *p. 773*	**SE** Hands-On Chemistry: Colorful Milk *p. 772*

Key			
SE Student Edition	**TE** Teacher Edition	**RP** Teacher Resource Package	
AR Additional Materials	**LM** Lab Materials	**▤** Transparencies	
◉ DVD	**▷** CD-ROM	**ⓘ** classzone.com	

All Learners	Technology	Review & Assessment	Standards
TE Teaching Tip *p. 753*	**EasyPlanner**	**SE** Key Terms *p. 776* **SE** Questions and Problems *p. 778*	**TE** **NSES** UCP1, UCP3, UCP5, A1, A2, B2, C5, E1, E2
TE Teaching Tips *pp. 754–755*	**EasyPlanner**	**SE** Active Reading Question *p. 755* **TE** More Examples *p. 756* **SE** Key Terms *p. 776* **SE** Questions and Problems *p. 778*	
TE Meeting Individual Needs *p. 756* **TE** Meeting Individual Needs *p. 757*	**Transparency: Figure 21.3** **EasyPlanner**	**SE** Active Reading Question *p. 757* **SE** Key Terms *p. 776* **SE** Questions and Problems *p. 778*	
TE Teaching Tip *p. 758*	**EasyPlanner**	**SE** Key Terms *p. 776* **SE** Questions and Problems *p. 778*	
	EasyPlanner	**SE** Key Terms *p. 776* **SE** Questions and Problems *p. 778*	
TE Teaching Tip *p. 760* **RP** Team Learning Worksheet (Sec. 21.1)	**Lab Generator CD** **EasyPlanner**	**SE** Active Reading Question *p. 760* **SE** Review Questions (21.1.A–21.1.F) *p. 761* **SE** Key Terms *p. 776* **SE** Questions and Problems *pp. 778–779*	
TE Teaching Tips *pp. 762–763, 766* **RP** MINT: Challenge Projects *TE p. 762*	**Lab Generator CD** **EasyPlanner**	**SE** Active Reading Question *p. 764* **SE** Key Terms *p. 777* **SE** Questions and Problems *p. 779*	**TE** **NSES** UCP1, UCP5, A1, A2, B2, B3, C2, C5, E1, E2, F2, F6
TE Teaching Tips *pp. 766, 768* **TE** Meeting Individual Needs *p. 767* **TE** Meeting Individual Needs *p. 768*	**EasyPlanner**	**SE** Active Reading Question *p. 766* **SE** Active Reading Question *p. 768* **SE** Key Terms *p. 777* **SE** Questions and Problems *p. 779*	
TE Teaching Tips *pp. 769–771* **TE** Meeting Individual Needs *p. 774* **RP** Team Learning Worksheet (Sec. 21.2)	**Transparency: Figure 21.20** **Animation: Micelle Formation** **EasyPlanner**	**SE** Active Reading Question *p. 771* **SE** Review Questions (21.2.A–21.2.C) *p. 775* **SE** Key Terms *p. 777* **SE** Questions and Problems *p. 779*	

Resource Materials for Chapter 21

SE Chapter Review *pp. 776–777*

SE Critical Thinking *p. 780*

SE Standardized Test Practice *p. 781*

AR English/Spanish Summaries

English Summaries Audio

Spanish Summaries Audio

RP Meeting Individual Needs Toolkit (MINT)
    Challenge Projects
    Chapter Review Worksheets
    Chapter Summaries

RP Solutions Guide

RP Standardized Test Practice

RP Chapter Tests

RP Test Bank

Test Generator

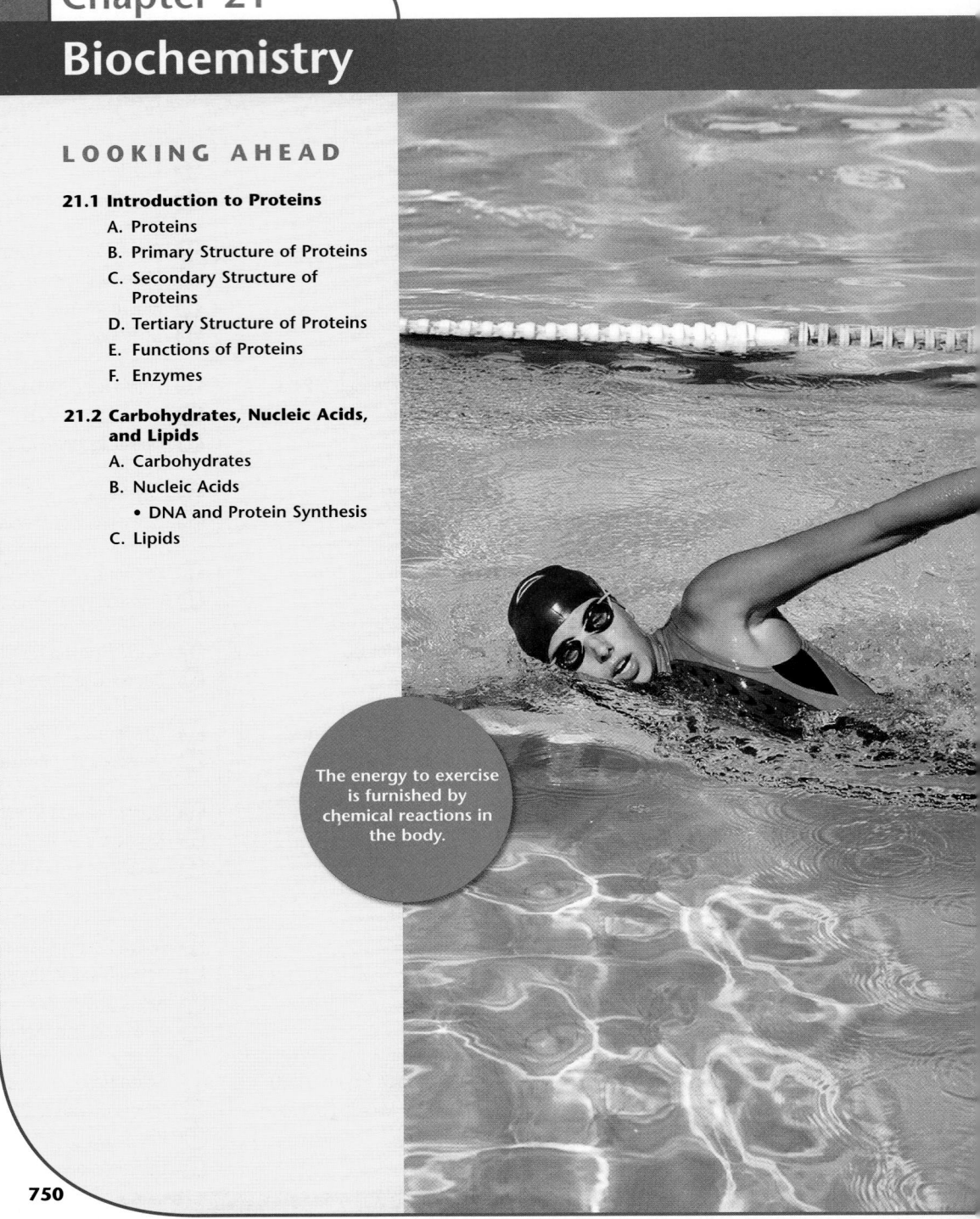

Chapter 21
Overview

In this chapter our goals are for students to:

- Learn about proteins
- Understand the primary structure of proteins
- Understand the secondary structure of proteins
- Understand the tertiary structure of proteins
- Learn about the various functions served by proteins
- Understand how enzymes work
- Understand the fundamental properties of carbohydrates
- Understand the fundamental nucleic acid structure
- Learn the four classes of lipids

Chapter 21
Biochemistry

The energy to exercise is furnished by chemical reactions in the body.

750

IN YOUR LIFE

Biochemistry, the study of the chemistry of living systems, is a vast and exciting field in which important discoveries about how life is maintained and how diseases occur are being made every day. In particular, there has been rapid growth in the understanding of how living cells manufacture and use the molecules necessary for life. This not only has been beneficial for detection and treatment of diseases but also has spawned a new field—**biotechnology**, which uses nature's "machinery" to synthesize desired substances. For example, insulin is a complex biomolecule that is used in the body to regulate the metabolism of sugars. People who have diabetes are deficient in natural insulin and must take insulin by injection or other means. In the past this insulin was obtained from animal tissues (particularly that of cows). However, our increased understanding of the biochemical processes of the cell has allowed us to "farm" insulin. We have learned to insert the "instructions" for making insulin into the cells of bacteria such as *E. coli* so that as the bacteria grow they produce insulin that can then be harvested for use by diabetics. Many other products, including natural pesticides, are also being produced by the techniques of biotechnology.

An understanding of biochemistry also allows our society to produce healthier processed foods. For example, the food industry is making great efforts to reduce the fat levels in food without destroying the good taste that fats bring to food.

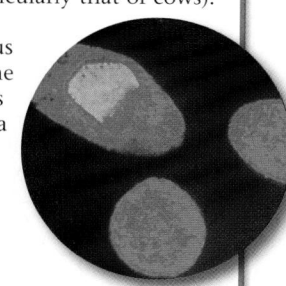

This sample of E. coli bacteria has been genetically altered to produce human insulin. The insulin production sites are colored orange. The bacteria are cultured and pure human insulin is harvested from them.

WHAT DO YOU KNOW?

Prereading Questions

1. What is meant by the phrase "like dissolves like"?

2. What do catalysts do to a chemical reaction?

3. What is a carbohydrate?

4. What do you know about DNA?

5. What do you know about the term "gene"?

Biochemistry • Chapter 21 • **751**

Prereading Questions

1. Polar solvents will dissolve polar solutes. Nonpolar solvents will dissolve nonpolar solutes.

2. A catalyst lowers the activation energy for a chemical reaction. Thus, at a given temperature, more molecules have enough energy to react. This speeds up the chemical reaction.

3. Many students will know that carbohydrates serve as food sources for organisms and that sugars are carbohydrates.

4. *Answers will vary.* Some students may be aware that DNA stores and transmits genetic information.

5. *Answers will vary.* Some students will know that a gene is a segment of DNA that contains a genetic code.

TECHNOLOGY IN THE CLASSROOM

 Transparencies
Figures: 21.3, 21.20

 Power Presentation DVD
PowerPoint Slides
Animation
Micelle Formation
eEdition
EasyPlanner

 Lab Generator CD
English Summaries CD
Spanish Summaries CD
ML Test Generator

 classzone.com

Student Preparation

Assign students to read Section 21.1 and to answer the Review Questions at the end of the section before coming to class.

 Active Learning
Team Learning Worksheet

After introducing the material in Section 21.1 in class, place students in groups and have them work together on **Section 21.1: Team Learning Worksheet.**

Homework

You may wish to assign these selected end-of-chapter problems as homework for this section:
2, 4, 5, 7, 8, 9a–b, 12, 13, 14, 16, 19, 21, 22, 23, 26

Additional end-of-chapter problems can be used for extra practice.

Introduction to Proteins

Key Terms

- Essential elements
- Trace elements
- Cell
- Proteins
- Fibrous proteins
- Globular proteins
- Alpha-amino acids
- Side chains
- Dipeptide
- Peptide linkage
- Polypeptide
- Primary structure
- Secondary structure
- Alpha-helix
- Pleated sheet
- Tertiary structure
- Disulfide linkage
- Denaturation
- Enzymes
- Lock-and-key model
- Substrate
- Active site

Objectives

- *To learn about proteins*
- *To understand the primary structure of proteins*
- *To understand the secondary structure of proteins*
- *To understand the tertiary structure of proteins*
- *To learn the functions of proteins*
- *To understand how enzymes work*

At present, 30 elements are definitely known to be essential to human life. These **essential elements** are shown in color in **Figure 21.1.** The most abundant elements are hydrogen, carbon, nitrogen, and oxygen; sodium, magnesium, potassium, calcium, phosphorus, sulfur, and chlorine are also present in relatively large amounts. Although present only in trace amounts, the first-row transition metals are essential for the action of many enzymes (biological catalysts). For example, zinc, one of the **trace elements**, is found in nearly 200 biologically important molecules. The functions of the essential elements are summarized in **Table 21.1.** In time, other elements will probably be found to be essential.

Life is organized around the functions of the **cell**, the smallest unit in living things that exhibits the properties normally associated with life, such as reproduction, metabolism, mutation, and sensitivity to external stimuli.

As the fundamental building blocks of all living systems, aggregates of cells form tissues, which in turn are assembled into the organs that make up complex living systems. Therefore, to understand how life is maintained and reproduced, we must learn how cells operate on the molecular level. This is the main thrust of biochemistry.

Essential elements
The 30 elements currently known to be essential to human life

Trace elements
First-row transition metals that are present in very small (trace) amounts in the human body

1																	8
1 H	2											3	4	5	6	7	2 He
3 Li	4 Be											5 B	6 C	7 N	8 O	9 F	10 Ne
11 Na	12 Mg											13 Al	14 Si	15 P	16 S	17 Cl	18 Ar
19 K	20 Ca	21 Sc	22 Ti	23 V	24 Cr	25 Mn	26 Fe	27 Co	28 Ni	29 Cu	30 Zn	31 Ga	32 Ge	33 As	34 Se	35 Br	36 Kr
37 Rb	38 Sr	39 Y	40 Zr	41 Nb	42 Mo	43 Tc	44 Ru	45 Rh	46 Pd	47 Ag	48 Cd	49 In	50 Sn	51 Sb	52 Te	53 I	54 Xe
55 Cs	56 Ba	57 La	72 Hf	73 Ta	74 W	75 Re	76 Os	77 Ir	78 Pt	79 Au	80 Hg	81 Tl	82 Pb	83 Bi	84 Po	85 At	86 Rn
87 Fr	88 Ra	89 Ac	104 Rf	105 Db	106 Sg	107 Bh	108 Hs	109 Mt	110 Ds	111 Rg	112 Uub	113 Uut	114 Uuq	115 Uup			

58 Ce	59 Pr	60 Nd	61 Pm	62 Sm	63 Eu	64 Gd	65 Tb	66 Dy	67 Ho	68 Er	69 Tm	70 Yb	71 Lu
90 Th	91 Pa	92 U	93 Np	94 Pu	95 Am	96 Cm	97 Bk	98 Cf	99 Es	100 Fm	101 Md	102 No	103 Lw

Figure 21.1
The chemical elements essential for life. Those most abundant in living systems are shown as purple. Nineteen elements, called the trace elements, are shown as green.

Table 21.1

Some Essential Elements and Their Major Functions

Element	Percent by Mass in the Human Body	Function
oxygen	65	in water and many organic compounds
carbon	18	in all organic compounds
hydrogen	10	in water and many inorganic and organic compounds
nitrogen	3	in both inorganic and organic compounds
calcium	1.5	in bone; essential to some enzymes and to muscle action
phosphorus	1.2	essential in cell membranes and to energy transfer in cells
potassium	0.2	cation in cell fluid
chlorine	0.2	anion inside and outside the cells
sulfur	0.2	in proteins
sodium	0.1	cation in cell fluid
magnesium	0.05	essential to some enzymes
iron	<0.05	in molecules that transport and store oxygen
zinc	<0.05	essential to many enzymes
cobalt	<0.05	found in vitamin B_{12}
iodine	<0.05	essential to thyroid hormones
fluorine	<0.01	in teeth and bones

A. Proteins

In Chapter 20 we saw that many useful synthetic materials are polymers. A great many natural materials are also polymers: starch, hair, silk and cotton fibers, and the cellulose in woody plants, to name only a few.

In this section we introduce a class of natural polymers, the **proteins**, which make up about 15% of our bodies and have molar masses that range from approximately 6,000 to over 1,000,000 grams. Proteins have many functions in the human body. **Fibrous proteins** provide structural integrity and strength for many types of tissue and are the main components of muscle, hair, and cartilage. Other proteins, usually called **globular proteins** because of their roughly spherical shape, are the "worker" molecules of the body. These proteins transport and store oxygen and nutrients, act as catalysts for the thousands of reactions that make life possible, fight invasion of the body by foreign objects, participate in the body's many regulatory systems, and transport electrons in the complex process of metabolizing nutrients.

Striated muscle tissue is composed of fibrous proteins.

21.1 • Introduction to Proteins • **753**

21.1.A Proteins
Objective To learn about proteins

 TEACHING TIP

Table 21.1 gives mass percents of elements and their functions. Reviewing the table is an excellent way to emphasize the importance of chemistry in everyday life.

Objective To understand the primary structure of proteins

 TEACHING TIP

This section is an excellent place to review what causes a side group to be polar or nonpolar. Refer students back to the ideas they learned about bonding and work with students to determine why each side chain is classified as polar or nonpolar.

B. Primary Structure of Proteins

The building blocks of all proteins are the α-amino acids:

α-amino acid
An organic acid in which an amino group is attached to the carbon atom next to the carboxyl group

The R in this structure may represent H, CH_3, or more complex substituents. These molecules are called α-amino acids because the amino group ($-NH_2$) is always attached to the α-carbon, the one next to the carboxyl group ($-COOH$). The 20 amino acids most commonly found in proteins are shown in **Figure 21.2.**

Nonpolar R Groups (hydrophobic)

Glycine (gly) Alanine (ala) Proline (pro) Valine (val)

Tryptophan (trp) Isoleucine (ile) Methionine (met) Leucine (leu) Phenylalanine (phe)

Polar R Groups (hydrophilic)

Serine (ser) Asparagine (asn) Glutamine (gln) Tyrosine (tyr) Histidine (his)

Threonine (thr)

Aspartic acid (asp) Cysteine (cys) Glutamic acid (glu) Lysine (lys) Arginine (arg)

Figure 21.2
The 20 α-amino acids found in most proteins. The R group is shown in color.

Note from Figure 21.2 that the amino acids are grouped into polar and nonpolar classes on the basis of the composition of the R groups, also called the **side chains**. Nonpolar side chains contain mostly carbon and hydrogen atoms; polar side chains contain nitrogen and oxygen atoms. This difference is important because polar side chains are *hydrophilic* (water-loving), but nonpolar side chains are *hydrophobic* (water-fearing). This greatly affects the three-dimensional structure of the resulting proteins, because they exist in aqueous media in living things.

information

At the pH in biological fluids, the amino acids shown in Figure 21.2 exist in a different form, with the proton of the —COOH group transferred to the —NH$_2$ group. For example, glycine would be in the form $^+$H$_3$NCH$_2$COO$^-$.

Active Reading Question

How does the nature of the side chain affect the three dimensional structure of a protein?

The protein polymer is built by reactions between amino acids. For example, two amino acids can react as follows, forming a C—N bond with the elimination of water.

The product shown is called a **dipeptide**. The term *peptide* comes from the structure

which chemists call a **peptide linkage** or a peptide bond. The prefix *di-* indicates that two amino acids have been joined. Additional reactions lengthen the chain to produce a **polypeptide** and eventually a protein.

The 20 amino acids can be assembled in any order, which makes possible an enormous number of different proteins. This variety allows for the many types of proteins needed for the functions that organisms carry out.

The *order* or *sequence* of amino acids in the protein chain is called the **primary structure**. We indicate the primary structure by using three-letter codes for the amino acids (see Figure 21.2), where it is understood that the terminal carboxyl group is on the right and the terminal amino group is on the left. For example, one possible sequence for a tripeptide containing the amino acids lysine, alanine, and leucine is

which is represented in the shorthand notation (three-letter codes) as
lys-ala-leu

Primary structure
The order or sequence of amino acids in a protein chain

TEACHING TIPS

• The term *hydrophobic* is actually a misnomer. While the nonpolar side chains do not mix well with water, they do not repel the water. Instead, water molecules are simply more attracted to other water molecules than to the nonpolar side chains.

• When students first begin to make peptide linkages, they often link the carboxyl group on one amino acid to the R group of the next. Work through several examples of the linkages with students. It is helpful to mark the different parts of the amino acid (carboxyl, amine, R groups) with different colors so that students can more easily identify which groups should interact.

Active Reading Question

Most proteins exist in aqueous media. Polar side chains attract water, and nonpolar side chains move away from water. Thus, the protein will "fold" to maximize polar side chain and water interactions and to minimize nonpolar side chain and water interactions.

MINI-DEMO

Use a set of children's pop beads to illustrate the primary structure of a protein. The differently shaped beads can represent different amino acids. The pop connections can represent peptide linkages. Have students translate your primary structure into the three-letter-coded structure by assigning a code sequence to each bead.

EXAMPLE 21.1

More Examples

Write the sequences of all possible tripeptides composed of the amino acids serine (ser), glutamic acid (glu), and arginine (arg).

ser-glu-arg	glu-arg-ser	arg-ser-glu
ser-arg-glu	glu-ser-arg	arg-glu-ser

21.1.C Secondary Structure of Proteins

Objective To understand the secondary structure of proteins

TECHNOLOGY

📖 Figure 21.3

EXAMPLE 21.1

Understanding Primary Structure

Write the sequences of all possible tripeptides composed of the amino acids tyrosine (tyr), histidine (his), and cysteine (cys).

Solution

There are six possible sequences:

tyr-his-cys	his-tyr-cys	cys-tyr-his
tyr-cys-his	his-cys-tyr	cys-his-tyr

Secondary structure
The arrangement in space of the chain of the protein chain

A Closer Look The importance of the primary structure of polypeptides can be seen in the differences between *oxytocin* and *vasopressin*. Oxytocin is a hormone that triggers contraction of the uterus and milk secretion. Vasopressin raises blood pressure and regulates kidney function. Both of these molecules are nine-unit polypeptides, and they differ by only two amino acids.

cys-tyr-ile-gln-asn-cys-pro-leu-gly
oxytocin

cys-tyr-phe-gln-asn-cys-pro-arg-gly
vasopressin

These molecules have completely different functions in the human body.

C. Secondary Structure of Proteins

So far we have considered the primary structure of proteins—the order of amino acids in the chain as shown below.

A second level of structure in proteins is the arrangement in space of the chain of the long molecule. This is called the **secondary structure** of the protein.

One common type of secondary structure resembles a spiral staircase. This spiral structure is called an α-**helix** (see **Figure 21.3**). A spiral-like secondary structure gives the protein elasticity (springiness) and is found in the fibrous proteins in wool, hair, and tendons. Another type of secondary structure involves joining several different protein chains in an arrangement called a **pleated sheet**, as shown below.

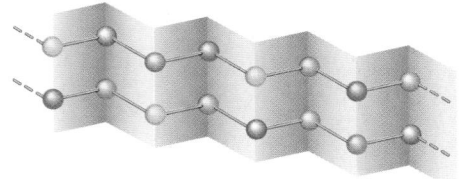

Figure 21.3
One type of secondary protein structure is like a spiral staircase and is called the α-helix. The spheres represent individual amino acids.

Meeting Individual Needs
VISUAL LEARNERS

An excellent example of a secondary structure is the coiled cord from a telephone. Another possibility is to twist children's pop beads into a helix to represent the secondary structure while showing the primary structure by the order of the pop beads. A folded piece of paper can represent the pleated sheet secondary structure.

Silk has this arrangement of proteins, making its fibers flexible but very strong and resistant to stretching. The pleated sheet is also found in muscle fibers.

Active Reading Question

What is it about a pleated sheet arrangement that makes it suitable for muscle fibers?

As you might imagine, a molecule as large as a protein has a great deal of flexibility and can assume a variety of overall shapes. The function the protein is to serve influences the specific shape that it will have. For long, thin structures such as hair, wool and silk fibers, and tendons, an elongated shape is required. This may involve an α-helical secondary structure, as found in the protein α-keratin in hair and wool or in the collagen that occurs in tendons (see **Figure 21.4a**), or it may involve a pleated-sheet secondary structure, as found in silk (see **Figure 21.4b**).

Many of the proteins in the body that have nonstructural functions (such as serving as enzymes) are globular. One is myoglobin (see **Figure 21.5**), which absorbs an O$_2$ molecule and stores it for use by the cells as it is needed. Note that the secondary structure of myoglobin is basically α-helical. However, in the areas where the chain bends to give the protein its compact globular structure, the α-helix breaks down so that the protein can "turn the corner."

(a)   (b)

Figure 21.4
(a) Collagen, a protein found in tendons, consists of three protein chains (each with an α-helical structure) twisted together to form a super-helix. The result is a long, relatively narrow protein.
(b) Many proteins are bound together in the pleated-sheet arrangement to form the elongated protein found in silk fibers.

Active Reading Question

The pleated sheet arrangement makes the fibers flexible, but strong and resistant to stretching.

α-helix

Random coil

Figure 21.5
The protein myoglobin. Note that the secondary structure is basically α-helical except at the bends. The tertiary structure is globular.

21.1 • Introduction to Proteins • **757**

Meeting Individual Needs
ENGLISH LANGUAGE LEARNERS

Before introducing the terms *helix* and *pleated*, explain some of the more common uses of each word. Relate a helix to a spiral staircase and the words *coil, twirl, twist,* and *curl*. Point out that a pleat is a fold or crease, and that pleats are found in pants, skirts, and curtains.

Objective To understand the tertiary structure of protein

 TEACHING TIP

Figure 21.6 shows how a permanent wave causes hair to curl. It provides an interesting way to introduce the denaturation of proteins and the disruption of protein function that can result. The formation of disulfide linkages demonstrates that R groups can play an active role in protein structure (other than in the primary structure).

MINI-DEMO

One way to illustrate the tertiary structure is to use a coiled phone cord or a Slinky. The coils represent the secondary structure of the protein, which can be bent, folded, or coiled to illustrate the tertiary structure.

21.1.E Functions of Proteins

Objective To learn about various functions served by proteins

MINI-DEMO

You can easily demonstrate the denaturation of a protein by cooking an egg on a hot plate. The whites are denatured as we cook them. You can produce the same result by adding sulfuric acid to the egg, but this activity renders it useless as food. You can denature milk protein by adding dilute acetic acid to nonfat dry milk dissolved in water. Students are familiar with the results of these reactions but usually do not associate them with chemistry.

Tertiary structure
The overall shape of a protein

Chemicals used in permanent wave solutions create curls in hair.

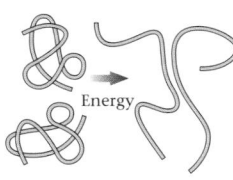

Figure 21.7
A schematic representation of the thermal denaturation of a protein

---

D. Tertiary Structure of Proteins

The overall shape of the protein, long and narrow or globular, is called its **tertiary structure**. To make sure the difference between secondary and tertiary structure is clear, examine Figure 21.5 again. The secondary structure of the myoglobin protein is helical except in the regions where it bends back on itself to give the overall compact (globular) tertiary structure. If the bends did not occur, the tertiary structure would be like a long tube (tubular). In both tertiary arrangements (globular and tubular), the secondary structure of the protein is basically helical.

The amino acid *cysteine* (cys) plays a special role in stabilizing the tertiary structure of many proteins, because the —SH groups on two cysteines can react to form an S—S bond called a **disulfide linkage**.

The formation of a disulfide linkage can fasten together two parts of a protein chain to form and hold a bend in the chain, for example. A practical application of the chemistry of disulfide bonds is the permanent waving of hair (see **Figure 21.6**). The S—S linkages in the protein of hair are broken by treatment with a reducing agent. Next the hair is set in curlers to change the tertiary protein structure to the desired shape. Then treatment with an oxidizing agent causes new S—S bonds to form, which make the hair protein retain the new structure.

Natural cysteine linkages in hair — Reduction — Chains shift — Hair set in curlers alters tertiary structure — Oxidation — New cysteine linkages in waved hair

Figure 21.6
The permanent waving of hair

E. Functions of Proteins

The three-dimensional structure of a protein is crucial to its function. The process of breaking down this structure is called **denaturation** (see **Figure 21.7**). For example, heat causes the denaturation of egg proteins when an egg is cooked. Any source of energy can cause denaturation of proteins and is thus potentially dangerous to living organisms. For example, ultraviolet radiation, X-ray radiation, or nuclear radioactivity can disrupt protein structure, which may lead to cancer or genetic damage. The metals lead and mercury, which have a very high affinity for sulfur, cause protein denaturation by disrupting disulfide bonds.

The tremendous variability in the several levels of protein structure allows proteins to be tailored specifically to serve a wide range of functions, some of which are given in **Table 21.2.**

F. Enzymes

Enzymes are proteins that catalyze specific biological reactions. Without the several hundred enzymes now known, life would be impossible. Almost all of the critical biochemical reactions would occur far too slowly at the temperatures at which life exists. Enzymes are impressive for their tremendous efficiency (they are typically 1 to 10 million times as efficient as inorganic catalysts) and their incredible selectivity (an enzyme "ignores" the thousands of molecules in body fluids that are not involved in the reaction it catalyzes).

Enzyme
A protein that catalyzes a specific biological reaction

Table 21.2

Common Functions of Proteins

Function	Comment/Example
Structure	Proteins provide the strength of tendons, bones, and skin. Cartilage, hair, wool, fingernails, and claws are mainly protein. Viruses have an outer layer of protein.
Movement	Proteins are the major components of muscles and are directly responsible for the ability of muscles to contract. The swimming of sperm results from the contraction of protein filaments in their tails.
Catalysis	Nearly all chemical reactions in living organisms are catalyzed by enzymes, which are almost always proteins.
Transport	Oxygen is carried from the lungs to tissues by the protein hemoglobin in red blood cells.
Storage	The protein ferritin stores iron in the liver, spleen, and bone marrow.
Energy transformation	Cytochromes are proteins found in all cells. They extract energy from food molecules by transferring electrons in a series of oxidation–reduction reactions.
Protection	Antibodies are special proteins that are synthesized in response to foreign substances and cells, such as bacterial cells. They then bind to those substances or cells and provide us with immunity to various diseases. Interferon, a small protein made and released by cells when they are exposed to a virus, protects other cells against viral infection. Blood-clotting proteins protect against bleeding (hemorrhage).
Control	Many hormones are proteins produced in the body that have specific effects on the activity of certain organs.
Buffering	Because proteins contain both acidic and basic groups on their side chains, they can neutralize both acids and bases and thus provide buffering for blood and tissues.

Use drawings to illustrate the lock-and-key model. Show that potential substrates will not react if they do not fit the active site.

 Active Reading Question

A substrate is a molecule that reacts with an enzyme. An enzyme is a biological catalyst that speeds up a reaction. A substrate molecule undergoes a chemical change in the reaction, but an enzyme does not. They are related because they are able to "fit" together like a lock and key in the active site of the enzyme.

Figure 21.8
Schematic diagram of the lock-and-key model of the functioning of an enzyme

Substrate
The molecule that interacts with an enzyme

Active site
The part of the enzyme to which the specific substrate is bound as a reaction is catalyzed

 nformation

An enzyme often changes shape slightly as the substrate is bound. This "clamps" the substrate into place.

Although the mechanisms of enzyme activity are complex and not fully understood in most cases, a simple theory called the **lock-and-key model** (see **Figure 21.8**) seems to fit many enzymes. This model postulates that the shapes of the reacting molecule (the **substrate**) and the enzyme are such that they fit together much as a key fits a specific lock. The substrate and enzyme attach to each other in such a way that the part of the substrate where the reaction is to occur occupies the **active site** of the enzyme. After the reaction occurs, the products are liberated and the enzyme is ready for a new substrate. We can represent enzyme catalysis by the following steps:

Step 1 The enzyme E and the substrate S come together.
$$E + S \rightleftharpoons E \cdot S$$

Step 2 The reaction occurs to give the product P, which is released from the enzyme.
$$E \cdot S \rightarrow E + P$$

After the product is released, the enzyme is free to engage another substrate.
    Because this process occurs so rapidly, only a tiny amount of enzyme is required.

 Active Reading Question

What is the difference between a substrate and an enzyme? How are they related?

In some cases a substance other than the substrate can bind to the enzyme's active site. When this occurs, the enzyme is said to be *inhibited*. If the inhibition is permanent, the enzyme is said to be inactivated. Some of the most powerful toxins act by inhibiting, or inactivating, key enzymes.
    Because enzymes are crucial to life and because we hope to learn how to mimic their efficiency in our industrial catalysts, the study of enzymes occupies a prominent place in chemical research.

CHEMISTRY IN YOUR WORLD

Science, Technology, and Society

Urine Farming

Nature is a very good chemist—organisms make hundreds of complex chemicals every second to survive. The rapidly expanding science of biotechnology is learning more every day about how to use natural chemical pathways to make valuable molecules. For example, insulin for diabetics is now made almost exclusively by "farming" genetically altered *E. coli* or yeast.

Turning livestock into four-footed pharmaceutical factories has seemed an attractive option ever since we learned to carry out "genetic engineering." In fact, a great deal of effort has been expended on creating cows, sheep, and goats that are genetically modified to produce useful human proteins that are secreted into the animals' milk, from which they can then be harvested. None of these proteins has yet reached the market—tests are now under way to check their efficacy and safety—but a blood-clotting agent, antithrombin III, developed by Genzyme Transgenics Corporation of Framingham, Massachusetts, is close to commercial application. Creating a transgenic (genetically modified) animal is expensive (costing approximately $60,000), but then standard breeding techniques can lead to an entire herd of animals programmed to produce commercially interesting molecules.

As a medium, milk has some disadvantages. It is produced only by mature females and contains a wide variety of proteins that complicate the purification process to obtain the desired product. Urine may be a better alternative. It contains fewer natural proteins and is produced at an early age by both male and female animals. Robert J. Wall and his colleagues at the U.S. Department of Agriculture in Beltsville, Maryland, have developed transgenic mice that produce human growth hormone in the walls of their bladders. For obvious reasons, mice are not ideal for large-scale production of chemicals, but Wall's experiments nevertheless show that the concept works. At present it is too early to know whether urine farming will prove feasible. Yields from the bladder are about 10,000 times lower than those from the mammary glands. In addition, collecting urine from farm animals could prove to be a very tricky business.

A New Zealand goat, one of the animals used for urine farming

SECTION 21.1
REVIEW QUESTIONS

❶ What are the major types and functions of proteins?

❷ What property of the side chain on an amino acid affects the three-dimensional structure of the protein?

❸ Draw the general structure for an amino acid.

   a. Circle the side chain group.

   b. Draw a second amino acid next to the first and circle the water removed to form a peptide bond to link the two amino acids.

❹ What are the differences among primary, secondary, and tertiary structure in proteins?

❺ What level of protein structure is changed by denaturation?

❻ What is the role of enzymes in biochemical reactions?

❼ Explain the lock-and-key model of enzymes.

RESEARCH LINKS
CLASSZONE.COM

21.1 • Introduction to Proteins • **761**

 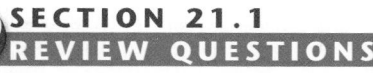

Student Preparation

Assign students to read Section 21.2 and to answer the Review Questions at the end of the section before coming to class.

 Active Learning
Team Learning Worksheet

After introducing the material in Section 21.2 in class, place students in groups and have them work together on **Section 21.2: Team Learning Worksheet.**

SECTION 21.2

GUIDE THE LEARNING

Homework

You may wish to assign these selected end-of-chapter problems as homework for this section: 27, 30, 31, 33, 34, 35, 37, 39, 40, 41

Additional end-of-chapter problems can be used for extra practice.

21.2.A Carbohydrates

Objective To understand the fundamental properties of carbohydrates

 LABORATORY
EXPERIMENT 91:
Vitamin C in Juices, Microscale

🍎 TEACHING TIP

Use glucose and fructose to compare the structures of common monosaccharides. Both have six carbons, but glucose has an aldehyde functional group on carbon 1 and fructose has a ketone on carbon 2. Both have —OH groups on the remaining carbons.

SECTION 21.2
Carbohydrates, Nucleic Acids, and Lipids

Key Terms

- Carbohydrates
- Monosaccharides (simple sugars)
- Disaccharide
- Sucrose
- Glycoside linkage
- Polysaccharides
- Starch
- Cellulose
- Glycogen
- DNA (deoxyribonucleic acid)
- RNA (ribonucleic acid)
- Nucleotide
- Protein synthesis
- Gene
- mRNA (messenger RNA)
- tRNA (transfer RNA)
- Lipids
- Fats
- Fatty acids
- Saponification
- Micelles
- Surfactant
- Phospholipids
- Waxes
- Steroids
- Cholesterol
- Adrenocorticoid hormones
- Sex hormones
- Bile acids

Objectives

- *To understand the fundamental properties of carbohydrates*
- *To understand nucleic acid structures*
- *To learn the four classes of lipids*

A. Carbohydrates

The **carbohydrates** are another class of biologically important molecules. Carbohydrates serve as food sources for most organisms and as structural materials for plants. Because many carbohydrates have the empirical formula CH_2O, it was originally believed that these substances were hydrates of carbon ($C \cdot H_2O$), which accounts for their name.

Like proteins, carbohydrates occur in almost bewildering varieties. Many of the most important carbohydrates are polymers—large molecules constructed by hooking together many smaller molecules. We have seen that proteins are polymers constructed from amino acids. The polymeric carbohydrates are constructed from molecules called **simple sugars** or, more precisely, **monosaccharides**. Monosaccharides are aldehydes or ketones that contain several hydroxyl (—OH) substituents. An example of a monosaccharide is fructose, with the structure

$$CH_2OH$$
$$|$$
$$C=O \quad \leftarrow \text{Ketone}$$
$$|$$
$$HO-C-H$$
$$|$$
$$H-C-OH$$
$$|$$
$$H-C-OH$$
$$|$$
$$CH_2OH$$
Fructose

Breads contain high levels of carbohydrates and fruits are a dietary source of fructose.

762 • Chapter 21 • Biochemistry

Meeting Individual Needs
CHALLENGE PROJECTS

For ideas on research topics related to biochemistry, see *Investigating Biological Topics* located in the *Teacher Resources.*

Fructose is a sugar found in honey and fruits. Monosaccharides can have various numbers of carbon atoms, and we name them according to the number of carbon atoms they contain by adding prefixes to the root *-ose*. The general names of monosaccharides are shown in **Table 21.3.** Notice that fructose is a ketone with six carbon atoms and five —OH substituents. Fructose is a member of the hexose family, where the prefix *hex-* means six.

Table 21.3

The General Names of Monosaccharides

Number of Carbon Atoms	Prefix	General Name of Sugar
3	*tri-*	triose
4	*tetr-*	tetrose
5	*pent-*	pentose
6	*hex-*	hexose
7	*hept-*	heptose
8	*oct-*	octose
9	*non-*	nonose

Top Ten Sugar-Consuming Countries	
Country	kg per Person per Year
Swaziland	320
Belize	280
Israel	276
Réunion	264
Costa Rica	251
New Zealand	242
Barbados	238
Brazil	231
Trinidad and Tobago	225
Malaysia	223

The most important monosaccharides found in living organisms are pentoses and hexoses. The most common pentoses and hexoses are shown in **Table 21.4.**

Table 21.4

Some Important Monosaccharides

Pentoses (five carbon atoms)

Ribose
$$
\begin{array}{c}
\text{CHO} \\
\text{H—C—OH} \\
\text{H—C—OH} \\
\text{H—C—OH} \\
\text{CH}_2\text{OH}
\end{array}
$$

Arabinose
$$
\begin{array}{c}
\text{CHO} \\
\text{HO—C—H} \\
\text{H—C—OH} \\
\text{H—C—OH} \\
\text{CH}_2\text{OH}
\end{array}
$$

Ribulose
$$
\begin{array}{c}
\text{CH}_2\text{OH} \\
\text{C=O} \\
\text{H—C—OH} \\
\text{H—C—OH} \\
\text{CH}_2\text{OH}
\end{array}
$$

Hexoses (six carbon atoms)

Glucose
$$
\begin{array}{c}
\text{CHO} \\
\text{H—C—OH} \\
\text{HO—C—H} \\
\text{H—C—OH} \\
\text{H—C—OH} \\
\text{CH}_2\text{OH}
\end{array}
$$

Mannose
$$
\begin{array}{c}
\text{CHO} \\
\text{HO—C—H} \\
\text{HO—C—H} \\
\text{H—C—OH} \\
\text{H—C—OH} \\
\text{CH}_2\text{OH}
\end{array}
$$

Galactose
$$
\begin{array}{c}
\text{CHO} \\
\text{H—C—OH} \\
\text{HO—C—H} \\
\text{HO—C—H} \\
\text{H—C—OH} \\
\text{CH}_2\text{OH}
\end{array}
$$

Fructose
$$
\begin{array}{c}
\text{CH}_2\text{OH} \\
\text{C=O} \\
\text{HO—C—H} \\
\text{H—C—OH} \\
\text{H—C—OH} \\
\text{CH}_2\text{OH}
\end{array}
$$

TEACHING TIPS

- It is helpful to illustrate how a sugar cyclizes by using a model. Build a model of glucose and then carefully close the ring, showing students what happens as you proceed.

- Point out that in glucose, the aldehyde group reacts to form the ring, whereas in fructose, the ketone group reacts to form the ring. This difference changes the number of atoms in the ring for the two sugars.

21.2 • Carbohydrates, Nucleic Acids, and Lipids • **763**

Carbon and oxygen are involved in a glycoside linkage. The linkage is a C—O—C bond between the rings of monosaccharides.

Figure 21.9
The formation of a ring structure for fructose

Although we have so far represented the monosaccharides as straight-chain molecules, they usually form ring structures in aqueous solution. **Figure 21.9** shows how the ring forms for fructose. Note that a new bond is formed between the oxygen of a hydroxyl group and the carbon of the ketone group. In the cyclic form, fructose is a five-membered ring containing a C—O—C bond. Glucose, a hexose that is an aldehyde, forms a six-membered ring structure. The six-membered glucose ring is shown in **Figure 21.10a.** Note that the ring is nonplanar.

Figure 21.10
Sucrose (c) is a disaccharide formed from glucose (a) and fructose (b)

(a) Glucose (b) Fructose

(c) Sucrose

Glycoside linkage

Disaccharide
A sugar formed from two monosaccharides formed by a glycoside linkage

Sucrose
Table sugar; a disaccharide formed between glucose and fructose

Glycoside linkage
The C—O—C bond formed between monosaccharide rings in a disaccharide

More complex carbohydrates are formed by the combining of monosaccharides. For example, two monosaccharides can combine to form a **disaccharide**. **Sucrose**, common table sugar, is a disaccharide formed from glucose and fructose by elimination of water to form a C—O—C bond between the rings that is called a **glycoside linkage** (see **Figure 21.10c**). When sucrose is consumed in food, this reaction is reversed (the glycoside bond is broken). An enzyme in saliva catalyzes the breakdown of sucrose into its two monosaccharides.

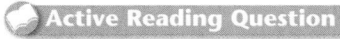 Active Reading Question

What elements are involved in a glycoside linkage?

CELEBRITY CHEMICAL Aspartame ($C_{14}H_{18}N_2O_5$)

Most humans love things that taste sweet—chocolate candy, cake, ice cream, and so on. The problem with sweet things is they have lots of calories and tend to make us gain weight. Wouldn't it be great to have sweets without the calories? Of course, this dream has now become reality through the magic of chemistry—artificial sweeteners, or molecules that taste sweet but do not add to the calorie count. Many molecules have a sweet taste—even sweeter than sugar. The earliest of these compounds were discovered in the late 1800s when tasting a new compound was accepted procedure. Most of the current artificial sweeteners were discovered by accident, however, when scientists were not observing proper lab hygiene.

Today a widely used artificial sweetener is a compound called aspartame, which is formed by coupling together two amino acids naturally found in humans: aspartic acid and phenylalanine

Aspartame is 200 times sweeter than sugar and leaves no unpleasant aftertaste. It is now found in most diet drinks and many other low-calorie products. One disadvantage of aspartame is that it decomposes at baking temperatures and thus cannot be used in products that are heated.

Like all artificial sweeteners, aspartame has had some critics. When this substance breaks down in the body it forms aspartic acid, phenylalanine, and methanol. The first two compounds are naturally present in the body and pose no hazard to most people. However, about one person in 15,000 suffers from a disease called phenylketonuria, which makes an individual sensitive to excess phenylalanine. People with this condition must avoid aspartame. Also, the fact that methanol is a product of the breakdown of aspartame makes some people concerned, because methanol is a toxic substance. Nevertheless, studies have shown that the small amount of methanol produced from aspartame poses no risk. In fact, a glass of natural fruit juice contains as much methanol as is produced from typical use of aspartame.

The label on a product containing aspartame

Large polymers containing many monosaccharide units are called **polysaccharides** and can form when each ring forms two glycoside linkages, as shown in **Figure 21.11.** Three of the most important of these polymers are starch, cellulose, and glycogen. All of these substances are polymers of glucose; they differ in the way the glucose rings are linked together.

Polysaccharide
Polymers containing many monosaccharide units

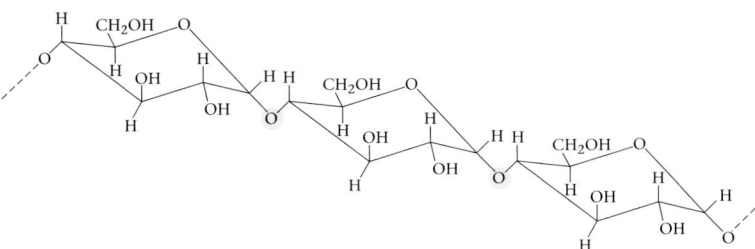

Figure 21.11
Starch is made by hooking together many glucose rings. Only a small part of the chain is shown here.

21.2 • Carbohydrates, Nucleic Acids, and Lipids • **765**

CELEBRITY CHEMICAL

Aspartame ($C_{14}H_{18}N_2O_5$)

Have students bring in samples of items containing aspartame. Alternatively, have them find items containing aspartame in the grocery store and bring in a list of these products. Discuss the need to label products properly, as some people are sensitive to this chemical.

TEACHING TIP

Students often have difficulty seeing how starch and cellulose form from glucose. You will need to mark the molecules and number the carbons to show students when an —OH from carbon 1 links with an —OH from carbon 4.

21.2.B Nucleic Acids

Objective To understand the fundamental nucleic acid structures

TEACHING TIPS

• This section offers an excellent opportunity to link to previous biology courses. The information presented here is much more detailed than students will have seen previously.

• Students should be able to identify both differences and similarities between DNA and RNA. You may want to summarize these differences and similarities in a table.

Active Reading Question

DNA polymers are larger than RNA polymers.

Starch
The main carbohydrate reservoir in plants; a polymer of glucose

Cellulose
The major structural component of woody plants and natural fibers, such as cotton; a polymer of glucose

Glycogen
The main carbohydrate reservoir in animals; a polymer of glucose

Deoxyribonucleic acid (DNA)
A huge nucleotide polymer having a double-helical structure with complementary bases on the two strands; functions include protein synthesis and the storage and transport of genetic material

Ribonucleic acid (RNA)
Large nucleotide polymer that, along with DNA, functions to transport genetic material

Nucleotide
A monomer of DNA and RNA consisting of a nitrogen-containing base, a five-carbon sugar, and a phosphate group

Note that the prefix *de-* refers to the absence of the substance that follows. Thus deoxyribose means ribose with a missing oxygen (see Figure 21.12).

Starch (Figure 21.11) is the carbohydrate reservoir in plants. It is the form in which glucose is stored by the plant for later use as cellular fuel—both by the plants themselves and by organisms that eat plants.

Cellulose, the major structural component of woody plants and natural fibers such as cotton, is also a polymer of glucose. However, in cellulose the way in which the glucose rings are linked is different from the way they are linked in starch. This difference in linkage has very important consequences. The human digestive system contains enzymes that can catalyze breakage of the glycoside bonds between the glucose molecules in starch. These enzymes are *not* effective on the glycoside bonds of cellulose, however, presumably because the different structure causes a poor fit between the enzyme's active site and the carbohydrate. Interestingly, the enzymes necessary to cleave the glycoside linkages in cellulose are found in bacteria that exist in the digestive tracts of termites, cows, deer, and many other animals. Therefore, unlike humans, these animals can derive nutrition from the cellulose in wood, hay, and other similar substances.

Glycogen is the main carbohydrate reservoir in animals. For example, it is found in muscles, where it can be broken down into glucose units when energy is required for physical activity.

B. Nucleic Acids

Life is possible only because each cell, when it divides, can transmit the vital information about what it is to the next generation of cells. It has been known for a long time that this process involves the chromosomes in the nucleus of the cell. Only since 1953, however, have scientists understood the molecular basis of this intriguing cellular "talent."

The substance that stores and transmits the genetic information is a polymer called **deoxyribonucleic acid (DNA)**, a huge molecule with a molar mass as high as several billion grams. Together with other similar nucleic acids called the **ribonucleic acids (RNA)**, DNA carries the information needed for the synthesis of the various proteins the cell requires to carry out its life functions. The RNA molecules, which are found in the cytoplasm outside the cell nucleus, are much smaller than DNA polymers, with molar mass values of only 20,000 to 40,000 grams.

Active Reading Question

Which are larger, DNA polymers or RNA polymers?

Both DNA and RNA are polymers—they are constructed by the hooking together of many smaller units. The fundamental unit in these polymers is called a **nucleotide**.

A nucleotide has three parts:
1. A nitrogen-containing organic base
2. A five-carbon sugar
3. A phosphate group

A nucleotide can be represented as follows:

In the DNA polymer, the five-carbon sugar is deoxyribose (see **Figure 21.12a**); in the RNA polymer, it is ribose (see **Figure 21.12b**). This difference in the sugar molecules present in the polymers is responsible for the names DNA (deoxyribonucleic acid) and RNA (ribonucleic acid).

A molecular model of part of the DNA structure

Figure 21.12
The structure of the pentoses (a) deoxyribose and (b) ribose. Deoxyribose is the sugar molecule present in DNA; ribose is found in RNA. The difference in these sugars is the substitution, in ribose, of an OH for one H in deoxyribose.

The organic base molecules in the nucleotides of DNA and RNA are shown in **Figure 21.13.** Notice that some of these bases are found only in DNA, some are found only in RNA, and some are found in both. To form the DNA and RNA polymers, the nucleotides are hooked together. DNA polymers can contain up to a *billion* nucleotide units. **Figure 21.14** shows a small portion of a DNA chain.

Uracil (U)
RNA

Thymine (T)
DNA

Adenine (A)
DNA
RNA

Cytosine (C)
DNA
RNA

Guanine (G)
DNA
RNA

Figure 21.13
The organic bases found in DNA and RNA. Note that uracil is found only in RNA and that thymine is found only in DNA.

Figure 21.14
A portion of a typical nucleic acid chain, half of the DNA double helix shown in Figure 21.15.

21.2 • Carbohydrates, Nucleic Acids, and Lipids • **767**

Thymine and adenine are complementary bases, which means that they form hydrogen bonds with one another.

TEACHING TIP

You can use the analogy of a ladder to help students understand the structure of DNA. The sides of the ladder represent the alternating sugar and phosphate groups, and the rungs of the ladder represent the base pairs that are hydrogen-bonded together.

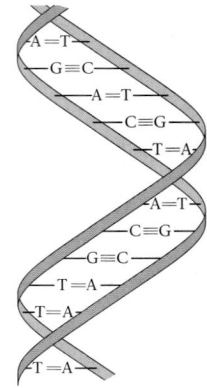

Figure 21.15
The DNA double helix contains two sugar–phosphate backbones with the bases from the two strands hydrogen-bonded to each other.

The key to DNA's functioning is its *double-helical structure with complementary bases on the two strands.* **Figure 21.15**. Complementary bases form hydrogen bonds to each other, as shown in **Figure 21.16.** Note that the structures of cytosine and guanine make them perfect partners (complementary) for hydrogen bonding and that they are *always* found as pairs on the two strands of DNA. Thymine and adenine form similar hydrogen-bonding pairs.

 Active Reading Question

Why are thymine and adenine always found as pairs on the two strands of DNA?

Figure 21.16
The (a) thymine–adenine and (b) cytosine–guanine pairs show complementarity. The hydrogen-bonding interactions are shown by dotted lines.

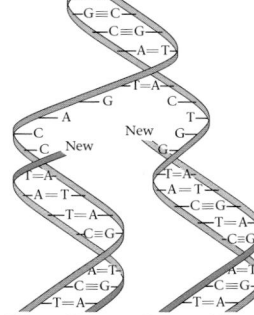

There is much evidence to suggest that the two strands of DNA unwind during cell division and that new complementary strands are constructed on the unraveled strands (see **Figure 21.17**). Because the bases on the strands always pair in the same way—cytosine with guanine and thymine with adenine—each unraveled strand serves as a template for attaching each complementary base (along with the rest of its nucleotide). This process results in two new double-helix DNA structures that are identical to the original one. Each new double strand contains one strand from the original DNA double helix and one newly synthesized strand. This replication of DNA makes possible the transmission of genetic information when cells divide.

DNA and Protein Synthesis

Besides replication, the other major function of DNA is **protein synthesis**. The proteins consumed by an organism in its food are typically not the specific proteins that organism needs to maintain its existence. The nutrient proteins are broken down into their constituent amino acids, which are then used to construct those proteins that the organism needs. The information for constructing each protein needed by a particular organism is stored in that organism's DNA.

Figure 21.17
During cell division, the original DNA double helix unwinds and new complementary strands are constructed on each original strand. In this way, the two cells resulting from the division have exact copies of the DNA of the original cell.

Meeting Individual Needs
INCLUSION STRATEGIES

Help students develop a mnemonic to remember that in a DNA strand, adenine and thymine are always paired and guanine and cytosine are always paired.

A given segment of the DNA, called a **gene**, contains the code for a specific protein. This code for the primary structure of the protein (the sequence of amino acids) can be transmitted to the construction "machinery" of the cell.

DNA stores the genetic information, and RNA molecules are responsible for transmitting this information to cell components called ribosomes, where protein synthesis actually occurs. This process involves, first, the construction of a special RNA molecule called **messenger RNA (mRNA)**. The mRNA is built in the cell nucleus, where a specific section of DNA (a gene) is used as the pattern. The mRNA then migrates from the nucleus into the cytoplasm of the cell, where, with the assistance of the ribosomes, the protein is synthesized.

Small RNA fragments, called **transfer RNA (tRNA)** molecules, attach themselves to specific amino acids and bring them to the growing protein chain as dictated by the pattern built into the mRNA. This process is summarized in **Figure 21.18.**

Gene
A given segment of the DNA molecule that contains the code for a specific protein

Lipids
Water-insoluble substances that can be extracted from cells by nonpolar organic solvents

Fat
An ester composed of glycerol and fatty acids

Fatty acid
A long-chain carboxylic acid

21.2.C Lipids
Objective To learn the four classes of lipids

 TEACHING TIPS

- Formation of lipids involves the same reaction as the formation of esters, which are discussed in Chapter 20. The glycerol is a multihydroxyalcohol.

- Fats containing more unsaturated fatty acids are liquids at room temperature.

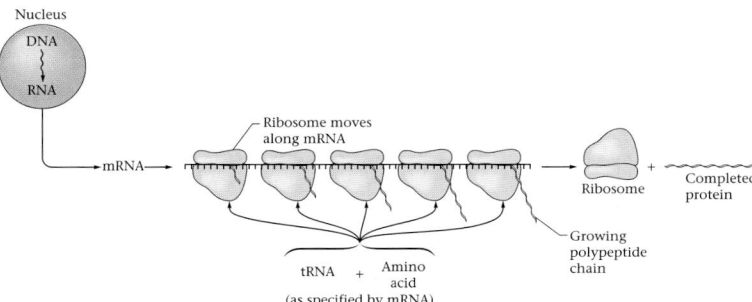

Figure 21.18
The mRNA molecule, constructed from a specific gene on the DNA, is used as the pattern for construction of a given protein with the assistance of ribosomes. The tRNA molecules attach to specific amino acids and put them in place, as dictated by the patterns on the mRNA. This sequence (left to right) shows the protein chain growing.

C. Lipids

The **lipids** are a group of substances defined in terms of their solubility characteristics. They are water-insoluble substances that can be extracted from cells by organic solvents such as benzene. The lipids found in the human body can be divided into four classes according to their molecular structure: fats, phospholipids, waxes, and steroids.

The most common **fats** are esters composed of the trihydroxy alcohol known as glycerol and long-chain carboxylic acids called **fatty acids** (see **Table 21.5**). *Tristearin*, the most common animal fat, is typical of these substances.

$$CH_2-O\boxed{H + H-O}-\overset{\overset{O}{\|}}{C}-(CH_2)_{16}-CH_3 \qquad CH_2-O-\overset{\overset{O}{\|}}{C}-(CH_2)_{16}-CH_3$$

$$CH-O\boxed{H + H-O}-\overset{\overset{O}{\|}}{C}-(CH_2)_{16}-CH_3 \rightarrow CH-O-\overset{\overset{O}{\|}}{C}-(CH_2)_{16}-CH_3 + 3H_2O$$

$$CH_2-O\boxed{H + H-O}-\overset{\overset{O}{\|}}{C}-(CH_2)_{16}-CH_3 \qquad CH_2-O-\overset{\overset{O}{\|}}{C}-(CH_2)_{16}-CH_3$$

Glycerol   Three stearic acid molecules   Tristearin (fat)

21.2 • Carbohydrates, Nucleic Acids, and Lipids • **769**

TEACHING TIP

Now is a good time to discuss soaps and how they work. Figures 21.19 and 21.20 show how a micelle forms and then breaks down globules of fats. Making soap in the laboratory is a good way for students to learn more about this process.

Table 21.5

Some Common Fatty Acids and Their Major Sources

Name	Formula	Major Source
Saturated		
arachidic acid	$CH_3(CH_2)_{18}-COOH$	peanut oil
butyric acid	$CH_3(CH_2)_2-COOH$	butter
caproic acid	$CH_3(CH_2)_4-COOH$	butter
lauric acid	$CH_3(CH_2)_{10}-COOH$	coconut oil
stearic acid	$CH_3(CH_2)_{16}-COOH$	animal and vegetable fats
Unsaturated		
oleic acid	$CH_3(CH_2)_7CH=CH(CH_2)_7-COOH$	corn oil
linoleic acid	$CH_3(CH_2)_4CH=CH-CH_2-CH=CH(CH_2)_7-COOH$	linseed oil
linolenic acid	$CH_3CH_2CH=CH-CH_2CH=CH-CH_2-CH=CH-(CH_2)_7COOH$	linseed oil

Triglyceride
A fat that is an ester of glycerol

Saponification
The process of breaking down a triglyceride by treatment with aqueous sodium hydroxide to produce glycerol and the fatty acid salts; the fatty acid salts produced are soaps.

ℹ nformation

Unsaturated fats contain one or more C=C bonds.

Fats that are esters of glycerol are called **triglycerides** and have the general structure

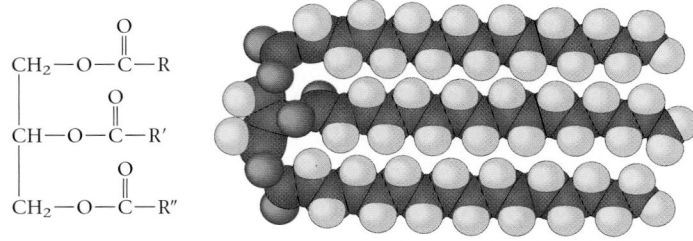

where the three R groups may be the same or different and may be saturated or unsaturated. Vegetable fats tend to be unsaturated and usually occur as oily liquids; most animal fats are saturated (contain only C—C single bonds) and occur as solids at room temperature.

Triglycerides can be broken down by treatment with aqueous sodium hydroxide. The products are glycerol and the fatty acid salts; the latter are known as soaps. This process is called **saponification**.

Much of what we call greasy dirt is nonpolar. Grease, for example, consists mostly of long-chain hydrocarbons. However, water, the solvent most commonly available to us, is very polar and does not dissolve "greasy dirt." We need to add something to the water that is somehow compatible with both the polar water and the nonpolar grease. Fatty-acid anions are perfect for this role, because they have a long nonpolar tail and a polar head. For example, the stearate anion can be represented as

Nonpolar tail

Polar head

Such ions can be dispersed in water because they form **micelles** (see **Figure 21.19**). These aggregates of fatty-acid anions have the water-incompatible tails in the interior; the anionic parts (the polar heads) point outward and interact with the polar water molecules. A soap solution does not contain *individual* fatty-acid anions dispersed in the water but rather groups of ions (micelles).

Soap dissolves grease by taking the grease molecules into the nonpolar interior of the micelle (see **Figure 21.20**), so they can be carried away by the water. Soap thus acts to suspend the normally incompatible grease in the water. Because of this ability to assist water in suspending nonpolar materials, soap is also called a *wetting agent*, or **surfactant**.

i n f o r m a t i o n

Like dissolves like.

Surfactant
A wetting agent that assists water in suspending nonpolar materials; soap is a surfactant.

 Active Reading Question

Soap helps to suspend nonpolar materials in water.

TECHNOLOGY

 Figure 21.20

 Animation
Micelle Formation

Active Reading Question

Why is soap sometimes called a *wetting agent*?

Nonpolar tail   Polar head
○ Positive ion
◉ Water molecule

Figure 21.19
A two-dimensional "slice" of the structure of a micelle of fatty-acid anions. Cations surround the negatively charged micelle.

Figure 21.20
Soap micelles absorb grease molecules into their interiors so that the molecules are suspended in the water and can be washed away.

21.2 • Carbohydrates, Nucleic Acids, and Lipids • **771**

Colorful Milk

Materials
- shallow colorless container
- whole milk
- food coloring
- cotton swab
- detergent

Procedure
1. Half-fill a shallow colorless container with whole milk.
2. Add 1–2 drops of food coloring to the surface of the milk. Do not stir.
3. Add 1–2 drops of a different food coloring to the surface in a different area. Do not stir.
4. Without moving or shaking the container, observe the food coloring and record what you see.
5. Dip one end of a cotton swab in a liquid dishwashing detergent. Touch the center of the surface of the milk with this end of the swab. Be careful not to stir the milk.
6. Record your observations. If the motion stops, add another drop of the detergent (see step 5).

Results/Analysis
1. Explain your observations from step 4.
2. Compare what the food coloring did in the milk to what happens when you add food coloring to water (see "Chemistry in Action: Mysterious Mixing" on page 39).
3. How did the detergent affect the food coloring in the milk? Explain.

A major disadvantage is that soap anions form precipitates in hard water (water that contains large concentrations of ions such as Ca^{2+} and Mg^{2+}). These precipitates occur because the Ca^{2+} and Mg^{2+} ions form insoluble solids with soap anions. These precipitates ("soap scum") dull clothes and drastically reduce soap's cleaning efficiency. To help alleviate this problem, a huge industry has developed to produce artificial soaps, called detergents. Detergents are similar to natural soaps in that they have a long nonpolar tail and an ionic head. However, detergent anions have the advantage of not forming insoluble solids with Ca^{2+} and Mg^{2+} ions.

Phospholipids are similar in structure to fats in that they are esters of glycerol. Unlike fats, however, they contain only two fatty acids. The third group bound to glycerol is a phosphate group, which gives phospholipids two distinct parts: the long nonpolar "tail" and the polar substituted-phosphate "head" (see **Figure 21.21**).

Phospholipid
An ester of glycerol containing two fatty acids; consists of a long nonpolar "tail" and a polar substituted-phosphate "head"

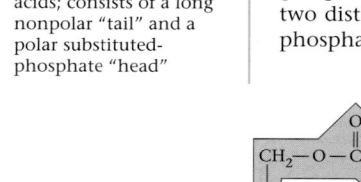

Nonpolar tails

Polar head

Figure 21.21
Lecithin, a phospholipid, with its long nonpolar tails and polar substituted-phosphate head

772 • Chapter 21 • Biochemistry

Hands-On Chemistry
MINI-LAB

Colorful Milk

Materials Each group will need a shallow colorless container, whole milk, food coloring, cotton swabs (at least one), and dishwashing detergent.

Purpose Students will examine the effect of milk fat on the movement of food coloring and determine the effect of soap on this movement.

Discussion When food coloring is added to whole milk, the drops do not spread as they do in water. This lack of effect occurs because food coloring is water-soluble and milk is a suspension of fat globules in water. Students should recall that food coloring mixes well with water. Upon adding dishwashing detergent to the center of the milk sample, the food coloring will move to the edges of the cup. In essence, the soap forms micelles that trap the fat globules and "push" away the water. When the water is "pushed," the food coloring goes with it.

Waxes are another class of lipids. Like fats and phospholipids, waxes are esters, but unlike these other lipids, they involve monohydroxy alcohols instead of glycerol. For example, beeswax, a substance secreted by the wax glands of bees, is mainly myricyl palmitate,

$$CH_3(CH_2)_{14}-\overset{\overset{\textstyle O}{\|}}{C}-O-(CH_2)_{29}-CH_3$$

formed from palmitic acid,

$$CH_3(CH_2)_{14}-C\overset{\textstyle O}{\underset{\textstyle OH}{\diagdown}}$$

and carnaubyl alcohol

$$CH_3(CH_2)_{29}-OH$$

Waxes are solids that furnish waterproof coatings on leaves and fruit and on the skins and feathers of animals. Waxes are also important commercially. For example, whale oil is largely composed of the wax cetyl palmitate. It has been used in so many products, including cosmetics and candles, that the blue whale has been hunted almost to extinction.

Steroids are a class of lipids that have a characteristic carbon ring structure of the type

Steroids comprise four groups: cholesterol, adrenocorticoid hormones, sex hormones, and bile acids.

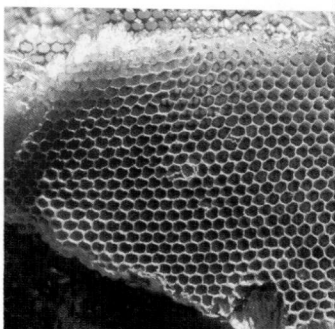

Beeswax in a honeycomb from Indonesia

> **Waxes**
> A class of lipids that involve monohydroxy alcohols instead of glycerol

Whale oil is largely composed of the wax cetyl palmitate.

CHEMISTRY EXPLORERS

Percy Julian • 1899–1975

Percy Julian was born in Birmingham, Alabama, in 1899, the son of a railway mail clerk and a schoolteacher, and the grandson of slaves. He earned a master's degree from Harvard University, where he graduated at the top of his class. After serving as associate professor of chemistry at Howard University for two years, he moved to Austria and received a Ph.D. in organic chemistry in 1931 from the University of Vienna.

Julian is noted for his work with steroids from natural products. Specifically, he synthesized chemicals used in the treatment of glaucoma and rheumatoid arthritis. In 1953, he founded The Julian Laboratories, Inc.

Percy Julian was awarded over 100 chemistry patents, was elected to the National Academy of Sciences in 1973, and was inducted into the National Inventors Hall of Fame in 1990.

21.2 • Carbohydrates, Nucleic Acids, and Lipids • **773**

CHEMISTRY EXPLORERS

Percy Julian

Julian also developed an inexpensive way to produce male and female hormones (progesterone and testosterone) from soy beans. Progesterone has been used to prevent miscarriages and to fight cancer and other ailments. Julian and his wife lived in Chicago for a time, and in 1950, Julian was named Chicagoan of the Year. Julian's numerous patents included one for a fire-extinguishing foam that was used on oil and gasoline fires during World War II.

Cholesterol (see **Figure 21.22a**) is found in virtually all organisms and is the starting material for the formation of the many other steroid-based molecules, such as vitamin D (see **Figure 21.22b**). Although cholesterol is essential for human life, it has been implicated in the formation of plaque on the walls of arteries (a process called atherosclerosis, or hardening of the arteries), which can lead eventually to clogging. This effect seems especially important in the arteries that supply blood to the heart. Blockage of these arteries leads to heart damage that often results in death from a heart attack.

Figure 21.22
Several common steroids and steroid derivatives

(a) cholesterol

(b) vitamin D$_3$

(c) cortisol

(d) testosterone

(e) progesterone

(f) estradiol

(g) ethynodiol diacetate

(h) cholic acid

Meeting Individual Needs

ADVANCED LEARNERS

Have students prepare a PowerPoint presentation detailing the progression of damage that occurs when people do not control their cholesterol intake. Presentations should also include acceptable cholesterol limits, ways to control cholesterol intake, and ways to learn of cholesterol levels.

The **adrenocorticoid hormones**, such as cortisol (see **Figure 21.22c**), are synthesized in the adrenal glands (glands that lie next to each kidney) and are involved in various regulatory functions.

Of the **sex hormones**, the most important male hormone is *testosterone* (see **Figure 21.22d**), a hormone that controls the growth of the reproductive organs and hair and the development of the muscle structure and deep voice that are characteristic of males. There are two types of female sex hormones of particular significance: *progesterone* (see **Figure 21.22e**), and a group of estrogens, one of which is *estradiol* (see **Figure 21.22f**). Changes in the concentrations of these hormones cause the periodic changes in the ovaries and uterus that are responsible for the menstrual cycle. During pregnancy, a high level of progesterone is maintained, which prevents ovulation.

The **bile acids** are produced from cholesterol in the liver and stored in the gallbladder. The primary human bile acid is *cholic acid* (see **Figure 21.22h**), a substance that aids in the digestion of fats by emulsifying them in the intestine. Bile acids can also dissolve cholesterol ingested in food and are therefore important in controlling cholesterol in the body.

SECTION 21.2
REVIEW QUESTIONS

❶ How is a protein different from a carbohydrate?

❷ Where does the name *carbohydrate* come from?

❸ How are starch and cellulose similar? Why can we not digest cellulose?

❹ What is a nucleotide? What are the fundamental parts of a nucleotide?

❺ In the double helix that forms DNA, what are the substances which form the steps in the ladder? How are they held together?

❻ What are the major functions of DNA?

❼ What are lipids? List the types of lipids and give a function for each.

❽ Explain how water cannot dissolve grease, and why soap in water dissolves grease.

RESEARCH LINKS
CLASSZONE.COM

🔍 SECTION 21.2
Review Questions

1. Proteins contain nitrogen and sometimes sulfur atoms. Carbohydrates contain only carbon, hydrogen, and oxygen.

2. Many carbohydrates have the empirical formula CH_2O, so it was believed that these substances were hydrates of carbon.

3. Starch and cellulose are both formed from glucose linked between the carbon 1 and carbon 4 atoms. The link is different in each substance, and humans have only the enzyme necessary to digest the link found in starch.

4. A nucleotide is a monomer of DNA and RNA. The fundamental parts of a nucleotide are sugar, phosphate, and base.

5. The substances that form the steps are the base pairs. They are held together by hydrogen bonding.

6. The major functions of DNA are replication and protein synthesis.

7. Lipids are water-insoluble substances that can be extracted by nonpolar solvents. Four classes of lipids exist: fats, phospholipids, waxes, and steroids.

8. Water is a polar substance and grease is a mixture of nonpolar substances, so they do not mix. However, soap molecules have long nonpolar "tails" (which interact with the grease) and polar "heads" (which interact with the water).

Chapter 21 Review

Key Terms

21.1
Biochemistry
Biotechnology
Essential elements
Trace elements
Cell
Proteins
Fibrous proteins
Globular proteins
Alpha-amino acids
Side chains
Dipeptide
Peptide linkage
Polypeptide
Primary structure
Secondary structure
Alpha-helix
Pleated sheet
Tertiary structure
Disulfide linkage
Denaturation
Enzymes
Lock-and-key model
Substrate
Active site

Key Ideas

21.1 Introduction to Proteins

■ Proteins are natural polymers made from various α-amino acids.

- Fibrous proteins are used in the body for structural purposes.

- Globular proteins are "worker" molecules that act as catalysts, as an O_2 storage system, as regulators of biological function, and so on.

- Protein structure has several levels

  ◆ Primary: the order of α-amino acids

  ◆ Secondary: arrangement of the protein in space

    ★ α-helix

    ★ β-pleated sheet

  ◆ Tertiary: overall shape of the protein

RESEARCH LINKS
CLASSZONE.COM

21.2 Carbohydrate, Nucleic Acids, and Lipids

- Carbohydrates
  - Serve as food sources for most organisms and structural materials for plants
  - Monosaccharides
    - Commonly 5 and 6 carbon polyhydroxy ketones and aldehydes
    - Combine to form more complex carbohydrates such as sucrose (table sugar), starch, and cellulose
- Nucleic acids
  - Deoxyribonucleic acid (DNA)
    - Has a double helical structure

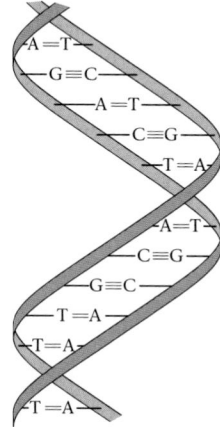

  - During cell division the double helix unravels to enable a copy of the DNA to be made.
  - Contains segments called genes that store the primary structure of various proteins
- Lipids
  - Water soluble substances found in cells divided into units
  - Four classes
    - Fats
    - Phospholipids
    - Waxes
    - Steroids

RESEARCH LINKS
CLASSZONE.COM

Chapter 21 Assessment

1. Oxygen is the element present in the human body in the largest percentage by mass (65%). Other elements present in the body and their uses are given in Table 21.1.

2. Proteins represent biopolymers of α-amino acids. Proteins make up about 15% of the human body by mass.

3. Molar masses of proteins range from a few thousand amu to more than 1 million amu. Such molar masses are consistent with proteins in that they are large polymeric molecules.

4. Fibrous proteins provide the structural material for many tissues in the body. They are the chief constituents of hair, cartilage, and muscles. Fibrous proteins consist of lengthwise bundles of polypeptide chains (a fiber). Globular proteins consist of polypeptide chains folded into a spherical shape. They are found in the bloodstream, where they transport and store various substances, act as antibodies (fight infections), act as enzymes (catalysts), and participate in the body's various regulatory systems.

5. The general structural formula for the α-amino acids is

$$\underset{\underset{R}{|}}{NH_2-\overset{\overset{H}{|}}{C}-\overset{\overset{O}{\parallel}}{C}-OH}$$

All α-amino acids contain the carboxyl group (—COOH) and the amino group (—NH₂) attached to the α-carbon atom as indicated. In this general formula, R represents the remainder of the amino acid molecule (side chain). It is this portion of the molecule that differentiates one amino acid from another.

6. The structures of the amino acids are given in Figure 21.2. A side chain is nonpolar if it is mostly

hydrocarbon in nature (like alanine). Polar side chains may contain the hydroxyl group (—OH), the sulfhydryl group (—SH), or a second amino (—NH₃) or carboxyl (—COOH) group.

7. Since most proteins exist in aqueous media (water) in living creatures, the presence of hydrophobic

(water-fearing) and hydrophilic (water-loving) side chains on the amino acids in a protein will greatly influence how that protein's chain interacts with water. The three-dimensional structure of the protein is greatly influenced by the types of side chains present in its constituent amino acids.

8. cys-ala-phe; cys-phe-ala; phe-ala-cys; phe-cys-ala; ala-cys-phe; ala-phe-cys

9. See *Solutions Guide* for labels.
   (a) ile-ala-gly

All exercises with blue numbers have answers in the back of this book.

21.1 Introduction to Proteins

A. Proteins

1. What element is present in the human body in the largest percentage by mass? Name ten other elements essential to life and list their uses in the body.

2. What are proteins? What portion of the human body (by mass) consists of proteins?

3. Describe the range of molar masses shown by proteins in the body. Are such molar masses consistent with proteins being polymers?

4. What uses do *fibrous* and *globular* proteins have in the body? Describe the general shape of these types of proteins.

B. Primary Structure of Proteins

5. Sketch the general formula for an α-amino acid, indicating the α-amino carbon atom. Circle the portion of the structure that all α-amino acids have in common.

6. Write the formulas of two amino acids with polar side chains and of two amino acids with nonpolar side chains. Explain *why* the side chains you have chosen have their respective polarities.

7. Why is it important to distinguish between hydrophilic and hydrophobic side chains? What solvent forms the natural environment for proteins in the body?

8. Write the amino acid sequences possible for a tripeptide containing the amino acids *cys*, *ala*, and *phe*, with each amino acid being used only once in each tripeptide.

9. Given the formulas of the common amino acids in Figure 21.2, sketch the structures of the following simple peptides. Circle the peptide bonds in your structures. Label the terminal amino and carboxyl groups clearly.

   a. ile-ala-gly
   b. gln-ser
   c. ser-gln
   d. cys-asn-gly

10. Given the formulas of the common amino acids in Figure 21.2, sketch the structures of the six different tripeptides possible containing phenylalanine, alanine, and glycine (each taken only once). Circle the peptide bonds in your structures. Label the terminal amino and carboxyl groups clearly.

C. Secondary Structure of Proteins

11. In general terms, what does the secondary structure of a protein represent?

12. How is the secondary structure of a protein related to its function in the body? Give examples.

13. Describe the secondary protein structure known as the pleated sheet. Give two examples of materials containing proteins with this structure.

14. Describe the secondary protein structure known as the α-helix. What types of proteins have this secondary structure?

D. Tertiary Structure of Proteins

15. In general terms, what does the tertiary structure of a protein describe? Clearly distinguish between the secondary and tertiary structures.

16. Describe the function of the amino acid cysteine in influencing the tertiary structure of a protein.

E. Functions of Proteins

17. What is meant by *denaturation* of a protein? Give three examples of situations in which proteins are denatured.

18. Describe the structure of the protein *collagen*. What function does collagen have in the body?

19. What name is given to proteins that catalyze biochemical reactions in the cell?

20. What are antibodies? Give an example of an important antibody.

21. Give several examples of proteins that serve a protective function in the body.

22. How does a "permanent wave" change the structure of the protein of hair? What amino acid undergoes reaction during a permanent wave? Which level of structure for the hair protein is affected?

F. Enzymes

23. How does the efficiency of an enzyme compare to that of inorganic catalysts? Are enzymes more or less efficient?

24. What general name is given to the molecule acted on by an enzyme? What does it mean to say that an enzyme is *specific* for this molecule?

25. What name is given to the specific portion of the enzyme molecule where catalysis actually occurs?

26. Describe the lock-and-key model for enzymes. Why are the shapes of the enzyme and its substrate important in this model?

21.2 Carbohydrates, Nucleic Acids, and Lipids

A. Carbohydrates

27. What functional groups are present in the simple sugars (monosaccharides)?

28. Sugars can be referred to as polyhydroxy carbonyl compounds. Explain this terminology.

29. In aqueous solution, the monosaccharides generally adopt a ring structure, rather than having straight chains. Sketch representations for the ring forms of glucose and fructose.

30. Sketch the straight-chain structures of the following monosaccharides.

    a. glucose   c. ribulose

    b. ribose   d. galactose

B. Nucleic Acids

31. What molecule stores and transmits genetic information in the cell? How large is this molecule? Where in the cell is this molecule found?

32. Name the five nitrogen bases found in DNA and RNA. Which base is found commonly in RNA but not in DNA? Which base is found commonly in DNA but not in RNA?

33. Describe the double-helical structure of DNA. What type of bonding occurs *within* the chain of each strand of the double helix? What type of bonding exists *between* strands to link them together?

34. Describe the *complementary base pairing* between the two individual strands of DNA that forms the overall double-helical structure. How is complementary base pairing involved in the replication of the DNA molecule during cell division?

35. What name is applied to the specific section of the DNA molecule that contains the code for construction of a particular protein?

36. Explain the distinction between, and the functions of, messenger RNA and transfer RNA.

C. Lipids

37. Under what circumstances is a biomolecule classified as a *lipid*? Is the classification based on a particular characteristic structure or on some physical property?

38. Referring to Table 21.5, list several saturated and several unsaturated fatty acids. What is the general source of most unsaturated fatty acids?

39. What is *saponification*? Write a general equation for the saponification of a triglyceride. What are the ionic products of a saponification reaction more commonly called?

40. What is a *micelle*? How do the micelles formed by soap molecules suspend greasy dirt in a solution?

41. What steroid serves as the starting material in the body for the synthesis of other steroids? What dangers are involved in having too large a concentration of this substance in the body?

ala-gly-phe

gly-phe-ala

gly-ala-phe

11. The secondary structure of a protein describes, in general, the arrangement in space of the protein's polypeptide chain. The most common secondary structures are the α-helix and the β pleated sheet.

12. Long, thin, resilient proteins (such as hair) typically contain elongated, elastic α-helical protein molecules. Other proteins (such as silk) that form sheets or plates typically contain protein molecules having the β pleated-sheet structure. Proteins without a structural function in the body (such as hemoglobin) typically have a globular structure.

13. A large number of similar polypeptide chains are arranged lengthwise next to each other to form a wide sheet of protein. The individual polypeptide chains contain the normal bond angles associated with the molecules involved and are not linear; when several chains are arranged next to each other to form a sheet, ripples ("pleats") appear in the overall sheet. Silk and muscle fibers have the pleated-sheet structure.

(b) gln-ser

(c) ser-gln

(d) cys-asn-gly

10. phe-ala-gly

phe-gly-ala

ala-phe-gly

14. The polypeptide chain forms a coil or spiral. Such proteins are found in wool, hair, and tendons.

15. The tertiary structure represents the protein's specific overall shape in its natural environment. To distinguish between secondary and tertiary structures, consider a given protein with an α-helical secondary structure. In the body, this helix is folded and twisted by interactions with the protein's environment until it forms a tight sphere (tertiary structure).

16. Cysteine contains the sulfhydryl (—SH) group in its side chain. It can therefore form disulfide linkages (—S—S—) with other cysteine molecules in the same polypeptide chain. This type of link produces a kink or a knot in the chain that leads to the tertiary structure (three-dimensional shape). For example, cysteine is responsible for the curling of hair.

17. Denaturation represents the breaking down of the protein's tertiary structure. Cooking a raw egg, adding heavy metal ions, and creating permanent hair waves are examples in which proteins are denatured.

18. Collagen has an α-helical secondary structure. Collagen functions as the raw material from which tendons are constructed.

19. enzymes

20. Antibodies are proteins made in the body in response to a foreign substance such as bacteria or viruses. Interferon is an important antibody because it offers general protection against viruses (many antibodies target specific invaders).

Critical Thinking

For exercises 42–63 choose one of the following terms to match the description given.

 a. aldohexose
 b. saliva
 c. antibody
 d. cellulose
 e. CH_2O
 f. cysteine
 g. denaturation
 h. disaccharides
 i. disulfide
 j. DNA
 k. enzymes
 l. fibrous
 m. globular
 n. glycogen
 o. glycoside linkage
 p. hormone
 q. hydrophobic
 r. inhibition
 s. ketohexoses
 t. oxytocin
 u. pleated sheet
 v. polypeptide
 w. polysaccharides
 x. primary structure
 y. substrate
 z. sucrose

42. polymer consisting of many amino acids
43. linkage that forms between two cysteine species
44. peptide hormone that triggers milk secretion
45. proteins with roughly spherical shape
46. sequence of amino acids in a protein
47. silk protein secondary structure
48. water-repelling amino acid side chain
49. amino acid responsible for permanent wave in hair
50. biological catalysts
51. breakdown of a protein's tertiary and/or secondary structure
52. molecule acted on by an enzyme
53. occurs when an enzyme's active site is blocked by a foreign molecule
54. special protein synthesized in response to foreign substance
55. substance that has a specific effect on a particular target organ
56. animal polymer of glucose
57. —C—O—C— bond between rings in disaccharide sugars
58. empirical formula leading to the name *carbohydrate*
59. where enzymes catalyzing the breakdown of glycoside link are found
60. six-carbon ketone sugars
61. structural component of plants, polymer of glucose
62. sugars consisting of two monomer units
63. six-carbon aldehyde sugars

780 • Chapter 21 • Biochemistry

21. Antibodies are synthesized in the body in response to foreign substances such as bacteria. Interferon is a protein that helps to protect cells against viral infection. The process of blood clotting involves several proteins.

22. The cross-linkages between adjacent polypeptide chains of one protein are broken chemically and then re-formed chemically in a new location. The primary cross-linkage involved is a disulfide linkage between cysteine units in the polypeptide chain. The tertiary structure is mainly affected, although the secondary structure can also be affected if the waving lotion is left on too long (making the hair very frizzy).

23. Enzymes are typically 1 to 10 million times more efficient than inorganic catalysts.

(continued on page 781a)

1 The order or sequences of amino acids in the protein chain is called the

A primary structure.

B secondary structure.

C tertiary structure.

D polypeptide.

2 A pleated sheet is a type of

A the primary structure of a protein.

B the secondary structure of a protein.

C the tertiary structure of a protein.

D disulfide linkage.

3 The lock-and-key model applies to

A the structure of carbohydrates.

B the shape of proteins.

C the functioning of enzymes.

D glycoside linkages.

4 Table sugar (sucrose) is a disaccharide formed from

A ribose and glucose.

B glucose and fructose.

C fructose and ribose.

D glucose and galactose.

5 Which of the following is not a carbohydrate?

A starch

B cellulose

C glycogen

D dipeptide

6 The fundamental units in both DNA and RNA are called

A nucleotides.

B amino acids.

C lipids.

D substrates.

7 Which if the following is not a steroid or steroid derivative?

A cholesterol

B cortisol

C adenosine

D cholic acid

8 Write the complementary pairs of bases.

Thymine

Guanine

Adenine

Cytosine

9 The phrase *like dissolves like* means that polar solvents dissolve polar solutes, and nonpolar solvents dissolve nonpolar solutes. Soap is dissolved in water (a polar molecule) to dissolve grease (nonpolar).

a. Explain how soap is able to dissolve in a polar solvent and dissolve nonpolar molecules.

b. Sketch a diagram showing how a soap solution is able to dissolve grease.

c. Explain what "hard" water is and why a soap solution is less effective in it.

Chapter 21 • Standardized Test Practice • **781**

1. A

2. B

3. C

4. B

5. D

6. A

7. C

8. Adenine is complementary to thymine, and cytosine is complementary to guanine.

9. a. Soap is a long-chain fatty acid ionic compound. The soap molecules form micelles in solution, and the micelles have nonpolar interiors. The nonpolar portion of the micelle can dissolve grease. The soap micelles dissolve in water because the outer portion of the micelles is ionic.

b. The drawing should look like Figure 21.20.

c. Hard water has ions such as Ca^{2+} and Mg^{2+} dissolved in it. These ions form insoluble solids with the soap anions, so the soap cannot dissolve in water as readily.

Test Taking Strategy

Help students to prepare mentally for a standardized test by discussing test anxiety and ways to overcome it. Show students how to use breathing exercises to calm their nerves. If known, review with students the way a test will be graded so that students will know whether they will be penalized for skipping a question. Review previous test-taking strategies. Also stress the importance of a good night's sleep before the test.

(continued from page 780)

24. The molecule acted upon by an enzyme is referred to as the enzyme's substrate. If an enzyme is said to be specific for a particular substrate, it will catalyze the reactions of only that molecule.

25. active site

26. The lock-and-key model postulates that the structures of the enzyme and its substrate are complementary. In this way, the active site of the enzyme and the portion of the substrate to be acted upon can fit closely together. The structures of these portions of the molecules are unique to the particular enzyme–substrate pair. They fit together in the same way that a particular key is necessary to open a specific lock.

27. Simple sugars typically contain several hydroxyl groups as well as the carbonyl functional group.

28. Sugars contain an aldehyde or ketone functional group (carbonyl group, $C=O$) as well as several hydroxyl groups (—OH).

29. See Figure 21.9.

30. (a)
```
        CHO
         |
   H — C — OH
         |
  HO — C — H
         |
   H — C — OH
         |
   H — C — OH
         |
        CH₂OH
```

(b)
```
        CHO
         |
   H — C — OH
         |
   H — C — OH
         |
   H — C — OH
         |
        CH₂OH
```

(c)
```
        CH₂OH
         |
         C = O
         |
   H — C — OH
         |
   H — C — OH
         |
        CH₂OH
```

(d)
```
        CHO
         |
   H — C — OH
         |
  HO — C — H
         |
  HO — C — H
         |
   H — C — OH
         |
        CH₂OH
```

31. DNA is responsible for coding and storing genetic information in the cell and for subsequently transmitting that information. It is found in the nucleus of each cell. The molar mass of DNA depends on the complexity of the species, but human DNA may have a molar mass as large as 2 billion g.

32. uracil (RNA only); cytosine (DNA, RNA); thymine (DNA only); adenine (DNA, RNA); guanine (DNA, RNA)

33. In a strand of DNA, the phosphate group and the sugar molecule of adjacent nucleotides become bonded to each other. The chain portion of the DNA molecule, therefore, consists of alternating phosphate groups and sugar molecules. The nitrogen bases are found sticking out from the side of this phosphate–sugar chain, being bonded to the sugar molecules.

34. A comparison of the two strands of a DNA molecule shows that a given base in one strand is always paired with a particular base in the other strand. Because of the shapes and side atoms along the rings of the nitrogen bases, only certain parts can hydrogen-bond with one another in the double helix. Adenine is always paired with thymine; cytosine is always paired with guanine. When a DNA helix unwinds for replication during cell division, only the appropriate complementary bases are able to approach and bond to the nitrogen bases of each strand. For example, when the two strands of DNA separate, only a new cytosine molecule can bond to the original guanine, and only a new guanine molecule can bond to the original cytosine.

35. gene

36. Messenger RNA molecules are synthesized to be complementary to a portion (gene) of the DNA molecule in the cell. They serve as the template or pattern upon which a protein will be constructed (a particular group of nitrogen bases on mRNA is able to accommodate and specify a particular amino acid in a particular location in the protein). Transfer RNA molecules are much smaller than mRNA, and their structure accommodates only a single, specific amino acid molecule. They "find" their specific amino acid in the cellular fluids and bring it to mRNA, where it is added to the protein molecule being synthesized.

37. Rather than having some common structural feature, substances are classified as lipids based on their solubility characteristics. Lipids are water-insoluble substances that can be extracted from cells by nonpolar organic solvents such as benzene or carbon tetrachloride.

38. Saturated: butyric acid, caproic acid, lauric acid, stearic acid; unsaturated: oleic acid, linoleic acid, linolenic acid. Most unsaturated fatty acids are derived from vegetable matter (plants).

39. Saponification is the production of a soap by treatment of a triglyceride with a strong base such as NaOH.

triglyceride + 3NaOH →
glycerol + 3Na$^+$soap$^-$

40. Soaps have a nonpolar nature and an ionic nature. In water, soap anions form aggregates called micelles, in which the hydrocarbon chains are oriented toward the interior of the aggregate and the ionic carboxyl groups are oriented toward the outside. The resulting micelle is able to interact with a grease molecule (pulling it into the hydrocarbon interior). See Figures 21.19 and 21.20.

41. Cholesterol is a naturally occurring steroid from which the body synthesizes other needed steroids. Because cholesterol is insoluble in water, having too large a concentration of this substance may lead to buildup on the walls of blood vessels, causing their eventual blockage.

42. v
43. i
44. t
45. m
46. x
47. u
48. q
49. f
50. k
51. g
52. y
53. r
54. c
55. p
56. n
57. o
58. e
59. b
60. s
61. d
62. h
63. a

Appendices

Appendix A

 Laboratory Safety Handbook

One of the first things a chemist learns is that working in a laboratory can be an exciting experience. But the laboratory can also be a dangerous place if safety rules are not followed. You must be responsible for your safety and the safety of others.

General Safety Rules

1. Read the directions for the experiment several times. Follow the directions exactly as they are written. If you have questions about any part of the procedure, ask your teacher for assistance.

2. Never perform any activities that are not authorized by your teacher. Do not work in the laboratory without teacher supervision.

3. Use the safety equipment provided for you. Safety goggles and a lab apron should be worn whenever you are working with chemicals or heating any substance.

4. Never eat or drink in the lab. Never inhale chemicals. Do not taste any chemicals.

5. Take care not to spill any material in the lab. If a spill occurs, immediately ask your teacher about the proper cleanup procedure. Do not pour chemicals or other substances into the sink or trash container.

6. Tie back long hair to keep it away from chemicals, burners, and other lab equipment.

7. Remove or tie back articles of loose clothing and jewelry that can hang down and come in contact with chemicals or flames.

8. Know the locations of the safety showers and eyewashes and know how to use them.

First Aid in the Lab

Report any accident or injury, no matter how minor, to your teacher.

Heating and Fire Safety

1. Maintain a clean work area and keep materials away from flames.

2. Never reach across an open flame.

3. Make sure you know how to use a Bunsen burner. Never leave a heat source unattended.

4. When heating a test tube, always point it away from you and others in case the substance bumps out of the tube.

5. Never heat a liquid in a sealed container. The increase in pressure could cause the container to break, injuring you or others.

Injury	Response
Burns	Apply cold water. Call your teacher immediately.
Cuts and Abrasions	Stop any bleeding by applying direct pressure. Call your teacher immediately.
Foreign Matter in Eye	Use eyewash to flush with plenty of water. Call your teacher immediately.
Fainting	Leave the person lying down. Loosen any tight clothing. Call your teacher immediately. Keep people away.
Poisoning	Note the suspected substance. Call your teacher immediately.
Spills on Skin	Flush with large amounts of water or use the safety shower. Call your teacher immediately.

6. Before picking up a container that has been heated, hold the back of your hand close to the container. If you can feel heat on your hand the container is too hot to handle. Use a clamp, tongs, or a hot pad. Remember that hot glass looks just like cold glass.

7. If a fire should break out in the classroom or if your clothing catches fire, smother it with a fire blanket or roll on the ground. NEVER RUN.

Working in the Laboratory Safely

1. Always use heat resistant (Pyrex) glassware for heating.

2. Use materials only from properly labeled containers. Read labels carefully before using chemicals.

3. Do not return chemicals to stock bottles. Discard extra chemicals as your teacher directs.

4. When diluting acids, *always add acid to water.*

5. Do not use the sink to discard matches or any other solid material.

6. Use glycerine or a lubricant when inserting glass tubing or thermometers through rubber stoppers. Protect your hand with a paper towel or a folded cloth.

7. Store backpacks, coats, and other personal items away from the immediate lab bench area.

Cleaning Up the Laboratory

1. After working in the lab, clean up your work area and return all equipment to its proper place.

2. Turn off all water and burners. Check that you have turned off the gas jet as well as the burner.

3. Dispose of chemicals and other materials as directed by your teacher.

4. Wash your hands thoroughly before leaving the lab.

Appendix B

Math Review

In solving chemistry problems you will use, over and over again, relatively few mathematical procedures. In this section we review the few algebraic manipulations that you will need.

Solving an Equation

In the course of solving a chemistry problem, we often construct an algebraic equation that includes the unknown quantity (the thing we want to calculate). An example is

$$(1.5)V = (0.23)(0.08206)(298)$$

We need to "solve this equation for V." That is, we need to isolate V on one side of the equal sign and all the numbers on the other side. How can we do this? The key idea in solving an algebraic equation is that *doing the same thing on both sides of the equal sign* does not change the equality. That is, it is always "legal" to do the same thing to both sides of the equation. Here we want to solve for V, so we must get the number 1.5 on the other side of the equal sign. We can do this by dividing *both sides* by 1.5.

$$\frac{(1.5)V}{1.5} = \frac{(0.23)(0.08206)(298)}{1.5}$$

Now the 1.5 in the denominator on the left cancels the 1.5 in the numerator:

$$\frac{(\cancel{1.5})V}{\cancel{1.5}} = \frac{(0.23)(0.08206)(298)}{1.5}$$

to give

$$V = \frac{(0.23)(0.08206)(298)}{1.5}$$

Using the procedures in "Using Your Calculator" for chain calculations, we can now obtain the value for V with a calculator.

$$V = 3.7$$

Sometimes it is necessary to solve an equation that consists of symbols. For example, consider the equation

$$\frac{P_1V_1}{T_1} = \frac{P_2V_2}{T_2}$$

Let's assume we want to solve for T_2. That is, we want to isolate T_2 on one side of the equation. There are several possible ways to proceed, keeping in mind that we always do the same thing on both sides of the equal sign. First we multiply both sides by T_2.

$$T_2 \times \frac{P_1V_1}{T_1} = \frac{P_2V_2}{\cancel{T_2}} \times \cancel{T_2}$$

This cancels T_2 on the right. Next we multiply both sides by T_1.

$$T_2 \times \frac{P_1V_1}{\cancel{T_1}} \times \cancel{T_1} = P_2V_2T_1$$

This cancels T_1 on the left. Now we divide both sides by P_1V_1.

$$T_2 \times \frac{\cancel{P_1V_1}}{\cancel{P_1V_1}} = \frac{P_2V_2T_1}{P_1V_1}$$

This yields the desired equation,

$$T_2 = \frac{P_2V_2T_1}{P_1V_1}$$

For practice, solve each of the following equations for the variable indicated.

a. $PV = k$; solve for P

b. $1.5x + 6 = 3$; solve for x

c. $PV = nRT$; solve for n

d. $\dfrac{P_1V_1}{T_1} = \dfrac{P_2V_2}{T_2}$; solve for V_2

e. $\dfrac{°F - 32}{°C} = \dfrac{9}{5}$; solve for $°C$

f. $\dfrac{°F - 32}{°C} = \dfrac{9}{5}$; solve for $°F$

Solutions

a. $\dfrac{P\cancel{V}}{\cancel{V}} = \dfrac{k}{V}$

$P = \dfrac{k}{V}$

b. $1.5x + 6 - 6 = 3 - 6$

$1.5x = -3$

$\dfrac{\cancel{1.5}x}{\cancel{1.5}} = \dfrac{-3}{1.5}$

$x = -\dfrac{3}{1.5} = -2$

c. $\dfrac{PV}{RT} = \dfrac{n\cancel{RT}}{\cancel{RT}}$

$\dfrac{PV}{RT} = n$

d. $\dfrac{P_1V_1}{T_1} \times T_2 = \dfrac{P_2V_2}{\cancel{T_2}} \times \cancel{T_2}$

$\dfrac{P_1V_1T_2}{T_1P_2} = \dfrac{P_2V_2}{\cancel{P_2}}\cancel{}$... $\dfrac{\cancel{P_2}V_2}{\cancel{P_2}}$

$\dfrac{P_1V_1T_2}{T_1P_2} = V_2$

e. $\dfrac{°F - 32}{\cancel{°C}} \times \cancel{°C} = \dfrac{9}{5}°C$

$\dfrac{5}{9}(°F - 32) = \dfrac{\cancel{5}}{\cancel{9}} \times \dfrac{\cancel{9}}{\cancel{5}}°C$

$\dfrac{5}{9}(°F - 32) = °C$

f. $\dfrac{°F - 32}{\cancel{°C}} \times \cancel{°C} = \dfrac{9}{5}°C$

$°F - \cancel{32} + \cancel{32} = \dfrac{9}{5}°C + 32$

$°F = \dfrac{9}{5}°C + 32$

Appendix C

Scientific Notation

The numbers we must work with in scientific measurements are often very large or very small; thus it is convenient to express them using powers of 10. For example, the number 1,300,000 can be expressed as 1.3×10^6, which means multiply 1.3 by 10 six times, or

$$1.3 \times 10^6 = 1.3 \times \underbrace{10 \times 10 \times 10 \times 10 \times 10 \times 10}_{10^6 = 1 \text{ million}}$$

A number written in scientific notation always has the form:

A number (between 1 and 10) times
the appropriate power of 10

To represent a large number such as 20,500 in scientific notation, we must move the decimal point in such a way as to achieve a number between 1 and 10 and then multiply the result by a power of 10 to compensate for moving the decimal point. In this case, we must move the decimal point four places to the left.

$$2\underset{4}{0}\underset{3}{5}\underset{2}{0}\underset{1}{0}$$

to give a number between 1 and 10:

2.05

where we retain only the significant figures (the number 20,500 has three significant figures). To compensate for moving the decimal point four places to the left, we must multiply by 10^4. Thus

$$20{,}500 = 2.05 \times 10^4$$

As another example, the number 1985 can be expressed as 1.985×10^3. To end up with the number 1.985, which is between 1 and 10, we had to move the decimal point three places to the left. To compensate for that, we must multiply by 10^3. Some other examples are given below.

Number	Exponential Notation
5.6	5.6×10^0 or 5.6×1
39	3.9×10^1
943	9.43×10^2
1126	1.126×10^3

So far, we have considered numbers greater than 1. How do we represent a number such as 0.0034 in exponential notation? First, to achieve a number between 1 and 10, we start with 0.0034 and move the decimal point three places to the right.

$$0.\underset{1}{0}\underset{2}{0}\underset{3}{3}4$$

This yields 3.4. Then, to compensate for moving the decimal point to the right, we must multiply by a power of 10 with a negative exponent, in this case, 10^{-3}. Thus

$$0.0034 = 3.4 \times 10^{-3}$$

In a similar way, the number 0.00000014 can be written as 1.4×10^{-7}, because going from 0.00000014 to 1.4 requires that we move the decimal point seven places to the right.

Mathematical Operations with Exponents

We next consider how various mathematical operations are performed using exponents. First we cover the various rules for these operations; then we consider how to perform them on your calculator.

Multiplication and Division

When two numbers expressed in exponential notation are multiplied, the initial numbers are multiplied and the exponents of 10 are *added*.

$$(M \times 10^m)(N \times 10^n) = (MN) \times 10^{m+n}$$

For example (to two significant figures, as required),

$$(3.2 \times 10^4)(2.8 \times 10^3) = 9.0 \times 10^7$$

When the numbers are multiplied, if a result greater than 10 is obtained for the initial number, the decimal point is moved one place to the left and the exponent of 10 is increased by 1.

$$(5.8 \times 10^2)(4.3 \times 10^8) = 24.9 \times 10^{10}$$
$$= 2.49 \times 10^{11}$$
$$= 2.5 \times 10^{11} \text{ (two significant figures)}$$

Division of two numbers expressed in exponential notation involves normal division of the initial numbers and subtraction of the exponent of the divisor from that of the dividend. For example,

$$\frac{4.8 \times 10^8}{\underbrace{2.1 \times 10^3}_{\text{Divisor}}} = \frac{4.8}{2.1} \times 10^{(8-3)} = 2.3 \times 10^5$$

If the initial number resulting from the division is less than 1, the decimal point is moved one place to the right and the exponent of 10 is decreased by 1. For example,

$$\frac{6.4 \times 10^3}{8.3 \times 10^5} = \frac{6.4}{8.3} \times 10^{(3-5)} = 0.77 \times 10^{-2}$$
$$= 7.7 \times 10^{-3}$$

Addition and Subtraction

In order for us to add or subtract numbers expressed in exponential notation, *the exponents of the numbers must be the same*. For example, to add 1.31×10^5 and 4.2×10^4, we must rewrite one number so that the exponents of both are the same. The number 1.31×10^5 can be written 13.1×10^4 because decreasing the exponent by 1 compensates for moving the decimal point one place to the right. Now we can add the numbers.

$$\begin{array}{r} 13.1 \times 10^4 \\ + \quad 4.2 \times 10^4 \\ \hline 17.3 \times 10^4 \end{array}$$

In correct exponential notation, the result is expressed as

$$1.73 \times 10^5.$$

To perform addition or subtraction with numbers expressed in exponential notation, we add or subtract only the initial numbers. The exponent of the result is the same as the exponents of the numbers being added or subtracted. To subtract 1.8×10^2 from 8.99×10^3, we first convert 1.8×10^2 to 0.18×10^3 so that both numbers have the same exponent. Then we subtract.

$$\begin{array}{r} 8.99 \times 10^3 \\ - \quad 0.18 \times 10^3 \\ \hline 8.81 \times 10^3 \end{array}$$

Powers and Roots

When a number expressed in exponential notation is taken to some power, the initial number is taken to the appropriate power and the exponent of 10 is *multiplied* by that power.

$$(N \times 10^n)^m = N^m \times 10^{m \times n}$$

For example,

$$\begin{aligned} (7.5 \times 10^2)^2 &= (7.5)^2 \times 10^{2 \times 2} \\ &= 56. \times 10^4 \\ &= 5.6 \times 10^5 \end{aligned}$$

When a root is taken of a number expressed in exponential notation, the root of the initial number is taken and the exponent of 10 is divided by the number representing the root. For example, we take the square root of a number as follows:

$$\sqrt{N \times 10^n} = (N \times 10^n)^{1/2} = \sqrt{N} \times 10^{n/2}$$

For example,

$$\begin{aligned} (2.9 \times 10^6)^{1/2} &= \sqrt{2.9} \times 10^{6/2} \\ &= 1.7 \times 10^3 \end{aligned}$$

Using a Calculator to Perform Mathematical Operations on Exponents

In dealing with exponents, you must first learn to enter them into your calculator. First the number is keyed in and then the exponent. There is a special key that must be pressed just before the exponent is entered. This key is often labeled $\boxed{\text{EE}}$ or $\boxed{\text{exp}}$. For example, the number 1.56×10^6 is entered as follows:

Press	Display	
1.56	1.56	
EE or exp	1.56	00
6	1.56	06

To enter a number with a negative exponent, use the change-of-sign key $\boxed{+/-}$ after entering the exponent number. For example, the number 7.54×10^{-3} is entered as follows:

Press	Display	
7.54	7.54	
EE or exp	7.54	00
3	7.54	03
+/-	7.54	-03

Once a number with an exponent is entered into your calculator, the mathematical operations are performed exactly the same as with a "regular" number. For example, the numbers 1.0×10^3 and 1.0×10^2 are multiplied as follows:

Press	Display	
1.0	1.0	
EE or exp	1.0	00
3	1.0	03
×	1	03
1.0	1.0	
EE or exp	1.0	00
2	1.0	02
=	1	05

The answer is correctly represented as 1.0×10^5.

The numbers 1.50×10^5 and 1.1×10^4 are added as follows:

Press	Display	
1.5	1.50	
EE or exp	1.50	00
5	1.50	05
+	1.5	05
1.1	1.1	
EE or exp	1.1	00
4	1.1	04
=	1.61	05

The answer is correctly represented as 1.61×10^5. Note that when exponential numbers are added, the calculator automatically takes into account any difference in exponents.

To take the power, root, or reciprocal of an exponential number, enter the number first, then press the appropriate key or keys. For example, the square root of 5.6×10^3 is obtained as follows:

Press	Display	
5.6	5.6	
EE or exp	5.6	00
3	5.6	03
$\sqrt{X}$	7.4833148	01

The answer is correctly represented as 7.5×10^1.

Practice by performing the following operations that involve exponential numbers. The answers follow the exercises.

a. $7.9 \times 10^2 \times 4.3 \times 10^4$ f. $\dfrac{1}{8.3 \times 10^2}$

b. $\dfrac{5.4 \times 10^3}{4.6 \times 10^5}$ g. $\log(1.0 \times 10^{-7})$

c. $1.7 \times 10^2 + 1.63 \times 10^3$ h. $-\log(1.3 \times 10^{-5})$

d. $4.3 \times 10^{-3} + 1 \times 10^{-4}$ i. $\sqrt{6.7 \times 10^9}$

e. $(8.6 \times 10^{-6})^2$

Solutions

a. 3.4×10^7 f. 1.2×10^{-3}

b. 1.2×10^{-2} g. -7.00

c. 1.80×10^3 h. 4.89

d. 4.4×10^{-3} i. 8.2×10^4

e. 7.4×10^{-11}

Appendix D

Graphing

In interpreting the results of a scientific experiment, it is often useful to make a graph. If possible, the function to be graphed should be in a form that gives a straight line. The equation for a straight line (a *linear equation*) can be represented in the general form

$$y = mx + b$$

where y is the *dependent variable*, x is the *independent variable*, m is the *slope*, and b is the *intercept* with the y-axis.

To illustrate the characteristics of a linear equation, $y = 3x + 4$ is plotted in Figure A.1. For this equation $m = 3$ and $b = 4$. Note that the y-intercept occurs when $x = 0$. In this case the y intercept is 4, as can be seen from the equation ($b = 4$).

The slope of a straight line is defined as the ratio of the rate of change in y to that in x:

$$m = \text{slope } \frac{\Delta y}{\Delta x}$$

For the equation $y = 3x + 4$, y changes three times as fast as x (because x has a coefficient of 3). Thus the slope in this case is 3. This can be verified from the graph. For the triangle shown in Figure A.1,

$$\Delta y = 50 - 14 = 36 \quad \text{and} \quad \Delta x = 15 - 3 = 12$$

Thus

$$\text{Slope} = \frac{\Delta y}{\Delta x} = \frac{36}{12} = 3$$

This example illustrates a general method for obtaining the slope of a line from the graph of that line. Simply draw a triangle with one side parallel to the y axis and the other side parallel to the x axis, as shown in Figure A.1. Then determine the lengths of the sides to get Δy and Δx, respectively, and compute the ratio $\Delta y/\Delta x$.

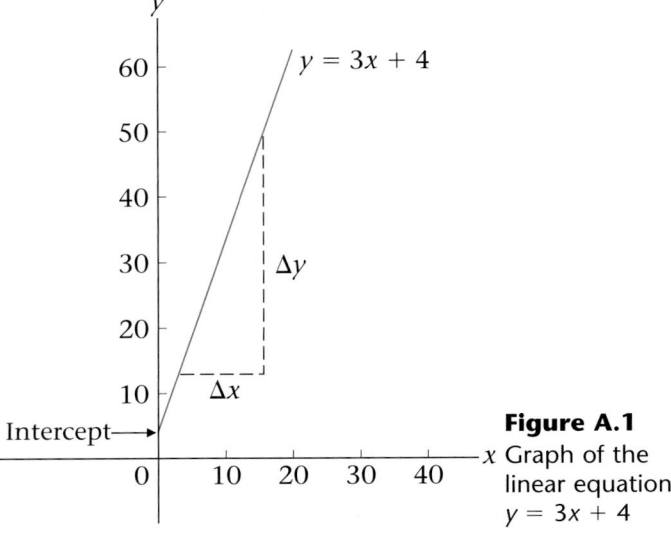

Figure A.1 Graph of the linear equation $y = 3x + 4$

Appendix E

Naming Common Ions

Common Simple Cations and Anions			
Cation	**Name**	**Anion**	**Name***
H^+	hydrogen	H^-	hydride
Li^+	lithium	F^-	fluoride
Na^+	sodium	Cl^-	chloride
K^+	potassium	Br^-	bromide
Cs^+	cesium	I^-	iodide
Be^{2+}	beryllium	O^{2-}	oxide
Mg^{2+}	magnesium	S^{2-}	sulfide
Ca^{2+}	calcium		
Ba^{2+}	barium		
Al^{3+}	aluminum		
Ag^+	silver		

*The root is given in color.

Common Type II Cations		
Ion	**Systematic Name**	**Older Name**
Fe^{3+}	iron(III)	ferric
Fe^{2+}	iron(II)	ferrous
Cu^{2+}	copper(II)	cupric
Cu^+	copper(I)	cuprous
Co^{3+}	cobalt(III)	cobaltic
Co^{2+}	cobalt(II)	cobaltous
Sn^{4+}	tin(IV)	stannic
Sn^{2+}	tin(II)	stannous
Pb^{4+}	lead(IV)	plumbic
Pb^{2+}	lead(II)	plumbous
Hg^{2+}	mercury(II)	mercuric
Hg_2^{2+}*	mercury(I)	mercurous

*Mercury(I) ions always occur bound together in pairs to form Hg_2^{2+}.

Names of Common Polyatomic Ions

Ion	Name	Ion	Name
NH_4^+	ammonium	CO_3^{2-}	carbonate
NO_2^-	nitrite	HCO_3^-	hydrogen carbonate (bicarbonate is a widely used common name)
NO_3^-	nitrate	ClO^-	hypochlorite
SO_3^{2-}	sulfite	ClO_2^-	chlorite
SO_4^{2-}	sulfate	ClO_3^-	chlorate
HSO_4^-	hydrogen sulfate (bisulfate is a widely used common name)	ClO_4^-	perchlorate
OH^-	hydroxide	$C_2H_3O_2^-$	acetate
CN^-	cyanide	MnO_4^-	permanganate
PO_4^{3-}	phosphate	$Cr_2O_7^{2-}$	dichromate
HPO_4^{2-}	hydrogen phosphate	CrO_4^{2-}	chromate
$H_2PO_4^-$	dihydrogen phosphate	O_2^{2-}	peroxide

SI Units and Conversion Factors

These conversion factors are given with more significant figures than those typically used in the body of the text.

Length

SI Unit: Meter (m)

1 meter	=	1.0936 yards
1 centimeter	=	0.39370 inch
1 inch	=	2.54 centimeters (exactly)
1 kilometer	=	0.62137 mile
1 mile	=	5280. feet
	=	1.6093 kilometers

Mass

SI Unit: Kilogram (kg)

1 kilogram	=	1000 grams
	=	2.2046 pounds
1 pound	=	453.59 grams
	=	0.45359 kilogram
	=	16 ounces
1 atomic mass unit	=	1.66057×10^{-27} kilograms

Volume

SI Unit: Cubic Meter (m³)

1 liter	=	10^{-3} m³
	=	1 dm³
	=	1.0567 quarts
1 gallon	=	4 quarts
	=	8 pints
	=	3.7854 liters
1 quart	=	32 fluid ounces
	=	0.94635 liter

Pressure

SI Unit: Pascal (Pa)

1 atmosphere	=	101.325 kilopascals
	=	760. torr (mm Hg)
	=	14.70 pounds per square inch

Energy

SI Unit: Joule (J)

1 joule	=	0.23901 calorie
1 calorie	=	4.184 joules

Solubility Rules

General Rules for Solubility of Ionic Compounds (Salts) in Water at 25 °C

1. Most nitrate (NO_3^-) salts are soluble.

2. Most salts of Na^+, K^+, and NH_4^+ are soluble.

3. Most chloride salts are soluble. Notable exceptions are $AgCl$, $PbCl_2$, and Hg_2Cl_2.

4. Most sulfate salts are soluble. Notable exceptions are $BaSO_4$, $PbSO_4$, and $CaSO_4$.

5. Most hydroxide compounds are only slightly soluble.* The important exceptions are $NaOH$ and KOH. $Ba(OH)_2$ and $Ca(OH)_2$ are only moderately soluble.

6. Most sulfide (S^{2-}), carbonate (CO_3^{2-}), and phosphate (PO_4^{3-}) salts are only slightly soluble.*

*The terms *insoluble* and *slightly soluble* really mean the same thing: such a tiny amount dissolves that it is not possible to detect it with the naked eye.

Practice Problem Exercises

Chapter 2

Practice Problem Exercise 2.1

Items (a) and (c) are physical properties. When the solid gallium melts, it forms liquid gallium. There is no change in composition. Items (b) and (d) reflect the ability to change composition and are thus chemical properties. Statement (b) means that platinum does not react with oxygen to form some new substance.

Practice Problem Exercise 2.2

a. Milk turns sour because new substances are formed. This is a chemical change.

b. Melting the wax is a physical change (a change of state). When the wax burns, new substances are formed. This is a chemical change.

Practice Problem Exercise 2.3

a. Maple syrup is a homogeneous mixture of sugar and other dissolved substances dispersed uniformly in water.

b. Helium and oxygen form a homogeneous mixture.

c. Oil and vinegar salad dressing is a heterogeneous mixture. (Note the two distinct layers the next time you look at a bottle of dressing.)

d. Common salt is a pure substance (sodium chloride), so it always has the same composition. (Note that other substances such as iodine are often added to commercial preparations of table salt, which is mostly sodium chloride. Thus commercial table salt is a homogeneous mixture.)

Chapter 3

Practice Problem Exercise 3.1

a. P_4O_{10} b. UF_6 c. $AlCl_3$

Practice Problem Exercise 3.2

1. In the symbol $^{90}_{38}Sr$, the number 38 is the atomic number, which represents the number of protons in the nucleus of a strontium atom. Because the atom is neutral overall, it must also have 38 electrons. The number 90 (the mass number) represents the number of protons plus the number of neutrons. Thus the number of neutrons is $A - Z = 90 - 38 = 52$.

2. The atom $^{201}_{80}Hg$ has 80 protons, 80 electrons, and $201 - 80 = 121$ neutrons.

Practice Problem Exercise 3.3

The atomic number for phosphorus is 15 and the mass number is $15 + 17 = 32$. Thus the symbol for the atom is $^{32}_{15}P$.

Practice Problem Exercise 3.5

Element	Symbol	Atomic Number	Metal or Nonmetal	Family Name
a. argon	Ar	18	nonmetal	noble gas
b. chlorine	Cl	17	nonmetal	halogen
c. barium	Ba	56	metal	alkaline earth metals
d. cesium	Cs	55	metal	alkali metals

Practice Problem Exercise 3.6

a. KI
   $(1+) + (1-) = 0$

b. Mg_3N_2
   $3(2+) + 2(3-) = (6+) + (6-) = 0$

c. Al_2O_3
   $2(3+) + 3(2-) = 0$

Chapter 4

Practice Problem Exercise 4.1

a. rubidium oxide   c. potassium sulfide

b. strontium iodide

Practice Problem Exercise 4.3

a. The compound $PbBr_2$ must contain Pb^{2+}, named lead(II), to balance the charges of the two Br^- ions. Thus the name is lead(II) bromide. The compound $PbBr_4$ must contain Pb^{4+}, named lead(IV), to balance the charges of the four Br^- ions. The name is therefore lead(IV) bromide.

b. The compound FeS contains the S^{2-} ion (sulfide) and thus the iron cation present must be Fe^{2+}, iron(II). The name is iron(II) sulfide. The compound Fe_2S_3 contains three S^{2-} ions and two iron cations of unknown charge. We can determine the iron charge from the following:

$$2(?+) + 3(2-) = 0$$

   ↑   ↑

  Iron S^{2-}

 charge charge

In this case, ? must represent 3 because

$$2(3+) + 3(2-) = 0$$

Thus Fe_2S_3 contains Fe^{3+} and S^{2-} and its name is iron(III) sulfide.

c. The compound $AlBr_3$ contains Al^{3+} and Br^-. Because aluminum forms only one ion (Al^{3+}), no Roman numeral is required. The name is aluminum bromide.

d. The compound Na_2S contains Na^+ and S^{2-} ions. The name is sodium sulfide. (Because sodium forms only Na^+, no Roman numeral is needed.)

e. The compound $CoCl_3$ contains three Cl^- ions. Thus the cobalt cation must be Co^{3+}, which is named cobalt(III) because cobalt is a transition metal and can form more than one type of cation. Thus the name of $CoCl_3$ is cobalt(III) chloride.

Practice Problem Exercise 4.4

Compound	Individual Names	Prefixes	Name
a. CCl_4	carbon chloride	none tetra-	carbon tetrachloride
b. NO_2	nitrogen oxide	none di-	nitrogen dioxide
c. IF_5	iodine fluoride	none penta-	iodine pentafluoride

Practice Problem Exercise 4.5

a. silicon dioxide

b. dioxygen difluoride

c. xenon hexafluoride

Practice Problem Exercise 4.6

a. chlorine trifluoride

b. vanadium(V) fluoride

c. copper(I) chloride

d. manganese(IV) oxide

e. magnesium oxide

f. water

Practice Problem Exercise 4.7

a. calcium hydroxide

b. sodium phosphate

c. potassium permanganate

d. ammonium dichromate

e. cobalt(II) perchlorate (Perchlorate has a $1-$ charge, so the cation must be Co^{2+} to balance the two ClO_4^- ions.)

f. potassium chlorate

g. copper(II) nitrite [This compound contains two NO_2^- (nitrite) ions and thus must contain a Cu^{2+} cation.]

Practice Problem Exercise 4.8

Compound	Name
a. $NaHCO_3$	sodium hydrogen carbonate
Contains Na^+ and HCO_3^-; (common name)	often called sodium bicarbonate
b. $BaSO_4$	barium sulfate
Contains Ba^{2+} and SO_4^{2-}	
c. $CsClO_4$	cesium perchlorate
Contains Cs^+ and ClO_4^-	
d. BrF_5	bromine pentafluoride
Both nonmetals (Type III binary)	
e. $NaBr$	sodium bromide
Contains Na^+ and Br^- (Type I binary)	
f. $KOCl$	potassium hypochlorite
Contains K^+ and OCl^-	
g. $Zn_3(PO_4)_2$	zinc(II) phosphate

Contains Zn^{2+} and PO_4^{3-}; Zn is a transition metal and may require a Roman numeral. However, because Zn forms only the Zn^{2+} cation, the II is left out. Thus the name of the compound is given as zinc phosphate.

Practice Problem Exercise 4.9

Name	Chemical Formula
a. ammonium sulfate	$(NH_4)_2SO_4$

Two ammonium ions (NH_4^+) are required for each sulfate ion (SO_4^{2-}) to achieve charge balance.

b. vanadium(V) fluoride $\quad VF_5$
The compound contains V^{5+} ions and requires five F^- ions for charge balance.

c. disulfur dichloride $\quad S_2Cl_2$
The prefix di- indicates two of each atom.

d. rubidium peroxide $\quad Rb_2O_2$
Because rubidium is in Group 1, it forms only $1+$ ions. Thus two Rb^+ ions are needed to balance the $2-$ charge on the peroxide ion (O_2^{2-}).

e. aluminum oxide $\quad Al_2O_3$
Aluminum forms only $3+$ ions. Two Al^{3+} ions are required to balance the charge on three O^{2-} ions.

Chapter 5

Practice Problem Exercise 5.2

$357 = 3.57 \times 10^2$
$0.0055 = 5.5 \times 10^{-3}$

Practice Problem Exercise 5.3

a. Three significant figures. The leading zeros (to the left of the 1) do not count, but the trailing zeros do.

b. Five significant figures. The one captive zero and the two trailing zeros all count.

c. This is an exact number obtained by counting the cars. It has an unlimited number of significant figures.

Practice Problem Exercise 5.5

a. $12.6 \times 0.53 = 6.678 = 6.7$
$\quad\quad\quad$ Limiting

b. $12.6 \times 0.53 = 6.7$; $\quad 6.7 \quad$ Limiting
$\quad\quad$ Limiting $\quad\quad \underline{-4.59}$
$\quad\quad\quad\quad\quad\quad\quad\quad 2.11 = 2.1$

c. $\quad 25.36$
$\quad \underline{-4.15} \quad\quad \dfrac{21.21}{2.317} = 9.15408 = 9.154$
$\quad\quad 21.21$

Practice Problem Exercise 5.6

$0.750 \, \cancel{L} \times \dfrac{1.06 \text{ qt}}{1 \, \cancel{L}} = 0.795 \text{ qt}$

Practice Problem Exercise 5.7

$225 \, \dfrac{\cancel{mi}}{h} \times \dfrac{1760 \, \cancel{yd}}{\cancel{mi}} \times \dfrac{1 \, \cancel{m}}{1.094 \, \cancel{yd}} \times \dfrac{1 \text{ km}}{1000 \, \cancel{m}} = 362 \, \dfrac{\text{km}}{h}$

Practice Problem Exercise 5.9

The best way to solve this problem is to convert 172 K to Celsius degrees. To do this we will use the formula $T_{°C} = T_K - 273$.

In this case

$$T_{°C} = T_K - 273 = 172 - 273 = -101$$

So 172 K = −101 °C, which is a lower temperature than −75 °C. Thus 172 K is colder than −75 °C.

Practice Problem Exercise 5.11

The problem is 41 °C = ? °F.
  Using the formula

$$T_{°F} = 1.80(T_{°C}) + 32$$

we have

$$T_{°F} = ? °F = 1.80(41) + 32 = 74 + 32 = 106$$

That is, 41 °C = 106 °F.

Practice Problem Exercise 5.12

This problem can be stated as 239 °F = ? °C.
Using the formula

$$T_{°C} = \frac{T_{°F} - 32}{1.80}$$

we have

$$T_{°C} = ? °C = \frac{239 - 32}{1.80} = \frac{207}{1.80} = 115$$

That is, 239 °F = 115 °C.

Practice Problem Exercise 5.14

We obtain the density of the cleaner by dividing its mass by its volume.

$$\text{Density} = \frac{\text{mass}}{\text{volume}} = \frac{2.81 \text{ g}}{35.8 \text{ mL}} = 0.785 \text{ g/mL}$$

This density identifies the liquid as isopropyl alcohol.

Chapter 6

Practice Problem Exercise 6.1

The average mass of nitrogen is 14.01 amu. The appropriate equivalence statement is 1 N atom = 14.01 amu, which yields the conversion factor we need:

$$23 \text{ N atoms} \times \frac{14.0 \text{ amu}}{1 \text{ N atom}} = 322.2 \text{ amu.}$$
(exact)

Practice Problem Exercise 6.2

The average mass of oxygen is 16.00 amu, which gives the equivalence statement 1 O atom = 16.00 amu. The number of oxygen atoms present is

$$288 \text{ amu} \times \frac{1 \text{ O atom}}{16.00 \text{ amu}} = 18.0 \text{ O atoms}$$

Practice Problem Exercise 6.4

Note that the sample of 5.00×10^{20} atoms of chromium is less than 1 mol (6.022×10^{23} atoms) of chromium. The fraction of a mole that it represents can be determined as follows:

$$5.00 \times 10^{20} \text{ atoms Cr} \times \frac{1 \text{ mol Cr}}{6.022 \times 10^{23} \text{ atoms Cr}}$$

$$= 8.30 \times 10^{-4} \text{ mol Cr}$$

Because the mass of 1 mol of chromium atoms is 52.00 g, the mass of 5.00×10^{20} atoms can be determined as follows:

$$8.30 \times 10^{-4} \text{ mol Cr} \times \frac{52.00 \text{ g Cr}}{1 \text{ mol Cr}} = 4.32 \times 10^{-2} \text{ g Cr}$$

Practice Problem Exercise 6.5

Each molecule of C_2H_3Cl contains two carbon atoms, three hydrogen atoms, and one chlorine atom, so 1 mol of C_2H_3Cl molecules contains 2 mol of C atoms, 3 mol of H atoms, and 1 mol of Cl atoms.

Mass of 2 mol of C atoms:	2×12.01	$= 24.02$ g
Mass of 3 mol of H atoms:	$3 \times 1.008 =$	3.024 g
Mass of 1 mol of Cl atoms:	1×35.45	$= 35.45$ g
		62.494 g

The molar mass of C_2H_3Cl is 62.49 g (rounding to the correct number of significant figures).

Practice Problem Exercise 6.6

The formula for sodium sulfate is Na_2SO_4. One mole of Na_2SO_4 contains 2 mol of sodium ions and 1 mol of sulfate ions.

1 mol of $Na_2SO_4 \rightarrow$ 1 mol of [Na⁺ SO₄²⁻ Na⁺] → 2 mol Na⁺, 1 mol SO₄²⁻

Mass of 2 mol of $Na^+ = 2 \times 22.99$		$= 45.98$ g
Mass of 1 mol of $SO_4^{2-} = 32.07 + 4(16.00) =$		96.07 g
Mass of 1 mol of Na_2SO_4		$= 142.05$ g

The molar mass for sodium sulfate is 142.05 g.
  A sample of sodium sulfate with a mass of 300.0 g represents more than 1 mol. (Compare 300.0 g to the molar mass of Na_2SO_4.) We calculate the number of moles of Na_2SO_4 present in 300.0 g as follows:

$$300.0 \text{ g } Na_2SO_4 \times \frac{1 \text{ mol } Na_2SO_4}{142.5 \text{ g } Na_2SO_4} =$$

$$2.112 \text{ mol } Na_2SO_4$$

Practice Problem Exercise 6.8

First we must compute the mass of 1 mol of C_2F_4 molecules (the molar mass). Because 1 mol of C_2F_4 contains 2 mol of C atoms and 4 mol of F atoms, we have:

$$2 \text{ mol C} \times \frac{12.01 \text{ g}}{\text{mol}} = 24.02 \text{ g C}$$

$$4 \text{ mol F} \times \frac{19.00 \text{ g}}{\text{mol}} = 76.00 \text{ g F}$$

Mass of 1 mol of C_2F_4:   100.02 g = molar mass

Using the equivalence statement 100.02 g C_2F_4 = 1 mol C_2F_4, we calculate the moles of C_2F_4 units in 135 g of Teflon.

$$135 \text{ g } C_2F_4 \text{ units} \times \frac{1 \text{ mol } C_2F_4}{100.02 \text{ g } C_2F_4} =$$

$$1.35 \text{ mol } C_2F_4 \text{ units}$$

Next, using the equivalence statement 1 mol = 6.022×10^{23} units, we calculate the number in C_2F_4 units in 135 g of Teflon.

$$135 \text{ mol } C_2F_4 \times \frac{6.022 \times 10^{23} \text{ units}}{1 \text{ mol}} =$$

$$8.13 \times 10^{23} \ C_2F_4 \text{ units}$$

Practice Problem Exercise 6.9

The molar mass of penicillin F is computed as follows:

C: $14 \text{ mol} \times 12.01 \dfrac{g}{mol} = 168.1 \text{ g}$

H: $20 \text{ mol} \times 1.008 \dfrac{g}{mol} = 20.16 \text{ g}$

N: $\ 2 \text{ mol} \times 14.01 \dfrac{g}{mol} = 28.02 \text{ g}$

S: $\ 1 \text{ mol} \times 32.07 \dfrac{g}{mol} = 32.07 \text{ g}$

O: $\ 4 \text{ mol} \times 16.00 \dfrac{g}{mol} = 64.00 \text{ g}$

Mass of 1 mol of $C_{14}H_{20}N_2SO_4$ = 312.39 g = 312.4 g

Mass percent of C = $\dfrac{168.1 \text{ g C}}{312.4 \text{ g } C_{14}H_{20}N_2SO_4} \times 100\%$ = 53.81%

Mass percent of H = $\dfrac{20.16 \text{ g H}}{312.4 \text{ g } C_{14}H_{20}N_2SO_4} \times 100\%$ = 6.453%

Mass percent of N = $\dfrac{28.02 \text{ g N}}{312.4 \text{ g } C_{14}H_{20}N_2SO_4} \times 100\%$ = 8.969%

Mass percent of S = $\dfrac{32.07 \text{ g S}}{312.4 \text{ g } C_{14}H_{20}N_2SO_4} \times 100\%$ = 10.27%

Mass percent of O = $\dfrac{64.00 \text{ g O}}{312.4 \text{ g } C_{14}H_{20}N_2SO_4} \times 100\%$ = 20.49%

Check: The percentages add up to 99.99%.

Practice Problem Exercise 6.12

Step 1 0.6884 g lead and 0.2356 g chlorine

Step 2 $0.6884 \text{ g Pb} \times \dfrac{1 \text{ mol Pb}}{207.2 \text{ g Pb}} = 0.003322 \text{ mol Pb}$

$0.2356 \text{ g Cl} \times \dfrac{1 \text{ mol Cl}}{35.45 \text{ g Cl}} = 0.006646 \text{ mol Cl}$

Step 3 $\dfrac{0.003322 \ \text{mol Pb}}{0.003322} = 1.000 \text{ mol Pb}$

$\dfrac{0.006646 \text{ mol Cl}}{0.003322} = 2.001 \text{ mol Cl}$

These numbers are very close to integers, so step 4 is unnecessary. The empirical formula is $PbCl_2$.

Practice Problem Exercise 6.13

Step 1 0.8007 g C, 0.9333 g N, 0.2016 g H, and 2.133 g O

Step 2 $0.8007 \text{ g C} \times \dfrac{1 \text{ mol C}}{12.01 \text{ g C}} = 0.06667 \text{ mol C}$

$0.9333 \text{ g N} \times \dfrac{1 \text{ mol N}}{14.01 \text{ g N}} = 0.06662 \text{ mol N}$

$0.2016 \text{ g H} \times \dfrac{1 \text{ mol H}}{1.008 \text{ g H}} = 0.2000 \text{ mol H}$

$2.133 \text{ g O} \ \times \dfrac{1 \text{ mol O}}{16.00 \text{ g O}} = 0.1333 \text{ mol O}$

Step 3 $\dfrac{0.06667 \text{ mol C}}{0.0667} = 1.001 \text{ mol C}$

$\dfrac{0.06662 \text{ mol N}}{0.06667} = 1.000 \text{ mol N}$

$\dfrac{0.2000 \text{ mol H}}{0.06662} = 3.002 \text{ mol H}$

$\dfrac{0.1333 \text{ mol O}}{0.06662} = 2.001 \text{ mol O}$

The empirical formula is CNH_3O_2.

Practice Problem Exercise 6.14

Step 1 In 100.00 g of Nylon-6 the masses of elements present are 63.68 g C, 12.38 g N, 9.80 g H, and 14.14 g O.

Step 2 $63.68 \text{ g C} \times \dfrac{1 \text{ mol C}}{12.01 \text{ g C}} = 5.302 \text{ mol C}$

$12.38 \text{ g N} \times \dfrac{1 \text{ mol N}}{14.01 \text{ g N}} = 0.8837 \text{ mol N}$

$9.80 \text{ g H} \times \dfrac{1 \text{ mol H}}{1.008 \text{ g H}} = 9.72 \text{ mol H}$

$14.14 \text{ g O} \times \dfrac{1 \text{ mol O}}{16.00 \text{ g O}} = 0.8838 \text{ mol O}$

Step 3 $\dfrac{5.302 \text{ mol C}}{0.8836} = 6.000 \text{ mol C}$

$\dfrac{0.8837 \text{ mol N}}{0.8837} = 1.000 \text{ mol N}$

$\dfrac{9.72 \text{ mol H}}{0.8837} = 11.0 \text{ mol H}$

$\dfrac{0.8838 \text{ mol O}}{0.8837} = 1.000 \text{ mol O}$

The empirical formula for Nylon-6 is $C_6NH_{11}O$.

Practice Problem Exercise 6.15

Step 1 First we convert the mass percents to mass in grams. In 100.0 g of the compound, there are 71.65 g of chlorine, 24.27 g of carbon, and 47.0 g of hydrogen.

Step 2 We use these masses to compute the moles of atoms present.

$71.65 \text{ g Cl} \times \dfrac{1 \text{ mol Cl}}{35.45 \text{ g Cl}} = 2.021 \text{ mol Cl}$

$24.27 \text{ g C} \times \dfrac{1 \text{ mol C}}{12.01 \text{ g C}} = 2.021 \text{ mol C}$

$4.07 \text{ g H} \times \dfrac{1 \text{ mol H}}{1.008 \text{ g H}} = 4.04 \text{ mol H}$

Step 3 Dividing each mole value by 2.021 (the smallest number of moles present), we obtain the empirical formula $ClCH_2$.

To determine the molecular formula, we must compare the empirical formula mass to the molar mass. The empirical formula mass is 49.48.

$$\begin{array}{ll} \text{Cl:} & 35.45 \\ \text{C:} & 12.01 \\ \text{2 H: } 2 \times & (1.008) \\ \text{ClCH}_2\text{:} & 49.48 = \text{empirical formula mass} \end{array}$$

The molar mass is known to be 98.96. We know that

Molar mass = $n \times$ (empirical formula mass)

So we can obtain the value of n as follows:

$$\frac{\text{Molar mass}}{\text{Empirical formula mass}} = \frac{98.96}{49.48} = 2$$

Molecular formula = $(\text{ClCH}_2)_2 = \text{Cl}_2\text{C}_2\text{H}_4$

This substance is composed of molecules with the formula $\text{Cl}_2\text{C}_2\text{H}_4$.

Chapter 7

Practice Problem Exercise 7.1

a. $\text{Mg}(s) + \text{H}_2\text{O}(l) \rightarrow \text{Mg(OH)}_2(s) + \text{H}_2(g)$

Note that magnesium (which is in Group 2) always forms the Mg^{2+} cation and thus requires two OH^- anions for a zero net charge.

b. Ammonium dichromate contains the polyatomic ions NH_4^+ and $\text{Cr}_2\text{O}_7^{2-}$ (you should have these memorized). Because NH_4^+ has a 1+ charge, two NH_4^+ cations are required for each $\text{Cr}_2\text{O}_7^{2-}$, with its 2- charge, to give the formula $(\text{NH}_4)_2\text{Cr}_2\text{O}_7$. Chromium(III) oxide contains Cr^{3+} ions—signified by chromium(III)—and O^{2-} (the oxide ion). To achieve a net charge of zero, the solid must contain two Cr^{3+} ions for every three O^{2-} ions, so the formula is Cr_2O_3. Nitrogen gas contains diatomic molecules and is written $\text{N}_2(g)$, and gaseous water is written $\text{H}_2\text{O}(g)$. Thus the unbalanced equation for the decomposition of ammonium dichromate is

$(\text{NH}_4)_2\text{Cr}_2\text{O}_7(s) \rightarrow \text{Cr}_2\text{O}_3(s) + \text{N}_2(g) + \text{H}_2\text{O}(g)$

c. Gaseous ammonia, $\text{NH}_3(g)$, and gaseous oxygen, $\text{O}_2(g)$, react to form nitrogen monoxide gas, $\text{NO}(g)$, plus gaseous water, $\text{H}_2\text{O}(g)$. The unbalanced equation is

$\text{NH}_3(g) + \text{O}_2(g) \rightarrow \text{NO}(g) + \text{H}_2\text{O}(g)$

Practice Problem Exercise 7.3

Step 1 The reactants are propane, $\text{C}_3\text{H}_8(g)$, and oxygen, $\text{O}_2(g)$; the products are carbon dioxide, $\text{CO}_2(g)$, and water, $\text{H}_2\text{O}(g)$. All are in the gaseous state.

Step 2 The unbalanced equation for the reaction is

$\text{C}_3\text{H}_8(g) + \text{O}_2(g) \rightarrow \text{CO}_2(g) + \text{H}_2\text{O}(g)$

Step 3 We start with C_3H_8 because it is the most complicated molecule. C_3H_8 contains three carbon atoms per molecule, so a coefficient of 3 is needed for CO_2.

$\text{C}_3\text{H}_8(g) + \text{O}_2(g) \rightarrow 3\text{CO}_2(g) + \text{H}_2\text{O}(g)$

Also, each C_3H_8 molecule contains eight hydrogen atoms, so a coefficient of 4 is required for H_2O.

$\text{C}_3\text{H}_8(g) + \text{O}_2(g) \rightarrow 3\text{CO}_2(g) + 4\text{H}_2\text{O}(g)$

The final element to be balanced is oxygen. Note that the left side of the equation now has two oxygen atoms, and the right side has ten. We can balance the oxygen by using a coefficient of 5 for O_2.

$\text{C}_3\text{H}_8(g) + 5\text{O}_2(g) \rightarrow 3\text{CO}_2(g) + 4\text{H}_2\text{O}(g)$

Step 4 *Check:*

$$3\text{ C, 8 H, 10 O} \rightarrow 3\text{ C, 8 H, 10 O}$$
$$\underset{\substack{\text{Reactant}\\\text{atoms}}}{} \qquad \underset{\substack{\text{Product}\\\text{atoms}}}{}$$

We cannot divide all coefficients by a given integer to give smaller integer coefficients.

Practice Problem Exercise 7.4

a. $\text{NH}_4\text{NO}_2(s) \rightarrow \text{N}_2(g) + \text{H}_2\text{O}(g)$ (unbalanced)

$\text{NH}_4\text{NO}_2(s) \rightarrow \text{N}_2(g) + 2\text{H}_2\text{O}(g)$ (balanced)

b. $\text{NO}(g) \rightarrow \text{N}_2\text{O}(g) + \text{NO}_2(g)$ (unbalanced)

$3\text{NO}(g) \rightarrow \text{N}_2\text{O}(g) + \text{NO}_2(g)$ (balanced)

c. $\text{HNO}_3(l) \rightarrow \text{NO}_2(g) + \text{H}_2\text{O}(l) + \text{O}_2(g)$ (unbalanced)

$4\text{HNO}_3(l) \rightarrow 4\text{NO}_2(g) + 2\text{H}_2\text{O}(l) + \text{O}_2(g)$ (balanced)

Chapter 8

Practice Problem Exercise 8.2

a. The ions present are

$$\underbrace{\text{Ba}^{2+}(aq) + 2\text{NO}_3{}^-(aq)}_{\substack{\text{Ions in}\\\text{Ba(NO}_3)_2(aq)}} + \underbrace{\text{Na}^+(aq) + \text{Cl}^-(aq)}_{\substack{\text{Ions in}\\\text{NaCl}(aq)}} \rightarrow$$

Exchanging the anions gives the possible solid products BaCl_2 and NaNO_3. Using Table 8.1, we see that both substances are very soluble (rules 1, 2, and 3). Thus no solid forms.

b. The ions present in the mixed solution before any reaction occurs are

$$\underbrace{2\text{Na}^+(aq) + \text{S}^{2-}(aq)}_{\substack{\text{Ions in}\\\text{Na}_2\text{S}(aq)}} + \underbrace{\text{Cu}^{2+}(aq) + 2\text{NO}_3{}^-(aq)}_{\substack{\text{Ions in}\\\text{Cu(NO}_3)_2(aq)}} \rightarrow$$

Exchanging the anions gives the possible solid products CuS and NaNO_3. According to rules 1 and 2 in Table 8.1, NaNO_3 is soluble, and by rule 6, CuS should be insoluble. Thus CuS will precipitate. The balanced equation is

$\text{Na}_2\text{S}(aq) + \text{Cu(NO}_3)_2(aq) \rightarrow \text{CuS}(s) + 2\text{NaNO}_3(aq)$

c. The ions present are

$$\underbrace{\text{NH}_4{}^+(aq) + \text{Cl}^-(aq)}_{\substack{\text{Ions in}\\\text{NH}_4\text{Cl}(aq)}} + \underbrace{\text{Pb}^{2+}(aq) + 2\text{NO}_3{}^-(aq)}_{\substack{\text{Ions in}\\\text{Pb(NO}_3)_2(aq)}} \rightarrow$$

Exchanging the anions gives the possible solid products NH_4NO_3 and PbCl_2. NH_4NO_3 is soluble (rules 1 and 2) and PbCl_2 is insoluble (rule 3). Thus PbCl_2 will precipitate. The balanced equation is

$2\text{NH}_4\text{Cl}(aq) + \text{Pb(NO}_3)_2(aq) \rightarrow \text{PbCl}_2(s) + 2\text{NH}_4\text{NO}_3(aq)$

Practice Problem Exercise 8.3

a. *Molecular equation:*
$$Na_2S(aq) + Cu(NO_3)_2(aq) \rightarrow CuS(s) + 2NaNO_3(aq)$$

Complete ionic equation:
$$2Na^+(aq) + S^{2-}(aq) + Cu^{2+}(aq) + 2NO_3^-(aq) \rightarrow$$
$$CuS(s) + 2Na^+(aq) + 2NO_3^-(aq)$$

Net ionic equation:
$$S^{2-}(aq) + Cu^{2+}(aq) \rightarrow CuS(s)$$

b. *Molecular equation:*
$$2NH_4Cl(aq) + Pb(NO_3)_2(aq) \rightarrow PbCl_2(s) + 2NH_4NO_3(aq)$$

Complete ionic equation:
$$2NH_4^+(aq) + 2Cl^-(aq) + Pb^{2+}(aq) + 2NO_3^-(aq) \rightarrow$$
$$PbCl_2(s) + 2NH_4^+(aq) + 2NO_3^-(aq)$$

Net ionic equation:
$$2Cl^-(aq) + Pb^{2+}(aq) \rightarrow PbCl_2(s)$$

Practice Problem Exercise 8.5

a. The compound NaBr contains the ions Na^+ and Br^-. Thus each sodium atom loses one electron ($Na \rightarrow Na^+ + e^-$), and each bromine atom gains one electron ($Br + e^- \rightarrow Br^-$).

$$Na + Na + Br - Br \rightarrow (Na^+Br^-) + (Na^+Br^-)$$

b. The compound CaO contains the Ca^{2+} and O^{2-} ions. Thus each calcium atom loses two electrons ($Ca \rightarrow Ca^{2+} + 2e^-$), and each oxygen atom gains two electrons ($O + 2e^- \rightarrow O^{2-}$).

$$Ca + Ca + O - O \rightarrow (Ca^{2+} O^{2-}) + (Ca^{2+} O^{2-})$$

Practice Problem Exercise 8.6

a. oxidation–reduction reaction; combustion reaction

b. synthesis reaction; oxidation–reduction reaction; combustion reaction

c. synthesis reaction; oxidation–reduction reaction

d. decomposition reaction; oxidation–reduction reaction

e. precipitation reaction (and double–displacement)

f. synthesis reaction; oxidation–reduction reaction

g. acid–base reaction (and double–displacement)

h. combustion reaction; oxidation–reduction reaction

Chapter 9

Practice Problem Exercise 9.3

The problem can be stated as follows:
$$4.30 \text{ mol } C_3H_8 \rightarrow ? \text{ mol } CO_2$$
$$\text{yields}$$
From the balanced equation
$$C_3H_8(g) + 5O_2(g) \rightarrow 3CO_2(g) + 4H_2O(g)$$
we derive the equivalence statement
$$1 \text{ mol } C_3H_8 = 3 \text{ mol } CO_2$$
The appropriate conversion factor (moles of C_3H_8 must cancel) is 3 mol CO_2/1 mol C_3H_8, and the calculation is

$$4.30 \text{ mol } C_3H_8 \times \frac{3 \text{ mol } CO_2}{1 \text{ mol } C_3H_8} = 12.9 \text{ mol } CO_2$$

Thus we can say

4.30 mol C_3H_8 yields 12.9 mol CO_2

Practice Problem Exercise 9.5

$$1.30 \text{ mol Al} \rightarrow 1.30 \text{ mol AlI}_3$$

$$1.30 \text{ mol AlI}_3 \times \frac{407.7 \text{ g AlI}_3}{1 \text{ mol AlI}_3} = 530. \text{ g AlI}_3$$

Practice Problem Exercise 9.6

a. We first write the balanced equation.
$$SiO_2(s) + 4HF(aq) \rightarrow SiF_4(g) + 2H_2O(l)$$
The map of the steps required is
$$SiO_2(s) + 4HF(aq) \rightarrow SiF_4(g) + 2H_2O(l)$$

We convert 5.68 g of SiO_2 to moles as follows:

$$5.68 \text{ g SiO}_2 \times \frac{1 \text{ mol SiO}_2}{60.09 \text{ g SiO}_2} =$$

$$9.45 \times 10^{-2} \text{ mol SiO}_2$$

Using the balanced equation, we obtain the appropriate mole ratio and convert to moles of HF.

$$9.45 \times 10^{-2} \text{ mol SiO}_2 \times \frac{4 \text{ mol HF}}{1 \text{ mol SiO}_2} =$$

$$3.78 \times 10^{-1} \text{ mol HF}$$

Finally, we calculate the mass of HF by using its molar mass.

$$3.78 \times 10^{-1} \text{ mol HF} \times \frac{20.01 \text{ g HF}}{1 \text{ mol HF}} = 7.56 \text{ g HF}$$

b. The map for this problem is
$$SiO_2(s) + 4HF(aq) \rightarrow SiF_4(g) + 2H_2O(l)$$

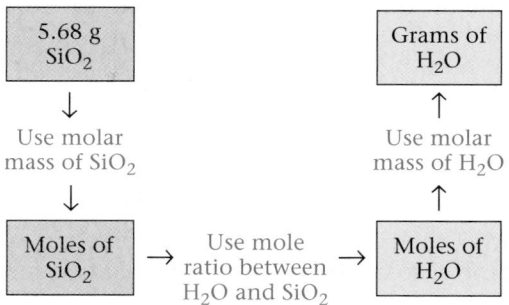

We have already accomplished the first conversion in part a. Using the balanced equation, we obtain moles of H_2O as follows:

$$9.45 \times 10^{-2} \text{ mol } SiO_2 \times \frac{2 \text{ mol } H_2O}{1 \text{ mol } SiO_2} =$$

$$1.89 \times 10^{-1} \text{ mol } H_2O$$

The mass of water formed is

$$1.89 \times 10^{-1} \text{ mol } H_2O \times \frac{18.02 \text{ g } H_2O}{1 \text{ mol } H_2O} = 3.41 \text{ g } H_2O$$

Practice Problem Exercise 9.8

Step 1 The balanced equation for the reaction is

$$6Li(s) + N_2(g) \rightarrow 2Li_3N(s)$$

Step 2 To determine the limiting reactant, we must convert the masses of lithium (atomic mass = 6.941 g) and nitrogen (molar mass = 28.02 g) to moles.

$$56.0 \text{ g } Li \times \frac{1 \text{ mol } Li}{6.941 \text{ g } Li} = 8.07 \text{ mol } Li$$

$$56.0 \text{ g } N_2 \times \frac{1 \text{ mol } N_2}{28.02 \text{ g } N_2} = 2.00 \text{ mol } N_2$$

Step 3 Using the mole ratio from the balanced equation, we can calculate the moles of lithium required to react with 2.00 mol of nitrogen.

$$2.00 \text{ mol } N_2 \times \frac{6 \text{ mol } Li}{1 \text{ mol } N_2} = 12.0 \text{ mol } Li$$

Therefore, 12.0 mol of Li is required to react with 2.00 mol of N_2. However, we have only 8.07 mol of Li, so lithium is limiting. It will be consumed before the nitrogen runs out.

Step 4 Because lithium is the limiting reactant, we must use the 8.07 mol of Li to determine how many moles of Li_3N can be formed.

$$8.07 \text{ mol } Li \times \frac{2 \text{ mol } Li_3N}{6 \text{ mol } Li} = 2.69 \text{ mol } Li_3N$$

Step 5 We can now use the molar mass of Li_3N (34.83 g) to calculate the mass of Li_3N formed.

$$2.69 \text{ mol } Li_3N \times \frac{34.83 \text{ g } Li_3N}{1 \text{ mol } Li_3N} =$$

$$93.7 \text{ g } Li_3N$$

Practice Problem Exercise 9.9

a. **Step 1** The balanced equation is

$$TiCl_4(g) + O_2(g) \rightarrow TiO_2(s) + 2Cl_2(g)$$

Step 2 The numbers of moles of reactants are

$$6.71 \times 10^3 \text{ g } TiCl_4 \times \frac{1 \text{ mol } TiCl_4}{189.68 \text{ g } TiCl_4} =$$

$$3.54 \times 10^1 \text{ mol } TiCl_4$$

$$2.45 \times 10^3 \text{ g } O_2 \times \frac{1 \text{ mol } O_2}{32.00 \text{ g } O_2} =$$

$$7.66 \times 10^1 \text{ mol } O_2$$

Step 3 In the balanced equation both $TiCl_4$ and O_2 have coefficients of 1, so

$$1 \text{ mol } TiCl_4 = 1 \text{ mol } O_2$$

and

$$3.54 \times 10^1 \text{ mol } TiCl_4 \times \frac{1 \text{ mol } O_2}{1 \text{ mol } TiCl_4} =$$

$$3.54 \times 10^1 \text{ mol } O_2 \text{ required}$$

We have 7.66×10^1 mol of O_2, so the O_2 is an excess and the $TiCl_4$ is limiting. This makes sense. $TiCl_4$ and O_2 react in a 1:1 mole ratio, so the $TiCl_4$ is limiting because fewer moles of $TiCl_4$ are present than moles of O_2.

Step 4 We will now use the moles of $TiCl_4$ (the limiting reactant) to determine the moles of TiO_2 that would form if the reaction produced 100% of the expected yield (the theoretical yield).

$$3.54 \times 10^1 \text{ mol } TiCl_4 \times \frac{1 \text{ mol } TiO_2}{1 \text{ mol } TiCl_4} =$$

$$3.54 \times 10^1 \text{ mol } TiO_2$$

The mass of TiO_2 expected for 100% yield is

$$3.54 \times 10^1 \text{ mol } TiO_2 \times \frac{79.88 \text{ g } TiO_2}{\text{mol } TiO_2} =$$

$$2.83 \times 10^3 \text{ g } TiO_2$$

This amount represents the theoretical yield.

b. Because the reaction is said to give only a 75.0% yield of TiO_2, we use the definition of percent yield.

$$\frac{\text{Actual yield}}{\text{Theoretical yield}} \times 100\% = \% \text{ yield}$$

to write the equation

$$\frac{\text{Actual yield}}{2.83 \times 10^3 \text{ g } TiO_2} \times 100\% = 75.0\% \text{ yield}$$

We now want to solve for the actual yield. First we divide both sides by 100%.

$$\frac{\text{Actual yield}}{2.83 \times 10^3 \text{ g } TiO_2} \times \frac{100\%}{100\%} = \frac{75.0}{100} = 0.750$$

Then we multiply both sides by 2.83×10^3 g TiO_2.

$$2.83 \times 10^3 \text{ g } TiO_2 \times \frac{\text{Actual yield}}{2.83 \times 10^3 \text{ g } TiO_2} =$$

$$0.750 \times 2.83 \times 10^3 \text{ g } TiO_2$$

Actual yield = $0.750 \times 2.83 \times 10^3$ g TiO_2

$$= 2.12 \times 10^3 \text{ g } TiO_2$$

Thus 2.12×10^3 g of $TiO_2(s)$ is actually obtained in this reaction.

Chapter 10

Practice Problem Exercise 10.1

The conversion factor needed is $\frac{1 \text{ cal}}{4.184 \text{ J}}$, and the conversion is

$$28.4 \text{ J} \times \frac{1 \text{ cal}}{4.184 \text{ J}} = 6.79 \text{ cal}$$

Practice Problem Exercise 10.2

We know that it takes 4.184 J of energy to change the temperature of each gram of water by 1 °C, so we must multiply 4.184 by the mass of water (454 g) and the temperature change (98.6 °C − 5.4 °C = 93.2 °C).

$$4.184 \, \frac{J}{g \, °C} \times 454 \, g \times 93.2 \, °C = 1.77 \times 10^5 \, J$$

Practice Problem Exercise 10.3

From Table 10.1, the specific heat capacity for solid gold is 0.13 J/g °C. Because it takes 0.13 J to change the temperature of *one* gram of gold by *one* Celsius degree, we must multiply 0.13 by the sample size (5.63 g) and the change in temperature (32 °C − 21 °C = 11 °C).

$$0.13 \, \frac{J}{g \, °C} \times 5.63 \, g \times 11 \, °C = 8.1 \, J$$

We can change this energy to units of calories as follows:

$$8.1 \, J \times \frac{1 \, cal}{4.184 \, J} = 1.9 \, cal$$

Practice Problem Exercise 10.4

Table 10.1 lists the specific heat capacities of several metals. We want to calculate the specific heat capacity (s) for this metal and then use Table 10.1 to identify the metal. Using the equation

$$Q = s \times m \times \Delta T$$

we can solve for s by dividing both sides by m (the mass of the sample) and by ΔT:

$$\frac{Q}{m \times \Delta T} = s$$

In this case,

Q = energy (heat) required = 10.1 J

m = 2.8 g

ΔT = temperature change = 36 °C − 21 °C = 15 °C

so

$$s = \frac{Q}{m \times \Delta T} = \frac{10.1 \, J}{(2.8 \, g)(15 \, °C)} = 0.24 \, J/g \, °C$$

Table 10.1 shows that silver has a specific heat capacity of 0.24 J/g °C. The metal is silver.

Practice Problem Exercise 10.5

We are told that 1652 kJ of energy is *released* when 4 mol of Fe reacts. We first need to determine what number of moles 1.00 g Fe represents.

$$1.00 \, g \, Fe \times \frac{1 \, mol}{55.85 \, g} = 1.79 \times 10^{-2} \, mol \, Fe$$

$$1.79 \times 10^{-2} \, mol \, Fe \times \frac{1652 \, kJ}{4 \, mol \, Fe} = 7.39 \, kJ$$

Thus 7.39 kJ of energy (as heat) is released when 1.00 g of iron reacts.

Practice Problem Exercise 10.6

Noting the reactants and products in the desired reaction

$$S(s) + O_2(g) \rightarrow SO_2(g)$$

We need to reverse the second equation and multiply it

by $\frac{1}{2}$. This reverses the sign and cuts the amount of energy by a factor of 2.

$$\frac{1}{2}[2SO_3(g) \rightarrow 2SO_2(g) + O_2(g)] \qquad \Delta H = \frac{198.2 \, kJ}{2}$$

or

$$SO_3(g) \rightarrow SO_2(g) + \frac{1}{2}O_2(g) \qquad \Delta H = 99.1 \, kJ$$

Now we add this reaction to the first reaction

$S(s) + \frac{3}{2}O_2(g) \rightarrow SO_3(g)$	$\Delta H = 2395.2 \, kJ$
$SO_3(g) \rightarrow SO_2(g) + \frac{1}{2}O_2(g)$	$\Delta H = 99.1 \, kJ$
$S(s) + O_2(g) \quad \rightarrow SO_2(g)$	$\Delta H = 2296.1 \, kJ$

Chapter 11

Practice Problem Exercise 11.1

a. Circular pathways for electrons in the Bohr model

b. Three-dimensional probability maps that represent the likelihood that the electron will occupy a given point in space. The details of electron motion are not described by an orbital.

c. The surface that contains 90% of the total electron probability. That is, the electron is found somewhere inside this surface 90% of the time.

d. A sublevel is a set of orbitals of a given type of orbital within a principal energy level. For example, there are three sublevels in principal level 3; they consist of the 3s orbital, the three 3p orbitals, and the five 3d orbitals.

Practice Problem Exercise 11.2

Element	Electron Configuration	Orbital Diagram
		1s 2s 2p 3s 3p
Al	$1s^2 2s^2 2p^6 3s^2 3p^1$ [Ne]$3s^2 3p^1$	⇅ ⇅ ⇅⇅⇅ ⇅ ↑ __ __
Si	[Ne]$3s^2 3p^2$	⇅ ⇅ ⇅⇅⇅ ⇅ ↑ ↑ __
P	[Ne]$3s^2 3p^3$	⇅ ⇅ ⇅⇅⇅ ⇅ ↑ ↑ ↑
S	[Ne]$3s^2 3p^4$	⇅ ⇅ ⇅⇅⇅ ⇅ ⇅ ↑ ↑
Cl	[Ne]$3s^2 3p^5$	⇅ ⇅ ⇅⇅⇅ ⇅ ⇅ ⇅ ↑
Ar	[Ne]$3s^2 3p^6$	⇅ ⇅ ⇅⇅⇅ ⇅ ⇅ ⇅ ⇅

Practice Problem Exercise 11.3

Fluorine (F): In Group 7 and Period 2, it is the fifth "2p element." The configuration is $1s^2 2s^2 2p^5$, or [He]$2s^2 2p^5$.

Silicon (Si): In Group 4 and Period 3, it is the second of the "3p elements." The configuration is $1s^2 2s^2 2p^6 3s^2 3p^2$, or [Ne]$3s^2 3p^2$.

Cesium (Cs): In Group 1 and Period 6, it is the first of the "6s elements." The configuration is $1s^2 2s^2 2p^6 3s^2 3p^6 4s^2 3d^{10} 4p^6 5s^2 4d^{10} 5p^6 6s^1$, or [Xe]$6s^1$.

Lead (Pb): In Group 4 and Period 6, it is the second of the "6p elements." The configuration is [Xe]$6s^2 4f^{14} 5d^{10} 6p^2$.

Iodine (I): In Group 7 and Period 5, it is the fifth of the "5p elements." The configuration is [Kr]$5s^2 4d^{10} 5p^5$.

Chapter 12

Practice Problem Exercise 12.1

Using the electronegativity values given in Figure 12.4, we choose the bond in which the atoms exhibit the largest difference in electronegativity. (Electronegativity values are shown in parentheses.)

a. H—C   >   H—P
   (2.1)(2.5)   (2.1)(2.1)

b. O—I   >   O—F
   (3.5)(2.5)   (3.5)(4.0)

c. S—O   >   N—O
   (2.5)(3.5)   (3.0)(3.5)

d. N—H   >   Si—H
   (3.0)(2.1)   (1.8)(2.1)

Practice Problem Exercise 12.2

H has one electron, and Cl has seven valence electrons. This gives a total of eight valence electrons. We first draw in the bonding pair:

   H—Cl, which could be drawn as H:Cl

We have six electrons yet to place. The H already has two electrons, so we place three lone pairs around the chlorine to satisfy the octet rule.

   H—$\ddot{\underset{..}{C}}$l: or   H:$\ddot{\underset{..}{C}}$l:

Practice Problem Exercise 12.3

Step 1 O_3: 3(6) = 18 valence electrons

Step 2 O—O—O

Step 3 $:\ddot{O}=\ddot{O}-\ddot{O}:$ and $:\ddot{O}-\ddot{O}=\ddot{O}$

   This molecule shows resonance (it has two valid Lewis structures).

Practice Problem Exercise 12.4

See table at the top top of page A22.

Practice Problem Exercise 12.6

a. NH_4^+

The Lewis structure is
$$\left[\begin{array}{c} H \\ | \\ H-N-H \\ | \\ H \end{array}\right]^+$$

(See Practice Problem Exercise 12.4.) There are four pairs of electrons around the nitrogen. This requires a tetrahedral arrangement of electron pairs. The NH_4^+ ion has a tetrahedral molecular structure (case 3 in Table 12.4), because all electron pairs are shared.

b. SO_4^{2-}

The Lewis structure is
$$\left[\begin{array}{c} :\ddot{O}: \\ | \\ :\ddot{O}-S-\ddot{O}: \\ | \\ :\ddot{O}: \end{array}\right]^{2-}$$

(See Practice Problem Exercise 12.4) The four electron pairs around the sulfur require a tetrahedral arrangement. The SO_4^{2-} has a tetrahedral molecular structure (case 3 in Table 12.4).

c. NF_3

The Lewis structure is
$$:\ddot{F}\underset{\overset{|}{\underset{:\ddot{F}:}{}}}{\overset{\overset{..}{N}}{}}\ddot{F}:$$

(See Practice Problem Exercise 12.4) The four pairs of electrons on the nitrogen require a tetrahedral arrangement. In this case only three of the pairs are shared with the fluorine atoms, leaving one lone pair. Thus the molecular structure is a trigonal pyramid (case 4 in Table 12.4).

d. H_2S

The Lewis structure is H—$\ddot{\underset{..}{S}}$—H

(See Practice Problem Exercise 12.4) The four pairs of electrons around the sulfur require a tetrahedral arrangement. In this case two pairs are shared with hydrogen atoms, leaving two lone pairs. Thus the molecular structure is bent or V-shaped (case 5 in Table 12.4).

e. ClO_3^-

The Lewis structure is
$$\left[:\ddot{O}-\overset{..}{Cl}-\ddot{O}: \atop :\ddot{O}: \right]^-$$

(See Practice Problem Exercise 12.4.) The four pairs of electrons require a tetrahedral arrangement. In this case, three pairs are shared with oxygen atoms, leaving one lone pair. Thus the molecular structure is a trigonal pyramid (case 4 in Table 12.4).

f. BeF_2

The Lewis structure is $:\ddot{F}—Be—\ddot{F}:$

The two electron pairs on beryllium require a linear arrangement. Because both pairs are shared by fluorine atoms, the molecular structure is also linear (case 1 in Table 12.4).

Chapter 13

Practice Problem Exercise 13.1

We know that 1.000 atm = 760.0 mm Hg. So

$$525\ \cancel{mm\ Hg}\times \frac{1.000\ atm}{760.0\ \cancel{mm\ Hg}} = 0.691\ atm$$

Practice Problem Exercise 13.2

Initial Conditions	**Final Conditions**
P_1 = 635 torr	P_2 = 785 torr
V_1 = 1.51 L	V_2 = ?

Solving Boyle's law ($P_1V_1 = P_2V_2$) for V_2 gives

$$V_2 = V_1 \times \frac{P_1}{P_2}$$

$$= 1.51\ L \times \frac{635\ \cancel{torr}}{785\ \cancel{torr}} = 1.22\ L$$

Note that the volume decreased, as the increase in pressure led us to expect.

Molecule or Ion	Total Valence Electrons	Draw Single Bonds	Calculate Number of Electrons Remaining	Use Remaining Electrons to Achieve Noble Gas Configurations	Check Atom	Electrons
a. NF_3	$5 + 3(7) = 26$	F—N (with F)	$26 - 6 = 20$	$:\!\ddot{F}\!-\!\ddot{N}\!-\!\ddot{F}\!:$ $:\!\ddot{F}\!:$	N	8
					F	8
b. O_2	$2(6) = 12$	O—O	$12 - 2 = 10$	$:\!\ddot{O}\!=\!\ddot{O}\!:$	O	8
c. CO	$4 + 6 = 10$	C—O	$10 - 2 = 8$	$:\!C\!\equiv\!O\!:$	C	8
					O	8
d. PH_3	$5 + 3(1) = 8$	H—P—H (with H)	$8 - 6 = 2$	$H\!-\!\ddot{P}\!-\!H$ H	P	8
					H	8
e. H_2S	$2(1) + 6 = 8$	H—S—H	$8 - 4 = 4$	$H\!-\!\ddot{S}\!-\!H$	S	8
					H	2
f. $SO_4{}^{2-}$	$6 + 4(6) + 2 = 32$	O—S—O (with O above and below)	$32 - 8 = 24$	$\left[:\!\ddot{O}\!-\!\overset{:\ddot{O}:}{\underset{:\ddot{O}:}{S}}\!-\!\ddot{O}\!:\right]^{2-}$	S	8
					O	8
g. $NH_4{}^+$	$5 + 4(1) - 1 = 8$	H—N—H (with H above and below)	$8 - 8 = 0$	$\left[H\!-\!\overset{H}{\underset{H}{N}}\!-\!H\right]^+$	N	8
					H	2
h. $ClO_3{}^-$	$7 + 3(6) + 1 = 26$	O, Cl, O, O	$26 - 6 = 20$	$\left[:\!\ddot{O}\!-\!\overset{}{\underset{:\ddot{O}:}{\ddot{C}l}}\!-\!\ddot{O}\!:\right]^-$	Cl	8
					O	2
i. SO_2	$6 + 2(6) = 18$	O—S—O	$18 - 4 = 14$	$\ddot{O}\!=\!\ddot{S}\!-\!\ddot{O}\!:$ and $:\!\ddot{O}\!-\!\ddot{S}\!=\!\ddot{O}$	S	8
					O	8

Answer to Practice Problem Exercise 12.4

Practice Problem Exercise 13.5

Because the temperature of the gas inside the bubble decreases (at constant pressure), the bubble gets smaller. The conditions are

Initial Conditions
$T_1 = 28\ °C = 28 + 273 = 301\ K$
$V_1 = 23\ cm^3$

Final Conditions
$T_2 = 18\ °C = 18 + 273 = 291\ K$
$V_2 = ?$

Solving Charles's law,

$$\frac{V_1}{T_1} = \frac{V_2}{T_2}$$

for V_2 gives

$$V_2 = V_1 \times \frac{T_2}{T_1} = 23\ cm^3 \times \frac{291\ K}{301\ K} = 22\ cm^3$$

Practice Problem Exercise 13.7

Because the temperature and pressure of the two samples are the same, we can use Avogadro's law in the form

$$\frac{V_1}{n_1} = \frac{V_2}{n_2}$$

The following information is given:

Sample 1
$V_1 = 36.7\ L$
$n_1 = 1.5\ mol$

Sample 2
$V_2 = 16.5\ L$
$n_2 = ?$

We can now solve Avogadro's law for the value of n_2 (the moles of n_2 in Sample 2):

$$n_2 = n_1 \times \frac{V_2}{V_1} = 1.5 \text{ mol} \times \frac{16.5 \, \cancel{L}}{36.7 \, \cancel{L}} = 0.67 \text{ mol}$$

Here n_2 is smaller than n_1, which makes sense in view of the fact that V_2 is smaller than V_1.

Note: We isolate n_2 from Avogadro's law as given above by multiplying both sides of the equation by n_2 and then by n_1/V_1,

$$\left(n_2 \times \frac{n_1}{V_1}\right)\frac{V_1}{n_1} = \left(n_2 \times \frac{n_1}{V_1}\right)\frac{V_2}{n_2}$$

to give $n_2 = n_1 \times V_2/V_1$.

Practice Problem Exercise 13.8

We are given the following information:

$P = 1.00 \text{ atm}$
$V = 2.70 \times 10^6 \text{ L}$
$n = 1.10 \times 10^5 \text{ mol}$

We solve for T by dividing both sides of the ideal gas law by nR:

$$\frac{PV}{nR} = \frac{\cancel{nR}T}{\cancel{nR}}$$

to give

$$T = \frac{PV}{nR} = \frac{(1.00 \, \cancel{atm})(2.70 \times 10^6 \, \cancel{L})}{(1.10 \times 10^5 \, \cancel{mol})\left(0.08206 \, \frac{\cancel{L} \, \cancel{atm}}{K \, \cancel{mol}}\right)}$$
$$= 299 \text{ K}$$

The temperature of the helium is 299 K, or $299 - 273 = 26 \, °C$.

Practice Problem Exercise 13.9

We are given the following information about the radon sample:

$n = 1.5 \text{ mol}$
$V = 21.0 \text{ L}$
$T = 33 \, °C = 33 + 273 = 306 \text{ K}$
$P = ?$

We solve the ideal gas law ($PV = nRT$) for P by dividing both sides of the equation by V:

$$P = \frac{nRT}{V} = \frac{(1.5 \, \cancel{mol})\left(0.08206 \, \frac{\cancel{L} \, atm}{K \, \cancel{mol}}\right)(306 \, \cancel{K})}{21.0 \, \cancel{L}}$$
$$= 1.8 \text{ atm}$$

Practice Problem Exercise 13.10

To solve this problem we take the ideal gas law and separate those quantities that change from those that remain constant (on opposite sides of the equation). In this case volume and temperature change, and number of moles and pressure (and, of course, R) remain constant. So $PV = nRT$ becomes $V/T = nR/P$, which leads to

$$\frac{V_1}{T_1} = \frac{nR}{P} \text{ and } \frac{V_2}{T_2} = \frac{nR}{P}$$

Combining these gives

$$\frac{V_1}{T_1} = \frac{nR}{P} = \frac{V_2}{T_2} \text{ or } \frac{V_1}{T_1} = \frac{V_2}{T_2}$$

We are given

Initial Conditions
$T_1 = 5 \, °C = 5 + 273 = 278 \text{ K}$
$V_1 = 3.8 \text{ L}$

Final Conditions
$T_2 = 86 \, °C = 86 + 273 = 359 \text{ K}$
$V_2 = ?$

Thus

$$V_2 = \frac{T_2 V_1}{T_1} = \frac{(359 \, \cancel{K})(3.8 \text{ L})}{278 \, \cancel{K}} = 4.9 \text{ L}$$

Check: Is the answer sensible? In this case the temperature was increased (at constant pressure), so the volume should increase. The answer makes sense.

Note that this problem could be described as a "Charles's law problem." The real advantage of using the ideal gas law is that you need to remember only one equation to do virtually any problem involving gases.

Practice Problem Exercise 13.11

We are given the following information:

Initial Conditions
$P_1 = 0.747 \text{ atm}$
$T_1 = 13 \, °C = 13 + 273 = 286 \text{ K}$
$V_1 = 11.0 \text{ L}$

Final Conditions
$P_2 = 1.18 \text{ atm}$
$T_2 = 56 \, °C = 56 + 273 = 329 \text{ K}$
$V_2 = ?$

In this case the number of moles remains constant. Thus we can say

$$\frac{P_1 V_1}{T_1} = nR \text{ and } \frac{P_2 V_2}{T_2} = nR$$

or

$$\frac{P_1 V_1}{T_1} = \frac{P_2 V_2}{T_2}$$

Solving for V_2 gives

$$V_2 = V_1 \times \frac{T_2}{T_1} \times \frac{P_1}{P_2} = (11.0 \text{ L})\left(\frac{329 \, \cancel{K}}{286 \, \cancel{K}}\right)\left(\frac{0.747 \, \cancel{atm}}{1.18 \, \cancel{atm}}\right)$$
$$= 8.01 \text{ L}$$

Practice Problem Exercise 13.12

As usual when dealing with gases, we can use the ideal gas equation $PV = nRT$. First consider the information given:

$P = 0.91 \text{ atm} = P_{\text{total}}$
$V = 2.0 \text{ L}$
$T = 25 \, °C = 25 + 273 = 298 \text{ K}$

Given this information, we can calculate the number of moles of gas in the mixture:

$n_{\text{total}} = n_{N_2} + n_{O_2}$. Solving for n in the ideal gas equation gives

$$n_{\text{total}} = \frac{P_{\text{total}} V}{RT} = \frac{(0.91 \, \cancel{atm})(2.0 \, \cancel{L})}{\left(0.08206 \, \frac{\cancel{L} \, \cancel{atm}}{\cancel{K} \, \text{mol}}\right)(298 \, \cancel{K})} = 0.074 \text{ mol}$$

We also know that 0.050 mol N_2 is present. Because

$$n_{total} = n_{N_2} + n_{O_2} = 0.074 \text{ mol}$$
$$\underset{(0.050 \text{ mol})}{\uparrow}$$

We can calculate the moles of O_2 present.

$$0.050 \text{ mol} + n_{O_2} = 0.074 \text{ mol}$$
$$n_{O_2} = 0.074 \text{ mol} - 0.050 \text{ mol}$$
$$= 0.024 \text{ mol}$$

Now that we know the moles of oxygen present, we can calculate the partial pressure of oxygen from the ideal gas equation.

$$P_{O_2} = \frac{n_{O_2}RT}{V} = \frac{(0.024 \text{ mol})\left(0.08206 \frac{L \text{ atm}}{K \text{ mol}}\right)(298 \text{ K})}{2.0 \text{ L}}$$
$$= 0.29 \text{ atm}$$

Although it is not requested, note that the partial pressure of the N_2 must be 0.62 atm, because

$$\underbrace{0.62 \text{ atm}}_{P_{N_2}} + \underbrace{0.29 \text{ atm}}_{P_{O_2}} = \underbrace{0.91 \text{ atm}}_{P_{total}}$$

Practice Problem Exercise 13.13

The volume is 0.500 L, the temperature is 25 °C (25 + 273 = 298 K), and the total pressure is given as 0.950 atm. Of this total pressure, 24 torr is due to the water vapor. We can calculate the partial pressure of the H_2 because we know that

$$P_{total} = P_{H_2} + P_{H_2O} = 0.950 \text{ atm}$$
$$\underset{24 \text{ torr}}{\uparrow}$$

Before we carry out the calculation, however, we must convert the pressures to the same units. Converting P_{H_2O} to atmospheres gives

$$24 \text{ torr} \times \frac{1.000 \text{ atm}}{760.0 \text{ torr}} = 0.032 \text{ atm}$$

Thus

$$P_{total} = P_{H_2} + P_{H_2O} = 0.950 \text{ atm} = P_{H_2} + 0.032 \text{ atm}$$

and

$$P_{H_2} = 0.950 \text{ atm} - 0.032 \text{ atm} = 0.918 \text{ atm}$$

Now that we know the partial pressure of the hydrogen gas, we can use the ideal gas equation to calculate the moles of H_2.

$$n_{H_2} = \frac{P_{H_2}V}{RT} = \frac{(0.918 \text{ atm})(0.500 \text{ L})}{\left(0.08206 \frac{L \text{ atm}}{K \text{ mol}}\right)(298 \text{ K})}$$
$$= 0.0188 \text{ mol} = 1.88 \times 10^{-2} \text{ mol}$$

The sample of gas contains 1.88×10^{-2} mol of H_2, which exerts a partial pressure of 0.918 atm.

Practice Problem Exercise 13.14

We will solve this problem by taking the following steps:

$$\boxed{\begin{array}{c}\text{Grams}\\\text{of}\\\text{zinc}\end{array}} \Rightarrow \boxed{\begin{array}{c}\text{Moles}\\\text{of}\\\text{zinc}\end{array}} \Rightarrow \boxed{\begin{array}{c}\text{Moles}\\\text{of}\\H_2\end{array}} \Rightarrow \boxed{\begin{array}{c}\text{Volume}\\\text{of}\\H_2\end{array}}$$

Step 1 Using the atomic mass of zinc (65.38 g), we calculate the moles of zinc in 26.5 g.

$$26.5 \text{ g Zn} \times \frac{1 \text{ mol Zn}}{65.38 \text{ g Zn}} = 0.405 \text{ mol Zn}$$

Step 2 Using the balanced equation, we next calculate the moles of H_2 produced.

$$0.405 \text{ mol Zn} \times \frac{1 \text{ mol } H_2}{1 \text{ mol Zn}} = 0.405 \text{ mol } H_2$$

Step 3 Now that we know the moles of H_2, we can compute the volume of H_2 by using the ideal gas law, where

$$P = 1.50 \text{ atm}$$
$$V = ?$$
$$n = 0.405 \text{ mol}$$
$$R = 0.08206 \text{ L atm/K mol}$$
$$T = 19 \text{ °C} = 19 + 273 = 292 \text{ K}$$

$$V = \frac{nRT}{P} = \frac{(0.405 \text{ mol})\left(0.08206 \frac{L \text{ atm}}{K \text{ mol}}\right)(292 \text{ K})}{1.50 \text{ atm}}$$
$$= 6.47 \text{ L of } H_2$$

Practice Problem Exercise 13.15

Although there are several possible ways to do this problem, the most convenient method involves using the molar volume at STP. First we use the ideal gas equation to calculate the moles of NH_3 present:

$$n = \frac{PV}{RT}$$

where $P = 15.0$ atm, $V = 5.00$ L, and $T = 25 \text{ °C} + 273 = 298$ K.

$$n = \frac{(15.0 \text{ atm})(5.00 \text{ L})}{\left(0.08206 \frac{L \text{ atm}}{K \text{ mol}}\right)(298 \text{ K})} = 3.07 \text{ mol}$$

We know that at STP each mole of gas occupies 22.4 L. Therefore, 3.07 mol has the volume

$$3.07 \text{ mol} \times \frac{22.4 \text{ L}}{1 \text{ mol}} = 68.8 \text{ L}$$

The volume of the ammonia at STP is 68.8 L.

Chapter 14

Practice Problem Exercise 14.2

Energy to melt the ice:

$$15 \text{ g } H_2O \times \frac{1 \text{ mol } H_2O}{18 \text{ g } H_2O} = 0.83 \text{ mol } H_2O$$

$$0.83 \text{ mol } H_2O \times 6.02 \frac{\text{kJ}}{\text{mol } H_2O} = 5.0 \text{ kJ}$$

Energy to heat the water from 0 °C to 100 °C:

$$4.18 \frac{\text{J}}{\text{g °C}} \times 15 \text{ g} \times 100 \text{ °C} = 6300 \text{ J}$$

$$6300 \text{ J} \times \frac{1 \text{ kJ}}{1000 \text{ J}} = 6.3 \text{ kJ}$$

Energy to vaporize the water at 100 °C:

$$0.83 \text{ mol } H_2O \times 40.6 \frac{kJ}{\text{mol } H_2O} = 34 \text{ kJ}$$

Total energy required:

$$5.0 \text{ kJ} + 6.3 \text{ kJ} + 34 \text{ kJ} = 45 \text{ kJ}$$

Practice Problem Exercise 14.4

a. Contains SO_3 molecules—a molecular solid.

b. Contains Ba^{2+} and O^{2-} ions—an ionic solid.

c. Contains Au atoms—an atomic solid.

Chapter 15

Practice Problem Exercise 15.1

$$\text{Mass percent} = \frac{\text{mass of solute}}{\text{mass of solution}} \times 100\%$$

For this sample, the mass of solution is 135 g and the mass of the solute is 4.73 g, so

$$\text{Mass percent} = \frac{4.73 \text{ g solute}}{135 \text{ g solution}} \times 100\%$$

$$= 3.50\%$$

Practice Problem Exercise 15.2

Using the definition of mass percent, we have

$$\frac{\text{Mass of solute}}{\text{Mass of solution}} =$$

$$\frac{\text{grams of solute}}{\text{grams of solute} + \text{grams of solvent}} \times 100\% = 40.0\%$$

There are 425 g of solute (formaldehyde). Substituting, we have

$$\frac{425 \text{ g}}{425 \text{ g} + \text{grams of solvent}} \times 100\% = 40.0\%$$

We must now solve for grams of solvent (water). This will take some patience, but we can do it if we proceed step by step. First we divide both sides by 100%.

$$\frac{425 \text{ g}}{425 \text{ g} + \text{grams of solvent}} \times \frac{\cancel{100\%}}{\cancel{100\%}} = \frac{40.0\%}{100\%} = 0.400$$

Now we have

$$\frac{425 \text{ g}}{425 \text{ g} + \text{grams of solvent}} = 0.400$$

Next we multiply both sides by (425 g + grams of solvent).

$$(\cancel{425 \text{ g} + \text{grams of solvent}}) \times \frac{425 \text{ g}}{\cancel{425 \text{ g} + \text{grams of solvent}}}$$

$$= 0.400 \times (425 \text{ g} + \text{grams of solvent})$$

This gives

$$425 \text{ g} = 0.400 \times (425 \text{ g} + \text{grams of solvent})$$

Carrying out the multiplication gives

$$425 \text{ g} = 170. \text{ g} + 0.400 \text{ (grams of solvent)}$$

Now we subtract 170. g from both sides,

$$425 \text{ g} - 170. \text{ g} = \cancel{170. \text{ g}} - \cancel{170. \text{ g}} + 0.400$$
$$\text{(grams of solvent)}$$

$$255 \text{ g} = 0.400 \text{ (grams of solvent)}$$

and divide both sides by 0.400.

$$\frac{255 \text{ g}}{0.400} = \frac{\cancel{0.400}}{\cancel{0.400}} \text{ (grams of solvent)}$$

We finally have the answer:

$$\frac{255 \text{ g}}{0.400} = 638 \text{ g} = \text{grams of solvent}$$

$$= \text{mass of water needed}$$

Practice Problem Exercise 15.4

The moles of ethanol can be obtained from its molar mass (46.1).

$$1.00 \cancel{\text{ g } C_2H_5OH} \times \frac{1 \text{ mol } C_2H_5OH}{46.1 \cancel{\text{ g } C_2H_5OH}}$$

$$= 2.17 \times 10^{-2} \text{ mol } C_2H_5OH$$

$$\text{Volume in liters} = 101 \cancel{\text{ mL}} \times \frac{1 \text{ L}}{1000 \cancel{\text{ mL}}} = 0.101 \text{ L}$$

$$\text{Molarity of } C_2H_5OH = \frac{\text{moles of } C_2H_5OH}{\text{liters of solution}}$$

$$= 2.17 \times \frac{10^{-2} \text{ mol}}{0.101 \text{ L}} = 0.215 \text{ M}$$

Practice Problem Exercise 15.5

For a. and b.: When Na_2CO_3 and $Al_2(SO_4)_3$ dissolve in water, they produce ions as follows:

$$Na_2CO_3(s) \xrightarrow{H_2O(l)} 2Na^+(aq) + CO_3^{2-}(aq)$$

$$Al_2(SO_4)_3(s) \xrightarrow{H_2O(l)} 2Al^{3+}(aq) + 3SO_4^{2-}(aq)$$

Therefore, in a 0.10 M Na_2CO_3 solution, the concentration of Na^+ ions is 2×0.10 M = 0.20 M and the concentration of CO_3^{2-} ions is 0.10 M. In a 0.010 M $Al_2(SO_4)_3$ solution, the concentration of Al^{3+} ions is 2×0.010 M = 0.020 M and the concentration of SO_4^{2-} ions is 3×0.010 M = 0.030 M.

Practice Problem Exercise 15.6

When solid $AlCl_3$ dissolves, it produces ions as follows:

$$AlCl_3(s) \xrightarrow{H_2O(l)} Al^{3+}(aq) + 3Cl^-(aq)$$

Thus a 1.0×10^{-3} M $AlCl_3$ solution contains 1.0×10^{-3} M Al^{3+} ions and 3.0×10^{-3} M Cl^- ions.

To calculate the moles of Cl^- ions in 1.75 L of the 1.0×10^{-3} M $AlCl_3$ solution, we must multiply the volume by the molarity.

$$1.75 \text{ L solution} \times 3.0 \times 10^{-3} \text{ M } Cl^-$$

$$= 1.75 \cancel{\text{ L solution}} \times \frac{3.0 \times 10^{-3} \text{ mol } Cl^-}{\cancel{\text{ L solution}}}$$

$$= 5.25 \times 10^{-3} \text{ mol } Cl^- = 5.3 \times 10^{-3} \text{ mol } Cl^-$$

Practice Problem Exercise 15.7

We must first determine the number of moles of formaldehyde in 2.5 L of 12.3 M formalin. Remember that volume of solution (in liters) times molarity gives moles of solute.

In this case, the volume of solution is 2.5 L and the molarity is 12.3 mol of HCHO per liter of solution.

$$2.5 \text{ L solution} \times \frac{12.3 \text{ mol HCHO}}{\text{L solution}} = 31 \text{ mol HCHO}$$

Next, using the molar mass of HCHO (30.0 g), we convert 31 mol of HCHO to grams.

$$31 \text{ mol HCHO} \times \frac{30.0 \text{ g HCHO}}{1 \text{ mol HCHO}} = 9.3 \times 10^2 \text{ g HCHO}$$

Therefore, 2.5 L of 12.3 M formalin contains 9.3×10^2 g of formaldehyde. We must weigh out 930 g of formaldehyde and dissolve it in enough water to make 2.5 L of solution.

Practice Problem Exercise 15.8

We are given the following information:

$$M_1 = 12 \frac{\text{mol}}{\text{L}} \qquad\qquad M_2 = 0.25 \frac{\text{mol}}{\text{L}}$$

$$V_1 = ? \text{ (what we need to find)} \qquad V_2 = 0.75 \text{ L}$$

Using the fact that the moles of solute do not change upon dilution, we know that

$$M_1 \times V_1 = M_2 \times V_2$$

Solving for V_1 by dividing both sides by M_1 gives

$$V_1 = \frac{M_2 \times V_2}{M_1} = \frac{0.25 \frac{\text{mol}}{\text{L}} \times 0.75 \text{ L}}{12 \frac{\text{mol}}{\text{L}}}$$

and

$$V_1 = 0.016 \text{ L} = 16 \text{ mL}$$

Practice Problem Exercise 15.10

Step 1 When the aqueous solutions of Na_2SO_4 (containing Na^+ and SO_4^{2-} ions) and $Pb(NO_3)_2$ (containing Pb^{2+} and NO_3^- ions) are mixed, solid $PbSO_4$ is formed.

$$Pb^{2+}(aq) + SO_4^{2-}(aq) \rightarrow PbSO_4(s)$$

Step 2 We must first determine whether Pb^{2+} or SO_4^{2-} is the limiting reactant by calculating the moles of Pb^{2+} and SO_4^{2-} ions present. Because 0.0500 M $Pb(NO_3)_2$ contains 0.0500 M Pb^{2+} ions, we can calculate the moles of Pb^{2+} ions in 1.25 L of this solution as follows:

$$1.25 \text{ L} \times \frac{0.0500 \text{ mol } Pb^{2+}}{\text{L}} = 0.0625 \text{ mol } Pb^{2+}$$

The 0.0250 M Na_2SO_4 solution contains 0.0250 M SO_4^{2-} ions, and the number of moles of SO_4^{2-} ions in 2.00 L of this solution is

$$2.00 \text{ L} \times \frac{0.0250 \text{ mol } SO_4^{2-}}{\text{L}} =$$

$$0.0500 \text{ mol } SO_4^{2-}$$

Step 3 Pb^{2+} and SO_4^{2-} react in a 1:1 ratio, so the amount of SO_4^{2-} ions is limiting because a smaller number of SO_4^{2-} moles is present.

Step 4 The Pb^{2+} ions are present in excess, and only 0.0500 mol of solid $PbSO_4$ will be formed.

Step 5 We calculate the mass of $PbSO_4$ by using the molar mass of $PbSO_4$ (303.3 g).

$$0.0500 \text{ mol } PbSO_4 \times \frac{303.3 \text{ g } PbSO_4}{1 \text{ mol } PbSO_4} =$$

$$15.2 \text{ g } PbSO_4$$

Practice Problem Exercise 15.11

Step 1 Because nitric acid is a strong acid, the nitric acid solution contains H^+ and NO_3^- ions. The KOH solution contains K^+ and OH^- ions. When these solutions are mixed, the H^+ and OH^- react to form water.

$$H^+(aq) + OH^-(aq) \rightarrow H_2O(l)$$

Step 2 The number of moles of OH^- present in 125 mL of 0.050 M KOH is

$$125 \text{ mL} \times \frac{1 \text{ L}}{1000 \text{ mL}} \times \frac{0.050 \text{ mol } OH^-}{\text{L}}$$

$$= 6.3 \times 10^{-3} \text{ mol } OH^-$$

Step 3 H^+ and OH^- react in a 1:1 ratio, so we need 6.3×10^{-3} mole of H^+ from the 0.100 M HNO_3.

Step 4 6.3×10^{-3} mole of OH^- requires 6.3×10^{-3} mole of H^+ to form 6.3×10^{-3} mole of H_2O.

Therefore,

$$V \times \frac{0.100 \text{ mol } H^+}{\text{L}} = 6.3 \times 10^{-3} \text{ mol } H^+$$

where V represents the volume in liters of 0.100 M HNO_3 required. Solving for V, we have

$$V = \frac{6.3 \times 10^{-3} \text{ mol } H^+}{\frac{0.100 \text{ mol } H^+}{\text{L}}} = 6.3 \times 10^{-2} \text{ L}$$

$$= 6.3 \times 10^{-2} \text{ L} \times \frac{1000 \text{ mL}}{\text{L}} = 63 \text{ mL}$$

Practice Problem Exercise 15.13

From the definition of normality, N = equiv/L, we need to calculate (1) the equivalents of KOH and (2) the volume of the solution in liters. To find the number of equivalents, we use the equivalent weight of KOH, which is 56.1 g (see Table 15.2).

$$23.6 \text{ g KOH} \times \frac{1 \text{ equiv KOH}}{56.1 \text{ g KOH}} = 0.421 \text{ equiv KOH}$$

Next we convert the volume to liters.

$$755 \text{ mL} \times \frac{1 \text{ L}}{1000 \text{ mL}} = 0.755 \text{ L}$$

Finally, we substitute these values into the equation that defines normality.

$$\text{Normality} = \frac{\text{equiv}}{\text{L}} = \frac{0.421 \text{ equiv}}{0.755 \text{ L}} = 0.558 \ N$$

Practice Problem Exercise 15.14

To solve this problem, we use the relationship

$$N_{\text{acid}} \times V_{\text{acid}} = N_{\text{base}} \times V_{\text{base}}$$

where

$$N_{\text{acid}} = 0.50 \frac{\text{equiv}}{\text{L}}$$

$V_{acid} = ?$

$N_{base} = 0.80 \dfrac{\text{equiv}}{L}$

$V_{base} = 0.250 \text{ L}$

We solve the equation

$$N_{acid} \times V_{acid} = N_{base} \times V_{base}$$

for V_{acid} by dividing both sides by N_{acid}.

$$\frac{N_{acid} \times V_{acid}}{N_{acid}} = \frac{N_{base} \times V_{base}}{N_{acid}}$$

$$V_{acid} = \frac{N_{base} \times V_{base}}{N_{acid}} = \frac{\left(0.80 \dfrac{\text{equiv}}{\cancel{L}}\right) \times (0.250 \text{ L})}{0.50 \dfrac{\text{equiv}}{\cancel{L}}}$$

$$V_{acid} = 0.40 \text{ L}$$

Therefore, 0.40 L of 0.50 N H_2SO_4 is required to neutralize 0.250 L of 0.80 N KOH.

Chapter 16

Practice Problem Exercise 16.2

The conjugate acid–base pairs are

H_2O, H_3O^+

Base   Conjugate acid

and

$HC_2H_3O_2$, $C_2H_3O_2{}^-$

Acid   Conjugate base

The members of both pairs differ by one H^+.

Practice Problem Exercise 16.3

Because $[H^+][OH^-] = 1.0 \times 10^{-14}$, we can solve for $[H^+]$.

$$[H^+] = \frac{1.0 \times 10^{-14}}{[OH^-]} = \frac{1.0 \times 10^{-14}}{2.0 \times 10^{-2}} = 5.0 \times 10^{-13} \text{ M}$$

This solution is basic: $[OH^-] = 2.0 \times 10^{-2}$ M is greater than $[H^+] = 5.0 \times 10^{-13}$ M.

Practice Problem Exercise 16.5

a. Because $[H^+] = 1.0 \times 10^{-3}$ M, we get pH = 3.00 by using the regular steps.

b. Because $[OH^-] = 5.0 \times 10^{-5}$ M, we can find $[H^+]$ from the K_w expression.

$$[H^+] = \frac{K_w}{[OH^-]} = \frac{1.0 \times 10^{-14}}{5.0 \times 10^{-5}} = 2.0 \times 10^{-10} \text{ M}$$

Then we follow the regular steps to get pH from $[H^+]$.

1. Enter (−).

2. Push $\boxed{\text{log}}$.

3. Enter 2.0×10^{-10}.

pH = 9.70

Practice Problem Exercise 16.7

pOH + pH = 14.00

pOH = 14.00 − pH = 14.00 − 3.5

pOH = 10.5

Practice Problem Exercise 16.8

pH = 3.50

−pH = −3.50

$\boxed{\text{2nd}}$ $\boxed{\text{log}}$ $-3.50 = 3.2 \times 10^{-4}$

$[H^+] = 3.2 \times 10^{-4}$ M

Practice Problem Exercise 16.9

pOH = 10.50

−pOH = −10.50

$\boxed{\text{2nd}}$ $\boxed{\text{log}}$ $-10.50 = 3.2 \times 10^{-11}$

$[OH^-] = 3.2 \times 10^{-11}$ M

Practice Problem Exercise 16.10

Because HCl is a strong acid, it is completely dissociated:

5.0×10^{-3} M HCl →
$\quad$ 5.0×10^{-3} M H^+ and 5.0×10^{-3} M Cl^-

so $[H^+] = 5.0 \times 10^{-3}$ M.

pH = $-\log(5.0 \times 10^{-3}) = 2.30$

Practice Problem Exercise 16.11

The reaction is

$$H^+ + OH^- \rightarrow H_2O$$

75.00 mL of 0.1500 M KOH contains

$$\text{moles OH}^- = 75.00 \text{ mL} \times \frac{1.000 \text{ L}}{1.000 \times 10^3 \text{ mL}} \times$$

$$0.1500 \frac{\text{mol OH}^-}{L} = 1.125 \times 10^{-2} \text{ mol OH}^-$$

To neutralize the KOH solution, we need an equal number of moles of H^+ from the 0.3000 M HCl solution.

$$1.125 \times 10^{-2} \text{ mol H}^+ = V \times 0.3000 \frac{\text{mol H}^+}{L}$$

$$V = \frac{1.125 \times 10^{-2} \text{ mol H}^+}{0.3000 \dfrac{\text{mol H}^+}{L}} = 3.750 \times 10^{-2} \text{ L}$$

$$3.750 \times 10^{-2} \text{ L} \times \frac{1.000 \times 10^3 \text{ mL}}{1.000 \text{ L}} = 37.50 \text{ mL}$$

The volume of 0.3000 M HCl required is 37.50 mL.

Chapter 17

Practice Problem Exercise 17.1

Applying the law of chemical equilibrium gives

Coefficient of NO_2 Coefficient of H_2O

$$K = \frac{[NO_2]^4[H_2O]^6}{[NH_3]^4[O_2]^7} \leftarrow \text{Coefficient of } O_2$$

↑
Coefficient of NH_3

Practice Problem Exercise 17.3

a. $K = [O_2]^3$ The solids are not included.

b. $K = [N_2O][H_2O]^2$ The solid is not included. Water is gaseous in this reaction, so it is included.

c. $K = \dfrac{1}{[CO_2]}$ The solids are not included.

d. $K = \dfrac{1}{[SO_3]}$ Water and H_2SO_4 are pure liquids and so are not included.

Practice Problem Exercise 17.4

When rain is imminent, the concentration of water vapor in the air increases. This shifts the equilibrium to the right, forming $CoCl_2 \cdot 6H_2O(s)$, which is pink.

Practice Problem Exercise 17.5

a. No change. Both sides of the equation contain the same number of gaseous components. The system cannot change its pressure by shifting its equilibrium position.

b. Shifts to the left. The system can increase the number of gaseous components present, and so increase the pressure, by shifting to the left.

c. Shifts to the right to increase the number of gaseous components and thus its pressure.

Practice Problem Exercise 17.6

a. Shifts to the right away from added SO_2.

b. Shifts to the right to replace removed SO_3.

c. Shifts to the right to decrease its pressure.

d. Shifts to the right. Energy is a product in this case, so a decrease in temperature favors the forward reaction (which produces energy).

Practice Problem Exercise 17.8

a. $BaSO_4(s) \rightleftharpoons Ba^{2+}(aq) + SO_4^{2-}(aq)$; $K_{sp} = [Ba^{2+}][SO_4^{2-}]$

b. $Fe(OH)_3(s) \rightleftharpoons Fe^{3+}(aq) + 3OH^-(aq)$; $K_{sp} = [Fe^{3+}][OH^-]^3$

c. $Ag_3PO_4(s) \rightleftharpoons 3Ag^+(aq) + PO_4^{3-}(aq)$; $K_{sp} = [Ag^+]^3[PO_4^{3-}]$

Practice Problem Exercise 17.9

$[Ba^{2+}] = [SO_4^{2-}] = 3.9 \times 10^{-5}\ M$

$\begin{aligned} K_{sp} = [Ba^{2+}][SO_4^{2-}] &= (3.9 \times 10^{-5})^2 \\ &= 1.5 \times 10^{-9} \end{aligned}$

Practice Problem Exercise 17.10

$PbCrO_4(s) \rightleftharpoons Pb^{2+}(aq) + CrO_4^{2-}(aq)$

$K_{sp} = [Pb^{2+}][CrO_4^{2-}] = 2.0 \times 10^{-16}$

$[Pb^{2+}] = x$

$[CrO_4^{2-}] = x$

$2.0 \times 10^{-16} = x^2 = K_{sp}$

$x = 1.4 \times 10^{-8}\ M = $ Solubility of $PbCrO_4(s)$

Chapter 18

Practice Problem Exercise 18.1

a. CuO contains Cu^{2+} and O^{2-} ions, so copper is oxidized ($Cu \rightarrow Cu^{2+} + 2e^-$) and oxygen is reduced ($O + 2e^- \rightarrow O^{2-}$).

b. CsF contains Cs^+ and F^- ions. Thus cesium is oxidized ($Cs \rightarrow Cs^+ + e^-$) and fluorine is reduced ($F + e^- \rightarrow F^-$).

Practice Problem Exercise 18.2

a. SO_3
We assign oxygen first. Each O is assigned an oxidation state of -2, giving a total of -6 (3×-2) for the three oxygen atoms. Because the molecule has zero charge overall, the sulfur must have an oxidation state of $+6$.
Check: $+6 + 3(-2) = 0$

b. SO_4^{2-}
As in part a, each oxygen is assigned an oxidation state of -2, giving a total of -8 (4×-2) on the four oxygen atoms. The anion has a net charge of -2, so the sulfur must have an oxidation state of $+6$.
Check: $+6 + 4(-2) = -2$
SO_4^{2-} has a charge of -2, so this is correct.

c. N_2O_5
We assign oxygen before nitrogen because oxygen is more electronegative. Thus each O is assigned an oxidation state of -2, giving a total of -10 (5×-2) on the five oxygen atoms. Therefore, the oxidation states of the *two* nitrogen atoms must total $+10$, because N_2O_5 has no overall charge. Each N is assigned an oxidation state of $+5$.
Check: $2(+5) + 5(-2) = 0$

d. PF_3
First we assign the fluorine an oxidation state of -1, giving a total of -3 (3×-1) on the three fluorine atoms. Thus P must have an oxidation state of $+3$.
Check: $+3 + 3(-1) = 0$

e. C_2H_6
In this case it is best to recognize that hydrogen is always $+1$ in compounds with nonmetals. Thus each H is assigned an oxidation state of $+1$, which means that the six H atoms account for a total of $+6$ ($6 \times +1$). Therefore, the *two* carbon atoms must account for -6, and each carbon is assigned an oxidation state of -3.
Check: $2(-3) + 6(+1) = 0$

Practice Problem Exercise 18.4

We can tell whether this is an oxidation–reduction reaction by comparing the oxidation states of the elements in the reactants and products:

$$N_2 + 3H_2 \rightarrow 2NH_3$$

Oxidation states: 0   0 -3 $+1$ (each H)

Nitrogen goes from 0 to -3. Thus it gains three electrons and is reduced. Each hydrogen atom goes from 0 to $+1$ and is thus oxidized, so this is an oxidation–reduction reaction. The oxidizing agent is N_2 (it takes electrons from H_2). The reducing agent is H_2 (it gives electrons to N_2).

$$N_2 + 3H_2 \rightarrow 2NH_3$$
$$6e^-$$

Practice Problem Exercise 18.6

The unbalanced equation for this reaction is

$$Cu(s) + HNO_3(aq) \rightarrow Cu(NO_3)_2(aq) + H_2O(l) + NO(g)$$

Copper metal   Nitric acid   Aqueous copper(II) nitrate (contains Cu^{2+})   Water   Nitrogen monoxide

Step 1 The oxidation half-reaction is

$$Cu + HNO_3 \rightarrow Cu(NO_3)_2$$

Oxidation states: 0   +1 +5 −2   +2   +5   −2
                              (each 0)   (each 0)

The copper goes from 0 to +2 and thus is oxidized.

     The reduction reaction is

$$HNO_3 \rightarrow NO$$

Oxidation states: +1 +5 −2   +2 −2
                              (each 0)

In this case nitrogen goes from +5 in HNO_3 to +2 in NO and so is reduced. Notice two things about these reactions:

1. The HNO_3 must be included in the oxidation half-reaction to supply NO_3^- in the product $Cu(NO_3)_2$.
2. Although water is a product in the overall reaction, it does not need to be included in either half-reaction at the beginning. It will appear later as we balance the equation.

Step 2 *Balance the oxidation half-reaction.*

$$Cu + HNO_3 \rightarrow Cu(NO_3)_2$$

a. Balance nitrogen first.

$$Cu + 2HNO_3 \rightarrow Cu(NO_3)_2$$

b. Balancing nitrogen also caused oxygen to balance.

c. Balance hydrogen using H^+.

$$Cu + 2HNO_3 \rightarrow Cu(NO_3)_2 + 2H^+$$

d. Balance the charge using e^-.

$$Cu + 2HNO_3 \rightarrow Cu(NO_3)_2 + 2H^+ + 2e^-$$

This is the balanced oxidation half-reaction.

Balance the reduction half-reaction.

$$HNO_3 \rightarrow NO$$

a. All elements are balanced except hydrogen and oxygen.

b. Balance oxygen using H_2O.

$$HNO_3 \rightarrow NO + 2H_2O$$

c. Balance hydrogen using H^+.

$$3H^+ + HNO_3 \rightarrow NO + 2H_2O$$

d. Balance the charge using e^-.

$$3e^- + 3H^+ + HNO_3 \rightarrow NO + 2H_2O$$

This is the balanced reduction half-reaction.

Step 3 We equalize electrons by multiplying the oxidation half-reaction by 3:

$$3 \times (Cu + 2HNO_3 \rightarrow Cu(NO_3)_2 + 2H^+ + 2e^-)$$

which gives

$$3Cu + 6HNO_3 \rightarrow 3Cu(NO_3)_2 + 6H^+ + 6e^-$$

Multiplying the reduction half-reaction by 2

$$2 \times (3e^- + 3H^+ + HNO_3 \rightarrow NO + 2H_2O)$$

gives

$$6e^- + 6H^+ + 2HNO_3 \rightarrow 2NO + 4H_2O$$

Step 4 We can now add the balanced half-reactions, which both involve a six-electron change.

$$3Cu + 6HNO_3 \rightarrow 3Cu(NO_3)_2 + 6H^+ + 6e^-$$

$$6e^- + 6H^+ + 2HNO_3 \rightarrow 2NO + 4H_2O$$

$$\overline{\cancel{6e^-} + \cancel{6H^+} + 3Cu + 8HNO_3 \rightarrow 3Cu(NO_3)_2 + 2NO + 4H_2O + \cancel{6H^+} + \cancel{6e^-}}$$

Canceling species common to both sides gives the balanced overall equation:

$$3Cu(s) + 8HNO_3(aq) \rightarrow 3Cu(NO_3)_2(aq) +$$
$$2NO(g) + 4H_2O(l)$$

Step 5 Check the elements and charges.

Elements   3Cu, 8H, 8N, 24O → 3Cu, 8H, 8N, 24O

Charges   0 → 0

Chapter 19

Practice Problem Exercise 19.1

a. An alpha particle is a helium nucleus, ^4_2He. We can initially represent the production of an α particle by $^{226}_{88}Ra$ as follows:

$$^{226}_{88}Ra \rightarrow {}^4_2He + {}^A_ZX$$

Because we know that both A and Z are conserved, we can write

$$A + 4 = 226 \text{ and } Z + 2 = 88$$

Solving for A gives 222 and for Z gives 86, so ^A_ZX is $^{222}_{86}X$. Because Rn has $Z = 86$, ^A_ZX is $^{222}_{86}Rn$. The overall balanced equation is

$$^{226}_{88}Ra \rightarrow {}^4_2He + {}^{222}_{86}Rn$$

Check: $Z = 88$ $Z = 86 + 2 = 88$
                    $\longrightarrow$
         $A = 226$ $A = 222 + 4 = 226$

b. Using a similar strategy, we have

$$^{214}_{82}Pb \rightarrow {}^0_{-1}e + {}^A_ZX$$

Because $Z - 1 = 82$, $Z = 83$, and because $A + 0 = 214$, $A = 214$. Therefore, $^A_ZX = {}^{214}_{83}Bi$. The balanced equation is

$$^{214}_{82}Pb \rightarrow {}^0_{-1}e + {}^{214}_{83}Bi$$

Check: $Z = 82$ $Z = 83 - 1 = 82$
                    $\longrightarrow$
         $A = 214$ $A = 214 + 0 = 214$

Practice Problem Exercise 19.2

a. The missing particle must be ^4_2He (an α particle), because

$$^{222}_{86}Rn \rightarrow {}^{218}_{84}Po + {}^4_2He$$

is a balanced equation.

Check: $Z = 86 \qquad Z = 84 + 2 = 86$

$\qquad\qquad\longrightarrow$

$\qquad A = 222 \qquad A = 218 + 4 = 222$

b. The missing species must be $^{15}_{7}X$ or $^{15}_{7}N$, because the balanced equation is

$$^{15}_{8}O \rightarrow {}^{15}_{7}N + {}^{0}_{1}e$$

Check: $Z = 8 \qquad Z = 7 + 1 = 8$

$\qquad\qquad\longrightarrow$

$\qquad A = 15 \qquad A = 15 + 0 = 15$

Practice Problem Exercise 19.3

Let's do this problem by thinking about the number of half-lives required to go from 8.0×10^{-7} mol to 1.0×10^{-7} mol of $^{228}_{88}Ra$.

8.0×10^{-7} mol $\xrightarrow[\substack{\text{First}\\\text{half-life}}]{}$ 4.0×10^{-7} mol $\xrightarrow[\substack{\text{Second}\\\text{half-life}}]{}$

2.0×10^{-7} mol $\xrightarrow[\substack{\text{Third}\\\text{half-life}}]{}$ 1.0×10^{-7} mol

It takes three half-lives, then, for the sample to go from 8.0×10^{-7} mol of $^{228}_{88}Ra$ to 1.0×10^{-7} mol of $^{228}_{88}Ra$. From Table 19.3, we know that the half-life of $^{228}_{88}Ra$ is 6.7 years. Therefore, the elapsed time is 3(6.7 years) = 20.1 years, or 2.0×10^{1} years when we use the correct number of significant figures.

Chapter 20

Practice Problem Exercise 20.1

The alkane with ten carbon atoms can be represented as $CH_3-(CH_2)_8-CH_3$ and its formula is $C_{10}H_{22}$. The alkane with fifteen carbons,

$$CH_3-(CH_2)_{13}-CH_3$$

has the formula $C_{15}H_{32}$.

Practice Problem Exercise 20.4

a.

This molecule is 5-ethyl-3-methyloctane.

b.

This molecule is 5-ethyl-3-methylheptane. Note that this chain could be numbered from the opposite direction to give the name 3-ethyl-5-methylheptane. These two names are equally correct.

Practice Problem Exercise 20.5

The root name decane indicates a ten-carbon chain. There is a methyl group at the number 4 position and an isopropyl group at the number 5 position. The structural formula is

Practice Problem Exercise 20.6

a. The longest chain has eight carbon atoms with a double bond, so the root name is octene. The double bond exists between carbons 3 and 4, so the name is 3-octene. There is a methyl group on the number-2 carbon. The name is 2-methyl-3-octene.

b. The carbon chain has five carbons with a triple bond between carbons 1 and 2. The name is 1-pentyne.

Practice Problem Exercise 20.7

a. 2-chloronitrobenzene or o-chloronitrobenzene

b. 4-phenyl-2-hexene

Practice Problem Exercise 20.8

a. 1-pentanol; primary alcohol

b. 2-methyl-2-propanol (but this alcohol is usually called tertiary butyl alcohol); tertiary alcohol

c. 5-bromo-2-hexanol; secondary alcohol

Practice Problem Exercise 20.9

a. 4-ethyl-3-hexanone
Because the compound is named as a hexanone, the carbonyl group is assigned the lowest possible number.

b. 7-isopropyldecanal

Selected End-of-Chapter Problems

Chapter 1

2. (a) cellular processes, drug mechanisms; (b) understanding forensic reports, examination of the crime scene; (c) drug interactions, dosages; (d) properties of paints and thinners, properties of sculpture media; (e) film-developing process, properties of papers and coatings; (f) fertilizers, plant hormones; (g) drug interactions, dosages

4. Many examples exist. Chemical and biological weapons are produced in some countries. Although the development of plastics has been a benefit in many endeavors, their use depletes fossil fuel reserves and increases our solid waste problems. Although biotechnology has produced many exciting new drugs and treatments, the testing procedures that have been developed for determining whether a person has a genetic likelihood of developing a particular disease might be used to make it difficult or impossible for that person to obtain health or life insurance.

6. Answers will depend on the student's choices.

7. Answers will depend on student's experience.

8. David and Susan first recognized the problem (unexplained medical problems). A possible explanation was then proposed (the glaze on their china might be causing the lead poisoning). The explanation was tested by experiment (it was determined that the china did contain lead). A full scenario is given in the text.

10. (a) quantitative—a number (measurement) is indicated explicitly; (c) quantitative—a numerical measurement is indicated; (e) quantitative—a number (measurement) is implied

12. A natural law is a summary of observed, measurable behavior that occurs repeatedly and consistently. A theory is an attempt to explain such behavior.

14. Most applications of chemistry are oriented toward the interpretation of observations that solve problems. Although memorization of facts may *aid* in these endeavors, it is the ability to combine, relate, and synthesize information that is most important in the study of chemistry.

16. In real-life situations, the problems and applications likely to be encountered are not simple textbook examples. You must be able to observe an event, hypothesize a cause, and then test this hypothesis. You must be able to carry forward what has been learned in class to new, different situations.

Chapter 2

2. Atoms are very tiny.

5. In general, the properties of a compound are very different from the properties of its constituent elements.

For example, the properties of water are very different from the properties of the elements (hydrogen gas and oxygen gas) that make up water.

7. Because gases are mostly open space, they can be compressed easily to smaller volumes. In solids and liquids, most of the sample's bulk volume is filled with the molecules, leaving little empty space.

9. chemical **10.** the orange color

13. (a) chemical; (c) chemical; (e) chemical; (g) chemical; (i) physical

16. (a) mixture; (c) mixture

17. (a) homogeneous; (c) heterogeneous

20. Consider a mixture of table salt (sodium chloride) and sand. Salt is soluble in water, sand is not. The mixture is added to water and stirred to dissolve the salt, and then filtered. The salt solution passes through the filter, but the sand remains on the filter. The water can then be evaporated from the salt.

22. The solution is heated to vaporize (boil) the water. The water vapor is then cooled so that it condenses back to the liquid state, and the liquid is collected. After all the water is vaporized from the original sample, pure sodium chloride remains. The process consists of physical changes.

23. compound **25.** physical

29. chemical

Chapter 3

2. Alchemists discovered several previously unknown elements (mercury, sulfur, antimony) and were the first to prepare several common acids.

4. over 115 elements are known; 88 occur naturally; the others are man-made. Table 3.1 lists the most common elements on earth.

6. The four most abundant elements in living creatures are oxygen, carbon, hydrogen, and nitrogen. In the nonliving world, the most abundant elements are oxygen, silicon, aluminum, and iron.

8. Sb (antimony), Cu (copper), Au (gold), Pb (lead), Hg (mercury), K (potassium), Ag (silver), Na (sodium), Sn (tin), W (tungsten), Fe (iron)

9. (a) Ne; (c) K; (e) Ba

11. (a) copper; (c) calcium; (e) chromium; (g) chlorine

13. According to Dalton, a given compound always consists of the same number and type of atoms; thus the composition of the compound on a mass percentage basis is always the same.

15. According to Dalton, all atoms of the same element are identical; in particular, every atom of a given element has the same mass as every other atom of that element. If a given compound always contains the same relative numbers of atoms of each kind, and those atoms always have the same masses, then the compound made from those elements always contains the same relative masses of its elements.

16. (a) PCl_3; (c) $CaCl_2$; (e) Fe_2O_3

18. (a) False. Rutherford's bombardment experiments suggested that alpha particles were being deflected by a dense, positively charged nucleus. (b) False. The proton and electron do have opposite electrical charges, but the mass of the electron is much smaller than the mass of the proton. (c) True

20. protons   **22.** electrons

24. false

26. Atoms of the same element (atoms with the same number of protons in the nucleus) may have different numbers of neutrons, and so will have different masses.

27. (a) 32; (c) 24; (e) 38; (g) 4

28. (a) $^{17}_{8}O$; (c) $^{60}_{27}Co$; (e) $^{131}_{53}I$

29. (a) 94p, 150n, 94e; (c) 89p, 138n, 89e; (e) 77p, 116n, 77e

32. vertical; groups

34. Metallic elements are found toward the left and bottom of the periodic table; there are far more metallic elements than nonmetals.

36. hydrogen, nitrogen, oxygen, fluorine, chlorine, plus all the Group 8 elements (noble gases)

38. A metalloid is an element that has some properties common to both metallic and nonmetallic elements. The metalloids are found in the "stairstep" region marked on most periodic tables.

39. (a) 7, halogens; (c) 1, alkali metals; (e) 8, noble gases; (g) 8, noble gases

40. (a) rubidium, Rb, atomic number 37, Group 1, metal; (c) magnesium, Mg, atomic number 12, Group 2, metal

42. These elements are found uncombined in nature and do not react readily with other elements. Although these elements were once thought to form no compounds, this now has been shown to be untrue.

44. liquids: bromine, gallium, mercury; gases: hydrogen, nitrogen, oxygen, fluorine, chlorine, the noble gases (helium, neon, argon, krypton, xenon, radon)

47. (a) Ca: 20 protons, 20 electrons; Ca^{2+}: 20 protons, 18 electrons; (c) Br: 35 protons, 35 electrons; Br^-: 35 protons, 36 electrons; (e) Al: 13 protons, 13 electrons; Al^{3+}: 13 protons, 10 electrons

48. (a) I^-; (c) Cs^+; (e) F^-

51. The total number of positive charges must equal the total number of negative charges so that the crystals of an ionic compound have no net charge. A macroscopic sample of a compound ordinarily has no charge.

52. (a) FeP; (c) $FeCl_3$; (e) MgO; (g) Na_3P

54. Most of the atom's mass is concentrated in the nucleus; thus the protons and neutrons contribute most to the mass of the atom. The chemical properties of an atom depend on the number and location of the electrons.

56. (a) CO_2; (c) $HClO_4$

Chapter 4

2. compounds containing a metal and a nonmetal; compounds containing two nonmetals

4. cation (positive ion)

5. Sodium chloride consists of Na^+ ions and Cl^- ions in an extended crystal lattice array. No discrete NaCl pairs are present.

6. (a) sodium iodide; (c) aluminum sulfide; (f) silver(I) chloride (silver chloride); (h) lithium oxide

7. (a) incorrect; BaH_2 is barium hydride; (c) correct

8. (a) iron(III) iodide; (c) mercury(II) oxide; (e) copper(II) oxide

9. (a) cobaltous chloride; (c) plumbous oxide; (e) ferric oxide

10. (a) iodine pentafluoride; (c) selenium monoxide; (e) nitrogen triiodide

11. (a) germanium tetrahydride; (c) diphosphorus pentasulfide; (e) ammonia (nitrogen trihydride)

12. (a) diboron hexahydride, nonionic; (c) carbon tetrabromide, nonionic; (e) copper(II) chloride, ionic

13. (a) radium chloride; (c) phosphorus trichloride; (e) manganese(II) fluoride

14. An oxyanion contains a particular element plus oxygen. If there are two oxyanions of that element, the higher oxidation state is given the *-ate* ending and the lower oxidation state is given the *-ite* ending. If there are four oxidation states, the highest is given the prefix *per-* and the lowest is indicated by the prefix *hypo-*. For example: ClO (hypochlorite), ClO_2^- (chlorite), ClO_3^- (chlorate), ClO_4^- (perchlorate)

16. hypobromite; IO_3^-; periodate; IO^-

19. (a) $MgCl_2$; (b) $Ca(ClO)_2$; (c) $KClO_3$; (d) $Ba(ClO_4)_2$

21. (a) iron(III) nitrate, ferric nitrate; (c) chromium(III) cyanide, chromic cyanide; (e) chromium(II) acetate, chromous acetate

24. (a) hydrochloric acid; (c) nitric acid; (e) nitrous acid; (g) hydrobromic acid

25. (a) Li_2O; (c) Ag_2O; (e) Ca_3P_2; (g) Na_2S

26. (a) CO_2; (c) N_2Cl_4; (e) PF_5

27. (a) $Ca_3(PO_4)_2$; (c) $Al(HSO_4)_3$; (e) $Fe(NO_3)_3$

28. (a) HCN; (c) H_2SO_4; (e) HClO or HOCl; (g) $HBrO_2$

29. (a) LiCl; (c) HBr; (e) $NaClO_4$; (g) $Ba(HCO_3)_2$; (i) B_2Cl_6; (k) K_2SO_3

30. A moist paste of NaCl would contain Na^+ and Cl^- ions in solution and would serve as a conductor of electrical impulses.

31. A binary compound is a compound containing two, and only two, elements. A polyatomic anion is several atoms bonded together; as a whole, it carries a negative electrical charge. An oxyanion is a negative ion containing a particular element and one or more oxygen atoms.

32. (a) gold(III) bromide; (c) magnesium hydrogen phosphate; (e) ammonia

33. (a) ammonium carbonate; (c) calcium phosphate; (e) manganese(IV) oxide

34. (a) K_2O; (c) FeO; (e) ZnO

37.

$Ca(NO_3)_2$	$CaSO_4$	$Ca(HSO_4)_2$	$Ca(H_2PO_4)_2$	CaO	$CaCl_2$
$Sr(NO_3)_2$	$SrSO_4$	$Sr(HSO_4)_2$	$Sr(H_2PO_4)_2$	SrO	$SrCl_2$
NH_4NO_3	$(NH_4)_2SO_4$	NH_4HSO_4	$NH_4H_2PO_4$	$(NH_4)_2O$	NH_4Cl
$Al(NO_3)_3$	$Al_2(SO_4)_3$	$Al(HSO_4)_3$	$Al(H_2PO_4)_3$	Al_2O_3	$AlCl_3$
$Fe(NO_3)_3$	$Fe_2(SO_4)_3$	$Fe(HSO_4)_3$	$Fe(H_2PO_4)_3$	Fe_2O_3	$FeCl_3$
$Ni(NO_3)_2$	$NiSO_4$	$Ni(HSO_4)_2$	$Ni(H_2PO_4)_2$	NiO	$NiCl_2$
$AgNO_3$	Ag_2SO_4	$AgHSO_4$	AgH_2PO_4	Ag_2O	AgCl
$Au(NO_3)_3$	$Au_2(SO_4)_3$	$Au(HSO_4)_3$	$Au(H_2PO_4)_3$	Au_2O_3	$AuCl_3$
KNO_3	K_2SO_4	$KHSO_4$	KH_2PO_4	K_2O	KCl
$Hg(NO_3)_2$	$HgSO_4$	$Hg(HSO_4)_2$	$Hg(H_2PO_4)_2$	HgO	$HgCl_2$
$Ba(NO_3)_2$	$BaSO_4$	$Ba(HSO_4)_2$	$Ba(H_2PO_4)_2$	BaO	$BaCl_2$

39. (a) Al $(13e^-) \rightarrow Al^{3+}$ $(10e^-) + 3e^-$; (c) Cu $(29e^-) \rightarrow$ Cu^+ $(28e^-) + 1e^-$; (e) Zn $(30e^-) \rightarrow Zn^{2+}$ $(28e^-) + 2e^-$

40. (a) none likely; (c) Te^{2-}; (e) Br^-

41. (a) Na_2S; (c) BaO; (e) $CuBr_2$; (g) Al_2O_3

42. (a) beryllium oxide; (c) sodium sulfide; (e) hydrogen chloride (gaseous); hydrochloric acid (aqueous); (g) silver(I) sulfide; usually called silver sulfide

43. (a) incorrect; (c) incorrect

44. (a) iron(II) bromide; (c) cobalt(III) sulfide; (e) mercury(I) chloride

45. (a) xenon hexafluoride; (c) arsenic triiodide; (e) dichlorine monoxide

46. (a) iron(III) acetate; (c) potassium peroxide; (e) copper(II) permanganate

47. (a) lithium dihydrogen phosphate; (c) lead(II) nitrate; (e) sodium chlorite

48. (a) $CaCl_2$; (c) Al_2S_3; (e) H_2S; (g) MgI_2

49. (a) SO_2; (c) XeF_4; (e) PCl_5

50. (a) NaH_2PO_4; (c) $Cu(HCO_3)_2$; (e) BaO_2

51. (a) $AgClO_4$; (c) NaClO or NaOCl; (e) NH_4NO_2; (g) NH_4HCO_3

Chapter 5

2. 4512

4. (a) −5; (b) 6; (c) −4; (d) 4

5. (a) 9.367421×10^6; (c) 5.519×10^{-4}; (f) 6.319×10^1; (h) 7.21×10^{-1}

6. (a) 483; (c) 6.1; (e) 4,221,000; (g) 9999; (i) 101,600; (k) 97,100

7. (a) 1.423×10^5; (c) 2.27×10^4; (e) 2.51×10^2; (g) 9.7752 (9.7752×10^0)

8. (a) 3.1×10^3; (c) 1 or 1×10^0; (e) 1×10^7; (g) 1.00×10^{-7}

9. (a) 10^3; (c) 10^{-3}; (e) 10^{-9}

10. (a) mega; (c) nano; (e) centi

11. 100 miles   **12.** quart

14. the woman   **16.** d

18. d   **20.** 40 quarters

23. The scale of the ruler is marked to the nearest tenth of a centimeter. Writing 2.850 would imply that the scale was marked to the nearest hundredth of a centimeter (and that the zero in the thousandths place had been estimated).

24. (a) 4; (c) 4; (e) 3; (g) 6

25. (a) probably 2; (c) infinite (definition)

26. (a) 1,570,000 or 1.57×10^6 ; (c) 84,600 or 8.46×10^4

27. (a) 3.42×10^{-4}; (c) 1.7992×10^1

29. 3   **31.** none

32. (a) 641.0; (c) 77.34

33. (a) 124; (c) 1.14×10^{-2}

34. (a) 2.045; (c) 5.19×10^{-5}

38. 1 lb/$0.79

39. (a) 2.44 yd; (c) 115 in; (e) 648.1 mi; (g) 0.0362 km

40. (a) 0.2543 kg; (c) 6.06 lb; (e) 1.177 lb; (g) 2.5×10^2 g

42. 3.1×10^2 km; 3.1×10^5 m; 1.0×10^6 ft

47. (a) 118 K; (c) 221 K; (e) 226 K

48. (a) 2 °C; (c) − 273 °C; (e) 9727 °C

49. (a) − 40 °F ; (c) 241 °C

50. (a) 144 K; (c) 664 °F

54. Density is a characteristic property of a pure substance.

56. (a) 20.1 g/cm^3; (c) 0.907 g/cm^3

57. 0.843 g/mL   **59.** float

60. 11.7 mL

62. (a) 966 g; (b) 394 g; (c) 567 g; (d) 135 g

63. (a) cm; (c) km

65. $1   **68.** 959 g

69. (a) 4; positive; (c) 0; zero

71. (a) 1; (c) 4; (e) infinite (definition)

72. 38.2 g/mL

Chapter 6

2. 307 corks; 116 stoppers; 2640 g

4. The average atomic mass is a weighted average including a contribution based on the mass of the individual isotopes of an element and their abundance in nature.

5. (a) 640. amu; (c) 1642 amu

6. (a) one; (c) 100

9. Avogadro's number (6.022×10^{23})

11. 177 g   **13.** 0.50 mol O

14. (a) 0.133 mol Au; (c) 2.44×10^{-3} mol Ba; (e) 5.20×10^{-13} mol Ni

15. (a) 112 g Fe; (c) 0.240 g Pt; (e) 0.0248 g Mg

16. (a) 1.05×10^{19} atoms; (c) 0.0467 mol cobalt; (e) 249 g

18. adding (summing)

19. (a) 82.98 g; (c) 97.94 g; (e) 82.09 g

20. (a) 336.2 g; (c) 278.1 g; (e) 260.5 g

21. (a) 6.14×10^{-4} mol SO_3; (c) 0.495 mol $CHCl_3$; (e) 0.167 mol LiOH

22. (a) 3.55×10^{-5} mol; (c) 2704 mol

23. (a) 612 g AlI_3; (c) 721 g $C_6H_{12}O_6$

24. (a) 0.0559 g CO_2; (c) 0.361 g NH_4NO_3

25. (a) 3.84×10^{24} molecules; (c) 8.76×10^{16} molecules

26. (a) 0.0141 mol S; (c) 0.0258 mol S

27. (a) 32.37% Na, 22.58% S, 45.05% O; (c) 58.91% Na, 41.09% S; (e) 55.26% K, 14.59% P, 30.15% O; (g) 28.73% K, 1.481% H, 22.76% P, 47.03% O

28. (a) 28.45% Cu; (c) 44.06% Fe; (e) 18.84% Co; (g) 88.12% Sn

29. (a) 49.32% C; (c) 49.47% C; (e) 71.92% C; (g) 85.03% C

30. (a) 33.73% NH_4^+; (c) 64.94% Au^{3+}

32. The empirical formula represents the smallest whole-number ratio of the elements present in a compound. The molecular formula indicates the actual number of atoms of each element found in a molecule of the substance.

33. (a) NaO; (c) $C_{12}H_{12}N_2O_3$

34. (a) these have the same empirical formulas; (c) these have the same empirical formulas

36. CaO   **37.** $BaSO_4$

39. Co_2S_3 **41.** CuO

43. Na_3N; NaN_3 **45.** molar mass

48. $C_6H_{24}O_6$

50. empirical formula, C_3H_3O; molecular formula, $C_6H_6O_2$

52. 5.00 g Al, 0.185 mol, 1.12×10^{23} atoms; 0.140 g Fe, 0.00250 mol, 1.51×10^{21} atoms; 270 g Cu, 4.3 mol, 2.6×10^{24} atoms; 0.00250 g Mg, 1.03×10^{-4} mol, 6.19×10^{19} atoms; 0.062 g Na, 2.7×10^{-3} mol, 1.6×10^{21} atoms; 3.95×10^{-18} g U, 1.66×10^{-20} mol, 1.00×10^4 atoms

55. Cu_2O, CuO   **57.** 2.12 g Fe

60. $C_3H_7N_2O$ **61.** HgO

62. $BaCl_2$

Chapter 7

2. decrease in mass; change in texture

4. change in odor as acetic acid is produced

6. atoms

8. water

10. $C_3H_8(g) + O_2(g) \rightarrow CO_2(g) + H_2O(g)$

12. $(NH_4)_2CO_3(s) \rightarrow NH_3(g) + CO_2(g) + H_2O(g)$

14. $CO(g) + H_2(g) \rightarrow CH_3OH(l)$

16. $Ca(s) + H_2O(l) \rightarrow Ca(OH)_2(s) + H_2(g)$

18. $Mg(OH)_2(s) + HCl(aq) \rightarrow MgCl_2(aq) + H_2O(l)$

20. $H_2S(g) + O_2(g) \rightarrow SO_2(g) + H_2O(g)$

22. $Fe_2O_3(s) + CO(g) \rightarrow Fe(l) + CO_2(g)$

24. $O_2(g) \rightarrow O_3(g)$

26. $NH_3(g) + HNO_3(g) \rightarrow NH_4NO_3(aq)$

28. $Xe(g) + F_2(g) \rightarrow XeF_4(g)$

30. $Ag(s) + HNO_3(aq) \rightarrow AgNO_3(aq) + H_2(g)$

32. whole numbers

33. (a) $2H_2O_2(aq) \rightarrow 2H_2O(l) + O_2(g)$; (c) $2FeO(s) + C(s) \rightarrow 2Fe(l) + CO_2(g)$

34. (a) $CaF_2(s) + H_2SO_4(l) \rightarrow CaSO_4(s) + 2HF(g)$; (c) $TiCl_4(l) + 4Na(s) \rightarrow 4NaCl(s) + Ti(s)$

35. (a) $SiI_4(s) + 2Mg(s) \rightarrow Si(s) + 2MgI_2(s)$; (c) $8Ba(s) + S_8(s) \rightarrow 8BaS(s)$

36. (a) $Ba(NO_3)_2(aq) + Na_2CrO_4(aq) \rightarrow BaCrO_4(s) + 2NaNO_3(aq)$; (b) $C_2H_5OH(l) + 3O_2(g) \rightarrow 2CO_2(g) + 3H_2O(l)$

37. $Al(s) + O_2(g) \rightarrow Al_2O_3(s)$

39. $C_{12}H_{22}O_{11}(aq) + H_2O(l) \rightarrow 4C_2H_5OH(l) + 4CO_2(g)$

41. $2Al_2O_3(s) + 3C(s) \rightarrow 4Al(s) + 3CO_2(g)$

43. $2Li(s) + S(s) \rightarrow Li_2S(s)$; $2Na(s) + S(s) \rightarrow Na_2S(s)$; $2K(s) + S(s) \rightarrow K_2S(s)$; $2Rb(s) + S(s) \rightarrow Rb_2S(s)$; $2Cs(s) + S(s) \rightarrow Cs_2S(s)$; $2Fr(s) + S(s) \rightarrow Fr_2S(s)$

44. $2KClO_3(s) \rightarrow 2KCl(s) + 3O_2(g)$

48. $K_2CrO_4(aq) + BaCl_2(aq) \rightarrow BaCrO_4(s) + 2KCl(aq)$

Chapter 8

2. Driving forces are types of changes in a system that pull a reaction in the direction of product formation; they include formation of a solid, formation of water, formation of a gas, and transfer of electrons.

3. The net charge of a precipitate must be zero. The total number of positive charges equals the total number of negative charges.

7. "Insoluble" and "slightly soluble" have roughly the same meanings. However, if a substance is highly toxic and found in a water supply, for example, the difference could be crucial.

8. (a) soluble (most nitrate salts are soluble); (c) soluble (most sodium salts are soluble); (e) insoluble; (g) insoluble (most sulfide salts are only slightly soluble)

9. (a) rule 5: most hydroxide compounds are only slightly soluble; (c) rule 6: most phosphate salts are only slightly soluble

10. (a) calcium sulfate; (c) lead(II) phosphate; (e) no precipitate: all potassium and sodium salts are soluble

11. (a) no precipitate; (c) $H_2SO_4(aq) + Pb(NO_3)_2(aq) \rightarrow PbSO_4(s) + 2HNO_3(aq)$; (e) no precipitate

12. (a) $2AgNO_3(aq) + H_2SO_4(aq) \rightarrow Ag_2SO_4(s) + 2HNO_3(aq)$

13. (a) $(NH_4)_2S(aq) + CoCl_2(aq) \rightarrow CoS(s) + 2NH_4Cl(aq)$

14. (a) $Ca^{2+}(aq) + SO_4^{2-}(aq) \rightarrow CaSO_4(s)$; (c) $Ag^+(aq) + I^-(aq) \rightarrow AgI(s)$; (e) $Hg_2^{2+}(aq) + 2Cl^-(aq) \rightarrow Hg_2Cl_2(s)$

15. $Ag^+(aq) + Cl^-(aq) \rightarrow AgCl(s)$; $Pb^{2+}(aq) + 2Cl^-(aq) \rightarrow PbCl_2(s)$; $Hg_2^{2+}(aq) + 2Cl^-(aq) \rightarrow Hg_2Cl_2(s)$

18. The strong bases are those hydroxide compounds that dissociate fully when dissolved in water. The strong bases that are highly soluble in water (NaOH, KOH) are also strong electrolytes.

19. 1000; 1000

21. $RbOH(s) \rightarrow Rb^+(aq) + OH^-(aq)$; $CsOH(s) \rightarrow Cs^+(aq) + OH^-(aq)$

22. (a) $HCl(aq) + RbOH(aq) \rightarrow H_2O(l) + RbCl(aq)$; (c) $HBr(aq) + NaOH(aq) \rightarrow H_2O(l) + NaBr(aq)$

23. (a) $H_2SO_4(aq) + 2NaOH(aq) \rightarrow 2H_2O(l) + Na_2SO_4(aq)$; (c) $HClO_4(aq) + KOH(aq) \rightarrow H_2O(l) + KClO_4(aq)$

25. the metal loses electrons; the nonmetal gains electrons

26. Each potassium atom would lose one electron to become a K^+ ion. Each sulfur atom would gain two electrons to become a S^{2-} ion. Two potassium ions would have to react for every one sulfur atom.

27. $AlBr_3$ is made up of Al^{3+} ions and Br^- ions. Aluminum atoms each lose 3 electrons and bromine atoms each gain 1 electron (Br_2 gains 2 electrons).

29. (a) $2Fe(s) + 3S(s) \rightarrow Fe_2S_3(s)$; (c) $2Sn(s) + O_2(g) \rightarrow 2SnO(s)$; (e) $2Cs(s) + 2H_2O(l) \rightarrow 2CsOH(s) + H_2(g)$

31. Examples of the formation of water: $H_2SO_4(aq) + 2NaOH(aq) \rightarrow 2H_2O(l) + Na_2SO_4(aq)$; $HClO_4(aq) + KOH(aq) \rightarrow H_2O(l) + KClO_4(aq)$. Examples of formation of a gaseous product: $Mg(s) + 2HCl(aq) \rightarrow MgCl_2(aq) + H_2(g)$; $2KClO_3(s) \rightarrow 2KCl(s) + 3O_2(g)$

33. (a) oxidation–reduction; (b) oxidation-reduction; (c) acid–base; (d) acid–base; (e) precipitation; (f) precipitation; (g) oxidation–reduction; (h) oxidation–reduction; (i) acid–base

35. A decomposition reaction is one in which a given compound is broken down into simpler compounds or constituent elements. These may be classified in other ways. For example, the reaction $2HgO(s) \rightarrow 2Hg(l) + O_2(g)$ is both a decomposition reaction, and an oxidation–reduction reaction.

36. (a) $C_2H_5OH(l) + 3O_2(g) \rightarrow 2CO_2(g) + 3H_2O(g)$

37. (a) $2C_2H_6(g) + 7O_2(g) \rightarrow 4CO_2(g) + 6H_2O(g)$

38. (a) $2Co(s) + 3S(s) \rightarrow Co_2S_3(s)$; (c) $FeO(s) + CO_2(g) \rightarrow FeCO_3(s)$

39. (a) $2NI_3(s) \rightarrow N_2(g) + 3I_2(s)$; (c) $C_6H_{12}O_6(s) \rightarrow 6C(s) + 6H_2O(g)$

41. (a) silver ion: $Ag^+(aq) + Cl^-(aq) \rightarrow AgCl(s)$; lead(II) ion: $Pb^{2+}(aq) + 2Cl^-(aq) \rightarrow PbCl_2(s)$; mercury(I) ion: $Hg_2^{2+}(aq) + 2Cl^-(aq) \rightarrow Hg_2Cl_2(s)$; (c) hydroxide ion: $Fe^{3+}(aq) + 3OH^-(aq) \rightarrow Fe(OH)_3(s)$; sulfide ion: $2Fe^{3+}(aq) + 3S^{2-}(aq) \rightarrow Fe_2S_3(s)$; phosphate ion: $Fe^{3+}(aq) + PO_4^{3-}(aq) \rightarrow FePO_4(s)$; (e) sulfide ion: $Hg_2^{2+}(aq) + S^{2-}(aq) \rightarrow Hg_2S(s)$; carbonate ion: $Hg_2^{2+}(aq) + 2CO_3^{2-}(aq) \rightarrow Hg_2CO_3(s)$; chloride ion: $Hg_2^{2+}(aq) + 2Cl^-(aq) \rightarrow Hg_2Cl_2(s)$

43. (a) $HNO_3(aq) + KOH(aq) \rightarrow H_2O(l) + \underline{KNO_3}(aq)$; (c) $HClO_4(aq) + NaOH(aq) \rightarrow H_2O(l) + \underline{NaClO_4}(aq)$

45. (a) $AgNO_3(aq) + HCl(aq) \rightarrow \underline{AgCl}(s) + HNO_3(aq)$; (c) $FeSO_4(aq) + K_2CO_3(aq) \rightarrow \underline{FeCO_3}(s) + K_2SO_4(aq)$; (e) $Pb(NO_3)_2(aq) + Li_2CO_3(aq) \rightarrow \underline{PbCO_3}(s) + 2LiNO_3(aq)$

46. (a) $Ag^+(aq) + Cl^-(aq) \rightarrow AgCl(s)$; (c) $Pb^{2+}(aq) + 2Cl^-(aq) \rightarrow PbCl_2(s)$

48. (a) 1; (c) 2; (e) 3

49. (a) 2; (c) 3

50. (a) $2C_3H_8OH(l) + 9O_2(g) \rightarrow 6CO_2(g) + 8H_2O(g)$; oxidation–reduction, combustion; (c) $3HCl(aq) + Al(OH)_3(s) \rightarrow AlCl_3(aq) + 3H_2O(l)$; acid–base, double-displacement

Chapter 9

2. Balanced chemical equations tell us in what proportions on a mole basis substances combine; since the molar masses of $C(s)$ and $O_2(g)$ are different, 1 g of each reactant cannot represent the same number of moles of each reactant.

4. (a) $3MnO_2(s) + 4Al(s) \rightarrow 3Mn(s) + 2Al_2O_3(s)$. Three formula units of manganese(IV) oxide react with four aluminum atoms, producing three manganese atoms and two formula units of aluminum oxide. Three moles of solid manganese(IV) oxide react with four moles of solid aluminum, producing three moles of solid manganese and two moles of solid aluminum oxide. (c) $3NO_2(g) + H_2O(l) \rightarrow 2HNO_3(aq) + NO(g)$. Three molecules of nitrogen dioxide react with one molecule of water to produce two molecules of nitric acid and one molecule of nitrogen monoxide. Three moles of gaseous nitrogen dioxide react with one mole of liquid water to produce two moles of aqueous nitric acid and one mole of nitrogen monoxide gas.

7. $2Ag(s) + H_2S(g) \rightarrow Ag_2S(s) + H_2(g)$. For Ag_2S: 1 mol $Ag_2S/2$ mol Ag; for H_2: 1 mol $H_2/2$ mol Ag

8. (a) 0.125 mol Fe, 0.0625 mol CO_2; (c) 0.500 mol H_3BO_3, 0.125 mol Na_2SO_4

9. (a) 0.50 mol NH_4Cl (27 g); (c) 0.50 mol H_3PO_3 (41 g), 1.5 mol HCl (55 g)

10. (a) 0.469 mol O_2; (c) 0.625 mol CH_3CHO

12. Stoichiometry is the process of using a chemical equation to calculate the relative masses of reactants and products involved in a reaction.

13. (a) 1.86×10^{-4} mol Ag; (c) 2.59×10^{-7} mol U; (e) 1.12 mol $Fe(NO_3)_3$

14. (a) 0.0221 g; (c) 0.312 g; (e) 73.4 g

15. (a) 1.03 mol $CuCl_2$; (c) 0.240 mol NaOH

16. (a) 7.63 mg $FeCO_3$, 11.5 mg K_2SO_4; (c) 21.6 mg Fe_2S_3

18. 0.44 g O_2

20. 45.0 mg $FeCl_3$

22. 0.631 g S

24. 2.07 g MgO

25. 1.61×10^4 g I_2

28. 1.42 g NH_3

29. The limiting reactant is the reactant that limits the amounts of products that can form in a chemical reaction. All reactants are necessary for a reaction to continue.

33. A reactant is present in excess if more of that reactant is present than is required to react with the limiting reactant. The limiting reactant, by definition, cannot be present in excess. No.

34. (a) HCl is the limiting reactant; 18.3 g $AlCl_3$; 0.415 g H_2; (c) $Pb(NO_3)_2$ is the limiting reactant; 12.6 g $PbCl_2$; 5.71 g HNO_3

35. (a) Na is the limiting reactant; 84.9 g $NaNH_2$; (c) NaOH is the limiting reactant; 78.8 g Na_2SO_3

36. (a) CO is the limiting reactant; 11.4 mg CH_3OH; (c) HBr is the limiting reactant; 12.4 mg $CaBr_2$; 2.23 mg H_2O

38. 1.79 g Fe_2O_3

41. If the reaction occurs in a solvent, the product may have a substantial solubility in the solvent; the reaction may come to equilibrium before the full yield of product is achieved (see Chapter 17); loss of product may occur to error.

44. $2LiOH(s) + CO_2(g) \rightarrow Li_2CO_3(s) + H_2O(g)$; 142 g of CO_2 can be ultimately absorbed; 102 g is 71.8% of the canister's capacity.

46. 82.6%

47. 28.6 g $NaHCO_3$

49. $C_6H_{12}O_6(s) + 6O_2(g) \rightarrow 6CO_2(g) + 6H_2O(g)$; 1.47 g CO_2

51. for O_2, 5 mol O_2/1 mol C_3H_8; for CO_2, 3 mol CO_2/1 mol C_3H_8; for H_2O, 4 mol H_2O/1 mol C_3H_8

53. (a) 0.0587 mol NH_4Cl; (b) 0.0178 mol $CaCO_3$; (c) 0.0217 mol Na_2O; (d) 0.0323 mol PCl_3

54. 0.667 g O_2

57. 0.624 mol N_2, 17.5 g N_2; 1.25 mol H_2O, 22.5 g H_2O

58. 5.0 g

Chapter 10

2. Some energy is given off in other forms such as heat or light.

4. Ball A has higher potential energy because of its higher position initially.

7. (a) No; temperature is a measure of average kinetic energy. (b) Yes; the thermal energy is the total energy.

9. There is more heat involved in mixing 100.0-g samples of 60 °C and 10 °C water.

11. The potential energy is the energy available to do work. Potential energy is due to the bond energies.

14. (a) endothermic; (c) exothermic

15. The process is exothermic; the process is endothermic.

17. The chemist chooses the sign based on whether energy flows from the system (negative sign) or into the system (positive sign).

19. (a) 36 kJ   **20.** 16 kJ

23. lower

25. (a) 32.82 kJ; (c) 2.600×10^5 J

28. 1.42 J/g °C

30. (a) 2.54×10^3 kJ; (b) 7.4×10^3 kJ; (c) 693 kJ

33. 226 kJ   **35.** -11 kJ

36. The quality of energy tells us the form of the energy (potential or kinetic). The quantity of energy tells us how much. The total amount (or quantity) is conserved. However, when concentrated potential energy is converted to spread kinetic energy, we say that the quality is decreasing.

39. If it were not for greenhouse gases the surface temperature of the earth would be much colder. Having too large a quantity of greenhouse gases may cause the surface temperature of the earth to rise to levels that cause severe environmental changes.

41. The first law of thermodynamics tells us that the total amount of energy is constant. It does not tell us anything about direction or energy transfer.

43. The driving force of an exothermic reaction is energy spread. In an exothermic reaction, energy is transferred from the system to the surroundings.

46. (a) 110.5 kcal; (c) 0.2424 kcal

47. (a) 190.9 kJ; (c) 657.5 cal

49. 1.6×10^3 g silver   **51.** 0.031 cal/g °C

53. For a given mass of substance, the substance with the smallest specific heat capacity (gold, 0.13 J/g °C) will undergo the largest increase in temperature. Conversely, the substance with the largest specific heat capacity (water, 4.184 J/g °C) will undergo the smallest increase in temperature.

55. 22 °C

57.

Substance	Heat Required
water (*l*)	7.03×10^3 J
water (*s*)	3.41×10^3 J
water (*g*)	3.4×10^3 J
aluminum	1.5×10^3 J
iron	7.6×10^3 J
mercury	2.4×10^2 J
carbon	1.2×10^3 J
silver	4.0×10^2 J
gold	2.2×10^2 J

59. (a) 41 kJ; (c) 47 kJ

60. (a) exothermic; (c) endothermic

Chapter 11

1. This experiment is explained in Chapter 3.

4. The different forms of electromagnetic radiation all exhibit the same wavelike behavior and move through space at the same speed (the speed of light). The types of electromagnetic radiation differ in their frequency and wavelength and in the resulting amount of energy carried per photon.

6. The speed of electromagnetic radiation represents how fast energy is transferred through space; the frequency of the radiation tells us how many waves pass a given point in a certain amount of time.

8. The wave–particle nature of light refers to the fact that a beam of electromagnetic energy can be considered not only as a continuous wave, but also as a stream of discrete packets of energy moving through space.

9. The colors are due to the releasing of energy.

12. It is emitted as a photon.

14. When excited hydrogen atoms emit their excess energy, the photons of radiation that are emitted always have the exact same wavelength and energy. Thus the hydrogen atom possesses only certain allowed energy states.

16. The ground state of an atom is its lowest possible energy state.

18. According to Bohr, electrons move in fixed circular orbits around the nucleus. An electron can move to a larger orbit if a photon of applied energy equals the difference in energy between the two orbits.

20. Bohr's theory explained the line spectrum of hydrogen exactly. It did not explain measurements made for atoms other than hydrogen.

22. An orbit refers to an exact circular pathway for the electron around the nucleus. An orbital represents a region in space in which there is a high probability of finding an electron.

25. Pictures representing orbitals are probability maps. They do not imply that the electron moves on the surface of, or within, the region of the picture. The mathematical probability of finding an electron never becomes zero moving out from the nucleus (the electron could possibly be "anywhere").

26. The $2s$ orbital is similar in shape to the $1s$ orbital, but the $2s$ orbital is larger.

28. increases

30. The Pauli exclusion principle states that an orbital can hold a maximum of two electrons, and those two electrons must have opposite spin.

32. increases

35. Valence electrons are those in the outermost energy level. They can interact with the (valence) electrons of another atom in a chemical reaction.

37. (a) $1s^2 2s^2 2p^6 3s^2 3p^6 4s^2 3d^{10} 4p^6 5s^2$; (c) $1s^2$

38. (a) $1s^2 2s^2 2p^6 3s^2 3p^6 4s^2$; (c) $1s^2 2s^2 2p^5$

39. (a) $(\uparrow\downarrow)\ (\uparrow\downarrow)\ (\uparrow\downarrow)(\uparrow\downarrow)(\uparrow\downarrow)\ (\uparrow\downarrow)\ (\uparrow\ )(\ )(\ )$;
$1s2s2p3s3p$

(c) $(\uparrow\downarrow)\ (\uparrow\downarrow)\ (\uparrow\downarrow)(\uparrow\downarrow)(\uparrow\downarrow)\ (\uparrow\downarrow)\ (\uparrow\downarrow)(\uparrow\downarrow)(\uparrow\downarrow)\ (\uparrow\downarrow)$
$1s2s2p3s3p4s$

$(\uparrow\downarrow)(\uparrow\downarrow)(\uparrow\downarrow)(\uparrow\downarrow)(\uparrow\downarrow)\ (\uparrow\downarrow)(\uparrow\downarrow)(\uparrow\ )$
$3d4p$

40. (a) 1; (c) 7

42. The properties of Rb and Sr suggest that they are members of Groups 1 and 2, respectively. This means that the outer electrons are filling the $5s$ orbital. The $5s$ orbital, then, must be lower in energy and fills before the $4d$ orbitals.

43. (a) $[Ar]4s^2$; (c) $[Kr]5s^2 4d^1$

44. (a) $[Ne]3s^2 3p^3$; (c) $[Ne]3s^2$

45. (a) 1; (c) 0   **46.** (a) $5f$; (c) $4f$

47. (a) $[Rn]7s^2 6d^1 5f^3$; (c) $[Xe]6s^2 4f^{14} 5d^{10}$

48. The metallic elements lose electrons and form positive ions (cations); the nonmetallic elements gain electrons and form negative ions (anions).

52. The elements of a given period (horizontal row) have valence electrons in the same subshells. Nuclear charge increases across a period from left to right. Atoms at the left side have smaller nuclear charges and bind their valence electrons less tightly.

54. The nuclear charge increases from left to right within a period. The greater the nuclear charge, the more tightly the valence electrons are "pulled."

55. (a) Na; (c) Br   **56.** (a) Li; (c) Cl

57. (a) Xe < Sn < Sr < Rb

59. speed of light   **61.** orbital

62. (a) $(\uparrow\downarrow)\ (\uparrow\downarrow)\ (\uparrow\downarrow)(\uparrow\downarrow)(\uparrow\downarrow)\ (\uparrow\downarrow)\ (\uparrow\downarrow)(\uparrow\downarrow)(\uparrow\downarrow)\ (\uparrow)$;
$1s2s2p3s3p4s$
$1s^2 2s^2 2p^6 3s^2 3p^6 4s^1$; $[Ar]4s^1$;

(c) $(\uparrow\downarrow)\ (\uparrow\downarrow)\ (\uparrow\downarrow)(\uparrow\downarrow)(\uparrow\downarrow)(\uparrow\downarrow)\ (\uparrow)(\uparrow)(\ )$;
$1s2s2p3s3p$
$1s^2 2s^2 2p^6 3s^2 3p^2$; $[Ne]3s^2 3p^2$

63. (a) ns^2; (c) $ns^2 np^4$

64. (a) 2 (d electrons are not counted as valence); (c) 2

65. Light is emitted from the hydrogen atom only at certain wavelengths. If the energy levels of hydrogen were continuous, a hydrogen atom would emit energy at all possible wavelengths.

67. (a) $1s^2 2s^2 2p^6 3s^2 3p^6 4s^2 3d^{10} 4p^5$;
(c) $1s^2 2s^2 2p^6 3s^2 3p^6 4s^2 3d^{10} 4p^6 5s^2 4d^{10} 5p^6 6s^2$

69. (a) Ca

Chapter 12

3. ionic; covalent

5. By bonding with each other, the H and F atoms share

a pair of valence electrons. Because the atoms have different attractions for the electrons, this sharing is not equal. The bonding in HF is polar covalent.

7. A bond is polar if the shared electron pair is attracted more strongly by one of the bonded atoms than the other. The polarity is due to differences in electronegativity values.

8. (a) K < Ca < Sc

9. (a) covalent; (c) polar covalent

10. (a) no polar covalent bonds; (c) no polar covalent bonds

11. (a) H—O; (c) H—F

12. (a) Na—O; (c) K—Cl

14. The presence of strong dipoles and a large overall dipole moment makes water a very polar substance. Properties of water that are dependent on its dipole moment include its freezing point, melting point, vapor pressure, and ability to dissolve many substances.

15. (a) H

16. (a) $^{\delta+}P \rightarrow F^{\delta-}$; (c) $^{\delta+}P \rightarrow C^{\delta-}$

17. (a) $^{\delta+}P \rightarrow S^{\delta-}$; (c) $^{\delta+}S \rightarrow N^{\delta-}$

18. gaining

20. (a) Li: $[He]2s^1$; Li^+: [He]; (c) Cs: $[Xe]6s^1$; Cs^+: [Xe]

21. (a) Ca^{2+}; (c) Br^-

22. (a) Na_2S; (c) $MgBr_2$; (e) KH

23. (a) Al^{3+}, [Ne]; S^{2-}, [Ar]; (c) Rb^+, [Kr]; O^{2-}, [Ne]

25. An ionic solid such as NaCl consists of an array of alternating positively and negatively charged ions. In most ionic solids, the ions are packed as tightly as possible.

27. In forming an anion, an atom gains additional electrons in its outermost (valence) shell. Having additional electrons in the valence shell increases the repulsive forces between electrons, and the outermost shell becomes larger to accommodate this repulsion.

28. (a) F^- is larger than Li^+. The F^- ion has a filled $n = 2$ shell. A lithium atom has lost the electron from the $n = 2$ shell, leaving $n = 1$ as its outermost shell. (c) Ca is larger than Ca^{2+}. The calcium ion has $n = 3$ as its outer shell, and the calcium atom has $n = 4$ as its outer shell.

29. (a) I^-; (c) Cl^-

31. When atoms form covalent bonds, they try to attain a valence-electron configuration similar to that of the nearest noble gas element. Thus hydrogen in a bond would have two electrons (like helium, the duet rule) and others would have eight electrons (like neon and argon, the octet rule).

33. (a) 32; (c) 30

34. (a) H—N̈—H;   (c) :C̈l—N—C̈l:
               | |
               H   :C̈l:

35. (a) H—S̈—H;   (c) H   H
                                  | |
                                  C = C
                                  | |
                                  H   H

36. (a) :C̈l—Ö—C̈l:

37. (a)
$$\left[\begin{array}{c} :\ddot{O}: \\ | \\ :\ddot{O}—S—\ddot{O}: \\ | \\ :\ddot{O}: \end{array} \right]^{2-}$$

38. (a)
$$\left[\begin{array}{c} :\ddot{O}: \\ | \\ H—\ddot{O}—P—\ddot{O}: \\ | \\ :\ddot{O}: \end{array} \right]^{2-}$$

40. Trigonal pyramid structure with four electron pairs (three bonding pairs and one lone pair). The bond angle is somewhat less than 109.5° (due to the lone pair).

42. Tetrahedral structure with four bonding electron pairs. The bond angle is 109.5°.

44. The general molecular structure is determined by the number of electron pairs around the central atom (bonding and lone pairs).

46. In NF_3 the nitrogen is surrounded by four electron pairs (tetrahedral geometry); in BF_3 the boron is surrounded by three electron pairs (trigonal planar).

47. (a) four electron pairs (tetrahedral geometry)

48. (a) tetrahedral

49. (a) <109.5° (about 105°); (c) 109.5°

50. (a) tetrahedral

52. The actylene molecule would be linear, with bond angles of 180°, because of the presence of the triple bond between carbon atoms.

54. (a) S—F

55. The bond energy is the energy required to break the bond.

56. (a) Be

57. (a) O

58. (a) Na^+; (c) K^+; (e) S^{2-}; (g) Al^{3+}

59. (a) nonlinear (V-shaped or bent); (c) trigonal planar

Chapter 13

1. A solid is rigid and incompressible and has a definite shape and volume. A liquid is less rigid than a solid; although it has a definite volume, a liquid takes the shape of its container. A gas has no fixed volume or shape; it takes the volume and shape of its container and is affected more by changes in its pressure and temperature than is a liquid or a solid.

4. (a) 1.038 atm; (c) 0.989 atm

5. (a) 758.1 mm Hg; (c) 748 mm

6. (a) 1.03×10^5 Pa; (c) 1.125×10^5 Pa

7. (a) 59.7 mL   **8.** (a) 146 mL

10. 20.0 atm

12. Measure the volume of a gas at several different temperatures (keep pressure and moles of gas constant). Plot these data and extrapolate the line (continue past the points you have measured). The temperature at which the gas has zero volume is absolute zero.

13. 49.2 mL   **14.** (a) 273 °C

15. (a) −238 °C

17. The volume of the neon gas would become half the initial value at 149 K. The volume would double at 596 K.

20. 10.8 L

21. Real gases behave most ideally at relatively high temperatures and low pressures.

23. (a) 5.02 L   **24.** (a) 0.201 L

26. 4,430 g He; 2,230 g H_2

27. 655 K   **30.** 464 mL

32. The pressure of the water vapor must be subtracted from the total pressure.

34. 5.0 atm N_2; 3.3 atm O_2; 1.7 atm CO_2

36. $P_{O_2} = 732$ torr, 1.98×10^{-2} mol O_2

38. 14.7 L O_2

40. 5.03 L (dry volume)

43. 15.6 L, 0.225 atm O_2, 0.256 atm N_2, 0.163 atm CO_2, 0.356 atm Ne

45. 0.709 L Cl_2

46. A theory is successful if it explains known experimental observations; no

48. We assume that the volume of the gas molecules in a sample is negligible compared to the bulk volume. This helps explain why gases are so compressible.

49. Pressure is due to atoms or molecules of a gas colliding with the walls of the container.

51. The temperature is a measure of the average kinetic energy of a sample of atoms or molecules. At high temperatures, the gas particles have, on average, greater kinetic energy and are moving faster than the same gas particles at a lower temperature.

54. When the volume of a gas is decreased, the gas particles take up a greater percentage of the volume of the container. The assumption in the KMT that gas particles take up a negligible volume is less reliable.

55. 125 balloons

58. The volume would be 3.0 L, so the balloon will burst.

61. 5.8 L O_2; 3.9 L SO_2

62. 32 L; $P_{He} = 0.86$ atm; $P_{Ar} = 0.017$ atm; $P_{Ne} = 0.12$ atm

Chapter 14

2. Dipole–dipole forces are stronger at shorter distances; they are relatively short-range forces.

4. Hydrogen bonding can exist when H is bonded to O, N, or F. This additional intermolecular force requires more energy to separate the molecules for boiling.

6. All atoms and molecules exhibit London dispersion forces between each other.

7. (a) London dispersion forces; (c) dipole–dipole forces and London dispersion forces

9. Strong hydrogen bonding occurs in both ethanol and water. Thus the molecules have great attraction for one another and are able to approach each other very closely; in fact, they must approach each other more closely in the mixture than either can approach a like molecule in the separate liquids.

11. Water, as perspiration, helps cool the human body. Some nuclear power plants use water to cool the reactor core.

13. Water pipes can be broken during cold weather. Also, ice can float on water, which is crucial for aquatic life (and ultimately for humans).

15. Sloped portions represent changes in temperature. The flat portions represent phase changes.

17. These processes are explained in detail in the text.

19. Intermolecular

21.

22. 8.35 kJ; 84.6 kJ; 23.1 kJ

25. Vapor pressure is the pressure of vapor present at equilibrium above a liquid in a sealed container at a given temperature. Molecules in the liquid evaporate, but as the number of molecules in the vapor state increases, some of these rejoin (condense). Eventually dynamic equilibrium is reached between evaporation and condensation.

27. See Figure 14.5 and the corresponding explanation.

28. (a) H_2S. H_2O exhibits hydrogen bonding and H_2S does not.

30. Hydrogen bonding can exist in ethyl alcohol but not dimethyl ether. Therefore ethyl alcohol would be less volatile (higher boiling point).

31. At higher altitudes the boiling temperatures of liquids are lower because there is less atmospheric pressure above the liquid. The temperature at which food cooks is determined by the temperature to which water in the food can be heated before it escapes as steam. By boiling at a lower temperature, the food will have to cook longer.

34. Ionic solids (NaCl); molecular solids (ice); atomic solids (copper)

36. Ionic solids tend to be harder and have higher melting and boiling points. Compare table salt (NaCl) to table sugar (sucrose), for example.

38. Ionic solids have strong electrostatic forces (due to the attraction of positively and negatively charged ions). These forces require a great deal of energy to be overcome.

42. The presence of a second metal's atoms in a metal's lattice changes the properties (usually making the alloy stronger because irregularities arise, keeping the crystal from being easily deformed). Steels with relatively high carbon content are exceptionally strong. Steels produced by alloying iron with nickel, chromium, and cobalt are more resistant to corrosion (rusting) than iron itself.

53. Diethyl ether should have a higher vapor pressure because it does not exhibit hydrogen bonding while 1-butanol does.

54. (a) KBr (exhibits ionic bonding)

56. Steel is a general term applied to alloys consisting mostly of iron. Steel is much stronger and harder than iron, which is relatively soft, malleable, and ductile.

57. Dipole–dipole interactions are typically 1% as strong as covalent bonds.

58. London dispersion forces arise from instantaneous dipoles; they are weaker than dipole–dipole forces or covalent bonds.

59. (a) London dispersion forces; (c) London dispersion forces

61. In NH_3, strong hydrogen bonding can exist. Because CH_4 molecules are nonpolar, only the relatively weak London dispersion forces exist.

Chapter 15

1. A homogeneous mixture is a combination of two (or more) pure substances that is uniform in composition and appearance throughout. Examples of homogeneous mixtures include rubbing alcohol (70% isopropyl alcohol and 30% water) and gasoline (a mixture of hydrocarbons).

4. The intermolecular forces must be similar in the two substances for them to mix. Polar and ionic solids may dissolve in water.

6. unsaturated   **8.** large

9. Increasing the surface area of a solid increases the amount of solid that comes in contact with the solvent.

12. (a) 5.00% $CaCl_2$; (c) 5.00% $CaCl_2$

13. (a) 0.719 g NaCl; (c) 0.494 g NaCl

15. 19.6% $CaCl_2$

17. 4.8 g heptane; 2.7 g pentane; 86 g hexane

19. 0.221 mol Ca^{2+}; 0.442 mol Cl^-

21. (a) 2.0 M; (c) 0.67 M

22. (a) 0.253 M; (c) 0.434 M

24. 0.0902 M

25. 0.623 M Fe^{3+}; 1.87 M Cl^-

27. (a) 0.0133 mol; 0.838 g; (c) 0.00505 mol; 0.490 g

28. 6.04 g NH_4Cl

29. (a) 4.60×10^{-3} mol Al^{3+}; 1.38×10^{-2} mol Cl^-; (c) 2.19×10^{-3} mol Cu^{2+}; 4.38×10^{-3} mol Cl^-

31. (a) 0.0837 M; (c) 0.0964 M

33. Transfer 6.21 mL of the 3.02 M solution to a 125-mL volumetric flask and add water to the calibration mark.

36. 7.5 mL   **38.** 0.976 g $PbCrO_4$

40. 0.107 M NaOH

41. (a) 3.85 mL NaOH; (c) 4.29 mL NaOH

43. 1.53 equivalents OH^- ion. By definition, one equivalent of OH^- ion exactly neutralizes one equivalent of H^+ ion.

44. (a) 0.277 N **45.** (a) 0.134 N

46. 0.359 M; 1.08 N **47.** 47.4 mL

49. Colligative properties are properties of a solution that depend only on the number, not the identity, of the solute particles.

52. 0.167 M Co^{3+}; 0.117 M Ni^{2+}; 0.567 M Cl^-

54. 1.93 g   **56.** 2.56 M

57. (a) 0.0909 M; (c) 0.192 M

58. (a) 0.50 N $HC_2H_3O_2$

Chapter 16

2. In the Arrhenius definition, an acid is a substance that produces hydrogen ions (H^+) when dissolved in water. An Arrhenius base produces hydroxide ions (OH^-) when dissolved in water. These definitions are not complete because they limit the bases to compounds with a hydroxide ion, and the only allowable solvent is water.

4. A conjugate acid–base pair differs by one hydrogen ion, H^+. For example, $HC_2H_3O_2$ (acetic acid) differs from its conjugate base $C_2H_3O_2^-$ (acetate ion) by a single hydrogen ion.

6. When an acid is dissolved in water, the hydronium ion (H_3O^+) is formed. The hydronium ion is the conjugate acid of water.

7. (a) The conjugate base of H_2SO_4 is the HSO_4^- ion. The conjugate acid of SO_4^{2-} is also the HSO_4^- ion. (c) The conjugate base of $HClO_4$ is the ClO_4^- ion. The conjugate acid of Cl^- is HCl.

8. (a) NH_3 (base), NH_4^+ (acid); H_2O (acid), OH^- (base)

9. (a) H_2SO_4; (c) $HClO_4$

10. (a) CO_3^{2-}; (c) Cl^-

11. (a) $NH_3 + H_2O \rightarrow NH_4^+ + OH^-$;
(c) $O^{2-} + H_2O \rightarrow OH^- + OH^-$

12. (a) $HClO_4 + H_2O \rightarrow ClO_4^- + H_3O^+$;
(c) $HSO_3^- + H_2O \rightarrow SO_3^{2-} + H_3O^+$

14. If an acid is weak in aqueous solution, it does not easily transfer protons to water (and does not fully ionize). Thus the anion of the acid must attract protons rather strongly.

15. A strong acid loses its protons easily and fully ionizes in water. Thus the acid's conjugate base is poor at attracting protons (that is, a very weak base). A weak acid does not ionize fully, so its conjugate base must have a rather strong attraction for a proton (that is, it must be a relatively strong base).

17. (a) $CH_3COO^-(C_2H_3O_2^-)$ is a relatively strong base;
(c) HS^- is relatively strong base

18. (a) HSO_4^- is a moderately strong acid; (c) HCN is a weak acid

20. $H_2O + H_2O \rightleftharpoons H_3O^+ + OH^-$; $K_w = [H_3O^+][OH^-]$

22. (a) $[H^+] = 2.5 \times 10^{-10}$ M; basic;
(c) $[H^+] = 1.4 \times 10^{-13}$ M; basic

23. (a) $[OH^-] = 1.0 \times 10^{-7}$ M; neutral;
(c) $[OH^-] = 1.4 \times 10^{-14}$ M; acidic

24. (a) $[H^+] = 1.2 \times 10^{-3}$ M is more acidic

25. (a) $[H^+] = 1.04 \times 10^{-8}$ M

27. household ammonia (pH 12); blood (pH 7–8); milk (pH 6–7); vinegar (pH 3); lemon juice (pH 2–3); stomach acid (pH 2)

29. The pH of a solution is defined as the negative logarithm of the hydrogen ion concentration; that is, $pH = -\log[H^+]$. Mathematically, as the $[H^+]$ increases, pH must decrease.

30. (a) pH = 3.000 (acidic); (c) pH = 10.037 (basic)

31. (a) 7.000 (neutral); (c) 10.017 (basic)

32. (a) pH = 9.68; solution is basic;
(c) pH = 12.19; solution is basic

33. (a) $[OH^-] = 1.0 \times 10^{-7}$ M; pH = 7.00; pOH = 7.00;
(c) $[OH^-] = 2.3 \times 10^{-4}$ M; pH = 10.37; pOH = 3.63

34. (a) 0.091 M; (c) 1.0×10^{-6} M

35. (a) $[H^+] = 8.1 \times 10^{-11}$ M; (c) $[H^+] = 1.4 \times 10^{-13}$ M

36. (a) $[H^+] = 7.6 \times 10^{-6}$ M; $[OH^-] = 1.3 \times 10^{-9}$ M;
(c) $[H^+] = [OH^-] = 1.0 \times 10^{-7}$

37. We can measure the pH of a solution with a pH meter, pH paper, and indicators. The pH meter is the most accurate.

40. The solution contains water molecules, H_3O^+ ions (protons), and NO_3^- ions. No HNO_3 molecules are present because HNO_3 is a strong acid.

42. (a) $[H^+] = 1.0 \times 10^{-4}$ M; pH = 4.00;
(c) $[H^+] = 4.21 \times 10^{-5}$ M; pH = 4.376

43. 500.0 mL

46. A buffered solution consists of a mixture of a weak acid and its conjugate base; one example of a buffered solution is a mixture of acetic acid ($HC_2H_3O_2$) and sodium acetate ($NaC_2H_3O_2$).

48. The weak acid component of the buffered solution reacts with the strong base. For example, hydroxide reacts with the acetic acid as follows:
$OH^- + HC_2H_3O_2 \rightarrow H_2O + C_2H_3O_2^-$.

49. (a) no; (c) yes

53. (a) basic solution; (c) not a basic solution (acidic)

54. (a) strong acid; (c) strong acid

55. (a) this is a conjugate acid–base pair;
(c) this is a conjugate acid–base pair

56. (a) CH_3NH_2 (base), $CH_3NH_3^+$ (acid); H_2O (acid), OH^- (base)

58. (a) $[OH^-] = 3.2 \times 10^{-6}$ M

Chapter 17

2. A nitrogen–nitrogen triple bond and three hydrogen–hydrogen bonds must be broken. Six nitrogen–hydrogen bonds must form.

4. The activation energy is the minimum energy required by two molecules for their collision to result in a reaction. If this energy requirement is not met, a collision will not result in a reaction.

6. The catalysts found in living cells are called enzymes. They are necessary for life because most of the cell's chemical processes would proceed too slowly at room temperature without a catalyst.

8. For a chemical reaction to occur, the reactants must collide with one another. As the temperature is increased, the average kinetic energy is increased. The particles are moving faster and the collisions will occur more frequently and have higher energies.

11. A state of equilibrium is reached when two opposing processes are exactly balanced. The development of a vapor pressure above a liquid in a closed container is an example of a physical equilibrium. Any chemical reaction that appears to "stop" before completion is an example of chemical equilibrium.

13. A system has reached equilibrium when no more product forms, even though significant amounts of all reactants are present. This indicates that the reverse process is now occurring at the same rate as the forward process. In other words, every time a product molecule is formed, another product molecule reacts to give back the reactants. Reactions that come to equilibrium are indicated by a double arrow.

15. We recognize a state of chemical equilibrium by the fact that the concentrations of reactants and products no longer change with time. However, this does not mean the reaction has "stopped." The concentrations remain the same because the forward and reverse reactions are occurring at the same rate.

17. Depending on the amounts of reactants that were present originally, differing amounts of products and reactants will be present at equilibrium. However, the ratio of the products to the reactants (which is represented by the equilibrium constant) will always be the same. For example, 4/2 and 6/3 involve different numbers, but each of these ratios is equal to 2.

18. (a) $K = \dfrac{[NCl_3(g)]^2}{[N_2(g)][Cl_2(g)]^3}$

19. (a) $K = \dfrac{[CH_3OH(g)]}{[CO(g)][H_2(g)]^2}$

21. $K = 2.5 \times 10^{10}$

24. Equilibrium constants represent ratios of the concentrations of the products and reactants present at equilibrium. The concentration of a pure liquid or solid is constant and is determined by the density of the solid or liquid.

25. (a) $K = [H_2O(g)][CO_2(g)]$

26. (a) $K = [N_2(g)][Br_2(g)]^3$

28. When more of one reactant is added to an equilibrium system, the system shifts to the right and adjusts to use up some of the added reactant. A net increase in the amount of product results, compared with the equilibrium position before the additional reactant was added. The numerical value of the equilibrium constant does not change when a reactant is added. The concentrations of all reactants and products adjust until they satisfy the value of K.

30. If heat is applied (the temperature is raised) to an endothermic reaction, the equilibrium shifts to the right. More product will be present (and less reactant will be present) at equilibrium than if the temperature had not been increased. The value of K increases.

32. (a) no change; (b) shifts left; (c) shifts right; (d) shifts right

34. For an endothermic reaction, an increase in temperature will shift the position of equilibrium to the right (toward the products).

37. A small equilibrium constant means that at equilibrium the concentration of the products is small compared with the concentration of reactants. The position of equilibrium lies far to the left. A reaction with a small equilibrium constant is therefore not useful as a means of producing the products. To become useful, the equilibrium position would have to be shifted to the right.

38. $K = 3.2 \times 10^{11}$ **40.** $K = 2.1 \times 10^{-3}$

42. $[N_2O_4] = 5.4 \times 10^{-4}\ M$

45. Stirring or grinding the solute increases the speed with which the solute dissolves. However, the amount of solute that dissolves is set by the equilibrium constant for that process.

47. (a) $PbBr_2(s) \rightleftharpoons Pb^{2+}(aq) + 2Br^-(aq)$;

$K_{sp} = [Pb^{2+}(aq)][Br^-(aq)]^2$;

(c) $PbCO_3(s) \rightleftharpoons Pb^{2+}(aq) + CO_3{}^{2-}(aq)$;

$K_{sp} = [Pb^{2+}(aq)][CO_3{}^{2-}(aq)]$

49. $K_{sp} = 1.6 \times 10^{-11}$ **51.** 1.7×10^{-4} g/L

52. $K_{sp} = 1.9 \times 10^{-4}$; 10. g/L

55. An increase in temperature increases the fraction of molecules with energy greater than the activation energy.

56. To say a reaction is reversible means that the reaction may occur in either direction.

58. In an exothermic process heat can be considered a product of the reaction. Adding heat (by increasing the temperature) opposes the forward process.

59. $9.0 \times 10^{-3}\ M$

61. At higher temperatures, the average kinetic energy of the reactant molecules is larger. Therefore, the probability that the molecules will have enough energy for a reaction to take place is greater. At the molecular level a higher temperature means a given molecule will be moving faster.

63. (a) $K = \dfrac{[HBr(g)]^2}{[H_2(g)][Br_2(g)]}$;

(b) $K = \dfrac{[H_2S(g)]^2}{[H_2(g)]^2[S_2(g)]}$;

(c) $K = \dfrac{[HCN(g)]^2}{[H_2(g)][C_2N_2(g)]}$

64. (a) $K = \dfrac{1}{[O_2(g)]^3}$ **66.** $K_{sp} = 1.4 \times 10^{-8}$

Chapter 18

2. Reduction can be defined as the gaining of electrons by an atom, molecule, or ion. Reduction may also be defined as a decrease in oxidation state for an element. This decrease occurs because of the gaining of one or more electrons (thus the definitions are the same). The following equation shows the reduction of sulfur: $S(s) + 2e^- \rightarrow S^{2-}(aq)$.

3. (a) sodium is oxidized, nitrogen is reduced; (c) aluminum is oxidized, bromine is reduced

4. (a) Mg is oxidized, Br_2 is reduced; (c) Cl_2 is reduced, Br is oxidized

5. The assignment of oxidation states is a bookkeeping method by which charges are assigned to the various atoms in a compound. This method allows us to keep track of electrons transferred between species in oxidation–reduction reactions.

7. A neutral molecule overall has a charge of zero.

8. The sum of all oxidation states of the atoms in a polyatomic ion must equal the overall charge on the ion.

9. (a) N, +3; Cl, −1; (c) P, +5; Cl, −1

10. (a) H, +1; Br, −1; (c) Br, 0

11. (a) H, +1; O, −2; N, +5; (c) H, +1; O, −2; S, +6

12. (a) Cu, +2; Cl, −1; (c) H, +1; O, −2; Cr, +6

13. (a) H, +1; C, −4; (c) K, +1; H, +1; C, +4; O, −2

15. When an atom gains an electron (which is negative), it gains a negative charge, which will lower its oxidation state. For example, in the reaction $Cl + e^- \rightarrow Cl^-$, the oxidation state goes from 0 to -1.

16. An oxidizing agent causes another species to be oxidized (to lose electrons). To do so, the oxidizing agent must take in electrons (be reduced). Thus an oxidizing agent is reduced (and a reducing agent is oxidized).

18. (a) Zn is oxidized (0 to $+2$); H is reduced ($+1$ to 0); (c) N is reduced (0 to -3); Br is oxidized (0 to $+1$)

19. (a) copper is oxidized (0 to $+2$); silver is reduced ($+1$ to 0); (c) sulfur is oxidized (0 to $+4$); iron is reduced ($+3$ to 0)

20. Silver is reduced [$+1$ in $AgBr(s)$, 0 in $Ag(s)$]; bromine is oxidized [-1 in $AgBr$, 0 in $Br_2(g)$]

23. Under ordinary conditions, it is impossible to have "free" electrons that are not part of some atom, ion, or molecule. Thus the total number of electrons lost by the species being oxidized must equal the total number of electrons gained by the species being reduced.

24. (a) $N_2 + 6e^- \rightarrow 2N^{3-}$; (c) $Zn \rightarrow Zn^{2+} + 2e^-$

25. (a) $4e^- + 4H^+ + O_2 \rightarrow 2H_2O$; (c) $e^- + 2H^+ + VO^{2+} \rightarrow V^{3+} + 2H_2O$

26. (a) $2MnO_4^-(aq) + 16H^+(aq) + 5Zn(s) \rightarrow 2Mn^{2+}(aq) + 8H_2O(l) + 5Zn^{2+}(aq)$;
(c) $2NO_3^-(aq) + 4H^+(aq) + Zn(s) \rightarrow NO_2(g) + 2H_2O(l) + Zn^{2+}(aq)$

27. (a) $IO_3^-(aq) + 6H^+(aq) + 5I^-(aq) \rightarrow 3I_2(aq) + 3H_2O(l)$

29. A salt bridge completes the electrical circuit in a cell. It allows ion flow from one half of the cell to another without allowing bulk mixing of the solutions. It is typically a U-shaped tube filled with an electrolyte that is not involved in the oxidation–reduction reaction. Any method that allows ion flow without large-scale mixing of solutions (such as a porous cup or frit) can be used in place of a salt bridge.

32. $Pb^{2+}(aq)$ ion is reduced; $Zn(s)$ is oxidized. The reaction at the anode is $Zn(s) \rightarrow Zn^{2+}(aq) + 2e^-$. The reaction at the cathode is $Pb^{2+}(aq) + 2e^- \rightarrow Pb(s)$.

34. Both normal and alkaline cells contain zinc as an electrode; zinc corrodes more slowly under alkaline (basic) conditions than in a normal dry cell (which is acidic).
Anode: $Zn(s) + 2OH^-(aq) \rightarrow ZnO(s) + H_2O(l) + 2e^-$.
Cathode: $2MnO_2(s) + H_2O(l) + 2e^- \rightarrow Mn_2O_3(s) + 2OH^-(aq)$.

36. Aluminum reacts very quickly with the oxygen in air to form a thin coating of Al_2O_3 on its surface. This coating is transparent and clings tightly to the aluminum. In addition, the aluminum oxide is much less reactive than aluminum and protects the surface from further reaction.

38. In cathodic protection of steel tanks and pipes, a more reactive metal than iron is connected to the item to be protected. The active metal is then oxidized instead of the iron of the tank or pipe.

40. The main recharging reaction for the lead storage battery is $2PbSO_4(s) + 2H_2O(l) \rightarrow Pb(s) + PbO_2(s) + 2H_2SO_4(aq)$. A major side reaction is the electrolysis of water, $2H_2O(l) \rightarrow 2H_2(g) + O_2(g)$.

42. The item to be plated should be made the cathode in a cell containing a solution of ions of the desired plating metal.

44. lose

45. hydrogen, oxygen

46. (a) $4Fe(s) + 3O_2(g) \rightarrow 2Fe_2O_3(s)$; iron is oxidized, oxygen is reduced

47. (a) $2MnO_4^-(aq) + 6H^+(aq) + 5H_2O_2(aq) \rightarrow 2Mn^{2+}(aq) + 8H_2O(l) + 5O_2(g)$

48. (a) zinc is oxidized, nitrogen is reduced;
(c) potassium is oxidized, oxygen is reduced

49. (a) Mn, $+4$; O, -2; (c) H, $+1$; S, $+4$; O, -2

50. (a) oxygen is oxidized, chlorine is reduced;
(c) carbon is oxidized, chlorine is reduced

Chapter 19

2. The radius of a typical atomic nucleus is on the order of 10^{-13} cm. This is about 100,000 times smaller than the radius of an atom overall.

3. The atomic number (Z) represents the number of protons in the nucleus. The mass number (A) represents the total number of protons and neutrons in the nucleus. For example, for $^{13}_{6}C$, with six protons and seven neutrons, we have $Z = 6$ and $A = 13$.

5. The atomic number (Z) is written as a left subscript, while the mass number (A) is written as a left superscript. The general symbol for a nuclide is $^A_Z X$. As an example, the isotope of oxygen with 8 neutrons would be $^{16}_{8}O$.

7. When a nucleus produces a beta particle, the atomic number of the parent nucleus is increased by one unit.

8. Gamma rays are high-energy photons of electromagnetic radiation; they are normally not considered to be particles. When a nucleus produces only gamma radiation, the atomic number and mass number remain the same.

10. Electron capture occurs when one of the inner orbital electrons is pulled into, and becomes part of, the nucleus.

12. (a) $^{192}_{83}Bi$

13. (a) $^{0}_{-1}e$

14. (a) $^{136}_{53}I \rightarrow ^{0}_{-1}e$ 1 $^{136}_{54}Xe$

15. (a) $^{226}_{88}Ra \rightarrow ^{222}_{86}Rn + ^{4}_{2}He$; (c) $^{239}_{94}Pu \rightarrow ^{235}_{92}U + ^{4}_{2}He$

17. The target nucleus and the bombarding particles often repel each other greatly. This is especially true if the bombarding particles are positively charged. Accelerators are needed to speed up the particles to overcome this repulsion.

19. $^{27}_{13}Al + ^{4}_{2}He \rightarrow ^{30}_{15}P + ^{1}_{0}n$

21. The half-life for a nucleus is the time required for one-half of the original sample of nuclei to decay. A given isotope of an element always has the same half-life. Different isotopes of the same element may have very different half-lives. Nuclei of different elements have different half-lives.

24. highest to lowest activity: $^{87}Sr > ^{99}Tc > ^{24}Na > ^{99}Mo > ^{133}Xe > ^{131}I > ^{32}P > ^{51}Cr > ^{59}Fe$

25. For ^{223}Ra, approximately 125 mg (after 36 days or 3 half-lives); for ^{224}Ra, approximately 4 mg (after 29 days or 8 half-lives); for ^{225}Ra, approximately 250 mg (after 30 days, or 2 half-lives).

28. Carbon-14 is produced in the upper atmosphere by the bombardment of nitrogen with neutrons from space: $^{14}_{7}N + ^{1}_{0}n \rightarrow ^{14}_{6}C + ^{1}_{1}H$.

30. When a plant dies, it no longer replenishes itself with carbon-14 from the atmosphere. As the carbon-14 it has undergoes decay, the amount decreases over time. This assumes that the concentration of carbon-14 in the atmosphere is constant over time.

32. These isotopes are listed in Table 19.4.

34. Nuclear fusion is the combining of two light nuclei to form a heavier, more stable nucleus. Splitting a heavy nucleus into nuclei with smaller mass numbers is nuclear fission.

36. $^{1}_{0}n + ^{235}_{92}U \rightarrow ^{142}_{56}Ba + ^{91}_{36}Kr + 3^{1}_{0}n$

38. A critical mass of fissionable material is the amount needed to sustain a chain reaction. Enough neutrons have to be produced to cause a constant fission of more material. A sample with less than the critical mass is still radioactive, but it cannot sustain a chain reaction.

40. The type of nuclear explosion produced by a nuclear weapon cannot occur in a nuclear reactor. The concentration of fissionable materials in a reactor is not sufficient to form a supercritical mass.

42. $^{1}_{0}n + ^{238}_{92}U \rightarrow ^{239}_{92}U$; $^{239}_{92}U \rightarrow ^{239}_{93}Np + ^{0}_{-1}e$; $^{239}_{93}Np \rightarrow ^{239}_{94}Pu + ^{0}_{-1}e$

44. The hydrogen nuclei are positively charged and therefore repel each other. Extremely high temperatures are needed to overcome this repulsion as they are shot into each other.

47. Somatic damage is damage directly to the organism itself, which causes nearly immediate sickness or death. Genetic damage is damage to the genetic machinery of the organism, which causes defects in future generations of offspring.

49. Alpha particles are much heavier than gamma rays so they can ionize biological materials very effectively. Gamma rays can penetrate long distances but seldom cause ionization.

51. The exposure limits given in Table 19.5 as causing no detectable clinical effect are 0–25 rem. The total yearly exposures from natural and human-induced radioactive sources are estimated in Table 19.6 as less than 200 millirem (0.2 rem)—well within the acceptable limits.

52. alpha, beta, beta, alpha, alpha, alpha, alpha, alpha, beta, beta, alpha, beta, beta, alpha

53. (a) cobalt is a component of vitamin B_{12}; (c) red blood cells contain hemoglobin, an iron–protein compound

55. Al-27: 13 protons, 14 neutrons; Al-28: 13 protons, 15 neutrons; Al-29: 13 protons, 16 neutrons

57. Breeder reactors convert nonfissionable U-238 into fissionable Pu-239. A combination of U-238 and U-235 is used. Excess neutrons from the U-235 fission are absorbed by U-238, converting it into Pu-239. The chemical and physical properties of Pu-239 make it very difficult and expensive to handle.

Chapter 20

2. Four. Carbon atoms have four valence electrons. By making four bonds, carbon atoms complete their valence octet.

4. four; tetrahedral

6. The geometry around each carbon is a tetrahedral, making the angles 109.5 °. To be "straight," the angles would have to be 180 °.

8. (a) H—C—C—C—C—H;

(c) H—C—C—C—C—C—H

10. a branch or substituent

13. The root name is derived from the number of carbon atoms in the longest continuous chain of carbon atoms.

14. The position of a substituent is indicated by a number that corresponds to the carbon atom in the longest chain to which the substituent is attached.

16. (a) 3-ethylpentane; (c) 2,2-dimethylpropane

17. (a) CH_3—CH—CH_2—CH_2—CH_2—CH_3;
$\quad\quad\quad\quad\quad$ |
$\quad\quad\quad\quad CH_3$

(c) CH_3—C—CH_2—CH_2—CH_2—CH_3
$\quad\quad\quad$ |
$\quad\quad\quad CH_3$

19.

Number of Carbon Atoms	Use
5–12	gasoline
10–18	kerosene, jet fuel
15–25	diesel fuel, heating oil
>25	asphalt

23. Combustion represents the vigorous reaction of a hydrocarbon (or other substances) with oxygen. It has been used as a source of heat and light.

25. Dehydrogenation reactions involve the removal of hydrogen atoms from adjacent carbon atoms in an alkane (or other substance). When two hydrogen atoms are removed from an alkane, a double bond is formed.

26. (a) $2C_6H_{14}(l) + 19O_2(g) \rightarrow 12CO_2(g) + 14H_2O(g)$

28. An alkyne is a hydrocarbon containing a carbon–carbon triple bond. The general formula is C_nH_{2n-2}.

29. (a) $CH_3CH_2CH_3(g)$

30. (a) 2-butene; (c) l-butyne

33. A set of equivalent Lewis structures can be drawn for benzene. Each structure differs only in the location of the three double bonds in the ring. Experimentally benzene does not have the chemical properties expected for molecules having any double bonds.

35. *ortho*-: adjacent substituents (1,2-); *meta*-: two substituents with one unsubstituted carbon between them (1,3-); *para*-: two substituents with two unsubstituted carbon atoms between them (1,4-)

36. (a) ; (c)

37. (a) 1,2-dimethylbenzene; (c) anthracene

39. (a) ether; (c) alcohol

41. Primary alcohols have *one* hydrocarbon fragment (alkyl group) bonded to the carbon atom where the —OH group is attached. Secondary alcohols have *two* such alkyl groups attached, and tertiary alcohols contain three such alkyl groups. Examples are

Ethanol (primary) CH_3-CH_2-OH

2-Propanol (secondary)

2-Methyl-2-propanol (tertiary)

42. (a) 1-pentanol (primary); (c) 3-pentanol (secondary)

43. (a) $CH_3-CH_2-CH_2-CH_2-CH_2-OH$; (primary);
(c) (secondary)

45. $C_6H_{12}O_6 \rightarrow 2CH_3CH_2OH + 2CO_2$ (yeast is a catalyst). The yeast are killed if the concentration of alcohol is greater than 13%. To make more concentrated ethanol solutions, distillation is needed.

47. methanol (CH_3OH): starting material for synthesis of acetic acid and many plastics; isopropyl alcohol (2-propanol, $CH_3-CH(OH)-CH_3$): rubbing alcohol

49. The location of the carbonyl group (C=O). Aldehydes contain the carbonyl group at the end of a hydrocarbon chain. Ketones contain the carbonyl group in the interior of a hydrocarbon chain.

50. (a) 3-hexanone (ethyl propyl ketone);
(c) 3,4-dimethylpentanal

51. (a) ; (c)

52. Carboxylic acids are typically weak acids;
$CH_3CH_2COOH + H_2O \rightleftharpoons CH_3CH_2COO_2^- + H_3O^+$

54. (a) 3-methylbutanoic acid; (c) 2-hydroxypropanoic acid

55. (a)

(c)

57. A polyester is a polymer in which the polymerization forms an ester group. The repeating unit is an ester; thus there are many esters, or "poly-esters." Dacron is an example.

59. nylon

Dacron

60. The general formula is C_nH_{2n+2}. Each successive alkane differs from the previous or following alkane by CH_2 (a methylene unit).

62. (a) 2-chlorobutane;
(c) triiodomethane (common name: iodoform)

63. (a)

(c)

64. (b) $CH_3-CH_2-CH_2-CH_3$

65. 1,2,3-trihydroxypropane (1,2,3-propanetriol)

67. (a)

(c)

68. (a) carboxylic acid; (c) ester

Chapter 21

2. Proteins represent biopolymers of α-amino acids. Proteins make up about 15% of the body by mass.

4. Fibrous proteins provide the structural material of many tissues in the body. They are the chief constituents of hair, cartilage, and muscles. Fibrous proteins consist of lengthwise bundles of polypeptide chains (a fiber). Globular proteins consist of polypeptide chains folded into a spherical shape; they are found in the bloodstream where they transport and store various substances, act as antibodies (fight infections), act as enzymes (catalysts), and participate in the body's various regulatory systems.

6. The structures of the amino acids are given in Figure 21.2. A side chain is nonpolar if it is mostly hydrocarbon in nature (like alanine). Polar side chains may contain the hydroxyl group (—OH), the sulfhydryl group (—SH), or a second amino (—NH₃) or carboxyl (—COOH) group.

8. cys-ala-phe; cys-phe-ala; phe-ala-cys; phe-cys-ala; ala-cys-phe; ala-phe-cys

10. phe-ala-gly

phe-gly-ala

ala-phe-gly

ala-gly-phe

gly-phe-ala

gly-ala-phe

12. Long, thin, resilient proteins (such as hair) typically contain elongated, elastic α-helical protein molecules. Other proteins (such as silk) that form sheets or plates typically contain protein molecules having the beta pleated-sheet structure. Proteins without a structural function in the body (such as hemoglobin) typically have a globular structure.

14. The polypeptide chain forms a coil or spiral. Such proteins are found in wool, hair, and tendons.

16. Cysteine contains the sulfhydryl (—SH) group in its side chain. It can therefore form disulfide linkages (—S—S—) with other cysteine molecules in the same polypeptide chain. This produces a kink or a knot in the chain, which leads to the tertiary structure (three-dimensional shape). For example, cysteine is responsible for the curling of hair.

18. Collagen has an a-helical secondary structure. Collagen functions as the raw material from which tendons are constructed.

20. Antibodies are proteins made in the body in response to foreign substances such as bacteria or viruses. Interferon is an important antibody because it offers general protection against viruses (many antibodies target specific invaders).

22. The cross-linkages between adjacent polypeptide chains of one protein are broken chemically and then re-formed chemically in a new location. The primary cross-linkage involved is a disulfide linkage between cysteine units in the polypeptide chain. The tertiary structure is mainly affected, although the secondary structure can also be affected if the waving lotion is left on too long (making the hair very "frizzy").

24. The molecule acted on by an enzyme is referred to as the enzyme's substrate. If an enzyme is said to be specific for a particular substrate, it will catalyze the reactions of only that molecule.

26. The lock-and-key model postulates that the structures of the enzyme and its substrate are complementary. In this way, the active site of the enzyme and the portion of the substrate to be acted on can fit closely together. The structures of these portions of the molecules are unique to the particular enzyme–substrate pair. They fit together like a particular key is necessary to open a specific lock.

28. Sugars contain an aldehyde or ketone functional group (carbonyl group, C=O) as well as several hydroxyl groups (—OH).

30. (a) glucose,   CHO   ; (c) ribulose,   CH$_2$OH

$$
\begin{array}{cc}
\text{H}-\text{C}-\text{OH} & \text{C}=\text{O} \\
\text{HO}-\text{C}-\text{H} & \text{H}-\text{C}-\text{OH} \\
\text{H}-\text{C}-\text{OH} & \text{H}-\text{C}-\text{OH} \\
\text{H}-\text{C}-\text{OH} & \text{CH}_2\text{OH} \\
\text{CH}_2\text{OH} &
\end{array}
$$

32. uracil (RNA only); cytosine (DNA, RNA); thymine (DNA only); adenine (DNA, RNA); guanine (DNA, RNA)

34. A comparison of the two strands of a DNA molecule shows that a given base in one strand is always paired with a particular base in the other strand. Because of the shapes and side atoms along the rings of the nitrogen bases, only certain parts can hydrogen-bond with one another in the double helix. Adenine is always paired with thymine; cytosine is always paired with guanine. When a DNA helix unwinds for replication during cell division, only the appropriate complementary bases are able to approach and bond to the nitrogen bases of each strand. For example, when the two strands of a guanine–cytosine pair in the original DNA separate, only a new cytosine molecule can bond to the original guanine, and only a new guanine molecule can bond to the original cytosine.

36. Messenger RNA molecules are synthesized to be complementary to a portion (gene) of the DNA molecule in the cell. They serve as the template or pattern on which a protein will be constructed (a particular group of nitrogen bases on mRNA is able to accommodate and specify a particular amino acid in a particular location in the protein). Transfer RNA molecules are much smaller than mRNA, and their structure accommodates only a single specific amino acid molecule. They "find" their specific amino acid in the cellular fluids and bring it to mRNA, where it is added to the protein molecule being synthesized.

37. Rather than having some common structural feature, substances are classified as lipids based on their solubility characteristics. Lipids are water-insoluble substances that can be extracted from cells by nonpolar organic solvents such as benzene or carbon tetrachloride.

39. Saponification is the production of a *soap* by treatment of a triglyceride with a strong base such as NaOH.
triglyceride + 3NaOH → glycerol + 3Na$^+$soap$^-$

$$
\begin{array}{ccc}
& \text{O} & \\
& \| & \\
\text{CH}_2-\text{O}-\text{C}-\text{R} & & \text{CH}_2-\text{OH} \quad \text{RCOONa} \\
& \text{O} & \\
& \| & \\
\text{CH}-\text{O}-\text{C}-\text{R}' + 3\text{NaOH} & \rightarrow & \text{CH}-\text{OH} + \text{R}'\text{COONa} \\
& \text{O} & \\
& \| & \\
\text{CH}_2-\text{O}-\text{C}-\text{R}'' & & \text{CH}_2-\text{OH} \quad \text{R}''\text{COONa}
\end{array}
$$

41. Cholesterol is a naturally occurring steroid from which the body synthesizes other needed steroids. Because cholesterol is insoluble in water, having too large a concentration of this substance in the bloodstream may lead to buildup on the walls of blood vessels, causing their eventual blockage.

43. i

45. m

47. u

49. f

51. g

53. r

55. p

57. o

59. b

61. d

63. a

Glossary

Absolute zero $-273\ °C$

Acid a substance that produces hydrogen ions in aqueous solution; a proton donor.

Acid–base indicator a chemical that changes color according to the pH of a solution.

Acidic oxide a covalent oxide that dissolves in water to give an acidic solution.

Actinide series a group of fourteen elements following actinium on the periodic table, in which the $5f$ orbitals are being filled.

Activation energy the minimum energy required in order to cause a chemical reaction.

Active site the part of the enzyme to which the specific substrate is bound as a reaction is catalyzed.

Addition polymerization the process in which monomers simply "add together" to form polymers.

Addition reaction a reaction in which new atoms form single bonds to the carbon atoms in unsaturated hydrocarbons that were involved in double or triple bonds.

Air pollution contamination of the atmosphere, mainly by the gaseous products of transportation and the production of electricity.

Alcohol a hydrocarbon derivative in which the hydroxyl group $(-OH)$ is the functional group.

Aldehyde an organic compound containing the carbonyl group bonded to at least one hydrogen atom.

Alkali metal a Group 1 metal.

Alkaline earth metal a Group 2 metal.

Alkane a saturated hydrocarbon with the general formula C_nH_{2n+2}.

Alkene an unsaturated hydrocarbon containing a carbon–carbon double bond. The general formula is C_nH_{2n}.

Alkyne an unsaturated hydrocarbon containing a carbon–carbon triple bond. The general formula is C_nH_{2n-2}.

Alloy a mixture of elements that has metallic properties.

Alloy steel a form of steel containing carbon plus metals such as chromium, cobalt, manganese, and molybdenum.

Alpha (α) particle a helium nucleus produced in radioactive decay.

Alpha-particle production a common mode of decay for heavy radioactive nuclides resulting in a loss of 4 in mass number and a loss of 2 in atomic number.

Amine a hydrocarbon derived from ammonia in which one or more of the hydrogen atoms are replaced by organic groups.

α-Amino acid an organic acid in which an amino group, a hydrogen atom, and an R group are attached to the carbon atom next to the carboxyl group.

Ampere the unit of measurement for electric current; 1 ampere is equal to 1 coulomb of charge per second.

Amphoteric substance a substance that can behave either as an acid or as a base.

Anion a negatively charged ion.

Anode the electrode in a galvanic cell at which oxidation occurs.

Aqueous solution a solution with water as a solvent.

Aromatic hydrocarbon one of a special class of cyclic unsaturated hydrocarbons, the simplest of which is benzene.

Arrhenius concept of acids and bases a concept postulating that acids produce hydrogen ions in solution, whereas bases produce hydroxide ions in solution.

Atmosphere the mixture of gases that surrounds the earth's surface.

Atom the fundamental unit of which elements are composed.

Atomic mass unit (amu) a small unit of mass equal to 1.66×10^{-24} grams.

Atomic number the number of protons in the nucleus of a given atom.

Atomic radius half of the distance between the atomic nuclei in a molecule consisting of identical atoms.

Atomic solid a solid that contains atoms at the lattice points.

Auto-ionization the transfer of a proton from one molecule to another of the same substance.

Average atomic mass (weight) the weighted average of the masses of all of the isotopes of an element.

Avogadro's law equal volumes of gases at the same temperature and pressure contain the same number of particles (atoms or molecules).

Avogadro's number the number of atoms in exactly 12 grams of pure ^{12}C, equal to 6.022×10^{23}.

Ball-and-stick model a molecular model that distorts the sizes of atoms but shows bond relationships clearly.

Barometer a device that measures atmospheric pressure.

Base a substance that produces hydroxide ions in solution; a proton acceptor.

Basic oxide an ionic oxide that dissolves in water to produce a basic solution.

Battery a group of galvanic cells connected in series.

Beta (β) particle an electron produced in radioactive decay.

Beta-particle production a decay process for radioactive nuclides in which the mass number remains constant and the atomic number increases by one. The net effect is to change a neutron to a proton.

Binary compound a two-element compound.

Binary ionic compound a two-element compound consisting of a cation and an anion.

Binding energy (nuclear) the energy required to decompose a nucleus into its component nucleons.

Biochemistry the study of the chemistry of living systems.

Biomolecule a molecule that functions in maintaining and/or reproducing life.

Bond (chemical bond) the force that holds two or more atoms together and makes them function as a unit.

Bond energy the energy required to break a given chemical bond.

Bond length the distance between the nuclei of the two atoms that are connected by a bond.

Bonding pair a pair of electrons that are shared between two atoms forming a covalent or polar-covalent bond.

Boyle's law the pressure of a given sample of a gas is inversely related to the volume of the gas at constant temperature. $PV = k$

Breeder reactor a nuclear reactor in which fissionable fuel is produced while the reactor runs.

Brønsted–Lowry model a model proposing that an acid is a proton donor and that a base is a proton acceptor.

Buffer capacity the ability of a buffered solution to absorb protons or hydroxide ions without a significant change in pH.

Buffered solution a solution that resists a change in pH when either an acid or base is added.

Buret a device for the accurate measurement of the delivery of a given volume of liquid or solution.

Calorie the amount of energy needed to raise the temperature of one gram of water by one Celsius degree.

Calorimeter a device used to determine the heat associated with a chemical or physical change.

Calorimetry the science of measuring heat flow.

Carbohydrate a polyhydroxyl ketone or polyhydroxyl aldehyde or a polymer composed of these.

Carbon steel an alloy of iron containing up to about 1.5% carbon.

Carboxyl group the —COOH group in an organic acid.

Carboxylic acid a hydrocarbon derivitave (—COOH) containing the carboxyl group.

Catalyst a substance that speeds up a reaction without being consumed.

Cathode the electrode in a galvanic cell at which reduction occurs.

Cathode rays the "rays" emanating from the negative electrode (cathode) in a partially evacuated tube; a stream of electrons.

Cathodic protection the connection of an active metal, such as magnesium, to steel to protect the steel from corrosion.

Cation a positively charged ion.

Cell the smallest unit in living things that exhibits the properties normally associated with life, such as reproduction, metabolism, mutation, and sensitivity to external stimuli.

Cell potential (electromotive force) the driving force in a galvanic cell that pushes electrons from the reducing agent in one compartment to the oxidizing agent in the other.

Cellulose the major structural component of woody plants and natural fibers, such as cotton; a polymer of glucose.

Chain reaction (nuclear) a self-sustaining fission process caused by the production of neutrons that proceed to split other nuclei.

Charles's law the volume of a given sample of a gas is directly related to the temperature of the gas at constant pressure. $V = bT$

Chemical change the change of substances into other substances through a reorganization of the atoms; a chemical reaction.

Chemical equation a representation of a chemical reaction using the formulas of the starting substances that react and the new substances that are formed.

Chemical equilibrium a dynamic state in which the concentrations of the reactants and the products remain constant over time, as long as the conditions are not changed.

Chemical formula a representation of a molecule in which the symbols for the elements are used to indicate the types of atoms present and subscripts are used to show the relative numbers of atoms.

Chemical kinetics the area of chemistry that concerns reaction rates.

Chemical property characteristic that describes the ability of a substance to change to a different substance.

Chemical reaction a process in which one or more substances are changed into one or more new substances by the reorganization of component atoms.

Chemical stoichiometry the quantities of materials consumed and produced in a chemical reaction.

Chemistry the science of materials and the changes that these materials undergo.

Coal a solid fossil fuel mostly consisting of carbon.

Coefficient the number written in front of the chemical formulas in a balanced chemical equation; coefficients indicate the relative numbers of reactants and products in the reaction.

Colligative property a property that depends only on the number of solute particles present in solution.

Collision model molecules must collide in order to react; used to account for the fact that reaction rate depends on temperature and concentrations of reactants.

Combustion reaction a chemical reaction involving oxygen as one of the reactants that produces enough heat so that a flame results.

Complete ionic equation a chemical equation for a reaction in solution representing all strong electrolytes as ions.

Compound a substance made of two or more different elements joined together in a specific way.

Concentrated describes a solution in which a relatively large amount of solute is dissolved in a solution.

Condensation the process in which a vapor is converted to a liquid.

Condensation polymerization the process in which a small molecule such as water is produced for each extension of the polymer chain.

Condensed states of matter liquids and solids.

Conjugate acid the substance formed when a proton is added to a base.

Conjugate acid–base pair two substances related to each other by the donating and accepting of a single proton.

Conjugate base the remaining substance when a proton is lost from an acid.

Continuous spectrum a spectrum that exhibits all the wavelengths of visible light.

Control rods in a nuclear reactor, rods composed of substances that absorb neutrons. These rods regulate the power level of the reactor.

Conversion factor a ratio used to convert from one unit to another.

Copolymer a polymer consisting of two different types of monomers.

Core electron an inner electron in an atom; one that is not in the outermost principal energy level of an atom.

Corrosion the process by which metals are oxidized in the atmosphere.

Covalent bonding a type of bonding in which atoms share electrons.

Critical mass the mass of fissionable material required to produce a chain reaction.

Critical reaction (nuclear) a reaction in which exactly one neutron from each fission event causes another fission event, thus sustaining the chain reaction.

Crystalline solid a solid characterized by the regular arrangement of its components.

Dalton's atomic theory a theory established by John Dalton in the early 1800s, used to explain the nature of materials.

Dalton's law of partial pressures for a mixture of gases in a container, the total pressure exerted is the sum of the partial pressures of each of the gases.

Decomposition reaction a chemical reaction in which a compound is broken down into simpler compounds, or into the component elements.

Denaturation the breaking down of the three-dimensional structure of a protein, resulting in the loss of its function.

Density the mass of a substance per a given volume of that substance.

Deoxyribonucleic acid (DNA) a huge nucleotide polymer having a double-helical structure with complementary bases on the two strands. Its major functions are protein synthesis and the storage and transport of genetic information.

Diatomic molecule a molecule composed of two atoms.

Dilution the process of adding solvent to a solution to lower the concentration of solute.

Dimensional analysis the process of using conversion factors to change from one unit to another.

Dimer a molecule consisting of two monomers joined together.

Dipole–dipole attraction the attractive force between the positively charged end of one polar molecule and the negatively charged end of another polar molecule.

Dipole moment a property of a molecule whereby the charge distribution can be represented by a center of positive charge and a center of negative charge.

Disaccharide a sugar formed from two monosaccharides joined by a glycoside linkage.

Distillation a method for separating the components of a liquid mixture that depends on the different boiling points of the substances.

Double bond a covalent or polar covalent bond in which two pairs of electrons are shared by two atoms.

Dry cell battery a common battery used in calculators, watches, radios, and tape players.

Electrical conductivity the ability to conduct an electric current.

Electrochemistry the study of the interchange of chemical and electrical energy.

Electrolysis a process that involves forcing a current through a cell to cause a chemical reaction that would not otherwise occur.

Electrolyte a material that dissolves in water to give a solution that conducts an electric current.

Electrolytic cell a cell that uses electrical energy to produce a chemical change that would not otherwise occur.

Electromagnetic radiation radiant energy that exhibits wavelike behavior and travels through space at the speed of light in a vacuum.

Electron a negatively charged subatomic particle.

Electronegativity the tendency of an atom in a molecule to attract shared electrons to itself.

Element a substance that cannot be decomposed into simpler substances by chemical or physical means. It consists of atoms all having the same atomic number.

End point the point in a titration at which the indicator changes color.

Endothermic refers to a process in which energy (as heat) flows from the surroundings into the system.

Energy the ability to do work or to produce heat.

Enthalpy at constant pressure, a change in enthalpy equals the energy flow as heat.

Entropy a function used to keep track of the natural tendency for the components of the universe to become disordered; a measure of disorder or randomness.

Enzyme a large molecule, usually a protein, that catalyzes biological reactions.

Equilibrium the exact balance of two processes, one of which is opposite of the other.

Equilibrium constant the value obtained when equilibrium concentrations of the chemical species are substituted into the equilibrium expression.

Equilibrium expression the expression (from the law of mass action) equal to the product of the product concentrations divided by the product of the reactant concentrations, each concentration having first been raised to a power represented by the coefficient in the balanced equation.

Equilibrium position a particular set of equilibrium concentrations of all reactants and products in a chemical system.

Equivalence point (stoichiometric point) the point in a titration at which enough titrant has been added to react exactly with the substance in solution that is being titrated.

Equivalent of an acid the amount of acid that can furnish one mole of hydrogen ions (H^+).

Equivalent of a base the amount of base that can furnish one mole of hydroxide ions (OH^-).

Equivalent weight the mass (in grams) of one equivalent of an acid or a base.

Essential elements the 30 elements currently known to be essential to human life.

Ester a hydrocarbon derivative produced by the reaction between a carboxylic acid and an alcohol.

Exothermic refers to a process in which energy (as heat) flows out of the system into the surroundings.

Fat (glyceride) an ester composed of glycerol and fatty acids.

Fatty acid a long-chain carboxylic acid.

Filtration a method for separating the components of a mixture containing a solid and a liquid.

First law of thermodynamics a law stating that the energy of the universe is constant.

Fission the process of splitting a heavy nucleus into two more stable nuclei with smaller mass numbers.

Fossil fuel fuel that consists of carbon-based molecules derived from decomposition of once-living organisms; coal, petroleum, or natural gas.

Frequency the number of waves (cycles) per second that pass a given point in space.

Fuel cell a galvanic cell for which the reactants are continuously supplied.

Functional group an atom or group of atoms in a hydrocarbon derivative that contains elements in addition to carbon and hydrogen.

Fusion the process of combining two light nuclei to form a heavier, more stable nucleus.

Galvanic cell a device in which chemical energy is converted spontaneously to electrical energy by means of oxidation–reduction reaction.

Galvanizing a process in which steel is coated with zinc to prevent corrosion.

Gamma (γ) ray a high-energy photon produced in radioactive decay.

Gas one of the three states of matter; substance with no definite shape or volume.

Geiger–Müller counter (Geiger counter) an instrument that measures the rate of radioactive decay by registering the ions and electrons produced as a radioactive particle passes through a gas-filled chamber.

Gene a given segment of the DNA molecule that contains the code for a specific protein.

Glycogen the main carbohydrate reservoir in animals; a polymer of glucose.

Glycoside linkage the C—O—C bond formed between monosaccharide rings in a disaccharide.

Greenhouse effect the process by which an atmosphere warms a planet.

Ground state the lowest possible energy state of an atom or a molecule.

Group a vertical column of elements on the periodic table.

Haber process the manufacture of ammonia from nitrogen and hydrogen, carried out at high pressure and high temperature with the aid of a catalyst.

Half-life (of a radioactive sample) the time required for half of the original sample of radioactive nuclides to decay.

Half-reactions the two parts of an oxidation–reduction reaction, one representing oxidation, the other reduction.

Halogen a Group 7 element.

Halogenation an addition reaction in which a halogen is a reactant.

Hard water water from natural sources that contains relatively large concentrations of calcium and magnesium ions.

Heat flow of energy due to a temperature difference.

Heating/cooling curve a plot of temperature versus time for a substance, where energy is added at a constant rate.

Heisenberg uncertainty principle a principle stating that there is a fundamental limitation to how precisely we can know both the position and the momentum of a particle at a given time.

Herbicide a pesticide applied to kill weeds.

Hess's Law the change in enthalpy in going from a given set of reactants to a given set of products does not depend on the number of steps in the reaction.

Heterogeneous equilibrium an equilibrium system in which all reactants and products are in different states.

Heterogeneous mixture a mixture that has different properties in different regions of the mixture.

Heterogeneous reaction reaction involving reactants and products in different states.

Homogeneous equilibrium an equilibrium system in which all reactants and products are in the same state.

Homogeneous mixture a mixture that is the same throughout.

Homogeneous reaction reaction involving reactants and products in the same state.

Homopolymer a polymer consisting of a single type of monomer.

Hydration the interaction between solute particles and water molecules.

Hydrocarbon a compound of carbon and hydrogen.

Hydrogen bonding unusually strong dipole–dipole attractions that occur among molecules in which hydrogen is bonded to a highly electronegative atom.

Hydrogenation reaction an addition reaction in which H_2 is a reactant.

Hydronium ion the H_3O^+ ion; a hydrated proton.

Hypothesis one or more assumptions put forth to explain observed phenomena.

Ideal gas a hypothetical gas that exactly obeys the ideal gas law. A real gas approaches ideal behavior at high temperature and/or low pressure.

Ideal gas law an equation relating the properties of an ideal gas, expressed as $PV = nRT$, where P = pressure, V = volume, n = moles of the gas, R = the universal gas constant, and T = temperature on the Kelvin scale. This equation expresses behavior closely approached by real gases at high temperature and/or low pressure.

Indicator a chemical that changes color and is used to mark the end point of a titration.

Indicator paper a strip of paper coated with a combination of acid–base indicators.

Insoluble solid a solid that dissolves to such a small degree that it is not detectable to the naked eye.

Intermolecular forces attraction forces that occur between molecules.

Internal energy the sum of the kinetic and potential energies of all particles in the system.

Intramolecular forces attractive forces that occur between atoms in a molecule; chemical bonds

Ion an atom or a group of atoms that has a positive or negative charge.

Ionic bonding the attraction between oppositely charged ions.

Ionic compound a compound that results when a metal reacts with a nonmetal to form cations and anions.

Ionic solid a solid containing cations and anions that dissolves in water to give a solution containing the separated ions, which are mobile and thus free to conduct an electric current.

Ionization energy the amount of energy required to remove an electron from a gaseous atom or ion.

Ion-product constant (K_w) the equilibrium constant for the auto-ionization of water; $K_w = [H^+][OH^-]$. At 25 °C, K_w equals 1.0×10^{-14}.

Isomers species that have the same chemical formula but different properties.

Isotopes atoms with the same number of protons but different numbers of neutrons.

Joule a unit of measurement for energy; 1 calorie = 4.184 joules.

Ketone a hydrocarbon derivative containing the carbonyl group bonded to two carbon atoms.

Kinetic energy ($\frac{1}{2}mv^2$) energy due to the motion of an object.

Kinetic molecular theory (KMI) a model that assumes that an ideal gas is composed of tiny particles (atoms or molecules) in constant motion.

Lanthanide series a group of fourteen elements following lanthanum on the periodic table, in which the 4f orbitals are being filled.

Lattice a three-dimensional system of points designating the positions of the centers of the components of a solid (atoms, ions, or molecules).

Law of chemical equilibrium a general description of the equilibrium condition; it defines the equilibrium expression.

Law of conservation of energy energy can be converted from one form to another but can be neither created nor destroyed.

Law of conservation of mass mass is neither created nor destroyed.

Law of constant composition a given compound always contains elements in exactly the same proportion by mass.

Law of mass action (also called the law of chemical equilibrium) a general description of the equilibrium condition; it defines the equilibrium expression.

Law of multiple proportions a law stating that when two elements form a series of compounds, the ratios of the masses of the second element that combine with one gram of the first element can always be reduced to small whole numbers.

Lead storage battery a battery used in cars in which the anode is lead, the cathode is lead coated with lead dioxide, and the electrolyte is sulfuric acid.

Le Châtelier's principle if a change is imposed on a system at equilibrium, the position of the equilibrium will shift in a direction that tends to reduce the effect of that change.

Lewis structure a representation of a molecule or polyatomic ion showing how valence electrons are arranged among the atoms in the molecule or ion.

Limiting reactant (limiting reagent) the reactant that is completely used up when a reaction is run to completion.

Line spectrum a spectrum showing only certain discrete wavelengths.

Linear accelerator a type of particle accelerator in which a changing electrical field is used to accelerate a beam of charged particles along a linear path.

Lipids water-insoluble substances that can be extracted from cells by nonpolar organic solvents.

Liquid one of the three states of matter; has a definite volume that takes the shape of its container.

London dispersion forces relatively weak intermolecular forces resulting from a temporarily uneven distribution of electrons that induces a dipole in a neighbor.

Lone pair electron pairs in a Lewis structure that are not involved in bonding.

Main-group (representative) elements elements in the groups labeled 1, 2, 3, 4, 5, 6, 7, and 8 on the periodic table. The group number gives the sum of the valence s and p electrons.

Mass the quantity of matter in an object.

Mass number the total number of protons and neutrons in the nucleus of a given atom.

Mass percent the percent by mass of a component of a mixture or of a given element in a compound.

Matter the material of the universe.

Measurement a quantitative observation

Metal an element that gives up electrons relatively easily and is typically lustrous, malleable, and a good conductor of heat and electricity.

Metalloid (semi-metals) an element that has both metallic and nonmetallic properties.

Metallurgy the process of separating a metal from its ore and preparing it for use.

Millimeters of mercury (mm Hg) a unit of measurement for pressure, also called a torr; 760 mm Hg = 760 torr = 101,325 Pa = 1 standard atmosphere.

Mixture a substance with variable composition.

Model (theory) a set of assumptions put forth to explain the observed behavior of matter. The models of chemistry usually involve assumptions about the behavior of individual atoms or molecules.

Moderator a substance used in a nuclear reactor to slow down the neutrons.

Molar heat of fusion the energy required to melt one mole of a solid.

Molar heat of vaporization the energy required to vaporize 1 mol of a liquid.

Molar mass the mass in grams of one mole of a compound.

Molar volume the volume of one mole of an ideal gas; equal to 22.42 liters at standard temperature and pressure.

Molarity moles of solute per volume of solution in liters.

Mole (mol) the number equal to the number of carbon atoms in exactly 12 grams of pure ^{12}C: Avogadro's number. One mole represents 6.022×10^{23} units.

Mole ratio (stoichiometry) the ratio of moles of one substance to moles of another substance in a balanced chemical equation.

Molecular equation a chemical equation showing the complete (undissociated) forms of all reactants and products.

Molecular formula the actual formula of a compound, giving the types of atoms and the number of each type of atom.

Molecular solid a solid composed of molecules.

Molecular structure the three-dimensional arrangement of atoms in a molecule.

Molecular weight (molar mass) the mass in grams of one mole of a substance.

Molecule a collection of atoms bonded together that behave as a unit.

Monoprotic acid an acid with one acidic proton.

Natural gas a gaseous fossil fuel mostly consisting of methane and usually associated with petroleum deposits.

Natural law a statement that summarizes generally observed behavior.

Net ionic equation a chemical equation for a reaction in solution showing only those components that are directly involved in the reaction. Strong electrolytes are represented as ions.

Network solid an atomic solid containing strong directional covalent bonds.

Neutralization reaction an acid–base reaction.

Neutron a subatomic particle in the atomic nucleus with no charge.

Noble gas a Group 8 element.

Nonelectrolyte a substance that, when dissolved in water, gives a nonconducting solution.

Nonmetal an element that does not exhibit metallic characteristics. Chemically, a typical nonmetal accepts electrons from a metal.

Normal boiling point the temperature at which the vapor pressure of a liquid is exactly one atmosphere; the boiling temperature under one atmosphere of pressure.

Normal melting/freezing point the melting/freezing temperature of a liquid under one atmosphere of pressure.

Normality the number of equivalents of a substance dissolved in a liter of solution.

Nuclear atom a concept of the atom as having a dense center of positive charge (the nucleus) surrounded by moving electrons.

Nuclear transformation the change of one element into another.

Nucleon a particle in an atomic nucleus, either a neutron or a proton.

Nucleotide a monomer of DNA and RNA consisting of nitrogen-containing base, a five-carbon sugar, and a phosphate group.

Nucleus the relatively small, dense center of positive charge in an atom.

Nuclide the general term applied to each unique atom; represented by $^A_Z X$, where X is the symbol for a particular element.

Octet rule the observation that atoms of nonmetals form the most stable molecules when they are surrounded by eight electrons (to fill their valence orbitals).

Orbital the three-dimensional region in which there is a high probability of finding an electron in an atom.

Organic acid an acid with a carbon-atom backbone and a carboxyl group.

Organic chemistry the study of carbon-containing compounds (typically containing chains of carbon atoms) and their properties.

Oxidation an increase in oxidation state; a loss of electrons.

Oxidation–reduction (redox) reaction a chemical reaction involving the transfer of electrons.

Oxidation states a concept that provides a way to keep track of electrons in oxidation–reduction reactions according to certain rules.

Oxidizing agent (electron acceptor) a reactant that accepts electrons from another reactant.

Oxyacid an acid in which the acidic proton is attached to an oxygen atom.

Oxyanion a polyatomic ion containing at least one oxygen atom and one or more atoms of at least one other element.

Ozone O_3, a form of elemental oxygen much less common than O_2 in the atmosphere near the earth.

Partial pressures the independent pressures exerted by a gas in a mixture of gases.

Particle accelerator a device used to accelerate nuclear particles to very high speeds.

Pascal the SI unit of measurement for pressure; equal to one newton per square meter.

Pauli exclusion principle in a given atom, no two electrons can occupy the same atomic orbital and have the same spin.

Percent yield the actual yield of a product as a percentage of the theoretical yield.

Periodic table a chart showing all the elements arranged in columns in such a way that all the elements in a given column exhibit similar chemical properties.

Petroleum a thick, dark liquid composed mostly of hydrocarbon compounds.

pH meter a device used to measure the pH of a solution.

pH scale a log scale based on 10 and equal to $-\log[H^+]$; a convenient way to represent solution acidity.

Phenyl group the benzene molecule minus one hydrogen atom.

Phospholipid an ester of glycerol containing two fatty acids; consists of a long nonpolar "tail" and a polar substituted-phosphate "head".

Photochemical smog air pollution produced by the action of light on oxygen, nitrogen oxides, and unburned fuel from auto exhaust to form ozone and other pollutants.

Photon a particle of electromagnetic radiation.

Physical charge a change in the form of a substance that does not affect the composition of a substance.

Physical property characteristic of a substance that can change without the substance's becoming a different substance.

Polar covalent bond a covalent bond in which the electrons are not shared equally because one atom attracts the shared electron more strongly than the other atom.

Polar molecule a molecule that has a permanent dipole moment.

Polyelectronic atom an atom with more than one electron.

Polymer a large, usually chain-like molecule made from small molecules called monomers.

Polymerization a process in which small molecules called monomers are joined together to form a large molecule.

Polyprotic acid an acid with more than one acidic proton. It dissociates in a stepwise manner, one proton at a time.

Polysaccharide polymers containing many monosaccharide units.

Positron production a mode of nuclear decay in which a particle is formed that has the same mass as an electron but opposite charge. The net effect is to change a proton to a neutron.

Potential the "pressure" on electrons to flow from the anode to the cathode in a battery.

Potential energy energy due to position or composition.

Precipitate the solid that forms in a precipitation reaction.

Precipitation the formation of a solid in a chemical reaction.

Precipitation reaction a reaction in which a solid forms and separates from the solution as a solid.

Precision the degree of agreement among several measurements of the same quantity; the reproducibility of a measurement.

Primary structure (of a protein) the order or sequence of amino acids in the protein chain.

Probability distribution (orbital) a representation indicating the probabilities of finding an electron at various points in space.

Product the new substance formed by a chemical reaction. It is shown to the right of the reaction arrow.

Protein a natural polymer formed by condensation reactions between amino acids.

Proton a positively charged subatomic particle located in the atomic nucleus.

Pure substance a substance with constant composition; a pure element or a pure compound.

Radioactive decay (radioactivity) the spontaneous decomposition of a nucleus to form a different nucleus.

Radiocarbon dating (carbon-14 dating) a method for dating ancient wood or cloth on the basis of the radioactive decay of the carbon-14 nuclide.

Radiotracer a radioactive nuclide introduced into an organism and traced for diagnostic purposes.

Random error an error that has an equal probability of being high or low.

Rate of decay the change per unit time in the number of radioactive nuclides in a sample.

Reactant the starting substance of a chemical reaction shown to the left of the reaction arrow.

Reactor core the part of a nuclear reactor in which the fission reaction takes place.

Reducing agent (electron donor) a reactant that donates electrons to another substance, reducing the oxidation state of one of its atoms.

Reduction a decrease in oxidation state (a gain of electrons).

Rem a unit of radiation dosage that accounts for both the energy of the dose and its effectiveness in causing biological damage (from roentgen equivalent for man).

Resonance a condition occurring when more than one valid Lewis structure can be written for a particular molecule.

Ribonucleic acid (RNA) large nucleotide polymer that along with DNA, functions to transport genetic material.

Salt an ionic compound.

Salt bridge a U-tube containing an electrolyte that connects the two compartments of a galvanic cell, allowing ion flow without extensive mixing of the different solutions.

Saponification the process of breaking down a triglyceride by treatment with aqueous sodium hydroxide to produce glycerol and the fatty acid salts; the fatty acid salts produced are soaps.

Saturated describes a hydrocarbon in which all carbon-carbon bonds are single bonds.

Saturated solution a solution that contains as much solute as can be dissolved in that solution at that temperature.

Scientific method a process of studying natural phenomena that involves making observations, forming laws and theories, and testing theories by experimentation.

Scientific notation expresses a number in the form $N \times 10^M$; a convenient method for representing a very large or very small number and for easily indicating the number of significant figures.

Scintillation counter an instrument that measures the rate of radioactive decay by sensing flashes of light that the radiation produces in a detector.

Second law of thermodynamics the entropy of the universe is always increasing.

Secondary structure (of a protein) the arrangement in space of the chain of the protein chain (for example, α-helix, random coil, or pleated sheet).

SI units International System of units based on the metric system and on units derived from the metric system.

Sigma (σ) bond a covalent bond in which the electron pair is shared in an area centered on a line running between the atoms.

Significant figures the certain digits and the first uncertain digit of a measurement.

Silica the fundamental silicon–oxygen compound, which has the empirical formula SiO_2 and forms the basis of quartz and certain types of sand.

Silicates salts that contain metal cations and polyatomic silicon–oxygen anions that are usually polymeric.

Single bond a covalent or polar covalent bond in which one pair of electrons is shared by two atoms.

Solid one of the three states of matter; has a fixed shape and volume.

Solubility the amount of a substance that dissolves in a given volume of solvent or solution at a given temperature.

Solubility product the constant for the equilibrium expression representing the dissolving of an ionic solid in water.

Soluble solid a solid that readily dissolves in water.

Solute a substance dissolved in a solvent to form a solution.

Solution a homogeneous mixture.

Solvent the dissolving medium in a solution.

Somatic damage radioactive damage to an organism resulting in its sickness or death.

Specific gravity the ratio of density of a given liquid to the density of water at 4 °C.

Specific heat another name for specific heat capacity.

Specific heat capacity the amount of energy required to raise the temperature of one gram of a substance by one Celsius degree.

Spectator ions ions present in solution that do not participate directly in a reaction.

Standard atmosphere a unit of measurement for pressure equal to 760 mm Hg or 101, 325 Pa.

Standard solution a solution in which the concentration is accurately known.

Standard temperature and pressure (STP) the condition 0 °C and 1 atmosphere of pressure.

Starch the main carbohydrate reservoir in plants; a polymer of glucose.

State function a property that is independent of the pathway.

States of matter the three different forms in which matter can exist: solid, liquid, and gas.

Stoichiometric quantities quantities of reactants mixed in exactly the amounts that result in their all being used up at the same time.

Stoichiometry the process of using a balanced chemical equation to determine the relative masses of reactants and products involved in a reaction.

Stoichiometry of a reaction the relative quantities of reactants and products involved in the reaction.

Strong acid an acid that completely dissociates (ionizes) to produce H^+ ions in solution.

Strong base a base that completely dissociates to produce OH^- ions in solution.

Strong electrolyte a substance that dissolves in water, dissociating completely into ions.

Structural formula the representation of a molecule in which the relative positions of the atoms are shown and the bonds are indicated by lines.

Structural isomerism describes what occurs when two molecules have the same atoms but different bonds

Subcritical reaction (nuclear) a reaction in which fewer than one of the neutrons from each fission event causes another fission event and the process dies out.

Sublimation the process by which a substance goes directly from the solid state to the gaseous state without passing through the liquid state.

Substitution reaction (hydrocarbons) a reaction in which an atom, usually a halogen, replaces a hydrogen atom in a hydrocarbon.

Substrate the molecule that interacts with an enzyme.

Sucrose table sugar; a disacchradie formed between glucose and fructose.

Supercooling the process of cooling a liquid to a temperature below its freezing point without its changing to a solid.

Supercritical reaction (nuclear) a reaction in which more than one of the neutrons from each fission event causes another fission event. The process rapidly escalates to a violent explosion.

Superheating the process of heating a liquid to a temperature above its boiling point without its boiling.

Supersaturated describes a solution that contains more solute than a saturated solution will hold at that temperature.

Surfactant a wetting agent that assists water in suspending nonpolar materials; soap is a surfactant.

Surroundings everything in the universe surrounding a thermodynamic system.

System (thermodynamic) that part of the universe on which attention is to be focused.

Systematic error an error that always occurs in the same direction.

Temperature measure of the random motions (average kinetic energy) of the components of a substance.

Tertiary structure (of a protein) the overall shape of a protein, long and narrow or globular, maintained by different types of intramolecular interactions.

Theoretical yield the maximum amount of a given product that can be formed when the limiting reactant is completely consumed.

Theory (model) a set of assumptions put forth to explain some aspect of the observed behavior of matter.

Thermodynamics the study of energy.

Titration a technique in which a solution of known concentration is used to determine the concentration of another solution.

Titration curve (pH curve) a plot of the pH of a given solution versus the volume of titrant added to the solution.

Torr another name for millimeters of mercury (mm Hg).

Trace elements first-row transition metals present in very small (trace) amounts in the human body.

Transition metals several series of elements in which inner orbitals (*d* or *f* orbitals) are being filled.

Transuranium elements the elements beyond uranium that are made artificially by particle bombardment.

Triglyceride a fat that is an ester of glycerol

Triple bond a covalent or polar covalent bond in which three pairs of electrons are shared by two atoms.

Uncertainty (in measurement) the characteristic reflecting the fact that any measurement involves estimates and cannot be exactly reproduced.

Unit factor an equivalence statement between units that is used for converting from one set of units to another.

Units the part of the measurement telling us the scale being used.

Universal gas constant the combined proportionality constant in the ideal gas law; 0.08206 L atm/K mol, or 8.314 J/K mol.

Unsaturated describes a hydrocarbon containing carbon-carbon multiple bonds.

Unsaturated solution a solution in which more solute can be dissolved than is dissolved already at that temperature.

Valence electrons the electrons in the outermost principal energy level of an atom.

Valence shell electron pair repulsion (VSEPR) model a model used to predict molecular geometry. Based on the idea that pairs of electrons surrounding an atom repel each other and that the atoms in a molecule are positioned to minimize this repulsion.

Vapor pressure the pressure exerted by a vapor in equilibrium with its liquid phase at a certain temperature.

Vaporization (evaporation) the process in which a liquid is converted to a gas.

Viscosity the resistance of a liquid to flow.

Volt the unit of measurement for electric potential; it is defined as one joule of work per coulomb of charge transferred.

Volume the amount of three-dimensional space occupied by a substance.

Wavelength the distance between two consecutive peaks or troughs in a wave.

Waxes a class of lipids that involve monohydroxy alcohols instead of glycerol.

Weak acid an acid that dissociates to a slight extent in aqueous solution.

Weak base a base that reacts with water to produce hydroxide ions to only a slight extent in aqueous solution.

Weak electrolyte a material that, when dissolved in water, gives a solution that conducts only a small electric current.

Weight the force exerted on an object by gravity.

Work force acting over a distance.

Photo/Illustration Credits

Chapter 1

pp. 2–3, © Royalty-Free/CORBIS; p. 3, PhotoDisc/Getty Images; p. 4, (top right) © David Young-Wolff/PhotoEdit; p. 4, (bottom left) Bart Eklund; p. 5, (bottom right) © David Katzenstein/CORBIS; p. 5, (top right) Sean Brady; p. 7, SW Productions/Index Stock Imagery; p. 8, Kaz Mori/The Image Bank/Getty Images; p. 11, (center) © Don Mason/CORBIS; p. 11, (center right) Sean Brady; p. 17, © Michael Newman/PhotoEdit.

Chapter 2

pp. 22–23, Royalty-Free/Materfile; p. 23, Sean Brady; p. 24, (center left) Sean Brady; p. 24, (bottom left) IBM Almaden Research Center; p. 25, (center right) Dr. Jeremy Burgess/Science Photo Library/Photo Researchers, Inc.; p. 25, (top right) Chuck Place; p. 25, (bottom left) The Art Archive/Chicago Art Institute; p. 25, (center left) The Art Archive/Chicago Art Institute; p. 27, (bl) Mark A. Schneider/Photo Researchers, Inc.; p. 27, (bottom center) © Daniel Templeton/Alamy Images; p. 27, (top center) Don Farall/PhotoDisc/Getty Images; p. 27, (top right) Sean Brady; p. 28, (center left) Lawrence Lawry/PhotoDisc/Getty Images; p. 28, (center) © Lester V. Bergman/CORBIS; p. 28, (center right) Tom Pantages; p. 29, (top right) Fred Hirschmann; p. 29, (bottom right) Richard Megna/Fundamental Photographs; p. 31, Sean Brady; p. 34, Jim Pickerell/Stone; p. 36, © JupiterMedia/Alamy; p. 38, (center right) © Ulrike Welsch/PhotoEdit; p. 38, (center left) PhotoDisc/Getty Images; p. 39, (center left) Richard Megna/Fundamental Photographs; p. 39, (center) Richard Megna/Fundamental Photographs; p. 45, Charles D. Winters/Photo Researchers, Inc.

Chapter 3

pp. 48–49, © Royalty-Free/CORBIS; p. 50, The Granger Collection, New York; p. 52, (top right) © Spencer Grant/PhotoEdit; p. 52, (bottom left) © Bettmann/CORBIS; p. 52, (bottom center) © Bettmann/CORBIS; p. 52, (bottom right) The Granger Collection, New York; p. 53, (top left) © Bob Daemmrich/PhotoEdit; p. 53, (top right) © Will & Deni McIntyre/CORBIS; p. 55, Ulf E. Wallin/The Image Bank/Getty Images; p. 57, Reproduced by permission, Manchester Literary and Philosophical Society; p. 59, © Archivo Iconografico, S.A./CORBIS; p. 61, © Bettmann/CORBIS; p. 66, Sean Brady; p. 70, API/Explorer/Photo Researchers, Inc.; p. 71, Mark A. Schneider/Photo Researchers, Inc.; p. 73, (bottom left) Sean Brady; p. 73, (bottom center) Sean Brady; p. 73, (center right) Sean Brady; p. 75, © Royalty-Free/CORBIS; p. 80, © Dynamic Graphics Group/Creatas/Alamy; p. 81, ER Degginger.

Chapter 4

pp. 92–93, © Royalty-Free/CORBIS; p. 93, Comstock Images/Index Stock Imagery; p. 94, © Bob Daemmrich/The Image Works; p. 96, Scala/Art Resource, NY; p. 99, Sean Brady; p. 105, (top left) Sean Brady; p. 105, (top right) Sean Brady; p. 108, Dr. Gopal Muri/Photo Researchers, Inc.; p. 116, Dan Suzio/Photo Researchers, Inc.

Chapter 5

pp. 124–125, Phillip Hayson/Photo Researchers, Inc.; p. 125, Sean Brady p. 129, NASA; p. 132, Courtesy Mettler-Toledo; p. 134, Russel D. Curtis/Photo Researchers, Inc.; p. 135, University Archives, Iowa State University Library; p. 137, © Jim Craigmyle/CORBIS; p. 141, (top left) © Royalty-Free/CORBIS; p. 141, (top right) © Michael Newman/PhotoEdit; p. 141, (bottom) David Fleetham/Index Stock Imagery; p. 147, © Davis Barber/PhotoEdit; p. 154, Warner Brothers/The Kobal Collection; p. 160, Dan McCoy/Rainbow; p. 161, Tom Pantages; p. 162, © Royalty-Free/CORBIS.

Chapter 6

pp. 170–171, © Iconotec/Alamy; p. 171, Jeff Greenberg/Visuals Unlimited; p. 172, Siede Preis/PhotoDisc/Getty Images; p. 173, PhotoDisc/Getty Images; p. 179, (center left) Ken O'Donoghue; p. 179, (center right) Ken O'Donoghue; p. 180, Ken O'Donoghue; p. 182, Sean Brady; p. 183, GK Hart/Vikki Hart/The Image Bank/Getty Images; p. 187, © Digital Archive Japan/Alamy; p. 189, Michael P. Gadomski/Photo Researchers, Inc.; p. 190, © Don Mason/CORBIS; p. 191, © Don Mason/CORBIS; p. 201, The Granger Collection, New York; p. 208, © Susan Van Etten/PhotoEdit.

Chapter 7

pp. 216–217, Charles D. Winters/Photo Researchers, Inc.; p. 217, J.C. Allen/Stock Boston; p. 218, (bottom left) © Spencer Grant/Photo Edit; p. 218, (center) Sean Brady; p. 219, (bottom left) © Ingram Publishing/SuperStock; p. 219, (bottom center) © Royalty-Free/CORBIS; p. 219, (bottom center) © Brand X Pictures/Alamy; p. 219, (bottom center) © Royalty-Free/CORBIS; p. 219, (top left) Richard Megna/Fundamental Photographs; p. 219, (top right) Richard Megna/Fundamental Photographs; p. 219, (center right) Richard Megna/Fundamental Photographs; p. 219, (center left) Sean Brady; p. 222, (center left) Richard Megna/Fundamental Photographs; p. 222, (center) Richard Megna/Fundamental Photographs; p. 222, (center right) Richard Megna/Fundamental Photographs; p. 223, Richard Megna/Fundamental Photographs; p. 229, Thomas Eisner and Daniel Aneshansley, Cornell University; p. 231, Richard Megna/Fundamental Photographs; p. 232, Sean Brady; p. 234, Richard Megna/Fundamental Photographs; p. 235, © Paul A. Souders/CORBIS.

Chapter 8

pp. 238–239, © Richard Megna/Fundamental Photographs, New York; p. 239, © BananaStock/Alamy; p. 240, Richard Megna/Fundamental Photographs; p. 242, Brigitte Wegner/StockFood Creative/Getty Images; p. 247, Sean Brady; p. 252, © GRANT HEILMANGrant Heilman Photography; p. 254, (center) © foodfolio/Alamy; p. 254, (center right) Lars Klove/The Image Bank/Getty Images; p. 257, Bruce Roberts/Photo Researchers, Inc.; p. 259, Richard Megna/Fundamental Photographs; p. 260, Sean Brady; p. 265, Courtesy, Morton Thiokol; p. 267, © Michael Newman/PhotoEdit.

Chapter 9

pp. 278–279, © Royalty-Free/CORBIS; p. 280, © Jeff Greenberg/PhotoEdit; p. 282, © Bill Bachmann/PhotoEdit; p. 287, PhotoLink/Photodisc/Getty Images; p. 290, (top left) Sean Brady; p. 290, (center left) Sean Brady; p. 293, Larry Larimer/Brand X Pictures/PictureQuest; p. 296, Raoul Minsart/Masterfile; p. 299, © GRANT HEILMAN/Grant Heilamn; p. 304, Ken O'Donoghue; p. 308, (top right) Sean Brady; p. 308, (center) Sean Brady; p. 308, (top left) © Joseph Sohm; Visions of America/CORBIS.

Chapter 10

pp. 318–319, DesignPics Inc./Index Stock Imagery; p. 319, Chad Ehler/Stock Connection/PictureQuest; p. 320, Lester Lefkowitz/Getty Images; p. 325, Image Source/PictureQuest; p. 327, Sean Brady; p. 331, Neil Lucas/BBC Wild; p. 333, Associated Press, AP; p. 336, Argonne National Laboratory; p. 338, John Pinkston and Laura Stern/USGS, Menlo Park; p. 341, © Royalty-Free/CORBIS; p. 342, (top right) © Bettmann/CORBIS; p. 342, (top left) © Bettmann/CORBIS; p. 343, © Alan Oddie/PhotoEdit; p. 345, Courtesy, National Biodiesel Fuel Board; p. 349, Courtesy, FPL Energy LLC.

Chapter 11

pp. 358–359, © Studio Photogram/Alamy; p. 360, Associated Press, AP; p. 363, Agricultural Research Service, USDA; p. 364, Sean Brady; p. 369, AIP Emilio Segre Visual Archives; p. 370, The Granger Collection, New York; p. 374, © Yann Arthus-Bertrand/CORBIS; p. 382, Courtesy of Professor Andrey K. Geim/High Field Magnet Laboratory/University of Nijmegen; p. 383, Dan McCoy/Rainbow; p. 385, Associated Press, THE CHARLESTON DAILY MAIL; p. 389, PhotoLink/PhotoDisc/PictureQuest; p. 390, AP Photo/Terry Renna; p. 392, Sean Brady.

Chapter 12

pp. 398–399, © Royalty-Free/CORBIS; p. 399, Tino Hammid; p. 406, © Roger Ressmeyer/CORBIS; p. 414, The Bancroft Library; p. 418, Stockbyte/Getty Images; p. 423, (center left) Frank Cox; p. 423, (bottom left) Frank Cox; p. 424, (top right) © Comstock Images/Alamy; p. 424, (center left) © Dennis MacDonald/PhotoEdit; p. 424, (bottom right) Andy Crawford/Dorling Kindersley/Getty Images; p. 425, Frank Cox.

Chapter 13

pp. 440–441, Juerg Alean; p. 441, Photo by Jean-Francois Luy with the kind authorization of Beitling SA; p. 443, (top left) Sean Brady; p. 443, (top center) Sean Brady; p. 445, Ken O'Donoghue; p. 449, Dave Jacobs/Stone/Getty Images; p. 451, John A. Rizzo/PhotoDisc/Getty Images; p. 463, Sean Brady; p. 464, Kurt Amsler/Vandystadt/Allsort USA; p. 471, Courtesy, Ford Motor Company.

Chapter 14

pp. 486–487, Photodisc/Getty Images; p. 487, Ray McVay/PhotoDisc/Getty Images; p. 489, © David Taylor/Alamy; p. 492, © Bob Daemmrich/The Image Works; p. 493, © Royalty-Free/John Foster/Masterfile; p. 494, © Flip Nicklin/Minden Pictures; p. 499, (top right) Terry Doyle/Stone/ Getty Images; p. 499, (bottom right) © Bettmann/CORBIS; p. 501, David Chasey/PhotoDisc/Getty Images; p. 504, (bottom left) Sean Brady; p. 504, (bottom center) Sean Brady; p. 504, (bottom right) Mark A. Schneider/Visuals Unlimited; p. 505, Erich Schrempp/Photo Researchers, Inc.; p. 507, (bottom right) James Worrell/Photonica/Getty Images; p. 507, (top left) Ken O'Donoghue; p. 507, (top right) Richard Megna/Fundamental Photographs; p. 508, (bottom right) M. Freeman/PhotoDisc/Getty Images; p. 508, (top left) © Royalty-Free/CORBIS; p. 509, T.J. Florian/Rainbow p. 510, (top left) Jose Luis Pelaez Inc./Blend Images/Getty Images; p. 510, (bottom right) © Nicholas Eveleigh/SuperStock; p. 510, (center left) Sean Brady; p. 510, (center) Sean Brady; p. 510, (center right) Sean Brady.

Chapter 15

pp. 518–519, Martin Rogers/Stone/Getty Images; p. 519, Siede Preis/Photoisc/Getty Images; p. 523, © Najiah Feanny/CORBIS SABA; p. 525, Charles D. Winters/Photo Researchers, Inc.; p. 526, D. Yeske/Visuals Unlimited; p. 527, Courtesy MIT Museum; p. 533, Tom Pantages; p. 539, Tom Pantages; p. 542, Richard Megna/Fundamental Photographs; p. 543, Ken O'Donoghue; p. 550, Photo Researchers, Inc.

Chapter 16

pp. 560–561, PhotoLink/PhotoDisc/Getty Images; p. 561, PhotoDisc/Getty Images; p. 562, Sean Brady; p. 564, Sean Brady; p. 566, Sean Brady; p. 568, Sean Brady; p. 576, Andrew Syred/Photo Researchers, Inc.; p. 577, David Woodfall/Stone/Getty Images; p. 579, (center right) Sean Brady; p. 579, (bottom right) Richard Megna/Fundamental Photographs; p. 581, Copyright Los Angeles Times Syndicate. Photo from Chemical Heritage Foundation; p. 583, (top left) Richard Megna/Fundamental Photographs; p. 583, (top center) Richard Megna/Fundamental Photographs; p. 583, (top right) Richard Megna/Fundamental Photographs; p. 585, Hans Reinhard/Bruce Coleman, Inc.

Chapter 17

pp. 594–595, Rafael Macia/Photo Researchers. Inc.; p. 595, Sean Brady; p. 598, (top left) NASA/Photo Reseachers, Inc.; p. 598, (bottom right) Courtesy, Amana; p. 599, Tom Pantages; p. 600, (top left) Associated Press, AP; p. 600, (bottom right) C Squared Studios/PhotoDisc/Getty Images; p. 610, (bottom left) Richard Megna/Fundamental Photographs; p. 610, (bottom right) Richard Megna/Fundamental Photographs; p. 611, Rod Planck/Photo Researchers, Inc.; p. 614, © GOODSHOOT/Alamy; p. 615, (top right) Paul Silverman/Fundamental Photographs; p. 615, (bottom right) Sean Brady; p. 620, (top left) Sean Brady; p. 620, (center left) Sean Brady; p. 622, CNRI/Photo Researchers, Inc.

Chapter 18

pp. 634–635, © Jeff J. Daly/Visuals Unlimited; p. 635, Sean Brady; p. 636, (top left) Sean Brady; p. 636, (top center) Ken O'Donoghue; p. 636, (top center) Ken O'Donoghue; p. 636, (top right) Sean Brady; p. 637, Sean Brady; p. 641, © GOODSHOOT/Alamy; p. 643, © Royalty-Free/CORBIS; p. 644, Sean Brady; p. 645, Paul Chesley/Stone/Getty Images; p. 648, (top left) Ken O'Donoghue; p. 648, (center left) Ken O'Donoghue; p. 651, Richard Megna/Fundamental Photographs; p. 653, © Tom Wagner/CORBIS; p. 654, © Bettmann/CORBIS; p. 657, © Owen Franken/CORBIS; p. 659, (center) © B. RUNK/S. SCHOENBERGER / Grant Heilman Photography; p. 659, (bottom right) The Granger Collection, New York.

Chapter 19

pp. 666–667, © John Joannides/Alamy; p. 667, © James L. Amos/CORBIS; p. 670, Kopal/Mediamed Publiphoto/Photo Researchers, Inc.; p. 672, Bettman/CORBIS; p. 675, Culver Pictures; p. 677, Ken O'Donoghue; p. 678, Lawrence Berkeley National Lab; p. 679, Mark A. Philbrick/BYU; p. 680, Smithsonian Institution, Natural History Museum, Department of Mineral Sciences; p. 681, (top left) SIU/Visuals Unlimited; p. 681, (top center) SIU/Visuals Unlimited; p. 686, © Roger Ressmeyer/CORBIS; p. 687, NASA; p. 688, NASA; p. 689, Associated Press/Lennox McLendon.

Chapter 20

pp. 698–699, © Marbo Stock/Alamy; p. 699, Tom Pantages; p. 705, CORBIS Images/PictureQuest; p. 710, Tony Freeman/PhotoEdit; p. 721, © Shaffer/Smith/SuperStock; p. 726, Agricultural Research/USDA/Photo by Scott Bauer; p. 731, Sean Brady; p. 737, John A. Rizzo/PhotoDisc/Getty Images; p. 738, Laguna Design/Photo Researchers, Inc.; p. 740, Dr. Harold Rose/Photo Researchers, Inc.

Chapter 21

pp. 750–751, John Cumming/Digital Vision/Getty Images; p. 751, Volker Steger/Science Photo Library/Photo Researchers, Inc.; p. 753, Michael Abbey/Science Source/Photo Researchers, Inc.; p. 758, D. Yeske/Visuals Unlimited; p. 761, Courtesy, Genzyme Transgenics Corporation; p. 762, (bottom left) USDA; p. 762, (bottom right) Mitch Hrdlicka/PhotoDisc/Getty Images; p. 765, RDF/Visuals Unlimited; p. 767, M. Freeman/PhotoLink/PhotoDisc/PictureQuest; p. 773, (center right) Digital Vision/Getty Images; p. 773, (bottom right) © Bettmann/CORBIS; p. 773, (top right) Will and Deni McIntyre/Photo Researchers, Inc.

Index

1A

1								
H Hydrogen 1.008	2A							
3 **Li** Lithium 6.941	4 **Be** Beryllium 9.012							
11 **Na** Sodium 22.99	12 **Mg** Magnesium 24.31							

Key

6	Atomic number
C	Element symbol
Carbon	Element name
12.01	Atomic mass

Period 4:
| 19 **K** Potassium 39.10 | 20 **Ca** Calcium 40.08 | 21 **Sc** Scandium 44.96 | 22 **Ti** Titanium 47.88 | 23 **V** Vanadium 50.94 | 24 **Cr** Chromium 52.00 | 25 **Mn** Manganese 54.94 | 26 **Fe** Iron 55.85 | 27 **Co** Cobalt 58.93 |

Period 5:
| 37 **Rb** Rubidium 85.47 | 38 **Sr** Strontium 87.62 | 39 **Y** Yttrium 88.91 | 40 **Zr** Zirconium 91.22 | 41 **Nb** Niobium 92.91 | 42 **Mo** Molybdenum 95.94 | 43 **Tc** Technetium (98) | 44 **Ru** Ruthenium 101.1 | 45 **Rh** Rhodium 102.9 |

Period 6:
| 55 **Cs** Cesium 132.9 | 56 **Ba** Barium 137.3 | 57 **La** Lanthanum 138.9 | 72 **Hf** Hafnium 178.5 | 73 **Ta** Tantulum 180.9 | 74 **W** Tungsten 183.9 | 75 **Re** Rhenium 186.2 | 76 **Os** Osmium 190.2 | 77 **Ir** Iridium 192.2 |

Period 7:
| 87 **Fr** Francium (223) | 88 **Ra** Radium 226.0 | 89 **Ac** Actinium (227) | 104 **Rf** Rutherfordium (261) | 105 **Db** Dubnium (262) | 106 **Sg** Seaborgium (263) | 107 **Bh** Bohrium (264) | 108 **Hs** Hassium (265) | 109 **Mt** Meitnerium (268) |

58 **Ce** Cerium 140.1	59 **Pr** Praseodymium 140.9	60 **Nd** Neodymium 144.2	61 **Pm** Promethium (145)	62 **Sm** Samarium 150.4
90 **Th** Thorium 232.0	91 **Pa** Protactinium (231)	92 **U** Uranium 238.0	93 **Np** Neptunium (237)	94 **Pu** Plutonium (244)